EDUCATIONAL RESOURCE CENTER
Greenville College
Greenville, Illinois 62246

P9-ASJ-643

EDUCATIONAL RESOURCE CENTER
Greenville College
Greenville, Illinois 62246

BIOLOGICAL SCIENCES CURRICULUM STUDY

Yellow Version
BIOLOGICAL SCIENCE: AN INQUIRY INTO LIFE,
Harcourt, Brace & World, Inc.

Green Version
HIGH SCHOOL BIOLOGY: BSCS GREEN VERSION,
Rand McNally & Co.

Blue Version
HIGH SCHOOL BIOLOGY: MOLECULES TO MAN,
Houghton Mifflin Company

LABORATORY BLOCKS
The Complementarity of Structure and Function
Animal Growth and Development
Plant Growth and Development
Microbes: Their Growth, Nutrition, and Interaction
    (Other titles in preparation) D. C. Heath & Company

Biological Investigations for Secondary School Students: Research Problems in Biology for the Schools, Doubleday & Company, Inc.

MATERIALS FOR THE TEACHER
Biology Teacher's Handbook, John Wiley & Sons, Inc.
Innovations in Equipment and Techniques for the Biology Teaching Laboratory, D. C. Heath & Company

BSCS Pamphlet Series, D. C. Heath & Company

CURRICULUM STUDY BULLETINS
Hurd, P. DeH. 1961. *Biological Education in American Secondary Schools, 1890–1960*. BSCS Curriculum Study Bulletin No. 1, American Institute of Biological Sciences, Washington, D.C.

Brandwein, P. F., J. Metzner, E. Morholt, A. Roe, W. Rosen, 1962. *Teaching High School Biology: A Guide to Working with Potential Biologists*. BSCS Curriculum Study Bulletin No. 2, American Institute of Biological Sciences, Washington, D.C.

BIOLOGICAL SCIENCES CURRICULUM STUDY

Initiated by the AMERICAN INSTITUTE OF BIOLOGICAL SCIENCES

BSCS *High School Biology*: *Yellow Version*

A REVISION PREPARED BY:

JOHN A. MOORE, SUPERVISOR
Department of Zoology
Columbia University

BENTLEY GLASS
Department of Biology
The Johns Hopkins University

WILLIAM V. MAYER
Department of Biology
and Associate Dean
College of Liberal Arts
Wayne State University

WILSON N. STEWART
Department of Botany
University of Illinois

J. MAXWELL DAVIS
Biology Department
Bosse High School
Evansville, Indiana

DONALD H. BUCKLIN
Department of Zoology
University of Wisconsin

GEORGE SCHWARTZ
Biology Department
Forest Hills High School
New York City

Edited by DON E. MEYER
and VIRGINIA M. DRYDEN
of the Harcourt, Brace & World *Staff*

BIOLOGICAL SCIENCE:

AN INQUIRY INTO LIFE

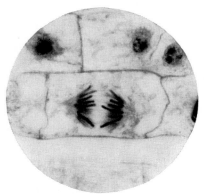

HARCOURT, BRACE & WORLD, INC.

New York   Chicago   Atlanta   Dallas   Burlingame

AMERICAN INSTITUTE OF BIOLOGICAL SCIENCES

PRESIDENT
James G. Dickson, 1959–60
Tracy Sonneborn, 1961
Frits Went, 1962
James Ebert, 1963

EXECUTIVE DIRECTOR
Hiden T. Cox, through 1962

EDUCATION COMMITTEE CHAIRMAN
Oswald Tippo, 1959–60
Gairdner Moment, 1961–63

BIOLOGICAL SCIENCES CURRICULUM STUDY

CHAIRMAN
Bentley Glass

DIRECTOR
Arnold B. Grobman

ASSOCIATE DIRECTOR
Walter Auffenberg, 1960–63
William V. Mayer, 1963–64

The many writers, artists, consultants, and reviewers who have contributed to experimental editions of BSCS *High School Biology: Yellow Version* are acknowledged on pages 724–27.

Artwork by CARU Studios

COVER PHOTOGRAPH: Courtesy of J. H. Tjio and T. T. Puck, from *Proc. Nat. Acad. Sci.*, 44, 1229 (1958). The chromosomes are shown in an arrested stage of mitosis (text pages 538 and 547). The field of the photograph has been reversed by use of a negative print.

SOURCE OF PHOTOGRAPHS ON TITLE PAGE: *upper*, Gen. Biological Supply House, Inc.; *lower*, Philip Gendreau.

© 1963 by the American Institute of Biological Sciences, Washington, D.C.

All rights reserved. No part of this book may be reproduced in any form, by mimeograph or any other means, without permission in writing from the publisher.

PRINTED IN THE UNITED STATES OF AMERICA

CONTENTS

PART 1 UNITY

The earth is populated by millions of different types of living creatures. Each has its own way of living, but all share *the only known kind* of structural and chemical organization that means *being alive*. Whatever their dissimilarities, plants, animals, and other creatures solve their big problems—those of being alive—in much the same way. Investigation into the unifying features of living will emphasize two things: *what* biologists know about life and *how* they have managed to acquire this knowledge.

CHAPTER
1
BIOLOGY—WHAT IS IT ABOUT?   3

Biology is the sum of man's knowledge about life—his own life and that of all other creatures. This knowledge consists not only of a collection of facts, but more importantly, of the way these facts are associated and interpreted in general theories. Clues to the study of biology appear in the principal themes introduced in this chapter. An example of a biological investigation follows as a case history of one problem—the cause of mankind's most serious disease, malaria.

CHAPTER
2
LIFE FROM LIFE   23

Less than a century ago scientists debated furiously the question of whether life could rise spontaneously from nonliving substances. The far-reaching implications of this biological question are not necessarily the same for life today and life in its most distant past. But they *are* the same for all kinds of living things, as investigation of this biological problem in terms of life today has abundantly illustrated.

CHAPTER
3
BASIC STRUCTURE   44

Unifying theories explain isolated facts. Science is at its best when it seeks a new theory to organize an accumulation of poorly understood facts. One of the greatest unifying theories of biology is that all, or nearly all, forms of life have a common basic structure. That this is true is not at all obvious: a

EDUCATIONAL RESOURCE CENTER
Greenville College
Greenville, Illinois 62246   01314

fish and a tree really do not seem to resemble one another. Yet both are alike in being composed of cells. Cells were first discovered almost 200 years before their nature was understood well enough to lead to the cell theory.

PART 2 DIVERSITY

Diversity among the earth's microorganisms, plants, and animals is more obvious in many ways than the fundamental unity in life. Historically, diversity emerged as modifications upon a common pattern. Unity continues to be shown in the recognition that different organisms are similar chemically, have a common structural basis (cells), reproduce, evolve, respond to stimuli, and constitute parts of an interrelated whole. Yet diversity in life is seen in the millions of different types of living organisms, the three principal groups being microorganisms, plants, and animals. This section of the book will be concerned with the many variations upon the fundamental theme.

A. MICROORGANISMS

No living thing is simple, but relatively speaking, the viruses are the simplest forms of life. They cannot in any way provide for themselves—they live only in cells of bacteria, plants, and animals. The host cells provide energy for the virus particles and materials for their reproduction—and often are killed in the process.

The bacteria, a step more complex than the viruses, are the simplest organisms that can be called cells. They also are the smallest organisms that can be studied with the compound microscope. Their activities are the basic ones that are characteristic of *every* living organism. Life in the simplest cells can be very complex—even to reproduction by sexual means.

The bacteria, in spite of their microscopic size, are essential organisms in the complex web of life. Some species are of prime importance in the carbon and nitrogen cycles, which make possible the life of other plants and animals. Other species are used in a variety of manufacturing processes. Still other species cause diseases—in man as well as in other animals and plants. The discoveries leading to the proof that bacteria can produce disease furnish one of the most interesting examples of the methods of science.

B. PLANTS

Collectively known as fungi, the molds, yeasts, and mushrooms are more complex than bacteria. They represent distinctive lines in the evolution of organisms that cannot carry out photosynthesis. They, like the animals, are dependent ultimately upon the green plants. The fungi are important in the nitrogen cycle and other cycles of life. Together with the bacteria they are the chief decomposers—they break down the bodies of dead animals and plants and release substances that are needed by the living.

C. ANIMALS

tion (such as a circulatory system). All events relating to oxygen and carbon dioxide exchange, including the energy-liberating reactions within cells, are a part of respiration.

PART 3 CONTINUITY

Living organisms of today are the temporary manifestations of a lineage of life that extends backward in time for several billion years. Individuals die, but life continues in their offspring. Two aspects of the continuity of life by reproduction must be considered: a short-term continuity based on resemblances between parents and offspring, and a long-term continuity based on changes and their accumulation, through evolution.

A. GENETIC CONTINUITY

particular combinations of chromosomes that occur at fertilization, determine the pattern of heredity. There is also a physical basis for recombination of genes located on the same chromosome.

his own undoing. By poor agricultural practices he has destroyed vast areas of productive soil; he has devastated forests, only to find his water supply diminishing and his soil supply eroding; he has fouled the rivers and streams, thereby making their water unsuitable to his needs. But today he is beginning to behave as he must—as a living creature who depends on other life for his own existence.

FOREWORD

With each new generation our fund of scientific knowledge increases fivefold; this remarkable growth of knowledge has led to more inadequate and more formalized science instruction. In biology, the routines of teaching have drifted ever farther from any approach that a scientist could recognize as an introduction to a science. As a consequence, there has been widespread dissatisfaction with the content and methods of our science courses in secondary schools. In January 1959, the AIBS, a professional society representing 85,000 biologists, established the Biological Sciences Curriculum Study as a means of contributing to the improvement of secondary school biological education. For the purposes of formulating basic policy, there was organized at an early date a BSCS Steering Committee (composed of college biologists, high school biology teachers, and other educators—all interested in improving the quality of the teaching of biology). Headquarters for the Study were established on the campus of the University of Colorado. Primary financial support for the Biological Sciences Curriculum Study has been provided by the National Science Foundation.

Two tasks in improving and modernizing instructional materials in biology stood out as imperative. First was the fullest possible consideration of the new perspectives in biology growing from the astonishing increase in scientific knowledge. At the current rate of scientific advance, there is about four times as much significant biological knowledge today as in 1930, and about sixteen times as much as in 1900. By the year 2000, at this rate of increase, there will be a hundred times as much biology to "cover" in the introductory course as at the beginning of the century. Obviously, then, we must be highly selective in our choice of what scientific facts, concepts, and principles to present, so that the most important developments of the new biology, together with the most profound insights of the older biology, may be included. This highly selective approach means, however, that many feasible viewpoints and approaches may claim equal validity and equally high merit. We have consequently refrained from any attempt to develop a single authoritative program for the study of biology in the secondary schools. Instead, we have prepared and now present a varied, balanced, and enriched program that may utilize either Yellow, Green, or Blue Versions, with the possible inclusion of any of a number of Laboratory Blocks, Invitations to Enquiry, and Special Investigations.

Secondly, we are profoundly convinced that the major fault in the teaching of biology and other sciences in the secondary schools is that emphasis has been placed on authoritative content—facts, concepts, principles—instead of being placed on the investigative processes of science and the history of scientific ideas. In order to live in a scientifically based civilization with some appreciation of the forces that are shaping the lives of modern citizens, what is especially needful is an understanding of what science really is—not a modern magic but a variety of ways of finding out verifiable information and building up concepts and principles that adequately explain what we know of nature's ways. Our primary emphasis has thus been laid upon science as investigation and inquiry. Observation, experiment, hypothesis, and verification are the four corners of this structure. The student, by personal participation in scientific processes, must come to know them and respect them. For these reasons we have eschewed the possibility of providing textbooks that could be used without the complementary laboratory programs. We have done our best to prepare, instead, a laboratory- (and field-) centered program of instruction that makes use of the textbook only as a supplement to learning. For these reasons, too, we have placed special stress on the value of the Laboratory Blocks and the Invitations to Enquiry, as well as the Special Investigations that individual students may perform. Taken together, the BSCS materials comprise a series of integrated, balanced, and enriched programs —not simply a set of independent books, films, and laboratory exercises.

Particularly important in the integration of the materials was a sort of three-dimensional framework of ideas. In one dimension we determined to include a balanced consideration of microorganisms, plants, and animals, and not to ignore or slight any one of these three great subdivisions of living organisms. In another dimension we have been concerned with a balanced consideration of all levels of living organization, from the molecule through the cell, the tissue and organ, the individual, the population and species, and the community, to the entire world biosphere. In the third conceptual dimension we conceived of nine great themes that would course through all treatments of subjects and topics, extend through all levels of organization, and relate to microorganisms, plants, and animals alike. These major themes were as follows: science as investigation and inquiry; the history of biological concepts; the complementarity of structure and function; diversity of type and unity of pattern; change of organisms through time—evolution; genetic continuity; the complementarity of organism and environment; regulation and homeostasis; and the biological roots of behavior.

We were also firmly convinced that in our new courses nothing should prevent a thorough, unbiased, and scientifically objective presentation of such supposedly controversial biological subjects as organic evolution, the nature of individual and racial differences, sex and reproduction in the human species, or the problems of population growth and control. A sound biological understanding of such matters as these is the inalienable birthright of every future parent and citizen. To establish a basis for a better public understanding of the wise management of natural resources, of the biological hazards of nuclear agents in peace and in war, and of the methods by which scientific information is achieved, as primary sources of national strength and well-being in this new era of history, was clearly also an inescapable obligation of the new biology curriculum.

Perhaps the most significant feature in the development of the BSCS materials has been the fruitful cooperation between research biologists on the frontiers of science and high school teachers on the frontiers of teaching. The design and production of these teaching materials has involved a major intensive effort extending over several years.

During the summer of 1960, the BSCS assembled a group of 70 high school biology teachers and university research biologists to prepare preliminary trial materials. The books produced were tested in approximately 100 schools throughout the country, and based on that classroom experience the materials were thoroughly revised during the summer of 1961. The revised trial materials were then used in 500 schools during the 1961–62 academic year and in 950 schools the following year. The books now available reflect this very extensive experience with trial editions. The BSCS appreciates the singularly important contributions to the improvement of biological education made by over 1,000 teachers and 150,000 students through their use of the trial instructional materials.

Each one of the three versions, as we have said, has its own flavor and thematic approach. One of these versions, known during the three-year trial period as the Yellow Version, has evolved into the present materials. The rationale underlying the development of the Yellow Version is given in the following Preface by Dr. John A. Moore, who has served as supervisor of the writing team that developed the Yellow Version.

Hundreds of the nation's biological scientists and teachers have worked diligently on the BSCS materials. We hope that high school students and their teachers will continue to find that these efforts have been of value.

BENTLEY GLASS, CHAIRMAN, BSCS   ARNOLD B. GROBMAN, DIRECTOR, BSCS
The Johns Hopkins University   *University of Colorado*
Baltimore, Maryland   *Boulder, Colorado*

February 1, 1963

PREFACE

With the publication of BIOLOGICAL SCIENCE: AN INQUIRY INTO LIFE, the Yellow Version enters a new phase of its existence. It began in the summer of 1960, in Boulder, Colorado, at the first BSCS writing conference. During the academic year 1960–61 a preliminary Yellow Version was tested by dozens of teachers and thousands of students. It was rewritten, again in Boulder, during the summer of 1961; and during the academic years 1961–62 and 1962–63 it was tested by hundreds of teachers and tens of thousands of students. A second revision was then undertaken in New York in the period from July 1962 until July 1963.

A very large number of students and teachers have molded the product now in your hands. From the teachers and, through them, from the students, we have received many thousands of pages of comments: errors to be corrected; ideas for improvement of illustrations; suggestions for improving the development of biological ideas in the text; new approaches to difficult topics; evaluations of the level of presentation; and, now and then, words of praise. These comments were needed, for what we were attempting to do had not been done before. Hence there existed no prescription for success. Our procedure could only be to present the science of biology as we thought it might be presented and then test the results. The test was, and will continue to be, pragmatic: Is the Yellow Version, under its new title and in its new edition, a useful means of helping the teacher convey not only the data, but the questions, hypotheses, and theories of biology to the students?

All of us who have been engaged in the preparation of the three editions of the Yellow Version share in our admiration of the teachers and students who have been part of this joint educational experiment. Our first products were crude; their newness made life difficult for both students and teachers. We demanded the impossible, but the students and teachers fulfilled their obligations to the program in an admirable fashion. Of course, this was as it should be—education is everybody's business. Because it was so, the impossible bore fruit, yielding the teachable.

Now that we have passed from the stage of crudely printed experimental editions to a better printed experimental edition, we hope that our work—and its goal —will not appear more impersonal. We still need close contact with, and constant suggestions from, those using this book. May we have them?

There is nothing mysterious about the goal. Of the three BSCS teams of authors, the Yellow Version team accepted the broad responsibility for an up-to-date course in the whole of biology. We were not to emphasize one or a few fields to the disadvantage of others, but—to the best of our abilities—give as much insight as possible into every field, old and new, that is a part of modern biology. We were to impart an understanding of biological inquiry, not merely the data it has yielded. We were also to eliminate the awkwardness of unnecessary terms and unnecessary facts—that is, terms and facts not useful to the integration of all the fields of biology into one.

There remain today widely known biology textbooks that are little more than an accumulation of biological data. They have served a useful purpose and could be excused in times when biology was without a very clear conceptual structure. But times and biology have changed. Today this science is undergoing the greatest revolution in its history. Education in biology must reflect this event.

JOHN A. MOORE, SUPERVISOR
BSCS Yellow Version

July 5, 1963

1

UNITY

All living things resemble one another in many ways: in the substances of which they are composed; in the manner in which their body structures are put together of these substances; in the ways in which they use energy to maintain the living state; and in how they respond to stimuli, reproduce, and change with time. All are dependent and similar parts of an interrelated system—the world of life.

1

BIOLOGY—

WHAT IS IT ABOUT?

One of the best ways to understand your own country is to leave it to travel elsewhere. At home many things are so familiar to us that we scarcely notice them any more. Abroad, not only do the people and the buildings, the different ways of travel, and the strange foods startle and interest us, but different kinds of plant and animal life reveal to us that we are not at home. Elephants in the street, and tribes of monkeys scuttling over the temples, mean India. Palms and jungle signify the tropics. Old World plants and animals differ vastly from those of North America. Australia has its kangaroos, koala bears, and eucalyptus trees. Coming back to our land after a journey abroad, we look with fresh eyes at the living things we have for so long taken for granted. Indeed, what is homesickness but the longing to be surrounded once more by the familiar things of life?

All these impressions would be exaggerated if we were to visit another planet of our solar system. No one can be sure what awaits the first visitor, but the best guess is a dead world, something almost inconceivable to us. There would be no animals or plants as we know them. All matter would be in the form of gases, rocks, sand, dust, and possibly water.

Returning to earth, the familiar sights of the natural world would seem more interesting and important: the grasses and trees, the crops in the farmers' fields, the birds, the insects, and that most astounding of all animals, man. We would see more clearly that these are alive, and that being alive is a rare and wondrous thing. There *may* be life of some sort on some of the thousands of planets that circle the distant stars. Yet, so far as we positively know, only on our own earth are there living objects.

But is the gulf between the living and nonliving really absolute? Living things die, and when they die what becomes of them? A tree is blown down in a storm. The leaves wither, turn brown, and drop from the branches. The trunk decays. Eventually all is dust, dust in no way distinguishable from that formed by the breakup of the rocks of the earth's crust.

What, then, is the difference between a living tree and the nonliving dust formed through its decay? Can the same matter be alive, then dead, and then alive again? Man has asked questions of this sort throughout recorded history.

BIOLOGICAL QUESTIONS

There is no way to estimate the number of questions that have been asked throughout the years about animals, plants, and microorganisms, the three groups of things that are alive. All that man has learned in trying to answer these questions is **biology,** the science of living things.

Structure and Function

Some of the first questions that might be asked about a living creature are: What is it like? What does it do? What are its parts, and what does each part do? In other words, what is the structure, and what are the functions, of the animal or plant? When its body is opened, what parts does one find within? What are the functions of these parts, alone and together? These are morphological and physiological questions. **Morphology** (mor·FOL·o·jee) is the science of the *structure* of living things. **Physiology** (fiz·ih·OL·o·jee) is the science of the *functions* of living things.

Morphology and physiology are actually two different ways of viewing the same thing. Morphology deals with how an **organism** (OR·gan·iz'm—another name for *living thing*) is constructed; physiology deals with how it works. You cannot fully understand structure without knowing the functions involved, nor fully understand function without knowing the structures involved. Ultimately, when you know a lot about biology, it will be possible to tell a good deal about function just from seeing a structure, even in an unfamiliar organism. An eye like ours implies vision; wings like a bird's imply flight. You may never have heard of an Andean condor, but a picture of it would at once lead you to suppose it had keen vision and powers of flight.

Kinds of Organisms

If every kind of plant and animal were totally different from every other, we could never make much sense of nature. The tremendous variety would be totally bewildering. The question "What is it?" would require a complete new set of standards for studying each organism. Fortunately, this is not the case. Many kinds of organisms resemble each other in certain ways. Thus, when we see an unfamiliar animal with two wings and feathers, we at once say, "a bird." When the animal, instead of having wings and two legs, has four legs, is covered with hair, and produces milk for the feeding of the newborn, we say (if we know the word), "a mammal." Most of the familiar

plants have flowers, but the flowers of different kinds of plants differ. Some are one color, some another, some large, some quite small, some familiar in the way that they are put together, others so strange in structure that we have to look very closely to identify them.

In short, the biologist is impressed by the diversity, or differences, among living things, but in spite of this great diversity, he is aware that organisms are not *entirely* different from one another (Figure 1-1). We all recognize that there are "groups" of organisms. We recognize a group "birds," which includes chickens, pigeons, robins, wrens, gulls, and other feathered creatures. We recognize another group, "mammals," which includes dogs, cats, horses, bears, and many others. Biologists study the morphology, physiology, and behavior of organisms in an effort to arrange them, or classify them, in natural groups.

Growth and Development

Other questions a biologist may ask relate to **growth** and to **development**. At the start of your life, you were smaller than the period at the end of this sentence (Figure 1-2). You were no more than a little sphere of living substance, with none of the structures you now have: arms, heart, eyes, stomach, liver, or brain. What were the morphological and physiological steps that took place between this beginning and the way you now are? They were of two general sorts. First, there was a development, that is, the gradual changes from a relatively formless early embryo to the fully differentiated adult. Second, a part of this development was growth, which means an increase in size. The ability to grow and develop is universal, or nearly so, among living things. The seed of a plant germinates, develops and grows into a seedling, and later becomes a mature plant; the egg of an animal is fertilized, and develops and grows into a mature animal. The study of development

1-1 Every part of the world has its characteristic animals and plants. A densely massed rain forest of the tropics (above) is unlike the widely spaced plant life of a desert (below). A tree-dwelling monkey from the rain forest has no counterpart in the desert, and the desert's kangaroo rat is surprisingly different from rats of other parts of the world. In spite of such contrasts in life, however, basic similarities also exist. What are some of the similarities?

Photos: *above*, E. Aubert de la Rüe; *below*, David Muench

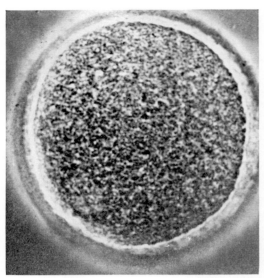

Dr. L. B. Shettles

1-2 All animals and plants, however complex, begin their life simply—generally as a single microscopic structure called a *cell*. This cell is a human egg, magnified about 200 times (usually written "200 X").

in plants and animals is therefore another important branch of biology, called **embryology** (em·brih·OL·o·jee).

Organisms and Their Environments

Animals and plants are not simply an assemblage of parts living in isolation from the world. After all, each individual is an organism, in which all parts are adjusted to the life of the whole. How do organisms behave? How do they respond to other creatures of their own kind, to other kinds of plants and animals and **microorganisms** (my·kro·OR·gan·iz'mz—organisms so small that one must use a microscope to study them), and to their physical environment? How does a tree respond to drought, low temperature, or injury? How does a bird feed its young, escape other animals, survive climatic extremes, and migrate to distant lands in spring and autumn?

Living organisms are remarkably able to regulate their own lives in the presence of change around them. They maintain a normal morphology and physiology in spite of changes in the surrounding world. This state of constancy, which is vital for life, is known as **homeostasis** (hoh·me·o·STAY·sis). We say organisms are sensitive to changes in their environments and that their behavior involves responses to particular environmental changes.

In many animals these responses are clearly related to sensory organs, such as eyes, ears, taste receptors, and the like; and to the presence of a nervous system that coordinates the responses of the whole organism. But appropriate responses are not at all limited to organisms with nervous systems, as we shall see; they are a universal characteristic of organisms. The physiology of these responses leads directly into a consideration of the basis of behavior. What is it that enables a living creature to adjust itself to its environment? Does it inherit its responses? Does it learn them by experience? Are the responses it can make flexible or rigid—adaptable or unchanging? We must look into all these and many other questions before we are done.

The relation between the living system and its environment is one that needs consideration at every level of organization. The smallest part of a living organism finds its activities and needs influenced by the neighboring parts. Every organ of the body lives in relation to all the other organs. Each individual in a population is influenced profoundly by the presence of other members of its family or social group, by the size of the group, and by the modifications the group makes of its environment. Every individual is also profoundly influenced by the physical features of its environment: light or darkness, moisture, chemicals, temperature, presence of minerals and foods, and many other things. Each population is a part of a total community of plants and animals and microorganisms of many species, all interacting in friendly, unfriendly, or blind fashion with each other and conditioning the behavior of the others. The end is reached only with the consideration of the entire living world, the **biosphere** (BY·o·sfeer), consisting of all the living things there are on this planet, and the physical environment in which they dwell —one vast complex interacting so fully that, directly or indirectly, everything influences everything else.

The larger aspects of this part of biology, the behavior of whole organisms and groups of organisms in relation to their total living and nonliving environments, is **ecology** (e·KOL·o·jee). The finer aspects of these relationships, within a single individual, we see as a part of physiology, morphology, or the chemistry of life. Really, there is no distinct boundary between the great and the small in this constant interplay between the internal system and the outside.

Like Produces Like

Some of the most profound of all biological questions are concerned with problems of reproduction. Living things produce offspring that resemble their parents, generation after generation. How does this come about? What biological forces insure that the offspring of cats are always baby cats, and not baby rabbits? This sounds like a silly question—but can you give a satisfactory answer? Perhaps both your parents and a brother or sister have brown eyes, yet yours are blue. What made you different? Questions and answers of these sorts make up the branch of biology called **genetics** (je·NET·iks).

Time and Change

Biology has its long-term questions, too. Half a billion years ago, there were no animals with backbones living on the earth. Now animals with backbones are an important group—the group to which man belongs. In the course of the earth's history, some very lowly animals with backbones

appeared (Figure 1-3). These were fishlike creatures. On a time scale that is measured in millions of years, descendants of these fishlike creatures came out on land. Through a long series of changes, so slight as to be unnoticeable in even a thousand years, man was formed. All animals and plants have a similar history. This is shown by remains of them preserved in the rocks as **fossils.** The beginnings of animals and plants go back to the origin of life itself, and over the course of time their descendants have changed to become the animals and plants of today. This is **evolution,** once hotly debated, but now a well-established theory.

The concept of evolution has been of prime importance in aiding our understanding of the diversity and unity of animals and plants. What they are today is the result of changes that have occurred in the past, changes that on each occasion rendered the possessors slightly better equipped to live in the environments they found—as we now say, made them better **adapted.** Less well-adapted and less fertile forms died out, as fossils of animals and plants that no longer exist abundantly show. The tremendous variety of kinds of animals and plants living on earth today is a consequence of evolution—each kind becoming modified for living in its own way.

Biological Themes

What we have described to this point in our introductory chapter outlines the major biological themes that will thread through all our future discussions. They are to be detected everywhere, forming the warp and woof, the main threads that run lengthwise and crosswise, of which the fabric of our biological thinking is woven. It will help to summarize these ideas. On the next page they are listed briefly (not in the same order as in the preceding discussion). See if you can identify which theme belongs with each preceding paragraph of explanation.

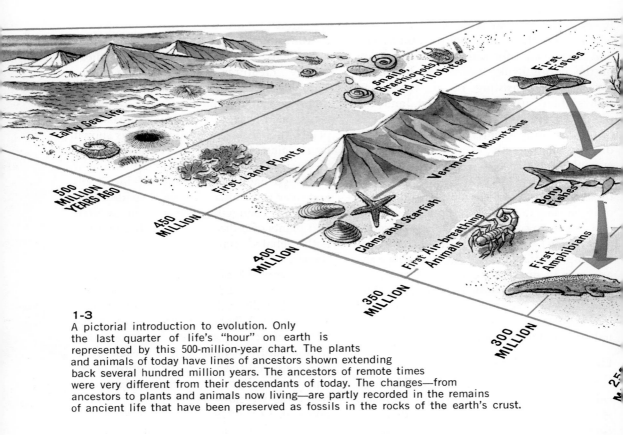

1-3
A pictorial introduction to evolution. Only the last quarter of life's "hour" on earth is represented by this 500-million-year chart. The plants and animals of today have lines of ancestors shown extending back several hundred million years. The ancestors of remote times were very different from their descendants of today. The changes—from ancestors to plants and animals now living—are partly recorded in the remains of ancient life that have been preserved as fossils in the rocks of the earth's crust.

Eight major biological themes have been included in the framework of introductory topics so far presented:

1. Change of living things through time: evolution
2. Diversity of type and unity of pattern among living things
3. The genetic continuity of life
4. Growth and development in the individual's life
5. The complementarity of structure and function
6. Regulation and homeostasis: the preservation of life in the face of change
7. The complementarity of organism and environment
8. The biological basis of behavior

There are two other major themes to be worked into the frame of our thinking, two other themes which it is most important to appreciate. One of these relates to the way in which science advances, its methods of inquiry and investigation, its logic, its dependence upon quantitative measurements and accurate observations, and its refinement of "the experiment." The other concerns the history of biological discoveries and concepts. One needs to understand how scientific ideas grow and develop, how mistakes and limitations of method confine and restrict the concepts of a particular time. We will learn that what often seem to be irreconcilable ideas each turn out to have something of the truth in them, and how in time a synthesis is made by throwing out the errors, clarifying the confusions, and putting together the ideas that hold true.

We must also appreciate that biology, like every science, is a record of the work

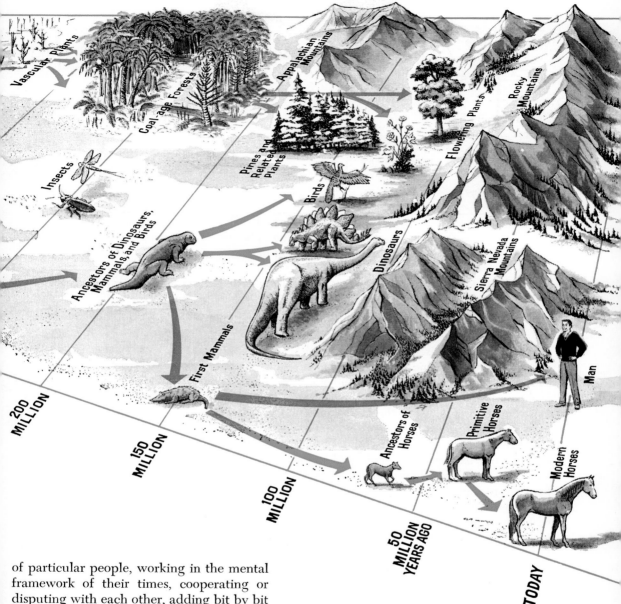

Vascular Plants

Coal age Forests

Appalachian Mountains

Rocky Mountains

Flowering Plants

Pines and Related Plants

Insects

Birds

Ancestors of Dinosaurs, Mammals, and Birds

Dinosaurs

Sierra Nevada Mountains

First Mammals

Man

200 MILLION

150 MILLION

100 MILLION

Ancestors of Horses

Primitive Horses

50 MILLION YEARS AGO

Modern Horses

TODAY

of particular people, working in the mental framework of their times, cooperating or disputing with each other, adding bit by bit to the current ideas of living nature. Science is a social enterprise, not only in the sense that it is built by the labors of many people, but also in the sense that its discoveries change the ways of life of people. To live in health, to have plenty of the right foods, to understand the origins of life, to rid one's mind of superstitions and fears, and to appreciate more fully the riches of nature—

these are human goals that biology is particularly able to help us achieve. The two themes just discussed may be named as follows:

9. Science as inquiry and investigation
10. The history of biological concepts and discoveries

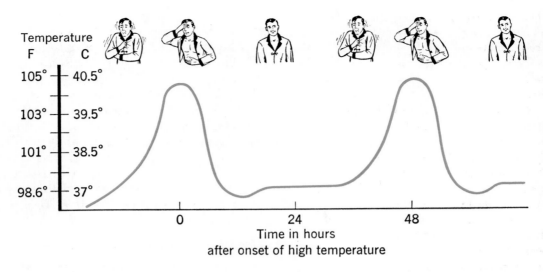

1-4 The temperature cycle in malaria. The irregular line of the graph shows the changes in body temperature that occur in one common type of malaria. The typical severe chill before each major rise in temperature is shown in the drawings above the graph.

Better than any discussion of these in the abstract, a truly graphic illustration of man's efforts to cope with a particular biological problem will help to bring out what we most desire to emphasize, *the nature of science and the history of its ideas and its social consequences.* The disease malaria will serve as our example of a biological problem. We will learn how biological problems are recognized and how they are studied; how difficult it is to answer questions that may seem simple; how the scientific ideas held by one generation are replaced by other ideas in the next; that the biological problems of man cannot be considered apart from nature; and that understanding of biological problems comes slowly as a result of the careful work of many individuals.

BIOLOGICAL PROBLEMS— AN EXAMPLE: MALARIA

Malaria is common in the tropical parts of the world. A century ago it was frequent as far north as Ohio and New York in the United States. Until recently it was even common in parts of Western Europe.

Malaria is a dramatic disease. In a typical attack, the unfortunate victim first experiences a severe chill. He feels very cold, even though a clinical thermometer would show that his temperature was above the normal value of 37° C (98.6° F). Gooseflesh forms, and his teeth chatter violently. A pile of blankets will not prevent this feeling of being very cold (Figure 1-4).

Several hours later the sufferer feels very hot—and indeed he is. His temperature may have risen to 41° C (106° F). He probably has a terrible headache and a feeling of nausea. Still later he begins to sweat profusely. In a few hours he feels much improved—though obviously weak and exhausted. In half a day he may even feel rather well.

If he has not been receiving medical treatment, he will not feel well for long! In a typical case, this whole series of events would be repeated two days later. The attacks will probably occur every other day for several weeks. Eventually the person would appear to be over his disease, but unless he had received medical treatment this probably would not be so. A few months or a year later, there might be a second attack of the disease, much like the first.

Clearly the person's physiology has been greatly upset by malaria. This disease, like all diseases, is a biological problem. Actually we will find that it includes a large number of biological problems. And important problems they are: over man's long history, malaria has been the disease that has most affected his health, economy, and politics. It has killed more people than any other malady. Questions about it have naturally been asked for a long time.

Malaria in Ancient Times

The ancient centers of civilization in Egypt, Iraq, India, China, Greece, and Italy were all areas where malaria occurred. Some physicians of more than two thousand years ago seem to have been familiar with the disease we now recognize as malaria. They described the chills and fevers, and the recurring attacks of the disease. They distinguished three *intermittent* fevers, which we now realize are different kinds of malaria, from the *continuous* fevers, which have many causes. They also noted that the disease was most frequent among people living in low, marshy areas. Somehow the stagnant waters of the marshes were thought to poison the air. As a result of breathing this "bad air," people became ill with malaria. This belief was, in fact, responsible for the name of the disease. The Italian words for "bad" and "air" are *mala* and *aria*. Malaria, then, was a disease associated with the bad air of marshy places. You may dismiss this belief as a silly superstition, but it was an early step toward solving the problem of man's most serious disease.

The Romans were not only familiar with the disease but they even attempted to control malaria by draining marshes. They had no way of treating persons ill with malaria —except by methods based on superstition.

Some historians believe that the decline of Roman civilization was caused partly by malaria—as it may earlier have led to the decline of Greek civilization. In any event, the western world entered a period lasting more than a thousand years during which little progress was made in solving the problems of malaria—or any other biological problem, for that matter. In scientific matters, these were truly the Dark Ages in Western Europe.

The Discovery of Quinine

The next advance of great importance, not only in understanding malaria but also in the advance of medicine, came in the seventeenth century. During the seventeenth century a tremendous variety of substances were used as medicines. Some were mineral substances; others were derived from animals and plants (Figure 1-5). The vast majority were worthless, and some were even harmful. For example, parts of nettle plants were mixed with whites of egg and placed on the forehead to cure headaches. Toothaches were thought to be cured by cutting up another plant, the spirewort, placing the pieces in the shell of a small snail-like animal, the limpet, and then applying the shell to the temple.

With the discovery of the New World, many new plants were sent back to Europe to be used as medicines. The bark of a Peruvian tree, known by its native name as **quina-quina** (KEE·na·KEE·na), was thought to be especially suitable for curing fevers. In fact, it was thought to be so good that soon it was impossible to ship enough to supply the demand in Europe. As it became more and more difficult to obtain, some not-so-honest merchants began to substitute the bark of another tree, the **cinchona** (sin·KOH-na), which closely resembled quina-quina. This mixup was of tremendous value to

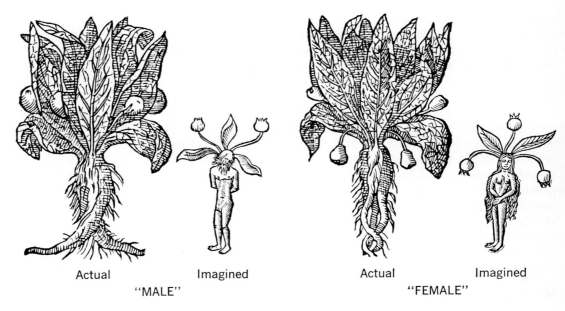

Actual   Imagined   Actual   Imagined

"MALE"   "FEMALE"

1-5 In the days before scientific medicine, man used many kinds of animal and plant products in an attempt to cure his diseases. Most were of little or no use. Special powers of healing were associated with plants (such as the mandrake shown here) that had a fancied resemblance to human beings.

mankind. Most physicians probably realized that quina-quina was worthless as a medicine. In contrast, the cinchona bark, which was being passed off as quina-quina, was found to be excellent for treating malaria. We now know the reason: cinchona bark contains quinine, a chemical substance that is effective in combating the disease. It was the only effective remedy known from the seventeenth to the twentieth century.

It is worth emphasizing that this discovery of the usefulness of cinchona was quite accidental. If the supply of quina-quina had been sufficient, cinchona would not have been substituted for it. Thus man narrowly escaped failure to discover the drug that would serve him so well for three centuries.

There are numerous examples, similar to the one just given, of important scientific discoveries being made quite accidentally. Time and again, a scientist will be studying one problem when he makes an observation that will lead to an important advance in another branch of science. Now that you have been told about quinine, the next example will interest you. When it was realized that quinine was so useful in treating malaria, chemists attempted to make it in the laboratory. In 1856, William Henry Perkin, a young chemist only eighteen years old, was carrying out such experiments in a crude laboratory in his home. He never succeeded—and no one else did for nearly a century—but he produced the first aniline dye (one of a group of synthetic dyes now widely used in industry). He failed in his primary purpose but "by accident" began the tremendously important aniline dye industry. Elsewhere, the investigation of malaria continued.

The Cause of Malaria

Although the importance of cinchona for treating malaria was recognized in the seventeenth century, physicians of the time knew nothing of the *cause* of malaria—apart from the ancient observation that it was associated with the "bad air" present in swampy places (Figure 1-6). But what in the "bad air" of swamps could be responsible? Possibly experiment would give the answer. Some brave investigators volunteered to drink swamp water from areas where malaria was common. They did not develop malaria. Thus, the illness did not result from drinking *this* particular swamp water. Where should they next look for the cause? Theories abounded, but none was proved. In the case of malaria, science marked time. The problem could not be studied effectively until there was a better understanding of the biology of disease in general. This came two hundred years later.

During the second half of the nineteenth century, it was found that some diseases are caused by very tiny living creatures—the bacteria. Once this was discovered, the belief grew that malaria might also be caused by some microscopic organism. The blood and parts of various organs of persons who were ill from malaria, or who had died of the disease, were studied. Some scientists thought that they had found bacteria to be the cause of the disease. Others could not confirm this finding.

The Discovery of *Plasmodium*

In 1878 a French army physician in Algeria began to search for the "cause" of malaria. After two years of careful work, he thought he had the answer. He had taken a small amount of blood from a patient ill with malaria, and as he examined it under his microscope he noticed some tiny living

1-6 Long before the biology of malaria was understood, some observers noticed that people living in lowlands suffered more from malaria than those living in towns built on hills. This observation suggested a hypothesis: malaria is caused by something associated with swamps. (The swamp below is in the Everglades of Florida. The town is San Gimignano, of north central Italy. Its towers date from the Middle Ages, when the noble families competed with one another to see who could have the highest tower. Probably this was not associated with the desire to get away from malaria!)

Left, Ewing Galloway; *right*, Ted Borsig from Rapho-Guilumette

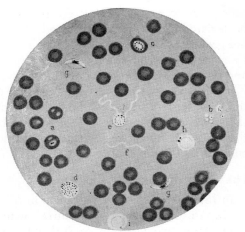

Photo from A. Laveran, *Paludism*, London,
The New Sydenham Society, 1893

1-7 The discovery of the malarial organism.
This drawing of blood from a person ill with
malaria is one of the original drawings of
the French army physician who made the
discovery. Objects such as those marked
c, d, e, and *f* were never observed in
healthy individuals. A reasonable hypothesis was that these objects, which are presumably living, are the cause of malaria.

creatures (Figure 1-7). They were long and
narrow—like little hairs—and so small that
they could hardly be seen under his microscope. In addition, some of the red blood
cells contained objects not seen in cells of
individuals who did not have malaria.

Now just because some peculiar objects
are found in the blood of a person ill with
malaria, we cannot conclude that they are
causing the malaria. In fact, this first report
was not believed by other scientists. But
two years later another physician, also in
Algeria, saw the same tiny creatures in the
blood of another patient ill with malaria.
Scientists were still not convinced that these
tiny creatures were causing malaria.

Five years after the first discovery, the
same peculiar creatures were observed for
the third time in the blood of a person
ill with malaria. This time the place was
Italy. The organism was described and giv-
en a name—*Plasmodium* (plaz·MOH·dih·um).

Gradually scientists began to accept the belief that malaria is caused by *Plasmodium*.
We now know, after years of observation
and experimentation, that this is true.

Possibly you wonder whether scientists
were just being stubborn in not believing
the first report that *Plasmodium* was the
cause of malaria. Actually they were merely
using the necessary caution in accepting a
new scientific discovery. (Many new "discoveries" are later shown to be incorrect.)

Studying Malaria Experimentally

Think of the situation of a scientist studying malaria in the last part of the nineteenth
century. Many *different* causes of malaria
were being suggested. How could he be
sure which, if any, was the true cause? He
could begin by reading the report of the
first scientist to discover *Plasmodium*. If it
was apparent that the report was based on
careful observations, he could conclude,
"Well, maybe this man is correct." He could
even provisionally accept the belief that
Plasmodium is the cause of malaria. If he
did so, he would be using one of the approaches to testing whether such a belief, or
hypothesis (hy·POTH·e·sis), is correct.

Suppose we accept, for the time being,
the hypothesis:

Plasmodium is the cause of malaria.

Now if this is true, we can make deductions
from the hypothesis. A deduction is a logical consequence of a statement or, in this
case, of the hypothesis. One deduction that
we could make would be:

*If Plasmodium is the cause of malaria,
then all persons ill with malaria should
have Plasmodium in their bodies.*

The next step is obvious—the blood of other
malaria patients must be examined for *Plasmodium*. This is the step that occurred
when *Plasmodium* was identified a second
time in Algeria and a third time in Italy.
The deduction was being confirmed; the hy-

pothesis of the cause of malaria was well on its way to becoming accepted as true.

It is impossible to estimate the number of scientists who looked for the cause of malaria—or the number of hours, days, and years they spent with their microscopes and other laboratory equipment in their quest. It is not surprising that the task was so hard and took so long. After all, no one knew what he was looking for, or where to look.

So far, we have established two important facts about malaria.

1. Quinine is an effective remedy.
2. *Plasmodium* may be what causes malaria.

What next?

How Does *Plasmodium* Get into the Blood of Man?

To know the enemy is not to defeat it. The next important problem would be to learn more about *Plasmodium*. Where is it found outside of man? How does it get into the blood of man? How can man prevent *Plasmodium* from entering his body?

Malaria tended to occur in marshy areas: this much was known, and there had even been some experimental attacks on the problem. If we work with this hypothesis:

Malaria is always associated with marshes.

then we can make the deduction:

If we eliminate the marshes we should eliminate malaria.

In several instances this was done. Marshes were drained in localities where malaria was abundant, and the disease was greatly reduced, or even eliminated altogether. This seemed to strengthen the hypothesis that in some way marshy areas are associated with malaria. But remember the human volunteers who drank the marsh water from highly malarial regions. They did not get malaria. If these crude experiments were to be believed, it could be concluded that *Plasmodium* was not in the marsh wa-

ter. But it must be associated with *something* that disappeared when the marshes were drained.

Mosquitoes and Malaria

If the marsh *water* was not the guilty agent, but if malaria was always associated with marshes, what could be responsible? What would be some of your guesses? When you recall visits to marshes, what do you remember most vividly? Possibly it is the abundance of insects, and especially mosquitoes.

This idea must have occurred to many scientists. As early as 1717, an Italian scientist suggested that malaria was transmitted by mosquitoes. He knew that malaria decreased when swamps were drained. The mosquito population decreased at the same time. (Their breeding sites were in the swamp water.) No mosquitoes, no malaria —could this be a cause-effect relation?

In the nineteenth century, several American scientists thought the evidence suggested that mosquitoes transmitted malaria. One was a physician, A. F. A. King, who in 1883 listed twenty observations that he believed pointed to mosquitoes as a factor in malaria. For example, he wrote that people who slept out of doors were more likely to contract malaria than those who did not; people sleeping under fine nets were less susceptible to malaria than those who did not sleep under nets; malaria seemed to be a disease of the night; and individuals sleeping near a smoky fire usually did not get the disease. These observations, and others King listed, were the data he used to suggest this hypothesis:

Mosquitoes are involved in the spread of malaria.

King had this to say: ". . . while the data . . . can not be held to prove the [hypothesis], they may go so far as to initiate and encourage experiments and observations by which the truth or fallacy of the views held may be demonstrated, which, either way, will be a step in the line of progress." (Note he is saying that science advances both by finding out what is true and by eliminating what is false.)

Apparently King's hypothesis was not convincing to many people. Experimental proof was needed.

What might this proof be? Let's begin by rewording King's hypothesis:

Mosquitoes transmit Plasmodium, the cause of malaria.

If so, here are some deductions we can make:

1. *Plasmodium* should occur in mosquitoes.
2. A mosquito can acquire *Plasmodium* by biting a person ill with malaria.
3. If a person is bitten by a mosquito infected with *Plasmodium,* he should develop malaria.

The Experiments of Ross

The investigation of mosquitoes as a possible carrier of *Plasmodium* was first begun by Ronald Ross, a British army physician working in India in the 1880's. Ross first wanted to answer the simple question of whether or not *Plasmodium* could be found in a mosquito after it had bitten a person ill with malaria. He allowed a mosquito of a kind scientists have named *Anopheles* (a·NOF·e·leez) to bite a person ill with malaria. He killed the mosquito some days later and found the *Plasmodium* parasites (any organisms that grow at the expense of others) multiplying in the mosquito's stomach. This was an exceedingly important discovery. It would not have been very important if he had merely found the parasite in the mosquito's stomach after it had bitten the patient. But the parasite was multiplying—a fact suggesting that the mosquito's stomach was one of its natural homes.

Another experiment would have been to allow an infected mosquito to bite a healthy person. If the hypothesis was correct, this person should become ill with malaria. But scientists are most reluctant to use human beings for experiments when the results can be so serious. What should Ross do? He did what biologists have done time after time: if it is difficult or impractical to study the problem in one animal, they study it in another.

Ross used sparrows. It had been discovered that many animals other than man may have malaria. Sparrows are one of them. (Nearly all robins have malarial parasites too.) Ross obtained some birds with the malarial parasites in their blood and allowed mosquitoes to feed on them (Figure 1-8). Some of the mosquitoes were killed and studied at various times after their meal of blood. In each mosquito that he studied, Ross found that the parasites grew and multiplied in the wall of the mosquito's stomach for some days. Later the parasites moved into the mosquito's salivary glands.

Ross did not kill all of the infected mosquitoes. He kept some and allowed these to bite healthy sparrows. When a mosquito bites, some of the fluid of the salivary glands enters the tiny wound. The salivary fluid of the infected mosquitoes contained the malarial parasites, and these entered the sparrows' blood vessels. When Ross examined the blood of these previously healthy birds some days later, he found it teeming with malarial parasites.

Plasmodium in Man

The experiments with birds, mosquitoes, and malaria suggested that a similar relation might exist between man, mosquitoes, and malaria. It was certainly not an identical relation. Ross realized that the malarial parasite of the birds, though very similar, was not exactly the same as the one in man. He also knew from his earlier experiments that the human malarial parasite could

a Was the malarial parasite transmitted by mosquitoes?

Same bird later

b Why was the hypothesis tested with sparrows rather than man?

1-8 One test of whether mosquitoes transmitted the malarial parasite was to give them the opportunity to do so, under strict conditions of control and observation.

grow in an *Anopheles* mosquito. In the experiment with the sparrows, however, it was another kind of mosquito—a *Culex* (KYOO·leks) mosquito—that transmitted the parasite (Figure 1-8).

In the end, the hypothesis that mosquitoes transmit malaria from one human being to another could be tested only by direct experiment. This step was taken in 1898 by some Italian biologists. They allowed an *Anopheles* mosquito to bite a person ill with malaria. The mosquito was kept for a few days, to allow the *Plasmodium* parasites to grow within its body, and then it was allowed to bite a healthy individual. This person later became ill with malaria (Figure 1-9).

These early experiments on malaria in sparrows and man were rapidly extended. In a few years the main facts about the biology of malaria were known. Most of the time while the *Plasmodium* parasite is in

man, it lives in the blood. The parasite enters a red blood cell, and here it reproduces to form as many as one or two dozen parasites. Then the red blood cell bursts and liberates the parasites. Each one of these can then enter another red blood cell and repeat the cycle.

For reasons that are still not fully understood, nearly all of the parasites in the blood seem to be doing the same thing at the same time. For example, most of the red blood cells with the parasites burst open and liberate the parasites simultaneously (Figure 1-10). This is the time when the patient experiences the chills and fevers that are so typical of the disease. It takes about 48 hours, in one common type of human malaria, for the parasite to enter a red blood cell, reproduce, and cause the cell to burst, releasing more parasites. This cycle explains why attacks of this type of malaria occur every two days.

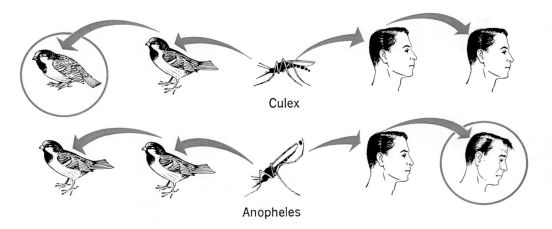

1-9 Malaria in bird and man, as transmitted by *Culex* and *Anopheles*. Malaria in man is transmitted by *Anopheles,* in birds by *Culex*.

Preventing Malaria

By the early years of the twentieth century, mankind possessed enough information to control malaria. By destroying breeding sites, such as puddles, marshes, and pools, he could reduce the *Anopheles* mosquitoes in number, or exterminate them. It was not necessary to drain the marshes—a layer of kerosene on top of the water would kill the developing mosquitoes. This would end malaria. If it proved impractical to do this, houses could be screened, and hence the chance of an individual's being bitten by *Anopheles* would be much reduced. Insect sprays were found to be of tremendous value. Another way of controlling the disease was to keep all people with malaria in screened places. When this was done, the mosquitoes could not become infected and spread the disease. Furthermore, persons who already had the disease could be treated with an efficient drug—quinine.

There is frequently a great interval between the time when man first learns how to solve a problem and the time when he has the impulse and the resources to do so. For most of the world, malaria remained a serious problem in the first half of the twentieth century. In some places public health methods did greatly reduce or even eliminate malaria. The northern United States is an example. Yet on a worldwide basis, *Plasmodium* continued to be man's number one biological enemy. As recently as 1946, in a report prepared for the Division of Medical Sciences of the National Research Council, the following statement was made: "What the actual total malarial incidence is today, no one knows, or can estimate closely. But one would venture to assume that there are not less than 3,000,000 malarial deaths and at least 300,000,000 cases of malarial fevers each year throughout the world." A decade earlier another scientist had written as follows in reference to malaria in northern India: "There is no aspect of life in that country which is not affected, either directly or indirectly, by the disease. It constitutes one of the most important causes of economic misfortune, engendering poverty, diminishing the quantity and quality of the food supply, lowering the physical and intellectual standard of the nation, and hampering increased prosperity and economic progress in every way." And this when man had the knowledge to control the disease!

This story will have a happy ending—malaria is on the way out in many nations. By 1950 the disease was essentially eradicated in the United States (Figure 1-11). In 1951 the National Malaria Society was dissolved —the job had been completed. What had happened?

Several centuries from now, when historians look back on the events of our time, they may decide that the most important consequence of World War II was that the nations of the world finally decided to join one another and battle their common enemy—malaria. It took the experience of that war to convince them that such a step was necessary. The research carried out during the war made the step economically possible.

In World War II, Japan quickly overran the countries of southeast Asia and the islands off the coast. Included in the sweep of her conquests was the island of Java. What does this have to do with the problem of malaria? In the seventeenth century, cinchona bark, from which quinine is made, was obtained from the bark of wild trees growing in South America. So many cinchona trees were killed by having their bark removed that they became scarce. Attempts were made then to grow them elsewhere. The Dutch in Java had been the most successful in this enterprise, and eventually they were producing nearly all of the cinchona bark used in the world.

When Japan conquered Java, therefore, the Allied nations lost their source of quinine. This was most unfortunate, since battles were being fought in parts of the world where malaria is a serious problem—southeast Asia, the western Pacific, and North Africa (you may recall that *Plasmodium* was discovered in Algeria). At the time the American army on Bataan in the Philippines surrendered, 85 percent of the soldiers

1-10 The temperature cycle and the *Plasmodium* cycle in malaria. Fluctuations in the temperature of the patient are correlated with the changes the parasite causes in the blood. High temperatures occur when red blood cells burst, liberating parasites.

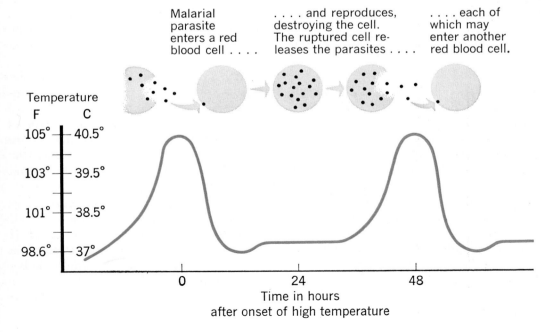

Malarial parasite enters a red blood cell . . . .

. . . . and reproduces, destroying the cell. The ruptured cell releases the parasites . . . .

. . . . each of which may enter another red blood cell.

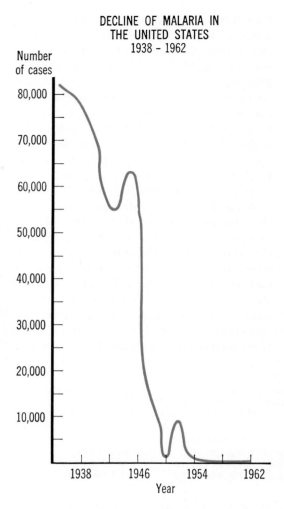

DECLINE OF MALARIA IN
THE UNITED STATES
1938 – 1962

Number
of cases

80,000

70,000

60,000

50,000

40,000

30,000

20,000

10,000

1938   1946   1954   1962
                    Year

1-11 What are some of the factors responsible for this dramatic decline in the number of people afflicted with malaria?

had malaria. During the South Pacific campaign, the armed forces of the United States suffered five times as many casualties from malaria as from combat.

Who was the real enemy? One scientist gave the simple answer, ". . . malaria had to be licked before the Japanese could be." The enemy, *Plasmodium*, was fought by the scientists, who eventually won their part of the war just as the armed forces won theirs.

Entomologists (biologists who study in-sects), physicians, and sanitary engineers went along with the soldiers. They determined the kinds of mosquitoes that were transmitting the malaria and where the mosquitoes bred. They tried to destroy the adult mosquitoes and the larval stages living in the pools and puddles of the jungle.

Back home some scientists were trying to make effective insecticides and insect repellents (the product called "6-12" was one). Others began a search for effective substitutes for quinine, so needed but no longer available for the treatment of soldiers ill with malaria. Some excellent drugs were eventually discovered, among them chloroquine. In this search thousands of chemical substances were tried. In fact, more research was undertaken to discover drugs for treating malaria than for any other wartime project except the one that led to the atomic bomb.

The chemical compound DDT, known before World War II but not used as an insecticide until 1939, was found to be effective in destroying the mosquitoes that could carry malaria. When DDT sprays are used in houses, some of the chemical remains on the walls. Months after the house has been sprayed, there may still be enough DDT on the walls to kill any *Anopheles* that happen to rest there.

With an arsenal composed of DDT, chloroquine, and many other chemical substances, it was possible to wage a successful war against *Plasmodium*. By 1960 malaria had been essentially eliminated from entire countries, such as Argentina, Italy, the U.S.S.R., The Netherlands, Venezuela, and the United States. Whereas malaria was responsible for about 3,000,000 deaths per year for the world in 1946, the total had been reduced to about 2,000,000 in 1961. If mankind continues his current strategy in the war with *Plasmodium*, malaria could become a rare disease by 1980. Thus, in your own lifetime, man's most serious biological enemy may be vanquished.

CONCLUDING REMARKS

This story has been an example of a biological problem and of how such problems are solved. As with most important biological problems, man has speculated about malaria for centuries. The folklore and imperfect observations of our ancestors provided the hints that enabled the scientists of the nineteenth century to make hypotheses about the causes of malaria. A laboratory scientist might never have thought of a possible relation between mosquitoes and malaria. But when he was told that malaria is more common in low, marshy places, he could set up a number of hypotheses to test. Could it be the humidity that promoted malaria, the stagnant water, the decaying vegetation, some plant, or some animal associated with the marshes? Any hypothesis he selected could be tested by experiment: marsh water could be drunk, mosquitoes could be destroyed, and so on.

We have learned now that it was the mosquitoes, not the marshes, that were primarily involved. But centuries went by before this hypothesis was proved. How many individuals thought that mosquitoes might be the factor but could never prove it? No one knows. But we do know that the odds against success were tremendous. In all the world there are about 2,000 species of mosquitoes, but we now know that only about 50 of these transmit malaria. Ross failed repeatedly in his early experiments with human malaria. We now know why—he was using the wrong kinds of mosquitoes (Figure 1-9). But he had an essential characteristic of a successful scientist—perseverance. Eventually he found that *Anopheles* was the kind of mosquito in which the *Plasmodium* of man would grow. With this discovery the problem of the control of malaria became answerable, in terms of eliminating the breeding places of the mosquito.

Possibly you were surprised at the slow rate of scientific progress in man's understanding of malaria. In 1717 good reasons were given for believing that mosquitoes transmit malaria. But Ross and others did not prove their theory until nearly two centuries had passed.

Why such a delay? Many factors are involved in the answer. There are endless unsolved biological problems, and far too few scientists to study them. Furthermore, as we will see time and again, progress in the biological sciences was exceedingly slow until the nineteenth century. Few biologists undertook to study malaria, and they lacked the necessary methods and equipment. The French army physician in Algeria in 1880 needed a very good microscope to see *Plasmodium* in human blood. Microscopes of the quality needed simply were not available to most physicians before about 1860.

What has it taken, then, to study the problem of malaria? Physicians and biologists to recognize the disease; physicians to treat the disease; biologists to study the mosquito; biologists and public health workers to eradicate the mosquito and its breeding places; chemists and biologists to develop insecticides to kill the adult mosquito and its young; other chemists and physicians to develop drugs to treat individuals ill with malaria; schools, books, and teachers to transmit what has been learned; and public officials to organize and direct the many projects involving malaria.

Malaria is everybody's business. All biological problems are.

Now that we have seen how one biological problem has been studied, let us begin another. This second problem is one of the most basic in all biology: what is the origin of living organisms? It has taken man a long time to solve this one—and, in fact, he is far from knowing the entire answer. The general methods we used for studying malaria will be useful for the next problem. We will also learn some of the other methods that scientists use.

GUIDE QUESTIONS AND PROBLEMS

1. a. What is morphology?
   b. What is physiology?
   c. How are morphology and physiology related?
   d. What biological principle is illustrated by the relationship in question 1c?
2. a. What is ecology?
   b. Why do different types of plants grow in a desert and in a marsh?
   c. What biological principle is illustrated by your answer to question 2b?
3. What does a biologist do when his original hypothesis is not supported by his experiments?
4. An estimated 200,000,000 cases of malaria occurred in 1961. Is the prediction that malaria will be all but wiped out by 1980 a reasonable one?
5. What is the relation between the life cycle of *Plasmodium* in the blood of man and the symptoms of malaria?
6. Suppose one of the volunteers who drank swamp water had contracted malaria. Would this fact alone have provided conclusive evidence of the cause of malaria? Why or why not?
7. How could it be demonstrated that animals such as dinosaurs once lived on the earth?
8. The limbs of the present-day horse bear evidence of a relationship to a three-toed ancestor. The lower leg bone of the modern horse ends in a single hoof. On either side of the bone are "splint bones," traces of bones in the three-toed ancestor. The splint bones have no function in the horse of today. Does this refute the idea that structure usually implies function?
9. What kind of environment would be suggested by
   a. A group of plants with very deep, much branched root systems?
   b. A clump of willow trees?
   c. Many cattail plants?
   d. A frog?
   e. A group of cactus plants?
10. What is the role of each of the following in solving a problem scientifically: data, hypothesis, deduction, experiment, confirmation, equipment?
11. Which of the following is the cause of malaria?
    a. Marshes
    b. *Anopheles*
    c. *Plasmodium*
    d. The rupture of red blood cells by the *Plasmodium*

SUGGESTIONS FOR ADDITIONAL READING

Books

Beveridge, W. I. B., *The Art of Scientific Investigation.* New York, Vintage Books, 1957.
> An interesting development of the "methods of operation" of working scientists. Most of the examples are biological.

Bonner, J. T., *The Ideas of Biology.* New York, Harper & Row, 1962.
> A well-written and interesting account of several of the themes introduced in this chapter.

De Kruif, Paul, *Microbe Hunters.* [1926] New York, Pocket Books, 1959.
> Excitingly written story of some discoveries and discoverers in biology. The chapter on Sir Ronald Ross contains a more complete account of the malaria story.

Magazines and Journals

Alvarado, C. A., and L. J. Bruce-Chwatt, "Malaria." *Scientific American,* Vol. 206 (May 1962), pp. 86–98.

2

LIFE FROM LIFE

When you think of "life," what first comes to mind? Is it movement, a rose, breathing, animals, a beating heart, or something else you associate with things that are alive? Think about this question and then define "life" as carefully as you can.

Now let us test your definition. Will it apply to all animals and all plants that are known to you? Will it apply to tiny living creatures, such as *Plasmodium,* mentioned in Chapter 1? Will it apply to a pea seed, a developing egg of a chicken, a potato? Will your definition distinguish between a pea seed, a chicken egg, and a potato when they are alive and these same objects after they have been cooked? Will your definition distinguish among a tree, a piece of firewood taken from the tree, and the ashes remaining when the wood has been burned?

The chances are that you did not succeed in making a definition of life that would work in *every* case. But do not feel discouraged—no one has ever done so.

When a scientist repeatedly finds himself unable to answer a question, he begins to wonder if he is asking the right question— or if he has asked the question in the right way. This is our trouble now. The question

"What is life?" is so general that it cannot easily be studied in a scientific manner. Scientists have learned time and again that it is usually better to ask a very specific question.

For example, we might have first decided that the chief characteristic of life is movement. Probably all of the animals with which you are familiar can move—fish swim, birds fly, and dogs run. We could ask our question: "Are all living things capable of movement?" The answer to this question could then be obtained by examining all the living creatures that we could find. Most of the things that we call animals would be found to be capable of movement. Some might be rather slow about it, however— think of snails! But what about mushrooms and trees? Do they move? Furthermore, a river moves, but is it alive?

The chances are that we would soon discover that "the ability to move" is not a very satisfactory definition of life. Some things that are alive do not move, and not all things that move are alive. If we are to define life adequately, all things that are alive must conform to our definition, and no things that are not alive can conform.

We can work toward a definition of life that is adequate for nearly all purposes by asking some more questions. "Where do living things come from?" We can all answer that one—from their parents. That is, the plants and animals of one generation come from the plants and animals of the preceding generation. And, of course, the parents and offspring are the same kind—or **species** (spee·sheez)—of plant or animal. But can you answer the next question: "Do living things come *only* from other living things?" Once again the answer is obvious for many situations. The familiar green plants grow from seeds produced by individuals of the same species. Puppies are produced only by the mating of dogs. Is it true that all living things come from parents that are similar to the offspring? What about tiny creatures such as the bacteria and viruses? Do they come *only* from other bacteria and viruses?

Questions of this sort have been asked for at least 2,500 years. You may be surprised, however, to learn that what is now regarded as the correct answer has been accepted for less than a century!

HYPOTHESES OF THE ORIGIN OF ORGANISMS

Until the last part of the nineteenth century, it was generally believed that living things originated in one of three ways (Figure 2-1). First, they could result from the reproduction of other living creatures of their own kind. Second, they could result from the reproduction of very different kinds of living creatures. Third, they could be formed, spontaneously, solely from materials that were not alive. We now believe that only the first method occurs on the earth at the present time. But let us trace the history of these various hypotheses, which relate to one of the most fundamental biological problems.

The Barnacle Goose

The idea that offspring are produced by parents of their own kind or species—or, as we say, that "like produces like"—is a familiar one. Another idea, however—that "like produces *unlike*"—was regarded for centuries as a way of reproduction. The origin of the barnacle goose can serve as one example. We will let a biologist writing in 1657 tell the story (his words have been modernized somewhat):

> There is a bird in Brittany that the English call a Barnacle or a Brant Goose. . . . It is smaller than a wild goose. The breast is somewhat black, the rest is ash-colored. It flies as wild geese do, cries, and haunts lakes, and spoils the corn. Scholars question the origin of it very much. Some say it breeds from rotten

wood, some from apples, some of fruit that is like a heap of leaves. . . . Boethius has written as follows: "If you throw wood into the sea, in time worms breed in it, and these gradually grow a head, feet, wings, and lastly, feathers. When they are fully grown, they are as large as geese and they fly upward as other birds do—using their wings to carry them through the air."

[Next the biologist describes an actual case that supports his quotation from Boethius.] A great ship, having the name *Christopher*, had been at anchor for three years in one of the Hebrides. It was drawn up on land and the part that had been below the water line was full of holes. There were worms in the holes. Some were unformed and not like birds. Others were perfect birds.

We now know this to be a charming myth (Figure 2-2). The point to be emphasized, however, is that before 1700 the prevailing view among those interested in animals was that one species of wild goose came from worms that lived in the sea. At the same time it was known, of course, that the domestic varieties of geese developed from eggs laid by individuals of the same kind as the young. Clearly nature was using very different methods to arrive at similar ends. There seemed to be little order or reason in nature. Nearly anything seemed possible.

Why was this hypothesis eventually abandoned? You might guess that some biologists began to attack the problem by experimental means. They might have brought some of the worms into their laboratories, subjected them to various experimental conditions, and waited to see if any changed into geese. But remember that this hypothesis dated to the middle of the seventeenth century. It would have been most unusual for anyone to study a problem by experimentation.

2-1 THREE IDEAS ABOUT REPRODUCTION

a Reproduction of offspring from parents of the same kind

b Transformation of one kind of living thing into another

c Spontaneous generation from mud or earth or remains of dead plants and animals

Goose barnacles

Barnacle goose

The problem was not solved in such a direct manner. However, careful observation revealed no support for the hypothesis that a certain kind of goose develops from worms. Biologists became more and more familiar with marine creatures. They observed that pieces of wood or the bottoms of ships became covered with many kinds of animals and plants. These living creatures were no more produced by the wood or the seawater than animals and plants living on land are produced by the earth.

Slowly the true story emerged (Figure 2-2). The worms, which have the common name shipworm, are really not worms at all, but marine animals related to mussels and clams. Of even greater interest is another animal known as the goose barnacle. The goose barnacle frequently grows on logs and other wooden objects floating in the sea. If one uses his imagination, he can see that the shape of the goose barnacle does have a vague resemblance to the shape of a bird's head (Figures 2-1 and 2-2).

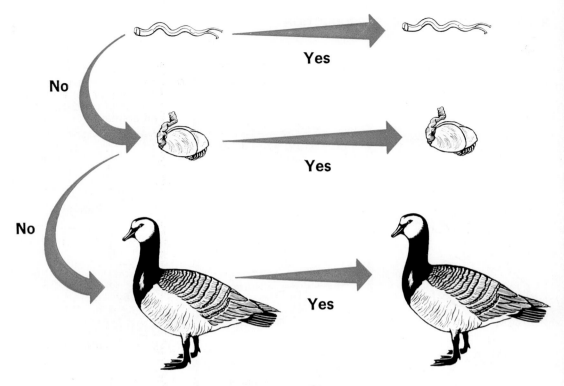

No

Yes

Yes

No

Yes

2-2 Life exhibits patterns in reproduction. Parent and offspring are always the same kind of organism. Worms cannot change into barnacles, nor barnacles into geese.

The shipworm and the goose barnacle are distinctive animals. They do not change into each other or into barnacle geese—any more than cows change into horses, or rye into wheat. The myth was exploded in part by better observations of shipworms and goose barnacles. It was also partly destroyed in another way. Other observers found that the barnacle goose breeds in the Far North—and it lays eggs and the young hatch, just as in the case of the barnyard goose. Why, then, was it necessary to assume a more complicated explanation?

This pleasant myth still lingers in the common names we give to the two principal animals involved: the "goose barnacle" and the "barnacle goose."

There were other tales of organisms of one kind producing organisms of a startlingly different kind. The tree that pro-

duces lambs is an example (Figure 2-3). As the years and centuries passed, however, biologists began to reject entirely the hypothesis that one species of animal or plant can suddenly change into another. This method of reproduction, therefore, was gradually eliminated from the list of possibilities being studied.

Spontaneous Generation

The third type of reproduction mentioned earlier in the chapter, the formation of living creatures from materials that are not alive, is known as the hypothesis of **spontaneous generation.** It was accepted as a fact by at least *some* competent biologists until the end of the nineteenth century.

Belief in spontaneous generation goes back to classical times. Aristotle (384–322 B.C.), the famous Greek philosopher, scientist, and teacher (Alexander the Great was his student), believed in spontaneous generation. Here are shortened and modified versions of some of his statements in the *Historia Animalium*:

> The great majority of fish develop from eggs. There are some fish, however, that proceed from mud and sand. A pond near Cnidos dried up—even the mud at the bottom. Later the pond was filled by rain. It was then observed that the pond contained many tiny fishes. The fishes in question are a kind of mullet. From this fact it is clear that certain fishes come spontaneously into existence, not being derived from eggs or from copulation.

Here is Aristotle's account of the spontaneous origin of eels:

> This species comes neither from pairing nor from the egg. There can be no doubt that this is so. For there are cases where a pond has been drained and the mud dredged away. Later, when the pond filled with rain, water eels appeared. The eels came from substances that form spontaneously in mud and in humid ground.

The same type of reproduction was thought to occur in insects:

> Some insects are derived from insects of the same kind. Other insects are not derived from living parents but they are formed spontaneously. Some of the latter are formed from dew falling on leaves; others in timber, either green or dry; some in the hair of animals; and still others in the flesh or in the excrements.

These beliefs, which were based on careless observations, seem quaint to us today, but their influence on the progress of biological thought was enormous. Aristotle was a recognized authority in classical times. During the Dark Ages of Western civilization, his writings were preserved and stud-

From Henry Lee, *The Vegetable Lamb of Tartary;*
A Curious Fable of the Cotton Plant. London, 1887.

2-3 Travelers returning to Europe from the Orient brought tales of "wool" growing on trees! What they had actually observed, or were told about, was tree cotton, which they mistook for wool. Tales were told and retold, with inevitable modifications, until "the mutton tree" shown here was described by one imaginative artist.

ied by Arabian scholars. In the early years of the Renaissance, Western scholars obtained copies of Aristotle's writings from the Arabs. There then followed a period of several centuries during which Aristotle's beliefs were accepted as fact by many scholars: one learned about biology more from Aristotle than from personal observation and experimentation. If this seems surprising today, we must recall again that scientific observation and experimentation were rare until recent centuries.

It is therefore not surprising that belief in spontaneous generation was widespread among educated people. Now if one believes in the occurrence of spontaneous generation, he cannot also strictly believe in an orderly origin of living things. Of course, Aristotle and other observers knew that many kinds of fishes mated, laid eggs, and that the eggs grew into fishes of the same kind as the parents. This is an example of genetic continuity, now regarded as a fundamental fact of biology. But these early writers also believed that other kinds of fishes might be formed solely from the mud in the bottom of a pond. In this case there would be no mating of the parents, no eggs deposited.

A young fish developing from eggs has ancestors; one formed from the ooze at the bottom of the pond has none. Both would give the same end products—animals recognized as "fishes" with scales, fins, and essentially the same internal organs—yet these would be formed in fundamentally different ways.

Nearly two thousand years after Aristotle wrote of spontaneous generation, biologists were expressing similar views. Jean-Baptiste van Helmont, in a book published in 1652, stated that if wheat grains and a dirty shirt were put in a pot, mice would be formed from the interaction of the grains and the dirt of the shirt.

It is probable that most of van Helmont's fellow biologists would have been dubious of this recipe for making mice. Yet nearly all of them would have explained some other familiar observations on the basis of spontaneous generation. The most familiar examples related to objects that were decaying. Who has not observed the appearance of maggots in decaying flesh? In warm weather the carcass of an animal rapidly becomes filled with writhing maggots. Where do the maggots, or "worms" as they are often called, come from? Most biologists of the seventeenth century would have answered, "From the meat through the process of spontaneous generation." One biologist did not, and by so doubting the prevailing theory, opened a new chapter in our understanding of life. This biologist was Francesco Redi.

The Experiments of Redi

Francesco Redi (1626–1697) was an Italian who served as a physician to the Medici family who ruled Florence. Like many physicians of those days, he was also a biologist. He was much interested in the question of the origin of living things, and he was, of course, aware of the general belief that maggots are generated spontaneously from rotting meat. To him, unlike others, the belief must have seemed ill-founded, for he decided to put the matter to a test. His action was especially noteworthy for one who lived in a time when it was customary to seek answers to biological questions in the writings of Aristotle and other ancient authorities. Perhaps we could say that the approach of most of Redi's contemporaries was, "Study books, not nature." But Redi thought otherwise, and his method of approach can be illustrated by an Arab proverb at the beginning of his book: "Experiment adds to knowledge, credulity leads to error." So Redi began to conduct experiments to test the theory of spontaneous generation. Here follows a modified version of his account of his experiments.

PRELIMINARY OBSERVATIONS. The belief of ancient and modern authorities, as well as the popular belief, is that maggots are generated from decaying bodies and filth. Being desirous of testing this belief, I made the following experiment.

I placed three dead snakes in a box and allowed them to decay. In three days the snakes were covered with small maggots. Eventually all of the flesh of the snakes was consumed and only the bones were left. On the nineteenth day some of the maggots stopped moving and behaved as if they were asleep. They seemed to shorten and take on an oval shape, like an egg. Later they became hard little balls, resembling the **pupae** (PYOO·pee) formed by caterpillars.

I put some of these little balls in a glass vessel, which was then carefully covered with paper. After eight days the little balls broke open and out of each came a gray fly. At first the fly moved very slowly and the wings were closed. After a few minutes the wings began to unfold and soon a fly of normal appearance had formed. All the flies matured likewise.

So far Redi had repeated a familiar observation: maggots appear in decaying meat. Others would have interpreted these facts as illustrating the spontaneous generation of maggots from decaying meat. But Redi had a different hypothesis.

HYPOTHESIS. Having considered these things, I began to wonder if the maggots could be the offspring of flies and not derived from the decay of the meat. Such a hypothesis seemed likely, for I had observed flies hovering over the meat before it became covered with maggots. Furthermore, the flies that hovered over the meat were of the same kind as those that later emerged from the meat.

Redi was here discarding the hypothesis of spontaneous generation. In its stead his hypothesis was: the flies that were observed to hover over the meat are the parents of those that later formed in the meat. The maggots then, could be merely a stage in the development of the flies. Now if Redi's hypothesis was true, he could (and did) make the simple deduction:

DEDUCTION. If adult flies are kept away from the decaying meat, maggots should not form in the meat.

A deduction of this sort can be put to an experimental test (Figure 2-4).

EXPERIMENT 1. Belief would be vain without the confirmation of experiment. Hence I took four wide-mouthed flasks. Into one I put a dead snake, into another some fish, into still another some eels, and into the last a slice of veal. I left these flasks open. I took four other flasks and filled them in the same way. These flasks, however, were closed.

It was not long before the meat and fish in the open flasks were covered with mag-

gots. Flies were seen entering and leaving at will. In the flasks that had been closed I saw no maggots, even after many days had passed.

CONCLUSIONS. From these experiments I thought I had proved that the flesh of dead animals could not generate maggots spontaneously. The maggots could only arise if flies laid eggs on the meat and these hatched into maggots.

SOURCES OF POSSIBLE ERROR. There is a possible objection to the experiment, however. The flasks in which no maggots appeared had been closed and the air could not penetrate or circulate. Possibly it was for this reason, and not for the absence of flies, that maggots were not spontaneously generated. Therefore, in order to remove all doubt, I carried out another experiment.

EXPERIMENT 2. I placed some meat and fish in a large vase and covered it with a fine net. This would allow air but not flies to enter the vase. As a further protection against flies, I placed the vase in a frame covered with the fine net.

Maggots never appeared in the meat. It was observed, however, that flies would light on the outside net and deposit maggots there.

Redi conducted many other experiments to test the prevailing belief that spontaneous generation was possible. His general conclusion was as follows:

When meats, fish, and milk products are protected from flies, they do not generate maggots. The same is true for fruits and vegetables, whether raw or cooked.

Just what had Redi proved? Had he shown that spontaneous generation is impossible? The answer to the second question is "No." What he had shown was that under the conditions of his experiments

a Redi prepared four flasks of animal flesh, and left each flask open to flies.

maggots did not arise spontaneously in decaying meat. Maggots appeared only if flies were allowed to lay eggs on the meat. Redi's experiments did not exclude the following possibilities.

1. Spontaneous generation of maggots might be possible under conditions that he did not provide in his experiments.
2. Other kinds of living things might be spontaneously generated.

Nevertheless Redi did feel justified in proposing a general theory:

I shall express my belief that after the first animals and plants were formed on the earth all others were formed by reproduction. There was no spontaneous generation.

Today we agree with this statement of Redi's. It is of interest to note, however, that Redi made other observations which convinced him that spontaneous generation *might* occur. In fact, he believed that some kinds of insects are produced not in the usual way by their parents, but by the juices of plants. In this instance, his observations were faulty and misleading.

The insects in question were those formed in the enlargements called **insect galls** in the leaves and stems of plants. Today we know how the galls are produced by insects, and we can understand the reasons why Redi was misled. He missed making one crucial observation.

A female gall wasp injects an egg into a leaf or stem of a plant (Figure 2-5). The egg develops into a maggotlike embryo. The plant responds by forming a large growth, the gall, around the developing insect embryo. Some galls are about the size of a pea; others may be as large as a walnut. The insect embryo eventually grows into an adult gall wasp and bores its way out of the gall. (Not all galls are formed by gall wasps. Some are caused by other kinds of insects, worms, bacteria, or even other kinds of plants.)

Redi was unaware that gall wasps cause the plant to produce galls. He did not observe the female insect laying her eggs in the plant. Since the developing gall had no hole in its surface, Redi concluded that the wasp embryo must be formed from within. Hence he believed the gall wasp arose not from gall wasp parents, but by spontaneous generation from plant juices.

OF SPONTANEOUS GENERATION

b Four other flasks were prepared identically, but these were covered to exclude flies.

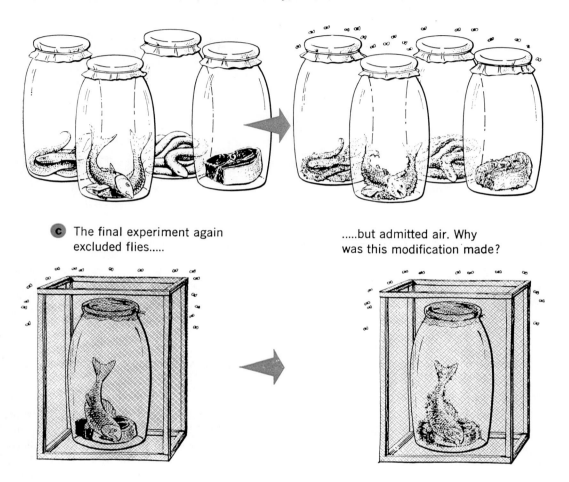

c The final experiment again excluded flies.....

.....but admitted air. Why was this modification made?

The mysterious origin of gall wasps was partially solved by another Italian biologist, Marcello Malpighi (1628–1694). Redi and Malpighi both lived at the same time, but Redi seems not to have known of Malpighi's work. Communication at that time was not as easy as it is today.

Apart from his doubts on gall insects, Redi was convinced that spontaneous generation did not occur. This was an important intellectual step in the development of biological theory. The chief importance of

Redi's work, however, was that he tested his beliefs with observation and experiment. In so doing, he was one of the first biologists to use an "Experimental Method." At a time when most philosophers believed that one could obtain answers to biological questions by thought or reading alone, Redi stated that "belief would be vain without the confirmation of experiment." This point of view proved a most fruitful one in the history of the science that came to be known as biology.

EDUCATIONAL RESOURCE CENTER
Greenville College
Greenville, Illinois 62246

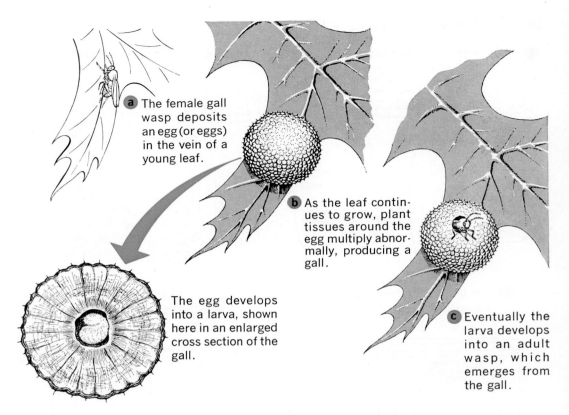

a The female gall wasp deposits an egg (or eggs) in the vein of a young leaf.

b As the leaf continues to grow, plant tissues around the egg multiply abnormally, producing a gall.

The egg develops into a larva, shown here in an enlarged cross section of the gall.

c Eventually the larva develops into an adult wasp, which emerges from the gall.

2-5 The life cycle of an oak gall wasp. Redi observed only steps **b** and **c**. Being unaware of step **a,** he assumed that the larva was formed spontaneously from plant juices.

Redi's results seemed conclusive, insofar as one man's work can be. But on such an important topic they alone would not have convinced many of his fellow scientists. What was needed was *confirmation*. Others must repeat his experiments or do similar experiments. If the same results were obtained, then Redi's general hypothesis that life comes only from life would be more secure. Many other men performed experiments similar to Redi's. The general conclusion was that maggots and other animals were not produced spontaneously. Redi's experimental findings were confirmed time after time.

The hypothesis that living things come only from other living things is called **biogenesis** (by·o·JEN·e·sis). In contrast, the hypothesis that living things can arise from nonliving things can be called either spontaneous generation or **abiogenesis** (ab·ih·o·JEN·e·sis). The work of Redi and others abolished the latter theory—but only for a time. The question was soon to arise again —on a different field of battle.

THE THREE HUNDRED YEAR DEBATE— BIOGENESIS OR ABIOGENESIS?

In the latter part of the seventeenth century, the entire question of spontaneous generation was reopened by the exciting world discovered by Antony van Leeuwenhoek (1632–1723). Leeuwenhoek lived most of his life in the Dutch town of Delft, where he spent much time studying objects with microscopes (Figure 2-6). He made many important discoveries, but the ones that concern us now are those that revealed to a much surprised seventeenth-century world the wonder of microscopic life.

Leeuwenhoek's Microscopic Life

Leeuwenhoek examined with his microscope drops of water from marshes, from the river at Delft, and from rainwater that had stood in pots. In water from all these sources, he saw numerous tiny living creatures (Figure 2-6). Here was a whole world of living organisms, tiny animals and plants, that no one had seen before. No one *could* have seen them, of course, until the necessary tool—a microscope—was available.

What was the origin of these tiny animals and plants? Leeuwenhoek's opinion was clear. His discovery "must surely convince all of the absurdity of these old opinions that living creatures can be produced from corruption or putrefaction."

But other biologists were not convinced. Gradually they gave up the idea that the larger animals—mice, worms, maggots, geese, and flies—could be produced spontaneously, but what about the microscopic forms? Perhaps these could arise spontaneously. There were many observations that could be interpreted this way. If small amounts of organic matter—for example, chopped hay or a few seeds—were put in pure rainwater, soon there would be a tremendous number of microscopic animals and plants. Were these generated from the materials put into the water? It was easy to see that all the philosophical ingredients necessary for a renewed debate were present in the question of the origin of these microscopic plants and animals. It was also easy to see that the question could not be settled one way or another by Leeuwenhoek's *opinion,* or by anyone else's opinion. Redi's remark was still valid: "Belief would be vain without the confirmation of experi-

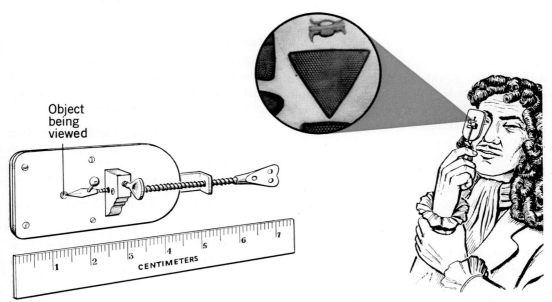

Object being viewed

Photo courtesy of J. G. Cittert-Eymers, Utrecht University Museum

2-6 Leeuwenhoek and one of his microscopes. Notice how different this instrument is from the microscopes of today. The photograph is of a diatom, a microscopic plant that is common in pond water. The photograph was taken recently through another of Leeuwenhoek's original microscopes.

ment." Only through experimentation could *either* of the opposing groups of scientists hope to establish its point of view as correct.

For the next three hundred years biologists debated fiercely the question of the origin of microorganisms. One group—the abiogenesists—maintained that the microorganisms were produced by spontaneous generation. The opposing group—the biogenesists—maintained that microorganisms were produced by the reproduction of other microorganisms.

Life in a Hay Infusion

Fortunately the debate between the biogenesists and the abiogenesists was usually based on the same general type of observation—the presence of life in a **hay infusion.** It was an observation that anyone could make. The recipe is simple: Take a few pieces of hay and chop them up; put the chopped hay in about 500 ml (or 2 cups) of water; boil for 10 minutes; pour the hay infusion into a glass container, and leave it exposed to the air (Figure 2-7).

For the first few days, the liquid in the hay infusion will be clear. If one examines a drop of the liquid under the microscope, it will seem to be free of organisms. After a few more days, however, the liquid will probably appear slightly cloudy. If a drop of the infusion is now examined under the microscope, it will be seen teeming with living creatures. Many will be animals we now call **protozoans** (pro·toh·ZOH·anz). There will also be much smaller creatures— bacteria. Molds, too, will frequently appear.

This was the basic observation, and it was made both by those biologists who believed in spontaneous generation and by those who believed life comes only from life. Furthermore, both groups agreed on an important point: since the hay infusion had been boiled at the start, any life within it would have been killed. Therefore, the protozoans and bacteria must have devel-

oped in one way or another after the hay infusion had cooled.

The believers in spontaneous generation —the abiogenesists—would give their expected explanation: the protozoans and bacteria were generated from the hay and water. The biogenesists had another explanation: the air to which the infusions were exposed must somehow contain the **spores** of protozoans and bacteria. These spores could be thought of as being the protozoans and bacteria in some inactive form and so small as to be invisible to the eye. The hypothetical spores were assumed to be inactive and not dead, because once they entered the hay infusion they would change into active creatures.

The explanation of the biogenesists seemed "farfetched" to the abiogenesists. If the explanation was correct, then pure air was pretty complex stuff. Every time a person took a breath, he could be inhaling bacteria and protozoans and all sorts of other weird microscopic creatures! The burden of proof was on the biogenesists.

Joblot and Biogenesis

The biogenesists' explanation, strange as it may have seemed, had one tremendous virtue: *it could be tested by the usual scientific procedures.* Let us try.

HYPOTHESIS. Protozoans and bacteria that appear in a boiled hay infusion come solely from "spores" of these organisms, which occur in the air.

If this is true, we can make a useful deduction.

DEDUCTION. If air containing spores is prevented from coming in contact with a boiled hay infusion, bacteria and protozoans should not develop in the infusion.

This deduction can be tested by simple experiments. Here is a paraphrased synopsis of one performed by Louis Joblot (1645– 1723) in 1711 (Figure 2-8).

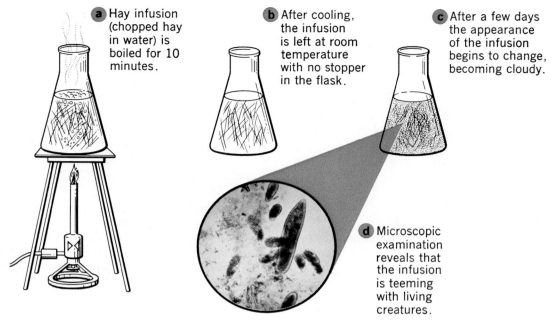

a Hay infusion (chopped hay in water) is boiled for 10 minutes.

b After cooling, the infusion is left at room temperature with no stopper in the flask.

c After a few days the appearance of the infusion begins to change, becoming cloudy.

d Microscopic examination reveals that the infusion is teeming with living creatures.

Photo by George Schwartz

2-7 Preparation of a hay infusion. The appearance of microorganisms in an infusion that has been boiled to kill such organisms is easily explained today. For three hundred years, however, it misled many biologists into believing that the microscopic life they observed in boiled infusions was proof of spontaneous generation.

EXPERIMENT. I boiled some hay in water for half an hour. I then put equal quantities of this hay infusion in two vessels of approximately the same size. Before the infusion had cooled, I closed one of the vessels with parchment. The other vessel was left uncovered. After several days organisms appeared in the vessel that had been left open. There were none in the vessel that had been closed. The closed vessel was kept for a considerable time to see if any organisms appeared, but none did.

We can sum up Joblot's experimental finding as follows:

CONCLUSION. In this experiment, no organisms appeared in the vessel from which the air was excluded—but they did appear in the vessel that was open to the air. If the organisms were spontaneously produced by the hay infusion, they should have appeared in *both* vessels. They did not. The results of the experiment, therefore, can be explained better on the basis of spores of organisms coming from the air.

Why did Joblot use two vessels—one closed and one open? If he suspected that the air was the source of contamination, would not the closed vessel be the only one he needed? Not in a proper experiment. If he had used only the closed vessel, one could criticize the experiment as follows: the reason that life never appeared in the vessel is that the infusion was no good. Joblot had to make sure that the infusion was suitable for the growth of organisms— hence the need for a vessel to be left open.

The open vessel was the **control** in his experiment. The control vessel and the ex-

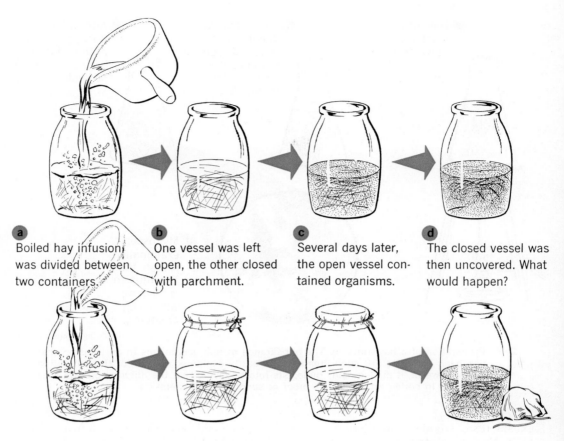

2-8 Joblot's experiment. One set of vessels was the control, the other the experimental set. The results led Joblot to agree with Leeuwenhoek that air was the source of the microorganisms that appeared in hay infusions.

perimental vessel were identical: they contained samples of the same infusion, kept at the same temperature, and with all other conditions identical—except for one. In this and all experiments, a scientist tries to keep his experiments and controls under the same conditions—except for the one condition he is testing. In Joblot's experiment the condition being tested was exposure to air. The experimental vessel was closed; the control vessel was open. Everything else was the same. (Suppose that microorganisms had appeared neither in the control vessel nor in the experimental vessel. What conclusions about the origin of microorganisms would then have been possible?)

Can you apply the same line of reasoning to Redi's experiments (Figure 2-4)? What condition was Redi testing? What conclusions would have been possible if he had obtained the same results with both sets of flasks?

Joblot studied his findings and decided to carry his observations one step further. Possibly the hay infusion in the closed vessel had lost some "vital force" by being closed. He could test this by removing the parchment cover. He did so and found that the infusion, which had remained clear for days, soon was cloudy with microorganisms.

Joblot, then, agreed with Leeuwenhoek that air was the source of the bacteria and protozoans that developed in hay infusions. But the opinions of the two are not of equal merit. Leeuwenhoek's opinion was unsupported by evidence. Joblot's opinion was supported by the results of a well-planned experiment.

Needham and Abiogenesis

Possibly you are convinced by Joblot's experiments, but the question was far from closed. For the next two and a half centuries, experiments were performed with hay infusions and other liquids, and conflicting results were obtained. The English biologist John Turberville Needham (1713–1781) boiled mutton gravy, poured it into a glass vial, corked the vial, and waited. In a few days the gravy was swarming with living creatures. The same results were obtained when he made infusions by boiling seeds of corn, wheat, and pumpkin. This gave comfort to the biologists who believed in spontaneous generation.

Spallanzani and Biogenesis

An Italian biologist, Lazzaro Spallanzani (1729–1799), repeated Needham's experiments but failed to obtain any evidence for spontaneous generation. When his infusions were boiled and carefully closed, they remained free of microorganisms. But the more Spallanzani worked, the more he realized that these "simple" experiments are not really so simple to perform. First he found that his infusions must be boiled for many minutes if they were to remain sterile, or free of life. He also found it necessary to close the vessels very carefully. In fact, they had to be closed so carefully that air could not seep into the vessels. Needham had used corks. These did not make an airtight seal. Spallanzani found it necessary to make airtight seals on his vessels.

Spallanzani then did an experiment that proved to be very important, since it revealed the *source of error* in Needham's work. He put infusions into eight contain-ers and boiled all of them. Four were carefully closed with corks. The other four were closed with airtight seals. The results were dramatic. There were abundant growths of organisms in all the vessels closed with corks. There were no organisms in the vessels with airtight seals.

Was the matter settled? Not at all. Prevailing opinions are hard to change. Those who believed in spontaneous generation were clearly on the defensive, but they were far from being defeated. They suggested that *air* was needed for spontaneous generation to occur! When Spallanzani made airtight seals, he may have been setting up conditions that prevented spontaneous generation from occurring. How could the biogenesists answer that one?

What a dilemma! The abiogenesists argued that air was necessary for spontaneous generation to occur. Their opponents, the biogenesists, maintained that air was a source of contamination. The abiogenesists needed air to *prove* the theory of spontaneous generation, and the biogenesists required that air be excluded if the theory was to be *disproved!*

Pouchet and Abiogenesis

A climax to the long debate came in the last half of the nineteenth century. It began in this way. A respected and skillful French scientist, F. A. Pouchet (1800–1872), performed hundreds of experiments with infusions. He was aware of the criticism of the biogenesists; namely, that natural air was contaminated with the spores of microorganisms. To avoid this difficulty, he made his own "air" in one of his experiments. That is, he prepared a hay infusion and then added nitrogen and oxygen to form an artificial air above the infusion. In a few days the infusion contained a rich variety of protozoans, bacteria, and molds.

In another experiment, Pouchet even made the water for the infusion! He burned hydrogen gas in air to form water. This water was then boiled with hay to make an infusion. In spite of all his care to prevent contamination, the infusion soon became filled with organisms.

Pouchet reached the conclusion that seemed reasonable to him: spontaneous generation was possible.

Pasteur and Biogenesis

Pouchet's claims did not go unchallenged. One of the greatest biologists of all time, Louis Pasteur (1822–1895) of France, was one challenger (Figure 2-9). According to Pasteur, the organisms that appeared in infusions were derived only from spores present in the air. Thus, if life appeared in Pouchet's infusions, this probably meant that the experiments had not been carried out properly. Pasteur's reasoning was easy to identify: he was obviously a biogenesist.

Pasteur made infusions of yeast and sugar. When exposed to air, they soon had a rich growth of bacteria and protozoans. When he was careful to prevent air from reaching some of the infusions, however, no organisms appeared.

But how could this solve the matter? Pouchet and Pasteur were both doing the same, or nearly the same, experiments. True, Pouchet generally used a hay infusion, and Pasteur used an infusion of yeast to which sugar was added. Yet spontaneous generation occurred for Pouchet and not for Pasteur.

You must feel by now that this argument is of the "yes it is, no it isn't" type. Each side contradicts the other, and there is no progress. The French Academy of Science sought to hasten a solution by offering a prize for the best essay on spontaneous generation. Pasteur described his experiments and beliefs, and in 1862, was awarded the prize. Pasteur concluded that if air was really pure—that is, without spores—it would never contaminate infusions.

And yet Pasteur had not won his argument. Pouchet and others who believed in spontaneous generation attacked Pasteur's experiments and conclusions. Finally the French Academy appointed a Commission of noted biologists to judge the dispute. In order to make the problem as specific as possible, the commission agreed on a statement that could be tested. This is a synopsis of what they said:

> It is possible to take the air of certain places, air that has not been subjected to any physical or chemical changes, and demonstrate that this air will *not* cause organisms to grow in infusions.

Pouchet disputed the statement; he believed that air, if not modified by physical or chemical means, would enable spontaneous generation to occur in an infusion. Pasteur, on the other hand, supported the statement: he believed that if he could get really pure air, that is, air free of spores of microorganisms, then this air could not cause the infusion to produce organisms.

The rules were agreed upon. The battle began. On June 22, 1864, Pouchet and Pasteur appeared before the Commission of the French Academy. Each was to perform his experiments in the presence of the members of the Commission.

How was Pasteur to get his "pure" air? He began by submitting the evidence of past experiments. In 1860, four years before, he had thought that perhaps the air of the high mountains would be relatively free of dust and the spores of microorganisms. To test this hypothesis, he had carried out the following experiment. Infusions were prepared and boiled in a number of glass flasks. While the infusions were still hot, the necks of the flasks were sealed with a flame. Every infusion prepared in this way remained free of organisms. Some time later, Pasteur took some of the sealed flasks, packed them on a mule, and set off for the French Alps.

When he and the mule had reached their destination, a point high on a mountain near Mont Blanc in the Alps, the experiment was continued. The necks of the flasks were cut open with a file. The infusions were exposed briefly to the air and then the openings in the necks were sealed again. Back down the mountain came the mule. The flasks were returned to the laboratory. What was observed to happen in the flasks subsequently?

Of 20 flasks exposed at one place, in only one did organisms grow. This was indeed an impressive demonstration of the probable truth of his hypothesis.

Remember that the experiment had taken place in 1860. Pasteur kept some of the flasks, and on the historic day of June 22, 1864, when he appeared before the Commission of the French Academy, he had three of the flasks with him. He showed them to the judges, who saw that there appeared to be no life within them.

But the members of the Commission wanted to know more. Was Pasteur's report of his experiment really accurate? And was there really oxygen, which they knew to be necessary for life, in the flasks? Flask No. 1 was opened and the air analyzed. It contained almost 21 percent oxygen—the normal proportion.

Were the infusions capable of supporting life? Perhaps they had remained lifeless for four years simply because they did not contain the necessary substances for the growth of the microorganisms. Flask No. 2 was opened and left exposed to the air. In three days it contained a huge population of organisms.

Flask No. 3 was left unaltered and it remained sterile—as it had been for four years.

Some of the flasks that Pasteur used in his experiments of 1860 are still on exhibit at the Pasteur Institute in Paris (Figure 2-10). A century has passed: spontaneous generation has yet to begin within them!

Pasteur then began his new experiments before the Commission. A total of 60 flasks

© 1962 Parke, Davis & Company

2-9 Pasteur in his laboratory. The great French biologist is shown examining a flask that is cloudy with microorganisms. The fluid in the gooseneck flask in his left hand is clear and sterile (see also Figure 2-11).

were prepared. Each contained an infusion of yeast and sugar. The infusions in all the flasks were boiled for two minutes, then the necks of 56 flasks were sealed by flame. (We will return to the other four flasks shortly.) The 56 flasks were divided into three groups and used as follows:

GROUP A: 19 flasks were opened briefly inside the amphitheatre of the building where the Commission was holding its scientific hearings. The flasks were then resealed and set aside.

GROUP B: 19 flasks were opened briefly high up in the dome of the amphitheatre. These were then resealed and set aside.

GROUP C: 18 flasks were opened outside the building, then resealed and set aside.

The reasoning here was that the air inside the building would be freer of particles than air outside the building, making the chances of contamination less.

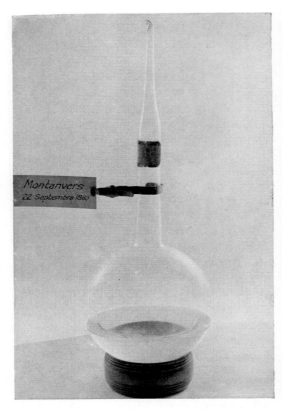
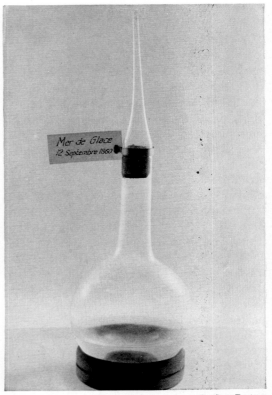

Institut Pasteur

2-10 Two of Pasteur's original flasks as they appear today. Pasteur opened these flasks high in the French Alps, where he hoped the air would be without spores of microorganisms. He then resealed the flasks and labeled them with the place of exposure and the date. They are now a permanent exhibit at the Pasteur Institute (*Institut Pasteur*) in Paris and are still sterile, after more than a century.

The results were as follows: In group A, 5 flasks (26 percent) developed growths of organisms. In group B, 6 (32 percent) developed growths of organisms. In group C, 16 (89 percent) developed growths.

In every group, some infusions exposed to air remained sterile. In these there was no evidence of spontaneous generation. *Most* of the infusions exposed indoors remained sterile, but only a *few* of those exposed outdoors did.

It was the four flasks not yet accounted for that proved most interesting of all. From the outset they were handled differently. Before the infusions in them were subjected to their two-minute boiling, Pasteur heated the glass neck of each of the four flasks and drew it out into a long curve (Figure 2-11). The ends of the necks were left open. Pasteur then boiled the infusions in the flasks and let steam issue out of the neck of each flask. This live steam killed any living creatures that might be present in the neck of the flask.

Then the flasks were allowed to cool. The purpose of the long, curved necks will now be apparent. As air entered the necks of the flasks, any particles would tend to settle on the curving walls of the glass. In some cases, at least, no particles should be expected to reach the infusions. As a matter of fact, all four flasks remained sterile! Yet none of the four was sealed!

What did Pouchet do? Although somewhat critical of the way Pasteur had conducted his experiments, Pouchet refused to do any more of his own. He refused to be judged, and the Commission of the French Academy decided in Pasteur's favor. On the basis of data submitted to them, there was no reason to believe that spontaneous generation occurred in infusions.

Pouchet and Pasteur in Retrospect. Pasteur had won a resounding scientific victory when the Commission decided in his favor. He seemed to have established for all time the fact of biogenesis—and to have discredited for all time the theory of spon-

taneous generation on the earth today. But the outcome might have been very different —in fact it *should* have been very different. Had Pouchet not lost his nerve, it is highly likely that he could have convinced the Commission of the occurrence of spontaneous generation. How could this be?

One should never forget the data on which scientific conclusions are based. Pasteur, in his experiments, used an infusion made of yeast, sugar, and water. Pouchet, in his earlier work, had used a hay infusion. Neither Pasteur nor Pouchet thought this difference was important. The Commission probably did not either. They may have thought it no more important than for the two biologists to use slightly different glassware.

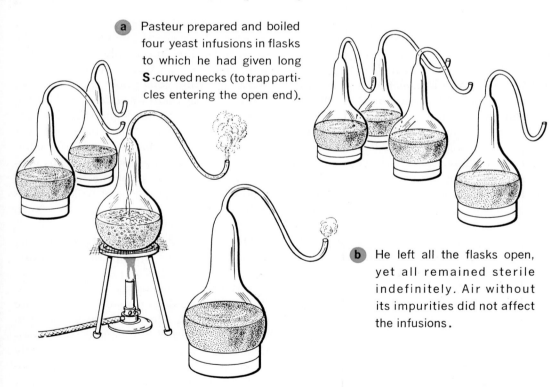

a Pasteur prepared and boiled four yeast infusions in flasks to which he had given long S-curved necks (to trap particles entering the open end).

b He left all the flasks open, yet all remained sterile indefinitely. Air without its impurities did not affect the infusions.

2-11 Pasteur's experiments with gooseneck flasks. These flasks were always open to the air, but only through long, curving necks that trapped spores of microorganisms. Using these flasks, Pasteur was able to counter one of the arguments of the abiogenesists. They had maintained that spontaneous generation failed to occur in sealed vessels because fresh air was excluded.

TABLE 2-1 Average Time That Different Organisms (or Their Spores) Can Survive Being Boiled in Infusions

Organisms	Survival time (in minutes)
Protozoa	0
Bacteria	
Most species	0
Bacillus subtilis	14
Clostridium perfringens	20
Clostridium botulinum	360

But was the type of infusion really *un*important? It was not, as we know today. Had Pasteur tried to repeat Pouchet's experiments he would have discovered that Pouchet had been "correct"! The hay infusion could have been boiled, closed carefully, and life would nonetheless have appeared! No doubt Pasteur would have been exceedingly perplexed. What would he have done to locate the problem? Would he have been able to proceed successfully?

We now know that both Pasteur and Pouchet made an initial error. Both made the assumption that boiling would destroy all organisms or spores. Today we know that this is not so. Although most microscopic animals and plants are killed by boiling water, some, such as *Clostridium* (klos-TRID·ih·um), a species of bacteria, can withstand boiling for minutes or even hours (Table 2-1). Dried hay, as used by Pouchet, would be likely to contain spores of *Clostridium* and other highly resistant organisms. Pasteur's yeast and sugar solution would be much less likely to contain them. Hence, both men could have done their experiments equally carefully and reached opposite conclusions!

What a strange accident in the history of brilliant biological research!

CONCLUDING REMARKS

After Pasteur, few competent biologists continued to believe that spontaneous generation occurs on the earth today. By the beginning of the twentieth century, perhaps none did. But had the long line of scientists from Redi to Pasteur actually proved that spontaneous generation cannot occur? Not at all. Perhaps this conclusion comes as a shock to you. All that had been scientifically demonstrated was as follows:

1. All observations and experiments thought to be examples of spontaneous generation were shown to be false.
2. In no experiment could it be shown convincingly that spontaneous generation could occur.

All competent biologists today are biogenesists. They accept the view that on the earth today life comes only from life. But wait, have we answered all parts of the question? If life comes only from life, does this mean that there was *always* life on the earth? It must, yet we know that this cannot be so. We know that the world was once without life—that life appeared later. How? We think it was by spontaneous generation! But this was not the same as the events occurring in a flask of boiled hay infusion. We must wait until Chapter 36 to continue this part of the story.

Three hundred years of debate and only a qualified answer. Did all those scientists waste their time? Is the question really that important? For biologists, of course it is. But for others, does it matter whether life comes only from life or can arise, at least in a few instances, by spontaneous generation? Yes, for all of us it is tremendously important to have the answer. Consider the problem of bacteria that cause diseases such as tuberculosis and diphtheria. If the disease-producing bacteria arise spontaneously within the sick person, a physician could devote his efforts only to combating the organism within the body of his patient. But the physician now knows that these bacteria come only from other living bacteria. A person becomes ill with tuberculosis or diphtheria only when he is infected from without. Preventive medicine becomes possible when we accept biogenesis as the most likely hypothesis for the origin of living things.

We began this chapter with a question, "What is life?" We are far from our answer, but perhaps we have established one of life's most important characteristics—its genetic continuity. The bacteria, the animals, the plants—all living creatures—are the offspring of other living creatures like themselves.

Now we shall explore other characteristics of life. Our next chapter will introduce the essential features of morphology and physiology. In other words, it will begin to answer two more questions of life: "What is it made of?" and "What does it do?" Each of these questions will help us to distinguish life from nonlife.

GUIDE QUESTIONS AND PROBLEMS

1. Why is the ability to move not a useful criterion for distinguishing a living thing?
2. How did more accurate observations provide a more acceptable explanation of the origin of "shipworms," "goose barnacles," and "barnacle geese"?
3. What observations, based on experiment, led Redi to his first hypothesis?
4. What conclusion was Redi justified in reaching on the basis of his experiments alone?
5. What observation did Redi interpret as an example of spontaneous generation?
6. What was the effect of the improvement of the microscope in the late seventeenth century on the idea of spontaneous generation?
7. What is a "control" in an experiment? How did Joblot use a control in his experiments on hay infusions?

8. What were the results achieved by Spallanzani when he repeated Needham's experiments?
9. How did Pasteur's preliminary experiments verify his hypothesis that infusions would not produce microorganisms if pure air (without spores of microorganisms) was available?
10. Explain the importance of the crucial demonstration in Pasteur's experiments before the Commission of the French Academy.
11. What did the experimentation by Redi and Pasteur really demonstrate?
12. Can spontaneous generation ever be disproved entirely? Why do you suppose that biologists today are no longer undertaking experiments similar to Redi's and Pasteur's?

SUGGESTIONS FOR ADDITIONAL READING

Books

De Kruif, Paul, *Microbe Hunters.* New York, Pocket Books, 1959.
  Excellently and excitingly written accounts of the contributions of Leeuwenhoek, Redi, Spallanzani, Needham, Joblot, Pouchet, and Pasteur.
Dobell, C. (ed.), *Antony van Leeuwenhoek and His "Little Animals."* New York, Dover Publications, 1962.
  Translations of the letters in which Leeuwenhoek describes his discovery of bacteria and protozoans.
Dubos, R., *Pasteur and Modern Science.* New York, Doubleday, 1960.
  Well-written and authoritative account of Pasteur and his work.
Schwartz, G., and P. Bishop (eds.), *Moments of Discovery.* New York, Basic Books, 1958. 2 vols.
  A selection of original writings including sizable parts of the experiments of Redi, Spallanzani, and Pasteur.

Magazines and Journals

Wald, G., "The Origin of Life." *Scientific American,* Vol. 191 (August 1954), pp. 44–53.

3

BASIC STRUCTURE

Man has always been a biologist of sorts. He had to be in order to live. Early in his history he was a hunter of animals and a gatherer of fruits, seeds, roots, and berries. He needed to know the different kinds of animals and their habits. The more he knew, the more successful he was as a hunter. He also needed to know the different kinds of plants. It was important that he be able to distinguish those which were edible from those which were not. In those days the penalty for being a poor biologist was a severe stomachache, or worse!

Early Knowledge of Plants and Animals

Primitive man used many wild plants for food, shelter, medicine, tools, and other purposes. Frequently his knowledge of varieties of plants, and the uses to which they could be put, was staggering. As a present-day example, the Indians of Brazil are known to use at least 66 different species of plants as fish poisons alone. Each of these plants contains some substance that makes the fish sluggish, or that paralyzes them. The plants are mashed and thrown into a stream. The poisons are washed out of the plants and carried downstream. Soon the

fish float to the surface and are easily caught. (Can you think of any reason why the Indians may have found it advisable *not* to use certain poisons from their arsenal in catching fish for food?)

The Plains Indians of western North America exploited to a remarkable degree a single species of animal—the buffalo, or American bison (Figure 3-1). The flesh was their main source of food. It could be eaten fresh or preserved. After a successful hunt, there was a feast of fresh meat. Blood was used as a soup. The surplus meat was dried by various methods, usually by being exposed in thin slices to the hot sun. The dried meat could be saved as it was or used to make pemmican. Here is the Indian's recipe for pemmican: Pound the meat into a powder, then mix with crushed cherries, marrow, and melted fat. Dried meat and pemmican last almost indefinitely—and so they tided the Indians over the periods when other food was not available.

Buffalo skins were used in many ways. Robes, tepee covers, storage sacks, war shields, and ropes and thongs were all made of skins. Some tribes also used skins to make boats—the skins being stretched over a wooden frame. Even cooking vessels were made of skins! One way of doing this was to dig a hole and line the bottom and sides of the hole with a buffalo skin. Water and food were then put into the skin. Finally, rocks were heated in a fire and put into the water. In this manner the food was cooked.

Buffalo stomachs were another source of cooking vessels; they were used also as buckets.

Buffalo heads, complete with horns, were used as headdresses in Indian ceremonies. Horns were used separately to make spoons, arrowheads, and cups. Other tools were made from bones: a shoulder blade, for example, could be attached to a stick to make a hoe. Children made sleds from the ribs. The tendons, especially the long ones ex-

American Museum of Natural History

3-1 The Indians of the North American Plains depended heavily on the buffalo. How many of the articles shown here were obtained from the buffalo? What would you guess is the significance of the painting on the first tepee? This illustration is reproduced from a painting by George Catlin, who visited many Indian tribes in the nineteenth century and left a valuable pictorial record of the Indians' way of life—a way of life that entailed much biological knowledge of the environment.

tending down the back, were used as sewing thread and bow strings. A glue was obtained from the hoofs. The brains were used in the hide-curing process; they were rubbed into the hides to help soften them. The skin of the rough side of the tongue was dried to make a comb.

Finally, the dried dung, which came to be known as "buffalo chips," was the principal fuel in a region that had few trees.

Thus it was that the Plains Indians relied upon the buffalo for the major portion of their needs for food, clothing, shelter, and fuel. Little of a slain animal was wasted, for the Indians possessed a great store of knowledge about this species which had

come to be so necessary for their existence.

All primitive peoples had a detailed knowledge of the plants and animals that formed their immediate "world." They depended upon this knowledge of other living things for their own well-being. Not infrequently they seemed to have a feeling of awe for life itself. Thus, in some tribes the warrior performed a brief ceremony after the hunt—apologizing to the spirit of the animal he had killed. He was sorry to take a life, but he must to preserve his own. The warrior referred to the animal as "little brother," which implies an understanding that life in man and life in beast were not so very different after all.

Scientific Knowledge

Was primitive man's tremendous knowledge of animals and plants *science?* Let us think about this. Obviously our task is to decide how we wish to use the word *science.* It is so common a term today that we should not be surprised that it has many meanings. But for us it has a restricted and useful meaning. Science, above all, means *organized* knowledge of natural phenomena. That is, it implies an attempt to relate many separate facts through the discovery of one or more general principles. We have already had one example: in spite of the many different ways organisms are produced, we can relate all origins by means of one general principle—biogenesis. Science is knowledge based upon data derived from observation and experiment. Sometimes it seems to be "impractical" knowledge—that is, knowledge gained solely to satisfy someone's curiosity. We will find, however, that what seems to be impractical knowledge at one time may eventually provide the basis for important discoveries.

Were our fishermen and our buffalo hunters scientists? Not in the strict sense of the word. There is no evidence that they *organized* their knowledge of living organisms the way a biologist would. Their knowledge of plants and animals can better be described as *technological.* Technology is *practical* knowledge, which is, of course, the kind primitive man had to possess if he was to survive.

The technical knowledge that flocks of wild geese would appear in the marshes at specific times every spring and fall was of great importance to a hunter who must feed his family. But man must begin to ask such questions as "Why do geese migrate?"—and obtain answers to his questions—before he is a scientist.

Necessity is the mother of technology: curiosity is the mother of science.

The distinction between what is science and what is not often is not as sharp as we have implied. The first Indian warrior to note that animals with hair also nursed their young, and had other characteristics in common, had the gleam of a scientific idea—the classification of organisms based upon natural groupings. He was recognizing a group we call **mammals.**

Biological science had its beginnings in the chance observations of primitive man. Yet even by the time of the early civilizations in Egypt and Iraq there was little that could be called theoretical science. These people, of the Valley of the Nile and of the land between the Tigris and the Euphrates of four thousand years ago, had much practical knowledge that they used in agriculture and medicine, but there is little evidence that they had a love of knowledge for its own sake. Their interests were more technological than scientific.

The first people to make comprehensive attempts to *organize* the data of the natural world were the Greeks. Aristotle and others of the fourth century B.C. were so superior as scientists to all who came before them that we sometimes tend to think of science as a Greek product. Of course, much that Aristotle wrote is incorrect—recall his observations on spontaneous generation of fish and frogs (Chapter 2). His tremendous contribution was his attempt to synthesize all knowledge of animals and plants. He was not satisfied with answers to the question "What?" He also wanted to find the answers to the questions "How?" and "Why?"

Aristotle died in 322 B.C., and science began a long decline. The Romans added little to the Greek achievement in science. Their greatest biologist, Pliny (A.D. 23–79) is remembered for a huge book, *Natural History.* This book consists of little more than folklore and excerpts from the writings of others—chiefly the Greeks. It was not until the sixteenth century that biological science again reached the intellectual level to which Aristotle had carried it.

THE DISCOVERY OF CELLS

Perhaps you see that the main theme of the preceding discussion is that observations do not become scientific observations until they are organized—until they are related to a question. The relation between isolated observations and organized science can be illustrated well if we trace the history of one important question:

Is there a fundamental unit of structure shared by all organisms?

By this we mean, "Is there any evidence that microorganisms, plants, and animals are constructed of the same parts?"

This is an example of a scientific question. We are seeking knowledge for knowledge's sake. When we first ask the question, there seems little likelihood that the answer will have any practical value. A good guess would be that the answer would satisfy one's curiosity and nothing more. But it so happens that the answer to this question has proved most important, not only for the advance of science but also for many problems of medicine.

At the moment this is being written, the author is also eating a pear. Author and pear are both alive—but the life expectancy of the pear is exceedingly brief! One could examine both carefully and reach the conclusion that there is no morphological similarity between man and pear. The pear and man are constructed in totally different ways. There is no trick here. This *is* the answer when the two are examined with the unaided eye. There is, however, another answer when we use different methods of study.

Early Work with the Microscope

There is no common structural unit that the unaided human eye can perceive among plants and animals. Primitive man found none, the Greeks found none, and early observers in the developing Western civiliza-

tions found none. But with the invention of the microscope, far more detailed comparisons became possible (Figure 3-2).

Crude microscopes seem to have been made for the first time in Holland, shortly before 1600. By about 1610, Galileo (1564–1642), the Italian astronomer and physicist who supported the theory that the earth and other planets revolve around the sun, had made a microscope and used it to observe tiny animals. He was followed by many others, among them Leeuwenhoek,

3-2 When Robert Hooke studied a common fly with a microscope (see Figure 3-4), this is what he saw. Simple lenses and microscopes have revealed a wealth of biological knowledge that otherwise would have eluded our understanding. (The letters on the fly and its wing refer to structures that Hooke described in his book *Micrographia,* published in 1665.)

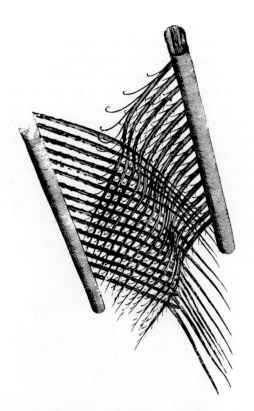

The Bettmann Archive

3-3 What is seen through a microscope often confirms evidence gained in another way. Running a finger along one side of a feather suggests that the parts of the feather are held together—and they are. This drawing by Hooke shows the interconnections as revealed under magnification.

3-4 Hooke's microscope. This instrument was a vast improvement over the microscopes used by Leeuwenhoek (Figure 2-6). Notice that Hooke's design for the microscope is similar in many ways to the design of microscopes used by scientists today—and to the one you use in the laboratory.

who, as we have already learned, discovered microscopic life in water (Chapter 2).

The microscope revealed that animals so small that the details of their structure could not be seen by the unaided eye have as complex a morphology as larger species. The common fly, for example, was found to be covered with many bristles.

Have you ever looked closely at a feather? The small threadlike structures that come out of each side of the shaft appear to be separated from one another. Yet when you run your finger along the underside of the feather, these structures seem to be held together. How can this be? If

you look at Figure 3-3, reproduced from a book of 1556, you can think of a hypothesis to explain this phenomenon.

There must have been a tremendous feeling of excitement when biologists began using microscopes for the first time. (Did you have similar feelings when you first looked at things under a microscope?) Magnified images not only revealed a world hitherto hidden but also answered questions that could not have been answered before. One biologist, writing in 1630, reported that he was learning about matters unknown even to Aristotle. That was about as far as one could go in 1630!

Hooke's *Micrographia*

In 1665, Robert Hooke (1635–1703) published a book entitled *Micrographia*. Hooke was an English scientist and inventor. He constructed a compound microscope (Figure 3-4), which was much better than the crude models available in his day. He examined many things with his microscope—minerals, textiles, and small plants and animals (Figures 3-2 and 3-3 are from his book). One of the things he examined was cork, which is part of the outer bark of the cork oak (Figure 3-5). Hooke's description of cork occupies so prominent a position in the history of man's attempt to understand the basic structure of living things that you may wish to read what he had to say. Here follows the description as it appeared in *Micrographia*. The type is quaint, but once you notice that an *s* is often much like an *f*, you fhould have little trouble reading it.

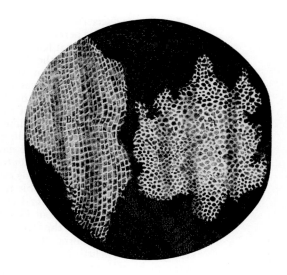

3-5 The microscopic structure of a piece of cork. *A* and *B* are Hooke's drawings of two slices of a piece of cork. This illustration, like Figures 3-2 and 3-3, is reproduced from *Micrographia*.

Obſerv. XVIII. *Of the* Schematiſme *or* Texture *of* Cork, *and of the* Cells *and* Pores *of ſome other ſuch frothy Bodies.*

I Took a good clear piece of Cork, and with a Pen-knife ſharpen'd as keen as a Razor, I cut a piece of it off, and thereby left the ſurface of it exceeding ſmooth, then examining it very diligently with a *Microſcope*, me thought I could perceive it to appear a little porous; but I could not ſo plainly diſtinguiſh them, as to be ſure that they were pores, much leſs what Figure they were of: But judging from the lightneſs and yielding quality of the Cork, that certainly the texture could not be ſo curious, but that poſſibly, if I could uſe ſome further diligence, I might find it to be diſcernable with a *Microſcope*, I with the ſame ſharp Pen-knife, cut off from the former ſmooth ſurface an exceeding thin piece of it, and placing it on a black objeᴄt Plate, becauſe it was it felf a white body, and caſting the light on it with a deep *plano-convex Glaſs*, I could exceeding plainly perceive it to be all perforated and porous, much like a Honey-comb, but that the pores of it were not regular; yet it was not unlike a Honey-comb in theſe particulars.

Firſt, in that it had a very little ſolid ſubſtance, in compariſon of the empty cavity that was contain'd between, as does more manifeſtly appear by the Figure A and B of the XI. *Scheme*, for the *Interſtitia*, or walls (as I may ſo call them) or partitions of thoſe pores were neer as thin in proportion to their pores, as thoſe thin films of Wax in a Honey-comb (which encloſe and conſtitute the *ſexangular cells*) are to theirs.

Next, in that theſe pores, or cells, were not very deep, but conſiſted of a great many little Boxes, ſeparated out of one continued long pore, by certain *Diaphragms*, as is viſible by the Figure B, which repreſents a ſight of thoſe pores ſplit the long-ways.

I no sooner discern'd these (which were indeed the first *microscopical* pores I ever saw, and perhaps, that were ever seen, for I had not met with any Writer or Person, that had made any mention of them before this) but me thought I had with the discovery of them, presently hinted to me the true and intelligible reason of all the *Phænomena* of Cork; As;

First, if I enquir'd why it was so exceeding light a body? my *Microscope* could presently inform me that here was the same reason evident that there is found for the lightness of froth, an empty Honey-comb, Wool, a Spunge, a Pumice-stone, or the like; namely, a very small quantity of a solid body, extended into exceeding large dimensions.

Next, it seem'd nothing more difficult to give an intelligible reason, why Cork is a body so very unapt to suck and drink in Water, and consequently preserves it self, floating on the top of Water, though left on it never so long : and why it is able to stop and hold air in a Bottle, though it be there very much condens'd and consequently presses very strongly to get a passage out, without suffering the least bubble to pass through its substance. For, as to the first, since our *Microscope* informs us that the substance of Cork is altogether fill'd with Air, and that that Air is perfectly enclosed in little Boxes or Cells distinct from one another. It seems very plain, why neither the Water, nor any other Air can easily insinuate it self into them, since there is already within them an *intus existens*, and consequently, why the pieces of Cork become so good floats for Nets, and stopples for Viols, or other close Vessels.

And thirdly, if we enquire why Cork has such a springiness and swelling nature whem compres'd ? and how it comes to suffer so great a compression, or seeming penetration of dimensions, so as to be made a substance as heavie again and more, bulk for bulk, as it was before compression, and yet suffer'd to return, is found to extend it self again into the same space? Our *Microscope* will easily inform us, that the whole mass consists of an infinite company of small Boxes or Bladders of Air, which is a substance of a springy nature, and that will suffer a considerable condensation (as I have several times found by divers trials, by which I have most evidently condens'd it into less then a twentieth part of its usual dimensions neer the Earth, and that with no other strength then that of my hands without any kind of forcing Engine, such as Racks, Leavers, Wheels, Pullies, or the like, but this onely by and by) and besides, it seems very probable that those very films or sides of the pores, have in them a springing quality, as almost all other kind of Vegetable substances have, so as to help to restore themselves to their former position.

And could we so easily and certainly discover the *Schematisme* and *Texture* even of these films, and of several other bodies, as we can these of Cork; there seems no probable reason to the contrary, but that we might as readily render the true reason of all their *Phænomena*; as namely, what were the cause of the springiness, and toughness of some, both as to their flexibility and restitution. What, of the friability or brittleness of some others, and the like; but till such time as our *Microscope*, or some other means, enable us to discover the true *Schematism* and *Texture* of all kinds of bodies, we must grope, as it were, in the dark, and onely ghess at the true reasons of things by similitudes and comparisons.

But, to return to our Observation. I told several lines of these pores, and found that there were usually about threescore of these small Cells placed end-ways in the eighteenth part of an Inch in length, whence I concluded there must be neer eleven hundred of them, or somewhat more then a thousand in the length of an Inch, and therefore in a square Inch above a Million, or 1166400. and in a Cubick Inch, above twelve hundred Millions, or 1259712000. a thing almost incredible, did not our

Microscope assure us of it by ocular demonstration; nay, did it not discover to us the pores of a body, which were they *diaphragm'd,* like those of Cork, would afford us in one Cubick Inch, more then ten times as many little Cells, as is evident in several charr'd Vegetables; so prodigiously curious are the works of Nature, that even these conspicuous pores of bodies, which seem to be the channels or pipes through which the *Succus nutritius,* or natural juices of Vegetables are convey'd, and seem to correspond to the veins, arteries and other Vessels in sensible creatures, that these pores I say, which seem to be the Vessels of nutrition to the vastest body in the World, are yet so exceeding small, that the *Atoms* which *Epicurus* fancy'd would go neer to prove too bigg to enter them, much more to constitute a fluid body in them. And how infinitely smaller then must be the Vessels of a Mite, or the pores of one of those little Vegetables I have discovered to grow on the back-side of a Rose-leaf, and shall anon more fully describe, whose bulk is many millions of times less then the bulk of the small shrub it grows on; and even that shrub, many millions of times less in bulk then several trees (that have heretofore grown in *England,* and are this day flourishing in other hotter Climates, as we are very credibly inform'd) if at least the pores of this small Vegetable should keep any such proportion to the body of it, as we have found these pores of other Vegetables to do to their bulk. But of these pores I have said more elsewhere.

To proceed then, Cork seems to be by the transverse constitution of the pores, a kind of *Fungus* or Mushrome, for the pores lie like so many Rays tending from the center, or pith of the tree, outwards; so that if you cut off a piece from a board of Cork transversly, to the flat of it, you will, as it were, split the pores, and they will appear just as they are express'd in the Figure B of the X I. *Scheme.* But if you shave off a very thin piece from this board, parallel to the plain of it, you will cut all the pores transversly, and they will appear almost as they are express'd in the Figure A, save onely the solid *Interstitia* will not appear so thick as they are there represented.

So that Cork seems to suck its nourishment from the subjacent bark of the Tree immediately, and to be a kind of excrescence, or a substance distinct from the substances of the entire Tree, something *analogus* to the Mushrome, or Moss on other Trees, or to the hairs on Animals. And having enquir'd into the History of Cork, I find it reckoned as an excrescency of the bark of a certain Tree, which is distinct from the two barks that lie within it, which are common also to other trees; That 'tis some time before the Cork that covers the young and tender sprouts comes to be discernable; That it cracks, flaws, and cleaves into many great chaps, the bark underneath remaining entire; That it may be separated and remov'd from the Tree, and yet the two under-barks (such as are also common to that with other Trees) not at all injur'd, but rather helped and freed from an external injury. Thus *Jonstonus* in *Dendrologia,* speaking *de Subere,* says, *Arbor est procera, Lignum est robustum, dempto cortice in aquis non fluitat, Cortice in orbem detracto juvatur, crascescens enim praestringit & strangulat, intra triennium iterum repletur: Caudex ubi adolescit crassus, cortex superior densus carnosus, duos digitos crassus, scaber, rimosus, & qui nisi detrahatur dehiscit, alioque subnascente expellitur, interior qui subest novellus ita rubet ut arbor minio picta videatur.* Which Histories, if well consider'd, and the tree, substance, and manner of growing, if well examin'd, would, I am very apt to believe, much confirm this my conjecture about the origination of Cork.

Nor is this kind of Texture peculiar to Cork onely; for upon examination with my *Microscope,* I have found that the pith of an Elder, or almoſt any other Tree, the inner pulp or pith of the Cany hollow ſtalks of ſeveral other Vegetables: as of Fennel, Carrets, Daucus, Bur-docks, Teaſels, Fearn, ſome kinds of Reeds, &c. have much ſuch a kind of *Schematiſme*, as I have lately ſhewn that of Cork, ſave onely that here the pores are rang'd the long-ways, or the ſame ways with the length of the Cane, whereas in Cork they are tranſverſe.

The pith alſo that fills that part of the ſtalk of a Feather that is above the Quil, has much ſuch a kind of texture, ſave onely that which way ſo-ever I ſet this light ſubſtance, the pores ſeem'd to be cut tranſverſly; ſo that I gheſs this pith which fills the Feather, not to conſiſt of abundance of long pores ſeparated with Diaphragms, as Cork does, but to be a kind of ſolid or hardned froth, or a *congeries* of very ſmall bubbles conſolidated in that form, into a pretty ſtiff as well as tough concrete, and that each Ca-vern, Bubble, or Cell, is diſtinctly ſeparate from any of the reſt, without any kind of hole in the encompaſſing films, ſo that I could no more blow through a piece of this kinde of ſubſtance, then I could through a piece of Cork, or the ſound pith of an Elder.

But though I could not with my *Microſcope*, nor with my breath, nor any other way I have yet try'd, diſcover a paſſage out of one of thoſe cavities into another, yet I cannot thence conclude, that therefore there are none ſuch, by which the *Succus nutritius*, or appropriate juices of Ve-getables, may paſs through them; for, in ſeveral of thoſe Vegetables, whilſt green, I have with my *Microſcope*, plainly enough diſcover'd theſe Cells or Poles fill'd with juices, and by degrees ſweating them out: as I have alſo obſerved in green Wood all thoſe long *Microſcopical* pores which appear in Charcoal perfectly empty of any thing but Air.

Now, though I have with great diligence endeavoured to find whe-ther there be any ſuch thing in thoſe *Microſcopical* pores of Wood or Piths, as the *Valves* in the heart, veins, and other paſſages of Animals, that open and give paſſage to the contain'd fluid juices one way, and ſhut themſelves, and impede the paſſage of ſuch liquors back again, yet have I not hitherto been able to ſay any thing poſitive in it; though, me thinks, it ſeems very probable, that Nature has in theſe paſſages, as well as in thoſe of Animal bodies, very many appropriated Inſtruments and contrivances, whereby to bring her deſigns and end to paſs, which 'tis not improbable, but that ſome diligent Obſerver, if help'd with better *Microſcopes*, may in time detect.

And that this may be ſo, ſeems with great probability to be argued from the ſtrange *Phænomena* of ſenſitive Plants, wherein Nature ſeems to perform ſeveral Animal actions with the ſame *Schematiſm* or *Orginiza-tion* that is common to all Vegetables, as may appear by ſome no leſs inſtructive then curious Obſervations that were made by divers Emi-nent Members of the *Royal Society* on ſome of theſe kind of Plants, where-of an account was delivered in to them by the moſt Ingenious and Excel-lent *Phyſician*, Doctor *Clark*, which, having that liberty granted me by that moſt Illuſtrious Society, I have hereunto adjoyn'd.

The Significance
of Hooke's Observations

Do you feel as though you have just read one of the important works in biology? Probably not. But you have read one that was later to be regarded as very important.

Hooke was the first person to describe cells, which we now regard as the basic struc-tural units of most organisms. There is no suggestion in Hooke's report that his dis-covery would be of such tremendous bio-logical importance.

Hooke used his discovery of cells to explain the properties of cork. Why is cork so light? Because it is composed of air-filled cells. Why does cork not absorb water? Because the cells are entirely surrounded by the **cell walls**, through which water cannot pass. Why was cork so springy? Because the little cells, which contained air, could be compressed, yet resume their shapes when the pressure was released. Thus Hooke speculated on the significance of his observations and suggested how they aid our understanding of the properties of cork. His observations were related to other scientific knowledge and became part of science itself.

Hooke also examined a few vegetables. All of the pieces he examined seemed to be composed entirely of cells. Of course he did not look at a whole cork oak tree, or even at a whole vegetable. He looked at tiny parts and *assumed* that the whole would be the same. We call this *sampling*. Do you think that this is a legitimate scientific procedure?

Soon others were observing cells under microscopes (Figure 3-6). Usually, these isolated observations were of little general importance. The structure of cork or of a plant stem as it appeared under the microscope was being described. This was not so very different from describing the minute structure of a flea or a feather. All were separate descriptions, which were wholly unrelated to any general theory. Isolated observations such as these might become important at some later time. They are a first step in science, but not enough to be called science itself.

Scientific Societies and Publications

We must pause at this point to consider an important aspect of science: how does scientific knowledge become generally known? If Hooke had looked at cork, but had failed to report what he saw, his observations would not have contributed to science. Of course, most people probably would not have been very interested in Hooke's report—after all, the structure of cork does not seem to be an exciting subject! But there would be a few individuals, seeking knowledge for its own sake, who would wonder about the world they could not see except with a microscope. How could Hooke communicate with those who might share his interests?

In the 1640's a group of men interested in science began meeting informally each week in London. They would discuss topics that interested them and report any observations or experiments. In 1660 the group was organized more formally, and in 1662 it was given a charter by King Charles II. It was to be called the "Royal Society of London for Improving Natural Knowledge."

The Royal Society was one of the first scientific societies. Among early members we find Robert Hooke, Isaac Newton, the chemist Robert Boyle, and the architect Christopher Wren. Marcello Malpighi (page 31) and Antony van Leeuwenhoek (page 32) were elected as foreign members when the Society was quite young. The Society provided a place where those interested in science could meet and discuss their problems. Not infrequently, members actually performed experiments at the Society's meetings. The Society also corresponded with other scientists throughout the world. Thus, it was to the Royal Society that Leeuwenhoek reported his discoveries made with the microscope.

The Royal Society was of enormous influence in stimulating science in still another way: it arranged to publish the observations by its members and other scientists. These appeared in *Philosophical Transactions*, which was the Society's journal. Publication began in 1665, and by 1962 volume number 245 had been reached.

The Royal Society published Hooke's *Micrographia* and many other books on scientific subjects. Since the King was the Pa-

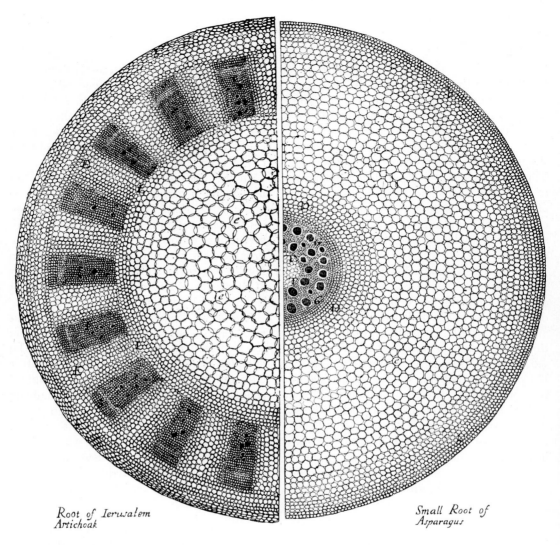

Root of Ierusalem
Artichoak

Small Root of
Asparagus

3-6 Less than twenty years after the publication of Hooke's *Micrographia,* Nehemiah Grew published *Anatomy of Plants.* Here are two of his drawings of cells in plant roots (the roots were cut open crosswise and examined with a microscope to give the sections shown here). If you had lived during the seventeenth century, do you think that you would have recognized a fundamental similarity in the microscopic structure of these two plants and of cork (Figure 3-5)?

tron of the Society, it is not surprising that Hooke begins *Micrographia* with the dedication, "To the King, Sir, I do here most humbly lay this small present at Your Majesties Royal feet."

Soon other societies were formed, and the number has increased through the years. It is difficult to obtain an accurate estimate of the total number of such societies in the world. In the United States there are now hundreds devoted to all aspects of science. The American Association for the Advancement of Science is one of the largest. It has 60,000 members.

The American Institute of Biological Science is an association of many separate societies specializing in the biological sciences. The total membership of the association is about 84,000. It not only arranges scientific meetings but supports the publication of books in the biological sciences—including the one you are reading.

Scientific societies typically hold meetings at which the members can discuss their problems and discoveries. The societies also publish articles having scientific value. Living as we do in an age of tremendous scientific activity, it is not surprising that the number of articles being published is enormous. In 1961 it was estimated that 50,000 scientific journals containing a total of about 2,000,000 articles were published around the world.

Now that we have seen how scientific information, from the time of Hooke onward, has been made known to all who might help one another in studying scientific questions, let us return to the main question that we are considering: Is there a fundamental unit of structure shared by all organisms?

THE CELL THEORY

It took a century and a half to progress from Hooke's initial observations on the structure of cork to the **cell theory.** On the basis of Hooke's data, we could have concluded only that *some* plants are composed of cells. According to the cell theory, the bodies of *all* plants and *all* animals are composed of cells or cell products.

Accumulation of the Evidence

As more and more scientists were able to obtain microscopes, they examined many different animals and plants. Their methods and microscopes were crude, but frequently they observed structures that resembled Hooke's cells. They knew this because Hooke had published his observations; they had but to read his book, *Micrographia.*

In the first decades of the nineteenth century, a new concept began to crystallize. Could it be that all living things are composed of cells? A French botanist, Dutrochet, published some data in 1824 that suggested this was so. He found that when plant material was boiled in nitric acid it broke up into tiny pieces. When examined with a microscope, the tiny pieces were seen to be boxlike units similar to those Hooke had described as cells.

More and more plants were found to be composed of cells. *But what about the animals?* Most of the evidence so far accumulated was based upon observations of plants. When small parts of animal tissue were examined, however, cells could not be seen. In fact, it was difficult to make out anything at all. Certainly there were no boxlike structures of the type so common in plants.

The Interpretation by Schwann and Schleiden

The next major advance was made in 1839 by a German zoologist, Theodor Schwann (1810–1882). His contribution was not *what* he saw, but *how he interpreted* what he saw. In a sense he changed the definition of "cell." Previous investigators had emphasized the walls of the box. He emphasized what was inside the box.

It had previously been discovered that within the boxlike cells of *living* plants there was a little sphere, the **nucleus** (NEW-kle·us). We owe this discovery to Robert Brown (1773–1858), who first observed nuclei in cells of orchids. Compared to cell walls, nuclei seemed inconspicuous. It was therefore only natural to identify plant cells on the basis of their walls.

When Schwann looked at little bits of animals under his microscope, he observed that nuclei were present. The nuclei were surrounded by a watery substance, and

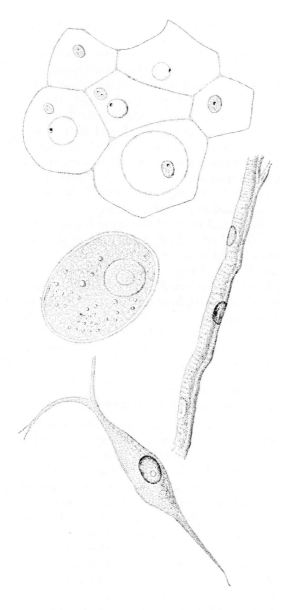

Redrawn from Th. Schwann, 1839

3-7 The microscopic structure of small parts of animals as seen by Schwann. The cluster of six cells at the top is from a fish. The oval cell is from the nervous system of a frog. The long cell on the right is from the muscle of an unborn pig. The spindle-shaped cell at the bottom is also from an unborn pig. These and other drawings of a variety of animal cells were published by Schwann in support of the cell theory.

usually by a thin outer membrane as well (Figure 3-7). There was little here that seemed much like plant cells with their conspicuous walls. But Schwann thought there might be a fundamental resemblance. Possibly one should think of the substance *within* the walls of plant cells as corresponding to what he saw in parts of animals. Nuclei, for example, were present in both. In Schwann's opinion, a cell could be said to consist of a nucleus, with its surrounding substance, plus some sort of a wall or membrane. The thick walls of plant cells could then be considered a characteristic of *plant* cells alone, and not of *all* cells.

Thus, Schwann developed a concept of the cell as a structure with a nucleus, rather than as a structure with a thick wall. He gave a new definition of a cell and then proposed a fundamental hypothesis:

> The bodies of animals and plants are composed of cells and the products of cells.

A German botanist, M. J. Schleiden (1804–1881), also came to this conclusion at about the same time. From the observations of Schwann and Schleiden, as well as those of others, a new theory was born. This was the cell theory, one of the most important scientific statements of the nineteenth century.

Schwann had proposed a hypothesis—the cell hypothesis. It led to a theory—the cell theory. What is the difference? For our purposes let us say that a hypothesis is a statement to be tested; it is a possibility. Schwann and others could test the hypothesis by making observations on the microscopic structure of numerous kinds of animals and plants. If they found that the hypothesis was true, that is, if all the animals and plants examined were found to be composed of cells, we could speak of the cell theory. But a theory is more than just a true hypothesis. A theory is a body of interrelated facts, and broad and important facts at that. If observation had shown that only cork was composed of cells, we would not speak of this as the *theory* of cork cells. We would merely say that the cellular nature of cork was a fact. But when cork, frogs, carrots, man, wheat, fish, and all other living things examined seemed to be composed of cells, we have a body of important and interrelated facts. We unite this body of important and interrelated facts as the cell theory.

It was clearly realized by Schwann and others that cells are tremendously varied in appearance, especially in animals (Figures 3-7 and 3-11). Some cells are spheres, others are flattened disks; some are long and narrow, others are branched; some are relatively large, others are small. But in animals and plants there is this fundamental similarity: the various structures called cells contain nuclei. A cell with its nucleus is the smallest structural unit common to animals and plants. Cells are the building blocks of life.

The Origin of Cells

With the statement of the cell theory, a new question immediately arose. Where do cells come from? Using the crude methods and microscopes of the first part of the nineteenth century, biologists could not be sure. Schwann believed that new cells were formed spontaneously out of the living substance, much in the way crystals form in an evaporating solution of salt. He was wrong.

Other biologists noticed occasions on which one cell seemed to divide into two (Figure 3-8). Could it be that this is the way new cells are formed—by the parent cell dividing into two parts? Many biologists thought so. Their view was expressed concisely in 1855 by a German biologist, Rudolf Virchow (1821–1902), who wrote, "*omnis cellula e cellula*" (all cells from cells).

Now this was a difficult hypothesis to establish. If one observes a cell dividing into

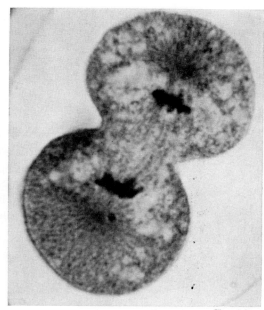

Clay Adams

3-8 Two cells from one. This dividing cell is a worm's egg. Similar divisions of cells, both plant and animal, were observed by many nineteenth-century biologists. Did this mean that *all* cells come from other cells?

two, does it mean that other origins of cells are impossible? Some observers believed that cells could form in several ways. For example, it was claimed that the cells in young embryos are carved out of the substance of the egg. This was similar to Schwann's belief. Gradually this view was abandoned. With better microscopes and more careful observations it was found that cells in embryos arise by cell division.

There were, of course, other scientists who believed that living cells could arise by spontaneous generation. We have already considered this hypothesis in Chapter 2.

Today all biologists accept the cell theory of Schwann and Schleiden, and Virchow's hypothesis that all cells come from pre-existing cells. While some animals and plants are single-celled (**unicellular**—yoo-nih·sEL·yoo·ler), the ones with which you

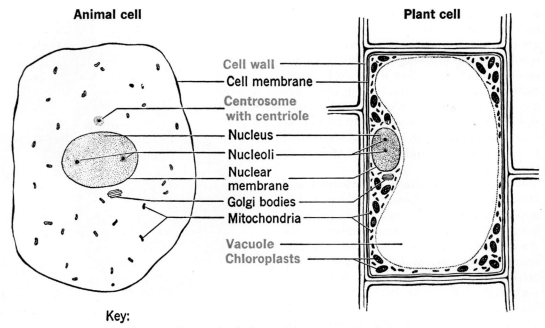

Animal cell　　　　　　　　　　　　　　　　　**Plant cell**

Cell wall
Cell membrane
Centrosome
with centriole
Nucleus
Nucleoli
Nuclear
membrane
Golgi bodies
Mitochondria
Vacuole
Chloroplasts

Key:

Black type— structures common to both cells
Color type— structures not common to both cells

3-9　All cells have many structures in common. Certain differences exist, however, between most animal cells and most plant cells. Both the similarities and the differences are shown in this illustration of a generalized animal cell and a generalized plant cell. Have you observed all of the cell structures shown here in your laboratory study of cells? If you have not, what do you think is the reason? (Any biological generalization, such as the one represented by this illustration, is inadequate in some ways. Thus, many animal cells do have small vacuoles, but they are never like the large central vacuole that is present in many mature plant cells.)

are most familiar are usually made up of many cells of many kinds. These different kinds of cells are variations on a theme—a variety of cells that accomplish a variety of functions.

There are limits—even with the best microscopes—to what one can observe in living cells. Usually dead cells are more revealing—but not just any dead cells, for they must be killed and treated in special ways. The methods used are designed to preserve the cells with as few structural changes as possible, and to stain the parts to make them more easily visible.

Briefly, the methods used are these. First, the cells are *fixed*. This means that they are treated with chemical agents that solidify the normally jellylike parts. The various parts are thus fixed in position (and of course, the cells are killed by the fixation process). Second, if the cells are in thick masses (making it nearly impossible to observe details within individual cells), sometimes they can be spread out in thin sheets before being studied. Otherwise it is necessary to make very thin slices of the material. Third, the cells are *stained* with one or more of a variety of dyes. It has been discovered, largely by trial and error, that some dyes will selectively stain specific structures in cells. Thus, a dye known as **hematoxylin** (hee·ma·ᴛᴏᴋ·sih·lin) will stain the nucleus much more than other parts of the cell. Other dyes will selectively stain other structures. Until recently, most of our information about structures in cells was based on observations of cells that had been fixed and stained as described here.

Animal Cells

Biologists realize that cells are more than just the structural units of organisms. They are also units of function, each kind being specialized to perform specific tasks. Muscle cells are specialized in contracting, nerve cells in carrying messages from one part of the body to another, gland cells of the intestinal lining in aiding the digestion of foods, and some of the cells of the eye in responding to light. In spite of this great variability, however, cells do have much in common.

What are these common features? Let us begin with an animal cell (Figure 3-9). The most conspicuous structure that one observes within the cell is the nucleus. In some cells the nucleus is spherical in shape, but in others it may be irregular. The nucleus of a living cell, when examined with an optical microscope, usually appears almost transparent, with little visible internal structure.

When a cell has been fixed and suitably stained, the nucleus no longer appears to have so little internal structure. Within the nucleus, usually one or two small spherical bodies, the **nucleoli** (new-KLEE-o-ly; sing., nucleolus—new-KLEE-o-lus), can be seen. (In some cells there may be more nucleoli.) The rest of the nucleus may appear to contain a network of threads. Around the outside of the nucleus is seen a thin membrane, the **nuclear membrane.**

Our methods of preparing cells for study lead to an incorrect impression about the material within the nucleus. There is, for example, considerable indirect evidence (from genetics; see Chapter 31) to suggest that in the living nucleus there is no actual

network of the threadlike material. Instead the data indicate that within the nucleus there exist *separate* threads, the **chromosomes.** They are plainly visible when cells divide, as we will see in Chapter 7, but not at other times. The chromosomes are independent structures—they do not fuse with one another to form a network.

Chromosomes are of tremendous importance. They control the activities of the cell. In addition, they are the structures of the cell that are of the greatest importance in inheritance.

With few exceptions (such as sex cells), the nucleus of every cell in the body of an animal or plant has the same number of chromosomes. For example, most of the cells of your body contain 46 chromosomes. This number is characteristic for man. A frog's cells have 26. A chimpanzee's cells have 48.

The portion of the cell substance outside the nucleus and within the cell membrane has been named the **cytoplasm** (SY-toh-plaz'm). It is a region and not a single substance any more than the nucleus is a single substance. Like the nucleus, the cytoplasm is relatively fluid in living cells. It contains a variety of structures, identifiable on the basis of their shape, staining properties, and chemical activities.

The **mitochondria** (my-toh-KON-drih-uh) are common structures in the cytoplasm. In some cells they are short rods; in others they may be long filaments. In recent years the function of mitochondria has been discovered: they are important in providing energy for the cell.

The **Golgi** (GOL-je) **bodies** are a collection of tiny platelike structures in the cytoplasm. Their function has not been established definitely, but there is some evidence that they are concerned with cell secretions. Secretions are products formed within the cell and then passed to the outside.

The cytoplasm also contains a number of small granules. Some, such as the **ribosomes**

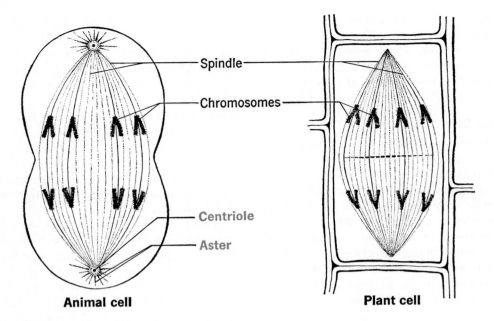

Spindle

Chromosomes

Centriole

Aster

Animal cell

Plant cell

Key:

Black type — Structures common to both cells
Color type —Structures not common to both cells

3-10 Cell division in a generalized animal cell and a generalized plant cell. When cells divide, structures that are not visible in nondividing cells make their appearance.

(RY·bo·sohmz), are too small to be seen with the compound microscope—one must use the electron microscope. Ribosomes are necessary for the cell to make its proteins.

A thin **cell membrane** covers the cell. The cell membrane occupies a strategic position, since everything that enters or leaves the cell must pass through it.

Earlier it was stated that all cells come from pre-existing cells by a process of division. The animal cell we have been describing was not in the process of dividing. Other structures make their appearance when a cell is dividing (Figure 3-10). At this time, for example, the chromosomes become clearly stainable. We believe that their shapes in fixed and stained dividing cells are much like their shapes in living dividing cells. The chromosomes of dividing cells are situated in what is called the **spin-**

dle. At each end of the spindle there are one or more tiny granules, the **centrioles** (SEN·trih·ohlz). The centrioles may or may not be contained within larger structures, the **centrosomes** (SEN·tro·sohmz). An **aster**, made up of radiating fibers, surrounds each centriole or centrosome.

The spindle, centrioles, and asters have their functional importance in the division of animal cells. They will be discussed further in Chapter 7.

Plant Cells

So far we have looked closely at an animal cell. When we examine plant cells, many similarities to animal cells will be apparent. There will also be some differences between the two.

A plant cell (Figure 3-9) typically possesses a nucleus, one or more nucleoli, mitochondria, Golgi bodies, ribosomes, and a cell membrane. In these respects it resembles an animal cell. Generally, plant cells differ from animal cells in having thick cell walls and large central **vacuoles** (VAK·yoo-ohlz). The cell walls were the prominent structures that were first observed in cork by Hooke. They form a relatively rigid outer case for the rest of the cell. Vacuoles are large liquid-filled structures bounded by a membrane. Frequently these are in the middle of the cell and so large that the bulk of the cytoplasm is pushed into a thin film next to the cell wall.

The cell membrane is ordinarily applied closely to the inner surface of the cell wall. It usually cannot be seen unless one uses some method to shrink the contents of the cell away from the cell wall.

Many of the cells of green plants contain **chloroplasts** (KLOR·o·plasts). These are microscopic bodies which contain the green pigment **chlorophyll** (KLOR·o·fill). Chloroplasts are of enormous biological importance, for they are key structures in the processes by which the plant manufactures food—not only food for the plant, but ultimately food for the entire animal kingdom. Nearly all living creatures, plant and animal, are dependent on the food-producing activities of plant cells that contain chlorophyll.

When a plant cell divides, the chromosomes and spindle are prominent (Figure 3-10), as in the case of animal cells. However, in nearly all the plants with which you are familiar, the cells lack centrioles and asters.

Sizes of Cells

Most cells are very small. White blood cells of man range from about 8 to 12 microns in diameter. (A **micron** [MY·kron] is about 1/1000 the thickness of a dime. Refer to Laboratory Exercise 3-2 for a discussion of measurements.) A nerve cell's width at its widest point is—like that of white blood cells—measured in microns, but its length may be more than a meter! (A meter is about 39 inches—slightly more than a yard.) Single nerve cells, for example, extend from the lower end of your spinal cord to the muscles in your feet.

The largest cells are the yolks of birds' eggs. Before a young bird begins to develop, the yolk of the egg is a single cell. In the course of time, this single cell forms the young bird.

You can determine for yourself the diameter of an egg cell of a hen. In the process you will be confronted with one of the problems that plagued the earlier students of living cells, namely, the difficulty of studying a semifluid object. When you break the shell, the egg will flow out and produce a flattened disk. If you are watching closely, you may notice that the yolk was originally a sphere, but that it becomes flattened when removed from the supporting shell. You can solve the problem, as did biologists of a century ago, by fixing the cell. For your purposes, heat is a suitable fixing agent. Boil the egg for ten minutes, remove the shell, and then measure the diameter of the yolk.

If the yolks of birds' eggs are the largest of cells, you might guess that if you repeat this experiment with an ostrich egg, you will have measured the largest cell of any living animal or plant. The elephant bird, which is now extinct, had an egg with a volume of about 8 liters (about 2 gallons).

CONCLUDING REMARKS

With a microscope we can see that there is a basic similarity in the structures of living things. Nearly all are composed of cells. There are a few exceptions, such as viruses (Chapter 9) and slime molds (Chapter 12). There are so few exceptions, however, that one can recognize a general theory, the cell theory. Today we look upon this as one of

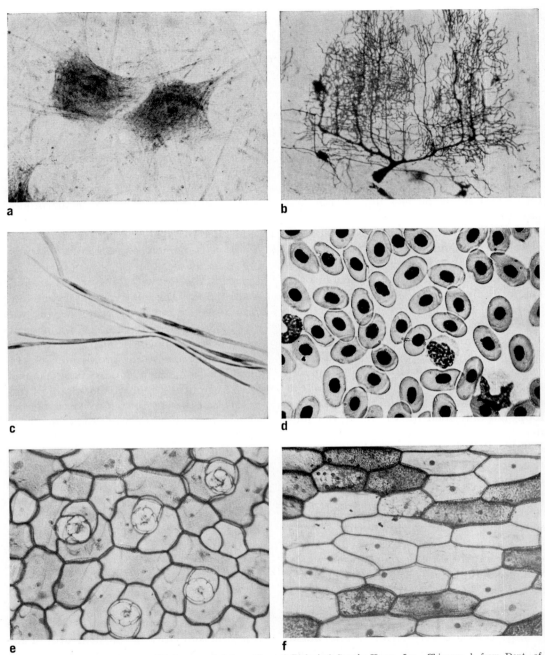

Photos *a* and *d* from General Biological Supply House, Inc., Chicago; *b* from Dept. of
Anatomy, Columbia Presbyterian Medical Center, N.Y.C., *e* and *f* from Hugh Spencer

3-11   Variety in animal and plant cells: **a** nerve cells; **b** cells of the brain; **c** muscle cells;
d blood cells of the frog; **e** cells from the surface of a plant leaf; **f** cells of onion
skin. If you had been given these six photographs before reading about the cell
theory, would you have recognized any fundamental similarities among the pictured structures? What evidence do you see now for calling all the structures cells?

the basic theories of biological science.

The intellectual steps from Hooke's observations to the cell theory were numerous and difficult. Hooke stumbled upon cells, so to speak, when he was using his microscope to look at common objects. Cork happens to be a substance that shows cell walls clearly. Neither Hooke nor other microscopists of the seventeenth century who saw cell-like structures in plants made much of their observations. They were adding facts to biological knowledge. They were not, however, relating these facts to any general theory.

It was exceedingly difficult to recognize cells as the common structural basis of living things. The reason is that cells differ tremendously in appearance. Most plant cells are surrounded by prominent cell walls, and the cell membrane is not readily seen. Most animal cells are surrounded by a delicate cell membrane alone. Some cells are flat, others are spheres, still others are long and narrow (Figure 3-11). It is unlikely that anyone would unite all these various structures in a class of similar objects. In external appearance, cells are *not* similar.

It was Schwann's lasting contribution that gave us a new way of defining cells. To him it was not the general shape and form that made a cell, but the nucleus and the surrounding living matter—all enclosed in a wall or a membrane.

Arriving at a hypothesis was then but a short step. Perhaps the bodies of all microorganisms, plants, and animals are composed of cells and the products of cells. One obvious deduction from the hypothesis would be:

If the body of any organism is examined, it will be found to be composed of cells.

This deduction was tested by observation. Biologists examined thousands of different species. Nearly all were found to be composed of cells. Most plants and animals were found to have bodies composed of many cells. Others, including some first seen by Leeuwenhoek, were single-celled organisms. One could even interpret the exceptions, such as slime molds, as having bodies modified from a cellular type. Because of abundant confirmations of the hypothesis, the cell theory is clearly established.

Now that we have traced the history of the cell theory, let us reconsider some of the early observations. What was Hooke's contribution? Actually it was slight, and herein lies an important point. Hooke's observation was not a contribution to organized knowledge—it was an isolated fact. It was not until the first years of the nineteenth century that observations of many plants and animals were combined to suggest that cells are the basic structural units of all life. The time lag of a century and a half between Hooke and Schwann was indeed unfortunate. If Hooke and others had pursued the original discovery, possibly the cell theory would have been established by 1700. If so, biological science would have advanced much more rapidly.

Hooke and his microscope started biologists along a fruitful line of inquiry, leading to the recognition that cells are the structural units of living matter. Today an understanding of cells is necessary for all branches of biology that deal with morphology and physiology. Our digestive juices are secreted by cells. Vision, taste, and hearing are all made possible by cells. The contraction of a muscle is no more than the contraction of its individual cells. Much in embryonic development is understandable in terms of interactions of cells. As Virchow was first to emphasize, a physician studies the cells of a sick person and can often identify the disease. Hooke's discovery of cells in cork, which was of little value when first made, is now of great theoretical and practical importance.

It was not until the nineteenth century that biologists were agreed that there is a basic unit of structure—the cell. Structure is what things are; function is what they do. Are there also basic functions of living organisms? That is, can one discover any activities that are common to all living organisms? Let us see.

GUIDE QUESTIONS AND PROBLEMS

1. What problems required that early man develop information about the plants and animals of his environment?
2. What are some of the uses that primitive man made of wild plants?
3. How did practical and detailed knowledge of the buffalo and its ways aid the Plains Indians?
4. How is technology distinguished from science? Does the distinction always exist?
5. Is there really such a thing as pure science—that is, science with no possible practical use? Explain.
6. Microscopes are used far more frequently by biologists than by chemists. Why do you think this is so?
7. What was Hooke's contribution to our knowledge of cells?
8. Were Hooke's observations science? Explain.
9. What was the role of the first scientific societies and their publications in the development of science?
10. How did Schwann change the concept of the cell?
11. What was Schwann's definition of a cell?
12. According to Schwann, how do new cells arise? According to Virchow?
13. What may happen to cells as a result of the action of chemicals used to prepare them for observation? How can one check for the possible production of artifacts?
14. What structures do most cells have in common?
15. What is the role in the cell of the mitochondria? the chromosomes? the chloroplasts?

SUGGESTIONS FOR ADDITIONAL READING

Books

Butler, John A. V., *Inside the Living Cell.* New York, Basic Books, 1959.
    Fine summary of recent experimental studies of cell structure, chemistry, and function.
Gerard, Ralph W., *Unresting Cells.* New York, Harper & Row, 1961.
    Easy-to-read, interesting account of cell functions.
Mercer, E. H., *Cells: Their Structure and Function.* New York, Doubleday, 1962.
    Well-written summary of recent work on the structure of cells, and some current theories of cell function.
Swanson, C. P., *The Cell.* Englewood Cliffs (N. J.), Prentice-Hall, 1960.
    An up-to-date account of cell structures, cell theory, and some information on the tools and techniques of cell study.

Magazines and Journals

Kopac, M. J., "Microsurgery." *Scientific American,* Vol. 183 (October 1950), p. 48.
Lwoff, A., "The Life Cycle of a Virus." *Scientific American,* Vol. 190 (March 1954), pp. 34–37.
Mazia, D., "Cell Division." *Scientific American,* Vol. 189 (August 1953), pp. 53–63.
Siekevitz, P., "Powerhouse of the Cell." *Scientific American,* Vol. 197 (July 1957), pp. 131–34.
Taylor, J. H., "The Duplication of Chromosomes." *Scientific American,* Vol. 198 (June 1958), pp. 36–42.

(Also, *Scientific American* for September 1961 is devoted entirely to cells.)

4

BASIC FUNCTIONS

Have you ever seen an animal die? Possibly you have seen a bird accidentally fly into the closed window of a building or a beetle drowning in a puddle. All of us have noticed plants dying—flowering plants withering in the late summer. The leaves of trees turn brown and slowly die in the autumn. If one closely examines an organism before and after it dies, it is often impossible to detect any immediate, obvious morphological difference. The unfortunate bird that flew into the building probably broke its neck. It might, however, take an exceedingly careful examination to show that this was so. The part of the bird actually damaged might be much less than 1 percent of the whole bird.

The change occurring in the less than 1 percent portion of the organism leads to a much greater result. In a moment the living organism is no longer alive. What happened? If we were to weigh an organism immediately before and after death, we would detect no difference. We could conclude that whatever the organism lost when it died was not a material that we could weigh. In fact, a series of elaborate experiments and observations would show that the "lost" property had none of the known characteristics of matter. Our failure to detect what was lost narrows the problem, but if anything, makes it more difficult.

Once again (see page 23) we are faced with the basic question, "What is life?" We have learned many things that contribute to an answer. In Chapter 1 we learned that one of the most important properties of the living state is the ability to reproduce. In Chapter 2 we learned that life, whatever it is, is part of a genetic process—living organisms of today are the descendants of other living organisms. In Chapter 3 we learned that living organisms have a basic structural similarity—they are composed of cells and the products of cells. Not one of these properties, however, seems to help much in answering our question of what life is. Organisms are not constantly reproducing; the chances are that the bird was not so engaged immediately before its death. As for the origin of the bird, its parentage has not been affected by the fact that it has died. And finally, if we were to study parts of the bird shortly after its death, we would find that they appear to consist of the same cells of which the living bird was made.

There must be important features of life apart from these three, which are so ineffectual in accounting for the difference between life and its absence in what seem to be the same structures.

TWO PHILOSOPHIES— VITALISM AND MECHANISM

There have been two main philosophies to account for the relation of life and matter. One is **vitalism**, a philosophy that assumes that life is made possible by some force that is neither chemical nor physical. The other is **mechanism**, a philosophy that assumes that life can be explained entirely in chemical and physical terms. Adherents to these opposing philosophies have debat-

Alinari Photo

The Louvre, Paris

4-1 Aristotle (left) and Descartes (right). Aristotle was a vitalist; he believed that life was associated with a unique force that defied the kind of investigation suitable for non-living phenomena. Descartes believed otherwise; he was fundamentally a mechanist, although he made a partial exception in his outlook toward human life.

ed with one another for at least several thousand years. This is not surprising, since questions about the nature of life have always been of great interest to man.

Aristotle and Vitalism

Fairly early in man's intellectual history, it became apparent that the substance of living and nonliving objects might be essentially the same. An organism dies and decays; the residue seems identical with other substances in the earth's crust. At one moment in time, the same substance was alive; at another, not. It seemed necessary, therefore, to assume that there was something more to life than its substance.

Let us begin with the opinions of the Greek biologist and philosopher, Aristotle (Figure 4-1). Aristotle was a vitalist: he believed that life was associated with some unique force, or principle, which does not exist apart from life. He called this unique force **psyche** (sy·kee). There were three main kinds of psyche, according to Aristotle: a vegetable psyche, an animal psyche, and a rational psyche (Figure 4-2).

The vegetable psyche was restricted to plants, and it was to be regarded as per-

mitting the lowest type of life. It was sufficient for using food, for growth, and for reproduction.

The animal psyche was associated with these basic biological processes plus two others—movement and responsiveness. In a general way, the power to move and to respond to stimuli from the surrounding world *does* distinguish animals from plants.

The rational psyche, restricted to man as you might have guessed, was associated with the properties found in the vegetable and animal psyches, plus another—the ability to reason.

The essential feature of Aristotle's vitalism was this *extra*. Living organisms were nonliving matter plus the life-directing psyche. Such was the prevailing view among biologists until the seventeenth century.

Descartes and Mechanism

René Descartes (1596–1650) was a young man living in France when the first European colonists were landing on the east coast of what is now the United States. He was a great philosopher and one of the early physiologists. Descartes lived at a time when astronomers and physicists such as Kepler and Galileo were having considerable success in describing the physical world. They studied the movements of the planets, the swing of the pendulum, and the rise and fall of the tides. And, so a myth goes, Galileo dropped heavy balls and light balls from the leaning tower at Pisa. Again and again it proved possible to describe the physical world in mechanical and mathematical terms.

Descartes was interested in these studies, and he was also interested in life. He attempted to explain all the activities of living organisms in terms of mechanics. The movement of fluids within the body, the contraction of muscles, the pumping of the heart, were obvious examples. Descartes went on to explain how the brain and nerves could act on mechanical principles. To him, therefore, life could be understood in terms of the laws that applied to nonliving objects. There was no need to invoke a vegetable or animal psyche.

It is noteworthy that Descartes did not extend these views to man completely. In most respects—breathing, moving, eating—man's body was a machine, and understandable as such. But man seemed to Descartes to have a rational soul or mind, which set him apart from other living creatures. Descartes even suggested that the rational soul of man might be located in the **pineal** (PIN·e·al) **body** (a tiny structure in the brain).

Vitalism Versus Mechanism

The preceding two examples of Aristotle the vitalist and Descartes the mechanist set the stage for our discussions. Before we continue, one point must be emphasized. Neither Aristotle nor Descartes was dealing with fact or even a reasonably well-established hypothesis. Vitalism and mechanism were no more than exploratory ideas. Whether either could be proved true would depend upon its being stated as a hypothe-

4-2 ARISTOTLE'S IDEAS OF PSYCHE

Vegetable Psyche	**Animal Psyche**	**Rational Psyche**
1. Food use	**1.** Food use	**1.** Food use
2. Growth	**2.** Growth	**2.** Growth
3. Reproduction	**3.** Reproduction	**3.** Reproduction
	4. Movement	**4.** Movement
	5. Responsiveness	**5.** Responsiveness
		6. Ability to reason

sis (or a set of hypotheses) that could be checked by experiment and observation.

The history of the debate between the vitalists and the mechanists will not be discussed in any detail. For generations the two groups argued with each other, but victory came for neither. This was inevitable, since so little was known about the true nature of the processes associated with life.

There is an interesting difference in the ways that the vitalists and the mechanists approached biological problems. Let us suppose, for example, that we are interested in discovering what controls the contractions of the heart. We know this to be an important physiological phenomenon, for when the heart stops, so does the life of the animal. A vitalist would say that the ultimate cause was some vital force, or psyche, of the animal. A mechanist, on the other hand, would believe that the heart was controlled by the same laws that hold for all chemical and physical events. He might not know what these laws were, but at least he would believe them to be *discoverable* (Figure 4-3). Thus, for the mechanist there was hope that continued study would lead to an answer. The vitalist, however, would find it difficult, if not impossible, to experiment on vital forces—it would be like trying to study the anatomy and physiology of ghosts! Furthermore, he might tend to think that he already knew the answer. The mechanists' hypothesis, then, tended to encourage observation and experiment to a greater degree than did the vitalists' hypothesis.

What would be some of the basic facts available to vitalists and mechanists in the seventeenth century, when they began their debates? They would know that animals needed air, food, and water. They were sure that plants needed air and water. Furthermore, Aristotle had told them that the earth manufactures plant food, and that the food enters the plants through their roots.

They would have noticed how seemingly slight changes can kill an animal or plant.

For example, many plants die after exposure to temperatures below freezing— 0° C. They also would have made the common observation mentioned at the start of the chapter—that a bird which flies into an obstacle may die of a broken neck. If injury to such a small part of the bird has such a great effect, they could conclude that a living being was highly organized. That is, the parts depended on one another. If one part failed, the whole would fail. One characteristic of life, therefore, was its association with *organized* structures. In fact, that is why we talk of living things as *organisms*.

The vitalists and mechanists began their arguments when there was almost no useful chemical knowledge. This made it rather difficult for the mechanists who, after all, hoped eventually to explain life in physical and chemical terms! (Before the seventeenth century, would-be chemists were more interested in practical than scientific knowledge: they were nearly always alchemists hoping to find some way of making gold.) But let us see how an early problem was investigated.

What Makes a Willow Tree?

Biologists are animals, and as such, they are quite aware of the role of food. Without it animals do not grow, or even maintain themselves. Instead they waste away and finally die.

What about plants? They do not eat, yet they maintain themselves and grow. Naturally, when they grow, the material of which they are composed increases in amount. An acorn may weigh less than an ounce; an oak tree may weigh more than ten tons. When the acorn grows into the oak, where does all the extra material come from?

Aristotle had suggested the answer. The earth manufactures the food, which enters through the roots. This explanation correlated well with some of the facts known to farmers. If crops were grown year after

Question: What causes the heart to contract?

Hypothesis: A "vital force"

Deduction:

?

How can useful deductions be made – deductions which can be tested?

Question: What causes the heart to contract?

First hypothesis: If the nerve from the brain to the heart is responsible ......

Deduction: ......then cutting the nerve will stop the heartbeat.

Test: In an experimental animal, the nerve is severed; the heart continues to contract.

Second hypothesis: If the cause is ......

4-3 What distinguishes science from other quests for understanding? The answer lies in how we *seek* an answer. Science progresses only if questions can be investigated by observation and experiment. Questions posed by vitalism may be debated, but they are rarely answerable experimentally. The same questions, from the point of view of mechanism, include the assumption that if an event is observed, its cause can be discovered and explained according to principles that hold for all matter.

year in the same field, the yield became less and less. It seemed as though the earth was not able to make plant food rapidly enough. This was borne out by the additional observation that if the field was left fallow for a year or more, better yields could then be expected.

If we accept the suggestion of Aristotle as a hypothesis, this deduction would follow logically:

If we grow a plant in a large container of earth, the earth should lose weight—because the food it produced would pass into the plant. The plant would gain the weight that the earth lost.

An experiment testing this deduction was performed by J. B. van Helmont (1577–1644), whom we first encountered in the controversy over spontaneous generation

(Chapter 2). Here is a paraphrased account of his experiment:

> I dried 200 pounds of earth in a furnace and then put it into a large pot. The earth was then moistened with rainwater and a small willow tree was planted. At this time the willow tree weighed 5 pounds. The earth was kept moist with rainwater or distilled water. Nothing else was added. In order that no dust would get into the pot, and add to the weight of the earth, I put a cover on the pot, leaving a hole for the trunk of the tree.

> After five years the entire tree was removed and found to weigh 169 pounds and 3 ounces. Since the tree had weighed 5 pounds at the start, the gain in weight was more than 164 pounds.

If Aristotle was correct, there should have been a great decrease in the weight of the earth—possibly a 164-pound decrease. However, as van Helmont reported:

> I removed the earth from the pot, dried and then weighed it. It weighed 199 pounds and 14 ounces.

Thus, while the earth had lost two ounces, the tree had gained 164 pounds. Clearly, earth-food was not being converted into "willow tree" in the way Aristotle had suggested. But where did the 164 pounds of willow tree (Figure 4-4) come from? Here is van Helmont's conclusion:

> Therefore, 164 pounds of wood, bark, and roots were formed out of water only.

According to van Helmont, then, water can be converted into living matter—in this case a willow tree. At the time, this seemed an unassailable conclusion, since all that he had added was water. Remember also that he added *pure* water (either rain or distilled water), so that there could be little or no source of error in added substance dissolved in the water.

This was indeed a staggering experiment. There seemed no doubt that the observation was correct. Robert Boyle (page 53) did similar experiments and obtained the same results, except that he was not sure the earth decreased even a trifling amount in weight.

How was one to interpret such results? Van Helmont thought the water was converted into the living substance of the willow tree. The water was nonliving; the willow tree was living. Somehow the nonliving substance had been transformed into the living.

How? It seemed obvious that more knowledge of the chemistry and physics of the process was necessary.

EARLY CHEMISTRY

In every science there is an attempt to reduce the complex to the simple; to get down to the basic facts. We have had one example—the quest for some unit of structure common to all living creatures. Biologists resolved this example with the discovery of the cellular nature of organisms.

Could there be units of structure in the nonliving world as well? Many thought so —in fact, ideas of this sort can be traced back to classical times. Aristotle thought that all matter was composed of varying proportions of earth, water, air, and fire. This could easily be demonstrated in some instances. Thus, when wood was burned, the fire left the wood. Smoke (air) was formed. If the wood was burned near a cold wall, one could be sure that the wood was liberating water, because moisture condensed on the wall. Finally only ashes (earth) were left. Thus wood was a combination of fire, air, water, and earth.

These four substances were supposed to be **elements**—that is, substances that could not be altered, or destroyed, or divided into simpler substances. The belief that all matter was composed of varying proportions of these four elements lasted for two thousand years. It was still widely accepted in the seventeenth century. Boyle, however, thought the view to be sheer nonsense and suggested that scientists should base their knowledge upon more careful observation and experimentation.

Another belief, held by van Helmont among many other persons, was that one substance could be changed into another. Recall that van Helmont believed water could be changed into the substance of a willow tree. The entire school of alchemists also believed that substances could be changed, one into another. In fact, their work was inspired by the hope of becoming wealthy by finding some way of changing base metals into gold. They never succeeded, but the isolated facts they learned in

their attempts were eventually organized into the science of chemistry.

The chemists of those times had as little understanding of the fundamental laws applying to the activity of nonliving matter as the biologists had of the fundamental laws applying to the activity we call life. The analysis of one problem—the nature of burning—was of tremendous help to both. The study of this problem, more than any other, was responsible for making chemistry a science. And once chemistry became a science, physiology could become a science, too.

The Burning Question

One of the most dramatic activities of the nonliving world is fire. It may be violent. It can be associated with tremendous

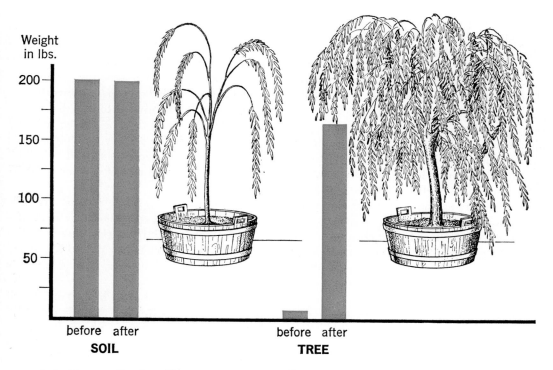

4-4 The growth of a willow tree. As van Helmont's little tree grew, its increase in weight was *not* associated with an equivalent decrease in the weight of the soil. (In the actual experiment, the container was covered; the cover had a hole for the trunk. Of what importance to the experiment was the cover?)

destruction and with tremendous pain. Is it a substance, an activity, or both?

A comprehensive theory to account for burning, or combustion, was proposed by a German chemist, G. E. Stahl (1660–1734). According to Stahl, combustible substances were composed of two sorts of material. One sort was inflammable, the other not. The inflammable material was named **phlogiston** (flo·JIS·ton). When wood was burned, the phlogiston combined with air. Ashes were left. Wood before burning, therefore, was ash plus phlogiston.

A similar result was obtained when copper was heated. The shiny metal was converted to a powdery substance called **calx.** Copper was therefore assumed to be composed of calx plus phlogiston. When heated, the phlogiston was driven off and only the calx remained.

In some cases it was possible to reverse the reactions. Thus, if the calx were heated with charcoal, copper was re-formed. This was easily explained by the nature of charcoal. Since charcoal would burn readily, it must contain large amounts of phlogiston. When heated with calx, some of the phlogiston of the charcoal would be transferred from the charcoal to the calx. Calx plus phlogiston would then become copper.

The Phlogiston Theory was found to account satisfactorily for many chemical reactions. It was useful, therefore, and remained a part of the science of chemistry throughout the eighteenth century. The theory also was stated in such a way that it could be tested. That is, one could make deductions and, by experiment and observation, see if these deductions were true.

Here is one example of a test for the Phlogiston Theory. We will assume that charcoal is made up of ash and phlogiston. According to the theory, when charcoal is heated the phlogiston is lost. (We must further assume that, since phlogiston is a substance, it has weight.) A logical deduction follows:

If we compare the weight of a piece of charcoal before and after combustion, we should find that it weighs less after combustion.

This deduction can be tested by a simple experiment. We will take a piece of charcoal weighing 50 grams. This we place in a crucible, which we hold in a fire. The charcoal will burn and leave an ash. We will then weigh the ash, which will be found to weigh no more than a few grams, let us say 3. We could conclude, therefore, that charcoal is composed of 47 parts (by weight) of phlogiston and 3 parts of ash. Few other substances are as rich in phlogiston.

So far so good. We have made a deduction from the hypothesis, tested the deduction, and found it to be true. Therefore, the hypothesis is *more probably* true than it was before we did our experiment.

But we must be careful. Let us test our deduction in another way—by substituting copper for the charcoal. Let us put 50 grams of copper in a crucible, which we will heat until the copper is converted to powdery calx. According to our deduction, the phlogiston will thus be driven off, and the calx should be lighter in weight than the copper with which we started. We find, however, that 50 grams of copper yield 57 grams of calx!

Diametrically opposed results are obtained in the two experiments. When phlogiston is removed from the charcoal, the charcoal is lighter. When phlogiston is removed from the copper, the copper is heavier.

The supporters of the Phlogiston Theory attempted to explain how the calx could be heavier than the copper. One need only assume, they wrote, that phlogiston had "negative weight." That is, the more phlogiston a substance had, the lighter it would be. Thus, the phlogiston in the copper actually decreased the weight of the copper. When the phlogiston was removed by fire, the calx was heavier.

But wait. How can we explain the first result we obtained when we burned charcoal? There the ash weighed far less than the charcoal. The phlogiston in the charcoal must have had "positive" weight. But how can phlogiston have "negative" weight in copper and "positive" weight in charcoal? Clearly the theory, which had explained so much, now seemed to be erroneous. Something other than phlogiston must be involved. What about the air? Could it be involved, somehow (Figure 4-5)? It was known to be necessary for combustion.

Air: Simple or Complex?

Many experiments and ideas of the eighteenth century suggested that air was not a simple elemental substance. Observation and experiment had shown that there are many kinds of "air," or *gases* (a name suggested by van Helmont).

In 1755 an English chemist, Joseph Black (1728–1799), collected a gas produced by burning charcoal. It was the gas now known as carbon dioxide. Black also established another exceedingly important point: carbon dioxide made up a noticeable part of the air exhaled from the lungs. Thus, the burning of charcoal and some reaction occurring in the human body were producing the same end result—the formation of carbon dioxide.

Lavoisier and Burning Phosphorus

Many new insights into the nature of burning, and into the composition of air, came from the work of the French chemist Antoine Lavoisier (1743–1794). Through his work the Phlogiston Theory was put to rest, and modern chemistry was born—and without modern chemistry there could be no solution to the problems of the nature of life.

Let us begin with one of Lavoisier's experiments. Phosphorus was allowed to burn

THE BURNING QUESTION

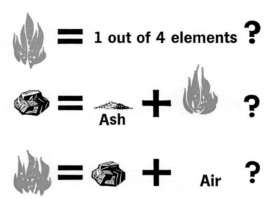

4-5 How were early scientists to explain burning? Was fire an element? a force? Was charcoal made of ash and fire? Or was fire an interaction between charcoal and air? The nature of burning was a crucial problem to man for thousands of years.

in a closed vessel containing air, and in the process it was converted into a white powder. After the phosphorus had burned, Lavoisier found that one fifth of the air (by volume) had disappeared. Furthermore, by varying the amounts of phosphorus in the container, he found that there was a limit to the amount of phosphorus that would burn in the closed container.

Lavoisier was an exceedingly careful experimenter (Figure 4-6). One of the things that he did was to weigh each of the substances he used, both before and after the experiment. Let us analyze his experiment.

1. For convenience, we will call the weight of the maximum amount of phosphorus that can burn in the closed container X.
2. After the phosphorus has burned and produced the white powder, we weigh the powder. Let us call this weight Y. We find that Y is considerably greater than X. Therefore, the difference in weight before and after burning is $Y - X$.

4-6 Careful observation and measurement is a foundation of scientific procedures. A true understanding of chemical reactions began to emerge when chemists carefully weighed the chemical substances before and after the reactions had occurred. Even the gases had to be weighed!

3. Let us call the weight of the air in the closed vessel before the phosphorus is burned A.
4. After the phosphorus has burned, we find that one fifth of the air (by volume) has disappeared. Let us call the weight of this air B. The difference in weight before and after will be A − B.
5. Lavoisier found again and again that Y − X = A − B. That is, the gain in weight of the phosphorus was exactly equal to the loss in weight of the air.

How can we interpret these results? It would seem that some substance in the air had combined with the phosphorus.

This leads us to another question (as all answers in science do). Why did only one fifth of the air disappear when the phosphorus burned? Why didn't the addition of more phosphorus cause all of the air to be used up? Repeated experiments showed that this was never so: no matter how much phosphorus was used, only one fifth of the air disappeared. We might therefore reach this tentative conclusion: air consists of two parts—one part that will combine with phosphorus, and another that will not.

Priestley, Candles, Mice, and Mint

In the same year that Lavoisier published the results of his experiments—1774—he was visited by an English parson who was a spare-time chemist, Joseph Priestley (1733–1804). Priestley had been performing similar experiments. Neither Priestley nor Lavoisier had been making rapid progress while working alone. When they discussed their experiments with one another, however, they began to understand things that were confusing before. New ideas suggested new experiments. New experiments gave new insight. Old questions were answered and new ones took their place. The endless cycle of scientific progress—question, answer, question, answer—continued.

What was Priestley able to tell Lavoisier? Early in his scientific life, Priestley lived in a house next to a brewery. It was wholly accidental that he happened to live near a brewery, but the fact that he did was of enormous importance for both biology and chemistry. He became interested in events occurring within the brewery. He noticed, for example, that bubbles of "air" were evolved in the fermentation vats. He collected some of the air and found it to be the gas we now call carbon dioxide (Priestley was unaware that Black had previously discovered this gas).

Carbon dioxide, then, was produced by fermentation. Here was an isolated fact that neither Priestley nor we would seem to be able to do much with—but let us "file and *not* forget."

Priestley found that carbon dioxide could also be obtained by heating limestone or by mixing acid and chalk. (He used the carbon dioxide so produced to make the first artificial carbonated water!) Experiment showed that the new gas differed in many ways from ordinary air. Candles would not burn in carbon dioxide, and a mouse placed in a container of it died quickly. A frog held for six minutes over a fermenting vat became inactive and seemed to be dead. It recovered after being removed to fresh air.

Other experiments showed that ordinary air was changed by a candle flame or a mouse. When a candle was placed in a closed container of air, it burned for a while, but then the flame went out. When a mouse was placed in a closed container of air, the mouse died after some time.

In an interesting double experiment, a lighted candle was placed in the container in which the mouse had died. The flame went out quickly. The mouse and the burning candle must have been using something in common from the air (Figure 4-7). Air that they had used was made "worthless" in some manner. But think what this seems to mean. We and many other animals are breathing all the time. Eventually we would destroy the life-supporting portion of the air. This point puzzled Priestley, too, until he made another important discovery (reported in an article in the *Philosophical Transactions* for 1772—see page 53):

It is evident . . . that there must be some provision in nature for this purpose, as well as for that of rendering the air fit for sustaining flame; for without it the whole mass of the atmosphere would, in time, become unfit for the purpose of animal life, and yet there is no reason to think that it is, at present, at all less fit for respiration than it has ever been. I flatter myself, however, that I have hit upon [a method] employed by nature for this great purpose.

. . . on the 17th of August, 1771, I put a sprig of mint in a quantity of air in which a wax candle had burned out, and found that on the 27th of the same month another candle burned perfectly well in it. This experiment I repeated, without the least variation in the event, not less than eight or ten times in the remainder of the summer. Several times I divided the quantity of air in which the candle had burned out, into two parts, and putting the plant into one of them, left the other in the same exposure, contained, also, in a glass vessel immersed in water, but without any plant [this was Priestley's control]; and never failed to find, that a candle would burn in the former but not the latter. I usually found that five or six days were sufficient to restore the air.

Priestley wrote to an American friend, Benjamin Franklin, to tell him of the experiments and received this reply:

That the vegetable creation should restore the air which is spoiled by the animal part of it, looks like a rational system. . . . We knew before, that putrid animal substances were converted into sweet vegetables, when mixed with the earth, and applied as manure; and now, it seems, that the same putrid substances mixed with the air, have a similar effect.

Priestley was able to tell Lavoisier about these interesting observations on mice, candles, mint, and carbon dioxide. But he had another observation that interested Lavoisier even more.

The Discovery of Oxygen

Priestley had taken a chemical substance, known now as red oxide of mercury, and heated it by focusing sunlight upon it with a "burning glass." The heated chemical gave off a gas—a gas unlike air or carbon dioxide. As Priestley reported:

> . . . what surprised me more than I can express, was, that a candle burned in this air with a remarkably vigorous flame . . . I was utterly at a loss how to account for it.

Furthermore, when a mouse was placed in a container with this new gas, it lived twice as long as did a mouse in another container of the same size but with air. Priestley breathed some of this gas and reported:

> . . . my breast felt peculiarly light and easy for some time afterwards . . . who can tell but that, in time, this pure air may become a fashionable article in luxury. Hitherto only two mice and myself have had the privilege of breathing it.

Priestley's was not the first discovery of the new gas, but to him must go the credit for the usefulness of the discovery. He published his results promptly, unlike another chemist who anticipated his work. Here we meet again one of the necessary conditions of scientific endeavor: making a discovery is not enough—it must be made known to other scientists.

Priestley's new gas, so invigorating for him to breathe, proved invigorating in an entirely different way to Lavoisier. As Priestley related his findings to his French host, Lavoisier's mind ticked rapidly through a comparison of Priestley's work with his own. A new theory began to emerge in his thoughts. A burning candle and a mouse used up something present in air; both were active longer in the presence of Priestley's new gas. Could these discoveries be related to the part of air that is used up when phosphorus burns?

After many months of thought and experiment, Lavoisier had the explanation. All of these observations could be explained by assuming that a gas, which he named *oxygen*, was involved. The gas was produced when red oxide of mercury was heated. It was also present in air, and was used up by a burning candle and a living mouse. On the basis of his finding that the burning of phosphorus removed one fifth of the volume of air, Lavoisier concluded that air must be about one-fifth oxygen by volume. The oxygen entered the body during inhalation and was involved in some sort of combustion process. Carbon dioxide was exhaled.

One test of the theory remained. Lavoisier had yet to *prove* that Priestley's new gas, obtained by heating red oxide of mercury, was a part of air. In an experiment brilliant in its directness and simplicity, he confined air and pure mercury together and slowly heated the mercury. At first nothing happened, then slowly—over a period of days—a change began to take place. The mercury was changing in appearance—and the volume of air began to decrease! At the end of twelve days, the reaction stopped. Almost one fifth of the air had been used up, and the mercury had been converted to red oxide of mercury—the substance Priestley had used to obtain his "pure air."

There was no longer any doubt (Figure 4-8). Oxygen was a part of air. It supported combustion and respiration alike. This was a tremendous concept. A living process—**respiration**—was being interpreted in the same way as a chemical reaction. Respiration was close to life itself. If it stopped for more than a moment, life ceased. Could anything so fundamental to life be explained by the laws of the nonliving world? Lavoisier was answering "Yes." This was one of the first examples of the successful explanation of a physiological problem in mechanistic terms.

The observations of Priestley, Lavoisier, and others suggested a fundamental rela-

4-7 PRIESTLEY'S FIRST EXPERIMENTS WITH AIR

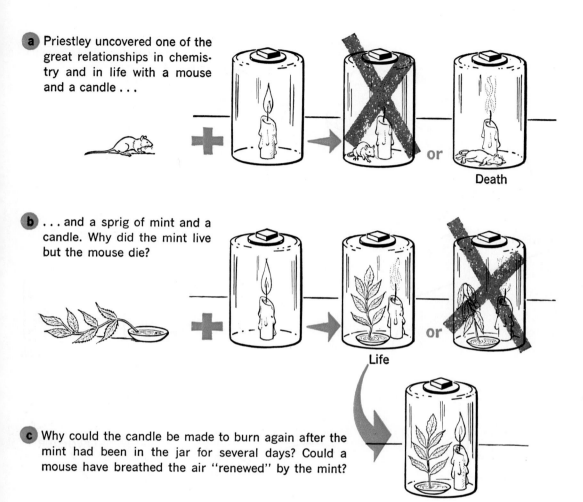

a Priestley uncovered one of the great relationships in chemistry and in life with a mouse and a candle . . .

or

Death

b . . . and a sprig of mint and a candle. Why did the mint live but the mouse die?

Life

or

c Why could the candle be made to burn again after the mint had been in the jar for several days? Could a mouse have breathed the air "renewed" by the mint?

tion between animals and green plants. Both mouse and mint are alive, but seem to function in chemically different ways. The mouse uses oxygen and produces carbon dioxide. The mint uses carbon dioxide and produces oxygen. The two balance one another (Figure 4-7).

The Phlogiston Theory was gradually abandoned after the discovery of oxygen. Lavoisier showed that burning, or combustion, could be understood by assuming that burning substances combine with oxygen.

An explanation based upon loss of phlogiston was unnecessary. Thus, phosphorus combined with the oxygen in air to form oxidized phosphorus—a phosphorus oxide. Charcoal, which is nearly pure carbon, combined with oxygen to form an oxide of carbon—carbon dioxide. Burning always involved a union of the substance being burned with oxygen—today we say that the substance is **oxidized.**

Not all substances are oxidized with the violence of burning charcoal—involving the

A CYCLE OF DISCOVERY AND CONFIRMATION—
The Discovery of Oxygen

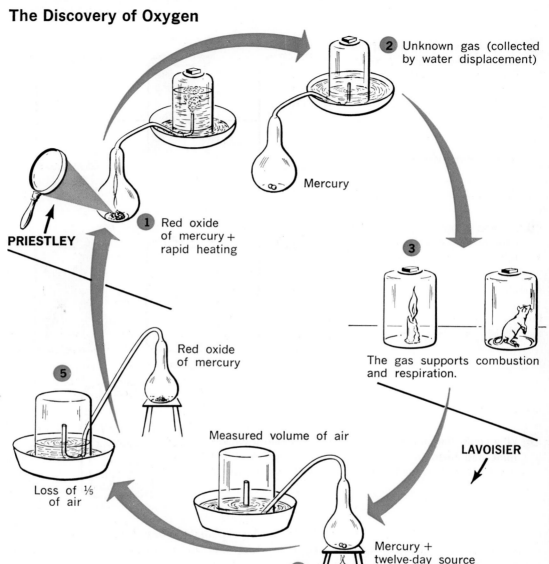

2 Unknown gas (collected by water displacement)

Mercury

1 Red oxide of mercury + rapid heating

PRIESTLEY

3 The gas supports combustion and respiration.

Red oxide of mercury

5 Loss of ⅕ of air

Measured volume of air

LAVOISIER

4 Mercury + twelve-day source of moderate heat

4-8   Scientific facts that are now well known were usually exceedingly difficult to establish. Reactions involving invisible gases (which were difficult to weigh and measure)
were especially hard to study. Priestley and Lavoisier both experimented on different
aspects of what proved to be related problems. The genius of Lavoisier lay in his
realization that their observations *were* related—as he demonstrated in this cycle of
discovery and confirmation. Priestley's observations began with the heating of red
oxide of mercury by concentrating the rays of the sun with a magnifying glass (then
often called a "burning glass"). A gas was liberated, and mercury was left. Lavoisier
correctly guessed the nature of the unknown gas and was able to demonstrate the
truth of his hypothesis by accomplishing the reverse reaction. By slowly and gently
heating mercury in the presence of a measured volume of ordinary air, he produced
red oxide of mercury. The critical feature of the process was that a gas from the
sample of air was used up, precisely as Lavoisier had anticipated.

liberation of great heat. When substances are oxidized in the mouse there are no flames! But Lavoisier realized that what went on in the living mouse, and in the burning phosphorus and charcoal, were much the same. All were oxidations, and all liberated energy. The energy was expressed in the flame and heat of the burning charcoal and, according to Lavoisier, in the "animal heat" of the mouse.

The Law of Conservation of Mass

Before we leave Lavoisier we must emphasize another of his magnificent contributions to science. Lavoisier was a careful experimenter. He measured and weighed with the finest analytical balances that he could obtain. He observed that the total weight of all the substances at the end of each reaction was the same as the weight of all the substances at the beginning. This fact also had been observed in many carefully performed experiments done years before Lavoisier's lifetime. Van Helmont, for example, had observed the same constancy of total weight.

These experiments suggested that matter could not be destroyed—though of course it could be changed. The total **mass,** or quantity of matter, remains the same. This fundamental principle became known as the:

Law of Conservation of Mass: Matter can neither be created nor destroyed. The mass of the substances present before and after a reaction or change are equal.

Note that the law has been stated in terms of *mass* rather than *weight.* Thus, with an exception to be noted later, it applies even today to reactions in a "weightless" laboratory in orbit around the earth.

Matter: Transformable and Nontransformable

Gradually it was becoming apparent that chemistry was not all chaos. Some exceptionally useful ideas were emerging. Rob-

ert Boyle (pages 53, 70) suggested a theory that, with many modifications, eventually proved to be true.

According to Boyle, there were two sorts of chemical substances—**elements** and **compounds.** The *elements* were the ultimate kinds of matter. They could not be divided into simpler substances, nor could they be changed into one another. The *compounds,* on the other hand, were composed of two or more elements, chemically united.

As time went on, more and more chemists regarded this as a good working hypothesis. Lavoisier added to it. He found that the elements in air seemed to be physically but not chemically united. Air, then, was a simple **mixture.** Unlike the elements in compounds, the parts of air seemed to separate or come together again without evidence of chemical reaction.

So there were elements, mixtures, and compounds. Compounds were those substances that could be broken down chemically into the simpler elements. Mixtures could simply be "unmixed." Elements could not be broken down at all. Thus gold, sulfur, silver, lead, copper, mercury, and carbon were regarded as elements. Air was a mixture. Sulfuric acid, mercuric oxide, and limestone were compounds.

The definitions seemed to be clear and untroublesome. In practice they were not. How could a chemist know whether an unknown substance was an element or a compound? He could not look it up in a book! Suppose that he took a substance X and used it in many experiments. He might find that it would combine with many other substances, but that no matter how he tried, he could not divide X itself into simpler substances. Could he safely conclude that X is an element? No. All he could conclude would be that on the basis of his experiments, X behaved as an element. It could be possible that X is really a compound, and that he did not perform the proper experiments to prove this.

Thus, often in the eighteenth century there was doubt about whether a substance was an element or a compound (Figure 4-9). Water is a good example. Repeated efforts to divide it into simpler substances failed. Then, near the end of the eighteenth century, it was found that hydrogen could be burned in the presence of oxygen to yield water. Water, therefore, was shown to be a compound composed of the elements oxygen and hydrogen. Efforts to break water down continued to fail, until electricity could be applied to the problem.

As one chemist expressed it in 1857, "The elements count as simple substances not because we know that they are, but because we do not know that they are not!"

Dalton and the Atomic Theory

Lavoisier had successfully challenged the Phlogiston Theory, proposed in its place the Theory of Oxidation to account for combustion, and firmly established the Law of Conservation of Mass. These were all intellectual feats of a high order. He had also made another contribution, which in the history of science proved to be of great importance: he insisted on the importance of making careful measurements of all that took place in experimentation.

Other chemists followed his lead, and soon many interesting facts and relations were discovered. Lavoisier himself did not live to participate in these developments: he was executed during the French Revolution. But John Dalton (1766–1844) pursued Lavoisier's doctrine of careful measurement and became the "modern father" of the Atomic Theory. (It is important to use the adjective "modern," because a belief in atoms goes back at least to the Greeks of more than two thousand years ago.)

We begin to approach the concept of an atom when we ask this question: What is the ultimate structure of matter? When Boyle, Lavoisier, and the others spoke of elements, they referred to *kinds* of matter.

But what are the elements really like? If one could examine carbon, mercury, oxygen, and hydrogen with a tremendously powerful microscope, what would one see? Would there be basic units of structure in the chemical world in the same sense that cells are the units of structure in the living world?

The compound microscope gives one answer: "No." The highest magnifications available, even today, reveal no unit of structure common to all elements. Oxygen and hydrogen are invisible. Both carbon and mercury have their own peculiar microscopic appearances—one as a solid, the other as a liquid. No chemical "cells" common to even two of these four elements are revealed by the microscope. But careful work with the chemists' balance has shown that there are other ways of "looking" at chemical substances.

If one measures very carefully the weights of the different elements that react to form a compound, a surprising fact is discovered: the ratio of weights is always the same. In water, for example, the oxygen always weighs 8 times as much as the hydrogen. If we burn 1 gram of hydrogen and 8 grams of oxygen, we get 9 grams of water. If we start with 2 grams of hydrogen and 8 grams of oxygen, we still get 9 grams of water—but this time we have 1 gram of hydrogen left over. The elements in a compound are in a constant proportion by weight.

The same elements that form *one* compound may combine in a different way to form another. For example, oxygen and hydrogen form not only water but also another compound, hydrogen peroxide. The weights of the hydrogen and oxygen in this case are in the proportion 1 (hydrogen) to 16 (oxygen).

Notice the difference. In water the ratio of hydrogen to oxygen is 1 to 8. In hydrogen peroxide it is 1 to 16. In other words, the proportional weight of oxygen is twice as great in the case of hydrogen peroxide.

The same relation was observed repeatedly with other elements in many different compounds. Carbon, for example, can be burned to form carbon monoxide or carbon dioxide. Under one set of conditions, 3 grams of carbon plus 4 of oxygen will yield 7 grams of carbon monoxide. Under other conditions, 3 grams of carbon plus 8 of oxygen will yield 11 grams of carbon dioxide. Notice the ratio of the weights of oxygen relative to the constant weight of carbon. In carbon dioxide, as compared with carbon monoxide, there is twice as much oxygen in proportion to the carbon.

Note more closely the ratios by weight in the two sets of examples:

Water: 1 (hydrogen) to **8** (oxygen)

Hydrogen peroxide:
    1 (hydrogen) to **16** (oxygen)

Carbon monoxide:
    3 (carbon) to **4** (oxygen)

Carbon dioxide:
    3 (carbon) to **8** (oxygen)

In each pair of ratios, the left-hand members remain unchanged. The right-hand members change in what appears to be *their own ratio of small whole numbers.* For example, the two oxygen ratios—8 to 16, and 4 to 8—are both 1-to-2 relationships. It is important to notice that the ratio is a small whole-number ratio (1 to 2). Neither member of the ratio is a fraction, such as $7/18$ to 1, or $29/11$ to 2.

What does all this mean? How can we use these data obtained by chemists with their balances?

Let us suggest an answer to these two questions by asking two more. Have you noticed from the examples that either 1 part of hydrogen or 3 parts of carbon can combine with 8 parts of oxygen? Can you predict the proportions of carbon and hydrogen that might combine with one another to form a carbon-hydrogen compound?

4-9 ELEMENT OR COMPOUND?

a For the eighteenth-century chemist, one test of whether a substance was an element or a compound was *heat.* Could the substance be decomposed by heat?

b Chemical tests also were made. Could the substance be broken down into simpler substances in this way?

c Even physical means were tried. Hammers, chisels, mortars and pestles, and other tools were called into use.

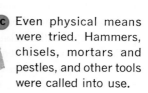
Moisture on glass

d Sometimes the evidence came in a surprising way. Efforts to decompose water, for example, failed, but what happened when the gas *hydrogen* was burned in air?

The chances are you guessed correctly. The smelly compound methane (or marsh gas) consists of 1 part by weight of hydrogen and 3 parts of carbon!

In 1808, data of this sort were put together by John Dalton in what is known as the Atomic Theory. Dalton suggested that:

1. Matter is composed of particles which are indestructible, indivisible, and discrete. He used the name **atoms** for these particles.
2. All atoms of a single element are the same. That is, all oxygen atoms are alike, especially in having the same mass.
3. The atoms of different elements differ from one another. That is, oxygen atoms, hydrogen atoms, and carbon atoms differ from one another, especially in having different masses.
4. Compounds are formed by the union of atoms, and only *whole* atoms can combine.

Dalton's theory gives us an explanation of the interesting relation between the relative proportions of oxygen in carbon monoxide and carbon dioxide, or in hydrogen peroxide and water. Let us assume that small particles of carbon monoxide are each made of one atom of carbon and one of oxygen. We know that the ratio by weight of carbon to oxygen in carbon monoxide is 3 to 4. Our reasoning now leads us to suggest that the union of one carbon atom and two oxygen atoms would give us carbon dioxide, with its carbon to oxygen ratio of 3 to 8. The ratio could not be 3 to 6, or 3 to 10, for according to Dalton only whole atoms can combine.

In 1808, Dalton's theory was only a *possible* explanation. It suggested that the data of chemistry could be interpreted in terms of indestructible atoms. There could be no transformation of the atoms of one element into another. The alchemists' dream would be over: base elements could not be transformed into the noble element gold.

The Atomic Theory threw doubt on the interpretation of van Helmont's willow tree experiment. It now appeared that water alone could not be transformed into the substance of a willow tree. Water is oxygen and hydrogen. A willow tree, on the other hand, is composed of compounds containing oxygen, hydrogen, and *many other elements*. It seemed probable that all these elements would obey mechanistic laws in the chemical laboratory, but would they obey the same laws in willow trees and wallabies? In the early years of the nineteenth century, chemists were not sure.

THE BEGINNING OF BIOCHEMISTRY

Lavoisier's and Dalton's new ideas in chemistry were exceedingly helpful in understanding many chemical phenomena. At first, however, they were not of much help in accounting for the activities that take place in plants and animals. It was true that the relation between respiration and combustion was established. Both involved reactions with oxygen.

It proved to be exceedingly difficult to study the chemistry of living organisms. For the most part, they seemed to consist of a tremendous variety of different compounds unanalyzable by the available chemical methods.

Not only were living organisms almost entirely unanalyzable, but in the early years of the nineteenth century chemists could not make any of the substances known to occur in living creatures. They might be quite skillful in juggling Dalton's atoms to produce the chemical compounds of the nonliving world. They could even obtain alcohol or sugar from living materials and determine its composition in terms of elements. They could not, however, make alcohol or sugar from the simple chemical elements or compounds available in their laboratories. This inability was all the more distressing when it was found that sugar was composed only of the elements carbon, hydrogen, and oxygen. It would seem easy, wouldn't it?

A justifiable conclusion in 1825 would have been this: Living organisms are made, at least in part, of chemical substances that can be **analyzed** (divided into parts) and shown to consist of the common elements, but it is impossible to **synthesize** (or unite from parts) these substances from the elements of which they are made. This synthesis, it was supposed, can be accomplished only by living creatures and seems to involve some kind of a "vital force."

The unique substances found in organisms were named **organic compounds.** Chemists soon found that all of these organic compounds contained carbon. In addition, most of them contained oxygen and hydrogen. Other elements were less frequent.

Compounds which were not restricted to living organisms were named **inorganic compounds.** Some inorganic compounds contained carbon, but this was not so frequently the case.

Wöhler's Synthesis of an Organic Compound

The most humble of green plants can assemble the atoms of carbon, hydrogen, and oxygen to make sugar. Why could not man, with all his scientific learning, produce this and other organic compounds? What is the power that enables the plant, but not the chemist, to perform these syntheses?

In 1828 Friedrich Wöhler (1800–1882) suggested it was not the "vital force" of the plant but the ignorance of the chemist that was at fault. He discovered one organic compound that could be produced in the laboratory. Wöhler heated a solution of a substance known as ammonium cyanate. A new substance was formed which on further study was found to be **urea** (yoo·REE·a). Urea is a compound found in urine and, as such, is a product of living organisms. Until Wöhler had performed this experiment, urea could be produced only by living cells.

Wöhler had not quite done the critical experiment, namely, to produce an organic compound while using only inorganic materials. Although ammonium cyanate would generally be classed as an inorganic compound, Wöhler had made it from substances obtained from animals. What he had shown was that an inorganic compound (coming from organic compounds) could be changed into a real organic compound.

It remained for one of Wöhler's students, Hermann Kolbe (1818–1884), to complete the achievement. Using the elements carbon, sulfur, and chlorine—plus water, which chemists knew could be produced by uniting the elements hydrogen and oxygen—he produced acetic acid. The date was 1844. This appears to be the first case of an organic compound's being made solely from inorganic materials. (Acetic acid is found in vinegar.)

Urea and acetic acid were humble beginnings, but their synthesis in the laboratory was a triumph of scientific endeavor. It was now clear that at least *some* organic compounds could be produced without the assistance of a vital force. Gradually more and more chemists and biologists began to suggest that perhaps all organic compounds could be made in the laboratory. *Knowledge* was what was required—not a vital force! Thus the chemistry of living things, which seemed to demand vitalism in 1800, was found approachable by the mechanists in 1850.

Let us continue to be cautious, however. Even if chemists could synthesize some organic compounds in the laboratory, it did not follow that all the activities of organisms were explainable by the laws of chemistry and physics. There were some obvious difficulties. In 1844, when Kolbe was synthesizing acetic acid, biologists were busy looking at cells. Schwann had published a book only five years before. There seemed to be little evidence of activity in living cells—that is, activity of sorts associated with chemical reactions.

Chemical reactions usually occurred with at least *some* noticeable changes. Few were violent in the sense that combustion so often was—but nearly all produced a change that could be detected readily (even if it required observation over a period of days, as with Lavoisier's synthesis of red oxide of mercury—see page 76). Perhaps the most noticeable change would be in color, or solubility in water, or taste, or change of state (from solid to liquid or liquid to gas, or vice versa, in association with some other property). The point was that *a change would be noticed.*

It was therefore disappointing to biologists and chemists alike that no obvious chemical changes were observed in living cells examined under the microscope. For pessimists among them, it may have seemed to confirm their worst fears, for they already knew that the moderate temperatures maintained by living organisms did not even approach the range necessary to activate most of the chemical changes that took place in the laboratory.

From another point of view, however, it appeared undeniable that a variety of chemical changes was occurring in cells. How else could organic compounds originate?

Clearly there was some immense flaw in the understanding of chemistry as it applied to living organisms. It was unthinkable that two opposing points of view were *both* correct—that a complex variety of chemical changes could take place in living organisms that apparently could *not* provide the conditions necessary for those changes (Figure 4-10). Some important piece of information was missing.

Spallanzani and Gastric Juice

During the period when Priestley and Lavoisier were performing their experiments in England and France, in Italy Lazzaro Spallanzani (1729–1799) was studying digestion. (Recall that he was also interested in the question of spontaneous generation.)

It was already known that foods such as meats and vegetables become liquid in the stomach and intestine. Was this a chemical reaction? And could it occur only in a living organism?

Spallanzani noticed a fluid, which he called **gastric juice,** in the stomachs of birds that he studied experimentally. He speculated that this gastric juice might be involved in the "dissolving" of food. He tested the hypothesis as follows:

I have found the gizzards of turkies and geese most abounding in gastric juices, probably on account of their superior size. I was induced by the quantity they afforded to attempt an experiment. . . . It consisted in trying, whether these juices retain their solvent power out of the stomach. For this purpose, I took two tubes sealed hermetically at one end, and at the other with wax: into one I put several bits of mutton, and into the other several bruised grains of wheat, and then filled them with the gastric liquor. In order that they might have the condition which in these animals precedes digestion, they had been macerated in the craw of a turkey cock. And as the warmth of the stomach is probably another condition necessary to the solution of food, I contrived to supply it by communicating to the tubes a degree of heat nearly equal, by fixing them under my arm-pits. In this situation I kept them at different intervals for three days, at the expiration of which time I opened them. The tube with the grains of wheat was first examined; most of them now consisted of the bare husk, the flour having been extract-

4-10 THE MISSING LINK

Chemistry in the Laboratory Chemistry in the Body

1 (a) Oxygen was found to be required for many reactions in the laboratory – chiefly combustion and other oxidation reactions.

(b) Similarly, oxygen was found to be required by the body of a man or a mouse or other animal during respiration.

2 (a) If a piece of charcoal was burned, carbon dioxide would be given off.

(b) Carbon dioxide was given off by the body during respiration.

3 (a) Combustion in the laboratory was almost never a self-starting process. An increase of temperature to the proper ignition temperature was required.

(b) Respiration seemed to take place in the body without change in temperature; no "ignition" temperature appeared to be involved at all.

4 (a) Combustion in the laboratory yielded visible or measurable light and heat – and often smoke.

(b) Respiration seemed to yield no light, no measurable heat (above the normal body temperature), and no smoke.

Was it possible that *similar* processes could be taking place under *different* conditions in the laboratory and in the body?

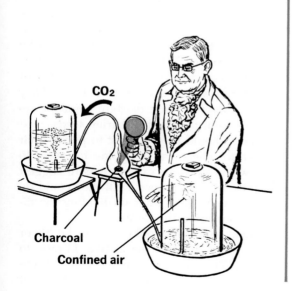

CO_2

Charcoal

Confined air

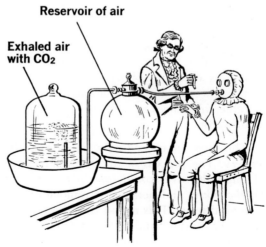

Reservoir of air

Exhaled air with CO_2

ed, and forming a thick grey sediment at the bottom of the tube. The flesh in the other tube was in great measure dissolved (it did not exhale the least putrid smell), and was incorporated with the gastric juice, which was hence rendered more turbid and dense. What little remained had lost its natural redness, and had become exceedingly tender. Upon putting it into another tube, and adding fresh gastric liquor, and replacing it under my arm-pits, the remainder was dissolved in the course of a day.

I repeated these experiments with other grains of wheat bruised and macerated in the same manner, and likewise upon some flesh of the same kind, but instead of gastric juice I employed common water. [This was a control.] After the two tubes had remained three days under my arm-pits, I found that the grains, where they were broken, were slightly excavated, which was occasioned by an incipient solution of the pulpy substance. The flesh had also undergone a slight superficial solution, but internally it appeared fibrous, red, firm, and in short, had all the characters of flesh. It was also putrid; and wheat too had acquired some acidity, two circumstances which did not take place in the grains and flesh immersed in the gastric liquor. These facts are then irrefutable proofs that the gastric juice retains even out of its natural situation the power of dissolving animal and vegetable substances in a degree far superior to water.

This was an exceedingly important discovery. The process of digestion, whatever it might involve, *could take place outside of the body*, and hence was removed from any vital force. This meant that the process could be studied under the controlled conditions of the laboratory. One could then try to isolate from gastric juice a substance that had the power of digesting food.

From Ferments to Enzymes

During the early part of the nineteenth century, biologists and chemists discovered similar situations. For example, two French chemists, Payen and Persoz, obtained in 1833 a substance that would digest starch.

Their substance was found in barley seeds, which could be ground up in water to make a crude mixture that would digest starch. Payen and Persoz gave the name **diastase** (DY·a·stays) to whatever it was that digested the starch. They did not know whether it was a substance or a vital force. If it was a substance, it might be possible to isolate it in a relatively pure form. If it was a vital force, it could not, of course, be separated from the living barley seeds.

Their problem was to begin with the crude mixture of barley seeds in water and try to extract a pure diastase. The first thing they did was to *filter* the mixture. That is, they poured the mixture into a funnel lined with a good grade of paper known as filter paper. The paper was designed to hold back particles even as small as cells but to allow the water and substances dissolved in it to pass through. The material that passed the filter was known as the **filtrate.**

The first step in their purification was the separation of the active mixture into two parts—the filtrate and the part held back by the filter paper. Which fraction was active? They tested each on starch and found that the filtrate was active (Figure 4-11). They knew, therefore, that diastase could be removed from the crushed barley seeds.

What should they do next to purify their material? There was no guide for them to follow—no previous experiments to suggest how they might proceed. All they could do was to try various ways of dividing the filtrate containing the diastase.

Their approach would have to be hit or miss. They heated the active filtrate to 70° C. The heat coagulated some of the material in the filtrate. They filtered it again. Once more they found that the ac-

4-11 THE SEARCH FOR THE MISSING LINK

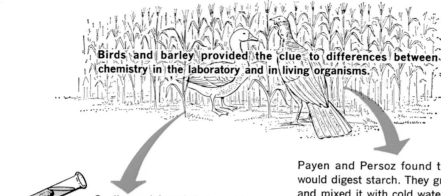

Birds and barley provided the clue to differences between chemistry in the laboratory and in living organisms.

Spallanzani found that gastric juices of turkeys and geese would decompose meats and grain even after removal from the gizzards of the animals.

Payen and Persoz found that barley grains would digest starch. They ground some barley and mixed it with cold water:

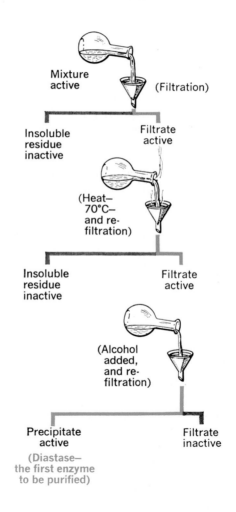

Mixture active (Filtration)

Insoluble residue inactive — Filtrate active

(Heat—70°C—and re-filtration)

Insoluble residue inactive — Filtrate active

(Alcohol added, and re-filtration)

Precipitate active (Diastase—the first enzyme to be purified) — Filtrate inactive

tivity was present in the filtrate. The coagulated materials were inactive.

Would a higher temperature purify the diastase more? The active filtrate was heated to 100° C. More substance was coagulated and removed by filtration. Tests showed that the coagulated material was inactive. What about the filtrate? It also was inactive. Too bad! This experiment had destroyed the diastase.

They had to start all over. This time they were careful not to heat the material to 100° C. The seeds were ground up in water, the mixture filtered, and the filtrate heated to 70° C as before. The filtrate was active. At this point they tried something else. Alcohol was added, and it produced a precipitate in the filtrate. Filtration then was used to separate the precipitate from the filtrate. Both the precipitate and the filtrate were tested, and this time only the precipitate was active. The precipitate, diastase, was a white, solid material. It could be purified further by dissolving it in water and precipitating it again with alcohol.

The purified diastase was very active in digesting starch. One part of diastase, dissolved in water, could digest 1,000 parts of starch in 10 minutes!

Diastase was a name first given for an activity associated with life—the ability to digest starch. The digestive action was found to be definitely a chemical change (and not a matter of dissolving). Payen and Persoz had shown that the chemical activity depends upon a substance. More important, this substance could be extracted and purified (Figure 4-11), then used to carry out its activities apart from a living system.

This was mechanism, not vitalism.

Diastase and similar substances provided a key to the understanding of many activities of organisms. Reactions that at first seemed impossible for the chemist to carry out were made possible with the aid of these substances isolated from living organisms. Sometimes the substances were called ferments (because they were sometimes associated with the process of fermentation). In 1879 the name **enzyme** was suggested, and it is the one we still use today. Diastase was one of the first enzymes obtained in a partially purified form. Two of the characteristics of diastase were found to be true of all enzymes: first, a temperature of 100° C destroys them; second, the enzymes are active even when only traces of them are present. (Recall that 1 part of diastase could digest 1,000 parts of starch.)

Enzymes provided the answer to why certain chemical changes can take place rapidly in the absence of high temperatures. In the presence of enzymes, high temperatures were not necessary *even for oxidation* ("burning") *of foods.*

As the nineteenth century progressed, biologists came more and more to the view that the many activities that occur within cells are controlled by enzymes. Most of these activities are so complex that even today the chemist cannot duplicate them in his laboratory without the aid of enzymes. No vital force is involved—the chemist uses enzymes as he uses other compounds.

There is more to the enzyme story, and we shall return to it in Chapter 6. What we must consider now is a more basic question: Why is chemical activity necessary to living organisms?

Chemical Activity for What?

When Priestley and Lavoisier compared the activity of a mouse and the activity of a burning candle, they suggested an important relation. The candle and mouse both used oxygen in reactions that liberate **energy**—the heat and light of the candle and the "animal heat" of the mouse.

What is energy and why does the mouse need it? Lavoisier listed heat and light in his table of elements. He knew they were different from other elements, such as oxygen and carbon. For one thing, neither light nor heat could be weighed on his balance. A closed container of water at 0° C had the same weight as at 50° C. The water had more heat, but since this extra heat did not add to the weight, Lavoisier realized it was not like the elements.

The relationship of heat to the elements did not make much sense until the following facts were discovered. Under one set of experimental conditions, substances A and B could combine to form AB. Under other conditions, AB could be broken down into A and B. In other words, the reaction was reversible. We can express these relations as follows:

$$A + B \rightarrow AB$$
$$AB \rightarrow A + B$$

Careful observations and measurements showed that if heat was needed to make A and B combine, then heat would be liberated when AB changed into A + B. Heat is a form of energy, so we will abbreviate it as "e." We can rewrite our equations as follows:

$$A + B + e_1 \rightarrow AB$$
$$AB \rightarrow A + B + e_2$$

The amount of heat required for the one reaction was found to be exactly the same as the amount liberated in the reverse reaction. In other words, $e_1 = e_2$. This relationship soon was verified for other chemical reactions.

Energy and Its Varieties

In the nineteenth century, chemists and physicists came to realize that there was a relationship between heat, light, and—once it was discovered—electricity. All are forms of energy. But again, what *is* energy? About the best general answer that could be given was: *energy* is the ability to do work.

There are many situations with which you are already familiar where energy is required to get things done. Perhaps you live in a community where the electricity is generated from water power. Even if you do not, we could illustrate the point by considering a power plant near a waterfall. The water has the ability to do work as it drops from the top of the falls to the bottom. We could show this to be the case by putting a waterwheel in the falls (Figure 4-12). The wheel would be rotated by the falling water.

In former times, mill wheels of this sort were used to grind wheat and corn. The wheel was attached to an axle. The axle was attached to heavy millstones which turned and crushed the grain. This was work!

A wheel of this sort could also be attached to a generator. In this case, the energy released by the falling water would be used to generate electricity.

The water at the top of the falls has the potentiality, or the ability, to do work. We say that it has **potential energy.** This potential energy is released as the water drops down on the waterwheel. The energy released moves the waterwheel, which then turns the generator shaft. The generator then produces electricity, which can do many sorts of work.

Now think of the many kinds of work

4-12 Energy from falling water. A waterwheel placed in the waterfall is connected to the grinding machinery of the mill. Energy conversion as a *practice* is quite old, even though knowledge of the *nature* of energy is quite recent—and indeed, is still being probed.

that electricity can do. It can be used to raise a heavy elevator from one floor to another. It can be used to light our homes. It can be used to produce heat in electric stoves.

Electricity can do some kinds of chemical work as well. When the elements sodium and chlorine unite to form sodium chloride (table salt), energy is released as heat. We can express this as:

sodium + chlorine $\rightarrow$ sodium chloride + e_1

By means of electrical energy, we can separate the sodium chloride into sodium and chlorine.

sodium chloride $+ e_2 \rightarrow$ sodium $+$ chlorine

We had to add energy, e_2, to separate the sodium chloride into sodium and chlorine. The amount of energy is exactly the same as the amount released in reaction 1. Once again, $e_1 = e_2$. It is important to note that in this example, e_1 was released as *heat,* and e_2 was supplied as *electricity.*

All forms of energy can be changed into one another. Not only is there a Law of Conservation of Mass (page 79), but there is also a similar law for energy.

Law of Conservation of Energy: Energy can neither be created nor destroyed, but it may be changed from one form to another. The amount of energy liberated in one reaction is always the same as the amount required for the reverse reaction.

There is a postscript to be added to the Laws of Conservation of Mass and of Energy. We now know that matter can be changed into energy, and energy into matter. But these are concerns of the physicist, with his nuclear reactors and cyclotrons, and of the astronomer, who seeks to learn more of what goes on inside the sun. So far as the reactions in chemistry and in living organisms are concerned, the laws as stated still suffice.

Where does all the energy consumed in living come from? Ultimately, as we shall see, nearly all of it comes from the sun (Chapter 6). More immediately, for plants and animals alike, it comes from complex chemical substances we call foods. Foods contain potential chemical energy. When the complex substances in foods are broken down and oxidized, the potential energy is released. It becomes active (kinetic) energy and is used in the processes of living. (Some, unavoidably, is lost from the organism in the form of heat.) Being energy us-

ers, all living creatures must be food makers or food hunters.

Some chemical changes release energy. Some require energy. The living organism is a sort of machine that uses the energy released by certain chemical changes to make other chemical changes take place. The chemical changes that release energy are generally **oxidations**—changes in which a substance with potential chemical energy unites with oxygen (or, as we will see in Chapter 6, what amounts to the same thing —has hydrogen or electrons removed from it). The opposite sorts of changes—those which require energy—are most usually **reductions**, that is to say, reactions in which oxygen is removed from (or hydrogen or electrons are added to) the substances.

The heat and light of a burning candle are evidences of energy's changing from one form to another as the wax is oxidized. The chemical energy of the wax is converted to heat and light.

The food used by a mouse is also oxidized. The energy released is used to keep the mouse going—to maintain its breathing, its heartbeat, the contraction of its muscles, and to keep its body at a temperature of about 37° C, even though the surroundings may be very cold.

CONCLUDING REMARKS

What are the basic activities of living things? Are they activities of matter obeying only the rules of physics and chemistry, or are they activities of matter controlled by a vital force? Possibly you have reached an answer of your own by now. We have surveyed a series of dramatic discoveries showing that the activities of living creatures can be studied by the methods of chemistry and physics. Is this convincing proof that there can be no vital force? No. But in our biological work it really does not matter. Here is why.

In the seventeenth century, Descartes began suggesting that the activities of animals and plants could be understood in mechanistic terms. His statement was only a hypothesis. There was very little that animals and plants do that he could explain. In fact, there were really no useful laws known at the time that would explain even the data of physics and chemistry. It was a little premature, therefore, to attempt to explain the activities of living organisms in terms of laws that were not known!

Gradually the orderly nature of the chemical and physical universe emerged. The old idea that matter is composed of the elements fire, air, earth, and water was found to be inadequate. Lavoisier and others began to recognize the elements that we know today: oxygen, carbon, hydrogen, sodium, and so on. Dalton suggested that one could explain much of the data of chemistry by assuming that all matter was composed of atoms—tiny particles far too small to be seen. An oxygen atom could on one occasion combine with hydrogen to form water, or on another combine with carbon to form carbon monoxide, but it always would maintain its integrity. It could be recovered from water or carbon monoxide and shown to be pure oxygen.

In the nineteenth century, the previously mysterious chemistry of living organisms was found to be approachable. It was discovered that in chemical composition, organisms consist of a large number of carbon compounds. The reactions of these and other compounds in living systems were found to be controlled by enzymes.

The physicist supplied the biologist with the concept of energy—the ability to do work. The energy required to keep an organism working was supplied by its food.

It all began with studies of a candle, a mouse, and a sprig of mint. Biologist, chemist, and physicist were soon to realize that the problems of living matter and nonliving matter were basically the same. When an ever-increasing number of plants and animals was studied, it was found that there are activities that are basic to all life; somehow everything that is alive must obtain chemical compounds for maintenance and growth of its own substance and for the energy it requires.

The sum of all these chemical events is **metabolism** (meh·TAB·o·liz'm).

By the end of the nineteenth century, this is how man stood on the question of mechanism versus vitalism:

There was no basic activity of life that could not be at least considered by way of the methods of chemistry and physics. Not everything was known—far from it—but every biological problem was approachable by the laboratory scientist.

This is not to say that scientists proved there is no vital force. They showed that it was unnecessary to invoke a vital force to explain the data of the physiology of cells and organisms. Vitalism was not discarded: it became unnecessary in explaining biological activities.

Clearly an understanding of the nature and behavior of matter is essential for an understanding of biology. In this chapter we have laid a background, but that is not enough. In the next chapter we will learn enough of twentieth-century chemistry to help us understand ourselves and other living organisms.

GUIDE QUESTIONS AND PROBLEMS

1. How would the mechanists' approach to the problem of living things encourage experiment and observation?
2. Van Helmont's experiment with the willow tree seemed to lead to a sound conclusion about the source of the material making up 164 pounds of tree. What chemical information would have revealed the error of this conclusion?

3. How did the use of scales and balances reveal a basic error in the phlogiston theory of burning?
4. What did Lavoisier's experiments with phosphorus show about burning? about air?
5. How did Priestley's observations of the bubbles given off by fermentation vats in a brewery lead to his more significant experiments on the atmosphere?
6. How did Priestley's experiments aid Lavoisier's explanation of burning?
7. What was the contribution of the chemical balance in establishing the atomic theory?
8. What assumptions did Dalton utilize in developing his Atomic Theory?
9. What was the significance of Wöhler's experiment? of Kolbe's?
10. How does oxidation of nonliving substances resemble oxidation (respiration) in a living body? How do the two differ?
11. How was the specific chemical nature of the enzyme diastase established?
12. How did the discoveries from the seventeenth century to the end of the nineteenth century make the concepts of vitalism unnecessary in the study of physiological problems?

SUGGESTIONS FOR ADDITIONAL READING

Books

Gabriel, M., and S. Fogel, *Great Experiments in Biology.* Englewood Cliffs (N. J.), Prentice-Hall, 1955.

> An excellent collection of original documents in the history of biology, including van Helmont's experiment with the willow tree, Payen and Persoz' memoir on diastase, and Priestley's observation on different kinds of air.

Moore, Ruth, *The Coil of Life.* New York, Knopf, 1961.

> Chapters 1, 2, 4, and 7 provide dramatic extensions of main ideas in this chapter.

Schwartz, G., and P. Bishop, *Moments of Discovery.* New York, Basic Books, 1958. 2 vols.

> A collection of original documents, including Black on carbon dioxide, Priestley on oxygen, Lavoisier on the role of oxygen in burning, and Wöhler on the production of urea.

Magazines and Journals

Duveen, D. I., "Lavoisier." *Scientific American,* Vol. 194 (May 1956), pp. 84–88.

Wilson, M., "Priestley." *Scientific American,* Vol. 191 (October 1954), pp. 68–70.

5

LIVING CHEMISTRY

After the foundations of our understanding of chemistry were laid in the eighteenth and nineteenth centuries, knowledge of both inorganic and organic substances advanced rapidly. Boyle and Lavoisier had opened one avenue of investigation with their ideas of elementary substances that could not be broken down by any known chemical means. Dalton had suggested that these elementary substances were composed of discrete, uniform particles, the atoms. Here were two theories, then: one relating to the *basic chemical types* of matter, or *elements;* and the other relating to the *basic physical structure* of matter, or *atoms.*

It was soon discovered that single atoms are rarely found in nature. Instead they occur in various associations and combinations. The behavior of atoms in chemical reactions was found to depend on the type of association. It will be important for us, therefore, to distinguish among the various ways that atoms occur together.

COMBINATIONS OF ATOMS AND ELEMENTS

We will begin by comparing three examples of matter: air, water, and a diamond. If we think of all three of these substances as composed of atoms (of one or more elements), what can they reveal to us of the ways in which atoms associate with one another?

The Analysis of Air

First, let us analyze air. It is invisible, odorless, colorless, and tasteless. It is so light in weight that you may think of it as next to nothing. Yet we can pump it into tires where it will support the weight of an automobile. We are also familiar with the fact that air contains something that we need in order to live and that a candle needs in order to burn.

Air is a gas. At first, chemists believed that it was an element. But when Priestley and Lavoisier removed oxygen from the air, they still had gas left. In fact, the remaining gas accounted for about $4/5$ of ordinary air. After many experiments, the properties of this gas became known. It was named nitrogen.

Air, then, was shown to consist of about $1/5$ oxygen and about $4/5$ nitrogen. Careful analysis later showed that there are tiny quantities of other gases in air. Carbon dioxide, which is exhaled in breathing and is a product of the combustion of carbon compounds (such as wood and coal), is present. There is not very much, to be sure—about 0.03 to 0.04 percent. There are also varying amounts of water vapor. Traces of other gases, such as argon and neon, are also present.

Could we think, then, of a small container of air as being composed of a huge number of nitrogen atoms, many oxygen atoms, and fewer atoms of argon and neon (excluding carbon dioxide for the present)? The answer is a mixed one—partly yes, partly no. The argon and neon *do* exist in air as individual atoms. (Some chemists call these atoms **monatomic** [mon·a·TOM·ik] **molecules,** to indicate that they do not normally react chemically with one another.) The nitrogen and the oxygen, however, are *not* present as individual atoms. The oxygen atoms react with one another chemically to form pairs. Chemists refer to this arrangement as O_2. The "O" is the symbol for an oxygen atom, and the "$_2$" means that two atoms of oxygen have formed a **chemical bond** between them. The nitrogen atoms of air also react with one another to form pairs; hence chemists refer to atmospheric nitrogen as N_2.

When two or more atoms form chemical bonds in the manner of O_2 and N_2, chemists call the resulting particle a **molecule.**

Air, then, is an association of molecules of nitrogen, molecules of oxygen, atoms of argon, and atoms of neon—together with traces of carbon dioxide and water vapor. The important point to be made about this association is as follows: the atoms and molecules found in air are separate. They do not influence one another except for an occasional collision.

In the last chapter, we learned that Lavoisier spoke of air as a *mixture* of gases. We speak of it in the same way today—and for the same reason. The gases found in air do not interact chemically. To look at this idea another way, suppose we emptied some flour and salt in a bowl and stirred them. The salt and flour would retain their identity; there would be no chemical interaction.

In a mixture of substances, one can vary the amounts of the different ingredients. Thus, one could make an artificial air by mixing 49 percent nitrogen, 49 percent oxygen, and 2 percent carbon dioxide. Any proportions of these substances will mix.

The Analysis of Water

The nature of water was first revealed not by analysis, but by synthesis (page 80). Water was originally regarded as an element, for at that time it could not be divided into simpler substances. The clue to its identification as a compound, rather than an element, came when hydrogen was burned in the presence of oxygen. The water so formed was identical to other water.

Chemists have found that water is composed of hydrogen and oxygen in the ratio of two atoms of hydrogen to each atom of oxygen. The ratio is always the same. We represent it, in the chemists' symbolic shorthand, as H_2O. Constant proportions of composition characterize all compounds. Here is a situation in marked contrast to mixtures, in which the proportions of the different substances may vary. (Recall that the recognition of constant proportions of composition was one of the observations that led Dalton to the Atomic Theory.)

Is H_2O a molecule, like O_2? Yes. But we have also called it a compound, a term that we do not use for O_2. What is the distinction? A *molecule* is a particle formed by a chemical reaction between two or more atoms. These atoms may be of the same element, as in O_2, or different elements, as in H_2O. A *compound*, on the other hand, *always* is composed of atoms of two or more different elements. Water is a compound because it is composed of the elements hydrogen and oxygen chemically bonded to one another.

The analysis of water into hydrogen and oxygen was finally accomplished when electricity became available to the chemist. The general method involves wiring the two poles of a battery to two electrodes immersed in water. (A bit of sulfuric acid is added to the water.) Bubbles of gas soon begin to form at each electrode. The water begins to disappear.

If one arranges to collect and test the two gases (one produced at each electrode), he will find that one is oxygen and the other hydrogen. The experiment might continue until all the water was used up; the only products formed would be hydrogen and oxygen (in the ratio of two volumes of hydrogen and one of oxygen). Thus, by means of electrical energy, the water would be separated into two simpler substances.

TABLE 5-1 THE MOST ABUNDANT ELEMENTS OF AIR, LAND, OCEANS, AND ORGANISMS

AIR	LAND	OCEANS	ORGANISMS
1. **Nitrogen**			
2. **Oxygen**	1. **Oxygen**	1. **Oxygen**	1. **Oxygen**
	2. Silicon		
			2. Carbon
		2. **Hydrogen**	3. **Hydrogen**
	3. Aluminum		
	4. Iron		
			4. **Nitrogen**
		3. Chlorine	
		4. Sodium	
	5. Calcium		
			5. Sulfur
			6. Phosphorus

Elements common to two or more columns are shown in **boldface** type.

The Analysis of a Diamond

There was a third substance on our original list of materials to study—namely, a diamond. With it we would encounter a new situation. All of the methods of the chemist could be used, but it would be impossible to separate the diamond into other substances. It would still be a diamond, or as the chemist says, pure crystalline carbon.

The Elements

The analyses of air, water, and a diamond have given different results. Air is composed of oxygen, nitrogen, and other gases. It is a mixture. Water is composed of hydrogen and oxygen. It is a compound. The diamond, on the other hand, is pure carbon. It is an element. No chemical method can divide it into simpler substances.

Can oxygen, nitrogen, and hydrogen be divided into simpler substances by chemical means? The answer is "No." No matter how the chemist tries to divide them, they still remain as oxygen, nitrogen, and hydrogen. Like carbon, they are chemically indivisible. All four substances are elements.

How many elements are there? If we attempted to analyze all of the hundreds of thousands of kinds of living and nonliving matter that are naturally present on the earth, a surprisingly simple conclusion would be reached. *Only 92 different kinds of elements would be present.* Physicists have been able to produce 11 more artificially—the total is now 103.

Some elements are abundant on earth; examples are hydrogen, oxygen, nitrogen, silicon, aluminum, sodium, calcium, chlorine, and iron (Table 5-1). Others are less abundant, such as carbon, magnesium, iodine, and phosphorus. Still others are rare.

The most common elements in living things are hydrogen, carbon, oxygen, nitrogen, sulfur, and phosphorus. Lesser quantities of potassium, sodium, magnesium, calcium, chlorine, iron, zinc, manganese, cobalt, and boron are also present. Iodine is required by some animals, but seemingly not by plants. Fluorine may be necessary in bony animals for the teeth and skeleton. Plants may have small amounts of aluminum and molybdenum.

The Structure of the Elements

The atoms of the 103 elements are not the smallest particles of matter. All atoms are built of varying combinations of still smaller particles, mainly **protons, neutrons,** and **electrons.** We must know a few general facts about the inner structure of atoms if we are to understand how they combine with one another to form molecules.

The atom with the simplest structure is hydrogen. It consists of one proton and one electron. Usually it does not have any neutrons. The proton is in the center, forming the nucleus of the atom. The single electron orbits around the proton. Figure 5-1 is a highly diagrammatic and simplified concept of a hydrogen atom. On the left, the electron is shown as a fixed point. Actually it is moving so rapidly that it would appear to be everywhere at once, forming a "cloud" around the proton, as on the right in the same figure.

Atoms of the other elements are more complex. Carbon atoms, for example, have a nucleus composed of six protons and six to eight (usually six) neutrons. Orbiting around the nucleus are six electrons (Figure 5-2).

As with hydrogen and carbon, the atoms of all other elements differ from one another in their numbers of protons, neutrons, and electrons. For any one element, however, the atoms have the same numbers of protons and electrons—but not necessarily

neutrons. There are **isotopes** (i·so·tohps) of all the known elements, in which one isotope may have a different number of neutrons than another.

Isotopes are important to us chiefly because some of them are **radioactive.** Thus, carbon-14 (6 protons, 8 neutrons) is a radioactive isotope of carbon. Unlike the more common carbon-12 (6 protons, 6 neutrons), carbon-14 is somewhat unstable. It emits radiation, and ultimately it breaks down altogether. This phenomenon is very useful to biologists, who can trace the path of carbon in living organisms by supplying foods made with carbon-14 instead of carbon-12.

Later in your reading you will encounter carbon-14, phosphorus-32, and other radioactive isotopes in their various uses, but at this point we are more interested in the protons, neutrons, and electrons themselves —the particles of which all atoms are made.

In one sense you are already familiar with electrons. An electric current passing along a wire is a flow of electrons. Both electrons and protons are **charged particles**—that is, they carry electrical charges. The charges that they carry are equal and opposite; we say that protons are *positively charged* (+) and electrons *negatively charged* (−).

In an atom, the charges balance one another, because the number of protons in the nucleus equals the number of electrons orbiting around the nucleus. The atom as a whole bears no charge, therefore; it is neu-

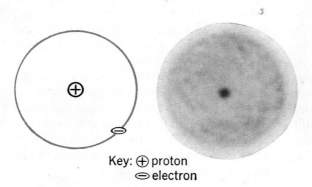

Key: ⊕ proton
⊖ electron

5-1
An atom of the element hydrogen. These two illustrations are highly diagrammatic. Both represent the same atom, but they convey different impressions of the atom. How does the "cloud" diagram on the right add to the impression gained from the diagram on the left?

tral. (The neutrons of the nucleus, as their name implies, are electrically neutral.)

We can think of an atom, then, as composed of a nucleus and its surrounding cloud of electrons. The nucleus consists of protons, which are positively charged, and of neutrons, which are uncharged. The electrons are negatively charged. The balance between opposite charges (between positively charged nucleus and negatively charged electrons) makes the atom neutral.

We now have the minimum amount of information required to understand how the atoms of the elements differ from one another: they differ in the number of protons and neutrons in the nucleus, and in the number of electrons surrounding the nucleus. Hydrogen has one proton, usually no neutrons, and one electron. Carbon has six protons, six to eight neutrons, and six electrons. The most complex of all of the elements that occur naturally on our earth is uranium. It has 92 protons, 140 to 147 (usually 146) neutrons, and 92 electrons.

CHEMICAL REACTIONS

Solitary atoms do not occur very often. Most atoms are chemically bonded together to form molecules and compounds. As they take part in chemical reactions in which substances are being built up or broken down, energy is either expended or released. Gasoline, for example, explodes in the cylinder and enough energy is released to move the automobile. Cooking gas is burned to heat water and to cook food. Chemical changes occur in our muscle cells and our arms move.

Chemical reactions are always going on in living organisms. The activities of living things are dependent upon a constant, complex pattern of chemical reactions.

The nonliving world is not nearly so chemically active. The rocks, air, and water of the earth's crust are rather stable. Chemical reactions occur slowly in them.

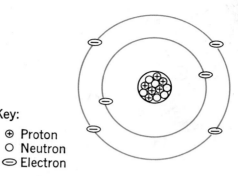

Key:
⊕ Proton
○ Neutron
⊝ Electron

5-2 A diagram of an atom of the element carbon. Would a "cloud" diagram of the atom look any different from the "cloud" diagram of hydrogen in Figure 5-1?

Chemical reactions, wherever they occur, involve only the outer parts of atoms. The nucleus is *not* involved; thus, no more need be explained about it here. The events that we call chemical reactions involve only the clouds or "shells" of electrons that surround the nucleus. Some additional information about electrons will therefore be important to our understanding of chemical reactions.

You are probably familiar with the fact that some substances will interact more readily than others. For example, at one time hydrogen was commonly used to fill balloons and dirigibles. Hydrogen is much lighter than air, hence balloons and dirigibles containing it will float. But hydrogen has one serious disadvantage: mixtures of hydrogen and oxygen, or hydrogen and air (containing oxygen), are highly explosive, given a spark, or a flash of lightning, or frictional heating. The dirigible *Hindenburg* exploded many years ago at Lakehurst, New Jersey, with a loss of many lives.

Helium, although it is about four times as heavy as hydrogen, is much better for filling balloons, because it will not react with oxygen, hence does not explode. In fact, helium is so stable that under ordinary conditions, it does not react with any other chemicals. Why should this be so?

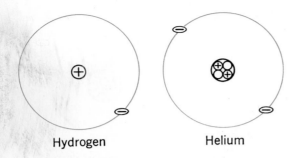

Hydrogen   Helium

5-3 Hydrogen and helium are the two simplest elements. One is extremely active chemically, the other normally inert (inactive). Why so great a difference? If chemical action does not involve the nuclei of atoms, what dissimilarity between hydrogen and helium could account for their difference in chemical activity?

We have learned that hydrogen has one electron. Helium has two (Figure 5-3). Why is a mixture of hydrogen and oxygen so violently explosive and a mixture of oxygen and helium so stable? The answer involves the number of electrons in each kind of atom. Atoms with certain numbers of electrons are stable, and those with other numbers are not. The unstable atoms tend to join with other atoms in a way that leads to greater stability. *The number of electrons that an atom possesses, therefore, is the chief determiner of its chemical behavior.*

If we consider only the more abundant elements found in living organisms, their atoms are most stable when the number of their electrons is 2, 10, or 18. (This seems to be because the electrons occupy concentric "shells" around the nucleus. The innermost shell can contain only 2 electrons, the next 8, the third, if it is the outermost shell, 8, etc. Thus, 2, 10, and 18 are the stable numbers for atoms with one, two, or three shells of electrons.)

A helium atom has two electrons. It is stable. A hydrogen atom, on the other hand, has only one electron. It would need one more to achieve a stable arrangement. An oxygen atom has eight electrons, two fewer than the stable number ten.

We have come a long way from Dalton's atoms. His ultimate units of matter have turned out to be very complex. Not only are they composed of electrons (negatively charged), protons (positively charged),

and neutrons (uncharged), but also they are the product of certain characteristic numbers and locations of each of these particles. Again disregarding the protons and neutrons of the nucleus, it develops that the chemical activity of atoms depends upon the numbers of, and the locations of, the orbital electrons.

It might be mentioned that today protons and neutrons are no longer thought to be elementary particles. They seem to be made up of various sorts of smaller particles—the **mesons** (MES·onz). Will there be any limit to this search for the ultimate structure of matter? A physicist writing in 1962 answers as follows: "One can only guess at future problems and future progress, but my personal conviction is that the search for ever smaller and ever more fundamental particles will go on as long as man retains the curiosity he has always demonstrated."

The Stability of Molecular Bonds

Interactions between atoms of an element, or between atoms of different elements, lead to greater stability for the atoms involved. Two hydrogen atoms can *share* their electrons, and thus each can attain the stable number two. The sharing of the electrons keeps the two hydrogen atoms close together, since each electron is attracted simultaneously to both of the atomic nuclei. We then say that a chemical bond exists between the two atoms. The result is a hydrogen molecule, which we can represent by H_2 or H—H. The line between the two H's in the latter symbol represents the chemical bond.

Nitrogen has seven electrons. Two nitrogen atoms can become more stable by sharing three electrons from each atom, or six altogether. In this way each nitrogen atom will *in effect* gain the stable number of ten electrons. Once again, the sharing of the electrons will produce a molecule, in this case a nitrogen molecule. We speak of electron-sharing bonds as **covalent** (koh-VAY-lent) **bonds,** or molecular bonds. In the example of the nitrogen molecule, there are three such bonds, and we may represent the molecule as N_2 or N≡N. In the latter symbol, note the designation of the triple bond; each line represents a shared electron. All the free nitrogen of the atmosphere is in the form of nitrogen molecules, not of separate nitrogen atoms.

The same is true of the free oxygen of the atmosphere. It exists as O_2 molecules, not as O atoms. The O_2 molecule is far more stable than elemental O, but even it is still reactive. That is, it can combine in other ways to form even more stable molecules. Thus, it combines with iron to form iron oxide, or rust. Oxygen can also combine with hydrogen. If oxygen and hydrogen molecules are mixed and enough energy is supplied to ignite the hydrogen, the atoms exchange partners explosively, liberating a great deal of energy. The reaction ends with a sharing of electrons between oxygen and hydrogen atoms that produces a more stable molecule than either the oxygen molecule or the hydrogen molecule. In the reaction, each oxygen atom, with eight electrons, needs to acquire two additional electrons to achieve stability. Of course, since each hydrogen atom has only one electron it may share, each oxygen atom will need to share electrons with two hydrogen atoms in order to have 10 electrons around it. A molecule is produced that has the structure H—O—H, or, as we commonly write it, H_2O. This is a molecule of water (Figure 5-4). The reaction may be expressed in what is known as a chemical equation:

$$2H_2 + O_2 \rightarrow 2H_2O + \text{energy}$$

This may be translated: "2 hydrogen molecules plus 1 oxygen molecule react to yield 2 molecules of water and to release energy." Since each molecule of oxygen contains two atoms of oxygen, two molecules

5-4 Two diagrams of a molecule of water. On the right, the molecule is shown as a Stuart model, to familiarize you with still another means of diagrammatic representation. What is the relation between these two different ways of representing the molecule?

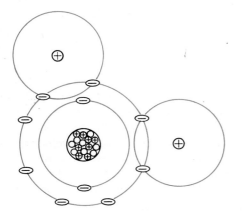
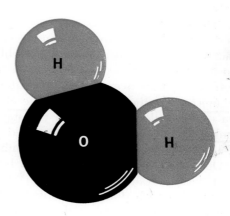

American Museum of Natural History

5-5 A model of a crystal of sodium chloride. The large balls represent chloride ions, the smaller balls sodium ions. In the actual crystal, what holds the ions together? Are the chemical bonds ionic or covalent?

of hydrogen $(2H_2)$ will be required for each molecule of oxygen when the exchange of partners occurs.

Bonds in a Salt Crystal

Sodium chloride (ordinary table salt) is a very stable substance, yet like water it is formed from two highly reactive atoms. A sodium atom has 11 electrons; a chlorine atom, 17. Recall that the stable numbers of electrons are 2, 10, and 18. The sodium atom has one more than the stable number ten. The chlorine atom has one fewer than the stable number 18. You can almost guess what will happen when sodium and chlorine combine. One electron from each sodium atom passes over to a chlorine atom. Sodium loses, rather than shares, one electron of its total of 11 to reach the stable number 10. The one electron is added to the 17 of chlorine to give the stable number 18. Once again energy is liberated as heat when these two atoms combine.

Recall that each atom of a particular element has the same number of electrons as protons. Expressed in another manner, it has equal numbers of negative and positive charges. When a sodium atom, which originally had 11 protons and 11 electrons, loses one electron, it is no longer neutral. It has 11 positive charges in its nucleus and only 10 negative charges among its electrons—an imbalance that gives the atom as a whole a positive charge of 1. Similarly, the chlorine, which originally had 17 protons and 17 electrons, gains 1 electron. Therefore, it has 1 extra negative charge. We show the relationship of the charges as part of the equation for the reaction which produces salt:

$$2Na + Cl_2 \rightarrow 2Na^+Cl^- + energy$$

The symbol for sodium is Na. This is an abbreviation of *natrium*, which is the Latin name for this element. The symbol for chlorine is Cl. The $^+$ and $^-$ signs indicate the charges that result when the electron of sodium passes to chlorine. (We rarely use this refinement. Sodium chloride is generally written NaCl.) Na^+ and Cl^- no longer are neutral atoms; they are charged particles. We call them **ions** (ɪ·onz). Na^+ is a sodium ion. Cl^- is a chloride ion.

The Na^+ ion strongly attracts each Cl^- ion, but the result is *not* a molecule. That is, the resulting particle contains *many* Na^+ and Cl^- ions. It is a _crystal_, in which each Na^+ ion is surrounded by Cl^- ions, and each Cl^- ion is surrounded by Na^+ ions (Figure 5-5). The chemical bonds are called **ionic** (ɪ·on·ik) **bonds,** as opposed to the covalent (molecular) bonds produced by electron-sharing.

When sodium chloride is dissolved in water, the sodium and chlorine separate—but not into a neutral atom of sodium and a neutral atom of chlorine. The electron that passed from sodium to chlorine when the atoms combined stays with the chlorine. Thus, the Na^+ ions and the Cl^- ions separate. The event can be expressed in the form of an equation:

$$\text{NaCl} \xrightarrow[\text{in water}]{} \text{Na}^+ + \text{Cl}^-$$

The process whereby a compound separates into ions in this way is called **ionization** (or dissociation).

Water is a particularly good solvent for compounds that can ionize.

The common ions in cells and body fluids of animals and plants are sodium ions (Na^+), chloride ions (Cl^-), hydrogen ions (H^+), hydroxide ions (OH^-), and potassium ions (K^+, in which K is an abbreviation of *kalium*, Latin for potassium). Also, calcium ions, (Ca^{++}), magnesium ions (Mg^{++}), phosphate ions ($PO_4^=$), sulfate ions ($SO_4^=$), carbonate ions ($CO_3^=$), bicarbonate ions (HCO_3^-), and nitrate ions (NO_3^-) occur. The superscript +'s and −'s show how many electric charges each sort of ion possesses. As you can see, some ions consist of only one element (Cl^-, Na^+), and others of two ($SO_4^=$, $CO_3^=$). One in our list (HCO_3^-) contains three elements.

Compounds—Molecular and Ionic

We now have two kinds of chemical bonds to consider in terms of the substances of which living organisms are made. Both molecular and ionic compounds are involved in the structures and processes of plants, animals, and microorganisms. Table 5-2 lists some of the more important elements in "living" chemistry. The table also shows electron changes that lead to maximum stability of the elements in the compounds they form (both molecular and ionic).

The electron changes listed in Table 5-2 do not indicate whether a given element will *share* electrons, rather than *gain* or *lose* them, in forming part of a compound. Generally, those marked "lose 1" or "lose 2" will do precisely that and form ionic compounds, but those marked "gain 1," "gain 2," etc., may either gain or share electrons.

The distinction between the meanings of *molecule* and *compound* is made clear by characteristics such as those we have been examining. Compounds may or may not be molecular, and molecules may or may not imply compounds. Ionic compounds, such as sodium chloride, do not exist as molecules at all, but many elements (O_2, H_2, N_2) and all covalently bonded (electron-sharing) compounds are molecules.

TABLE 5-2 THE COMMON ELEMENTS IN ORGANISMS

Element	Symbol	No. of electrons per atom	To achieve stability, it must . . .	. . . to reach the stable number . . .
Hydrogen	H	1	gain 1	2
Carbon	C	6	gain 4	10
Nitrogen	N	7	gain 3	10
Oxygen	O	8	gain 2	10
Sodium	Na	11	lose 1	10
Magnesium	Mg	12	lose 2	10
Phosphorus	P	15	gain 3	18
Sulfur	S	16	gain 2	18
Chlorine	Cl	17	gain 1	18
Potassium	K	19	lose 1	18
Calcium	Ca	20	lose 2	18

Organic Molecules

All of the molecular elements and many of the molecular compounds that occur on the earth's surface have relatively simple molecules. Water, for example, is H_2O; oxygen and nitrogen, O_2 and N_2.

The molecules that are found in living organisms tend to be much more complex. A molecule of table sugar, which comes from sugar cane or sugar beets, is composed of 45 atoms: 12 of carbon, 22 of hydrogen, and 11 of oxygen. Its chemical formula is $C_{12}H_{22}O_{11}$. Starch molecules, which are found in all plants, are composed of thousands of atoms of carbon, hydrogen, and oxygen. Protein molecules are often much larger still.

These large molecules are called organic molecules because of their association with living processes. All organic compounds contain carbon, in addition to other elements. Because of the tremendous size and complexity of their molecules, most organic compounds have been exceedingly difficult for chemists to study. Two of the things a chemist wishes to know are: what atoms make up a compound, and how these atoms are bonded to one another.

Recall from Chapter 4 (page 82) that many chemists of the eighteenth and early nineteenth centuries felt that it was impossible to learn much about organic compounds. They felt that these compounds could be made by an animal or plant but not by a chemist in his laboratory. Some went so far as to suggest that a "vital force," some mystical power associated with life, was necessary to produce organic compounds, but this belief became less prevalent after Wöhler synthesized urea and Kolbe synthesized acetic acid (page 83).

It was found that urea was made of carbon, hydrogen, oxygen, and nitrogen in the proportions expressed by the formula CON_2H_4. For reasons that will become clear shortly, this is written $CO(NH_2)_2$. As study of organic molecules progressed, however, it became apparent that a simple formula for a compound is not sufficient. For example, it was found that three different sugars all have the same formula! They are composed of the very same numbers of the same atoms. How, then, do they differ? The answer was found to be this: the characteristics of an organic molecule depend not only upon the *number* and *kinds* of atoms of which it is made, but also on the *positions* the atoms occupy.

Suppose we compare words and molecules. Just as the position of letters determines the word, so the position of atoms determines the type of molecule. The same letters a, e, and t, can be combined one way to form "ate" and another to form "tea." Position is important in words and molecules.

The formula $CO(NH_2)_2$, for urea, does not fully indicate the relative positions of the atoms. A better way of showing what we know of the makeup of the urea molecule is to use a *structural formula:*

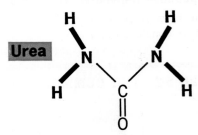

The two distinctive NH_2 groups are shown in boldface type. They are attached to a central carbon. A single oxygen atom is also attached to the carbon. Altogether, there are eight atoms in the molecule.

Note that different numbers of bonds are attached to each element. Carbon has four (one to each N and two to the O). This means that the carbon is sharing four electrons (see Table 5-2). The N has three bonds; it shares three electrons with other atoms. Two bonds for O, and one for each H, indicate the sharing of two electrons and one electron, respectively.

This method of representing organic compounds is most useful. It does have one serious limitation, however. Molecules have three dimensions, while the paper on which the structural formulas are shown is only two-dimensional.

THE PRINCIPAL COMPOUNDS OF CELLS

Living cells are composed of many sorts of substances. The most abundant are water, proteins, carbohydrates, fats, and nucleic acids. In addition, there are many other kinds about which you will learn in time, such as vitamins, steroid hormones, and mineral salts.

Water

The amount of water in living cells varies, but it is usually at least 65 percent, and in some organisms may be 96 percent or more of the total substance. Water is *by far* the most abundant compound in organisms. The activities of cells, therefore, are activities that occur in the presence of water.

Chemically speaking, water is not an organic compound. It does not contain carbon, and it is not produced only by living things. Its properties, however, make it enormously important in living activities.

One of its properties is this: it is the best solvent known. That is, more chemical substances dissolve in it than in any other liquid. What is the importance of this fact? The answer has to do with the way in which chemical substances react. In most cases it is necessary that the reacting substances be in very small particles, such as molecules or ions, and be well mixed, if they are to react.

Both the separation into small particles and the mixing occur when substances are dissolved in water. Chemical reactions occur between these molecules and ions, not between large chunks of matter. Water,

therefore, makes it possible for many chemical reactions to occur—reactions that would not occur if the substances were dry.

The mixing that occurs is partly explained by the motion of molecules. Molecules are always in motion. The higher the temperature of a substance, the greater the motion of its molecules. Water molecules are chiefly responsible for the mixing that occurs in a water solution; the water molecules bump into each other and into all other substances in the water.

In a living cell, substances are dissolved (or ionized) and mixed throughout the watery fluid of the cell in much the same way that they would be dissolved and mixed in water in the laboratory. In their dissolved or ionized state, they can react with one another more readily.

The movement of molecules and ions, as a result of their own motion or of being hit by other molecules and ions, is known as **diffusion** (dih·FEW·zh'n). The movement is in all directions. Eventually, it leads to an even distribution of the diffusing substances—even though they were not evenly distributed at the outset. We say, then, that the *net* result of the diffusion process is movement of substances from areas of greater concentration to areas of lesser concentration. In living cells this diffusion is largely the result of molecules and ions being hit and moved by water molecules.

Another important property of water is that it is a relatively *stable* compound. Imagine what would happen if this best of all solvents happened to be *unstable*. With hundreds of reactions constantly going on in a cell—reactions dependent upon the presence of water—it would be disastrous indeed if the water were to decompose into hydrogen and oxygen. To be sure, this reaction does occur in photosynthesis, the food-making process of green plants. A great deal of energy is required to split the relatively stable water molecules, however —and this energy is the source of nearly all the energy of living things, as we shall learn when we consider photosynthesis in Chapter 6.

Water does take part in many reactions within cells, but not in the uncontrolled manner of an unstable compound. Each reaction is controlled by—and indeed, made possible *only* because of—specific enzymes within the cell.

We can begin to see what *relative* stability means when we consider what we now know of water:

1. To serve as a solvent, it must have chemical stability.
2. To take part in enzyme-controlled reactions, however, it cannot be inert (that is, *completely* stable under all conditions).

We can now add another important property of water to our understanding of its relative stability. You may be surprised to learn that among the substances which ionize in water is *water itself!* To a very slight extent—that is, to the extent of about one in 500 million molecules—water ionizes. The few ions produced among hundreds of millions of water molecules are very important to cells.

A water molecule ionizes into H^+ and OH^- ions. The H^+, or hydrogen ion, is actually nothing more than a single proton (a hydrogen nucleus). Its missing electron is held by the OH^-, or hydroxide ion, which consists of an oxygen atom, a hydrogen atom, and the extra electron. (Older books list the hydroxide ion as the *hydroxyl* ion.) Chemists will tell you that the H^+ ion—and perhaps also the OH^- ion (they are not yet sure)—exists hydrated—that is, bonded to a water molecule. In other words, H_2O plus H^+ yields an H_3O^+ ion. For biological purposes we may ignore the hydration of the ions and represent the ionization of water as follows:

$$H_2O \rightarrow H^+ + OH^-$$

The reaction is reversible, so the equation may be written:

$$H_2O \rightleftharpoons H^+ + OH^-$$

H^+ and OH^- ions affect, and take part in, many of the reactions that occur in cells. If, as a result, more H^+ than OH^- ions remain in the solution, we say that the solution is **acidic.** (Such a solution is sour to our taste.) If more OH^- than H^+ ions remain in solution, we say that the solution is **basic.** (Such a solution is alkaline.) The relative concentration of H^+ and OH^- ions in living cells is very important, because the reactions controlled by enzymes each take place most readily at one particular concentration of H^+ and OH^- ions.

Chemists and biologists have a convenient device, known as the **pH scale,** which expresses the relative concentration of hydrogen and hydroxide ions in solution. The scale runs from 0 to 14. The greater the concentration of H^+ ions, or in other words, the greater the degree of acidity, the lower the number on the scale. Thus a pH value of 2 represents a solution that is a very strong acid. A pH value of 5 represents a solution that is much less acidic.

A pH value of 7 represents a solution that is neutral. That is, the concentrations of H^+ and OH^- ions are equal. At pH's above 7, the solutions are basic. That is, the concentration of H^+ ions becomes progressively less than the concentration of OH^- ions. A solution of pH 8 would be mildly basic. One with a pH of 10 would be very basic.

A pH change of *one* unit, that is, from pH 2 to pH 3, involves a *tenfold* change in the hydrogen ion concentration (see Figure 5-6).

Proteins

The most abundant carbon-containing (organic) compounds in plants and animals are the proteins. So important are these compounds that when they were named a

5-6 THE pH SCALE

For every 100,000,000,000,000 H+ ions at pH 0, there are			For every OH− ion at a pH value approaching pH 0, there are	
10,000,000,000,000	H+ ions	← at pH 1 →	10	OH− ions
1,000,000,000,000	H+ ions	← at pH 2 →	100	OH− ions
100,000,000,000	H+ ions	← at pH 3 →	1,000	OH− ions
10,000,000,000	H+ ions	← at pH 4 →	10,000	OH− ions
1,000,000,000	H+ ions	← at pH 5 →	100,000	OH− ions
100,000,000	H+ ions	← at pH 6 →	1,000,000	OH− ions
10,000,000	H+ ions	← at pH 7 →	10,000,000	OH− ions
1,000,000	H+ ions	← at pH 8 →	100,000,000	OH− ions
100,000	H+ ions	← at pH 9 →	1,000,000,000	OH− ions
10,000	H+ ions	← at pH 10 →	10,000,000,000	OH− ions
1,000	H+ ions	← at pH 11 →	100,000,000,000	OH− ions
100	H+ ions	← at pH 12 →	1,000,000,000,000	OH− ions
10	H+ ions	← at pH 13 →	10,000,000,000,000	OH− ions
1 Approaching 0	H+ ion H+ ions	← at pH 14 →	100,000,000,000,000	OH− ions

century ago, the term chosen was based upon the Greek word *proteios*, meaning "prime" or "first."

In living organisms, proteins serve a wide variety of functions. They are the principal organic substances within cells. They make up much of the substance of seeds and other plant parts. They also provide the bulk of the material of which skin, muscles, hair, and nails of familiar animals are made.

Hemoglobin (HEE·mo·glow·b'n), the ox-ygen-carrying compound of red blood cells, is protein; every cell in our bodies depends upon red blood cells and their hemoglobin for oxygen. Proteins play a key role in contraction of muscles, in digestion of foods (including other proteins!), in clotting of blood—indeed, there seems no limit to the variety of functions that proteins perform in living organisms. In each instance, the ability of a protein to serve a specific bio-logical role is a consequence of its molecu-

Gly
Val
Asp — NH_2
Glu — NH_2
His
Leu
Cy — S — S — Cy
Gly
Ser
His
Leu
Val
Glu
Ala
Leu
Tyr
Leu
Val
Cy — S — S — Cy
Gly
Glu
Arg
Gly }
Phe
Phe
Tyr
Thr
Pro
Lys
Ala }

Gly
Ileu
Val
Glu
Glu — NH_2
Cy
Cy
Ala
Ser
Val
Cy
Ser
Leu
Tyr
Glu — NH_2
Leu
Glu
Asp — NH_2
Tyr
Cy
Asp — NH_2

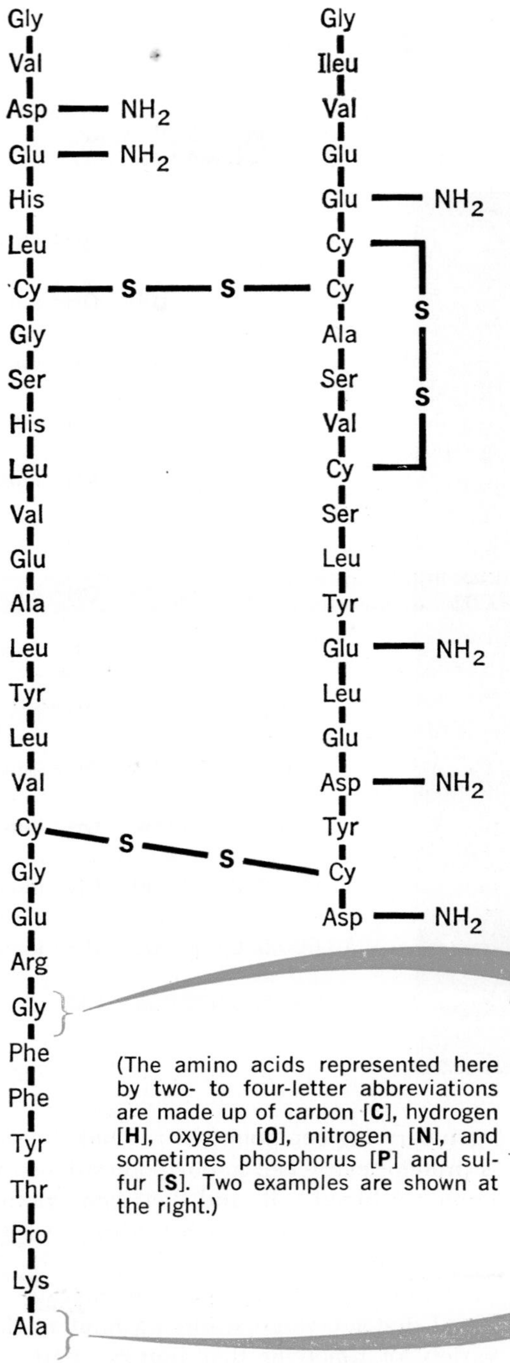

(The amino acids represented here by two- to four-letter abbreviations are made up of carbon [C], hydrogen [H], oxygen [O], nitrogen [N], and sometimes phosphorus [P] and sulfur [S]. Two examples are shown at the right.)

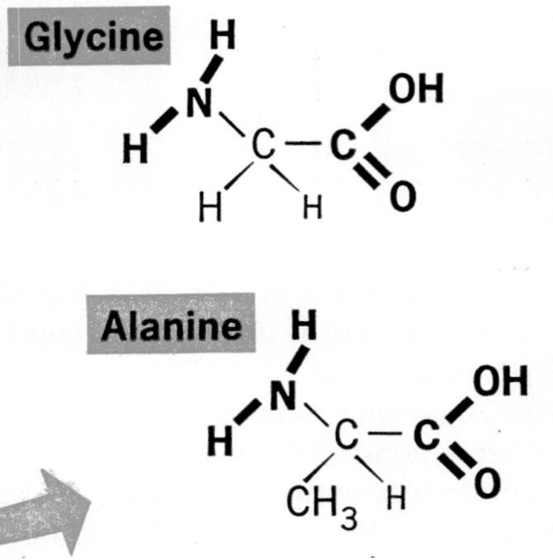

Glycine

Alanine

lar structure, that is, the way the atoms are arranged in the molecule (as will be seen in the next chapter).

Proteins are very large and complex molecules. This may be illustrated by the formula for human hemoglobin, which is $C_{3032}H_{4816}O_{872}N_{780}S_8Fe_4$. If you count all the atoms in this single molecule, you will get a total of 9,512.

Amino Acids

The proteins are built of various combinations of more than 20 kinds of organic compounds called amino (a·MEE·noh) acids. For example, insulin contains 16 different kinds of amino acid subunits. In Figure 5-7, some idea of the complexity of an insulin molecule is given. Each of the two- to four-letter abbreviations (*Gly, Val, Asp,* etc.) represents one of the 16 different kinds of amino acids. You can see that some of these are used more than once in the molecule (which has a total of 51 amino acids in two chains, plus other components as well).

The molecule looks very complex, but not nearly as complex as it really is. For example, suppose that in place of the two- to

5-7 The structure of an insulin molecule. Two of the component amino acids, glycine and alanine, are diagramed separately. Figure 5-8 shows the type of change that takes place as amino acids become chemically bonded to one another to form a long chain in a protein molecule.

four-letter abbreviations of the amino acids, we showed the actual chemical composition of each one, as we have done at the bottom of Figure 5-7 for just *two* of the amino acids. There would not be room on a page to "map" the insulin molecule!

For the moment, we are more interested in the amino acids than in the protein (insulin) molecule that they make up. Each amino acid is a distinctive kind of organic compound with both an **amino group** and a **carboxyl group** chemically bonded to the same carbon atom. The amino group is made up of a nitrogen atom and two hydrogen atoms bonded together ($-NH_2$). The carboxyl group is made up of carbon, oxygen (two atoms), and hydrogen ($-COOH$). The simplest amino acid is **glycine** (gly-SEEN), one of the two shown at the bottom of Figure 5-7. Note the amino and carboxyl groups (shown in **boldface** type in the diagram).

The other amino acids differ from glycine in having one of the hydrogen atoms (which in glycine are attached to the central carbon) replaced by some other combination of atoms. The amino acid **alanine** (AL·a·neen), for example, is shown along with glycine at the bottom of Figure 5-7. At what one point in the alanine molecule does it differ from glycine?

Proteins (the insulin of Figure 5-7, for example) are formed by the chemical linkage of amino acids in a characteristic manner. We can illustrate this with our molecules of glycine and alanine (Figure 5-8). Note that the reaction involves the removal of one molecule of water. The carboxyl group contributes an OH; and the amino group, an H. When these are removed, a chemical bond extends from the carbon of the carboxyl group to the nitrogen of the amino group. The new compound is **glycylalanine.**

Proteins are made of many amino acids chemically linked in this manner, in one or more chains. Notice that after the glycine and alanine have formed glycyl-alanine, there is still an amino group at the left and a carboxyl group at the right of the molecule. The amino group at the left can be bonded to the carboxyl group of a third amino acid. The carboxyl group at the right can be bonded to the amino group of a fourth amino acid. For each coupling, a molecule of water is split off.

This method of "chain-building" always leaves one free amino group and one free carboxyl group. Thus, there is an opportunity of building an ever larger molecule.

The molecules of the majority of proteins are built of 300 to 3,000 amino acid subunits. With so many individual amino acids in the protein molecule, and usually 20 kinds of amino acids to choose among, you can imagine the enormous number of possible protein molecules which might exist in plants and animals.

Once again an analogy may help to make the point. The number of kinds of amino acids found naturally is only a few less than the number of letters in the English alphabet. You are aware of the tremendous number of words that it is possible to construct with 26 letters. Remember also that the average number of letters to a word is fewer than ten. If words consisted of 300 to 3,000 letters, just as proteins consist of 300 to 3,000 amino acids, the possible number of words would be staggering.

It has been estimated that the cells of any one species of animal contain about 2,000 different kinds of protein molecules. Each kind of animal and plant has among its proteins numerous kinds found only in its own species. However, the more closely related two species are in an evolutionary sense, the more their proteins are alike.

Complex protein molecules are often broken down within organisms. For example, in digestion, protein molecules in foods are decomposed into amino acids. The bond between the N of a modified amino group and the C of a modified carboxyl group

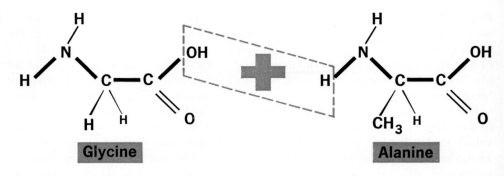

5-8 The chemical linkage of glycine and alanine to form glycyl-alanine. Amino acids are combined with one another in this manner to form the long chains of which protein

is broken by enzyme activity. Simultaneously, the equivalent of a water molecule is introduced to fill out the amino and carboxyl groups at the point of the broken bond. An H is bonded to the N, and an OH to the C. We call this process **hydrolysis** (hy·DROL·ih·sis). The term means "to break with water." The hydrolysis reaction can be described using Figure 5-8. All one has to do is to reverse the arrow.

Only a few proteins have been studied so intensively that their structure is fully known. The first was insulin, a protein that aids our use of sugar in the body. When not enough is present, the result is the disease diabetes. Insulin is a relatively small protein molecule, and therefore relatively easier to study than bigger ones, even though it has 51 amino acids in its two chains. In one of the most remarkable achievements of biochemistry, Frederick Sanger of Cambridge University was able to determine completely the structure of insulin. His research required years, but at the end, in 1954, he knew the precise position occupied by each amino acid in the molecule (Figure 5-7).

Sanger's feat of analysis has been duplicated for only a few other kinds of protein molecules. Let us pause a moment to see what such achievements mean. Remember that the proteins are among the most important of all organic molecules. Many of the properties of life itself are reflections of the structure and functions of proteins. A fuller understanding of the living processes must therefore be based on an intimate knowledge of proteins. In view of this, it is sobering to realize that we know the structural details of fewer than half a dozen proteins. Clearly this important branch of biochemistry is still in its infancy.

The *size* of a protein molecule depends upon the kinds and total number of amino acid molecules that have been bonded together. The *shape* of the molecule, however, depends upon the manner in which separate chains of amino acids have been connected, and *which* specific amino acids are present in the chains. Some proteins are long, thin fibers, such as those which form hair and silk. Others are globular; they appear to have their amino acid chains coiled up into a ball. Still others exhibit shapes resembling a cigar or a sausage. Figure 5-9 shows the manner in which the amino acid chain of a muscle protein, **myoglobin** (MY·o·glow·b'n), is coiled.

What is the significance of coiled or folded structure in a protein molecule? One can see from the structure of insulin, Figure 5-7, that it has at two places cross-linkages (disulfide bonds involving two sulfur atoms) that hold the two chains of the molecule together and in a particular shape. There is also a third such linkage between

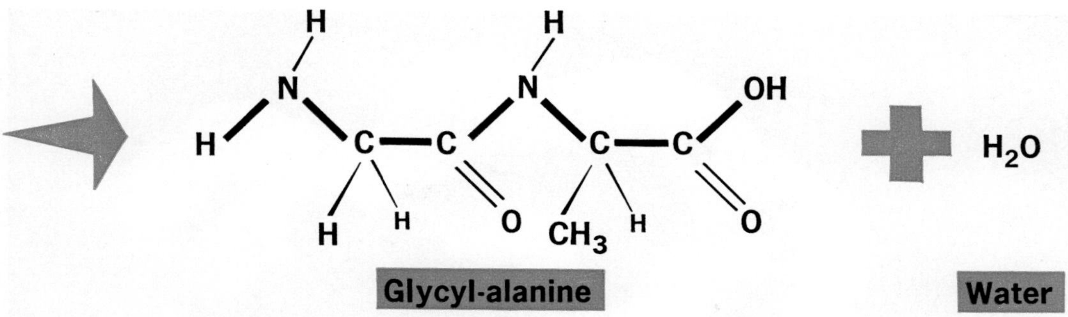

Glycyl-alanine + **Water**

molecules are composed. The linkage does not occur in a single step; several interrelated reactions involving enzymes are required, with the net result as shown here.

two different parts of one of the chains. Larger protein molecules are folded back and forth many times and held in shape by similar linkages between the folded chains. But the structure shown in Figure 5-9 brings out another feature. The myoglobin molecule pictured is very similar to the special part of the hemoglobin molecule that transports oxygen in the human circulatory system (and in that of many other animals). The functional part of the molecule (dark-colored) is held in a particular position by the coils of the remaining part of the molecule (light-colored). The ability to combine with another molecule and transport it or modify it obviously depends upon the over-all structure of the protein molecule. If the dark-colored, active part were tucked away deep inside the snakelike folds, its chemical activity would be greatly reduced and possibly eliminated altogether.

Proteins, therefore, are not quite so mysterious as they once were. Their enormous molecular size, however, does create great problems in studying them. They can now be isolated, crystallized, and characterized by chemical procedures, although to do so even for one kind of protein is a tremendous research task. It also is now possible to study the manner in which the structure of a protein molecule makes possible its biological function. As we proceed with our

study of biology, we will encounter many specific proteins in both plants and animals. It will be well to remember that each kind of protein has its own arrangement of amino acids, as well as a characteristic size and shape. It is these properties that make it possible for the protein to do its specific job for the plant or animal in which it is found. The correlation between structure and function, a prominent feature of all living organisms, is nowhere more striking than in the case of the proteins.

Carbohydrates

Carbohydrates are another class of carbon-containing compounds found in all living organisms. Their name, which we may express as "hydrated carbon," comes from the fact that, in addition to carbon, they contain hydrogen and oxygen *in the same ratio as in water* (2 to 1). This fact helps us remember their chemical structure.

Just as we found it convenient to picture proteins in terms of smaller units—amino acids—we can think of carbohydrates as being made of units of such simple sugars as **glucose.** Glucose has the formula $C_6H_{12}O_6$. The 24 atoms of each of its molecules are arranged as shown in Figure 5-10.

Small amounts of glucose occur in our food. For example, it is the common sugar of corn syrup. Within the body it is a key compound in many vital activities.

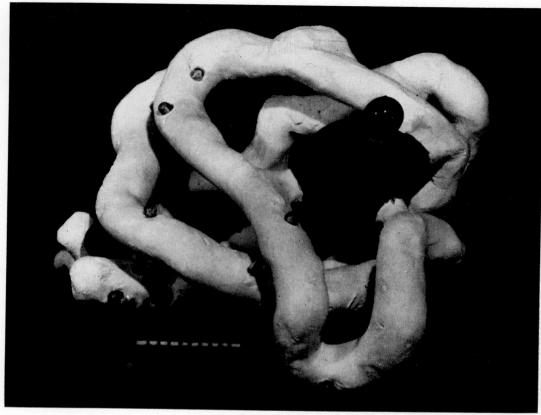

Courtesy John Kendrew; photo by Edward Leigh, Cambridge, England

5-9 A model of a myoglobin molecule. The long amino acid chains of which proteins are composed are often coiled and cross-connected as shown here. The active part of the molecule is the dark mass slightly to the right of center. What is the relation of a model of this type to the one diagramed in Figure 5-7? (The dash line beneath the model is a scale of size; its length represents ten millimicrons.)

Two other common simple sugars are **fructose** (FROOK·tohs), found in fruits, and **galactose** (ga·LAK·tohs), found as part of a larger sugar that we get from milk. These, like glucose, have the formula $C_6H_{12}O_6$. They are, therefore, composed of exactly the same numbers of each kind of atom. We have learned that the position of amino acids within the molecule determines the characteristics of a protein. In much the same way, the differences between glucose, fructose, and galactose are due to the position of atoms within the molecule. Figure 5-11 shows the structural formulas of the three simple sugars. You can count the numbers of carbon, hydrogen, and oxygen atoms and find them to be the same for each sugar. Yet the three sugars differ slightly in the relative positions of the atoms. Each sugar was recognized as different long before its molecular structure was understood. This is another example of the relation between structure and function. In this case, the three sugars had separately identifiable properties, because of their molecular structure.

The simple sugars are linked chemically to form the more complex carbohydrates.

The process will not be entirely strange to you, because it is not too unlike the linkage of amino acids. In Figure 5-12, for example, a molecule of water is split off, as two molecules of glucose undergo synthesis to form a molecule of the double sugar **maltose.**

The common substance that we call table sugar is sucrose. Most of it is obtained from sugar cane or sugar beets. Sucrose, like maltose, is a double sugar. One molecule of glucose and one of fructose undergo synthesis to form a molecule of sucrose. (As implied, a molecule of water is split off.)

Both in the laboratory and in living cells it is possible to put the water back into these double-sugar molecules to **hydrolyze** (HY·dro·lyz) them and re-form the two original molecules of simple sugars. The over-all reaction is roughly the reverse of that shown in Figure 5-12. Just reverse the direction of the arrow (as you have done once before to indicate hydrolysis of linked amino acids).

When two simple sugars form a double sugar, there are still H and OH groups at the ends of the molecule, where more simple sugars can be attached. Thus, either end of a maltose molecule (Figure 5-12) is a possible site for linkage to yet another glucose molecule to make a new molecule containing three glucose units. The larger mol-

Glucose:

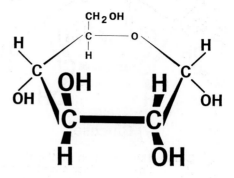

5-10 The simple sugar glucose. One can imagine the molecule as a hexagonal plate to which various H, OH, and CH₂OH groups are attached.

ecule can then react with a fourth molecule of glucose, etc. Giant molecules, built only of glucose units chemically linked by dehydration synthesis to form chains or huge branching structures, do occur in living organisms. Indeed, two of these giant molecules are plant **starch** and **glycogen** (GLY-ko·jen—which is sometimes called animal

5-11 The three common simple sugars—glucose, galactose, and fructose—all have the formula $C_6H_{12}O_6$. Yet each is a different compound. How does a molecule of glucose differ from a molecule of galactose? How do galactose and fructose differ?

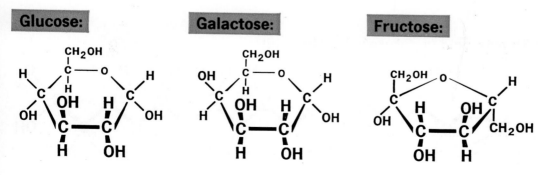

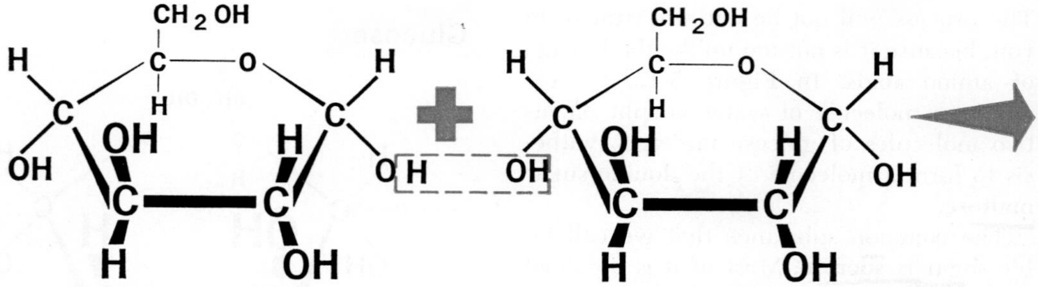

CH₂OH ... Glucose + Glucose →

5-12 The formation of the double sugar maltose. Simple sugars such as glucose are linked together chemically to produce double sugars (facing page) and more complex carbohydrates. The process requires several steps, involving numerous enzymes. Only the overall reaction is shown in this summarization.

starch because it is found in animal cells). Starch and glycogen molecules have no fixed size and may contain from 100 to 10,000 glucose units. Starch, and to a somewhat lesser extent glycogen, can be broken down like maltose by hydrolysis, in the reverse of the manner they were formed.

Without a doubt, the most abundant single carbohydrate in all of nature is **cellulose.** Its subunits, too, are made of glucose. Cellulose is found only in plants, where it makes up most of the material of plant cell walls. Pure cellulose is familiar to us as cotton fibers formed in the cotton plant. Wood is very largely cellulose. Paper is a common product made by man from the cellulose of plants.

Glycerol

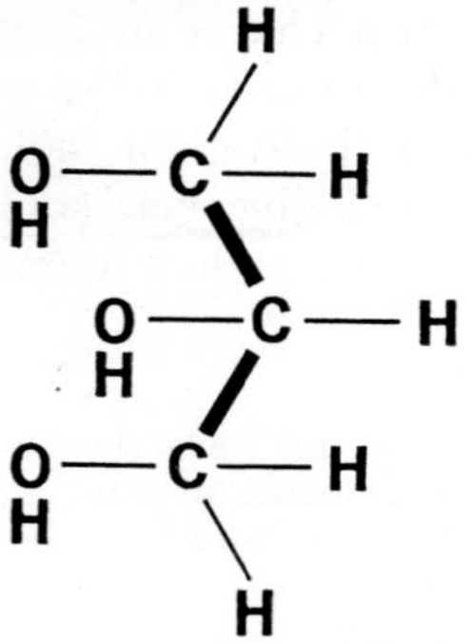

5-13 Glycerol and two fatty acids. There are two common kinds of fatty acids. *Saturated fatty acids,* such as stearic acid (shown below), have no double bonds between the carbon atoms. The carbon chain is saturated, so to speak, with all the hydrogens that can be held. *Unsaturated fatty acids,* such as linolenic acid (see facing page), have double bonds in the carbon chain wherever the number of hydrogens is less than two per carbon atom.

Stearic acid (a saturated fatty acid)

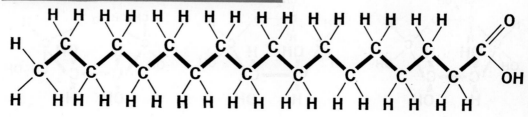

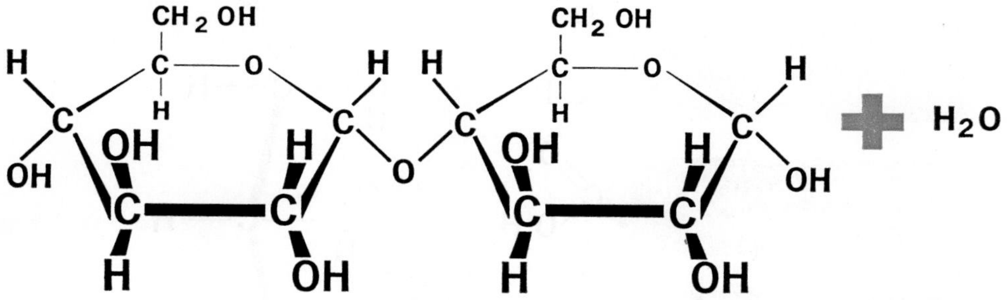

Maltose **Water**

Fats

Fats are familiar to us in several forms—as butter (which is the fat of milk), as the solid fat visible in meat, and as the oils that are obtained from cotton seeds, olives, and peanuts. The term *fat*, like the term *carbohydrate*, indicates a group of related compounds rather than any one specific compound. Upon analysis, all fats prove to be built of two major components known as glycerol (GLIS·er·ohl) and fatty acids (Figure 5-13).

It is the fatty acids that give fats their characteristic properties. Each fatty acid molecule consists of a long carbon chain with attached hydrogens and with a carboxyl group (−COOH) at one end. Although fatty acids with as few as 4 and as many as 24 carbon atoms per molecule can be found in animals and plants, most of the fatty acids in the common fats contain 16

or 18 carbon atoms per molecule. Two of these are diagramed structurally in Figure 5-13. The diagrams are rather complex, and usually we simplify them when we represent fatty acids taking part in chemical reactions. Thus, we show the active −COOH group as below, and represent the rest of the molecule, which does not take part in the formation of the new bonds, by a block or box.

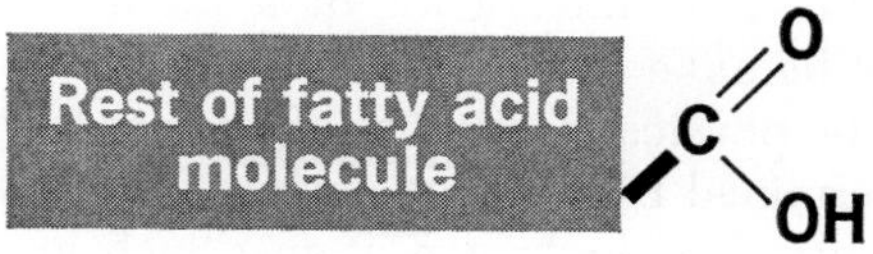

A molecule of a fat is formed by a chemical linkage of one molecule of glycerol to three of fatty acids. Each of the glycerol molecule's three hydroxyl (OH) groups [not the same as hydroxide ions, OH−] is

Linolenic acid (an unsaturated fatty acid)

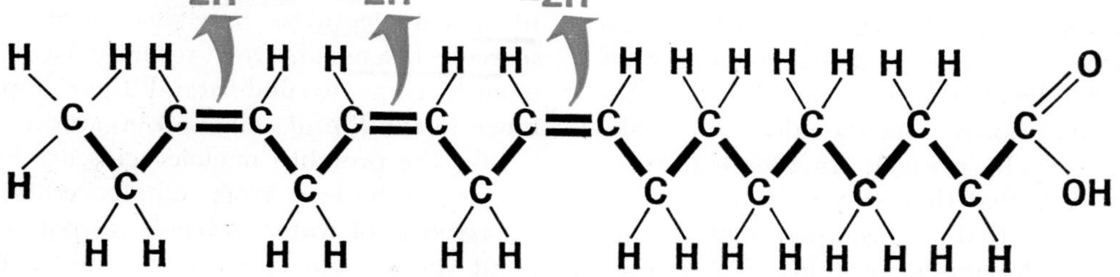

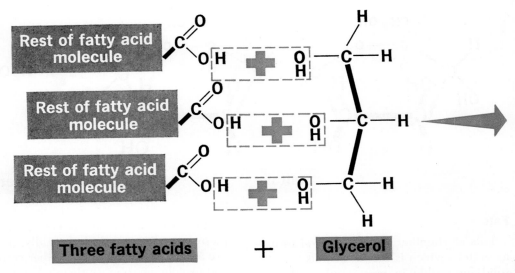

5-14 The formation of a fat. Three fatty acid molecules are bonded to a single molecule of glycerol to form a molecule of fat. The three fatty acid molecules entering the reaction may be three different kinds of fatty acids, or two of one kind and one of a

bonded to a different fatty acid molecule (Figure 5-14). Three water molecules are split off, one at each site of synthesis.

The three fatty acids of a fat molecule may be alike or of different kinds.

The physical properties of fats are largely determined by the long carbon chains with the attached hydrogen atoms. Such groupings prevent a molecule from dissolving in water. Molecules built in this way are lighter than water, and consequently float on water. This is why cream separates from natural milk, and why the oil in a vinegar-and-oil salad dressing rises shortly after mixing. (Skim milk and vinegar are largely water.)

At this time it is well to emphasize some common features of proteins, carbohydrates, and fats (Figure 5-15). All contain carbon, hydrogen, and oxygen; proteins contain nitrogen as well, and often sulfur and phosphorus. Occasionally, other elements may be present. Another feature of all three is that they may be thought of as compounds that are composed of smaller organic compounds: proteins of amino ac-

ids; carbohydrates of simple sugars; fats of fatty acids and glycerol.

The synthesis of proteins, carbohydrates, and fats from the organic units of which they are composed *always* involves the removal of water (Figures 5-8, 5-12, and 5-14).

When proteins, carbohydrates, and fats are broken down into amino acids, simple sugars, and glycerol plus fatty acids, respectively, there is also a common chemical event. Water is added at each place where the larger molecules are split. This is hydrolysis. Hydrolysis is fundamental to digestion, as well as to some other processes.

Nucleic Acids and Nucleotides

Not long ago, **nucleic** (new·KLEE·ik) acids and **nucleotides** (NEW·kle·o·tides) were scarcely discussed. Only recently have biologists come to understand their importance in the life of cells and organisms.

Like the proteins, nucleic acids are long chains synthesized from simpler units by the removal of water molecules at potential points of linkage between the units. The

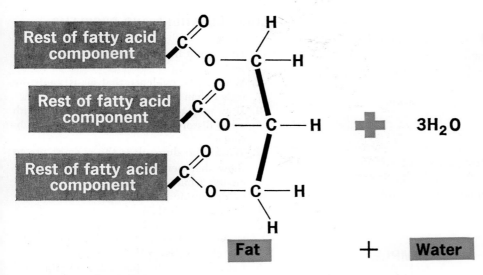

Fat + Water

second kind, or all three of the same kind, depending upon the identity of the particular fat molecule being synthesized. In what respect is the resulting synthesis similar to the synthesis of proteins and of complex carbohydrates?

nucleotides are the units. Their structure will be described in the following chapter, and in Chapter 32.

One nucleic acid, **deoxyribonucleic** (dee-OKS·ee·ry·boh·new·KLEE·ik) **acid** (DNA), has a key role in inheritance. It is the stuff that, passed down from one generation to another, controls development. One egg develops into a kitten and another into a human baby because each contains a different and specific type of DNA: cat DNA or human DNA.

In every living cell, the DNA appears to control the chemical machinery. This control seems to be exerted indirectly—through another nucleic acid known as **ribonucleic** (RY·boh·new·KLEE·ik) **acid** (RNA). RNA has a key role in directing protein synthesis.

Nucleotides also play other important roles in the cell. In Chapter 6 we will learn how one of them, **adenosine triphosphate** (a·DEN·o·seen try·FOS·fayt) (ATP), has a key role in providing energy for the cell's activities.

We could continue our inventory of the cell's molecules, but this is enough. We now have the necessary chemical information to understand many of the cell's activities.

Carbon and Life

Before we conclude the chapter, however, let us look again at the role of the element carbon in our living chemistry. Because carbon needs to gain four electrons to achieve a stable arrangement of its atoms, it is able to combine with four other atoms at once, or with three, or two, or only one. Thus, it has tremendous versatility. Carbon atoms also possess the most amazing ability to link up with each other, forming long chains and rings of various sizes. The tremendous diversity of the carbon compounds in living organisms, and the special roles each compound can play, depend upon these properties of the carbon atom. Thus, for example, a long fatty acid chain (Figure 5-13) permits many hydrogen atoms to be attached by covalent bonds to the carbon backbone of the molecule. Each of these bonds is a potential source of chemical energy, which may be released when the hydrogen atoms are removed in an oxidation process. One can just look at the structural formula of the fatty acid molecule, or of the carbohydrate molecule, and see that it is a storehouse of chemical energy, fuel for the needs of life, food for thousands of hungry mouths.

5-15 A Summary of Common Features in the Chemistry of Carbohydrates, Fats, and Proteins

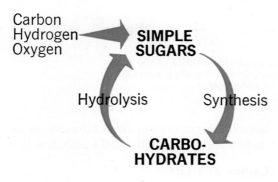

Carbon
Hydrogen → **SIMPLE SUGARS**
Oxygen

Hydrolysis   Synthesis

CARBO-HYDRATES

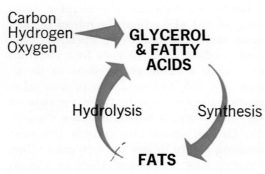

Carbon
Hydrogen → **GLYCEROL & FATTY ACIDS**
Oxygen

Hydrolysis   Synthesis

FATS

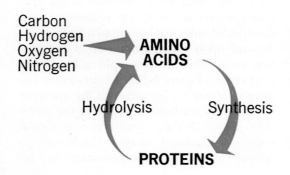

Carbon
Hydrogen
Oxygen → **AMINO ACIDS**
Nitrogen

Hydrolysis   Synthesis

PROTEINS

GUIDE QUESTIONS AND PROBLEMS

1. How can it be shown that air contains matter?
2. What is the evidence that air is a mixture rather than an element?
3. How might it be shown that water with some dissolved sugar is not a simple substance?
4. What procedures does the chemist use to show that neither water nor salt are elements? Could the same methods be used to determine whether wood is a simple substance? Explain.
5. The neon atom has 10 electrons. How could this fact be used to explain why this element is so highly stable?
6. Explain how the formation of chemical compounds involves the electrons in the outer shells of the reacting atoms.
7. What happens when table salt is dissolved in water? How does the result differ from dissolving sugar in water? Explain the difference in terms of the types of chemical bond involved.
8. The proteins in the cells of a bean plant differ from the proteins in the cells of a dog, yet they are built up from similar amino acids. How can the differences be explained?
9. What are the unique properties of water that make it so important a constituent of living bodies?
10. What are proteins? How do they differ from carbohydrates and fats?
11. What is the importance of Sanger's study of the insulin molecule?
12. What are nucleic acids? nucleotides? What is their importance in living cells?

SUGGESTIONS FOR ADDITIONAL READING

Books

Bogert, L. J., *The Fundamentals of Chemistry*, 8th ed. Philadelphia, Saunders, 1958.
    An easily understood basic chemistry text including both inorganic and organic chemistry, with emphasis on the structure of carbohydrates, fats, and proteins and their role in metabolism.

Bronowski, J., et al., *Doubleday Pictorial Library of Science* (Chemistry, Physics, Astronomy). New York, Doubleday, 1960.

Easy to read, beautifully illustrated historical development of the physical sciences, with up-to-the-minute information on recent achievements. The chemistry section includes the "Chemistry of Living Things."

Grunewald, E., and R. H. Johnson, *Atoms, Molecules, and Chemical Change.* Englewood Cliffs (N. J.), Prentice-Hall, 1960.

An introduction to chemistry for readers without a background in chemistry, emphasizing structure of matter and the concept of energy in chemical change.

Hecht, S., *Explaining the Atom,* rev. ed. New York, Viking Press, 1954.

An understandable explanation of modern atomic structure.

Lessing, L., *Understanding Chemistry.* New York, New American Library, 1959.

A well-written study of man's discoveries about the nature of matter and energy.

Read, J., *A Direct Entry to Organic Chemistry.* New York, Harper & Row, 1959.

An account of the nature and scope of organic chemistry for the reader who has no prior knowledge of chemistry.

Magazines and Journals

Gale, E. F., "Experiments in Protein Synthesis." *Scientific American,* Vol. 194 (March 1956), pp. 42–46.

Pauling, L., R. Corey, and R. Hayward, "The Structure of Protein Molecules." *Scientific American,* Vol. 191 (July 1954), pp. 51–59.

Stein, W. H., and S. Moore, "Chemical Structure of Proteins." *Scientific American,* Vol. 204 (February 1961), pp. 81–86.

Thompson, E. O. P., "The Insulin Molecule." *Scientific American,* Vol. 192 (May 1955), pp. 36–44.

6

THE PHYSIOLOGY

OF CELLS

Biological questions, however long they remain unanswered, have a way of persisting. When the cell theory established the similarity of structure among living organisms, biologists naturally questioned whether there were also similar functions shared by all organisms. (We first referred to this question in Chapter 3, page 64.) It was not a question to be answered soon; too little was then known of the chemistry of cells.

Today the situation has changed. Armed with the discoveries that were the subject of Chapters 4 and 5, biologists have learned a great deal of what goes on in living cells. It has not been an easy task, and it is far from complete. There exists, however, the beginning of a reasonable understanding, based largely upon two lines of investigation, **biochemistry** (by·o·KEM·iss·tree) and **electron microscopy** (my·KROS·ko·pee).

Biochemistry, a new term for the "living chemistry" with which you already are familiar, is revealing to us more and more about the reactions that go on in living cells. Electron microscopy, as the name im-plies, deals with the electron microscope and what it can reveal—a subject with which you became familiar in Laboratory Exercise 3-9. As you learned there, the electron microscope is bringing us near the point of observing particles so small that both structure and function become molecular and almost identical.

In this chapter we are ready to find out what some of the activities are that go on in cells. The physiology of a cell is—briefly stated—whatever the cell does, and some of the big problems concerned can be grasped by thinking of your own past history.

You began life as a single cell, the fertilized egg. At that time you were a tiny sphere about 0.1 mm in diameter. You were near the minimum size that the unaided human eye can detect.

In the years from then until now, you have changed beyond almost all means of recognition. Your volume has increased tremendously. Where did all the additional material come from? Clearly cells cannot create matter. Wondrous as they are, they cannot operate in defiance of the Law of Conservation of Mass (page 79). The matter that is required for growth comes from without, as food. It enters the cell as food particles—or in your body, as the products of digestion. Within the cell these supplies are used for the production of more living matter. Cells, therefore, use food materials for making more cells.

But food is required for more than growth. Actually, most food that enters the body is used for maintenance and energy. After all, man does not stop eating when he reaches his full size. He continues to consume about the same amount of food as when actively growing. Even a person at rest, with a minimum amount of muscular activity, must have food. Energy is required at all times to maintain the complex structure of living cells. The needed energy comes from food; if energy is not available, the cells die.

Thus, cells use food in two general ways: as a source of energy to maintain the living state, and as a source of materials to be converted into more living matter.

To be sure, cells that contain chlorophyll can make food within their chloroplasts, where glucose is synthesized from carbon dioxide and water. But even these cells must also be able to use food as a source of energy and as a source of materials.

A tremendous number of chemical reactions are involved in providing energy for the cell and in the formation of new living material. The kinds of reactions that occur are unusual, and by and large they tend to occur only in living cells. Cells can easily perform tasks that chemists find difficult or impossible in the laboratory. For example, all plant cells that contain chlorophyll can synthesize glucose from carbon dioxide and water. No chemist to date has carried out this fundamental synthesis.

It is not necessary to conclude that there is some mysterious vital force driving the chemical reactions within cells. The observations of Spallanzani on gastric juice (page 84), and of Payen and Persoz on diastase (page 86), indicated a more direct interpretation. The reactions that occur in cells are made possible by a special class of proteins, the enzymes, which in many cases can be removed from cells and used *in vitro* (VEET·roh). (The term "*in vitro*" means "in glass," referring to the fact that the event can occur in the chemist's glassware. A related term, *in vivo* (VEE·voh), means "in life." All enzymes work *in vivo*, and many are known to work *in vitro*.)

ENZYMES

Enzymes increase the rates of chemical reactions within cells. There are probably several thousands of different kinds of enzymes in every cell. Without them, no cell could live.

The importance of enzymes will be more apparent if an example of a reaction that occurs both with and without the participation of enzymes is given. The sugar glucose can be burned. That is, it will unite very rapidly with oxygen if the initial temperature is high enough. Water and carbon dioxide will be formed, and a great deal of energy will be released, as the C—H bonds of glucose are replaced by C=O and H—O bonds. The reaction occurs without the use of an enzyme.

A similar reaction, or rather a series of reactions that add up eventually to the same end result, is occurring in the cells of your body all of the time. The oxygen you breathe is carried by the circulating blood to the cells. Oxygen enters the cells, and glucose is oxidized. But there is no violence, no high temperature, no tremendous release of heat. The process proceeds in a gentle way—because the entire reaction is broken up into many steps, each regulated by a special enzyme. The energy is released in small amounts, and much of it is trapped as chemical energy in other compounds instead of being set free all at once. We will discuss this process in more detail later in the chapter.

Enzymes control essentially all reactions that occur in cells. Furthermore, each reaction is **catalyzed** (KAT·a·lyzd)—that is, brought about and accelerated—by a specific enzyme. It is estimated that a single liver cell, for example, may contain as many as 1,000 different enzymes, each of which is responsible for the control of a different chemical reaction. Of the many reactions which might conceivably occur among the hundreds of compounds present in a single cell, only those for which there is a specific enzyme *do* occur. Enzymes, therefore, give regulation and control to the chemical activities of living cells.

Without exception, enzymes are proteins. There are several hundred, or perhaps several thousand, individual molecules of each different enzyme in one cell. The total of all of these accounts for most of the protein of the cell.

Enzymes can be separated from biological material and purified by the methods used by chemists in separating proteins. Hundreds of different enzymes have been partially purified. Dozens have been crystallized. When substances can be obtained as crystals, we can be sure they are fairly pure. It is with these pure preparations that biochemists have studied the manner in which enzymes act.

Even though enzymes are large protein molecules, they are still much too small to be seen in living cells, even with the aid of the electron microscope. Their general mode of action is fairly well understood, however, and it is even possible to provide a visual model of how they work. The model at least approximates what must actually take place.

An Enzyme at Work

We learned earlier that maltose is formed (synthesized) by a chemical linkage of two molecules of glucose (Figure 5-12). In this process, the net result of several reactions is that a hydrogen atom (H) is removed from one glucose molecule, and a hydroxyl group (OH) from another, to form a molecule of water (H_2O). Enzyme molecules are involved in the reactions.

$$2C_6H_{12}O_6 \xrightarrow{\text{enzyme}} C_{12}H_{22}O_{11} + H_2O$$
$$\text{glucose} \qquad \text{maltose} \quad \text{water}$$

In the digestive tract of man and many other animals, there is an enzyme, **maltase**, that catalyzes the reverse reaction. That is, a molecule of maltose reacts with a molecule of water, and the product is two molecules of glucose.

$$C_{12}H_{22}O_{11} + H_2O \xrightarrow{\text{maltase}} 2C_6H_{12}O_6$$
$$\text{maltose} \quad \text{water} \qquad \text{glucose}$$

This chemical equation gives little indication of how the reaction actually occurs. The first step involves a chemical bonding of maltose and maltase. (A substance with which an enzyme reacts is called a **substrate** [SUB·strayt]. In this case, maltose is the substrate for maltase.) Apparently the maltose fits into a portion of the surface of the maltase molecule. This relationship is shown in a highly schematic way in Figure 6-1. (Maltase is a far larger molecule than maltose, but this difference is not shown.)

The next step is the breaking of the —O— chemical bond between the two glucose subunits, by hydrolysis. It is not fully understood how the enzyme does this. In any event, the bond is broken on one side of the O atom. The H from a water molecule reacts with this O atom to form OH. The OH group from the water molecule combines with the other glucose subunit.

At the end of the reaction, we have two molecules of glucose and the enzyme. The events could be written, therefore, as follows:

1. maltose + maltase → maltose-maltase
2. maltose-maltase + H_2O →
$$2 \text{ glucose} + \text{maltase}$$

Notice something that is of great significance: the maltase molecule is present at the end of the reaction just as at the start. It has not been altered in any way. Consequently, the same enzyme molecule can now react with another molecule of maltose and repeat the process. This characteristic is not unique to maltase: all enzymes can be used over and over in this way.

Enzymes are involved in all sorts of reactions: those in which large molecules are synthesized from smaller ones; those in which molecules are decomposed into smaller ones; those in which atoms are exchanged between molecules; and those in which the atoms of a molecule are rearranged.

The reactions controlled by enzymes occur extremely rapidly. An individual enzyme molecule may catalyze its specific reaction several hundred or even many thousand times in one second.

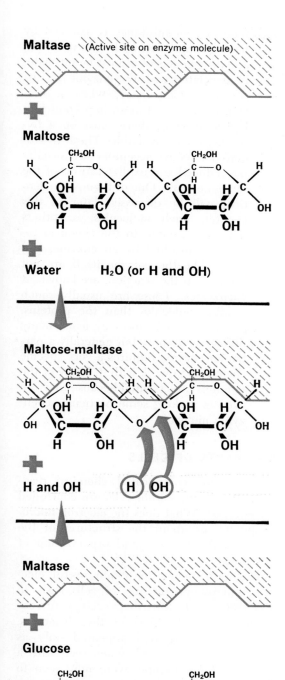

Maltase (Active site on enzyme molecule)

+

Maltose

+

Water H_2O (or H and OH)

Maltose-maltase

+

H and OH   (H) (OH)

Maltase

+

Glucose

Properties of Enzyme Action

These are some of the general properties of enzymes and their reactions:

1. Enzymes, being proteins, are affected by all factors that affect proteins. Thus, they are altered by heat. At temperatures above 55° C, most of them cannot function. High temperatures actually change the structure of these protein molecules and make them unable to react with the substrate. This is one reason why heat kills living organisms.

   Enzymes combine with the ions of metals like lead (Pb^{++}) and mercury (Hg^{++}) and are precipitated. This is why these metals are so poisonous.

2. Enzymes are specific. Each enzyme can enter into only one kind of reaction. Usually only one compound serves as substrate, but occasionally any member of a group of closely related compounds can react with a given enzyme. There are few exceptions to this otherwise universal rule.

3. The speed of the reactions that are controlled by enzymes is influenced by:
   a. the amount of enzyme present (if there is plenty of substrate). Thus, twice as much enzyme will make the reaction go twice as fast.
   b. the amount of substrate present (if there is plenty of enzyme). Thus, twice as much substrate will make the reaction go twice as fast.
   c. the pH of the solution in which the enzyme and substrate are in-

6-1
The digestion (or enzymatic hydrolysis) of maltose. Only a small part of the molecule of the enzyme maltase is represented here. A portion of its surface is shown as an active site at which a molecule of maltose is bonded to the enzyme, then split into two molecules of glucose.

teracting (Table 6-1). The majority of enzymes are most active at a pH near 7 (neutral). There are others that are most active when the pH is much higher (alkaline) or much lower (acid). The enzymes in your gastric juice, for example, are most active at a pH of 2 (this is very acid).

d. the temperature of the solution in which the enzyme and substrate are interacting. Most enzymes cannot act at 0° C. As the temperature is increased, a point is reached where they begin to act. As the temperature is further increased, enzymatic activity also increases. Eventually a temperature is reached where the activity is at a maximum. Beyond this the activity declines and finally ceases.

4. The requirement for coenzymes. Most of the important energy-yielding reactions are oxidations (see page 90). Oxidations and reductions must exist in coupled systems, since for every substance that gains electrons or hydrogen there must be some substance that loses them. So, in the cell, when a food or fuel substance is oxidized by having some of its hydrogen removed, a hydrogen acceptor must be intimately associated with the enzyme and its substrate. Conversely, when a substance is reduced in an important biological process, there must be a hydrogen donor available. These hydrogen donors or acceptors are usually the reduced and oxidized forms of the same molecule. One of them, a nucleotide, will be discussed later in this chapter. Such molecules, or others that are essential to the chemical reaction controlled by an enzyme, and which like the enzyme itself are not used up in the reaction, are known as **coenzymes.** These are usually much smaller molecules than the proteins. The same coenzyme may assist many different enzymes, but generally a particular enzyme requires a very specific coenzyme to work with it. Many of the vitamins are essential because they are used in making some particular coenzyme molecule.

THE PARTS OF CELLS

All of the complicated chemical reactions that occur within cells are controlled by enzymes. What does the electron microscope tell us about the structures of the cell and the location and organization of enzymes?

Biologists began to obtain useful electron microscope pictures of cells early in the 1950's. Naturally, their excitement rose to a high pitch. Most of the structures, which previously had appeared only as solid granules and rods when seen with a compound microscope, were now seen to have a complex internal structure. This specific structure suggested a relationship of some kind with the specific functions of the granules and rods. What could that relationship be?

TABLE 6-1 OPTIMAL pH VALUES FOR ENZYME ACTIVITY —SELECTED ENZYMES

Enzyme	Optimal pH	Substrate
Amylase (animal)	6.2–7.0	starch
Amylase (plant)	4.5–5.5	starch
Lactase	5.7	lactose
Maltase	7.0	maltose
Pepsin	1.5–2.2	proteins
Trypsin	7.8–9.0	proteins

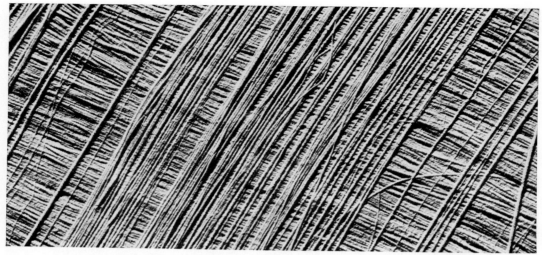

Eva Frei and R. D. Preston

6-2 The sturdy construction of plant tissues is evident in this electron microscope photograph of a plant cell wall. The cellulose fibers are arranged in layers, with the fibers of each layer at an angle to those of other layers. Some of the fibers from the uppermost layer shown in the photograph have been removed. (25,400 X)

We will begin our description at the outside boundary of a cell and work our way inward, learning as we go what the electron microscope tells us about the structure of cells.

The Cell Wall

In most plant cells, the outermost structure is the cell wall. The electron microscope shows that the wall is a network of fibers (Figure 6-2) consisting primarily of cellulose (page 112). The cell wall is non-living. In woody plants it may become very thick. In these cases the fibers are arranged in layers. In any single layer most of the fibers will be parallel to one another. The adjacent layer will also have its parallel fibers, but these will be at an angle to those in the first layer. This crisscross arrangement gives the cell wall great strength—the basis, of course, of the tremendous strength of the wood used for building houses and furniture. In woody tissues the cell wall is impregnated with minerals and tough, impervious organic material such as lignin.

The Cell Membrane

The cell membrane is beneath the cell wall in plants. In animal cells, and in those plants lacking cell walls, it forms the outer boundary of the cell. The cell membrane has a most important role in the life of the cell. Everything that enters and leaves the cell must pass across it.

The cell membrane has some interesting characteristics, in both structure and function. Recent studies with the electron microscope suggest that the cell membrane may have pores, much like those of the nuclear membrane shown in Figure 6-3. What is the significance of such pores in the cell membrane? No one is sure, but it is probable that they are concerned with materials entering or leaving the cell.

The cell membrane exerts a great deal of control over what enters and what leaves the cell. In general, very large molecules, such as those of proteins, fats, and large carbohydrates, cannot pass in or out. Some other substances such as water, oxygen, urea, and glycerol pass through easily.

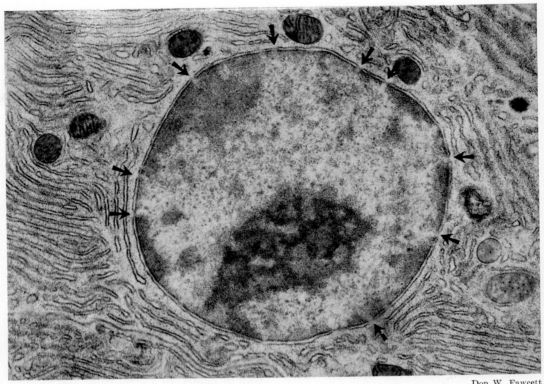

Don W. Fawcett

6-3 A nucleus and a small portion of the surrounding cytoplasm of a cell, as seen with an electron microscope. The arrows point to apparent pores in the nuclear membrane. The dark mass within the nucleus is the nucleolus, and the dark spheres in the cytoplasm are mitochondria. The narrow, tubelike structures are portions of the endoplasmic reticulum, on which ribosomes show as minute dots. (13,700 X)

A membrane that allows some but not all molecules to pass through it is said to be **differentially permeable** (PUR·me·a·b'l). The membranes of living cells are differentially permeable. We can learn something of the nature of these membranes by considering the movement of oxygen and carbon dioxide molecules across them. Cell membranes are permeable to both of these substances. As animal cells use oxygen and produce carbon dioxide in the oxidation of glucose, oxygen passes into the cells, and carbon dioxide passes out.

The movement of oxygen molecules is a consequence of their relative concentration outside and inside a cell. The cell is con-stantly using oxygen to combine with hydrogen. This lowers the concentration of free oxygen within the cell. There is, therefore, a higher concentration of oxygen molecules outside the cell. Many more oxygen molecules will, consequently, move into the cell than will tend to move out.

Carbon dioxide, on the other hand, is produced in the cell, and is consequently at a higher concentration in the cell than outside it, in the surrounding air or water or in body fluids. Therefore, much more CO_2 leaves the cell than enters it.

The movement of molecules—the net result of which is a more even distribution—is diffusion. You are already acquainted with the diffusion of dissolved substances in water (page 103). Now you see that diffusion can take place across a membrane.

Water molecules diffuse across the cell membrane in a similar way. This leads to some interesting problems. We can consider these problems in relation to some one-celled animals that live in fresh water. The interior of a typical specimen from among these aquatic animals contains a great deal of water. There is also a certain amount of material dissolved in this water. Not counting the large structures of the cell, such as mitochondria, Golgi bodies, granules, and even some very large organic molecules, we might say that the interior of the organism is 98 percent water and 2 percent dissolved material. The cell membrane is permeable to the water, but not to much of the dissolved material. What will happen to this cell in fresh water?

Fresh water contains a trace of dissolved materials, but the amount is so small that we can say the water is about 100 percent pure. More water molecules will diffuse from the fresh water into the cell than will leave the cell. This movement is a consequence of the differences in concentration of water: 100 percent outside and 98 percent inside. If there is nothing to counteract this movement, the cell will swell. However, the one-celled organisms in question do have a way of getting rid of the excess water (page 350). As a result, they remain about the same size.

Not all cells have a means of getting rid of excess water. If, for example, you place some blood cells of a frog (or your own) in pure water, the cells will swell and burst. The water concentration will be greater on the outside of the cells than within. Consequently, more water enters than leaves the cells until their cell membranes rupture.

For some cells the problem is reversed. They may be in solutions so rich in dissolved materials that water begins to leave the cells, and the solid contents of the cell become more and more condensed. Activity then ceases, and life itself may end. This is the reason that placing a cell, such as a bacterium, in a concentrated solution of salt or sugar will kill it.

For all organisms, the maintenance of the activities of life depends upon a variety of mechanisms that keep the internal concentration of water fairly constant. Thus, a few marine organisms retain concentrations of urea in the body fluids that balance the heavy concentration of salts in ocean water. Balance in the human body is maintained by blood and lymph, in which the concentration of dissolved substances is maintained at a level suitable for the cells. Changes in the concentration of substances in the lymph and blood are regulated by kidney action, by perspiration, and by a variety of other mechanisms.

In many one-celled organisms, there are vacuoles that pump excess water out of the cell. A large part of the energy of living in these organisms is spent in regulating the internal concentration of the cell.

Substances must be dissolved in order to enter a cell by diffusion. Either they must be soluble in water or they must be soluble in components of the cell membrane itself. The cell membrane is rich in fatty (lipid) materials. Other fatty materials and fat solvents (such as ether or ethyl alcohol) may enter by dissolving in the cell membrane and then diffusing through. This process explains why ether and alcohol can be dangerous to life: they can actually dissolve holes in cell membranes if they are in a sufficiently high concentration. This could lead to the breakdown or death of cells.

There are other ways, besides diffusion, in which materials can enter a cell. For example, the cell membrane may form a little pocket (Figure 6-4). Some of the water surrounding the cell, together with any material in the water, will be inside the pocket. The pocket may then detach itself from the cell membrane. Finally, the pocket—

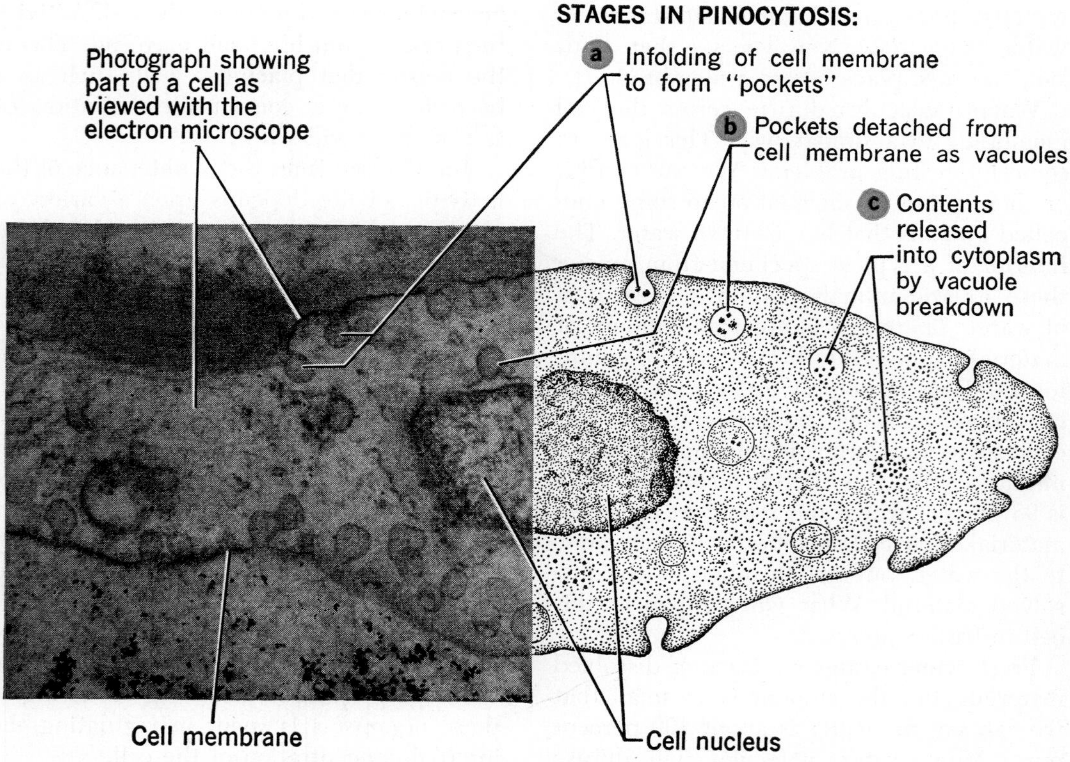

STAGES IN PINOCYTOSIS:

Photograph showing part of a cell as viewed with the electron microscope

a Infolding of cell membrane to form "pockets"

b Pockets detached from cell membrane as vacuoles

c Contents released into cytoplasm by vacuole breakdown

Cell membrane

Cell nucleus

6-4 Pinocytosis. The left half of this illustration shows a portion of a cell from the wall of a blood capillary, as photographed with an electron microscope. The right half of the cell has been reconstructed as an interpretative drawing. What are some of the substances that enter cells by pinocytosis?

which we would now call a vacuole—breaks down and liberates its contents into the cytoplasm. This method of admitting molecules that are too large to pass across the cell membrane by diffusion is known as **pinocytosis** (py·no·sy·TOH·sis).

The Endoplasmic Reticulum

Figure 6-5 shows a small portion of a cell as seen with the electron microscope. You will notice a portion of the nucleus at the bottom, and two mitochondria near the top.

We will learn more about these later. For the moment, concentrate on the numerous tubelike structures that occupy all of the cytoplasm in view. These are known as the **endoplasmic reticulum** (re·TIK·yoo·lum). Recent evidence suggests that the endoplasmic reticulum is a network of tubes extending throughout the cytoplasm. Some of these tubes seem to open on the cell membrane; thus, they appear to be continuous with the fluid surrounding the cell. Tubes of the endoplasmic reticulum also connect

6-5 Another electron microscope photograph of a small part of a cell (including part of the nucleus). The endoplasmic reticulum and the mitochondria referred to in the text show clearly here. How large would you guess the photograph would have been if the entire cell could be shown at this magnification? (44,000 X)

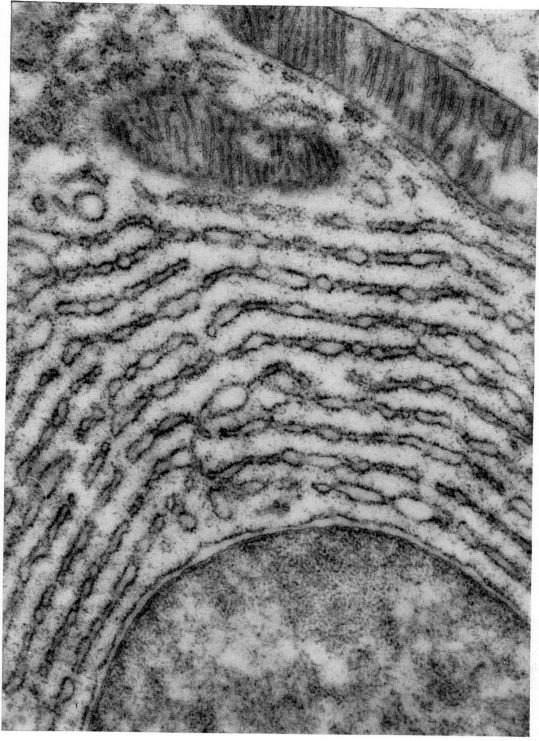

George E. Palade

inside the cell with the nuclear membrane.

You can see from the photograph that the endoplasmic reticulum is a prominent feature of the cytoplasm. One would suspect that it must play some exceedingly important role in the life of the cell, yet even its existence remained unknown until the electron microscope became available.

The function of the endoplasmic reticulum is not adequately known. The mere fact that it is a series of tubes suggests a role in transporting materials throughout the cytoplasm. Possibly this is what it does, but we must be careful not to assign a function merely from observing structure.

Ribosomes

If you examine Figure 6-5 closely, you will see that the endoplasmic reticulum is coated with tiny granules. They are so small that they do not look too important, but they are now known to have a major function in the cell. They are called **ribosomes** (RY·boh·sohmz). This name is given to them because they are known to be composed largely of ribonucleic acid, or RNA (page 115). They also contain protein.

Possibly you wonder how a biochemist would know that a ribosome contains RNA —or any other substance for that matter. A ribosome is so small that it can be seen only with the aid of an electron microscope, and even this remarkable instrument is not able to magnify ribosomes to a degree that permits us to see any internal structure in them. They appear only as granules. Can such tiny structures be isolated and studied? Yes.

One of the common ways of isolating the parts of cells is by **centrifugation** (sen·trif-yoo·GAY·sh'n). A centrifuge is an instrument for separating substances of different **densities.** Perhaps an example will best illustrate the meaning of density. If one allows whole (not homogenized!) milk to stand, the cream rises slowly to the top. The cream is less dense than the skim milk; that is, its

particles occupy more space but weigh less per unit of volume than those of the skim milk. The separation of the cream and skim milk can be speeded greatly—and indeed this is done in milk-processing plants—by centrifugation. The whole milk is put into a centrifuge machine, which whirls it around at high speeds. The heavier skim milk is thrown to the bottom of the container, and the cream comes to the top.

A similar technique can be used to separate those parts of cells that have different densities. Let us suppose that we wish to study the liver cells of a mouse. We can remove the liver from the animal and grind it up so fine that even the cells are broken. We will then have particles in a liquid medium (since cells are mostly water), which can be put into a centrifuge tube. Next we put the tube in the centrifuge and whirl it around for some time. After about 20 minutes we can stop the machine and remove the tube. The ground liver will have separated into several layers (Figure 6-6). We can examine the material in these layers with a compound microscope or with an electron microscope. The bottom layer (the heaviest) will consist largely of nuclei and any cells that were not broken. The next layer will consist of mitochondria. Above this is a layer consisting of broken pieces of the endoplasmic reticulum to which are attached the ribosomes. The upper (lightest) layer will consist of a nearly clear, watery solution.

These different layers are by no means pure. Compared to the ground-up cells, however, they are *relatively* pure. If one wishes to study the mitochondria, he can remove the layer in which they are present and carry out his various observations and experiments. In a similar way he could obtain a fairly pure mass of endoplasmic reticulum and attached ribosomes by using the second layer from the top.

Ribosomes may be isolated from the broken pieces of the endosplasmic reticulum

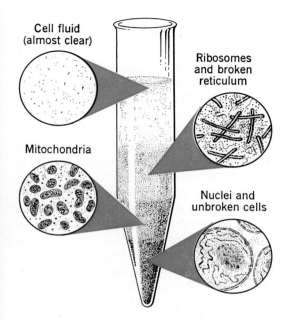

Cell fluid
(almost clear)

Ribosomes
and broken
reticulum

Mitochondria

Nuclei and
unbroken cells

6-6 The separation of cell structures by centrifugation. The cell fractions are shown in successive layers. Ordinarily, extra fluid would be added before the cells are centrifuged, with the result that the top layer would be disproportionately larger than that shown as cell fluid here.

by use of other methods. A purified sample can then be analyzed, and it will be found to consist largely of RNA and protein.

But what do the ribosomes do? Near the beginning of this chapter, the statement was made that cells require food for two general purposes: to provide energy to maintain life, and to provide materials to be converted into more living matter. How do cells synthesize living matter?

Proteins are made *within* the cell from amino acids. Very few protein molecules enter the cell already formed. (Almost none of the proteins have molecules small enough to diffuse through a cell membrane, and in most organisms, other methods of entry—see page 126—do not account for any significant transfer.)

It is amino acid molecules, rather than proteins as such, that enter the cell. With-

in the cell these amino acids are linked chemically to form proteins. But the process is more complicated than just hooking amino acids together. We learned earlier that there are many kinds of proteins in every cell. The amino acids, then, have to be chemically bonded to one another in very definite ways. It is the ribosomes that determine the manner in which the amino acids become bonded to each other. Somehow the amino acids are lined up in a specific way by these granules. As a consequence of this lining-up process, your cells do not make cow proteins from the beef you eat. They use the amino acids that come from the cow proteins to make human proteins.

The ribosomes, then, are concerned with the synthesis of proteins from amino acids.

ENERGY FOR THE CELL

So far we have not learned of any of the reactions concerned with the liberation of energy for the cell's activities (including the synthesis of proteins). Some of the reactions we will now consider seem to take place in the watery medium of the cell. Others occur in the mitochondria.

Reactions that occur within cells are of two general classes: one class requires energy; the other class liberates energy. As an example of the first class we can use the synthesis of a protein from amino acids:

amino acids + energy → protein + water

As an example of the second class, we can use the oxidation of glucose:

**glucose + oxygen →
energy + carbon dioxide + water**

In living cells there is a close relationship between the reactions that produce energy and those that require energy. Thus, the energy required for the synthesis of proteins can be obtained from the oxidation of glucose.

glucose + oxygen →
        energy + carbon dioxide + water

amino acids + ⬇ → protein + water

As a consequence of these two reactions, the glucose and free oxygen are used up. The amino acids are bonded to one another to form proteins. Carbon dioxide and water are left over.

The energy that is required for the ribosomes to synthesize proteins from amino acids is chemical energy. Only this form of energy can be used to bring about reactions in the cell. Chemical energy is used up or made available, depending on the reaction, when the atoms of molecules are chemically rearranged. Consider the case of the oxidation of glucose, which we can abbreviate as follows:

$$\underset{\text{glucose}}{C_6H_{12}O_6} + \underset{\text{oxygen}}{6O_2} \rightarrow \underset{\substack{\text{carbon} \\ \text{dioxide}}}{6CO_2} + \underset{\text{water}}{6H_2O} + \text{energy}$$

Note that the number of atoms remains the same: on both the left side and the right side of the arrow there are 6 carbon atoms, 12 hydrogen atoms, and 18 oxygen atoms. The arrangement of the atoms changes, however. In glucose the arrangement had more potential energy than the new arrangement in carbon dioxide and water. There were many C—H bonds in glucose, but there are none in the products. Thus when the atoms in glucose react with oxygen to form carbon dioxide and water, chemical energy becomes available.

When one thinks of the tremendous variety of cell types, it is natural to think that there might be an equal variety of biochemical patterns. This is far from true. Much to the surprise of everyone, including the biochemists, the basic biochemical events in all cells are much alike. The way your liver cells work is much the same as the way your muscle cells work. Many of the reactions that occur in your cells also occur in

those of frogs, mice, earthworms, mushrooms, rabbits, and raspberries. There is a surprising uniformity of cell functions in all living creatures. We can recognize a unity of life that is far more apparent than one would gather from comparing the external appearance of animals and plants.

Two examples of these basic biochemical similarities can be given and explored in some detail. First, in most animal and plant cells the oxidation of glucose is the principal source of energy. Second, nearly all of this energy is stored in adenosine triphosphate (see page 115). When energy is required for almost any cell process, it is obtained from adenosine triphosphate. Biochemists abbreviate the name of this compound to ATP; we shall, too.

Adenosine Triphosphate

ATP is a nucleotide (page 114). It is a key substance in the life of cells, apparently occurring in every living organism and in every cell. Its universal role in energy storage and supply was emphasized only in 1941, by Fritz Lipmann. The Nobel prize was later given to him in recognition.

ATP is not very complicated—as organic molecules go. Figure 6-7 shows the structure of this important molecule. The "triphosphate" part of the name comes from the three groups that contain a phosphorus (P) atom. You will notice them on the left side of the diagram.

It is the phosphate groups that give ATP its special significance. The two terminal chemical bonds that link the O and P atoms are known as "high-energy phosphate bonds." The replacement of one of these bonds by H—O bonds liberates two or three times as much energy as most chemical bonds. The high-energy phosphate bonds are shown as wavy lines in Figure 6-7.

The energy for cell activities is usually made available by the hydrolytic splitting of the ATP molecule at the outermost high-

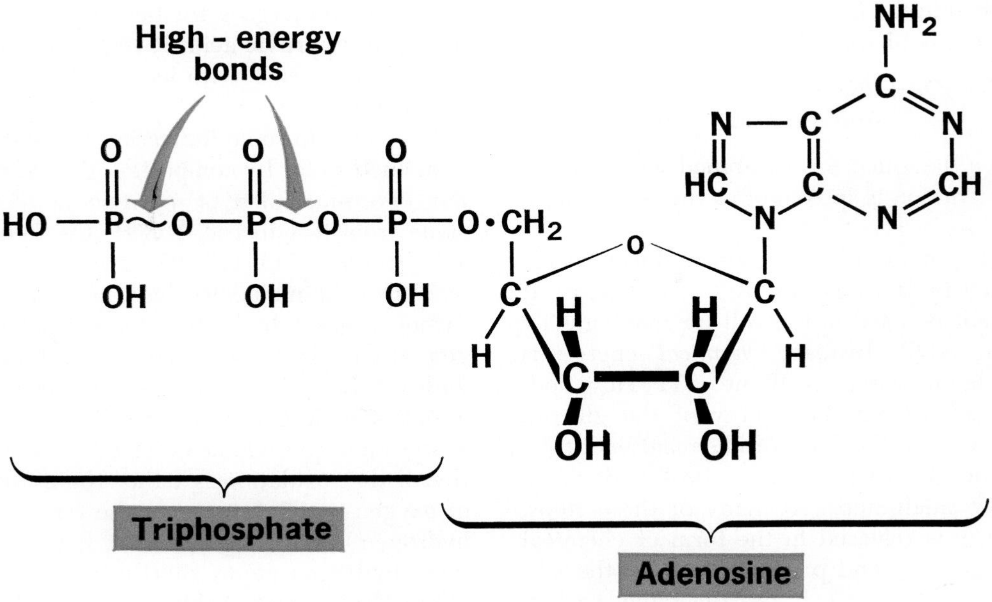

6-7 A diagram of a molecule of adenosine triphosphate (ATP), the substance that supplies most of the energy for the chemical reactions of a cell. Energy derived from the oxidation of foods is stored in ATP until needed for the cell's work. (Does the lower portion of the adenosine remind you of any other compound? Compare with Figure 5-11.)

energy phosphate bond (its position is marked by the left-hand arrow). When one phosphate group is removed, the adenosine *tri*-phosphate becomes adenosine *di*phosphate (ADP).

$$\text{ATP} \rightarrow \text{ADP} + \text{phosphate} + \text{energy}$$

The immediate source of energy for the cell's activities is provided by the change ATP → ADP. However, there is only a limited supply, and an active cell would soon use up all of its ATP. There must be some means of replenishing the supply. How is this done?

A living cell is constantly making ATP. It does so by putting a phosphate group back onto ADP. This sounds easy until we recall one important fact about the energy relations of chemical reactions. If the reaction ATP → ADP *yields* energy, then the reaction ADP → ATP will *require* energy. Furthermore, it will require the same amount

of energy to change ADP to ATP as is liberated by ATP → ADP. We have thus arrived at the reaction:

$$\text{ADP} + \text{phosphate} + \text{energy} \rightarrow \text{ATP}$$

So far we have learned that (1) the chemical energy needed for the cell's activities comes from the breakdown of ATP to ADP; (2) the cell makes new ATP from ADP; (3) this last process requires chemical energy.

Now we must seek the source of the energy needed to make ATP from ADP.

Energy from Glucose

The chemical energy required for the synthesis of ATP by animal cells and, in some cases, by most plant and bacterial cells, comes from glucose (or molecules related to it). The glucose molecule has a large amount of potential chemical energy. As we have said (page 119), glucose can be burned in the laboratory and a large amount of heat is liberated:

$$C_6H_{12}O_6 + 6O_2 \rightarrow$$
$$6H_2O + 6CO_2 + \text{heat energy}$$

Since the glucose is combined with oxygen, the reaction is spoken of as the oxidation of glucose.

The energy liberated when glucose is oxidized by burning is mostly heat energy. It cannot be used in the cell for making ATP from ADP. Instead, *chemical* energy is needed to change ADP into ATP. How does the cell obtain the energy of the glucose molecule in the form of chemical energy?

The glucose molecule is broken down in many small steps. At many of these steps, energy is released in the form of chemical energy. The end products, both in the laboratory and the cell, are the same: carbon dioxide, water, and energy. The oxidation of glucose in the laboratory produces heat energy. The oxidation of glucose in the cell produces some heat plus a large amount of chemical energy.

The reactions in the cell are controlled by enzymes. In this respect they differ from reactions in the laboratory. The glucose molecule is broken down in a series of several dozen steps, and each step is controlled by a specific enzyme. It requires a whole battery of enzymes, therefore, to break down the glucose molecule.

Biochemists have identified many of the steps in the oxidation of glucose in the cell. Louis Pasteur was one of the first to make a major contribution. In the succeeding century, and especially in the years since World War II, our knowledge has accumulated at an increasing pace.

We begin with a molecule having the chemical formula $C_6H_{12}O_6$. Energy is needed to start the reactions. This energy comes from ATP itself, the cell's source of all energy. The atoms within the glucose molecule are rearranged in a series of chemical reactions. Then the molecule is split in half.

Each half undergoes further changes until it becomes pyruvic acid. It requires at least ten reactions, each with its own enzyme, to reach this point.

We can gain some indication of what has happened so far by comparing glucose with the two molecules of pyruvic acid that came from it. Glucose is $C_6H_{12}O_6$. Pyruvic acid is $CH_3 \cdot CO \cdot COOH$. Thus, the two pyruvic acid molecules have a total of 6 carbon atoms, 8 hydrogen atoms, and 6 oxygen atoms. If these totals are compared with the $C_6H_{12}O_6$ of glucose, the net result is that 4 hydrogen atoms are lost between glucose and pyruvic acid. This is oxidation. Recall that oxidation is either the addition of oxygen to a substance or the removal of hydrogen. (We will see what happens to these hydrogen atoms shortly.)

Very little energy is liberated in the reactions from one glucose molecule to two pyruvic acid molecules. In fact, only enough is liberated to make four molecules of ATP from ADP. Even this is not much gain, for the energy of two molecules of ATP was used to make some of the reactions possible. Thus, the net result is an excess of two molecules of ATP.

Most of the energy is still to be released, but the pyruvic acid molecules must be broken down to obtain this chemical energy. In a series of about ten more reactions, each controlled by its specific enzyme, hydrogen atoms and carbon dioxide molecules are split off from pyruvic acid.

The over-all result of the breaking up of the glucose molecule is as follows:

$$\underset{\text{glucose}}{C_6H_{12}O_6} + \underset{\text{water}}{6H_2O} \rightarrow \underset{\substack{\text{carbon} \\ \text{dioxide}}}{6CO_2} + 24H$$

Within the cell, therefore, the glucose is broken down to form carbon dioxide molecules and hydrogen atoms. Most of the carbon dioxide leaves the cell as a waste product, since much more is produced than the cell uses. The hydrogen atoms are of great importance. In fact, they will provide most of the energy needed to convert **ADP to ATP**. Let us see what happens to them.

The Electron Transport Chain

As you will recall, a hydrogen atom is made of a proton and an electron (page 96). The hydrogen atoms that are released when glucose is oxidized in the cell separate into protons and electrons. These particles move along different pathways until they finally reach the oxygen with which they will react to form water as a by-product of respiration.

The protons are familiar to us as hydrogen ions (H^+), a product of the ionization of water molecules. The protons enter the cytoplasm, where they add to the hydrogen ion concentration of the cell, thus lowering the pH.

It is the electrons that provide a most fascinating picture. They combine successively with a series of compounds, known as the **electron transport chain.** A molecule of the first compound in the series picks up two electrons and is reduced. Then this compound passes the two electrons to a molecule of the next compound. The first thus reverts to the oxidized state and the second becomes reduced. Each compound in the electron transport chain is successively reduced and then oxidized as it first gains and then loses the pair of electrons. These reactions liberate the chemical energy that is used to make ADP into ATP.

The electron transport chain may be likened to the diagram in Figure 6-8 or to a bucket brigade of firemen. The buckets would represent the electrons, and the firemen the organic compounds of the chain.

When the two electrons reach the end of the chain, they are transferred to an oxygen atom. Two protons are necessary to complete each water molecule. These are taken up from the pool of protons (hydrogen ions) in the cell—the pool into which the protons went when they were separated from the electrons.

The first of the substances in the electron transport chain is either **diphosphopyridine nucleotide** (dy·fos·foh·PIR·a·deen NEW·klee-o·tide—abbreviated DPN) or a related substance. Each molecule of DPN that is to be involved in the reactions picks up two electrons that come from the hydrogen atoms. It should be mentioned in passing that niacin is part of the DPN molecule. Niacin is one of the vitamins. Can you imagine what would happen within cells if they did not have a sufficient supply of niacin to make DPN? The nucleotide DPN acts as a coenzyme (page 122).

The remaining steps in the electron transport chain are, in general, as follows. The electrons are transferred from reduced DPN to a **riboflavin coenzyme.** This also requires a vitamin as a part of the molecule. Can you guess what vitamin it is? (The name should give it away.)

From the riboflavin coenzyme, the electrons are passed to other molecules known as **cytochromes.** These molecules are very similar to the iron-carrying part of the hemoglobin molecule. The electrons are passed along by two or three cytochromes. Finally they pass from the last cytochrome to combine with oxygen. The hydrogen ions from the cytoplasmic pool also join up, and the product is water. Thus, hydrogen atoms removed from glucose eventually become parts of water molecules. The over-all process, if elaborate and complicated, has a most important result—energy release.

During the transfer of electrons from one substance to another, a large amount of chemical energy is made available. It is this energy that is used to make ADP into ATP. The removal of the hydrogens liberated in the breakdown of the two pyruvic acid molecules obtained from a single glucose molecule provides enough energy to synthesize 36 molecules of ATP.

We learned earlier that the reactions from glucose to pyruvic acid provide enough energy to make 2 molecules of

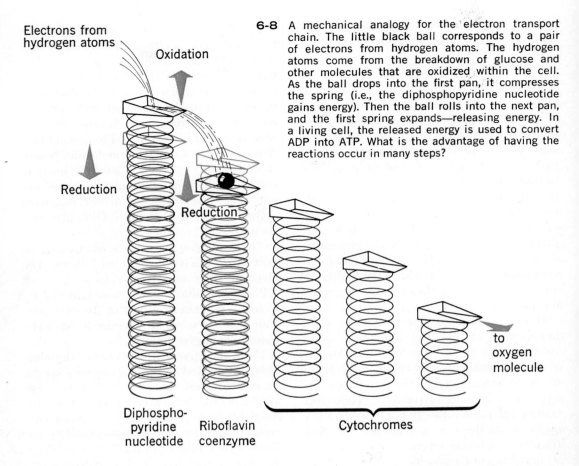

6-8 A mechanical analogy for the electron transport chain. The little black ball corresponds to a pair of electrons from hydrogen atoms. The hydrogen atoms come from the breakdown of glucose and other molecules that are oxidized within the cell. As the ball drops into the first pan, it compresses the spring (i.e., the diphosphopyridine nucleotide gains energy). Then the ball rolls into the next pan, and the first spring expands—releasing energy. In a living cell, the released energy is used to convert ADP into ATP. What is the advantage of having the reactions occur in many steps?

Electrons from hydrogen atoms

Oxidation

Reduction

Reduction

to oxygen molecule

Diphospho-pyridine nucleotide   Riboflavin coenzyme   Cytochromes

ATP. In summary, then, a single molecule of glucose provides enough chemical energy to make 38 molecules of ATP. Many individual reactions are involved. The whole sequence of events can be summarized in one equation:

$$C_6H_{12}O_6 + 6O_2 + 38ADP + 38P \rightarrow \\ 6CO_2 + 6H_2O + 38ATP$$

All of these reactions occur constantly in living cells. In recent years it has been possible to pinpoint the locations in the cell where some of them occur. The best evidence now is that the many reactions that convert glucose into two molecules of pyruvic acid occur in the watery medium of the cytoplasm. But what about the rest of the reactions? As knowledge of the func-

tions of the structures within the cell increased, it became apparent that the mitochondria have a most important role. They were found to contain all the enzymes necessary to oxidize pyruvic acid to carbon dioxide and water (and the entire electron transport chain composed of DPN, the riboflavin system, and the cytochromes as well). Consequently everything that happens to glucose from the pyruvic acid stage to the formation of CO_2 and H_2O occurs in the mitochondria. It is in mitochondria, therefore, that most of the ATP is formed. No wonder that the mitochondria are often called "the powerhouses of the cell." It is their job to use most of the energy of glucose to synthesize the cell's supply of energy-rich ATP.

Energy from Glucose—A Summary

We have learned that the energy for the cell's activities comes from a single source, the energy-rich phosphate bonds of ATP. This energy is made available as chemical energy when ATP changes to ADP.

The problem to solve then became: Where does the cell obtain its energy-rich ATP? We found that the cell re-forms ATP from ADP. But this requires energy—energy that is obtained from glucose. There is a cycle, then, of ATP liberating energy (and phosphate) to become ADP. The energy of glucose is then transferred to ADP (and phosphate) to make ATP again. The cycle of the energy changes in cells, therefore, can be represented as in Figure 6-9.

One might say that living things produce a kind of energy "coinage." Just as it was more convenient to replace primitive barter (direct trading or "swapping") of goods with coins and other forms of money, so it is convenient to have standard "coins" of energy. These standard coins of energy are high-energy phosphate bonds derived from the energy released by foods. They are conveyed from one point to another in the cell and can be spent in a variety of ways. Thus an amount of food that yields, say, 38 packets of energy can be used to supply chemical reactions that might require 16 packets in one place and 22 for use in another place. Like money put in the bank, the chemical packets of energy can be stored for use at some future time.

The story is not finished. We still have one large question remaining. Where does the glucose, with its store of chemical energy, come from? We will postpone considering this for a moment.

Other Sources of Energy

The proteins and fats that enter the body as food are used also for energy. Some of the reactions involved we already know.

For example, fats are first hydrolyzed to fatty acids and glycerol. This is the reverse of the process by which fats are made (Figure 5-14). The fatty acids are then oxidized in the mitochondria in much the same way that pyruvic acid is broken down. The simplest fatty acid is acetic acid; the **acetyl group** $(CH_3 \cdot CO \cdot)$ from this and other fatty acids is also the part of the pyruvic acid molecule that is oxidized.

When proteins are used for energy, they first are converted to amino acids. Later their amino groups are removed. The structure of the amino acid alanine is given in Chapter 5. When alanine has its amino (NH_2) group removed, the middle carbon atom is oxidized. That is, its H atom is replaced by an O atom. The molecule is then pyruvic acid! Pyruvic acid molecules formed in this way are broken down in the mitochondria.

Thus glucose, fatty acids, and amino acids all can be used to liberate energy. This energy is used to make ATP from ADP.

The Ultimate Source of Energy

Now let us return to the question, where does the energy of glucose itself come from? A partial answer will be given now; a more complete answer will be given later when we study green plants (Chapter 15).

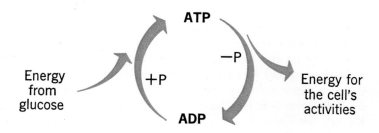

6-9
A cycle of energy relations within cells. ATP is the "currency" for energy exchange.

Energy from glucose +P ATP −P Energy for the cell's activities ADP

So far, we have discussed cells that obtain useful energy by the oxidation of glucose. Many cells, however, are able to use an even more abundant source of energy, the radiant energy of the sun. The processes that accomplish this most basic of all biological feats are collectively called **photosynthesis**. Photosynthesis is dependent on the presence of the green compound chlorophyll.

It has long been known that green plants use the energy of sunlight to carry out a process that appears to be the reverse of glucose oxidation, namely:

$$6CO_2 + 6H_2O + \text{light energy} \xrightarrow{\text{chlorophyll}} C_6H_{12}O_6 + 6O_2$$

Here again we have an equation that time and research proved inadequate to represent the process. It took biochemists a long time to work out the details. First it was found that green plants, in sunlight, take in carbon dioxide and give off oxygen. For a long time it was thought that heat energy rather than light energy was used in this process. Many experiments were necessary to demonstrate that light itself was the important energy source. Approximately one hundred years ago, however, the equation shown above could be stated with some confidence.

In Chapter 15 we will explore photosynthesis in some detail. At the moment all we need to know is that the ultimate source of energy for making glucose is the sun. (There are a few minor sources that we are ignoring.) Green plants are able to convert the light energy into chemical energy, which the plants then use to synthesize glucose and other organic compounds.

This adds up to a very simple but fascinating conclusion: nearly all life depends ultimately on the light of the sun. As you walked to school this morning, the energy that you expended may have come from the sunlight that fell on the wheat fields of Kansas last summer.

THE CELL NUCLEUS

Nearly all the events we have been describing occur in the cytoplasm of the cell. You may have wondered if the nucleus has any function at all. It does, and a most important function it is.

The nucleus controls the life and activities of the cell. (The evidence for this will come later, largely in the chapters devoted to genetics.) The key structures in this control are the chromosomes, which are composed largely of **deoxyribonucleoprotein** (dee·oks·i·ry·boh·new·klee·oh·pro·teen). This is a combination of protein and deoxyribonucleic acid (DNA).

There is ample reason to believe that DNA is one of the most vital substances in our cells. It seems to be the material that is important in inheritance. We are human beings because we have DNA of the human type. A rabbit is a rabbit because it has rabbit-type DNA.

Somehow the DNA controls the entire range of activities of the cell. We are not quite sure how this is accomplished. There is sufficient evidence, very recently obtained, to make us believe that the DNA controls the synthesis of specific types of RNA. These various types of RNA then leave the nucleus and enter the cytoplasm, where they associate with the ribosomes and there control the synthesis of all the specific types of proteins, including the enzymes. And, of course, it is the enzymes that control the types of chemical reactions that can go on in cells.

The nucleolus is largely ribonucleoprotein. Perhaps it is the storage place for some of the RNA before the RNA leaves the nucleus to enter the cytoplasm.

CONCLUDING REMARKS

Figure 6-10 is a schematic diagram of an animal cell. In most respects, it could also be considered a plant cell without the wall.

It can serve as the basis for our summary of cell structures and functions.

The cell membrane is more than a mere covering of the cell. It is a living membrane that regulates the passage of materials into and out of the cell. Some substances pass across by diffusion; others are taken in by pinocytosis. The amino acids, simple sugars, fatty acids, glycerol, vitamins, minerals, and oxygen that pass into the cell are used to synthesize living material.

The cell membrane may have pores that open into the endoplasmic reticulum. We are not too sure of the function of the endoplasmic reticulum. Many biologists believe it is a system of canals that transports materials throughout the cell. We do know that the ribosomes, which are attached to the endoplasmic reticulum, are the chief, if not exclusive, sites at which proteins are made in the cytoplasm of the cell.

Several mitochondria are shown in the

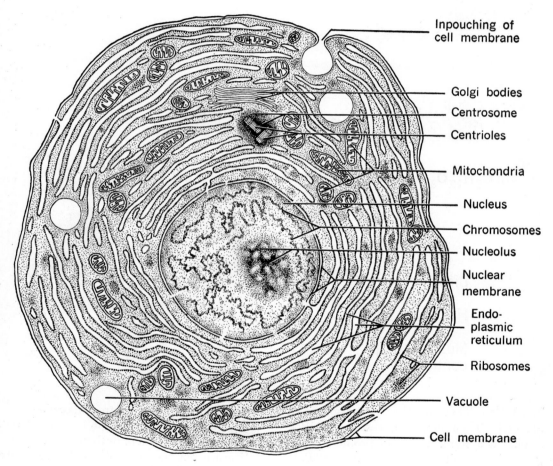

Inpouching of cell membrane

Golgi bodies

Centrosome

Centrioles

Mitochondria

Nucleus

Chromosomes

Nucleolus

Nuclear membrane

Endoplasmic reticulum

Ribosomes

Vacuole

Cell membrane

6-10 A generalized cell. The structures shown are found in most cells that are more complex than bacteria. Most of the structures are greatly enlarged in relation to the size of the cell. For example, the centrioles and mitochondria, if drawn to size, would be shown as dots, and the ribosomes and endoplasmic reticulum would be too small to show. (For the most part, the interpretation of the various structures in the diagram is based on electron microscope photographs.)

6-11 A SUMMARY OF ENERGY RELATIONSHIPS IN LIFE

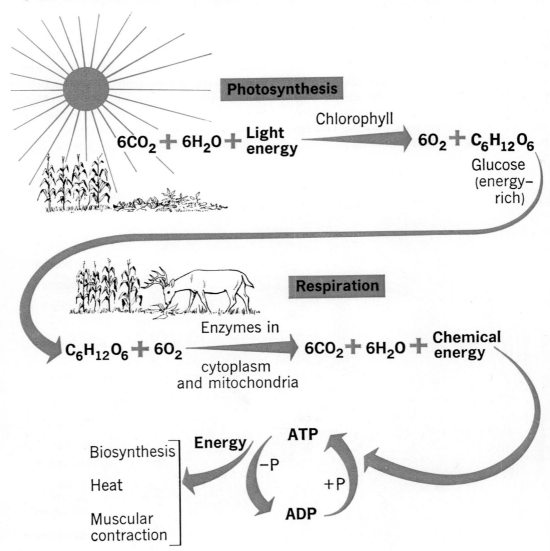

Photosynthesis

$$6CO_2 + 6H_2O + \text{Light energy} \xrightarrow{\text{Chlorophyll}} 6O_2 + C_6H_{12}O_6$$

Glucose (energy–rich)

Respiration

$$C_6H_{12}O_6 + 6O_2 \xrightarrow[\text{cytoplasm and mitochondria}]{\text{Enzymes in}} 6CO_2 + 6H_2O + \text{Chemical energy}$$

Biosynthesis
Heat
Muscular contraction

Energy
−P
ATP
+P
ADP

illustration. They are the "powerhouses of the cell." Their enzymes, and their DPN, riboflavin system, and cytochromes, transfer the energy of food molecules to ATP.

The nucleus is the sphere near the center of the cell. It contains the chromosomes, whose DNA controls all the cell's activities. The DNA controls the formation of RNA, some of which is found in the nucleolus.

The centriole and centrosomes are concerned with the reproduction of cells. More will be said about them in the next chapter.

We are not too sure of the function of the Golgi bodies. The best evidence is that they are concerned with the formation of granules. One of the organs of digestion, the pancreas, secretes granules which contain enzymes that aid digestion. The Golgi bodies seem to have a role in the formation of these granules.

Living cells require energy for their activities. The *ultimate* source of this energy is sunlight. The energy is captured in the C–H bonds of glucose and other organic compounds. Within a cell, these organic compounds are oxidized in small steps with the liberation of large amounts of energy. The energy is used to make ATP from ADP. The ATP is then the *immediate* source of energy in the cell. It is present everywhere in the cell.

The chemical reactions within cells occur rapidly though gently, because they are controlled by enzymes. The over-all relations of the energy cycle in the living world are shown in Figure 6-11.

GUIDE QUESTIONS AND PROBLEMS

1. What are the main ways in which food is used by cells?
2. How does the chemical combination of hydrogen and oxygen in a cell differ from the combination of the same elements in the laboratory?
3. What is an enzyme? What is the role of enzymes in living cells? What are coenzymes? What is their role?
4. How is a model of an enzyme used to explain the enzyme's action?
5. What are the characteristics of enzymes?
6. What does the electron microscope reveal about the structure of the cell wall? the cell membrane?
7. How are the smaller structures of the cell isolated for detailed study?
8. What is the role of the cell membrane in the life of the cell?
9. Which has more potential energy—amino acids or the proteins into which they can be synthesized?
10. How does ATP play so important a role in energy release and energy storage in living cells?
11. What part do the mitochondria play in the release of energy in a cell?
12. What is the relation of glucose to the energy cycle in cells?
13. How do enzymes function in the cell in providing energy for cell activities?
14. How do proteins and fats enter the energy stream in living cells?

SUGGESTIONS FOR ADDITIONAL READING

Books

Butler, John A. V., *Inside the Living Cell*. New York, Basic Books, 1959.
> An excellent summary of recent experimental studies of cell structure, chemistry, and function.

Harrison, K., *A Guidebook to Biochemistry*. New York, Cambridge University Press, 1959.
> Fine introductory biochemistry.

Mercer, E. H., *Cells: Their Structure and Function*. New York, Doubleday, 1962.
> Well-written summary of recent work on the structure of cells, and some current theories of cell function.

Swanson, Carl P., *The Cell*. Englewood Cliffs (N. J.), Prentice-Hall, 1960.
> A good account of cell structure, cell theory, and the tools and techniques of cell study.

Magazines and Journals

Brachet, J., "The Living Cell." *Scientific American*, Vol. 205 (September 1961), pp. 50–61.

Lehninger, A., "Energy Transformation in the Cell." *Scientific American*, Vol. 202 (May 1960), pp. 102–11.

——— "How Cells Transform Energy." *Scientific American*, Vol. 205 (September 1961), pp. 62–73.

Siekevitz, P., "Powerhouse of the Cell." *Scientific American*, Vol. 197 (July 1957), pp. 131–34.

Stumpf, P. K., "ATP." *Scientific American*, Vol. 188 (April 1953), pp. 85–86.

7

THE REPRODUCTION

OF CELLS

During the early years of the nineteenth century, many biologists saw dividing cells. One of the best places to observe them was in developing embryos. In most organisms embryos begin life as a single cell, the **fertilized egg.** Almost upon being formed by the union of an **egg cell** from the female parent and a **sperm cell** from the male, the fertilized egg divides—the first of many divisions. Frequently the divisions are regular —that is, the single cell divides into two, the two into four, the four into eight, and so on.

Cell reproduction must have seemed rather simple: a cell divides into two parts and that is all there is to it. It took biologists many decades to look beyond the apparent simplicity and realize that enormous problems are involved.

GENETIC CONTINUITY

The main problem is this: how can a single cell, the fertilized egg, have the ability to form all the complicated structures of the adult? Food and oxygen are required, but these and other things in the environment do not direct the outcome. A fertilized egg of a frog and one of a toad can be placed in the same dish, and the embryos can be given the same food. In every case one becomes a frog and the other a toad. There is no environment in which a fertilized frog egg will develop into a toad, or in which a fertilized toad egg will develop into a frog.

Somehow this knowledge, "How to become a frog," must be carried in the fertilized egg. Furthermore, this knowledge is transmitted from generation to generation. We speak of this as **genetic** (je·NET·ik) **continuity**—the production, generation after generation, of offspring that are similar (though not identical) to their parents.

The frog egg must have within it all the information required to produce a frog. Furthermore, there must be some mechanism to insure that some or all descendants of the fertilized egg also contain this information.

Think of it in this way. A single cell, the fertilized egg, develops into a frog. This frog becomes an adult. If it is a female, it produces egg cells. If it is a male, it produces another type of cell, sperm cells. When the mature frog mates with another frog, **fertilization** again occurs—that is, an egg cell and a sperm cell fuse to form a single cell, the fertilized egg. This fertilized egg will also develop into a frog. *What insures that it will?*

A basic problem of cell division, then, is this: What is the mechanism insuring genetic continuity? If a cell divides into two, would it not be more reasonable to assume that each daughter cell has only part, possibly half, of the genetic information of the original cell? Yet we know from observations of dividing cells that this cannot be the case. Somehow, each of the two daughter cells receives a complete set of the parent cell's genetic information.

There must be some means of insuring that all structures essential for genetic continuity are provided for each daughter cell when the cell divides. Perhaps we could obtain some clues as to what these structures might be by studying dividing cells.

MITOSIS

To a degree that is unusual in science, a single individual was responsible for describing the internal events of cell division. Walther Flemming, a German biologist, was the person. He published his discoveries in the 1880's. Of course, many details have been added in the last eighty years.

Flemming's work was outstanding for a variety of reasons. First of all, he was able to use the proper tools and methods. The compound microscopes of his day were reaching a high degree of perfection. Technology was supporting science, as it almost invariably does. The methods for fixing and staining cells were good and becoming better. A generation earlier it would not have been possible for anyone to do the work that Flemming did. He lived at the time when he, or someone else, could use recently improved tools and newly devised techniques to make meaningful observations about the internal events during cell division.

But Flemming did far more than be lucky enough to live at the right time! Cell division occurs throughout the world of living organisms, yet its secrets are not revealed equally in all cells. Flemming examined many kinds of animal and plant cells and selected those that showed the internal details of dividing cells most clearly. He was interested in events in *living* cells, yet he knew that it is easier to see certain structures in fixed and stained cells than in living cells. Herein lay a danger. When one sees a structure in a dead cell, can he be sure that the structure is part of the living process? Possibly it never existed in the living cell and is only an abnormality that arose during the fixing and staining process.

You can understand the danger from an example. When a hen's egg is boiled, there are changes much like those occurring in fixation. You could study the boiled egg and reach some conclusions regarding its structure. To what extent would these conclusions be true of the *living* egg?

Flemming carefully studied fixed and stained cells as well as living cells. He made it a rule never to believe what he saw in fixed and stained cells unless he could observe the same events in living cells. This made his studies much more difficult. But Flemming realized that some of the structures that stains help to bring out clearly in preserved cells might not be natural. That is, they could be produced by the chemicals used in fixing and staining.

Many other biologists, before and after Flemming, have made the mistake of assuming that what they see in preserved cells is a reliable picture of living cells. But Flemming was careful to check what he saw in preserved cells with what can be seen in living cells (Figure 7-1). As a result, his observations have stood the test of time. Other biologists have confirmed what he observed.

Flemming observed that in a dividing cell the nucleus passes through an orderly series of changes, which he called **mitosis** (my·TOH·sis). In all the cells he studied, both animal and plant, the events were approximately the same. There seemed in this, as in other features of organisms, a unity of life. Flemming's observations, plus the details added by later workers, provided us with a reasonable picture of *what* happens in cell division. Yet our knowledge of *how* it happens is most inadequate. Let us turn to a description of the process for information on which to base our questions.

A Study of a Cell Undergoing Mitosis

First, we will begin with an animal cell before it starts dividing. There is a central nucleus with one or more prominent nucle-

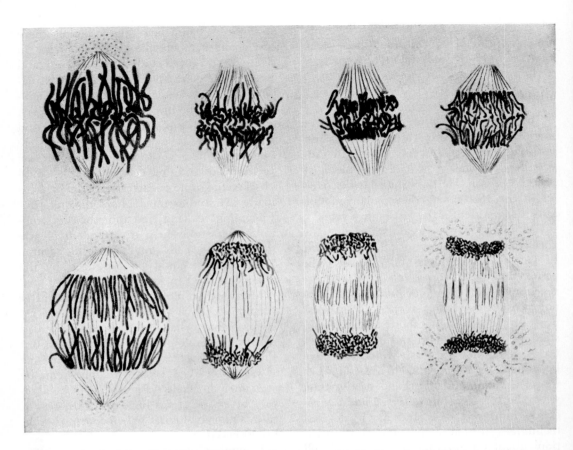

7-1 More than eighty years ago, the events of mitosis and cell division were observed and recorded by Walther Flemming. His drawings of mitosis in *stained* cells of a lily are reproduced above; similar events in *living* cells from the skin of a larval salamander appear in the drawings on the facing page. The sequence of events on both pages is from left to right, beginning at the upper left and ending at the lower right. The drawing at the right end of the second line in the salamander series is placed

oli. Generally, no chromosomes are visible. The cytoplasm contains the endoplasmic reticulum, mitochondria, Golgi bodies, and various granules. There is one centriole, or in some cells a cluster of centrioles. Sometimes the centrioles are contained in a centrosome.

The first indication that a cell is about to divide is generally given by the centriole and centrosome (Figure 7-2). The centriole divides into two, forming two daughter centrioles. The daughter centrioles then migrate, each with its surrounding centro-

some, to opposite sides of the nucleus. The nucleolus, a prominent feature of nondividing cells, disappears at this time.

We can follow this and succeeding events in photographs of cells of a whitefish embryo (Figure 7-3). These cells are prepared for examination in such a way that only the nucleus and structures relating directly to cell division are seen clearly. You will not see the mitochondria and Golgi bodies, because they have not been stained. Nor is the endoplasmic reticulum visible, because it is too small. The first photo-

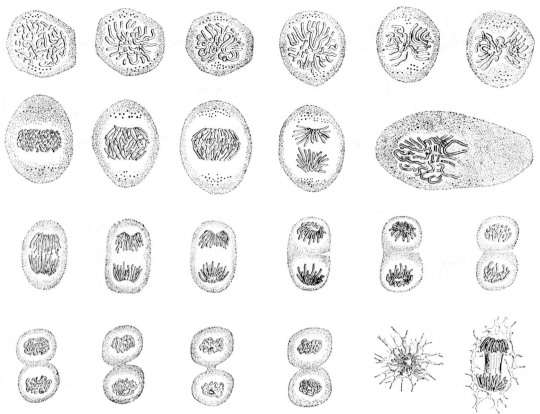

From Walther Flemming, *Zellsubstanz, Kern und Zelltheilung*, Leipzig, 1882

out of sequence, but shows one of Flemming's most important discoveries: each of the cell's chromosomes at this time appeared "double." *What was the significance of this observation?* The last two drawings at the lower right in the salamander series are Flemming's "postscript," in which he showed how differently things appear when viewed from two different angles—first, from one *end* of the spindle (next to last drawing), then from one *side* of the spindle (last drawing).

graph of Figure 7-3 shows a cell at the beginning of mitosis. The nucleus appears as a sphere containing darkly stained threads. The two darker spheres, to the right and left of the nucleus, are the centrosomes. (Centrioles are difficult to see in the whitefish. They do not show in the photographs.)

The most striking events in mitosis concern the chromosomes. They are nearly always invisible in nondividing cells. As mitosis gets under way, however, they become increasingly easy to see. They are the rather indistinct threads in the first photograph.

In the second photograph the chromosomes appear as tiny, dark rods (dark because they have been stained). The membrane surrounding the nucleus has disappeared. It will not re-form until the end of mitosis. The centrosomes are prominent. A series of fibers extends from one centrosome to the other. These form a structure known as the **spindle.** The spindle has roughly the shape of a football, and the chromosomes are situated *within* the spindle. One specialized part of each chromosome, known as the **centromere** (SEN·tro-

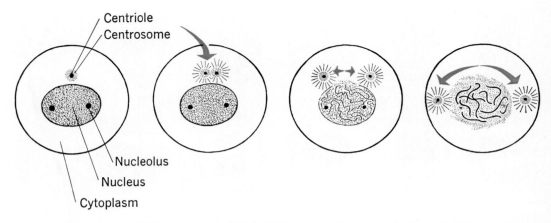

Centriole
Centrosome

Nucleolus
Nucleus
Cytoplasm

7-2 The division of the centriole and centrosome. Before mitosis begins, the centriole appears as a small granule within the centrosome. Actually, most animal cells have a double centriole, or two centrioles, at this time (see Figure 6-10), but so small that the two can be seen as separate structures only with the electron microscope. Slowly the two centrioles move to opposite sides of the nucleus. After they have separated, each characteristically doubles again. (What events begin to occur in the nucleus during the migration of the centrioles to opposite sides of the cell?)

meer), seems to be attached to the spindle. Centromeres cannot be seen in these photographs.

In the third photograph the chromosomes appear to be separating into two groups. One group is moving along the spindle toward one centrosome; the other group is moving toward the other centrosome.

A close examination of the part of the cell immediately surrounding each centrosome will reveal fibers. These are easiest to see surrounding the centrosome on the right in the third photograph. They appear to extend from the centrosome to the edges of the cell. This group of fibers surrounding each centrosome is the **aster**. It actually appears earlier than the stage of mitosis shown in photograph 3—look carefully at photographs 2 and 1.

In photographs 4 and 5, the two groups of chromosomes have moved progressively farther apart, and in the last photograph we approach the end of mitosis. The original cell has divided into two. The cell membrane has grown inward to cut across the spindle, thus pinching the cell in two. Each

daughter cell has a set of chromosomes. The asters and spindle have become indistinct.

At a time somewhat later than represented by photograph 6, a nuclear membrane forms around the chromosomes in each new cell. The chromosomes become progressively less distinct, and the nucleus in each new cell assumes the characteristic appearance found in a nondividing cell. Nucleoli reform within the two daughter nuclei. The asters and spindle disappear. The centrosomes decrease in size, and one remains, with its centriole, in each daughter cell.

In some cells the entire process of mitosis (nuclear division) and cell division is completed in about 15 minutes; in others it may require hours. Mitosis is not occurring all the time in all cells. It is frequent when the organism, or some part of it, is growing. When the individual is fully formed, mitosis is less frequent. In some tissues it may cease altogether. For example, there are no mitoses in your brain cells after you are born. Mitosis even occurs sometimes in cells that are *not* dividing; the result is

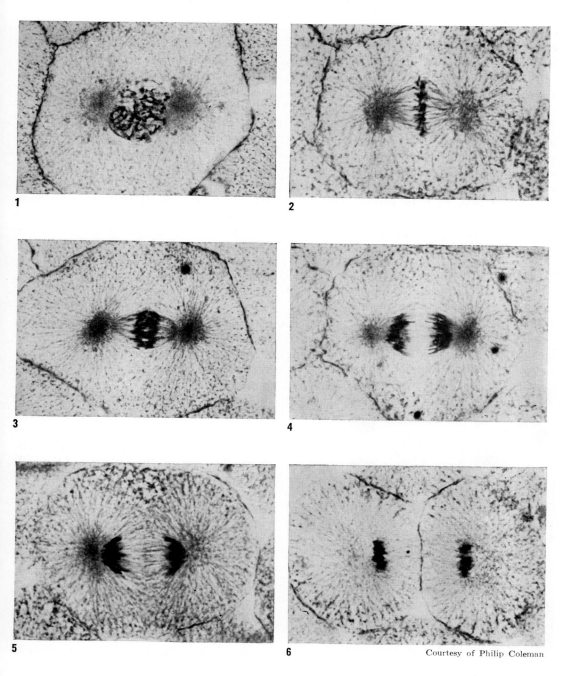

7-3 Mitosis in cells of a whitefish embryo. These six photographs, taken through a compound microscope, show stages of mitosis and cell division in sequence from upper left to lower right. The axis of the spindle is horizontal in each photograph. How do the events recorded here compare with Flemming's nineteenth-century drawings of mitosis in skin cells of a larval salamander (Figure 7-1)?

Courtesy of Philip Coleman

cells that have more than one nucleus (a common feature of your own skeletal muscle cells, for example).

By now you will have examined many kinds of cells in the laboratory. Do you recall seeing any in mitosis? The chances are that you do not. From most parts of your own body, you could examine thousands of cells and not find one dividing. There are several places where mitosis would be common—your skin and the lining of your intestine are two. In both places cells are constantly being worn away and replaced by the division of the remaining cells.

Mitosis in the cells of complex plants (such as the onion root tip in Figure 7-4)

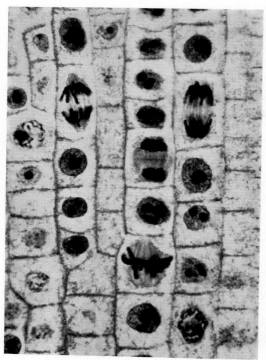

General Biological Supply House, Inc., Chicago

7-4 Mitosis in cells of the growing tip of an onion root. At the time the cells were fixed and stained, some were in the process of dividing, others not. Note the prominent nucleoli in the nuclei of nondividing cells. Why do some of the cells appear to be without nuclei?

is much the same as in animal cells. The chief points of difference are these: there are no centrioles or asters in the plant cells. Furthermore, the cell does not pinch in two. Instead, a new cell wall forms across the middle of the spindle.

The formation of the cell wall is a complex process. Tiny swellings appear on the spindle fibers at the middle of the spindle. These swellings fuse to form a partition that cuts across the cell, dividing the original cell into two daughter cells. This partition is not the new cell wall but a cementing substance that will hold the daughter cells together. The cytoplasm of each daughter cell lays down a new cell wall (of several layers) adjacent to the central partition. The cell walls consist largely of cellulose (Figure 6-2, page 123). In the walls of some plant cells there is also lignin, the substance that gives hardness to wood.

So much for the gross aspects of mitosis. We have yet to show its importance in genetic continuity.

Chromosome Reproduction

In Chapters 5 and 6 you were introduced to DNA. DNA is believed to be the substance that controls the activities of the cell. It is also believed to be the basic substance of inheritance—of genetic continuity. (The reasons for these beliefs will be developed in later chapters on genetics.)

DNA can have these important properties only if it passes intact from parent cell to daughter cell. If a fertilized egg develops into a frog, it is because it has frog DNA.

The fundamental importance of mitosis is this: It is a mechanism insuring that all daughter cells receive DNA identical or nearly identical to that of the parent cell. DNA is in the chromosomes, and in mitosis each daughter cell receives a set of chromosomes identical or nearly identical to those of the parent cell.

These important facts were not obvious from the photographs (Figures 7-3 and

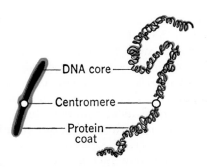

—DNA core—

—Centromere—

—Protein—
    coat

a During mitotic division, each chromosome is condensed in length and easily visible under the microscope.

b As the chromosome uncoils in the new daughter cell, it disappears from view. Replication begins at this stage.

c When next the chromosome becomes visible, it is "twins." Replication has been completed, except for the centromere.

d At mitosis, the chromosomes become attached to the spindle by the centromere. Finally the centromere divides, and....

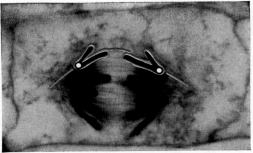

.....the two chromosomes separate.

Photo: General Biological Supply House, Inc., Chicago

7-5 One chromosome becomes two. The steps shown here begin with a chromosome in a newly formed cell (when division of the parent cell is almost over) and continue through the beginning stages of the next cell division.

7-4) and the description of mitosis and cell division. Some additional information must be considered.

Generally speaking, the nuclei of all cells in the body of an organism contain the same number of chromosomes. (Important exceptions are egg cells and sperm cells.) In man the typical number is 46. The problem of mitosis, then, is to insure that every human cell contains these 46 chromosomes. Consequently, if Figure 7-3 were of a human cell instead of cells from a developing whitefish embryo, each daughter cell in photograph 6 would contain 46 chromosomes. Let us follow the history of one of

these daughter cells, pretending that it is a human cell with 46 chromosomes.

Important events occur in the interval between the end of one cell division and the beginning of the next. *Each of the 46 chromosomes duplicates (or replicates).* The discovery that this occurs was one of Flemming's greatest achievements. Raw materials move from the cytoplasm into the nucleus, where they are used to form more DNA and protein. The DNA and protein are incorporated into new chromosome material, and each of the original chromosomes becomes a "double" chromosome, not yet separated completely (Figure 7-5).

At the beginning of the next cell division, close examination would reveal 46 "double" chromosomes, of which one is shown in Figure 7-5. Figure 7-6, which is an illustration of a human cell, shows this well. You can count 46 chromosomes and, in most cases, see that each is double. (This illustration will be confusing until you realize that the cell was prepared in a special way. It was flattened and broken to spread out the chromosomes. Stains affecting only the chromosomes were used. Other parts of the cell do not show.)

Later in division, each of the 46 "double" chromosomes separates into two daughter chromosomes. Thus two groups of chromosomes are formed, each with 46 single chromosomes. Each group has one chromosome of each kind that was present in the parent nucleus. One group of 46 chromosomes moves toward one centrosome. The other group of 46 moves toward the other

centrosome (as in photograph 4 of Figure 7-3). Then the cell divides into two daughter cells, each with 46 chromosomes.

Before each successive cell division, the process of mitosis is repeated. As a consequence, every cell of the organism normally will contain equivalent chromosomes.

Mitosis, then, is a mechanism insuring genetic continuity. The chromosomes replicate, and each daughter cell receives one of each kind of chromosome. Speaking in biochemical terms, the daughter cells will have DNA identical or nearly so to that of the parent cells.

The Mitotic Apparatus

The centrioles are so small, and the centrosomes usually so indistinct, that it is difficult to see them in nondividing cells. During mitosis they become easier to see, and other structures—the spindle and asters—make their appearance. The centrosomes together with their centrioles, the spindle, and the asters, are known as the **mitotic** (my·TOT·ik) **apparatus.**

Discouragingly little is known of the way the mitotic apparatus functions. Even its structure is not well understood. The spindle contains a number of fibers that extend from one end of the spindle to the other. These are easy to see in fixed and stained cells (see Figure 7-3). For many years it was not possible to see them in living cells —but now we know definitely that they exist in living cells. The spindle is composed largely of a single kind of protein. There are also traces of RNA in it.

The asters also seem to be composed of a protein through which fibers extend (Figure 7-3).

The entire mitotic apparatus forms an organized structure. Methods have recently been developed for isolating it from dividing cells. The methods consist of dissolving away the surrounding cytoplasm, leaving only the mitotic apparatus (Figure 7-7).

To biologists using the compound micro-

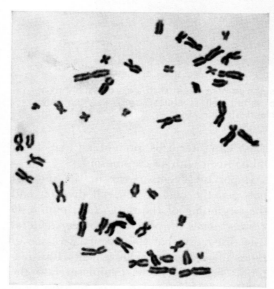

T. T. Puck

7-6 The chromosomes of man. How many are shown? Although this is the count normally found in a dividing cell, exceptions sometimes occur. Several types of abnormality in chromosome number are discussed in Chapter 31.

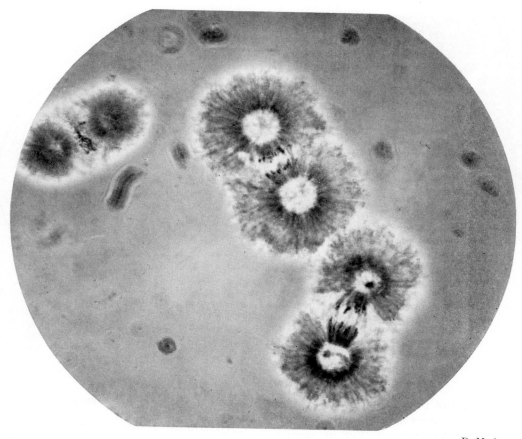

D. Mazia

7-7 Isolated mitotic apparatus of sea urchin eggs. At the center and the lower right of the photograph, the white spheres are centrosomes. The darker areas surrounding the centrosomes are the asters. Between each pair of centrosomes is a spindle, with chromosomes upon it (the chromosomes appear black in the photograph).

scope, the centriole appears as a tiny granule. The electron microscope has revealed considerable complexity. The centriole is a bundle of short rods surrounded by a belt of tiny spheres (Figure 7-8). What is the relation of this highly organized structure to the specific function of the centriole? No one yet knows.

MEIOSIS

Much has been made of the fact that although cells divide, the number of chromosomes per cell remains constant. The cells

of man have 46 chromosomes. Before a cell divides, each chromosome replicates, forming a total of 92. A mitotic division occurs, and each daughter cell receives 46 chromosomes—not just *any* 46, but the same assortment of 46 chromosomes that the parent cell had before its chromosomes replicated. The hereditary material has remained constant in each cell.

The chances are you have begun to question whether the number of chromosomes *always* remains the same when cells divide. Biologists also began to wonder about this, once Flemming and others had established

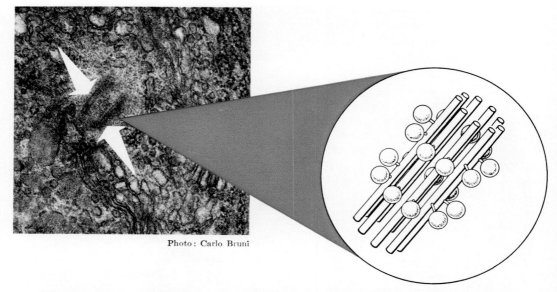

Photo: Carlo Bruni

7-8 From many photographs taken with the electron microscope, biologists have put together the structure of a centriole, as shown at the right. The photograph that appears here shows only a few of the rodlike structures from opposite sides of the centriole; the remainder of the centriole was sliced away in making a section thin enough to be viewed with the electron microscope. (Sometimes a microscopic section of a centriole shows a circle of nine tiny O's. Can you explain why?)

the basic fact of the constancy of the number of chromosomes in mitotic division.

This was the problem: Let us assume that when cells divide, the daughter cells *always* have the same number of chromosomes as the parent cell. In the case of man, the number will be 46. This will mean, therefore, that egg cells and sperm cells must also have 46 chromosomes. But if this were so, then the union of the egg nucleus and the sperm nucleus, which takes place at fertilization, would produce a total of 92. The fertilized egg would then undergo mitosis and all of the cells in the new individual would have 92 chromosomes! The same process would be repeated each generation. The grandchildren would have 184 chromosomes per cell, the great grandchildren 368. Observation of cells from successive generations of animals and plants shows that this is not the case. The chromosome number remains the same.

Let us review our dilemma:

HYPOTHESIS. If the number of chromosomes remains constant from cell division to cell division . . .

DEDUCTION. . . . then we would expect the individuals of the next generation to have twice the number of chromosomes their parents had.

This deduction, like all deductions, is a logical consequence of the hypothesis.

TEST OF DEDUCTION. By careful examination of a variety of plants and animals, it is found that successive generations of the same species have identical numbers of chromosomes.

CONCLUSION. We have checked the deduction and found it to be false. Therefore, the hypothesis cannot be correct as stated.

In every careful study of mitosis and cell division in animals and plants, the chromosome number in successive cell generations *does* remain constant. Obviously we have overlooked some important factors.

Let us recall the details of the test: what was actually done? Developing embryos and growing roots of plants were fixed and stained, and the cells were studied. It was found that the chromosome number remained the same. Actually we studied only *some* cells, and these during a *limited time period* of the individual's life. On the basis of these data we assumed that in all parts of the body and at all periods of life the number of chromosomes remains constant. In other words we have looked at a *few* cell divisions and assumed that *all* cell divisions are the same. Is this justifiable?

Arguments similar to these were advanced during the 1880's when biologists were first learning about mitosis and cell division. August Weismann (1834–1914) was one of these biologists. Because his eyesight was poor, it was difficult for him to use a microscope to study cells. But there were other things that he could do. Science is not advanced only by the collection of data. Someone must interpret the data. Weismann's poor eyesight forced him to spend more time thinking than looking.

Weismann considered the apparent facts:

1. In successive generations, individuals of the same species have the same number of chromosomes.
2. In successive cell divisions, the number of chromosomes remains constant.

Weismann realized, just as we have come to do, that both statements 1 and 2 cannot *always* be true. There was one way out: perhaps not *all* cell divisions are the same.

Weismann then suggested this hypothesis: there must be a kind of cell division in which the chromosome number is halved.

Let us see what the hypothesis means in terms of the cells of man. The normal number of chromosomes, 46, is doubled to give 92. The mitotic division then allots 46 chromosomes to each daughter nucleus in the daughter cells. But assume that there is one situation in which the chromosome number is not doubled before cell division. If so, 23 would be given to each daughter cell.

If this "other" type of division would occur during the formation of eggs and sperms, then all the facts could be explained. The egg would have 23 chromosomes. The sperm would also have 23 chromosomes. When egg and sperm combined the sum would be 46 chromosomes again. The fertilized egg would then divide by the usual sort of mitosis and every cell so formed would have 46 chromosomes.

Weismann's prediction was soon verified (Figure 7-9). Biologists carefully studied the cells that developed into eggs and into sperms. They found that just before the mature egg and sperm are formed, the chromosome number is halved. This process is called **meiosis** (my·OH·sis). As a result of meiosis, the sperm and the egg in human beings each have 23 chromosomes.

Meiosis occurs in all animals and plants that reproduce sexually. In animals it occurs before eggs and sperms are formed. In plants it characteristically occurs when spores (page 240) are formed.

Meiosis is of fundamental importance for an understanding of genetics and evolution, so we shall return to it in more detail in later chapters. For the present, however, we can work with these facts: eggs and sperms nearly always have half the number of chromosomes found in other cells. We speak of this number as the **monoploid** (MON·o·ploid) **number** (or use the abbreviation *n*). When the egg and sperm, each with a monoploid number of chromosomes, unite, a fertilized egg with the **diploid** (DIP·loid) **number** of chromosomes (abbreviated *2n*) is the result. These relations are shown in Figure 7-9, where meiosis and mitosis are compared.

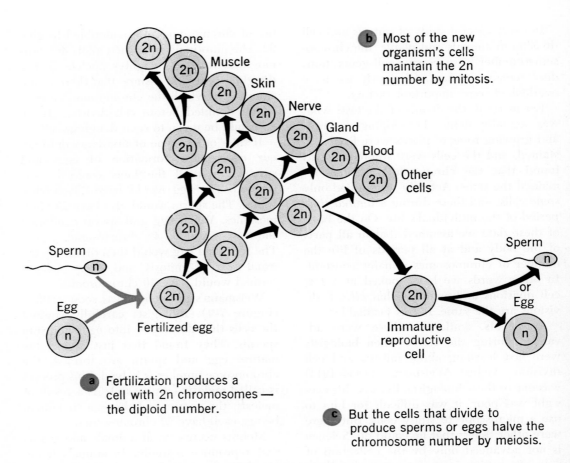

a Fertilization produces a cell with 2n chromosomes — the diploid number.

b Most of the new organism's cells maintain the 2n number by mitosis.

c But the cells that divide to produce sperms or eggs halve the chromosome number by meiosis.

7-9 The relationship between mitosis and meiosis in the life of an individual. How many kinds of cells are subject to mitosis? to meiosis? Can you explain why evidence that meiosis takes place was not observed by early investigators of cell division?

CONCLUDING REMARKS

In Chapters 3 through 6 we learned something of the tremendous complexity of cells. Their molecules are the largest and most complex associations of atoms known. Furthermore, cells undergo ceaseless activity. Molecules are being built up and broken down in fractions of a second. Biologists today have only a superficial understanding of the structure and function of a living cell. They understand enough, however, to be tremendously impressed by the mechanism that divides cells. Somehow the living, organized, intricate cell divides itself —and does so without becoming destroyed. More than that, in nearly every case the daughter cells have all the structure and potentialities of the parent cells.

The exact, or almost exact, replication of cells is made possible by a type of internal specialization. The life of a cell is not controlled equally by all of its parts. Some parts seem to be more important than others.

The chromosomes, and especially their organized DNA molecules, are the most important controlling elements. The structure and behavior of a cell is controlled by its specific DNA. The DNA contains the instructions necessary for the cell to carry on its vital activities.

In mitotic cell divisions, each chromosome makes a replica of itself. Then each double chromosome is divided—one chromosome going to each daughter cell. The replication of the chromosome involves a replication of its DNA. The rest of the cell is more or less equally divided. Each daughter cell, then, contains half of the original cell material but receives a *full* quota of the instructions in the DNA. With these instructions the daughter cell can grow and live as the parent cell did. It has all the information it needs.

Chromosome number remains constant from generation to generation. This is made possible by another type of division—meiosis. At some stage in the life of all plants and animals that reproduce sexually, there is a cell division without the replication of chromosomes. Meiosis halves the number of chromosomes to form the monoploid number. The full diploid number is restored again at the time of fertilization.

If you have followed this argument carefully, you must have wondered how in meiosis, when the daughter cells have only *half* the usual number of chromosomes, *all* of the instructions are transmitted from parent to daughter cells. Possibly you would like to suggest some hypotheses to explain this phenomenon. If so, you can test the hypotheses when you reach later chapters on genetics.

GUIDE QUESTIONS AND PROBLEMS

1. What is meant by genetic continuity? How is it illustrated in the frog or in the chicken?
2. What is the basic problem of cell division?
3. Why did Flemming make every effort to observe mitosis in living cells even though it was much easier to observe the fixed and stained preparations of dividing cells?
4. How do centrioles and centrosomes indicate the beginning of the mitotic process?
5. Chromosomes are rarely seen in nondividing cells. Does this mean they are re-formed for each cell division?
6. Where, other than in the developing egg, would you expect to find large numbers of dividing cells?
7. What is the most important result of the mitotic process? How is the result brought about?
8. What happens in the nucleus of a cell between the end of one mitosis and the beginning of the next one?
9. A dividing cell of the common fruit fly, *Drosophila*, has eight chromosomes. How many chromosomes will each of the new daughter cells have?
10. What might be learned from a study of the mitotic apparatus?
11. How could the existence of spindle fibers in living cells be shown?
12. What reason is there for assuming that there must be some exceptions to the idea of a constant number of chromosomes in all cells of an organism?
13. What is the important result of meiosis?

SUGGESTED READINGS

Books

McLeish, J., and B. Snoad, *Looking at Chromosomes.* New York, Macmillan, 1958.
> A clear, brief introduction to mitosis and meiosis, with excellent photomicrographs.

Swanson, C. P., *The Cell.* Englewood Cliffs (N. J.), Prentice-Hall, 1960.
> An up-to-date brief account of the cell and its functions.

Magazines and Journals

Mazia, D., "Cell Division." *Scientific American,* Vol. 189 (August 1953), pp. 53–63.

—— "Cell Division." *Scientific American,* Vol. 205 (September 1961), pp. 100–20.

Taylor, J. H., "Duplication of Chromosomes." *Scientific American,* Vol. 198 (June 1958), pp. 36–42.

8

THE BALANCE

OF NATURE

Levels of Biological Organization

So far in our study of life, we have concentrated upon two **levels of organization.** First, we have learned about *cells* and the structures found within them. Second, in an effort to understand more about the structure and functions of cells, we have studied the *atoms and molecules* that are the basis of life. But these are only two of the levels at which life must be studied. With the knowledge that we have obtained, we are still unprepared to deal with questions of the following sort: What controls the beating of your heart? What has been the history of our species in the past? What takes place when a fertilized egg develops into an embryo, and an embryo into an adult? What would life be like if there were no microorganisms or green plants on the earth? All these questions lead us to an important realization: cells and their molecules tell us much about life—but far from all. There are numerous other levels of biological organization (Table 8-1).

Most animals and plants are multicellu-lar, that is, they are composed of many cells. They are not just masses of cells, however. Their cells are organized in different ways. Morphologically similar cells with similar functions are associated as **tissues.** Thus the epidermis, the outer layer of cells in multicellular organisms, is a tissue (Figure 8-1). The important function of the epidermis is protection of the cells within the bodies of the organisms. The cells from the inside would die quickly if exposed to the air or water in which the organism lives.

The next higher level of organization above the tissue level is **organs.** An organ is a structure composed of different kinds of tissues that work in a specialized way to accomplish a highly organized function. Let us take as an example the eye of man.

The outermost tissue of the eye forms a tough protective layer over most of the eye. Protection of inner tissues is an important function, but in the case of the eye it would be of no value if the protective tissue blocked light from entering the eye. A second important function of the tissue, therefore, is *admitting light.*

The next tissue layer of the eye consists largely of blood vessels, which supply the cells of the eye with oxygen and digested food, and which remove the waste products. Finally, as we progress from tissue to tissue, we reach the innermost layer (actually several layers), the **retina** (RET·ih·na). The cells of the retina are specialized in reacting to light. Another tissue, the lens, serves to focus the rays of light on the retina. The end result of this organization of various tissues into an organ is our ability to see. Each tissue has important specific functions of its own, but vision depends on the integrated whole.

If we wish to make our list of levels of organization more complete, we should add **organ systems.** These are groups of organs that cooperate in some general function. Stomach, liver, and intestine are individual organs, yet together these organs are part of an organ system—the digestive system.

At the next higher level of organization are **organisms.** An organism is an individual—a microorganism, plant, or animal that possesses a certain structure and lives in a certain way. One organism is you.

It is natural for us to think of cells, tissues, organs, and organ systems as being incomplete and dependent. In complex plants and animals, they cannot exist alone; a heart, or an eye, or a brain by itself can do no more than die. It is just as natural for us to think of the individual organism —the man, the horse, the oak tree, or the eagle—as complete and independent. Each seems in control of its destiny. Yet this is far from being true, as even the following brief discussion will show.

All organisms are influenced in various ways by other organisms—both those now living and those that lived in the past. We can recognize four such influences upon any organism:

1. Influence by ancestors
2. Influence by others of its kind (which will introduce us to another level of organization—**species**)
3. Influence by different species of or-

TABLE 8-1   LEVELS OF BIOLOGICAL ORGANIZATION

In unicellular organisms	In multicellular organisms
Atoms and molecules	Atoms and molecules
Cells	Cells
↑	Tissues
(*Identical levels in unicellular organisms*)	Organs
	Organ systems
↓	
Individual organisms	Individual organisms
Species	Species
Communities	Communities
The biosphere	The biosphere

ganisms with which it lives (which will introduce us to still another level of organization—the **community**)
4. Influence by even the most distant (geographically speaking) organisms on the earth (which will introduce us to the highest level of organization—the entire world of life, the **biosphere**)

Table 8-1 for unicellular and multicellular organisms lists the levels of organization we have introduced.

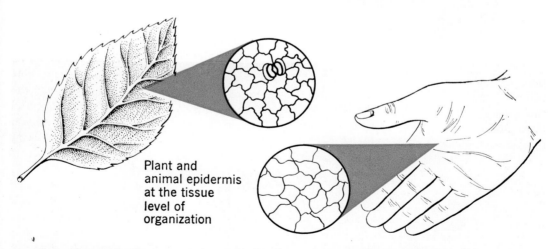

Plant and animal epidermis at the tissue level of organization

8-1   The epidermis of a plant or an animal is a tissue composed of similar cells. The function of the tissue in both organisms is essentially the same.

8-2
A great deal of energy and time go into studies of life in the past. From studies of fossil evidence, fairly reliable accounts of the influence of ancient organisms upon life today are often reconstructed. In the photograph above, the fossil bones of a dinosaur are being unearthed. At the left is a section of a petrified tree trunk, and below are imprints of the shells of animals from an ancient sea. The shell imprints are the oldest of the fossils shown here; they date to several hundred million years ago.

Above, American Museum of Natural History; *left*, G. Grant from National Park Service; *below*, Smithsonian Institution

INFLUENCES OF THE PAST

Biologically speaking, what we are today depends far more on what our ancestors did than what we ourselves do. "Ancestors" as used here means more than great-grandfather — or great-great-grandmother. The word will be used to refer to the entire line of ancestors from which we are descended — a line that stretches back to the origin of life on earth. The structure of our bodies, the ways the parts of our body function, and to a large degree our behavior, are inherited from the past. In the exceedingly remote past our ancestors solved the problems of cell division and mitosis, how to store chemical energy in ATP, and how to perpetuate the "instructions for living" in molecules of DNA. More recently they solved the problems of locomotion, first in water and later on land. And only yesterday, in the earth's scale of time, did they begin to use their hands for making and using tools.

These biological abilities are transmitted to us—transmitted solely in an egg cell and in a sperm cell. The sizes of these links with the past are exceedingly small—in our case they are combined in a little sphere, the fertilized egg, about 0.1 mm in diameter. (You will find it interesting to compute the total volume of this biological inheritance from the past for the entire population of the United States.)

Life in the Past

The species of animals and plants now living on the earth have not always been here. True, most of them have been here for a very long time—generally at least 1 million to 10 million years, and frequently much longer.

How can we possibly know this? We know it because some of the animals and plants that lived and died long ago have been partly preserved in the earth's crust. Most of the soft parts of their bodies de-cayed, but sometimes the harder parts—bones of animals and the cell walls of plants—became fossils. Mineral substances in the water and mud of the organisms' "graves" entered the plant cell walls or animal bones and slowly hardened into stone. We say that the remains of the organisms became *petrified* (which means "changed to stone"). Any remains of an ancient organism preserved by this or any other means is a fossil.

Perhaps you have visited or read about the Petrified Forest National Monument in Arizona or the Dinosaur National Monument on the Utah-Colorado boundary. In one you can see the fossil remains of trees. The other contains the petrified bones of huge reptiles, the dinosaurs. Most natural history museums have exhibits of fossils, such as those shown in Figure 8-2.

Fossils, then, tell us about life in the past. We can even determine the age of fossils by measuring the radioactivity and the products of radioactive decay in the past, in the rocks in which the fossils are found (page 243). We know, therefore, not only the kinds of animals and plants that lived in the past but also roughly when they lived.

The earliest evidences of life are at least 2 billion years old. There are not many fossils so old. Those that we do have suggest that all the ancient species lived in warm shallow seas. They were comparatively simple organisms. There were no trees, flowers, insects, fish, birds, or mammals.

With the passage of hundreds of millions of years, life became more complex. Nearly 500 million years ago, ancient plants began colonizing land. The early forms slowly evolved into the mosses, ferns, trees, and flowers that we know today.

The animals began to invade land about 300 million years ago. The insects, spiders, frogs, toads, reptiles, birds, and mammals evolved from these first groups of animals that came out on land.

In the course of time, then, the simple organisms of the past have given rise to all the species of microorganisms, plants, and animals of today. The name for this process is *evolution,* a term we have met before (Chapter 1).

Evolution

The chief mechanism of evolution, in general terms, is fairly simple. The hereditary materials of all species—the different kinds of DNA—are subject to change. So far as we know, the changes that occur "just happen," that is, they are chance events. We call these changes **mutations** (myoo-TAY·sh'nz). But because they occur in DNA, they are hereditary; they are passed on during reproduction, and they cause changes in the offspring. (Further details will be given in Chapters 30–33.) Most mutations are harmful; that is, they upset the carefully adjusted physiology of the organism. But if, by chance, mutations produce changes that help an organism to live and have offspring, we have the basis of an evolutionary change.

Let us use the example of a time about 400 million years ago when animals lived only in the sea. Life is always a struggle for animals. They must obtain food to eat, and they must keep from being eaten. The species that are successful in these two activities have a better chance of surviving and leaving offspring than those that are less successful. Species that are unsuccessful become extinct—and there are far more extinct species than living species.

There were many kinds of animals in these ancient seas. Huge fish and crablike forms fed on other animals. There were others that fed on plants. If any animals, as a result of mutations, were able to leave the sea and live on the shore, even for a short time, think of the immediate benefits. There would be no other animals there to eat them, hence their chance of survival would be greatly increased. The plants had be-

gun to colonize the land 100 million years before, hence for plant-eating species of animals there would be plenty of food.

Successful mutations, then, could produce by degrees a new species that could live in this new environment. In the new environment the chance of surviving and leaving offspring would be better than in the sea. The new species would survive—unless, in time, it was replaced by an even more successful species. Thus the interaction of organisms with the physical environment, and with other organisms around them, would result in a process of selection. That is, individuals and species with mutations that provided better chances for survival in the particular environment would be favored. We speak of this process as **natural selection.** This entire hypothesis of evolution, first clearly proposed by Charles Darwin, was his greatest contribution to biology. We will discuss it further in Chapter 34.

Mutation plus natural selection results in evolution. The changes that occur in DNA produce different varieties of individuals. Some of these varieties will be able to survive and leave offspring. Others will become extinct.

The tremendous diversity of organisms that we see today is the result of evolution. Each species has evolved a particular way of life. Take birds, for example. Some birds nest in the branches of trees, others in holes, still others on the ground. Some birds feed on insects, some on fish, some on other birds, some on berries, some on seeds, some on small mammals. Some live in the Arctic, some in the tropics, some on oceanic islands, some in deserts, some on mountaintops. In all, there are about 8,000 species of birds, each the product of mutation and natural selection.

As we continue our study of animals and plants, you should keep in mind that each species is the living representative of a long series of evolutionary changes. The

Utah Zoological Society

8-3 This liger was born in a zoo. The mother was a tiger and the father a lion. Different species rarely cross in nature, but closely similar species of animals and plants can often be crossed experimentally.

differences among the various species are the result of their evolving differently, leading to different ways of life.

We and all other organisms living today have a tremendous debt to the past. The patterns of our lives have been determined by evolutionary changes that have been going on for two or more billion years.

RELATIONS WITHIN SPECIES

The individual organism is one level of organization—an organization perfected in the course of time by the evolutionary process. The individual, however, is also part of several higher levels of organization. It may be part of an organization level such as a family group (as in man), of a group of similar organisms living in the same community, or of all the individuals of the same kind. The latter level is exceedingly important—it is the level we call the species (the singular and plural are spelled alike).

Species is not a new term to us. It is a group of individuals, related through common descent, which have the same general structure, physiology, and behavior. If the species is one consisting of males and females, we can expand the definition: in nature, individuals of the same species can breed with one another, but they rarely breed with individuals of other species. Each species then shares a common inheritance because of this interbreeding of its members and the absence, in nature, of interbreeding with other species. We must add the qualification "in nature" because there are many cases of different species crossing in captivity or under experimental conditions. Thus the tiger and the lion seem never to cross in nature, but they have been crossed in zoos. The offspring is a "tiglion" or a "liger," depending on which species is the mother and which species is the father (Figure 8-3).

There are also other interrelationships at this species level of organization. Some of these relationships may be of mutual benefit to the individuals, and others may be harmful to some of them.

So far as the species as a whole is concerned, the life of an individual is often of little importance. Generally it does not matter *which* individuals survive to leave offspring so long as *some* survive. In some instances it may be advantageous for a species to consist of a large number of individuals. In other instances it may be advantageous for the numbers to be small. In species differentiated as males and females, the individuals must be numerous enough for males and females to find one another and breed.

Since the individuals of the same species are so alike in structure, physiology, and behavior, it is not surprising that their requirements are essentially the same. In animal species, all the individuals generally eat the same kinds of food and live in the same sorts of places. In plant species, the individuals have similar requirements for light and types of soil. Since the requirements for the individuals are so much alike, members of a populous species naturally compete with one another for food and a place to live. After a section of forest has burned, a new population of trees of a given species starts to grow. Not infrequently the population may be larger than the available space can support. Most individuals will be crowded out; a few will survive.

It is impossible for us to catalogue the many interrelationships at the species level of organization. You will probably think of many others not mentioned here. Each additional example is more evidence that there is a clear-cut species level of organization.

Perhaps we should be reminded that man has developed a higher capacity for interaction with individuals of his own kind than has any other species. These interactions run the gamut from those of greatest benefit to those of greatest harm. Man has unequalled knowledge and abilities to help himself—he is also perhaps the only species with the power of destroying itself.

Organization in the Community

No species is complete in itself. Each has numerous and complex relations with other species. Groups of individuals belonging to different interdependent species, together with their nonliving environment, form another level of organization—the *community*. One example of a community is the total of all species that live together in a desert. Here, in a harsh environment characterized by little water, great extremes of temperature, intense sunlight, and soil with little humus, many microorganisms, plants, and animals make their homes. Over the course of time, evolution has perfected these various species for life under desert conditions. Each species has its role, and many species are needed to maintain the community. In a sense, a community is an almost self-sufficient portion of the entire living world. That is, if it were possible to erect a barrier around a community, life within it would go on almost as before.

In any self-sufficient community two conditions must be met:

1. There must be a source of energy, and a living system capable of incorporating this energy in organic compounds of cells.
2. There must be an adequate supply of necessary chemical substances, and mechanisms for keeping these substances in balance between the living and nonliving parts of the environment.

Green plants and a few other organisms are unique in the living world in being the **producers.** That is, they are the organisms that take energy from the nonliving environment and incorporate it in compounds that can be used by all living things. By photosynthesis, the green plants capture energy from sunlight and bind it into organic compounds needed for their own growth and reproduction. So plentifully do they store these compounds that they supply nearly all the nourishment for all nongreen plants and all animals. Energy from the sun, trapped by photosynthesis, is the power for living things. And oxygen, one by-product of photosynthesis, is required by almost all organisms in order to release this power.

We prefer to describe animals, including ourselves, as the **consumers.** Directly or indirectly all animals live at the expense of green plants. They could be regarded almost as parasites of plants. A community without green plants could not exist; a community without animals could.

The beetle grub eating a root, the grasshopper chewing up stems and leaves, and the mouse eating seeds and fruits are all **primary consumers;** that is, they live directly upon green plants. The mole eating a beetle grub, the coyote pouncing upon a grasshopper, and the hawk catching a mouse are all **secondary consumers,** so named because their food is made of the primary consumers. The cat that eats the mole, like the bat that catches a mosquito full of coyote blood, is a consumer, too—of a still higher order, since the energy of the sun has been handed on by further chemical steps of digestion and synthesis into still different compounds.

When the cat, bat, hawk, and coyote die, they become food for bacteria and molds, which serve as **decomposers** in the economy of nature. Decomposers work also on fallen leaves, dead trees, and other plant remains. They operate in relay teams, simplifying, step by step, the organic constituents of each dead body. In this way they derive energy and chemical substances for their own growth and reproduction. Their activities make the chemical substances available for other living things. Thus chemical substances pass constantly from organism to organism and between organism and the nonliving environment. We call these repeating patterns in the movement of materials **cycles.**

CYCLES

If the decomposing body of a plant or animal comes to rest in a pond, the decay bacteria that attack it can become food for mosquito wrigglers, which belong to a new generation of consumers. If the decomposing body is in a forest or a field, some of the products of decay are almost sure to find their way into the soil. They become raw materials important to the green plants living there. The same atoms are used over and over in cycles, which need only to be traced to be appreciated (Figures 8-4 and 8-5). The same atoms present in the earliest living things were re-used in the giant dinosaurs. Today they are incorporated into modern plants and animals.

Even water is constantly on the move into the roots of plants and out again by evaporation, and into and out of animals. Over the surface and through the earth it flows to the oceans. In the form of rain and snow it returns to the land.

We have become familiar with the fact that the living substance of all organisms is composed chiefly of carbon, hydrogen, oxygen, and nitrogen. In the balance of nature, the inflow and outgo of these four chemicals, as they cycle through living organisms, are especially important. Because the cycles of carbon, hydrogen, and oxygen are so intimately related, it is best to consider these three elements as if they formed one great cycle, the **carbon-hydrogen-oxygen cycle.** It is sometimes called just the **carbon cycle** for short. The **nitrogen cycle** has special features that deserve separate attention.

The Carbon-Hydrogen-Oxygen Cycle

All organic compounds—the building materials of which all living things are constructed—contain carbon. We have already seen this in the variety of carbohydrates, fats, proteins, and nucleic acids to which we have been introduced (Chapter 5). But where does all the carbon come from? In

8-4 THE PHOSPHORUS CYCLE ON LAND

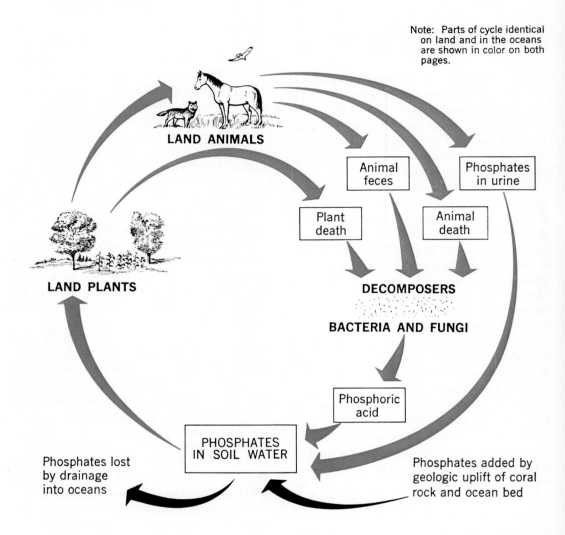

Note: Parts of cycle identical on land and in the oceans are shown in color on both pages.

LAND ANIMALS

Animal feces

Phosphates in urine

Plant death

Animal death

LAND PLANTS

DECOMPOSERS

BACTERIA AND FUNGI

Phosphoric acid

Phosphates lost by drainage into oceans

PHOSPHATES IN SOIL WATER

Phosphates added by geologic uplift of coral rock and ocean bed

the nonliving world there are only two conceivable sources of abundance:

1. The carbon dioxide of the air (0.03–0.04 percent), and that which is dissolved in water
2. The rocks containing carbonate (such as limestone) in the earth's crust

There are large amounts of carbon in coal and petroleum, but this does not become available to organisms unless it is burned to produce carbon dioxide. And coal and petroleum have their origin in trees and other vegetation that grew on the earth millions of years ago.

Our attention has already been directed to one carbon-trapping process. This process, of course, is photosynthesis, carried on by green plants. In photosynthesis, carbon dioxide is absorbed from air (or from the

8–5 THE PHOSPHORUS CYCLE IN THE OCEANS

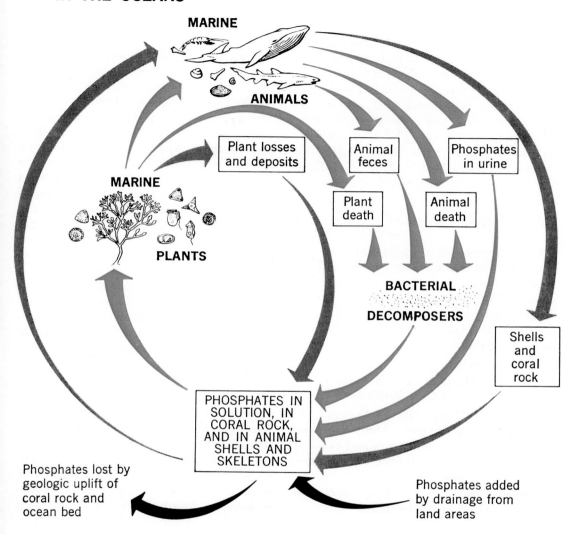

MARINE ANIMALS

MARINE PLANTS

Plant losses and deposits

Animal feces

Phosphates in urine

Plant death

Animal death

BACTERIAL DECOMPOSERS

Shells and coral rock

PHOSPHATES IN SOLUTION, IN CORAL ROCK, AND IN ANIMAL SHELLS AND SKELETONS

Phosphates lost by geologic uplift of coral rock and ocean bed

Phosphates added by drainage from land areas

water in which it has dissolved) and is then converted by union with hydrogen (from water) into molecules of carbohydrate. No source of carbon other than CO_2 used in photosynthesis is really important for living things.

The pure carbon of coal or graphite, the solid carbonates of limestone, and the like, must be burned or changed chemically before they become available to life. When CO_2 dissolves in water, some of it reacts to form carbonic acid (H_2CO_3), which immediately yields carbonate ($CO_3^=$) and bicarbonate (HCO_3^-) ions. Today the richest store of carbon in the waters of the earth is in the form of these ions. To an extent, they as well as dissolved CO_2 are used by marine organisms.

A mollusk, which deposits carbonate in its shell, cannot use the insoluble carbon so accumulated as a part of its fuel supply, or for its protein or nucleic acid, unless the carbonate is converted into carbon dioxide or soluble ions. Neither the mollusk nor any other animal is able to use large amounts of CO_2 directly. For most of its supply of carbon and oxygen, each animal depends upon carbohydrates, fats, amino acids, and still other carbon compounds that are in its food. So we come back to the green plants—the primary producers. The green plants, and they alone, take the carbon dioxide of the environment and make it into food. This is the meaning of our general equation for photosynthesis:

$$6CO_2 + 6H_2O + energy \rightarrow$$
$$C_6H_{12}O_6 + 6O_2$$

When sugar or fat or any other fuel molecule is broken down in a living cell, and its energy is released and transferred to molecules of ATP, what happens to the carbon, oxygen, and hydrogen atoms? The general equation for respiration in plants and animals is simply the reverse of the photosynthesis equation:

$$C_6H_{12}O_6 + 6O_2 \rightarrow$$
$$6CO_2 + 6H_2O + energy$$

In Chapter 11 we will see that not all respiration is so complete. Many microorganisms, known as fermenters and decomposers, respire in the absence of free oxygen. However, insofar as the carbon-hydrogen-oxygen cycle is concerned, they too produce CO_2 when they utilize glucose; and their other final products of respiration, such as ethyl alcohol, acetic acid, or lactic acid, are released and are utilized by organisms that are able to use free oxygen as a final hydrogen acceptor (see Chapter 6). The end of the matter is therefore that these microorganisms also help to carry out the chemical transformations of the cycle. The carbon dioxide and water formed during respiration go back into the air and the waters of the earth. Here, then, we see a tremendous cycle that involves carbon, hydrogen, and oxygen—all three at once. The cycle as it occurs for land organisms is shown in Figure 8-6. The same cycle, with a few changes and additions, occurs in the oceans.

The carbon-hydrogen-oxygen cycle may also be described as an energy cycle, for you will recall that energy from the sun is required to make the photosynthesis reaction go on in the plants throughout the world. The same amount of energy that photosynthesis stores in a glucose molecule is released in respiration. A part of it goes back immediately into the environment as heat. Most of it, trapped in the ATP molecules that are formed, is used in a thousand ways—in the contraction of a muscle, the chemical work of a gland, the transmission of impulses over nerves, in growth, in the lifting of water from the soil to the top of a plant, or in the circulation of blood in an animal. Eventually, as it is used, this chemical energy is converted into mechanical energy (producing motion) and ultimately into heat, which dissipates in the terrestrial surroundings.

Combustion of fuels, such as the burning of coal or oil, likewise releases heat and other forms of energy into the environment. The by-products are water vapor and carbon dioxide, which further replenish the reservoir of these substances in the atmosphere. So whether the CO_2 comes from combustion, industrial as well as natural (volcanoes, forest fires), or whether it comes from respiration, it renews the carbon supply of plants, and ultimately of animals as well.

One other group of organisms is essential to maintain the balance of the carbon-hydrogen-oxygen cycle. The bodies of living organisms contain a tremendous quantity of chemical substances. Generally these are not available to other living creatures while the organism is alive. Furthermore, suppose there were no bacteria or any other organisms, such as molds or other fungi,

-6 THE CARBON-HYDROGEN-OXYGEN CYCLE ON LAND

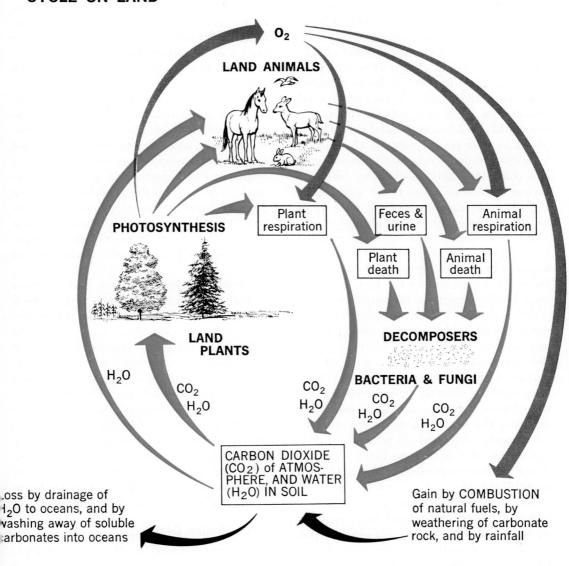

O_2

LAND ANIMALS

PHOTOSYNTHESIS

| Plant respiration |

| Feces & urine |

| Animal respiration |

| Plant death |

| Animal death |

LAND PLANTS

DECOMPOSERS

BACTERIA & FUNGI

H_2O

CO_2
H_2O

CO_2
H_2O

CO_2
H_2O

CO_2
H_2O

CARBON DIOXIDE (CO_2) of ATMOS-PHERE, AND WATER (H_2O) IN SOIL

Loss by drainage of H_2O to oceans, and by washing away of soluble carbonates into oceans

Gain by COMBUSTION of natural fuels, by weathering of carbonate rock, and by rainfall

to *decompose* dead plants and animals, or break down their wastes. We can imagine that dead organisms and the wastes of living organisms would then accumulate everywhere. We might try to burn them to get carbon dioxide back into the atmosphere, but this would dispose of only a small fraction of all things dying on the land, to say nothing of those in the oceans, where perhaps 85 percent of all living things pass their lives. And, clearly, this could not have been a possibility before man was present on the earth. What could we do even to dispose of our human sewage without the bacterial decomposers to assist? The problem would be great indeed!

Without the decomposers—the bacteria and fungi that produce decay—the carbon in wastes and dead organisms would quickly become "fixed"; it would no longer be returned to the carbon-hydrogen-oxygen cycle in the form of CO_2 as a product of "biological combustion." If we stop and think about this for a moment, it becomes appallingly clear that the small amount of *available carbon* (CO_2 or H_2CO_3 or HCO_3^-) in our world would soon be used up by green plants in their photosynthesis. The carbon-hydrogen-oxygen cycle would slow down and come to a halt, blocked by failure of carbon dioxide to return to the atmosphere. If that were really to happen, why would nearly all life on earth halt abruptly?

We have called this the carbon-hydrogen-oxygen cycle. We must now see what happens to the hydrogen and the oxygen in the cycle. First consider the hydrogen. It is abundantly present in the environment in water molecules (H_2O). In photosynthesis the water molecules are split into hydrogen and oxygen. The hydrogen becomes part of the sugar molecule, and then goes into the various organic compounds that are made from glucose, directly or indirectly. When the glucose is broken down in respiration, or when the decomposers get to work on the organic compounds of wastes and dead organisms, the hydrogen atoms are oxidized to form water again. This seems quite straightforward.

Now think about the oxygen in the cycle, which we may understand more easily if we treat it as though it were a separate part of the cycle (see the gray arrows in Figure 8-6). Oxygen (O_2) is necessary for all combustion, and it is the ultimate receiver of hydrogen atoms in respiration (Chapter 6). Combustion and respiration are the important sources of carbon dioxide in the atmosphere, as we have seen. Thus without O_2 there would be no combustion or respiration, no CO_2 production, and no carbon cycle.

Is the converse true? Could there be an oxygen cycle without a carbon cycle in nature? Green plants, during photosynthesis, release molecular oxygen to the atmosphere and to the earth's waters (the latter are known as the **hydrosphere**—HY·droh·sfeer), but—and this is crucial—these same plants require CO_2 from the atmosphere or hydrosphere to carry on their photosynthesis. There is good reason to believe that the amount of CO_2 actually limits the process. If photosynthesis were to stop, it would not take many thousand years for the combined respiration and combustion going on in the world to use up all the available oxygen—a point realized by Priestley long ago (page 75). That is, the oxygen would become combined in the form of organic and inorganic compounds, especially in the form of water.

Clearly, we human beings and all other animals require the presence of the green plants and their photosynthesis, not merely to supply us with sugar and other food substances, but just as significantly to keep replenishing the atmosphere with the oxygen we require for our respiration. On their side, the green plants must have the bacteria and other decomposers to replenish the supply of usable carbon (mainly CO_2) in the atmosphere and hydrosphere. Carbon, hydrogen, and oxygen cycles are really inseparable, and the producers, consumers, and decomposers all play essential roles in keeping the combined cycle going.

The Nitrogen Cycle

Nitrogen is found in all proteins and nucleic acids. It is, consequently, an essential element in living substance. One might suppose that plants and animals could capture the nitrogen they need directly from the air, since four fifths of our atmosphere is pure nitrogen. But no! Animals must have their nitrogen in the form of amino acids. Plants must have soluble nitrogen salts, from which, together with carbohydrates, they can make their proteins and nucleic acids. When amino acids are broken down in the bodies of animals, or when the animals die, the products are generally useless for green plants. It is the decomposers, especially some species of bacteria, that convert these useless compounds into compounds that the green plants can use for synthesizing their proteins. The decomposers are consequently of prime importance in the nitrogen cycle.

Essentially, the nitrogen cycle involves about five main steps. First, when a plant or an animal dies, when leaves fall from a tree, or when an animal excretes its waste products, the nitrogen compounds present in all of them pass into the soil or water. Next, certain bacteria in the soil, or in water, begin to break down these organic nitrogen compounds. One of the end-products is ammonia (NH_3). (In freshwater communities and in the oceans, many forms of life other than bacteria also produce ammonia as a metabolic end-product.) Much of the organic nitrogen is converted to ammonia. Yet even when combined in this relatively simple form, the nitrogen is of little use to green plants.

In the third step, chemical reactions occur in which ammonia gas is changed to an ammonium compound, a soluble salt. The salt ionizes to produce ammonium ions (NH_4^+) as well as some ions with a negative charge. Some green plants can take ammonium ions directly into their roots.

The fourth step is carried out in the soil by bacteria called **nitrifying** (NY·trih·fy·ing) **bacteria.** Some of these oxidize ammonium ions to water and **nitrites** (NY·tryts—salts containing the nitrite ion, NO_2^-). Others oxidize nitrites into **nitrates** (salts containing the nitrate ion, NO_3^-). In the fifth step, the highly soluble nitrates, dissolved in the soil water, are taken up by the roots of plants.

When ammonia is oxidized by bacteria to nitrites, and the nitrites are then oxidized by other bacteria to nitrates, energy is released. The bacteria use this energy for their own vital activities. The nitrates produced are waste products so far as the bacteria are concerned. The nitrates are of vital importance to green plants, however.

Another way in which nitrogen is made available for protein synthesis is by **nitrogen fixation.** Nitrogen-fixing algae (simple green plants) and bacteria live free in the soil. Other nitrogen-fixing bacteria grow in the roots of plants called **legumes** (LEG-yoomz). Examples of legumes with which you may be familiar are garden beans, soy beans, peas, vetches, alfalfa, and clover. After these bacteria invade the roots of the host they form **nodules**—little warty growths (Figure 8-7) on the roots. It might seem that these parasitic, nodule-forming bacteria would be harmful for the legumes. Actually, they improve the growth of these green plants. The bacteria utilize atmospheric nitrogen in their own metabolism, and convert it into nitrogen-containing substances. These substances are used by the legumes in making the proteins and nucleic acids which they need for growth. Just how the nitrogen-fixing bacteria "fix" the nitrogen is still one of nature's secrets.

Nitrogen fixation requires an expenditure of energy. To meet this requirement, carbohydrate and oxygen are needed by the nitrogen-fixing bacteria. The leguminous plant provides these. Thus, both the green plant and the bacteria benefit from their close association.

To a limited extent man supplies green plants with nitrogen from commercial fertilizers. In the great agricultural section of North America it is common to see farmers applying *ammonia* or *nitrate* to their fields to increase the yield and protein content of the crops. Green plants thus have at least three possible sources of nitrogen, but where do you and I and all of the other animals get nitrogen for proteins? We get it either directly from plants (when we eat a

a

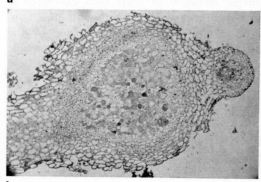

b

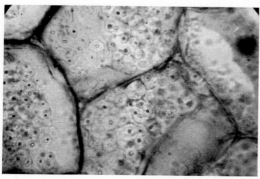

c

All photos by Hugh Spencer

8-7

The nodules on the clover roots in photograph **a** are the homes of nitrogen-fixing bacteria, so named because they "fix" nitrogen in compounds that green plants can use. This source of nitrogen compounds offsets "leaks" in the nitrogen cycle (Figure 8-8). In photograph **b**, a cross section of a single nodule is shown enlarged. The nodule is a structure of many cells, the inner ones of which contain the nitrogen-fixing bacteria. Photograph **c** shows some of the inner cells further enlarged (650 X). If you look closely, you will see that the cells are literally *packed* with evidence of bacterial activity.

←

salad or some green vegetable, peanuts, beans, etc.), or indirectly when we eat meat or cheese, or when we drink milk. For remember, the steer that provided our steak had to eat alfalfa and corn to get nitrogen in the form of amino acids to synthesize its own proteins.

For their part in the nitrogen and carbon-hydrogen-oxygen cycles, and in many other ways, bacteria are indirectly beneficial. Without them, plants could not get nitrogen to make proteins, and without the plants none of us could exist. In a way, nitrogen-fixing and nitrifying bacteria are, like the bacteria of disease, of life-and-death importance—but they aid life instead of making it more difficult.

The nitrogen cycle as we have just described it is simplified. It is actually more complicated. Some of the additional details are shown in Figure 8-8 where you can see that there are some "leaks" in this cycle. One such leak occurs when certain bacteria of the soil convert some of the all-important nitrates into nitrous oxide (NO_2), a gas that is lost to the atmosphere. Another leak involves loss of nitrifying bacteria. They are most abundant in the top six inches of soil and they will be lost if soil erosion occurs. Still another leak occurs when nitrogen-containing compounds are *leached* or washed away from the places where they could be absorbed by plant roots. In spite of these and other losses (Figure 8-8), the cycle keeps in balance. Can you say why?

8-8 THE NITROGEN CYCLE ON LAND

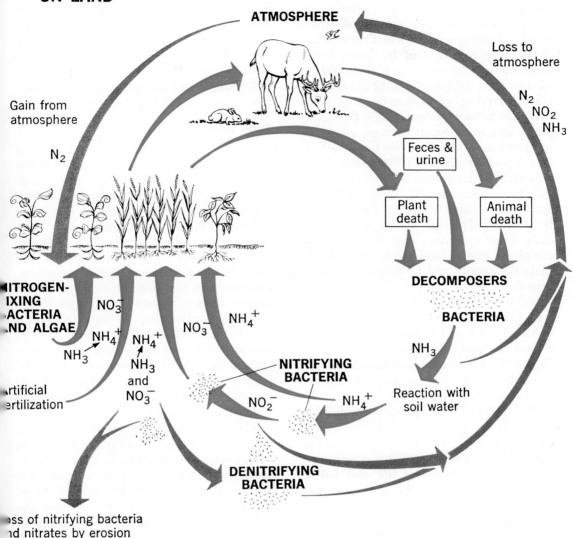

ATMOSPHERE

Loss to atmosphere

N_2
NO_2
NH_3

Gain from atmosphere

N_2

Feces & urine

Plant death

Animal death

NITROGEN-FIXING BACTERIA AND ALGAE

NO_3^-

NH_4^+

NO_3^-

NH_4^+

NH_3

NH_4^+

NH_3 and NO_3^-

Artificial fertilization

DECOMPOSERS

BACTERIA

NH_3

NITRIFYING BACTERIA

NO_2^-

NH_4^+

Reaction with soil water

DENITRIFYING BACTERIA

Loss of nitrifying bacteria and nitrates by erosion and leaching

INTERACTION BETWEEN ORGANISMS AND THEIR ENVIRONMENT

Usually we think of the environment as something that acts on living things, and we tend to think of the living things as merely being acted upon. Our discussion of the carbon-hydrogen-oxygen cycle and of the nitrogen cycle has shown that this is not so. The action goes in both directions. Our surroundings—atmosphere, soil, oceans, fresh waters—possess many of their present characteristics because of the presence of earlier plants and animals. Life is certainly affected by its environment. But it also modifies that environment and thus indirectly affects future generations of living things. This is another example of interaction at several levels of organization.

The cycles we have already discussed provide striking examples of this modification of the environment by living organisms. Animals as we know them could not exist without oxygen. Yet until green plants began carrying on modern photosynthetic processes millions of years ago, the atmosphere did not contain enough oxygen to support animal life. Someone has calculated that if photosynthesis were to cease, future populations of animals, no more numerous than those today, would use up all the oxygen in the atmosphere within about twenty centuries. Correspondingly, without animals releasing carbon dioxide into the atmosphere, green plants would gradually deplete the supply and be limited in further growth.

Soil is a complex and ever-changing system. Plants and animals are constantly removing from it and adding to it both organic and inorganic substances. Plants would deplete the soil of those substances it needs, were there not some mechanism for their constant replacement.

The water in the oceans, as another example, is no simple solution that can be easily duplicated in the chemistry laboratory. Instead, it is in equilibrium with myriad microscopic kinds of life and bottom sediments. Continually the ocean water acquires and loses particles of each of its characteristic substances. If the living things were removed, or if the water was somehow isolated away from the ocean bottom, the liquid would soon lose many of its distinctive qualities. This is the reason why it is so difficult to maintain a seawater aquarium with only a limited variety of species.

So far we have considered the interaction of organisms and their environment— that is, the organization of the community —with emphasis on events at the molecular level. We have learned that carbon, hydrogen, oxygen, nitrogen, and many other elements that have not been discussed, move from organism to organism and to and from the living and nonliving parts of the environment. Equally significant are the interactions of individual organisms with one another, singly and collectively. We shall now learn about some of these interactions.

Food Webs

A bat ate a mosquito that had bitten a coyote that had eaten a grasshopper that had chewed a leaf. All these living things together comprise part of a **food web**. This sequence is incomplete, however, for it does not show that many animals other than those mentioned eat grasshoppers and mosquitoes, or that coyotes and bats eat and are eaten by a great many other organisms. Grasshoppers and mosquitoes are related in similar ways to many other species. When we consider also that the kind of plant a grasshopper might eat may also be eaten by various other primary consumers, and these by several different secondary consumers, we start to build a picture of the food web that links together a whole community of living things (Figure 8-9).

The alternative pathways in a food web help maintain the stability of the living community. If the rabbits in some area decrease in number, perhaps because of some disease, the owls might be expected to go hungry. However, this is not the case. The rabbits eat less vegetation—hence, the greater number of plants produce more fruits and seeds and furnish better hiding places for mice. Soon a larger population of mice is present. The owls transfer their attention from rabbits to mice. This reduces the danger for surviving rabbits, and these primary consumers have a better chance to rebuild their numbers. The greater the number of alternative pathways a food web has, the more stable is the community of living things which make up the web.

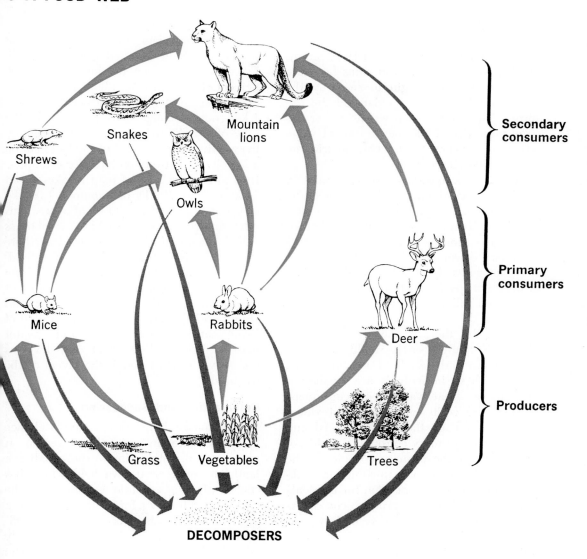

Secondary consumers

Primary consumers

Producers

Mountain lions

Snakes

Shrews

Owls

Mice

Rabbits

Deer

Grass

Vegetables

Trees

DECOMPOSERS

Stability results because, on the average, only a few of the possible offspring of a plant or animal survive to reproduce. Of all the seeds a plant forms, all but a few are eaten by animals or succumb to diseases or are killed by adverse weather conditions, either as seeds or somewhat later in life, as young plants that have not yet formed seeds of their own.

The world could not otherwise accommodate all the offspring that might be produced. Under normal circumstances a pair of meadow mice, for example, born early in the year, can produce 13 litters totaling about 78 young before the winter reduces their food supply. If each of these young were to survive and reproduce at the same rate, and all further generations likewise, the original pair would be ancestors to about 50,000 descendants and be great-great-great-great-great-grandparents before the year was out. If we consider that one meadow mouse requires about 10 kilograms of plant food per year and ruins far more than this, we can begin to see why the world could not accommodate all the offspring. The 50,000 mice would eat or destroy more than 1,500 metric tons of vegetation in a year's time. (One metric ton equals 1,000 kilograms.)

Actually, the meadow mouse population is fairly stable. About two offspring actually survive from each pair of parents. The others die of diseases or are caught by hawks, owls, foxes, martens, bobcats, and other secondary consumers.

We are so used to thinking of the welfare of our own species that we tend to regard as "wasted" all the offspring of any organisms that do not survive to reproductive maturity. But there is another side to the picture. Not only does the world lack space for so many individuals of any one kind, but also these individuals are needed as food by a great variety of consumers. Without the fruits and seeds and young plants and foliage that are produced and "wasted," the primary consumers could not exist. Without the primary consumers, the plants would die of overcrowding, or weaken from excessive competition for nutrients and light. Without the primary consumers produced and wasted, the secondary consumers would become extinct. Their elimination would doom the tertiary consumers. Through the presence of all these components in the food web, each species is held in check, and the community maintains its stability.

The transfer of energy from producer to primary consumer to secondary consumer, and so on, in a food web, involves many factors—among them energy loss. In any transfer of energy there is always some loss from the system in the form of escaping

heat—no transfer is 100 percent efficient. Among living beings, the transfer of energy in food from the "eaten" to the "eater" is really quite inefficient, and of course a great deal of the food does not get eaten at all. From grass to sheep the loss is about 90 percent. That is, it takes about 10 kilograms of organic matter in the grass to support 1 kilogram of sheep. If we suppose, for the sake of simplification, that each consumer lives entirely on one kind of food—a man on a lake living entirely on bass, for example—then to support 1 kg of man it takes about 10 kg of bass, 100 kg of minnows, 1,000 kg of water fleas, and 10,000 kg of algae. This relationship is shown in what is sometimes called a *pyramid of numbers,* because there are progressively fewer numbers of individuals in each category as one advances from producers through the different grades of consumers toward the top of the pyramid (Figure 8-10). It is also called a pyramid of living matter, because there is a far greater mass of living substance at each level as one moves down through the layers of the pyramid.

Colonization and Succession

Occasionally living things have a chance to spread into an uninhabited region. It may be a mountain slope exposed after a landslide, or a great lava field which has cooled after a volcanic eruption, or the land devastated by a forest fire, a flood, or a glacier. Some kinds of life prove more efficient than others as colonists, and quickly occupy the area. Others follow the pioneers and eventually crowd them out.

These changes in the landscapes are referred to as **succession.** Eventually a condition of reasonable stability is established. In some instances thousands of years are required, but in others the speed is remarkable. One example, which scientists studied with great care, is the island of Krakatoa, near Java in the East Indies. On August 27, 1883, two volcanoes on the island exploded simultaneously, entirely obliterating their previous cinder cones and producing a hole eight hundred feet deep where one of them had stood. Tidal waves created by the double blast took at least 36,417 human lives on this island and others more than 40 kilometers (25 miles) distant. Krakatoa and two adjacent islands were devastated.

Two months later when men visited Krakatoa they found it steaming from a recent rain, which had fallen on the still-hot rocks. A loose coating of pumice was washing away rapidly but in some places was still over 200 feet deep. Nine months after the eruption, a scientist found one lone spider spinning a web on Krakatoa, and some blue-green algae growing on rocks at the shore. Otherwise the island, and also another 12 miles distant, appeared to be lifeless.

Three years after the eruption an exploration team headed by a Dutch botanist saw that coastal plants had taken root along the shore from seeds carried to the island by waves. Ferns and grasses were growing over much of the island. These had developed from spores and seeds air-lifted to Krakatoa by wind and birds. Seven years later another party of scientists found half-grown coconut trees, young beefwoods, and an assortment of lizards and snakes living on one another or at the expense of a great variety of insects and spiders. Little by little, Krakatoa was acquiring new colonists by air and water and on occasional rafts of debris floating on the ocean.

A far more rapid recovery from devastation is seen on continental areas in temperate or tropical lands, because these areas are not isolated by broad stretches of water. After a forest fire, only one season may be needed before the burned area is again green with blackberry bushes, fireweed, and other plants whose seeds are dropped by birds. Wind and birds bring the seeds of pioneer trees: poplar, birch, and sumac, all of which are quick-growing and able to dominate the lower vegetation. Gradually oak and beech or evergreens rise above

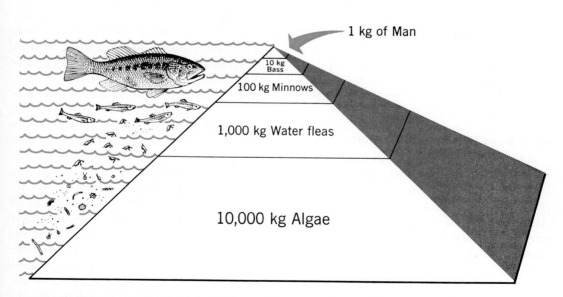

8-11 A pyramid of numbers. If the organisms are arranged according to predator-prey relations, one always finds many more of the prey species than of the predator.

This forest in western Pennsylvania shows no evidence of recent fire or other destruction. It has reached a stable state—it is a climax forest. The principal trees are beech and hemlock. Unless the forest is destroyed by fire or man, it is not likely to be invaded successfully by other types of trees. Some pine and birch seeds will be carried or blown into the area, but the seedlings will not survive in the summer shade of the forest floor. (What types of seedlings *are* likely to survive here?)

Helen Faye

the pioneer trees and provide so dense a shade that the quick-growing pioneer kinds can no longer survive. A forest of this kind represents a reasonably stable environment —a **climax community** (Figure 8-11). Unless some new event alters conditions drastically, the succession of plants and accompanying animals has essentially ended. The wound in nature has been healed.

Food Webs Under Natural Stress

Wherever some one feature of the environment limits the number of species that can live in an area, the food web is simpler. A tundra on a mountaintop or in the Arctic, for example, shows evidence of stress from winter cold. Comparatively few species inhabit it throughout the year; many migrate in during summer and away again in autumn. When the weather is warm on this tundra, insects and small plants reproduce to astonishing numbers, only to vanish as cold weather kills them, or as they become dormant in response to the cold. Nowhere on earth do mosquitoes, blackflies, and flower-visiting bees reach greater abundance. Nowhere more than in the Arctic do animals show such cyclic variations from abundance to scarcity.

On a much more restricted scale, the water of a thermal spring is a living space for plants and animals that can tolerate stress caused by high temperatures. Bacteria and blue-green algae (page 247) form crusts, often with bright pastel colors, in hot springs with water temperature as high as 85° C. At an elevation of 6,000 or 7,000 feet, as in Yellowstone National Park, this is not much below the boiling temperature of water. Few animals or plants, except the bacteria and blue-green algae, can live at temperatures above 50° C. Fish, for example, occur in thermal springs, but seldom tolerate a temperature above 40° C.

Brine shrimps, and insects called brine flies, are among the few inhabitants of lakes with a high concentration of salts. Sometimes the fly pupae (a developmental stage, similar to that observed by Redi in flies—see Chapter 2) are washed ashore from Great Salt Lake (in Utah) as a beach drift twenty feet wide at the lake's edge. They average 25 pupae to the square inch, or 370 million flies per mile of shore. At other seasons, scarcely a brine shrimp or fly can be found. Variations in the abundance of microscopic food organisms for both brine shrimp and fly may match variations in the salinity, which provides stress in the environment. Whatever causes the fluctuations in brine shrimp and fly populations, the food web in salt lakes is simple, and the changes in animal numbers extreme.

"Fossil" Food Webs

The pattern of exchange of energy and materials has existed for at least as long as the fossil record goes back in time. The most ancient known fossils include producers (green plants), and primary and secondary consumers among the animals. Many ancient forms of life were very different from any we know today, but they must have played similar parts in the interchange of energy and materials in ancient times. To give some impression of what might have been going on 150 million years ago, when dinosaurs were the biggest things around, a possible food web of that time is illustrated in Figure 8-12. Most of the actors in this scene have now disappeared from the earth, while others have evolved and taken their places.

The decomposers are largely missing as fossils, but we must assume that bacteria and molds existed then, too. Otherwise the balance of nature could not have been maintained. Without the decomposers, the cycles of carbon, hydrogen, oxygen, and nitrogen—and of minerals as well—could not have kept materials of life in circulation.

The balance of nature as revealed in the community is not static, nor is it fixed. It is a system with a great deal of flexibility, and it varies from place to place and time to time. It is a system of checks and balances, like a good system of human government; but the checks and balances are automatic responses to the changes produced in all of nature by natural forces and by living beings (including, as we will see in Chapters 38 and 40, man and his works).

The Biosphere

Spread out over the earth's surface, between the solid rocky crust of the earth and the upper reaches of the atmosphere, there extends the world of life, like a thin film of living matter. It is made up of grass and shrubs and trees, of worms, fish, rabbits, and wolves, of microorganisms and many other sorts of living things. This total world of life is called the **biosphere** (BY·o·sfeer).

Every organism within the biosphere affects the life of every other, directly or remotely. Man, for example, cannot continue to live without the bacteria in the soil, the green plants on land and in the sea, and even the scavengers of the dead. And what man does to the environment matters immensely to all the other living creatures that share this globe. The biosphere is a concept that embodies the balance of nature, but it is even broader than that idea, for it includes every relationship, the insignificant as well as the significant, that serves to bind all living beings into one inseparable world. It is the highest level of organization involving living organisms.

CONCLUDING REMARKS

The world of life can be studied at many levels of organization—molecules, cells, tissues, organs, organ systems, individuals, species, communities, and the biosphere. At each level there are specific problems for

8-12 FOOD WEB INVOLVING DINOSAURS

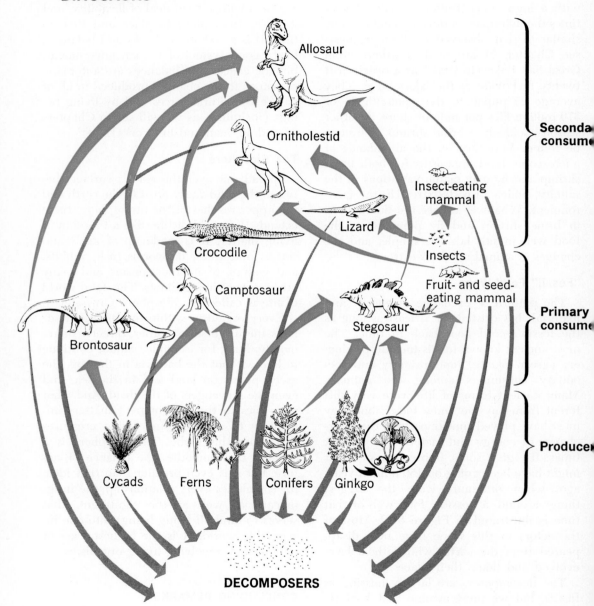

Allosaur

Ornitholestid

Insect-eating mammal

Lizard

Crocodile

Insects

Camptosaur

Fruit- and seed-eating mammal

Brontosaur

Stegosaur

Cycads   Ferns   Conifers   Ginkgo

DECOMPOSERS

Secondary consumers

Primary consumers

Producers

which one can seek specific biological answers. In most cases the problem at one level can be better understood if one knows the answers at other levels. Consider, as an example, problems concerned with breathing. We could (as we shall in Chapter 23) study the pumping of air in and out of the lungs. But think how much more meaningful the process of breathing becomes when we know that nearly all cells (cellular level) require oxygen, and that the oxygen is used to combine with the hydrogen atoms split from glucose (molecular level). At the level of the community we have now learned even more—that oxygen moves in a cycle that includes the bodies of microorganisms, plants, and animals, as well as the nonliving world.

We have observed that harmony and coordination exist at all levels of organization. Structure and function are always related. The living system is always in balance with what is outside it and around it —its environment. Individuals of the same species form populations with relationships between young and old, parents and offspring, males and females. Populations exist in communities made up of many interdependent kinds of organisms—plants, animals, and microorganisms. Consumers live at the expense of producers, and decomposers return the materials of the dead to the reservoirs of the atmosphere, fresh waters, seas, and soil.

The cycles of nature are illustrated by the movements of carbon, hydrogen, oxygen, and nitrogen, and those of other elements such as phosphorus and calcium, as they pass through the bodies of living organisms and re-enter the soil, water, and atmosphere. Some of these cycles are quite complex. They reveal to us the interdependence of living things.

Food webs constitute another way of looking at the interdependence of living organisms. Food webs must have existed in the remotest past, ever since the time when life first arose on the earth and different species assumed the roles of producers, consumers, and decomposers. We can see a dramatic bit of the adjustment that takes place when life is wiped out or grossly disturbed somewhere and then gradually returns to normal through a succession of relationships, leading up to a climax when the fullest possible balance of nature is restored. The invasion of a new volcanic is-

land by living things, or the renewal of life in an area devastated by fire, offers a picture of this kind.

The biosphere includes all living things on the earth. Each of them affects all the others, directly or indirectly, for all of them are a part of the balance of nature; all take part in the cycles of nature and form the food webs.

Man is a part of the biosphere and so are the microorganisms, which exist in incredible numbers in the soil, water, and bodies of other organisms. The biosphere could exist without man, but it could *not* exist without the microorganisms. A study of these most humble of living creatures will be our next assignment, as we begin to explore the variety of living things.

GUIDE QUESTIONS AND PROBLEMS

1. In what ways are living organisms affected by other living organisms?
2. How do the biological influences of the past affect the organisms of today?
3. What is the importance of the study of fossils?
4. What is the role of mutation in evolution?
5. How is natural selection related to mutation in evolution?
6. How does the species represent a level of biological organization?
7. In what sense is a community a self-sufficient unit?
8. What might happen to the "balance of nature" in a pond community if one kind of organism suddenly increased greatly in numbers? Would any of the changes that occur be permanent? Would it make a difference if the expanding population is a green alga (producer) or a fish (consumer)?
9. What is the role of decomposers in a biological community?
10. What part do microorganisms play in the carbon-hydrogen-oxygen cycle? the nitrogen cycle?
11. What is a food web?

12. An island devastated of all living things by the eruption of a volcano will eventually become repopulated.
    a. How are plants and animals able to repopulate this island?
    b. What types of plants and animals would be most likely to appear first on the island?
    c. What characteristics would you expect to find in the climax plants and animals?
13. How does the environment alter a food web?

SUGGESTIONS FOR ADDITIONAL READING

Books

Bates, Marston, *The Forest and the Sea*. New York, New American Library, 1959.
   A stimulating look at the world of life and its interrelations.

Buchsbaum, Ralph, and Mildred Buchsbaum, *Basic Ecology*. Pittsburgh, Boxwood Press, 1957.
   An excellent, brief treatment of ecological principles.
Dowdeswell, W. H., *Animal Ecology*. New York, Harper & Row, 1961.
   An excellent animal ecology.
Storer, J. H., *The Web of Life*. New York, New American Library, 1956.
   Well-written, easy to read treatment of ecology.

Magazines and Journals

Avery, G. S., "The Dying Oaks." *Scientific American*, Vol. 196 (May 1957), pp. 112–14.
Nicholas, G., "Life in Caves." *Scientific American*, Vol. 192 (May 1955), pp. 98–102.
Went, F. W., "The Plants of Krakatoa." *Scientific American*, Vol. 181 (September 1949), pp. 52–54.

2

DIVERSITY

The theme of unity in life has many variations—
each lived by one or more of millions
of kinds of microorganisms, plants, and animals.
Every niche on earth—in the sea or on the land,
in the tropics or near the poles—
requires some modification in way of life—
a different kind of organism.
This is the basis of diversity in life.

DIVERSITY

9

VIRUSES—

THE SMALLEST

LIVING THINGS

Now that the first part of our inquiry into life is completed, it should be clear that living things are organized as units of many sizes (Figure 9-1). Near one end of the scale are tiny atoms organized into molecules of varying degrees of complexity. At the other end is the biosphere, the world of organisms and their environments. Somewhere between is the organism itself, which may be a microscopic, single-celled bacterium, or a massive whale or giant redwood tree. As you look at the scale, you will see that viruses are placed relatively early in the scheme. We place them earlier than the cell with its distinct nucleus, mitochondria, chloroplasts, and other structures, yet following the giant molecule of DNA. What are the reasons for placing viruses at this particular level of organization? Why are viruses considered living? Perhaps the best way to answer these and other questions about viruses is to relate a little of the

story about the biological problems that resulted in the discovery of these remarkable particles.

DISCOVERY OF VIRUSES

If you look up the word *virus* in the dictionary, you will find that it is a Latin word meaning "poison." This use of the word goes back many hundreds of years, long before anyone really knew what a virus was, or that it even existed as we know it today. It was generally believed that these "viruses," or poisons, were carried in the night air and could cause many unexplained diseases. This is probably one reason why some people still insist on closing their windows at night to keep out the "bad air" (which is not really "malaria"— Chapter 1, pages 10 and 11).

By the late 1800's Louis Pasteur, Robert Koch, and other pioneer bacteriologists had demonstrated that many diseases of man and other organisms were caused by bacteria. Some diseases puzzled them, however, because they could find no bacteria or other organisms that were responsible for the disease symptoms. One such disease was found to occur in tobacco plants. It causes the leaves to wrinkle and become mottled. The mottled effect has the appearance of a mosaic, and the disease soon was called **tobacco mosaic disease.**

One of the early, and quite logical, ideas about the mysterious, disease-causing viruses was that they were toxins. Toxins are poisons produced by bacteria or by the cells of the infected organism. It was soon discovered that a virus could be transmitted from an infected organism to a healthy organism of the same kind. This was first demonstrated in 1892 by a Russian biologist named Iwanowsky. He extracted the juice from an infected tobacco plant and strained the juice through a very fine filter made of porcelain. The idea was to remove all the bacteria from the juice, leaving a

9-1 A SCALE OF SIZE AND COMPLEXITY—INORGANIC, ORGANIC AND LIVING STRUCTURES

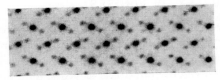

Inorganic molecules
These iron sulfide (FeS_2) molecules are magnified 18,000,000×.

Organic molecule
A DNA molecule, if also magnified 18,000,000×, would be about 3.6 cm wide — somewhat more than the thickness of this textbook.

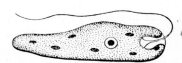

Virus (a bacteriophage)
If magnified 18,000,000×, it would be about 2.88 meters long — about the height of an average room.

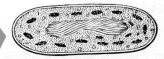

Bacterium (a cellular organism)
If magnified 18,000,000×, it would be 90 meters long — almost the length of a football field.

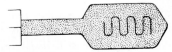

***Euglena* (a more complex cellular organism)**
If magnified 18,000,000×, it would be 1.2 kilometers long — about three quarters of a mile.

***Volvox* (a colonial organism)**
If magnified 18,000,000×, it would be about 3.7 kilometers in diameter — more than two miles.

A man of average height (175 cm), if represented on the same enlarged scale, would stand 31,500 kilometers tall — almost 20,000 miles.

Multicellular Organisms

A tree of average height (20 meters), on the same enlarged scale, would bridge the distance from the earth to the moon.

Photo by M. J. Buerger, Massachusetts Institute of Technology

bacteria-free filtrate—the juice that passed through the filter. Next, Iwanowsky rubbed some filtrate on leaves of a healthy tobacco plant. The healthy plant soon became infected with the disease (Figure 9-2a).

What was this strange substance in the filtrate that could cause disease when no bacteria were present? M. W. Beijerinck, a Dutch microbiologist, described the cause of the infection in the tobacco plant as a "*contagium vivum fluidum*," which is an elegant way of saying in Latin, "*living* fluid infectant." Without really understanding what viruses were, Beijerinck attributed the property of *life* to them because they apparently increased in amount in the infected plants and spread through their stems and leaves.

By 1900, "living fluid infectants" had been discovered in many organisms, both plant and animal. In 1898 it was demonstrated that foot-and-mouth disease of cattle could be transmitted by using bacteria-free filtrates made from blisters produced on diseased stock. The list of **filterable viruses** (viruses that can pass through a filter which has pores too small for bacteria to pass through) was growing. Today the list is long. Viruses cause many of the major diseases of plants, animals, and man. We have already mentioned that the tobacco mosaic virus (TMV) causes an important plant disease. Other viruses that cause plant diseases are the Y virus of potato, cucumber mosaic virus, mosaic virus of lettuce, and many others. In man, such diseases as yellow fever, influenza, poliomyelitis, the common cold, German measles, mumps, and chicken pox can be listed. Fever blisters are also caused by a virus.

Not all viruses cause disease in the sense that they bring about the death or serious malfunction of the organism in which they live—the **host.** Some species of bacteria are hosts for viruses called **bacteriophage** (bak-TEER-ih-o-fayj) or **phage.** Some of these bacterial viruses can remain in the cell in what

appears to be a passive state. In some species of fig trees and ornamental plants, the leaves are mottled because of a virus. In these organisms, the virus has little or no harmful effect that we can detect. It may destroy chlorophyll, but there is usually more than enough for the leaf to continue its photosynthetic activity.

If so many viruses were discovered during the early part of our century, then surely, you might suppose, someone must have seen them to prove their existence. No one had. By 1930 most people interested in viruses believed that the viruses were present as small particles, but *too* small to be seen with the compound microscope. (See Laboratory Exercise 3-9 for a discussion of the limitations of the compound microscope.) No one had even succeeded in obtaining a pure sample of viruses from the cells of a host—the only place, apparently, where viruses reproduced and increased in amount.

Isolation and Observation of Viruses

The year 1935 was important in unraveling the story of what viruses really are and how they behave. After many unsuccessful attempts, W. M. Stanley, an American microbiologist, succeeded in isolating TMV viruses from the host cells. Under the compound microscope, the isolated virus mass appeared as sliver-shaped crystals (Figure 9-2b). Within a short time it was shown that the virus crystals were nucleoproteins, closely resembling the nucleoproteins found in the chromosomes of plants and animals.

By 1935 a new kind of microscope—the electron microscope—had been constructed. (See Laboratory Exercise 3-9.) It was capable of producing magnifications far greater than the best compound microscope. Now it was possible for the first time to look at isolated viruses with the hope of seeing whether or not they really existed as individual particles. Sure enough, Stanley's

a   Rothamstead Expr. Station

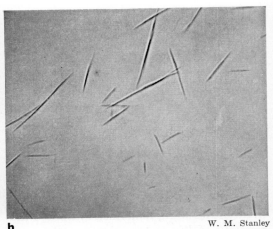

b   W. M. Stanley

9-2 **a** A tobacco plant showing the symptoms of tobacco mosaic disease. The virus causes a mottling of the leaves. Crystals of the purified virus are shown in **b**, as they appear under the compound microscope. Each crystal is composed of many rod-like virus particles, not visible under the compound microscope. Several of these particles are shown in **c**, as photographed with an electron microscope. (80,000 X)

c   H. L. Nixon, Rothamstead Expr. Station

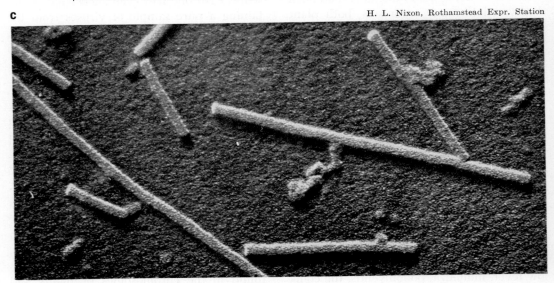

isolated crystalline TMV, its image magnified tens of thousands of times, was seen to be composed of many rod-shaped structures (Figure 9-2c).

In the isolated, purified condition, removed from the cells of the host, TMV seemed quite dead. Many attempts were made to get the virus to reproduce outside the tobacco plants. All failed. Again the question was asked: "Are viruses really living?" Stanley took some of the purified TMV, dissolved it in water, and rubbed it on the leaves of healthy tobacco plants. The leaves soon showed the mottled condition characteristic of tobacco mosaic disease. This result showed conclusively that reproduction of TMV occurred in living cells of the host species.

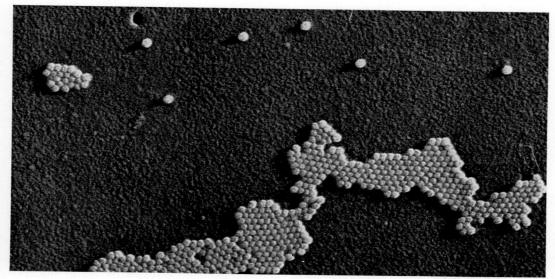

A. R. Taylor, Parke, Davis & Co.

9-3 Sphere-shaped particles of a polio virus. This electron micrograph (as any photograph taken with an electron microscope is sometimes called) has a magnification of 70,000 X. How do these virus particles compare in shape with TMV (Figure 9-2c)? How do they compare with the phage viruses in Figure 9-4?

Many biologists have since tried to get viruses of different kinds to grow and reproduce outside the living cells of their hosts. All attempts have failed. Thus it has been shown that viruses are strict **parasites,** requiring for their life processes the enzyme systems present in the living cells of other organisms. How should we interpret this phenomenon? Are viruses primitive living particles that have not yet evolved the enzyme systems required for an independent existence? Or were they once more complex living structures, which during the course of time have lost their capacity for an independent existence? We may never know. However, if we agree that viruses are alive, at least while in living cells of their hosts, where they reproduce, then they represent the simplest forms of life that we know.

Virus Size and Shape

Nearly all viruses are so small that as individual particles they cannot be seen with a compound microscope—a fact which means that most of them must be smaller than 210 millimicrons (mμ). Actually, viruses range in size from 15 mμ (the virus of foot-and-mouth disease) to 450 mμ (the virus of parrot fever). We might expect all such particles to look like no more than indistinct blobs even under the electron microscope. However, a photograph of polio virus (Figure 9-3), taken with the electron microscope, shows the virus particles as little spheres that look like tiny golf balls. Tobacco mosaic virus (Figure 9-2c) is rod-shaped, while some phage viruses of bacteria look like little tadpoles (Figure 9-4).

Virus Structure

Because of their small size, we might expect that very little would be known about the structure of viruses. However, with various ingenious techniques, biologists have discovered that plant and some animal viruses consist of a core of ribonucleic acid (RNA) and a sheath of protein. (Figure 9-5 shows a virus treated in a way to re-

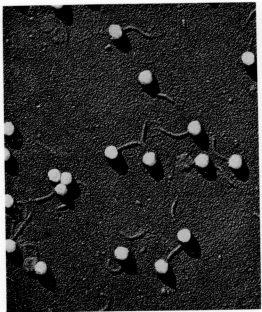

E. Kellenberger

9-4 An electron micrograph of phage viruses of bacteria. The tailpieces of these viruses are not used for locomotion. (50,000 X)

move the protein coat and leave the central strand of nucleic acid.) Bacteriophage (Figure 9-6) and most of the animal viruses consist of a central strand of deoxyribonucleic acid (DNA) surrounded by the protein sheath.

There is striking similarity in chemical composition between virus particles and the chromosomes of plant and animal cells. Could it be that viruses carry hereditary determiners or genes in the same way that chromosomes do? This question will be answered later.

VIRUSES AND THEIR WAY OF LIFE

Most plant viruses are spread by insects, with aphids and leafhoppers heading the list. Other plant viruses are transmitted by the mechanical rubbing of one leaf of a plant against another. Still others are spread by contact between the roots of different plants of the same species. The roots grow together to make a natural graft, a bridge from the infected plant to a neighboring healthy plant.

In a few cases, seeds of plants are known to carry virus particles and thus to transmit the virus from one generation to the next. This is true of lettuce mosaic disease, mentioned earlier. Vegetative parts of plants, such as leaves and cuttings of stems, may also harbor viruses. When the leaves or cuttings are used for propagation, the viruses are transmitted.

Animal viruses also are transmitted in a variety of ways. Viruses that cause infection of the respiratory tract are expelled in droplets by coughing, sneezing, or talking. Some common diseases spread to susceptible hosts in this way are virus pneumonia, the common cold, influenza, mumps, common measles, and German measles.

Some animal and human viruses, such as the polio viruses and the viruses of infectious hepatitis, are excreted in feces. Flies may carry the viruses to food, which is later ingested by human beings, or to water supplies used for drinking. This is one reason we should strive for the very best sanitary conditions in our communities.

Animal and human viruses can also be transmitted by direct contact. It is suspected that warts and fever blisters are transmitted in this way.

Virus Reproduction

What happens to a virus in a host organism? And what happens to the cells of a previously healthy host, once the transmission of a virus from an infected organism has taken place? We already know that viruses are completely inactive outside of the host's living cells. Once inside the host's cells, however, the virus DNA or RNA (depending on the kind of virus) assumes control of the cell's biochemical activities. The host cells, instead of making their own characteristic nucleic acids and proteins, begin

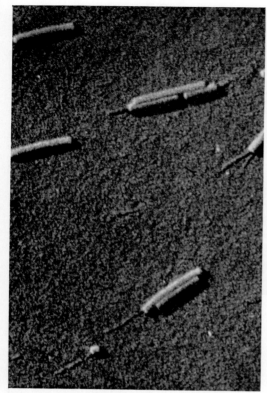

H. Fraenkel-Conrat

9-5 Tobacco mosaic virus particles with their protein coats partly removed. The core of ribonucleic acid can be seen as filaments projecting at the ends of the rods.

to make different ones specifically appropriate for the virus. The situation is somewhat like a master-slave relationship. As soon as the virus—the master—enters the host cell, it changes the activities of the cell and makes it a slave to the "needs" of the virus. In this changed cell environment, the virus replicates. Hundreds of virus particles may be produced, all exactly like the one that infected the host cell.

The phenomenon of virus reproduction has been studied in detail as it occurs among the bacteriophages. In some way phage particles are attracted to cells of bacteria, where they become attached by their tailpieces to the cell wall of the host (Fig-

ure 9-7a). At the point of attachment to the bacterial cell wall, a phage particle injects its DNA, and *only* its DNA (Figure 9-6), into the bacterial cell. In a remarkably short time, the DNA of the phage organizes the enzymes of the host so that they produce more phage DNA and protein sheaths for the phage. (Figure 9-7b shows a much enlarged bacterial cell with phage particles inside it.) After perhaps thirty minutes, the bacterial cell will usually burst, releasing hundreds of new phage particles (Figure 9-7c).

The introduction of phage DNA into a bacterium does not always have such violent results. Apparently the DNA of phage and bacterium can combine or associate in peaceful coexistence; many new generations of bacteria can be produced without any harmful results. Instead of a master-slave relationship, something more like a host-guest relationship results. The replication of the phage is evidently geared to be exactly in time with the growth cycle of the bacterium. Sometimes, however, the phage becomes reactivated and destroys the bacterium by reproducing rapidly in its helpless host. The outline of this cycle is shown in Figure 9-8.

How can the replication of the phage be timed so nicely to correspond to the reproduction of its host? It has been discovered that the DNA of the parasitic phage may become attached to the chromosome of the

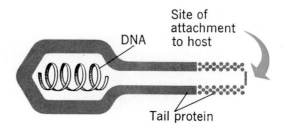

9-6 A diagram of the structure of a phage virus of bacteria. In what way does the virus resemble a chromosome? Is it alive?

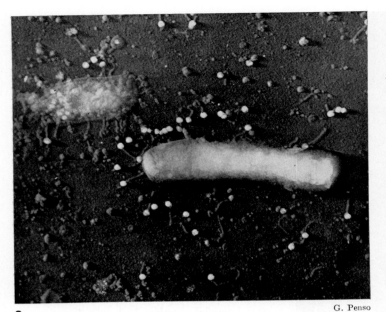

G. Penso

9-7
Three electron micrographs showing stages in virus replication. **a** Phage viruses attached by their tailpieces to a bacterium. (approx. 20,000 X) Note the remains of another bacterial cell, already destroyed by virus replication. **b** (below) A very thin section through a bacterium containing phage virus particles. The black, six-sided structures are the heads of the viruses. (60,000 X) **c** (facing page) Phage virus particles being released from a disintegrating bacterium. (35,000 X)

E. Kellenberger

a

b

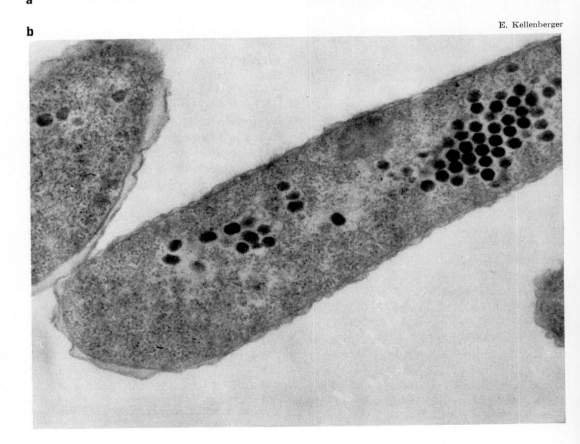

host. One interesting example of this phenomenon occurs in the bacteria long thought to cause diphtheria. It has recently been discovered that only those diphtheria bacteria that contain a specific phage DNA produce the poison which causes the disease. Is the bacterium, then, the cause of the disease? Or is the phage the cause?

Some scientists have suggested that a similar relation between our body cells and viruses may explain some types of cancer. This is just one of numerous ideas about causes of cancer now being investigated in many laboratories.

Variability of Virus Types

One of the characteristics of living things is their ability to produce offspring that may differ from the usual or normal parent type. These changes may be spontaneous and unpredictable in time. We call them mutations (page 158) if they are changes in the hereditary materials of the cell.

Many kinds of viruses are known to undergo mutations. Several mutant plant viruses produce disease symptoms in the host quite different from the normal type. Other mutations are known to occur in the bacteriophages. In fact, after only a decade of study, the known mutations of some phages are more numerous and better understood than are those of any other living things.

Certain kinds of mutant phage can be grown along with normal phage in the cells of susceptible bacteria. After the phage offspring have burst from the host cells, the virus particles can be isolated and their hereditary characteristics tested. It has been discovered that not only are the two parental types of phage (mutant and normal)

c

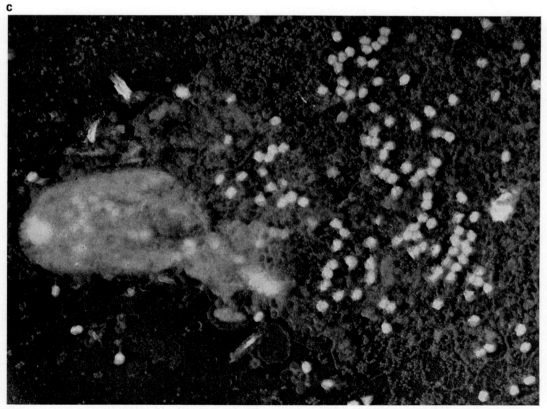

E. Kellenberger

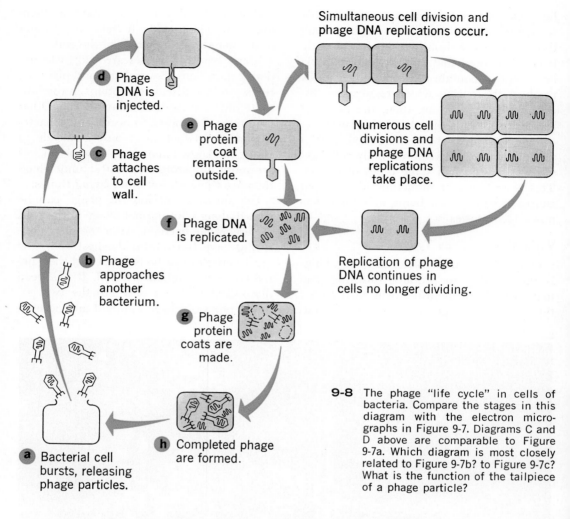

d Phage DNA is injected.

c Phage attaches to cell wall.

e Phage protein coat remains outside.

b Phage approaches another bacterium.

f Phage DNA is replicated.

g Phage protein coats are made.

a Bacterial cell bursts, releasing phage particles.

h Completed phage are formed.

Simultaneous cell division and phage DNA replications occur.

Numerous cell divisions and phage DNA replications take place.

Replication of phage DNA continues in cells no longer dividing.

9-8 The phage "life cycle" in cells of bacteria. Compare the stages in this diagram with the electron micrographs in Figure 9-7. Diagrams C and D above are comparable to Figure 9-7a. Which diagram is most closely related to Figure 9-7b? to Figure 9-7c? What is the function of the tailpiece of a phage particle?

present among the offspring, but also new forms in which characteristics of the parent viruses are combined. This reshuffling of heritable materials—the genes—is called **genetic recombination** and is another important characteristic of living things. The details of hereditary mechanisms, including mutation, recombination, and gene structure, are not the issue at this point. They are covered in Chapters 30–33. However, it is interesting to note here that such simple structures as viruses display the same hereditary principles found in the most complex organisms. There is unity to life!

CONCLUDING REMARKS

Although we have presented only a little of the total knowledge of viruses, you should now have enough information to understand better their position in the scale of organization (Figure 9-1) that was called to your attention at the beginning of this chapter.

Viruses show many of the properties of living organisms. Among these is the property of replication, though in the case of viruses this occurs only in the cells of a host. In complexity of structure, viruses—with their core of DNA (Figure 9-6) or RNA surrounded by a sheath of protein—somewhat resemble the chromosomes of higher plants and animals. The heritable materials—the **genes**—of viruses can mutate or be recombined when two different strains of viruses are brought together in the same host cell. This is characteristic of living things.

Where in the scale of organization do we reach the level of life? Is it at the lower end occupied by atoms or simple molecules? We all know that an atom of carbon, hydrogen, or oxygen has none of the properties of life shown by a virus. Atoms, even when they are combined into certain kinds of molecules—glucose ($C_6H_{12}O_6$), for example—cannot replicate in a living cell. The more complex molecules of the nucleic acids, however, do have the remarkable capacity of replication in living cells, a feature they share with viruses. Thus, as we go up the scale to the level of the most complex molecules, we approach the level of life. Viruses are placed only a little above this level.

Viruses are not as complex as cells, if for no other reason than the fact that they have none of the enzymes found in cells. Because of this, we place the virus just below the level of cellular organization.

How have viruses achieved their position in the scale of organization? We ask again: Do they represent the starting point of life in the evolution of living things? Or, on the other hand, have they been derived from some more complex cellular organisms, such as bacteria, which have become greatly reduced in structure? Could they be tiny parts of the hereditary materials of living cells which have gotten "out of hand" —that have escaped from the control of the cell and gone on to multiply and grow as parasites?

No matter what our hypothesis may be, we can see that viruses stand at the very threshold of life.

GUIDE QUESTIONS AND PROBLEMS

1. What characteristics of the tobacco mosaic virus caused Beijerinck to attribute life to it?
2. How did the electron microscope add information about the tobacco mosaic virus?
3. What factors limit the growth and reproduction of viruses? How do we interpret these limitations?
4. How do plant viruses differ in structure from bacterial and animal viruses?
5. How are virus particles reproduced? How does this relate to the cycle of the host cell?
6. What evidence of the role of viruses in bacterial activity was provided by a discovery concerning the diphtheria bacterium?
7. What properties of living organisms do viruses show? What characteristics of nonliving matter do they exhibit?
8. What are the advantages of using bacterial viruses in genetic experiments?

SUGGESTIONS FOR ADDITIONAL READING

Books

Burnet, F. M., *Viruses and Man.* Baltimore, Penguin Books, 1953.
An authoritative account of the viruses and their role in disease.

Smith, K. M., *Beyond the Microscope.* Baltimore, Penguin Books, 1949.
A popular introduction to the viruses.

Stanley, W. M., and E. G. Valens, *Viruses and the Nature of Life.* New York, Dutton, 1961.
An excellent group of essays on fundamental problems in the study of viruses.

Weidel, W., *Virus.* Ann Arbor, University of Michigan Press, 1959.
A good general introduction to the viruses.

Magazines and Journals

Fraenkel-Conrat, H., "Rebuilding a Virus." *Scientific American,* Vol. 194 (June 1956), pp. 42–47.

Horne, R. W., "The Structure of Viruses." *Scientific American,* Vol. 208 (January 1963), pp. 48–56.

Lwoff, A., "The Life Cycle of a Virus." *Scientific American,* Vol. 190 (March 1954), pp. 34–37.

10

BACTERIA—

PIONEERS OF

CELLULAR

ORGANIZATION

This page of your book, like all objects exposed to air, is covered with bacteria. Your skin may have more bacteria on its surface than there are human beings populating the earth. Your digestive tract, especially the intestines, is the home of many different kinds of bacteria. Without these microorganisms, many of the normal digestive processes of your body would not take place.

Cattle require special bacteria in their digestive tracts to break down the complex cellulose compounds in their food. Plants themselves would be lacking in certain important compounds needed for their growth if it were not for bacteria in the soil. Much of the carbon needed for the growth of all living things would be un-

available if there were no bacteria in soil, water, and air to cause the decay of dead plants and animals (Chapter 8).

Bacteria are found in the depths of the oceans. They have been collected miles above the earth. They have been isolated from the ice packs of the Arctic and Antarctic, and from the hot, humid rain forests of the tropics. It would be virtually impossible to name a part of the earth's land surfaces or oceans where bacteria are *not* found.

It is obvious that bacteria must be small in size to be present in such large numbers in so many places, yet not be seen with the unaided eye. How do we know that bacteria are so universally present? How do we know that bacteria exist at all, for that matter? These two questions were answered long ago when the story of the discovery of bacteria was gradually unfolded.

DISCOVERY OF BACTERIA

Advances in our understanding of living things are often dependent on the invention of special instruments. We know, for example, how important the electron microscope has been in the study of viruses. Without its tremendous power of magnification we would know very little about the shape and structure of these tiny objects. Similarly, the invention of the optical microscope had to occur before bacteria and other microorganisms could be discovered.

Leeuwenhoek—The First Bacteriologist

In the last years of the sixteenth century and the early years of the seventeenth century, the first microscopes were constructed (Figure 2-6). What an exciting new world of microscopic life was soon discovered! Marcello Malpighi, Nehemiah Grew, Robert Hooke, and Jan Swammerdam saw for the first time the microscopic parts of familiar organisms. Some of these men should seem like old friends by now.

One of the early microscopists, Antony van Leeuwenhoek, was the first to observe microorganisms. In much the same way that you and I might become interested in photography or stamp collecting, Leeuwenhoek became interested in lens grinding and the construction of microscopes. Suppose that you, instead of Leeuwenhoek, had just completed a new instrument that would magnify small objects many times and make them clearly visible for the first time. What would you choose to look at? Where would you start? The list would be endless, but it would have only a limited number of possibilities as imaginative as Leeuwenhoek's choice of a drop of water! You already know part of the story: we first encountered Leeuwenhoek in Chapter 2, where we learned of his role in the biogenesis-abiogenesis debate.

Leeuwenhoek discovered life in a form that was unexpected. He was amazed at the variety of tiny living objects he saw wriggling and darting across the field of his little microscope when he examined drops of various kinds of water (Figure 10-1). He became so enthusiastic about what he saw that he wrote several letters to the Royal Society in London. One letter with an account of what he saw was published by the Society in 1677, with the title "Concerning little Animals by him [Leeuwenhoek] observed in Rain-Well-Sea- and Snow-water; as also in water wherein Pepper had lain infused." In addition to drawings and descriptions of some protozoans and small aquatic animals, this article included the very first description of bacteria.

Some years later, in 1695, Leeuwenhoek submitted another letter with additional illustrations of these "little animals." Compare his drawings of bacteria (labeled "fig. E" and "fig. F") in Figure 10-1, with the bacteria you see in the laboratory when you use a modern microscope. Keep in mind that Leeuwenhoek made his observations nearly

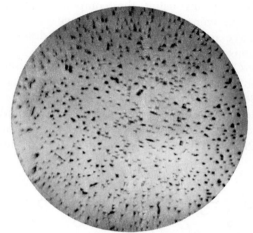

From *Arcana Naturae*, Detecta ab Antonio van Leeuwenhoeck, 1695

Courtesy of J. G. Van Cittert-Eymers, Utrecht University Museum

10-1 (Top) A reproduction of two drawings of bacteria made by Leeuwenhoek and published by the Royal Society of London in 1695. (Bottom) Photographic evidence that Leeuwenhoek could indeed see the shapes he recorded in his drawings. The photograph was taken recently, using one of Leeuwenhoek's original microscopes (see Figure 2-6). Although the photograph may seem fuzzy, if you look closely you will see many small rounded shapes and several rodlike ones, similar to the enlarged drawings above the photograph.

three hundred years ago, and perhaps you will agree that he made good microscopes and was a careful observer.

The Next Two Centuries

It is rather surprising that it took so long, after the invention of the microscope, for scientists to devote serious study to the bacteria. The word *bacterium,* derived from a Greek word meaning "little rod [or stick]," did not become a common part of the scientific vocabulary until the middle of the nineteenth century. It was even later in the same century before much was discovered about the structure and reproduction of bacteria. A German professor of botany, F. J. Cohn, eventually completed a magnificent book that represents the real beginnings of the study of bacteria. Cohn's observations using the compound microscope were so accurate that we can still make use of his illustrations and descriptions of bacteria.

Classification of the bacteria was a difficult problem because of their small size. Some biologists thought they were one-celled (**unicellular**) animals; others wanted to classify them in a separate kingdom—the **Protista** (pro·TIS·ta)—and not try to de-

scribe them as either plants or animals. Cohn was able to show that bacteria had a definite cell wall, often composed of two layers, and that in their structure they were very much like certain primitive plants called blue-green algae (see Chapter 13). The plantlike features of bacteria are generally recognized by most biologists today. However, as you study bacteria you will see why it is so difficult to decide how they should be classified.

Bacteria—Shape and Size

Until the structure and reproduction of viruses were clarified, bacteria were considered the smallest living things. When we talk about the sizes of viruses we use a scale of millimicrons. Bacteria are more conveniently measured in microns. (The comparative sizes of a virus and a bacterium were given in Figure 9-1.) Bacteria range in size from about 0.2 micron (μ) to 2μ in width, and from 2μ to 10μ in length. (For one type of bacteria, the terms "length" and "width" do not apply; these bacteria are sphere-shaped and can be described by a single dimension, their diameter.) All of the dimensions cited are within the range of the compound microscope.

Cohn in his pioneer work recognized three basic forms of bacteria (Figure 10-2): rod forms (**bacilli**—ba·SIL·i), spheres (**cocci** —KOK·si), and spiral or corkscrew forms (**spirilla**—spy·RIL·a). Although bacteria are unicellular organisms, the cells of some species may remain associated (after cell division) and form groups or colonies (Figure 10-2). Rod-shaped bacteria may form colonies that look like threads, or filaments, or chains of beads. These colonies are composed of the rod-shaped cells placed end to end. Sphere-shaped bacteria may occur in pairs, in groups of four, or in irregular grapelike clusters. Spiral-shaped bacteria seldom form colonies.

Differences in way of living usually are not correlated with bacterial shape.

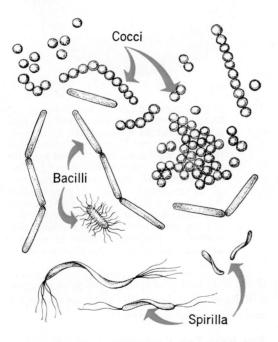

10-2 The three basic forms of bacteria. Some bacteria occur as single cells; others form colonies in pairs, chains, or irregular clusters. How do bacteria compare in size and shape with viruses?

STRUCTURE AND NUTRITION OF BACTERIA

By referring back to the scale of organization (Figure 9-1), you will see that the bacteria appear at the level of cellular organization—and immediately above the viruses. In many ways, however, a bacterium is much simpler in structure than the cells of the multicellular plants and animals you have examined.

Cell Structure

All who have studied the details of internal structure agree that bacteria do not have nuclei of the type found in cells of higher plants and animals. In the cells of these more complex organisms, the nucleus contains a nucleolus or two, is bounded by a visible membrane, and divides by mitosis. In bacteria there are no nucleoli, no nuclear membrane, and no typical mitosis. Yet, it has been demonstrated repeatedly that there is some kind of mechanism in bacteria for the transmission of hereditary characteristics.

Experiments have been performed showing that the bacterial hereditary determiners, or genes, have a linear arrangement (like beads in a chain)—an arrangement that is also characteristic of genes in the chromosomes of other organisms. Could it be that instead of a complex nucleus, the bacterial "nucleus" is a single chromosome?

Let us try another attack on the problem. We know that DNA comprises the genetic material of living cells. Perhaps we can answer the question by studying the DNA and its location in bacteria.

To locate DNA in a cell, special stains specific for DNA can be used. The results obtained from staining different kinds of bacteria are variable, but some carefully studied forms have their DNA concentrated in one or two deeply staining bodies (Figure 10-3a). Shortly before a bacterium divides, these DNA bodies divide and are equally distributed to the daughter cells. In this way the DNA bodies resemble chromosomes replicating in a dividing cell. More critical observations of bacterial "chromosomes" have been made by studying ultrathin sections of bacteria under the electron microscope (Figure 10-3b). Here the strands of DNA can be seen packed into a bacterial chromosome. It has been determined for some species of bacteria that the DNA molecule is about 3 millimicrons ($m\mu$) wide and as much as 1,000 microns (μ), or 1 mm, long! A bacterial DNA molecule is thus roughly 500 times as long as the bacterial cell that contains it! This may explain why the DNA appears to be twisted and folded as in Figure 10-3b. Are these structures similar to the chromosomes of more highly evolved organisms? Some investigators think they are, but until we know more about the fine structure of both kinds of chromosomes, it is difficult to determine their degree of resemblance.

Other structures of a bacterial cell (Figure 10-4) are small vacuoles, ribosomes, and granules of stored food. (The ribosomes are too small to show in Figure 10-4.) Water, of course, is an important constituent of bacterial cells. As much as 90 percent of the cell is water. The movement of dissolved materials in and out of the cell is regulated by a cell membrane, formed by the cytoplasm that lies next to the inner face of the cell wall. Structurally, the cytoplasm of a bacterial cell is quite similar to cytoplasm found in the living cells of organisms higher on the scale of organization.

In view of the importance of mitochondria in the oxidative reactions of the cell (Chapter 6), we might expect to find them in the cells of all organisms. Bacteria, however, lack mitochondria—at least of the sort found in most cells. Some bacterial species have structures that vaguely suggest mitochondria. In other species of bacteria the enzymes normally found in mitochondria are localized on or near the cell wall.

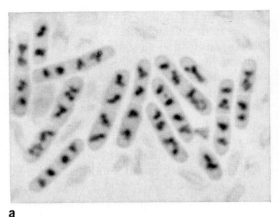
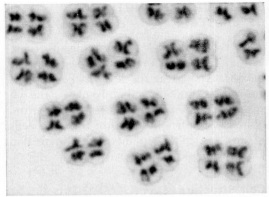

C. F. Robinow

a

10-3 **a** Bacteria of two of the basic forms (bacilli and cocci) prepared with a special stain to reveal their DNA. The DNA is localized in discrete bodies—the bacterial chromosomes—shown in various stages of division. The photographs were made through a compound microscope. **b** An ultrathin section of a dividing bacterium, photographed with an electron microscope. The sectioned bacterial chromosome in each daughter cell shows as twisted, contorted strands of DNA. (78,000 X)

C. F. Robinow

b

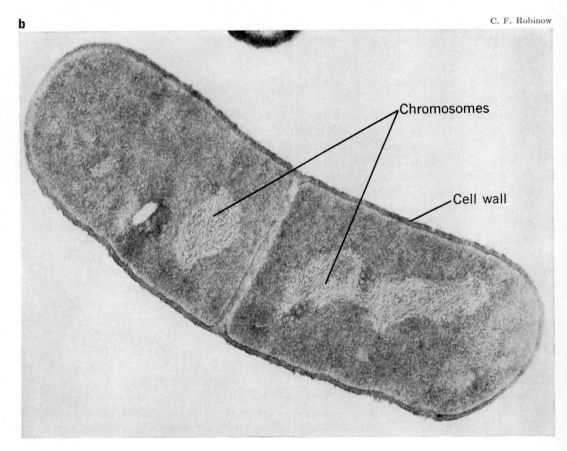

Chromosomes

Cell wall

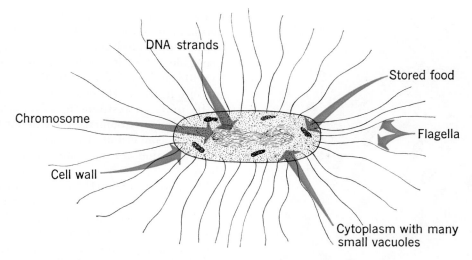

10-4 Diagram of a generalized bacterium. Acording to its shape, how would you classify this bacterium? Note that the flagella are embedded in the cytoplasm, inside the cell wall. Are all bacteria flagellated? What structure of this bacterial cell is like that of a plant? Is there also a structural resemblance to an animal? Which of the structures are regularly found in both plant and animal cells?

The bacterial cell wall (Figure 10-3b) is a complex structure composed of proteins and carbohydrates. Unlike the cell walls of plants, however, cell walls of most bacteria do not contain cellulose. Some bacteria may have a slime capsule surrounding the cell wall. Among bacteria that cause infections, those with capsules seem to be more resistant to the defenses of the body than those without capsules. The encapsulated forms, therefore, are more likely to cause disease. The bacterium causing pneumonia is an excellent example of a capsulated form that causes disease. A different strain of the same bacterium without capsules does not cause pneumonia.

A unique feature of some bacteria is their ability to form highly resistant **endospores** (EN·doh·sporz—Figure 10-5a). Endospores are produced when part of the living substance of a bacterium is surrounded by an almost indestructible wall. Mature endospores occur singly in the bacterium and look like tiny spheres or ovals occupying either the center or one end of the old cell

in which they are formed. When an endospore germinates (Figure 10-5b), it gives rise to a single bacterium. Endospores can survive the most adverse environmental conditions. Long periods of drying seem to have little or no effect upon them. In one experiment, endospores were kept in a dry condition for sixty years. At the end of this time, they readily germinated when provided with water and proper nutrients.

Most bacteria are killed by boiling water (100° C), but endospores resist this rough treatment. It requires a temperature of 121° C (250° F) for a period of fifteen minutes to kill endospores of most bacteria. If Pasteur, Spallanzani, Needham, and other early investigators of spontaneous generation (see Chapter 2) had known about endospores and their resistance to boiling, the mysteries of spontaneous generation would have been easy for them to solve.

Many diluted chemicals such as chlorine, "Merthiolate," and iodine may kill bacteria —but not their endospores. Even deepfreezing will not kill them. During recent expe-

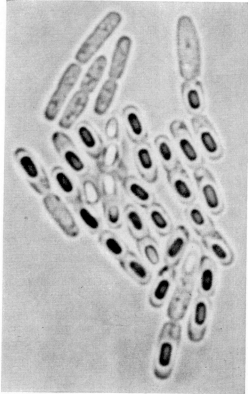

a

Both, C. F. Robinow

b

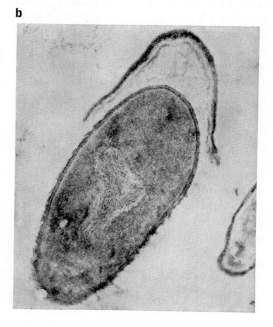

ditions to Antarctica, biologists isolated and germinated endospores obtained from snow and ice deposited centuries ago. What remarkable little bits of life endospores are to withstand such drastic treatment! Nothing else in the world of living things seems to be quite so resistant to adverse conditions of the environment. We can hardly escape the conclusion that endospores have survival value for the bacteria that form them.

Many kinds of bacteria are motile; that is, they can move. Motile bacteria have slender, whiplike threads called **flagella** (fla·JEL·a—Figure 10-6), which propel the bacteria through the water. Each flagellum is embedded at its base in the cytoplasm of the cell, from which it extends through the cell wall to the outside.

The diameter of a single flagellum is approximately 12 mμ—about the same dimension as the diameter of a molecule of some proteins. Because of their small size, the flagella of bacteria are invisible under a compound microscope unless first specially treated and stained. Studies using the electron microscope show that the flagella of most bacteria consist of a single strand (Figure 10-6). Chemical analyses have shown the substance of the strand to resemble the contractile proteins responsible for the contraction of animal muscle cells. The presence of the protein gives us an explanation of the physical basis for bacterial propulsion, just as it explains muscle contraction. (Propulsion by means of flagella will be discussed along with other types of locomotion in Chapter 26.)

←──────────────

10-5 **a** Bacteria with endospores. A single, thick-walled endospore is produced by each cell. In what way is an endospore of importance in the life of a bacterium? (36,000 X) **b** An electron micrograph of a germinating endospore. The remains of the old endospore wall can be seen at the top of the photograph, near one end of the new bacterium. (49,000 X)

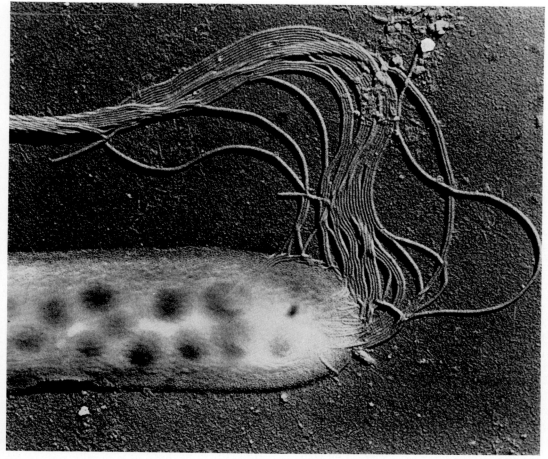

A. L. Houwink

10-6 A tuft of flagella at the end of a bacillus. This electron micrograph reveals that the base of a flagellum is in the cytoplasm of the cell. What substance is responsible for the movement of flagella in bacteria? (45,000 X)

Nutrition of Bacteria

Like all other living things, bacteria need energy for their growth, maintenance, and multiplication.

Most bacteria are **heterotrophic** (het·er·o-TROF·ik) in their nutrition. That is, they cannot synthesize their organic compounds from simple inorganic substances. They require a multitude of complex organic materials such as amino acids, glucose, and vitamins, in addition to inorganic substances. Since most bacteria are not photosynthetic, they cannot use light, as green plants do, to synthesize the substances they need. There is only one other source of energy readily available—the organic compounds in the environment. For example, the soil is full of organic compounds in the form of **humus,** which is the material resulting from the partial decay of plants and animals. Many soil-inhabiting bacteria have very extensive enzyme systems that break down the complex substances of humus to simpler compounds that the bacteria can absorb and utilize as a source of energy.

Organisms capable of obtaining their nutrition from organic compounds in this way are called **saprophytes** (SAP·ro·fyts). Bacterial saprophytes cause decay of dead animal and vegetable material as they convert complex organic compounds to simpler ones.

Some bacteria lack certain complex systems of enzymes; instead they depend on enzymes of other living organisms (hosts) to synthesize glucose, amino acids, vitamins, and other substances for growth. Thus these bacteria are parasites. Many parasitic bacteria cause disease and sometimes the death of their host, a topic discussed in the next chapter.

Some kinds of bacteria are **autotrophic** (au·toh·TROF·ik)—that is, they can synthesize their organic compounds from simple inorganic substances. A few of the autotrophic species are photosynthetic. Photosynthetic bacteria have a pigment very similar in molecular structure to the chlorophyll of

green plants. Unlike most green plants, which have their chlorophyll in chloroplasts, bacterial chlorophyll is dispersed in the bacterial cell. Other autotrophic species of bacteria obtain their energy from oxidation of some inorganic substance such as iron, sulfur, atmospheric hydrogen, or nitrogen compounds. No matter what the source of energy, some of it is directed to the production of new bacteria cells—that is, to reproduction.

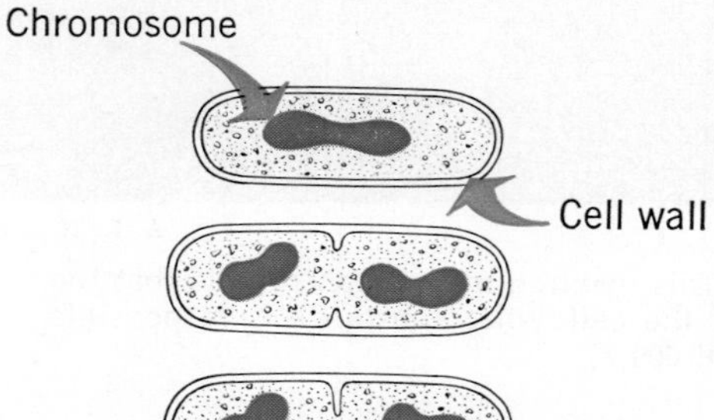

REPRODUCTION OF A UNICELLULAR ORGANISM

Using your microscope in the laboratory, you will look at cultures of living bacteria. In the same way that Leeuwenhoek and Pasteur saw them, you can see countless thousands of tiny cells. You might wonder, as they did, about the origin of these little cells. If all of them arose from pre-existing cells, as Pasteur and others suggested long ago (Chapter 2), then bacteria must have a rapid method of reproduction. Cell division is that method.

Cell Division in Bacteria

In multicellular organisms, the cells produced by cell division generally remain together, and larger organisms are the result. A bacterium, however, is a single-celled organism. When it divides and produces two cells, we have two organisms where we started with one (Figure 10-7). This kind of reproduction is **asexual** (ay·SEK·shoo·al), meaning that it does not involve the union of sex cells in the manner characteristic of so many animals and plants.

When there are sufficient amounts of water and nutrients, and when the temperature is favorable, bacteria can divide very rapidly. A bacterium can divide, and the two daughter cells can grow and start dividing—all in a period of twenty minutes. If we were to start with a single bacterium, it soon would divide to form 2 cells, then ap-

Chromosome

Cell wall

10-7 Division of a bacterium. The division of the cell is preceded by division of the chromosome. Compare this set of diagrams with Figure 10-3. Cell division of the kind illustrated here is called *fission*.

proximately twenty minutes later each of the 2 cells would divide simultaneously to form 4, each of the 4 dividing to form 8, then 16, 32, 64, 128, 256, and so on, doubling every twenty minutes. If this kind of cell increase, called a geometric increase (Figure 10-8), were to continue once every twenty minutes for twenty-four hours, a mass of bacteria weighing approximately 2,000 tons would be produced from a single cell! Actually this would never happen, because the bacteria would soon run out of sufficient water and nutrients needed for their reproduction. Also, as a bacterial population grows, the bacteria usually produce substances, such as alcohol or acids, which are poisonous to them. The accumulation of these substances can cause a decrease in the rate of reproduction, so that the number of new cells produced is about equal to the number of cells that die. As time passes, even greater concentrations of poisons accumulate. These can cause the death rate of cells to exceed the rate of reproduction, and sooner or later all the cells may die. Figure 10-9 is a graph showing changes in rates of reproduction of bacteria resulting from changes in the environment as described above. Experiments illustrating this are in the laboratory manual.

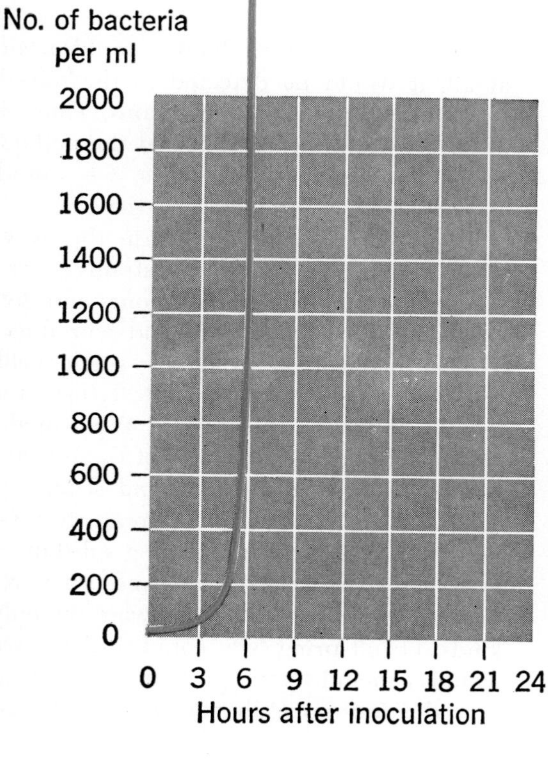

The Life Cycle—The Beginnings of Sexual Reproduction

Do bacteria reproduce sexually, that is, do they ever form sex cells, or **gametes** (GAM·eets), that unite with one another in the production of offspring? These questions have been asked for many years, but until recently the answers were very elusive. Many descriptions of a sexual stage were published, but these differed so much that they served only to emphasize the fact that no one was quite sure about the life cycle of bacteria.

It had long been known that bacteria mutate. Furthermore, it was found that mutations could be induced by exposing bacteria to high-energy radiation (X rays or ultraviolet radiation) or certain chemicals. Could an experiment be devised to combine two mutant strains of bacteria so that they would have the opportunity of exchanging or making new combinations of the mutant genes?

Such an experiment was undertaken in 1946 at Yale University. The investigators were Joshua Lederberg and Edward L. Tatum, who later were awarded the Nobel prize for this and other researches. First they had to obtain the two different bacterial strains that they hoped to cross. To do this, they first selected a "wild type" of

No. of bacteria
  per ml

2000
1800 —
1600 —
1400 —
1200 —
1000 —
 800 —
 600 —
 400 —
 200 —
   0

0   3   6   9   12 15 18 21 24
Hours after inoculation

10-8 Initial growth of a population of bacteria. The almost vertical ascent of the yellow line illustrates graphically the rapid reproduction of bacterial cells under ideal conditions. Could the increase go on indefinitely, as indicated by the yellow line that runs off the top of the page?

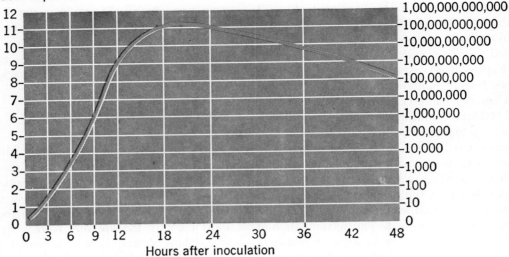

Hours after inoculation

10-9 What actually happens to the bacterial population in Figure 10-8 can be seen by using the logarithm of the actual number of bacterial cells present in the culture. The result is a graphic illustration of the growth and decline of the large population of cells. What point on this graph corresponds to the point at which the yellow line measuring population growth ran off the page in Figure 10-8?

bacteria capable of synthesizing the substances it needed for growth. Using irradiation to produce mutations, Lederberg and Tatum obtained a "triple nutritional mutant"—a strain that was unable to make three of the substances required for its growth. If it was to grow at all, it had to be supplied with the three substances it could not make for itself. Let us call these substances A, B, and C (see Figure 10-10).

A second triple nutritional mutant was obtained by once again irradiating the wild type bacteria. The second mutant could synthesize substances A, B, and C, but could not synthesize three other necessary compounds, which we will call D, E, and F. It appeared that six genes had been made to mutate, three in each mutant strain.

The two mutant strains could be grown together if the growth medium was supplied with all six substances—three that one mutant needed and three that the other

needed. If sexual reproduction could occur at all, it would be detected in the mixed culture of the two mutant strains. Thus, if any cells were formed that had the mutant genes combined in new ways, we would suspect sexual reproduction as the cause.

The experiment proceeded in this way. The genetically different strains were brought together for several hours and given the opportunity to grow and reproduce. The next step was to isolate single cells from the mixed culture and test them for their nutritional requirements. What might we expect to find as a result of these tests? It would be no surprise to find strains of offspring exactly like the parent strains— that is, some offspring requiring substances A, B, and C for their growth and others requiring D, E, and F. If these were the only kinds of offspring we could isolate, we would conclude that probably no sexual reproduction—no exchange of genetic ma-

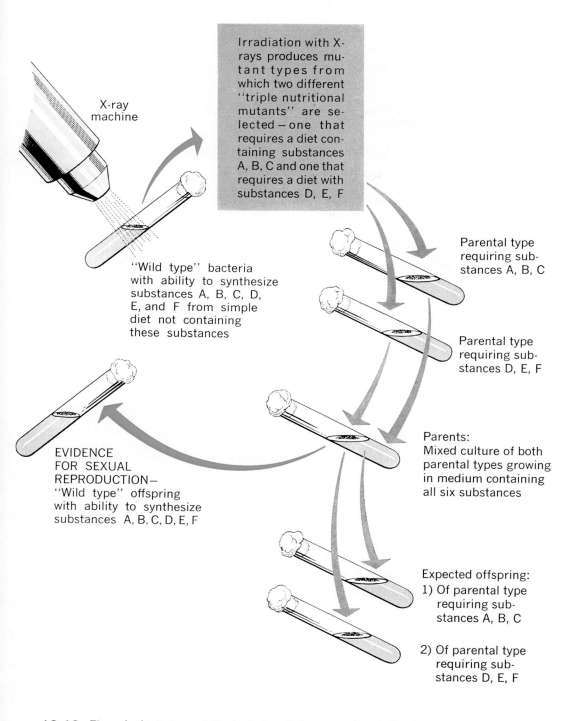

X-ray
machine

Irradiation with X-rays produces mutant types from which two different "triple nutritional mutants" are selected — one that requires a diet containing substances A, B, C and one that requires a diet with substances D, E, F

"Wild type" bacteria with ability to synthesize substances A, B, C, D, E, and F from simple diet not containing these substances

Parental type requiring substances A, B, C

Parental type requiring substances D, E, F

EVIDENCE FOR SEXUAL REPRODUCTION— "Wild type" offspring with ability to synthesize substances A, B, C, D, E, F

Parents: Mixed culture of both parental types growing in medium containing all six substances

Expected offspring:
1) Of parental type requiring substances A, B, C

2) Of parental type requiring substances D, E, F

10-10 The principal steps of the Lederberg-Tatum experiment. In what respect does the experiment offer proof that some bacteria do exchange genetic material and produce offspring with new combinations of genes?

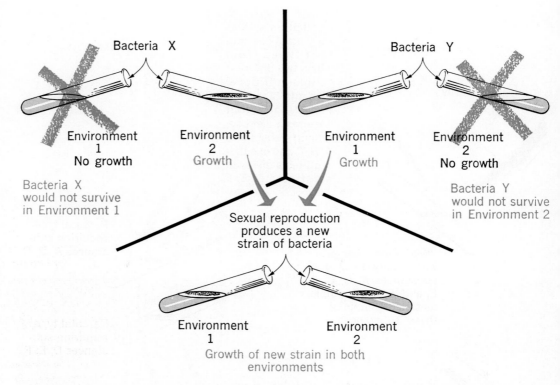

Bacteria X

Environment 1
No growth

Environment 2
Growth

Bacteria X
would not survive
in Environment 1

Bacteria Y

Environment 1
Growth

Environment 2
No growth

Bacteria Y
would not survive
in Environment 2

Sexual reproduction
produces a new
strain of bacteria

Environment 1

Environment 2

Growth of new strain in both
environments

10-11 An experiment to show the biological advantage of sexual reproduction. Two strains of bacteria (X and Y) have different requirements for growth. X cannot grow under the environmental conditions required by Y, and Y cannot grow in the environment of X. The new strain of bacteria, one of perhaps several resulting from sexual reproduction between X and Y, can grow in both environments.

terial—had occurred. On the other hand, if such an exchange *had* occurred, we might expect to find new kinds of offspring. Two new kinds would be (1) bacteria requiring all six substances for growth, and (2) bacteria that could synthesize all six substances. The second kind would be like the wild type; it could grow on a medium without supplements.

For Lederberg and Tatum, the testing of offspring proved rewarding. They isolated the wild type of bacteria from the mixed culture! But was this really an example of genetic recombination, resulting from sexual reproduction—or was it simply a case of "back mutation" in which the mutant genes reverted to the wild type? The latter expla-

nation seemed most improbable to the investigators, because the probability of *three* genes of either mutant strain changing back to the wild type all at once was very, very slight—about one chance in 1,000,000,000,-000,000,000. All biologists are now convinced, as a result of these experiments, that recombination *does* occur in at least some species of bacteria. This is best interpreted to show that some kind of sexual process is responsible.

This conviction was later confirmed by visual evidence. Electron microscopes were used to photograph cells in mixtures of two mutant strains, which could be distinguished by their structure. It was discovered that pairs of bacterial cells, one of each type, form little tubes (Figure 10-12), which make possible the physical transfer of genetic material from one cell to the other. It seems that we have been introduced to a simple means of sexual reproduction in the evolution of primitive organisms.

Advantages of Sexual Reproduction

Sexual reproduction appears to be an important, perhaps essential, property of most kinds of life. Is this an accidental occurrence in evolution, or is there some advantage to organisms in being able to reproduce sexually?

It is easy to demonstrate a biological advantage of sexual reproduction in the experiment just described. Let us start by comparing the offspring of bacteria isolated from the mixed culture, and ask ourselves which ones have the best chance for survival. It must be obvious that the sexually produced wild type, which does not require the addition of supplementary materials for growth, has the best chance for survival. The asexually formed triple nutritional mutants, on the other hand, require substances not provided by the usual environment. They can survive only in environments in which the substances are provided. Figure 10-11 illustrates the contribution sexual reproduction can make toward survival.

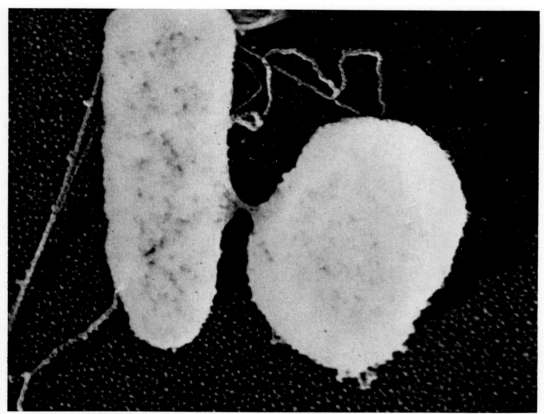

T. F. Anderson

10-12 Visible evidence that certain bacteria can exchange cell materials. This electron micrograph reveals a little tube between bacteria of two different strains. Biologists believe that genetic material moves from one cell to the other through the tube. What kind of reproduction is initiated by the exchange?

If all organisms had only asexual methods of reproduction, and the source of variability was restricted to mutations that occur in their own genes, then subsequent evolution among living things would be very slow indeed. With the introduction of sexual reproduction, a new source of variability is provided by the *exchange* of genes, making available to the species a whole new variety of genetic combinations. Thus, the greater the amount of variability appearing within a species, the greater the chances are that survival will be possible in the face of a radical change in the environment.

The mechanisms and factors affecting evolution are discussed fully in Chapters 34 and 35. In later chapters we will also see to what extent sexual reproduction has evolved in plants and animals more complex than the bacteria.

Not long ago it was thought that bacteria, because of their small size and simple structure, were at the bottom of the ladder of life. However, when compared with viruses—the simplest living particles we know—the bacteria seem to have come a long way along the path of evolution.

GUIDE QUESTIONS AND PROBLEMS

1. In view of the statement that it would be virtually impossible to name a part of the earth's land surfaces or oceans where bacteria are *not* found, what would happen if the world were suddenly left without bacteria?
2. What are the difficulties in classifying bacteria?
3. What were Professor Cohn's arguments for classifying bacteria as plants?
4. What is the evidence that heredity in bacteria is related to DNA, as it is in all higher organisms?

5. Of what advantage to the bacteria is the formation of endospores?
6. In what ways do saprophytic bacteria obtain their nutritive requirements? Parasitic bacteria? Autotrophic bacteria?
7. What factors prevent the continuation of the maximum rate of bacterial reproduction for very long?
8. How can the experiments of Lederberg and Tatum be interpreted?
9. What additional evidence supporting this interpretation has been obtained from electron microscopy?

SUGGESTIONS FOR ADDITIONAL READING

Books

Brock, T., *Milestones in Microbiology*. Englewood Cliffs (N. J.), Prentice-Hall, 1961.
An excellent sourcebook of original documents in the field of microbiology.
De Kruif, P., *Microbe Hunters*. [1926] New York, Pocket Books, 1959.
Excitingly written story of the work of the pioneers in microbiology.
Dobell, C. (ed.), *Antony van Leeuwenhoek and His "Little Animals."* New York, Dover Publications, 1962.
Translations of the letters in which Leeuwenhoek described his great discoveries of bacteria and protozoa. Good descriptions of his microscopes and his work.
Dubos, R., *Pasteur and Modern Science*. New York, Doubleday, 1960.
An exciting, accurate, and inspiring account of Pasteur's life and work.
Pelczar, M. J., and R. D. Reid, *Microbiology*. New York, McGraw-Hill, 1958.
College level textbook on general microbiology, with good diagrams and explanations.
Stanier, R. Y., M. Doudoroff, and E. A. Adelberg, *The Microbial World*. Englewood Cliffs (N. J.), Prentice-Hall, 1957.
An up-to-date, modern synthesis of microbiology on the college level.

11

SMALL

ORGANISMS OF

GREAT ECONOMIC

IMPORTANCE

The decomposition of dead plants and animals of all kinds may not be a very pleasant subject of thought, but we have learned in Chapter 8 how important decomposition is in maintaining a balance of nature. Without decomposition by bacteria and other organisms such as molds and yeasts, the cycling of the important elements nitrogen, carbon, hydrogen, and oxygen would soon cease, and so would life on earth. The nitrogen cycle and the carbon-hydrogen-oxygen cycle are examples of ways in which bacteria and other decomposers are indirectly, but vitally, important to us.

There are many other ways in which these microorganisms have a more direct effect on our everyday living.

HARMFUL BACTERIA

As is so frequently the case in scientific investigation, observations and experiments in one field of knowledge help us to gain understanding in seemingly unrelated areas. So it was in the late 1800's when Pasteur was conducting his famous experiments on the causes of fermentation. In the process of proving that yeasts and bacteria were responsible for fermentation (we will learn more of this later in the chapter), Pasteur noticed that frequently wine became "sick," or sour, and that certain kinds of bacteria were responsible. The bacteria produced acid, causing the wine to turn to vinegar. Pasteur reasoned, without good proof, that if bacteria could have such an adverse affect on wine, perhaps they could cause sickness or disease in animals and man.

It was *less than one hundred years ago* that Pasteur developed this hypothesis, which later became known as the Germ Theory of Disease. There was much opposition to this revolutionary idea, and Pasteur was hard pressed to defend himself. Such opposition is not unusual. New ideas are rarely well supported by data, so scientists are cautious in accepting them.

Koch's Postulates

Support for Pasteur's ideas came from Robert Koch (Figure 11-1), a young German physician who was a contemporary of Pasteur. Koch had become interested in a lethal disease called anthrax, which had caused 528 human deaths and over 56,000 deaths among horses, cows, and sheep during a three-year period in a single district of Novgorod, Russia. A bacillus (Figure 11-2) could always be found in the blood of diseased animals. Was it the cause of anthrax? Koch discovered that the bacillus multiplied rapidly in the aqueous (AY-kwee·us) humor (the fluid in the front part of the eye) of an ox's eye, and that he could watch its stages of development in extracts

Linda Hall Library

11-1 Robert Koch (1843–1910). This brilliant German physician, along with Louis Pasteur and F. J. Cohn, established the science of bacteriology in the latter part of the last century.

of aqueous humor under a microscope. As the bacillus aged, little dots developed in the cells. These, we now know, were endospores. Although Koch had discovered the life cycle of the organism, he had not yet proved any relationship between the organism and anthrax. What would happen, however, if blood containing the bacteria was taken from an animal showing symptoms of anthrax and injected into a healthy animal? There was only one way to find out. Koch began to inoculate living animals—guinea pigs, rabbits, and mice. Invariably they died of anthrax within 20 to 30 hours.

If blood containing the bacillus was dried, it lost its ability to infect after about five weeks. If spores were present and these were dried, however, then for at least five years the bacterium retained its **virulence** (VIHR·yoo·lentz)—that is, its capacity to produce poison (or for some bacteria, disease symptoms in some other way) in the host animal. As a result of these experiments, Koch provided final proof that bacteria do cause disease in animals.

In 1882 Koch completed another study, his monumental work, which demonstrated that another bacillus causes a disease of man—tuberculosis. In this particular work he devised experimental methods, based in part on his earlier work with anthrax. These methods of inquiry soon became rules for all who studied **pathogenic** (path-o·JEN·ik—disease-producing) organisms. The rules are usually called *Koch's postulates* (Figure 11-3). However, he never set them forth in a list of the kind that follows:

1. The organism believed to cause the disease must *always* be present in the host when the disease occurs. (Koch certainly realized that the anthrax bacillus was *always* present in cattle, mice, and rabbits diseased with anthrax. He had never failed to observe it under his microscope in blood from these diseased animals.)

2. The organism believed to cause the disease must be isolated from the host and grown in pure culture. (A pure culture of bacteria is one in which there is only one species of bacteria. The pure culture technique you will be using in the laboratory is essentially the same as that devised by Koch.)

3. The organisms obtained from pure culture, when inoculated into healthy hosts, must produce the characteristics of the disease. (In his early work on anthrax, Koch used the technique of inoculation when he injected blood from animals infected with anthrax into healthy animals; the blood was not a pure culture, though, since it probably contained other organisms.)

4. The organism believed to cause the disease must be re-isolated, grown in pure culture, and compared with the organism first injected. (This addition to the postulates was added at a later time by Erwin F. Smith of the U.S. Department of Agriculture.)

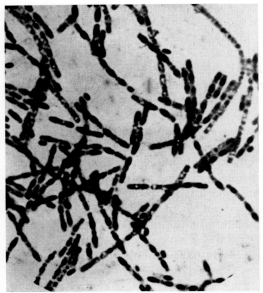

Armed Forces Institute of Pathology

11-2 Anthrax bacilli, shown forming endo-spores. From observations of these bacilli, Koch obtained evidence on which to base effective methods for studying disease-producing organisms.

We have seen how Robert Koch succeeded in proving Pasteur's hypothesis that bacteria can cause disease in animals and man. It was not long after Koch's epoch-making discoveries that Thomas Burrell (1829–1916), a botanist at the University of Illinois, demonstrated that a disease — fire blight of pears—was caused by bacteria. Since his discovery, more than one hundred diseases of plants have been attributed to bacteria. These hundred or more plant diseases, added to numerous diseases of animals and man caused by bacteria, further emphasize the important role bacteria play in our lives. But are bacterial diseases of humans as important now as they were one hundred years ago? Let us look at the list.

Here are some of the bacterial diseases of humans:

Anthrax, bacterial pneumonia, botulism, bubonic plague, cholera, diphtheria, bac-terial dysentery, syphilis, leprosy, meningitis, scarlet fever, septic sore throat, tetanus, tuberculosis, tularemia, typhoid fever, undulant fever, and whooping cough.

How many of these diseases have you or members of your family contracted? There are probably many of them that are not even familiar to you—yet all have at one time or another been important within the last two hundred years.

Tuberculosis was of major concern to every family until twenty years ago (Figure 11-4). To have tuberculosis meant a long period of rest, isolation, and treatment in a sanatorium, with only a remote prospect of complete recovery and a useful life. Bacterial pneumonia was even more often fatal than tuberculosis. There was no very useful drug, and only administration of oxygen relieved the patient. Today we no longer need live in such fear of bacterial pneumonia, *or any of the other bacterial diseases on the list.* We know that there are effective countermeasures—effective controls for these diseases—with all of us the beneficiaries in living longer, healthier lives.

What Is Disease?

Thus far we have talked about disease as sickness produced in an organism by bacteria (or viruses—see Chapter 9). Many other kinds of organisms besides bacteria and viruses are responsible for infectious diseases. Chapter 1 told us about the infectious disease malaria, caused by *Plasmodium,* a protozoan. Other diseases caused by protozoans are African sleeping sickness and amoebic dysentery. Many other organisms cause infectious diseases. Here we can list such notable examples as liver flukes, tapeworms, hookworms, and nematodes of plants. All these are wormlike animals.

Fungi cause some of the most important diseases in the world. Smuts and rusts of grain, and late blight of potatoes, are a few

11-3 KOCH'S POSTULATES

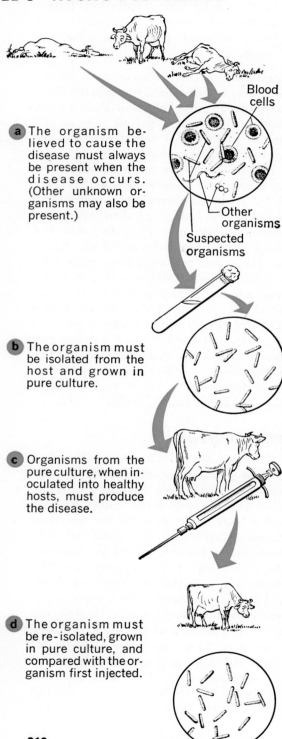

a The organism believed to cause the disease must always be present when the disease occurs. (Other unknown organisms may also be present.)

Blood cells

Suspected organisms

Other organisms

b The organism must be isolated from the host and grown in pure culture.

c Organisms from the pure culture, when inoculated into healthy hosts, must produce the disease.

d The organism must be re-isolated, grown in pure culture, and compared with the organism first injected.

that have had a profound effect on the lives of men.

By definition, *disease* includes not only all the infectious diseases of plants and animals, whether caused by bacteria, viruses, molds, protozoa, or other organisms, but any malfunction in an organism, no matter what the cause. With this definition in mind we would have to include as possible causes of disease the consequences of malnutrition, vitamin deficiency, air pollution, chemical poisons, inherited malfunctions, and even defects resulting from injury and imperfections in development.

Naturally, the methods of control of diseases are as diverse as the causes. But we are interested here chiefly in control of diseases caused by bacteria and viruses.

To understand how to control a disease, it is necessary, as pointed out in the case of malaria (Chapter 1), to know what the **pathogen** (PATH·o·jen), or disease-producing organism, is. Koch's postulates are the guide here. In addition, we need to know something about the way in which the pathogen enters the host, the degree of the pathogen's virulence, and whether or not the host is *resistant* to the pathogen.

How Pathogens Enter the Host

As you will discover from your laboratory experiments, microorganisms are everywhere around and on us. Fortunately only a small number of them are pathogens. In animals, including man, most pathogens enter the body of their host through its openings or through wounds. For example, the common pathway for entrance of the typhoid bacillus is through the mouth. The bacillus is usually present in water contaminated with sewage. The entrance of the organism causing gonorrhea is through the openings of the sex organs. Pores or wounds in the surfaces of plants provide a direct entrance for plant pathogens.

Although epidermal tissue protects plants and animals by excluding pathogenic organisms, it can be accidentally broken or injured. A wound or lesion allows bacteria, fungi, or viruses that normally would have remained inactive on an unbroken surface to invade the tissues and cells. The tobacco mosaic virus, for example, can be transmitted by rubbing juice containing the virus on the leaf of a healthy tobacco plant. The virus enters the host through breaks in the epidermis caused by the rubbing. Gas gangrene and other similar infections of animals can start in a wound that ruptures the skin.

The Virulence of Pathogens

Virulence depends on two major factors: the ability of the pathogen to invade, spread, and multiply in the host; and the **toxins** (TOK·sinz—poisons) or other ill effects it produces. To be virulent, an organism must be able to invade tissue and, once there, produce toxins or in some other way harm the host.

Many conditions influence the ability of a pathogen to invade, spread, and multiply in the host tissue. First of all, the site of invasion must provide favorable temperature, adequate nutrients, moisture, and proper oxygen level for the pathogen to become established. Differences in these conditions in the host may partially determine in which tissues a pathogen will become established. For example, the common cause of bacterial pneumonia is *Diplococcus pneumoniae* (dip·lo·KOK·us new·MOHN·ih-ee). This species thrives in an environment rich in oxygen, such as the lungs. The tetanus bacillus, by contrast, grows only in a deep cut or wound containing dead tissue, where the oxygen content has been greatly reduced. There the organism grows and secretes its deadly toxin, which diffuses eventually to the central nervous system and does its damage.

Some bacteria can protect themselves from being destroyed by their hosts. For example, *Diplococcus pneumoniae* pro-

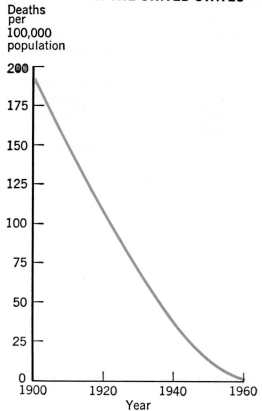

THE DECLINING DEATH RATE FROM TUBERCULOSIS IN THE UNITED STATES

Deaths per 100,000 population

11-4 Many diseases other than tuberculosis have shown a remarkable decline in death rate during the past 25 to 50 (or more) years. The average life expectancy of an infant born today in the United States is seventy years. What do you suppose the corresponding life expectancy was fifty years ago? seventy-five years ago? one hundred years ago?

duces a capsule that protects it from certain of the host's white blood cells, called **phagocytes** (FAG·o·sites). The virulent *Staphylococcus aureus* (staf·ih·lo·KOK·us AU-ree·us), which causes boils and abscesses, is protected in the host by the action of an enzyme—**coagulase** (ko·AG·yoo·lays). The enzyme forms a clot of microscopic proportions around the bacterium. The clot seems to act as a protective coat around the bacterium, keeping it from being ingested by phagocytes.

Growth of a pathogen clearly depends on favorable nutritional and environmental factors. But these factors alone are not enough to account for the successful invasion of the host. Several bacterial enzymes have been discovered that apparently help the microbe invade the host. One such enzyme, called the "spreading factor," is produced by pathogenic **streptococci** (strep-toh-KOK-si). The enzyme destroys the substance that holds the host cells together. As the cells separate, the streptococci invade the host and spread rapidly through its tissues.

Along with the capacity to invade the host, the ability to produce toxins is important in determining the virulence of bacteria and viruses. Pathogens vary in their toxicity, that is, in the amount of toxins they produce. Some highly virulent species, like those causing diphtheria, gas gangrene, or tetanus (lockjaw), secrete **exotoxins** (ek-so-TOK-sinz). These exotoxins spread rapidly throughout the host, by diffusion and circulation, from the site of infection. By contrast, organisms with comparatively low virulence are characterized by the production

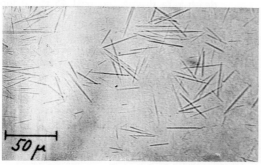

Society of American Bacteriologists

11-5 Crystals of purified botulinum exotoxin. Although these small crystals appear to be harmless, they harbor one of the most lethal toxins known (including snake venom). Fortunately, botulism food poisoning is extremely rare today.

of **endotoxins** (en-doh-TOK-sinz). These are retained inside the bacterial cell and are freed only if the cell is broken down.

Exotoxins are highly poisonous proteins. One of the most lethal (Figure 11-5) is formed by the common soil bacterium *Clostridium botulinum* (klos-TRID-ih-um bot-yoo-LY-num). This treacherous organism can be found on the surfaces of almost any type of vegetable (string beans, asparagus, etc.) that is canned—either at home or in a canning factory. Like all clostridia, this species forms endospores, which can survive the heat of the home pressure cooker. When the contaminated cans cool, endospores germinate, and the bacteria grow and produce exotoxins. Fortunately, there is usually some evidence that the bacterium is present, because it forms a gas that causes cans or their lids to show a suspicious bulge. Such a can should be thrown away for good reason; between 70 and 80 percent of all people who consume this exotoxin suffer a painful death. Fortunately, botulism food poisoning is rare, because the exotoxin produced by the bacterium is a protein and consequently is easily destroyed by heat or prolonged standing.

Endotoxins, by contrast, are relatively unaffected by heat and are comparatively weak poisons. Endotoxins are produced mainly by those pathogenic bacteria that cause diseases of the digestive system. We know little about how they act.

Although toxins have some properties in common, each appears to be different in its action upon the tissues of the host. There is diversity in toxins as there is diversity among microorganisms. Even though our knowledge of the action of toxins is not complete, we are gradually discovering how toxins produce their amazing and often disastrous physiological effects.

For example, the tetanus toxin affects the nerves that cause muscles to contract. In normal muscular action, when the muscle on one side of the arm contracts, the muscle on the opposite side relaxes. However, the tetanus toxin apparently allows the nerve impulse to go to both sets of muscles and so causes them both to contract at the same time. A painful rigidity of the muscles results.

The toxin produced by the diphtheria organism seems to interfere in some way with the formation and functioning of the respiratory enzymes of the host. Lack of sufficient energy because of depressed respiration could account for the general muscular weakness in the victim.

The nature of virulence in microbes that do not produce toxins, such as the bacillus (Figure 11-6) that causes tuberculosis, has been one of the mysteries that bacteriologists have been trying to solve ever since Koch discovered the organism nearly a hundred years ago.

CONTROL OF DISEASE

What happens in an organism after it has been invaded by a pathogen? How does it combat the toxins that may be formed by the virulent pathogen? In higher animals with efficient circulatory systems, intruding pathogenic bacteria are challenged almost immediately.

Host Resistance

The first line of resistance is by cells of the bloodstream. These are the phagocytes —certain white blood cells that engulf and destroy the invaders (Figure 11-7). In some instances, however, the host may not be able to cope with the rapidly multiplying pathogen. In this event the host may depend on an additional defense—the formation of proteins called **antibodies** (AN-tih·bod·eez). An antibody is produced in the host as a reaction to the introduction of a foreign substance, usually a protein, which is called the **antigen** (AN·tih·jen). In this example, the proteins of the bacteria themselves are the antigens. A unique feature of

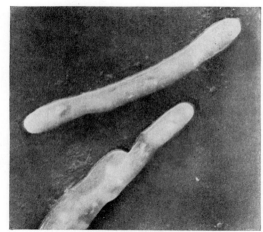

National Tuberculosis Assoc.

11-6 The bacillus that causes tuberculosis. Although the nature of its virulence is not yet known, this bacillus has been brought under control by trial-and-error identification of drugs that arrest or cure tuberculosis. (Trial-and-error also figured prominently in the malaria story of Chapter 1. Can it be that this hit-or-miss approach is one kind of scientific method?)

an antibody is its *specificity* for the antigen that stimulated its formation. Thus, in case of typhoid fever, the antigens of typhoid bacilli will cause the host to produce specific antibodies. The latter react with and inactivate the typhoid bacilli proteins with which they come in contact, but do not react with other bacilli — or react more weakly. Antibodies once formed may remain for years in the body of the host organism and impart varying degrees of immunity.

Without knowing the reason, peoples in early civilizations recorded the observation that if a tribesman was to become ill with a certain disease and was fortunate enough to recover, from that time on he would be immune to the disease. This same observation was familiar to the English physician Edward Jenner (1749–1823), who was the first to devise a safe and effective means of combating the dreaded virus disease smallpox. If you compare the time at which Jenner

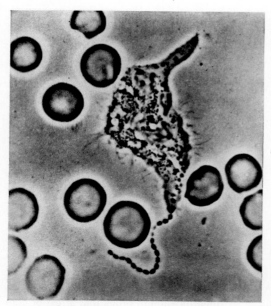

Chas. Pfizer & Co., Inc.

1.1-7 A phagocyte engulfing a chain of bacteria. The circular cells surrounding the phagocyte are red blood cells. The chain of bacteria extends from the phagocyte, near the bottom of the photograph.

lived with the date of the discovery of viruses and the date of proof that viruses can cause disease (1892), you will realize that he knew practically nothing about the cause of smallpox or any other virus disease. Nevertheless, he made two very astute observations. First, he noticed that milkmaids often contracted a mild case of cowpox from the cows infected with cowpox. The cowpox disease did not seriously affect either the cows or the milkmaids. When Jenner examined the histories of the milkmaids, he made the second observation: the milkmaids who had contracted cowpox at some time seldom contracted the far more serious disease, smallpox.

This second observation suggested a daring experiment. Could this be another case of natural immunity, such as had been recorded in the past? Perhaps by injecting a person with a little of the pus from a cowpox lesion, one could give him a mild case

of cowpox and spare him the ravages of smallpox. How much it would have helped Jenner, and how many doubts would have been erased from his mind, if he had only known about viruses, antibodies, and antigens.

In spite of his limited information, Jenner proceeded with his bold experiment by **vaccinating** (*vacca*—Latin for "cow") a young boy with pus from a cowpox blister. As anticipated, the boy contracted a mild case of the disease, which soon vanished. Now came the crucial step. Was the boy truly immunized against smallpox? There was only one way Jenner knew of finding out, and that was to inoculate the boy with pus from an active case of smallpox. In spite of what might have happened if he had failed, Jenner continued his experiment. You know the outcome—the boy did *not* contract the dreaded disease. He had indeed become immune. Can you explain what changes Jenner had brought about in the boy to produce immunity?

In Jenner's day it was difficult to persuade people to be vaccinated. They were suspicious of the things that they, as well as the physicians of the time, did not understand. Sooner or later, however, the fear of smallpox drove many to Jenner's door, where, in spite of their doubts about vaccination (Figure 11-8), they submitted to the new treatment.

Another century was to pass before it was learned *why* vaccination produces immunity. Again we can thank Louis Pasteur for helping to find some of the answers. Today we know that the milkmaids who had contracted cowpox as an occupational hazard acquired **active immunity**—their bodies produced antibodies in reaction to the pathogenic virus of cowpox. Fortunately, the viruses causing cowpox and smallpox were enough alike that the antibodies produced against cowpox were also effective against smallpox. Jenner, in his vaccination experiment, had *artificially induced* active immu-

11-8 An eighteenth-century cartoon showing the physician Edward Jenner using his cowpox extract to vaccinate patients against smallpox. The cartoonist, like the people portrayed, seems to have had misgivings about the results of vaccination.

The Bettmann Archive

nity by injecting pus containing cowpox virus (the antigen) into his patients.

Since Jenner's time, other methods of preparing antigens to produce immunity have been devised. Perhaps you recently have read about one of these methods in a magazine or newspaper. In the development of methods of immunization against poliomyelitis, Jonas Salk and his colleagues discovered that they could take active polio viruses, kill them with a poison called **formaldehyde** (for·MAL·de·hyd), and use the killed viruses as antigens. When injected, the antigens still caused the production of polio antibodies that protected the person from poliomyelitis.

Albert Sabin used a different method of producing polio antibodies in the host. He treated polio viruses to weaken them so that they would not produce the disease. A suspension of living but weakened viruses can then be swallowed, and the person will build antibodies against poliomyelitis.

Yet another method for producing active immunity involves the injection of antigens called **toxoids** (TOK·soidz). Certain diseases, such as diphtheria and tetanus, are due mainly to protein toxins that the bacteria secrete into the host's body. An effective immunization here requires the neutralization of the toxins by antibodies called **antitoxins** (an·tih·TOK·sinz). It is undesirable to inject the active toxin to cause protective antibody production, since the host would then become ill. Toxoids are used instead. Toxoids are produced by treating toxin, collected from laboratory cultures of bacteria, with a chemical substance such as formaldehyde. This treatment destroys the poisonous properties but not the ability of the molecule to cause a person to produce antitoxins. Would you say that this method is more like the Salk or the Sabin method of producing polio vaccine?

Active immunization usually lasts for months or even years. There is, however, a practical drawback to injecting weakened viruses, bacteria, or toxoids to produce antibodies. It usually takes several weeks for the body to build up an effective supply of antibodies. If exposure to a disease has already occurred, it may be too late to start active immunization. In cases such as this, the physician will often rely on measures of **passive immunity.**

Passive immunization depends on the use of antibodies made in another animal. Thus, if antigens are injected into a horse, the horse will produce the specific antibodies. The blood serum of the animal, now containing the antibodies, is known as **antiserum** (an·tih·SEER·um). The antiserum is injected into the person who requires immediate antibody protection. Physicians have supplies of various specific antisera on hand for just such emergencies. For example, horse serum collected from animals immunized with tetanus toxoid may be used to give protection against a potential case of tetanus. The protection is immediate, but is only temporary inasmuch as antibody production by the patient is not involved.

Chas. Pfizer & Co., Inc.

11-9 A colony of the blue-green mold *Penicillium*. Does this mold look familiar? Where might you have seen species of *Penicillium* growing? The name of the mold suggests clearly how certain species of it have become valuable to man.

Antibiotics

Approximately 75 percent of those who read this sentence have been given some **antibiotic** (an·tih·by·OT·ik) by a physician to help combat certain types of sore throat, bacterial pneumonia, tuberculosis, or some other bacterial disease. Antibiotics have become so important a part of our lives that we should know what they are and how they act. An antibiotic is any biological substance that is produced by an organism and that inhibits or retards the growth of microorganisms.

The effects of antibiotics have been known since about 1500 B.C., when it was observed by Chinese physicians that poultices and dressings containing mold worked very well in curing boils. It took another 3,500 years, however, before anyone understood how antibiotics worked. Near the end of the last century, two German investigators discovered that a blue pigment obtained from a certain pus-forming bacterium had an antibiotic effect against *Staphylococcus aureus*, the common cause of boils. The blue pigment had one serious drawback, however, that prevented its use on internal infections. It was much too toxic for direct injections. This is a major disadvantage of many antibiotics.

An event that was to lead to one of the greatest advances in the history of antibiotics was reported in 1929. At the time, it seemed relatively unimportant that a British microbiologist by the name of Alexander Fleming (1881–1955) should report the antibiotic activity of a blue-green mold in cultures of *Staphylococcus* growing on agar. Fleming had been working to isolate and grow the *Staphylococcus* in pure culture. As so often happens, the cultures became contaminated with a blue-green mold, *Penicillium* (pen·ih·SIL·ih·um—Figure 11-9). The mold was perhaps identical with the blue-green molds you have seen growing on spoiled oranges or grapefruit.

A contaminated culture usually ends up by being discarded. But Fleming did not throw this one away. It looked different from the usual contaminated plate because the agar immediately surrounding the mold was almost clear instead of being cloudy with staphylococci. The appearance of the clear area showed that the growth of *Staphylococcus* had been inhibited by some substance produced by the mold. Fleming isolated the antibiotic substance and named it *penicillin*. Further tests showed that penicillin was not toxic to humans and thus met one of the requirements of a useful antibiotic.

Very little was done to promote the use or production of penicillin until 1938, when two British biochemists started an intensive study. In addition to finding the range of bacteria affected by penicillin, they devised methods of growing the mold *Penicillium notatum* (no·TAY·tum) on a large scale. This accomplishment proved to be of tremendous value. Soon we were involved in World War II, during which penicillin was used in great quantities to control infections in wounded soldiers. It has been estimated that without penicillin the death rate during World War II and the Korean War would have been more than tripled because of gas gangrene and other bacterial infections in wounds.

Subsequently, new strains of *Penicillium* with greater capacity for penicillin production have been developed by introducing mutations in the original *P. notatum* stock. Some types of penicillin differ slightly from others, and tests are continually made to evaluate the effectiveness of each new type produced (Figure 11-10). There are even synthetic varieties of this antibiotic. To this day, penicillin is the most widely used, and among the least toxic, of the multitude of antibiotics now available.

It should be noted that Fleming's discovery was, in a sense, a lucky one. Had he simply discarded the contaminated culture, he might not have discovered penicillin. Others before him had observed that molds seem to inhibit bacterial growth, but Fleming wanted to know why. Many discoveries have been referred to as lucky "chances," but are they really? They are in part, but we might make the observation, as Pasteur did many years ago, that "chance favors the trained mind."

In America, much of the success in discovering new antibiotic-producing organisms can be attributed to Selman Waksman and his co-workers. For many years they studied microorganisms of the soil. They concentrated on organisms called **actinomycetes** (ak·tih·no·MY·seets—Figure 11-11), a group of threadlike fungi composed of bacterialike cells. Most of the antibiotics used today, except penicillin, are produced by actinomycetes, many of which were discov-

ered by Waksman and his associates. In 1944, Waksman and his co-workers discovered an antibiotic which we all know, one called **streptomycin** (strep·toh·MY·sin). This they isolated from the actinomycete *Streptomyces griseus* (strep·toh·MY·seez GREE·see·us). Since the discovery of streptomycin, pharmaceutical laboratories and independent investigators have isolated many species of actinomycetes that produce antibiotic substances. In addition to streptomycin, **aureomycin** (au·re·o·MY·sin), and **terramycin** (tehr·a·MY·sin), many others have been added to the list. Today about twenty-five antibiotics derived from molds are commercially produced (Figure 11-12). Some have their greatest effects against specific bacteria; others show a broad spectrum of action against many bacteria.

In addition to molds and actinomycetes, true bacteria have also been a source of antibiotics. Two of these antibiotics, **tyrothricin** (ty·ro·THRY·sin) and **polymyxin** (pah·lee·MIKS·in), have been obtained from spore-forming soil bacteria. Another, **bacitracin** (bas·ih·TRAY·sin), was isolated from an infected wound!

Many bacteria are inhibited only by certain specific antibiotics. This fact often makes it necessary for the microbiologist to isolate the pathogen and determine its sensitivity or resistance to a number of antibiotics. This may be done by growing the organism on an agar plate. On the surface of the agar, one places a number of filter paper disks saturated with different antibiotics. These antibiotics diffuse into the medium surrounding the disks. If the test organism is sensitive to the antibiotic in a specific disk, it fails to grow in the area surrounding that disk. You should be able to undertake this kind of experiment, called a **bioassay** (BY·oh·a·SAY) in the laboratory.

There are other reasons, too, for the proper selection of antibiotics. For instance, the widespread and unwise use of antibiotics

Eli Lilly and Co.

11-10 A test of the antibiotic activity of the penicillin produced by one strain of *Penicillium*. Each dark circular area is a disk saturated with a different strength of the penicillin. The width of the lighter circular zone around each disk indicates to what degree the penicillin has inhibited the growth of a species of *Streptococcus* in the nutrient medium of the dish. Which penicillin sample is the most concentrated?

may result in a number of undesirable side reactions. The patient may become allergic to the antibiotic and suffer severe reactions when it is used a second or third time. In other instances, some antibiotics, when taken by mouth, may practically sterilize the intestines. When this occurs, beneficial bacteria, which normally produce many of our B vitamins, will be killed, and an acute vitamin shortage may occur in our bodies.

Another reason for careful use of antibiotics is that strains of bacteria highly resistant to a given kind of antibiotic can develop by natural selection. The antibiotic then becomes useless against the resistant bacteria. Penicillin-resistant staphylococci have developed in many hospitals, where they occasionally become a major problem. In the presence of the drug, these organisms produce an enzyme, **penicillinase** (pen·ih·SIL·in·ase), which destroys penicillin. Clearly, penicillin cannot be used effectively under such circumstances.

Just how the majority of antibiotics operate in controlling bacterial infections is still a mystery. It is now known that penicillin will kill only actively growing bacteria. Its action seems to be to prevent the manufacture of new cell walls by the bacteria.

Disinfectants and Synthetic Drugs

Many chemical substances act as **disinfectants**—substances capable of killing or removing microorganisms that cause infection. Some disinfectants you may be familiar with are iodine, chlorine, formaldehyde, boric acid, carbolic acid, hydrogen peroxide, mercuric chloride, and silver nitrate.

One of the first recorded instances of the use of a disinfectant was in 1827, when a physician of the British navy added chloride of lime to water used on British naval vessels. He thought of the chloride of lime primarily as a deodorizer rather than as a "germ" killer. During the 1840's, Ignaz Semmelweis used this same compound to

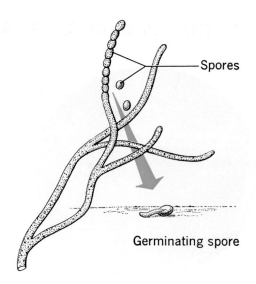

Spores

Germinating spore

11-11 The actinomycete *Streptomyces griseus,* shown much enlarged. Streptomycin, one of the most widely used antibiotics, is obtained from this soil fungus.

prevent the spread of childbed fever (a disease, often fatal, that occurred in maternity wards). Tincture of iodine began to be widely used to control bacterial infections during the War Between the States.

A major advance in the use of chemicals occurred about 1870 when Joseph Lister initiated the techniques of antiseptic surgery. Carbolic acid solution, which would kill bacteria, was sprayed over the skin of the patient, around the operating room, and over the instruments used for surgery. Infections, once horrifyingly common after surgery, were greatly reduced. Since the days of Semmelweis and Lister, the use of chemicals during surgery has undergone many improvements and refinements.

Another line of inquiry—a search for chemicals which would cure disease—has been going on ever since man first recognized that certain substances seemed to hasten recovery. Cure of disease by chemical means is called **chemotherapy** (kem-oh·THEHR·a·pee).

Paul Ehrlich (1854–1915) was a notable

11-12 THE PRODUCTION OF AN ANTIBIOTIC

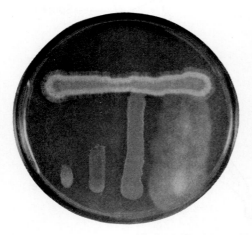

All photos Eli Lilly and Co.

a ▲

Soil samples from all over the world are screened for new antibiotics. Anything that inhibits growth of known pathogenic organisms is isolated for further study.

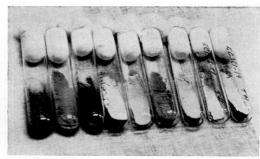

b ▲

Organisms that appear to produce effective antibiotics are transferred to agar slants (above) for incubation. The agar slants, in turn, are used to inoculate larger nutrient flasks. Soon the populations of microorganisms are large enough to provide quantities of the antibiotics for purification and eventual trial use.

When the final product has passed inspection, the antibiotic is packaged in a variety of ways—in a liquid medium suitable for injections, in tablets or capsules for oral use, and in the containers shown here. As a final safeguard, packaged samples are sent back to the laboratory for analysis.

The story is over—or is it just beginning? How many lives will the antibiotic help to protect in the years ahead?

h ▼

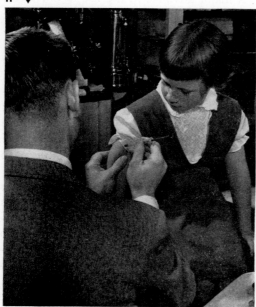

g ▼

c ▶

The commercial production of an antibiotic effective against pathogens, and nontoxic to man, duplicates many of the steps taken during its trial production. Here a nutrient flask containing the antibiotic-producing organism is emptied into a "transfer carrier" used to inoculate a large vat.

Several stages later, a large quantity of the antibiotic is isolated from the organism that produced it. Further extraction and purification procedures follow, using the equipment shown here.

d ▼

f ▲

The gray arrows leading to the laboratory technician are still another part of the story. At every step in production, samples are sent to the laboratory for analysis. The questions are always the same: Is the sample "clean"? Has any organism *other* than the antibiotic-producing one been cultured unintentionally?

◀ **e**

Contamination by a foreign organism or its toxin must be avoided at all costs. Sterile handling procedures keep the risk at a minimum, as the antibiotic (the white, crystalline substance in the scoop) is transferred to a bulk container.

pioneer in the search for chemical agents that would be toxic to pathogens but would not have harmful effects on their hosts, the patients. In 1910, after much trial and error, he discovered a synthetic compound called "salvarsan," which for years was the primary drug used in treating syphilis. Popular writers and the motion picture industry have immortalized Ehrlich's "salvarsan" as "the magic bullet."

The first of the recent so-called "wonder drugs" was first used during the 1930's. It was **sulfanilamide** (sul·fa·NIL·a·myd). The sulfa drugs, among which sulfanilamide and **sulfadiazine** (sul·fa·DY·a·zeen) are examples, are produced synthetically. Sulfa drugs as well as penicillin have saved countless lives, in hospitals and on battlefields throughout the world.

Control of Spoilage

Early in this chapter a point was made of the importance of bacteria and other decomposers in both the nitrogen cycle and the carbon-hydrogen-oxygen cycle. Without these decay-producers, the cycles of nature would soon be out of adjustment, resulting in the end of life as we know it. Many of the decomposers that play such an important role in nature's cycles also cause spoilage of foods, and decay of wood, fabrics, and leather. Like pathogenic organisms, these decomposers must be controlled. By making an imaginary trip through a large grocery store, we can illustrate most of the methods of control currently in use.

Heat. Suppose we start with the canned goods piled row on row—an immense variety of sizes, shapes, and contents. We take it for granted that the food inside the cans will be safe to eat even though it may have been on the shelf for months at room temperature. The canning of fruits and vegetables requires consideration of many factors, among which are the effects of heating on flavor and on the pH of the foods being canned. Boiling may provide suffi-

cient heat to kill the vegetative forms of bacteria, but endospores can survive in a temperature of 100° C. If the food being canned is an acid food (pH of 3 to 4), then boiling is sufficient; any endospores that survive will not grow in such an acid medium. Low-acid foods (pH above 4.5) are processed by heating in steam under 15 lbs. pressure, which raises the temperature to 120°–126° C. Depending on the food, exposure to these high temperatures is from 12 to 90 minutes. At the end of this time all organisms, including bacterial endospores, will be killed. The can and its contents will have been *sterilized* (Figure 11-13).

Techniques used in canning are not new. In 1810, Nicolas Appert, a French confectioner, reported success after using heat in canning. The first patent for a canning process was issued during the same year in England. In the United States, Boston was the site of the first canning company. It started operations in 1820. At first, glass containers were used, but tin cans soon became more popular and now are a familiar part of the American scene.

Let us move on to the grocer's cooler, where the supply of pasteurized milk is kept. Actually, two methods of bacterial control are used here—low temperature and **pasteurization** (Figure 11-13). Pasteurization requires the use of heat at temperatures high enough to kill nonspore-forming bacteria.

Pasteurization owes its name to Pasteur, who first used it in 1866 to save the French wine industry. Undesirable bacteria growing in the wine were spoiling its taste. Boiling, which would have killed the bacteria, would destroy the flavor of the wine. Pasteur conceived the simple idea of heating the fermented wine for about half an hour at a temperature considerably below the boiling point. This killed the organisms that were spoiling the wine, without impairing the flavor.

Later, a similar process was used for milk. Milk is an excellent food for bacteria as well as man. When milk is produced under careless conditions and is consumed raw (that is, without pasteurization), it can be dangerous. Pathogens that may grow in raw milk include those which cause typhoid fever, paratyphoid fever, scarlet fever, bovine tuberculosis, and undulant fever.

About 1880, a number of investigators recognized that many children, and often adults as well, were dying of these milk-borne diseases. It was therefore suggested that the milk should be heated, just as Pasteur had heated wine, in order to destroy the pathogens. At first, the pasteurization temperatures used were too high and the milk tasted scorched. Furthermore, the cream would not rise properly afterwards. On the other hand, if the milk was heated at too low a temperature the disease-producers were not killed.

After extensive and careful experimentation, using the tough bovine tuberculosis organism as a test organism, proper temperatures for pasteurizing milk were found. They were high enough to kill the tuberculosis bacterium, but not so high as to affect the taste and quality of the milk. Pasteurization kills not only the tuberculosis organism, but other nonspore-forming bacteria as well.

Two methods of pasteurizing milk are now used extensively. One method involves heating milk for 30 minutes at 62° C. The other uses a higher temperature (71° C) for a shorter period of only 15 seconds. Essentially, the same effects are achieved by either method.

Low Temperatures. The milk cooler, meat counter, and food freezers in the grocery, and the electric refrigerator and home freezer are all used to keep foods from spoiling for limited periods of time by refrigeration (Figure 11-13). The temperatures in these appliances, except for the freezers or the freezing compartment in a

11-13 HEAT, COLD, AND THE PREVENTION OF SPOILAGE

Canned foods

Sterilization

100° C plus 15 lbs. pressure—yielding 120° to 126° C (maintained 12 to 90 minutes)

Milk

Pasteurization

71° C (15 seconds)

62° C (30 seconds)

Eggs, milk vegetables, cheese, and meats

Low temperature storage

10° to 15° for several days

Meats and vegetables

Freezing

−10° to −18° C for several weeks to several months

refrigerator, is always above 0° C. Foods left at these temperatures indefinitely will spoil. At these low temperatures (10°–15° C) bacteria are not killed—nor are their metabolic activities and growth completely retarded.

Let us move on to the grocer's meat locker where meats are kept below freezing (−10° to −18° C), or to the display freezers where quick-frozen vegetables, ice cream, fruit juices, pizzas, fish, and many other products are kept. At these low temperatures, bacterial activity is practically nil, and many foods may be kept indefinitely without spoiling. In one instance, some beef was left in a cold-storage locker at −20° C from 1907 to 1947 without appreciably altering the flavor of the meat.

At temperatures below freezing, the vegetative cells of bacteria may be killed, and the endospores, although not killed, will not grow. Obviously, at these low temperatures such processes as respiration, digestion, and absorption cannot go on in the bacteria, because the water required is frozen and not available. Thus the environment of your home freezer is a dry one that prevents the growth of bacteria and other decomposers.

Drying. The prunes, dried apricots, dried milk, dried fish, and dried meat at the grocery store are all examples of preservation at room temperatures by *dehydration* (removal of water). If enough water can be removed from foods, the bacteria that are present on or in it cannot grow. For example, eggs, milk, and meat will not spoil if their water content is reduced to 10 percent or less. Fruits and vegetables will keep if the moisture content is below 20 percent.

Preservatives. While we are in the grocery store, let us look at the pickles in the pickle barrel. What keeps them from spoiling? If they are not treated in some way, they will soon decay. Two agents are used in preserving the pickles in the open barrel. Salt is dissolved in water to make a brine,

and vinegar is added. The high concentration of salt in brine will remove water by diffusion from the bacteria, molds, and other decomposers that fall into the barrel. Although water is present in the brine, it is not available for growth of microorganisms. For them the brine is a desert—a condition of *physiological dryness.* (For more explanation of this phenomenon, see the discussion of diffusion, pages 103 and 124.) Further, the vinegar is acidic and reduces the pH to a point where bacteria and most molds will not grow.

Sugar is another common preservative. It has the same antimicrobial action as the brine in the pickle barrel. Many fruits are preserved in sugar. Crystallized salt is a common preservative of meats (salt pork and salted fish, for example). Many other chemicals, spices, and even antibiotics are used as preservatives. However, their use is regulated by the Pure Foods and Drug Administration of the Federal Government.

BENEFICIAL BACTERIA

Having read the story of bacteria thus far, you will probably conclude that all but those bacteria taking part in the nitrogen cycle and the carbon-hydrogen-oxygen cycle are harmful, and that the world would indeed be a better place without them. We must look again at the "other side of the coin" and see in what other ways bacteria are beneficial. Some of the ways they help us in our everyday living will surprise you.

Bacteria for Better Health

Has your doctor ever prescribed vitamin capsules for you? Chances are that in addition to the usual collection of vitamins A, C, and D, members of the B complex also are included in the capsules. One member of the B complex is vitamin B_{12} (the cobalt vitamin), which in human beings prevents the blood disease **pernicious anemia** (per·NISH·us a·NEE·mih·a).

For many years it has been known that injections of crude liver extracts often helped the victims of pernicious anemia. It was not known until recently, however, what substance in the liver was responsible.

In the late 1940's, an American microbiologist, Mary Shorb, studied this problem. She was trying to devise a medium for growing the bacterium *Lactobacillus lactis* (lak·toh·ba·sɪʟ·us ʟᴀᴋ·tis). She could supply, in the form of purified chemicals, all but one of the nutrients this organism needed. That extra substance was present in crude beef-liver extract. Could the growth substance for the bacterium be the same as that which helped victims of pernicious anemia?

Several tons of beef liver were used in an effort to extract the growth factor. After much chemical extraction, a few milligrams of a highly active, pure, red compound were obtained. It not only was the missing growth substance Mary Shorb was looking for, but also proved to be the cure for pernicious anemia. Thus, by studying the biology of a bacterium, biologists were led to the discovery of a substance of great aid to man—vitamin B_{12}.

The recovery of large amounts of vitamin B_{12} from beef liver is a difficult and costly job. Nevertheless, the vitamin was needed for medical purposes, so it became important to find a better source. The bacteria helped to solve the problem.

So far as is known, all bacteria need vitamin B_{12} in their cells. Some species must have B_{12} added to the medium in which they are grown. Other species can grow in a medium that does not contain B_{12}. How does the second group of species obtain the needed B_{12}? They must have the ability to synthesize it! Investigation soon identified a number of bacteria species that synthesized B_{12} far in excess of their own needs. In an effort to obtain this excess B_{12}, these bacteria were grown in huge cultures containing thousands of gallons of media. From these cultures the vitamin B_{12} was removed and purified. It is now used not only for treating pernicious anemia patients, but also in commercial vitamin pills. This story of discovery affords an excellent example of one of the many ways in which bacteria can serve man.

Did you know that bacteria in your digestive system, especially in the small and large intestines, are important in completing certain digestive processes? They are so important that without them, digestion of foods is incomplete, and you can become ill. This explains why the family physician is reluctant to use penicillin and other antibiotics which will reduce the bacteria in the digestive tract to a dangerous level. Under normal conditions these intestinal bacteria secrete enzymes that convert many of the complex foods you eat to simple soluble compounds that can be absorbed by the lining of the intestinal tract.

It has been discovered that some of these enzymes can be obtained from bacteria in a fairly pure form and used in some very unusual ways. One of the extracts is composed of many protein-digesting enzymes, collectively known as **protease** (ᴘʀᴏʜ·tee-ase). Dry cleaners have found that protease is very effective in removing spots made by blood, meat juice, eggs, and other protein-containing substances. Similar enzymes may be used by your physician in treating an open wound or burn; the protease digests away the dead tissues and leaves the living tissues unharmed and ready to heal the wound.

Bacteria in Industry

The same protein-digesting enzymes that are so helpful to human digestion may have played an important part in the manufacture of the leather shoes you are wearing, or the leather pocketbook or purse you carry, or your leather gloves. Leather is made from the hides of animals, especially pigs, cows, and horses. The raw hides with bits of flesh, hair, and other foreign material are put into great, evil-smelling vats, where bacteria secrete enzymes that digest the unwanted flesh and hair, leaving the hides softened and ready for the next steps in tanning.

Many of the fabrics that are made into the clothes you wear depend upon bacteria for their manufacture. The coffee you drink in the morning may have had a "bacterial treatment" in its processing. The Swiss cheese or American cheese in your lunchtime sandwich was given its flavor and texture by the activity of bacteria.

Fermentation

Earlier in this chapter, and in Chapter 2, much of the work and genius of Louis Pasteur has been noted. Among his many accomplishments, he is famous for his researches which disproved the theory of spontaneous generation; he is credited with saving the silk industry in France by discovering the cause of a disease of silkworms; he formulated the Germ Theory of Disease, which was later proved by Robert Koch; and he devised a method for control of bacteria in wine and beer by using heat, a process we call pasteurization.

Much of Pasteur's research, especially that which led him to disprove abiogenesis (see Chapter 2), involved studies of the causes of "sick" wine and beer. The manufacture of wine, a great French enterprise, was faced with ruin in the mid-nineteenth century because of problems in controlling fermentation. In the summer of 1856 a request was made of Pasteur for his help. Pasteur was well acquainted with the fermentation process which produced alcohol and carbon dioxide. The fermentation was carried out by brewers' yeast, a common fungus you may have used in an experiment in the laboratory.

The wine makers' problem was simple. As soon as fermentation had been started by the brewers' yeast, substances appeared that turned the wine sour. The substances that ruined the wine were found to be lactic acid and acetic acid. The problems confronting Pasteur were to discover what caused formation of the acid and how to prevent it.

It did not take Pasteur long to find the cause. Whenever acids were produced in fermenting liquids, he was able to find bacteria. When bacteria were not present, there were no acids, and good wine was produced. A method of control was soon worked out. The bacteria were easily killed —and without affecting the flavor of the wine—by exposure to a temperature of 62° C for a period of thirty minutes. Pasteur saved the French wine industry and at the same time introduced the techniques of pasteurization.

Thus far we have said very little about what fermentation really is. Pasteur knew that fermentation resulted in the formation of alcohols and CO_2, or of acids. He knew that it was caused by microorganisms growing in **anaerobic** (an·ay·er·OH·bik) environments, that is, environments in which little or no atmospheric oxygen (O_2) was available. This was contrary to the requirements of most organisms with which Pasteur was familiar. It had already been demonstrated that most plants and animals were **aerobic** (ay·er·OH·bik)—that is, they required free oxygen for respiration. Many years were to pass after Pasteur's work before the details of "biological combustion," either aerobic or anaerobic, were worked out. Some of these details for aerobic respiration appear in Chapter 6. A review of this material will be helpful in understanding **anaerobic respiration** (fermentation).

Today we think that anaerobic respiration was the kind of respiration utilized by the first living things that populated the earth. There is good reason for believing that at that time the earth's atmosphere lacked free oxygen (see Chapter 36). Thus, anaerobic respiration, or fermentation,

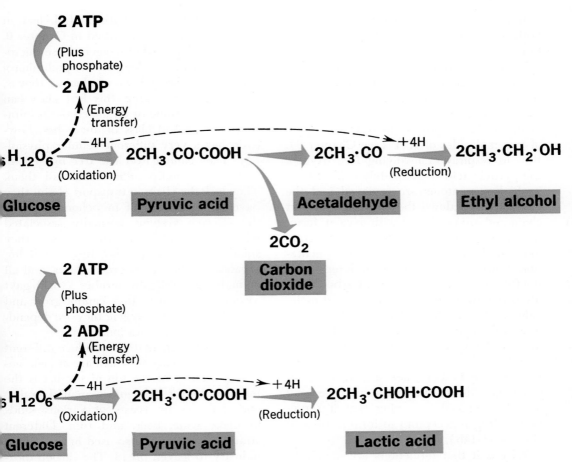

11-14 **a** A summary of the fermentation process as carried out by anaerobic microorganisms that produce carbon dioxide and alcohol. Compare this process (and the amount of ATP derived from it) with respiration as described in Chapter 6. Note that the *net* energy gain from the fermentation of a molecule of glucose is only two ATP molecules. (Three are formed, but they must offset the loss of one that supplied energy for the reaction.) No energy is derived from the two pyruvic acid molecules split from the molecule of glucose. **b** Steps similar to those in **a** occur in the fermentation process carried out by anaerobic microorganisms that produce lactic acid. The amount of energy derived from the fermentation is the same—a net gain of two ATP molecules per molecule of glucose.

would have been the only way energy could have been released for metabolism.

When compared with aerobic respiration, fermentation is most inefficient. It yields only about 5 percent of the total potential energy from a molecule of glucose ($C_6H_{12}O_6$). Thus, fermentation is an incomplete form of respiration. This is explained by the fact that the glucose molecule is only partially broken down in the process (Figure 11-14). Most of the total energy remains in the end products of alcohol or acid. (In aerobic respiration the breakdown is complete. The end products are water and carbon dioxide, not complex substances such as alcohol and organic acids.)

Although there are many differences between aerobic respiration and fermentation, both processes release energy from glucose; both are examples of "biological combustion."

What happens in fermentation that makes it different from aerobic respiration? In both cases a glucose molecule is split and oxidized to make two molecules of pyruvic acid, and in the process there is a net gain of two molecules of ATP (see Chapter 6). But, in respiration involving free oxygen, the pyruvic acid is completely oxidized; all its hydrogen atoms are removed and the electrons pass down the electron transport chain and are combined with oxygen, forming water. These are the steps that generate most of the ATP of the cell. In fermentation, however, the steps are different after the formation of pyruvic acid. Carbon dioxide is removed from the pyruvic acid molecules and is released, leaving $CH_3 \cdot CHO$, or **acetaldehyde** (as·et·AL·de·hyd). Depending on the species of microorganism, the acetaldehyde is converted into ethyl alcohol (Figure 11-14a), acetic acid, or other products. Alternatively, the pyruvic acid may be reduced (meaning that it serves as a hydrogen acceptor) to form lactic acid (Figure 11-14b).

Why is it that fermenters are unable to utilize free oxygen and unlock more efficiently the vast stores of energy in the glucose molecule? Why must they live in so impoverished a condition, in respect to their energy supply? One answer might be that they can afford to be wasteful, since they live immersed in an abundance of food. A better answer, probably, is that this ability to live without free oxygen adapts them to live where oxygen-breathers simply cannot exist. We will learn later (see Chapter 36) that the world was not always rich in an atmosphere of oxygen. From a cellular viewpoint it is significant that there are two classes of these anaerobic organisms. Some of them, given the opportunity, can utilize free oxygen and respire like other air-breathers. They possess the equivalent of mitochondria with the full electron transport chain, as described in Chapter 6. But, when deprived of oxygen, these microorganisms can get along on the preliminary stages of the breakdown of glucose, that is, on fermentation. Thus this first class can depend on aerobic or on anaerobic respiration. The second class of anaerobes, however, has a very different cellular physiology. They cannot ever use free oxygen; in fact, it is usually sufficient to kill them. They lack the electron transport chain; they have no equivalent of mitochondria or of the enzyme systems normally associated with mitochondria. In this respect they stand apart from all other forms of living organisms. Thus, most green plants, and all animals, are **obligate aerobes** (OB·lih·gayt AY·er·ohbs). That is, they cannot grow and reproduce without oxygen; they are dependent on aerobic respiration.

Different fermentations produce different by-products, many of which are of economic importance. At the top of the list is the fermentation of fruit juices, malted grains, and molasses by yeasts of various kinds to make wine, beer, and rum. Different strains of yeasts are also used in the baking industry to leaven bread. The carbon dioxide produced during fermentation makes bubbles in the dough and causes the bread to rise, giving it lightness and a desirable texture when it is baked. Yeasts also are an important source of vitamins, especially riboflavin (B_2).

Other bacterial fermentations produce a wide variety of metabolic by-products. Among these are lactic acid, a substance required in the manufacture of many dairy products, including cheeses, buttermilk, and yogurt.

In an earlier part of this chapter, the souring of wine was described as the result of an undesired fermentation. Actually, one very important and useful product, vinegar, is produced by oxidizing alcohol in wine to acetic acid. The organism responsible is an aerobic bacterium. To prevent wine from turning to vinegar, oxygen must be excluded and anaerobic conditions maintained.

CONCLUDING REMARKS

The ways in which bacteria and some other microorganisms are beneficial to us would make a long list. We have selected only a few examples to give you some appreciation of the importance of bacteria, yeasts, and molds. The impact of these beneficial organisms on our everyday living cannot be overemphasized. All too frequently the undesirable effects of bacteria as spoilers and disease producers are the only aspects that concern us. Actually these harmful effects are more than counterbalanced by the ways in which these microorganisms benefit us. Review in your mind the advances that have been made in the control of bacteria and the uses of their products, including enzymes, vitamins, organic acids, alcohols, and antibiotics. Nearly all of these products and their uses have been discovered since the 1860's. This has been indeed a century of discovery. The next century may bring to light many more new useful products obtained from microorganisms, perhaps new enzymes, vitamins, or antibiotics to benefit all mankind.

GUIDE QUESTIONS AND PROBLEMS

1. How did the development of Koch's postulates confirm Pasteur's Germ Theory of Disease?
2. What explanation can be given for the sharp reduction in the incidence of most bacterial diseases in the United States?
3. Why is it important to know how a pathogenic bacterium enters the host?
4. How does the environment in the body of the host determine the virulence of a pathogenic bacterium, such as the one causing tetanus or pneumonia?
5. What is the relation between virulence of a bacterium and its ability to produce toxins or otherwise infect the host?
6. What is the significance of the fact that antibodies are specific?
7. How did Jenner's observations and procedures anticipate our present knowledge of immunization?
8. What are the differences between active and passive immunity?
9. How can the specific effects of an antibiotic be determined?
10. What are some of the dangers of a continued widespread use of antibiotics?
11. How are chemicals used in the control and treatment of disease?
12. What would happen if every bacterium on the earth were to disappear? Explain.
13. If a freshwater microorganism is placed in a strong brine solution, what will happen to it? How might this result be used in preserving food?
14. How are bacteria beneficial to man?
15. How has the study of fermentation contributed to the development of concepts of broad significance to all living things?

SUGGESTIONS FOR ADDITIONAL READING

Books

Burnet, F. M., *Viruses and Man.* Baltimore, Penguin Books, 1953.
> An authoritative account of the viruses and their role in disease, by the 1960 Nobel prizewinner in medicine.

Dubos, R., *Pasteur and Modern Science.* New York, Doubleday, 1960.
> An exciting, accurate, and inspiring account of Pasteur's life and work.

Nicol, H., *Microbes by the Million.* Baltimore, Penguin Books, 1939.
> A witty book on microorganisms, including many interesting experiments that can be performed at home with a mimimum of equipment.

Stanier, R. Y., M. Doudoroff, and E. A. Adelberg, *The Microbial World.* Englewood Cliffs (N. J.), Prentice-Hall, 1957.
> An up-to-date, modern coverage of microbiology on the college level.

DIVERSITY

12

MOLDS, YEASTS, AND MUSHROOMS

The "Thing"

A slime mold is of no practical value whatever. You cannot make anything useful out of it, and it does not cause any serious disease. However, as you may have discovered in the laboratory (Exercise 12-2), a slime mold is a strange and truly wonderful "thing." Its structure and behavior have raised many questions. As you read our brief story of a slime mold, you will find that some of these questions are still unanswered.

At one stage, some species of slime molds are creeping masses of living substance, having the consistency of unboiled egg white and the color of the yolk (Figure 12-1a). The movement of this living thing brings to mind a giant amoeba, for it sends out arms, which engulf and digest bacteria from the surface of rotting logs or leaves. This amoeboid stage of the slime mold is called a **plasmodium.** (This same word also stands for the genus of the malaria organism—Chapter 1.) In nature, a large plasmodium may cover several square feet. It can crawl over

grass, creep up the sides of trees, or go almost anywhere where there is food and moisture. It is very much like an object from a science-fiction story. The plasmodium consists of cytoplasm in which are embedded many nuclei, food vacuoles, and undigested food particles. If you look at an active plasmodium through a microscope, you will see the most spectacular exhibition of cytoplasmic streaming you can find anywhere. As you watch, the cytoplasm flows rapidly in one direction. After about fifty seconds the flow slows down, stops, then reverses its direction. What causes this rhythmic, back-and-forth flow of cytoplasm? That is still one of nature's well-kept secrets.

The slime mold plasmodium is unusual. Certainly it is not on the borderline between the living and nonliving, like viruses. It is neither a cellular structure divided into many cells, each **uninucleate** (yoo·nih·NEW·kle·ayt —containing a single nucleus), nor is it restricted by a confining cell wall, like a bacterium. Perhaps if we understand how the plasmodium is formed, we can better understand its strange organization—so different from that of any other living thing.

Plasmodia move along the forest floor, onto dead logs and leaves that are bathed in sunlight. In this dry, often warm, environment a miraculous **metamorphosis** (met·a·MOR·fo·sis) takes place. In a matter of hours, the plasmodium changes into clusters of fruiting bodies. Depending on the species, the fruiting bodies (Figure 12-1b) look like diminutive golf balls, or feathers, or bird cages, or worms, in a great variety of colors. Part of each fruiting body produces a large number of microscopic, asexual reproductive cells called **spores.** Each spore has a single nucleus and a thick, protective wall. A spore may remain inactive for a long time, or it may germinate soon after it has been shed from the fruiting body. Germination of the spore occurs when there is plenty of water and a suitable temperature. The fruiting stage and the thick-walled

a Bob Gilpin, Courtesy of Leland Shanor   b   Constantine J. Alexopoulos

12-1 a A portion of the plasmodium of the slime mold *Physarum*. The plasmodium is growing on a nutrient medium of agar. If this were the only part of the organism you could find, how would you classify it? As plant or animal? As unicellular or multicellular? **b** Fruiting bodies of *Physarum*. The fruiting bodies are shown growing on the surface of rotting wood. How would you discover whether the plasmodium and the fruiting bodies are related? What do the fruiting bodies produce?

spores of the slime mold are very plantlike. *Spores are produced by all plants at some time in their life cycles.* They are very important reproductive cells, as you will see later. When a slime mold spore germinates, it produces one or more tiny cells. Each cell has a pair of flagella that propel it through the film of water that must be present for spore germination. These flagellated cells may function as gametes (sex cells) and fuse in pairs. This is true sexual reproduction, even though the gametes appear to be identical in structure.

Cells resulting from the fusion of gametes become amoeboid and form a new plasmodium that is **multinucleate** (mul·tih·NEW·kle·ayt—containing many nuclei). The multinucleate condition arises either by growth of the amoeboid cell and subsequent divisions of the nucleus, or by the fusion of many individual amoeboid cells, which thus lose their separate identity. This is a most unusual way for an organism to be formed. How would you interpret this phenomenon according to the cell theory (see Chapter 3)?

Looking back at our description of a slime mold, we can see that it combines characters of animals and plants. If we ob-

served only the plasmodium, we would certainly call a slime mold an animal; if fruiting bodies and spores were the only parts we could see, we would call the organism a plant. Is it plant or animal? Can we really relate this strange organism to other living things? What was its evolutionary origin? We can get some help answering these questions by examining some other more familiar fungi, which are called molds.

TRUE FUNGI

Common names for organisms are often misleading and hard to define. The fluffy mold on a piece of stale bread is certainly not the same thing as a slime mold. Yet both are called **molds.** In its organization, the bread mold *Rhizopus nigricans* (ry·ZOH·pus NY·grih·cans—Figure 12-2a) is a true **fungus.** This means that its vegetative structure—the fluffy mass—is composed of slender threads called **hyphae** (HY·fee). All hyphae have distinct cell walls and are branching structures. How does this compare with the vegetative structure (plasmodium) of a slime mold?

In *Rhizopus*, hyphae grow on and into the bread, secreting enzymes that digest the starch into soluble compounds. Hyphae then absorb the soluble carbohydrates, which serve as food for the fungus.

Adaptation to a Land Environment

Rhizopus has some structures that adapt it to a dry land environment. The hyphae that absorb water and soluble nutrients also anchor the plant. Large numbers of thick-walled spores are produced in spherical capsules, or **sporangia** (spo·RAN·jih·a), at the ends of upright hyphae (Figure 12-2a). From here they are easily dispersed by air currents and splashing water. Not only are the spores resistant to drying, but they are produced in tremendous numbers. These features may help you to understand why some molds are so widespread in nature, and why they may contaminate the agar plates used in your laboratory experiments.

Sexual reproduction in *Rhizopus*, as in the majority of true fungi, shows some of the evolutionary changes that adapt it to a terrestrial mode of life. Instead of forming gametes with flagella, as slime molds do, parent strains form special hyphae that fuse with one another (Figure 12-2b). Each contributes nuclei and cytoplasm to the **zygote** (zy·goht), the cell that forms in fertilization by the union of two gametes. In this modification of sexual reproduction, most true fungi (except for some aquatic molds) do not require "free" water (dew, rain, etc.) as a medium for the fusion of their gametes. (Mosses and certain other primitive types of land plants require water for fusion of gametes. The sperms swim to the eggs.)

You will see sexual reproduction of a mold when you mate two strains of *Rhizopus* in the laboratory. This is an important experiment, because it is the only one in which you will have a chance to see steps in the union of gametes—fertilization—and the formation of a zygote. *Rhizopus* forms a zygote with a very thick wall which, like the thick-walled spores, can withstand drying and other adverse terrestrial conditions.

Are the Fungi Plants?

Earlier we posed the unanswered question of whether slime molds are plants or animals. If we asked the same question about *Rhizopus*, it might appear to be answered easily, because *Rhizopus* has no flagellated cells or amoeboid stage, as do slime molds, to suggest that its ancestors were single-celled (unicellular) animals (Chapter 20). Furthermore, *Rhizopus* has well-developed cell walls and produces spores in sporangia—features that are characteristic of plants. Substantiating its relationship to plants is a discovery of long ago that some true fungi—*Rhizopus*, for example—are very similar to certain algae in their structure and their method of reproduction (see Figure 12-2). The hyphae of *Rhizopus* lack cross-walls, and in this characteristic they are similar to the filaments of the algae. It was also observed that the sexual reproduction of other algae is accomplished by a process similar to sexual reproduction in *Rhizopus*. Because of these and other similarities, biologists once supposed that the true fungi were evolved from the algae. According to this line of reasoning, fungi were algae that in the process of evolution had lost their ability to carry on photosynthesis—they had become heterotrophic.

Not long after this idea about the evolutionary origin of the true fungi had become widely accepted, an interesting group of primitive fungi was discovered. These were aquatic organisms having some characteristics of true fungi; however, they were not at all like algae. At different points in their life cycles they produced flagellated cells that looked more like **Protozoa** (proh·toh·ZOH·a—unicellular animals) than like the reproductive cells of algae. Further studies of flagellated cells of various true fungi have convinced biologists that the true fungi indeed evolved from protozoans and should be placed in groups quite unrelated to the algae, as shown in the illustrated

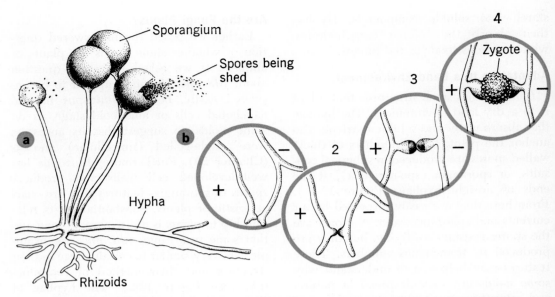

Sporangium

Spores being shed

4

Zygote

3

1

2

+ −

+ −

+ −

Hypha

+

+ −

+ −

Rhizoids

a

b

12-2 **a** A fragment of *Rhizopus* with sporangia. (What type of reproduction is indicated by the spores?) *Rhizopus* is a common contaminant of bread. To combat the organism, bakers put a mold inhibitor in bread dough. **b** Stages in sexual reproduction of *Rhizopus*. The two mating strains are labeled + and −. Although little or no visible difference exists between these mating strains, they are genetically different.

summary of plant classification at the end of Chapter 14 (pages 282–83).

But what about the slime molds, with their plant-like and animal-like characteristics? The plasmodium and the flagellated cells formed by the slime molds are also very much like protozoans. This, plus their animal-like mode of nutrition and the absence of cell walls in the plasmodium, leaves little doubt that slime molds, like the true fungi, also had their evolutionary beginnings with protozoans. But remember that protozoans live and reproduce in water, while slime molds and true fungi live and reproduce on land, where the environment is relatively dry. The slime molds and true fungi evolved a stage in their life cycles that could withstand drying and other adverse conditions of a land environment. This stage is the spore-stage, the plantlike part of the life cycle.

From the point of view of their evolution, it is not necessary to decide whether slime molds and true fungi are plants or animals. They are organisms that have evolved from an aquatic environment to become adapted for survival on land. It makes little difference how we classify the characteristics that evolved, as long as we understand what has happened in the evolution of the organism. Now what is your opinion about the classification of a slime mold or a true fungus? Is it animal or plant? Or is it really important which kingdom the fungi are placed in? Perhaps it is more important for us to understand *where* they came from, *how* they have become adapted to their environments, and *why* they are important components of the world we live in.

THE IMPORTANCE OF FUNGI

In many ways bacteria and fungi are similar in their importance to man. Some bacteria and fungi produce useful products from fermentations, while others produce life-saving antibiotics. Most bacteria and fungi are decomposers, and in this respect play an important role in the cycles of nature, as described in Chapter 8. Like some of the bacteria, some of the fungi produce disease. Especially important are the fungus diseases of plants, for fungi are far more harmful to plants than bacteria are to human beings.

Fungi cause tremendous amounts of spoilage, which each year costs millions of dollars in loss of foodstuffs, lumber, and leather goods (Figure 12-3). We should not forget the poisonous "toadstools" (from the German *Tod-Stuhl,* meaning "death-stool") that take their toll of human lives each year. At the same time we should remember the delicate flavor mushrooms add to our beefsteak, soups, and a great variety of other dishes.

To Eat

Not too many years ago, the cultivation of edible mushrooms was a carefully guarded secret. Today they are grown as a crop in many places throughout the world. They are grown in caves, cellars, and especially constructed mushroom-growing houses (Figure 12-4). "Do-it-yourself" mushroom kits (Laboratory Exercise 12-3) can be purchased so that one can raise mushrooms and study their growth rates at school or even at home.

The edible portion of a mushroom is really a fruiting body composed of compacted hyphae. Like the fruiting bodies of other fungi, that of a mushroom produces great numbers of spores. It has been estimated that a mushroom like the one shown in Figure 12-5a produces about 1,800,000,000 spores from its gills (Figure 12-6)! However, the number of mushrooms in nature remains roughly the same. This means that only a tiny percentage of the spores will ever germinate or ultimately produce a new generation of mushrooms.

Hugh Spencer

12-3 A bracket fungus on a tree. What you see is the fruiting (spore-producing) structure of the fungus. This fungus and many of its relatives kill or spoil unestimated amounts of lumber and untold numbers of shade trees each year.

12-4 The production of edible mushrooms in a special mushroom-growing house. Daylight is excluded, and temperature and humidity are controlled. The annual crop in the United States is about 85 million pounds. Baskets of fresh mushrooms can be found at the grocer's throughout most of the year.

American Mushroom Inst.

a Hugh Spencer

12-5 **a** Edible field mushrooms of the genus *Agaricus*. The fruiting bodies are tipped to one side to show the gills on the undersides of the caps. Great numbers of spores are produced and shed by the gills. **b** The white "death angel," *Amanita verna*. This pure white toadstool is one of the deadliest members of the poisonous mushrooms, not all of which are easily distinguished either by shape or by color from nonpoisonous varieties.

b L. L. Steimley

Whenever we find offspring, in this case the spores, produced in such tremendous numbers by any species, we can be sure that the chances of survival of the offspring are very, very small. This illustrates an important biological principle—the lower the probability of survival of offspring, the greater the rate of production of offspring. Can you apply this principle to other organisms?

Not to Eat

Some mushrooms (those often called toadstools) contain a poisonous chemical compound called **amanitin** (a·MAN·ih·tin), which may cause respiratory and circulatory failure when eaten. Altogether, approximately seventy species of gill fungi are poisonous to man. The most deadly are those belonging to the genus *Amanita* (am-a·NY·ta—Figure 12-5b). *Amanita verna* has a pure white fruiting body. Eating less

than one cap from this fungus can prove fatal within one day. It is well named the "death angel." Generally the amanitas and other poisonous mushrooms can be distinguished by a large cup at the base of the stalk (Figure 12-6). However, this may be buried in the ground and not easily detected. There are many "old wives' tales" about how to distinguish poisonous mushrooms from edible ones. Here are a few of these misconceptions. "A silver spoon will tarnish if put in the pot with poisonous mushrooms that are being cooked"; "The cap of an edible mushroom will peel readily, while that of a toadstool will not"; "If insects or other animals eat a mushroom, it is safe for human consumption." None of these, nor any other general rule, can be used to distinguish edible from poisonous species. The only rule to follow when selecting mushrooms for the table is to divide them into two groups, those produced commercially and purchased at the grocery store, and those that you collect in the field. Unless you intend to have them identified by an expert, dispose of all the mushrooms collected in the field and eat those from the grocery store.

Spoilage and Decay

There are a great many different kinds of fungi responsible for spoilage and decay. Some are wood-rotting fungi, which infect and destroy not only living trees but also railroad ties, fence posts, telephone poles, and all kinds of structural timbers. It is estimated that these fungi destroy more wood than all other destructive agencies put together—including fire and man.

This estimate holds true in spite of the preservatives such as creosote, tars, paints, and varnishes that are used in the endless battle to prevent wood decay.

Unfortunately, much of the damage to structural timbers and living trees is done long before there is any visible sign of rotting. Sooner or later, however, a bracket-like fruiting body (Figure 12-3) may appear, which will produce billions of spores. A few of the spores will infect living trees or start fungal rot in railroad ties, telephone poles, fence posts, and green lumber used in building inexpensive homes.

A trip to the basement in search of your leather boots, or the extra leather suitcase or knapsack, may have introduced you to the detrimental effects of blue and green molds that belong to the genus *Penicillium* (Chapter 11). Or perhaps you have had the misfortune of selecting an orange or grapefruit spoiled by one of these molds. If you have had any of these experiences, you certainly noticed a green powdery substance produced by the fungus on the leather or fruit. This substance is made up of spores formed by *Penicillium* on hyphal branches that look like little brushes (Figure 12-7). The thick walls of these spores are pigmented, and their color accounts for

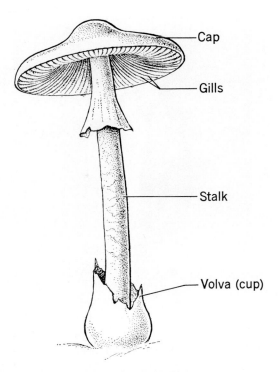

12-6 A drawing of the fruiting body of *Amanita verna*. Shown here is the cup, or volva, at the base of the stalk. This feature (it may be underground) is characteristic of many of the poisonous mushrooms. The radiating gills on the underside of the cap are characteristic of all gill fungi, whether edible or poisonous.

the beautiful greens and blue-greens of these handsome molds. The blue-green mold found in bleu and Roquefort cheeses is also produced by species of *Penicillium*. The cheeses get their distinctive flavor from the mold with which the cheese is inoculated. Spores of *Penicillium* are widely distributed and are common contaminants of sterile cultures in the laboratory.

Fungi and Disease

We have already discussed the importance of *Penicillium* and other molds in production of antibiotics (pages 217–19). Here we will discuss fungi from the other point of view—as *causes* of disease.

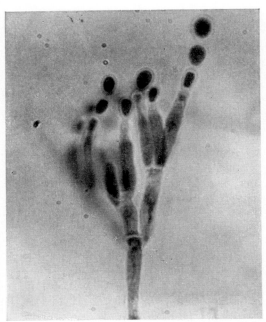

12-7 The brushlike hyphal branches of *Penicillium*. Thick-walled spores are produced at the tips of the branches. (675 X)

Do you have some Irish ancestors in your family tree? If you do, the chances are very good that they emigrated to the United States during the years following 1845. Up to that time, Ireland was a thriving state with a rapidly increasing population that had reached eight million. During this time of rapid expansion, the people of the "misty isles" had become almost totally dependent on one crop as a source of food. This was the "Irish potato," which had been introduced from South America many years earlier. It was the "luck of the Irish" that the year 1845 turned out to be a bad one for the potato crop. The days during the growing season were cool and damp, and as the young potato vines matured they became sick and died. At first it was thought that the poor growth of potatoes was the result of the bad weather, but it was soon demonstrated that a fungus, *Phytophthora infestans* (fy·TOF·tho·ra in·FEST·ans), was causing

a disease and that the cool, damp days were ideal for its rapid spread.

In the next fifteen years the potato crop failed repeatedly because of the fungus disease, and over a million Irishmen died of starvation and other diseases related to malnutrition. Rather than die on Irish soil, although they dearly loved it, another million and a half people emigrated to North America. Many settled in the rapidly growing cities of the United States, where they and their numerous descendants have played an important role in politics, law enforcement, and religious activities. If you examine your family tree, you may find that your existence today can be traced to a plant disease that occurred in Ireland more than one hundred years ago.

The disease of potatoes that scourged Ireland is still with us. It is estimated that in the United States alone, an annual average of over seven million bushels of potatoes is lost to this disease.

Crop failures resulting from rust and smut diseases of cereals (corn, wheat, rice) have displaced hundreds of millions of humans and caused countless deaths either by starvation or in wars motivated by starvation. In one recent five-year period alone, starvation in one nation took more than 12 million lives. Much of this loss of life can be attributed to loss of crops infected with rusts and smuts.

In the United States, starvation is infrequent, but crop loss is sometimes heavy. It is estimated that wheat rust disease causes a national reduction of more than 85 million bushels in production of wheat during a normal year! All diseases of field corn result in a loss of 335 million bushels. Of this total, 95 million bushels are lost because of corn smut.

In the face of increasing populations and food shortages in many parts of the world, these figures are important. The constant reduction in death rate resulting from the conquest of malaria (Chapter 1) and other

Eli Lilly and Co.

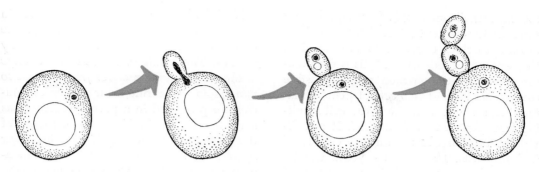

12-8 Asexual reproduction by budding in a brewers' yeast. How does this compare with reproduction in bacteria? With cell division in multicellular plants and animals?

diseases leads to a continual increase in the average life span and adds to the rapid increase of the earth's population. As a result of humanitarian efforts, it appears that man has created another imbalance in nature— one which an English clergyman, Thomas R. Malthus, predicted more than 160 years ago. Now that man is populating the earth more rapidly than ever before, he must turn his attention to increasing his food supply. But where is additional food to come from? There are several possibilities. One is to control diseases of important food crops as effectively as human diseases have been controlled. Improved control of plant diseases in the United States could produce an annual increase of 450 million bushels of grain of various kinds, with no increase in the acreage being farmed. This saving, however, is only a very small fraction of the food that will be necessary to feed mankind by the year 2000, if populations continue to increase at their present rate. Can you think of some other sources of food that are not utilized to any great extent? Making the most of the world's food supply is one problem biologists of the future will have to solve.

We have not exhausted the list of fungi that cause diseases of plants and animals. Perhaps you are unfortunate enough to live in a community where all of the American elm trees have died within the last few years. The chances are that the elm trees were infected with a vicious, fast-working fungus that causes the Dutch elm disease. Fungi also cause various skin diseases of man, apple scab, blights of native trees, and many other diseases.

Yeasts

Common brewers' and bakers' yeasts (Figure 12-8) are different from most true fungi, because they do not form hyphae. These yeasts are unicellular and reproduce asexually by a special kind of cell division called **budding.** When a yeast cell buds, it forms a bulge on one side of the cell. A nuclear division occurs in the parent cells, and one of the daughter nuclei moves into the developing bud. As the bud grows in size, it may separate from the parent cell.

In addition to asexual reproduction by budding, yeasts have a simple sexual cycle. To help understand the cycle, review Chapter 7. We will apply some of the ideas presented in Chapter 7 to this simple life cycle (Figure 12-9).

There are many different strains of commercial yeasts. They may be monoploid or diploid. Monoploid yeasts are distinguished from the diploid strains because their cells are smaller and they are metabolically less active. As monoploid yeasts age, there is a noticeable tendency for the cells of the culture to pair with one another. Where they touch, a small opening is formed, allowing some of the contents, including a nucleus, of one yeast cell to flow into and mix with the contents of its partner. This is the process of fertilization, which makes possible the combination of *two sets* of genetic material in a single cell. Thus, the cell resulting from fertilization is *diploid*. It can divide by budding, to form a new culture of diploid yeasts. These are the yeasts usually used by brewers and bakers, because of their greater production of carbon dioxide and alcohol in fermentation.

If diploid yeasts are subjected to certain unfavorable environmental conditions, some of the cells in the culture will divide by meiosis. *The result of meiosis is a change in the chromosome number from diploid to monoploid.* As a rule, four monoploid nuclei are produced in a parent yeast cell as a result of meiosis. Next, the contents of the parent yeast cell are divided into four spores. Each spore contains one of the monoploid nuclei. When the spores germinate, a new monoploid strain is started.

Knowing about the life cycle of yeasts

YEAST LIFE CYCLE

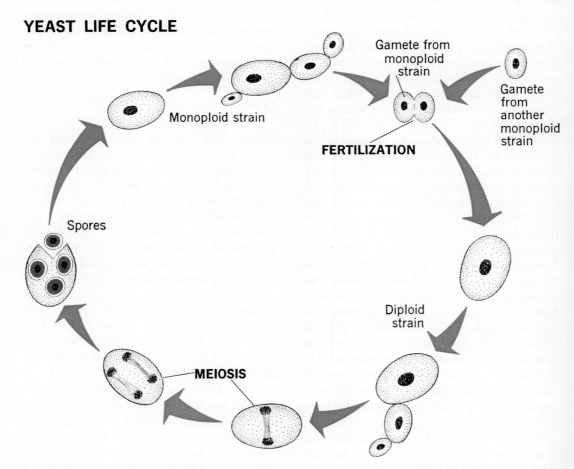

Monoploid strain

Gamete from monoploid strain

Gamete from another monoploid strain

FERTILIZATION

Spores

Diploid strain

MEIOSIS

12-9 The life cycle of a yeast is basically similar to the life cycles of all sexually reproducing organisms. What is the distinction between diploid and monoploid strains? What changes in chromosome number are involved in the life cycle?

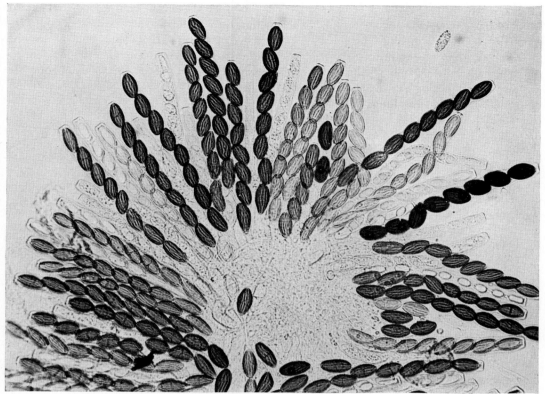

Bernard O. Dodge

12-10 A portion of the fruiting body of the pink bread mold *Neurospora*. The dark ellipti-cal bodies are the spores. They are arranged in a linear fashion inside saclike cells. How has *Neurospora* proved valuable in studies of inheritance in organisms?

has made it possible for us to utilize their potentialities better. For example, two mon-oploid strains of yeasts having desirable qualities may be mated to produce diploid cells. The offspring may differ from both parent strains in their ability to form vita-mins, or their efficiency in producing alco-hol or carbon dioxide, or in other qualities.

Yeasts have proved extremely useful as experimental organisms in our quest for knowledge of outer space. Scientists have been aware of the hazards to man of vari-ous kinds of radiation found in outer space. To test the effects of radiation on living or-ganisms prior to man's first flights, rockets were sent aloft carrying living yeast cells.

When the yeasts were returned to earth, they were cultured, and the degree of dam-age to their genetic material was studied.

Another fungus that has been used ex-tensively to help us understand the princi-ples of inheritance is the pink bread mold. Like the yeasts, this mold produces spores immediately following meiosis. There are usually eight of these spores in each of the saclike cells (Figure 12-10). These mono-ploid spores can be isolated individually from the sac, then cultured to analyze their hereditary characteristics. The order of the spores in the sac reflects the events that oc-cur in meiosis. The analysis of these events will be discussed in detail in Chapter 32.

CONCLUDING REMARKS— ADAPTATION TO LAND

The evolution of organisms capable of surviving on land is one of the most important of all biological events. The evidence indicates that the fungi, like all other terrestrial organisms, had their beginnings with more primitive, unicellular, aquatic ancestors. These ancestors, like the fungi, were probably heterotrophs and would best be described as protozoans. In the course of adaptation to life on land, certain changes occurred that made it possible for organisms (plants, animals, and fungi) to survive in the dry land environments.

More specifically, in the evolution of the fungi we can list the following important adaptations:

1. The disappearance of flagellated cells and the evolution of new methods of sexual and asexual reproduction. (Review spore and gamete formation in *Rhizopus*.)
2. The evolution of protective layers around spores and (in some cases) zygotes. The tiny bit of living substance within a spore or zygote provides the only continuity from one organism to the next. The mold or mushroom may die, but survival of the species is assured by the production of these resistant, almost indestructible reproductive cells. (Remember the spores of a slime mold, and of *Penicillium, Rhizopus*, and yeasts.)
3. The evolution of hyphae with thickened, supporting cell walls. Hyphae are structural units used for obtaining nutrition from the environment. They compose the structures (fruiting bodies) on which spores are produced and elevated for dispersal, and they also are modified for sexual reproduction.

Numerous other characters that adapt fungi to a terrestrial existence could be listed. It is time, however, to move on with our story of evolution and see how autotrophic plants succeeded in colonizing the land.

GUIDE QUESTIONS AND PROBLEMS

1. In what ways does the slime mold plasmodium resemble an animal?
2. What plantlike traits does the slime mold show in its life history?
3. What adaptations for living in a dry land environment are found in the bread mold *Rhizopus?*
4. What is the evidence that the true fungi have evolved from the protozoans rather than from algae?
5. Compare the fungi and the bacteria with respect to their importance to man.
6. How can it be shown that fungal diseases of plants have social, political, and economic consequences?
7. What is the economic importance of the yeasts?
8. What important adaptations occurred in the evolution of the fungi that enabled them to live on land?

SUGGESTIONS FOR ADDITIONAL READING

Books

Christensen, Clyde M., *The Molds and Man.* Minneapolis, University of Minnesota Press, 1961.

An accurate and interesting account of the importance of the fungi.

Hylander, C. J., *The World of Plant Life*, 2nd ed. New York, Macmillan, 1956.

A complete and concise description of important plant groups.

Smith, G. M., *Cryptogamic Botany.* New York, McGraw-Hill, 1955.

A two-volume, advanced-level text on the seedless plants. The first volume contains a good section on the slime molds and the fungi.

13

THE TREND

TOWARD

COMPLEXITY

By this time the importance of green plants in the world of living things has been made clear to you. Without green plants there would be practically no photosynthesis, a vital process in which light energy is transformed into stored chemical energy. Fortunately, the green plant stores more energy than it uses for its own growth and reproduction. It is this unused reservoir that *all* animals and other heterotrophs rely on, either directly or indirectly, for their existence.

Has it always been this way? Have there always been green plants on the land, and land animals to eat them? If not, when and where did green plants first appear? Do we have any evidence to give us some idea as to how long photosynthetic organisms have inhabited the earth? If so, what were these organisms like in the distant past? Clearly the answers to these questions—if there are answers—will have overtones of an evolu-

tionary nature. To study the evolution of photosynthetic plants and their ascendancy in the seas and on the land, we have to "go back in time" to search for evidences of ancient plants as recorded in the rocks. We must start with the fossil record—the history of life on earth.

THE EARLIEST EVIDENCES OF PLANT LIFE

Before we begin to search the fossil record for evidence of ancient photosynthetic organisms, we have to gain some perspective about the age of the earth. We must forget about time in terms of what happened yesterday, a year ago, or just when some historical event, such as the signing of the Declaration of Independence, took place. We must learn to relate events in the evolution of living things to the age of our earth.

According to the latest estimates, our earth is approximately 5,000,000,000 years old. Five billion is an easy number to say but, like all large numbers, its magnitude is difficult to understand. Let us try to give it some meaning by using an analogy. Imagine that the thickness of a dime (1 mm) represents the period of recorded history (about 6,000 years). Now let us lay the dime on its side next to a building 896 meters tall. Such a building would be twice as tall as the Empire State Building in New York City, at present the tallest building in the world. The height of this colossal tower would then represent 5 billion years if the thickness of the dime represented the entire duration of recorded history!

Telling Time by the Rocks

You might wonder how the age of the earth and the rocks that make up its crust can be determined with any degree of accuracy. One method is to measure the accumulation of certain isotopes (see Chapter 5) of lead and other elements that are products of the disintegration of radioactive materials originally present when the rocks were formed. This method is called the radioactive clock method and is the most accurate way to measure the age of **igneous** (IG·ne·us) **rocks** of the earth's crust. Igneous rocks are formed from molten materials such as those which come from the outflow of volcanoes. It is presumed that the oldest rocks in the earth's crust are igneous, having been derived from molten materials formed fairly early in the history of the earth.

Many igneous rocks contain lead-206 (Pb^{206}), which is a stable isotope of lead derived from the disintegration of radioactive uranium-238 (U^{238}). The disintegration of U^{238}, like the disintegration of any radioactive substance, is unaffected by factors of the environment such as temperature, humidity, and pressure. The rate of disintegration is constant and is measured in units of time called **half-lives.** Perhaps the best way to understand a half-life is to give an example.

Let us imagine that we have purified some U^{238}, and then taken exactly 2,000,000 atoms of U^{238} and sealed them in a bottle where there were no atoms of any other elements. We place a label on the bottle marking the year—1963. The U^{238} atoms in the bottle would continue to disintegrate at a given rate, so that at the end of 4.5 billion years there would be only 1,000,000 U^{238} atoms left, or just one half the number we started with. At the end of another 4.5 billion years the U^{238} atoms would be reduced by one half again, and so on, as shown below.

Date	Number of atoms of U^{238} in sample
A.D. 1963	2,000,000
A.D. 4,500,001,963	1,000,000
A.D. 9,000,001,963	500,000
A.D. 13,500,001,963	250,000

Thus the half-life of U^{238} is 4.5 billion years, which means that only half of the atoms of U^{238} present at a given moment will be on hand 4.5 billion years later.

As the U^{238} atoms in our sample disintegrate, a series of new radioactive substances forms, each with a specific half-life, until the final stable product, Pb^{206}, is produced. Since Pb^{206} represents the "end of the line" of the disintegration process that started with U^{238} atoms, each atom of Pb^{206} therefore represents an atom of U^{238} in the "original" sample. Let us suppose that our sample is a piece of igneous rock containing U^{238} and Pb^{206} atoms. We discover that the ratio of uranium to lead is approximately 2 to 1. How old would the rock be if we assume that only U^{238} atoms were present at the time the rock was formed? By using the radioactive clock method, the age of some of the oldest igneous rocks of the earth has been determined to be about 2.8 billion years.

There may seem to be little connection between dating the igneous rocks and determining the age of the earliest fossils. For fossils are found in **sedimentary** (sed·ih-MEN·ta·ree), or stratified, rocks—not in igneous rocks. Sandstone, limestone, shale, and coal are examples of stratified rocks. They are made up of particles of sand, clay, or plant debris, and have been converted to rock that may contain fossils. Because particles of which sedimentary rocks are composed have many different origins, it is impossible to use the radioactive clock method to date them. However, sedimentary rocks are often associated with dated igneous rocks in such a way that the age of the sedimentary rock can be inferred. Such an association occurs where molten igneous materials have filled the cracks and spaces in sedimentary rocks. Since the sedimentary rocks were formed first, they must be at least as old as the intrusive igneous material. Thus, by determining the age of the igneous material we can determine the minimum age of the associated sedimentary rocks.

There are also a few instances where one can make a more accurate determination of the age of sedimentary rocks. For example, geologists know of a few places where a layer of molten igneous material spread over a layer of sedimentary rock in the process of formation. In this case the ages of the sedimentary rocks and the igneous rocks would be nearly the same.

The Oldest Fossils

Now that we know of a method for determining the age of fossils, we can look at the fossil record for some of the answers to our questions about when and where photosynthetic plants first made their appearance. Fossil evidence of the first photosynthetic organisms comes from a period of the earth's history called the **Pre-Cambrian** (pre-KAM-brih-an—Figure 13-1). This period embraces about nine tenths of the total age of the earth, starting with the earth's beginning and continuing up to the time of the **Cambrian period.** Since the Cambrian period started, about 600 million years ago, all the evolution of land organisms has occurred.

During the Pre-Cambrian period, tremendous reefs of limestone ($CaCO_3$) were formed. Some of these limestones show a characteristic pattern, as though the limestone had been deposited in concentric layers to form large limestone heads (Figure 13-2a), of which the reefs are composed. One such Pre-Cambrian limestone reef in Southern Rhodesia is at least 2.3 billion years old! These unusual limestone deposits have been compared with similar limestone formations produced by some present-day blue-green algae. Could it be that blue-green algae were present in the Pre-Cambrian seas where the reefs were formed? No matter how hard we look, we cannot find conclusive evidence of the remains of algal cells in the ancient limestone.

In 1954 two Americans, S. A. Tyler and E. S. Barghoorn, reported a spectacular discovery. They had found fossilized remains of organisms in rocks of Pre-Cambrian age —at least 1.6 billion years old. These beautifully preserved specimens were discovered in a very hard rock called chert or flint (Figure 13-2b). By grinding sections of the rock thin enough to transmit light, Tyler and Barghoorn were able to examine the sections under the compound microscope. These examinations revealed organisms similar to fungal hyphae and spores, and colonies of cells very much like modern blue-green algae! This unique discovery confirmed what had been suspected many years before, that blue-green algae were among the earliest cellular inhabitants of the earth.

Perhaps the most important conclusion to be drawn from this discovery is that both autotrophic and heterotrophic organisms had evolved during the Pre-Cambrian period. The further accumulation of evidence from Pre-Cambrian fossils has led to two additional conclusions: the organisms of the Pre-Cambrian period were very primitive in structure, and they lived in water.

Before we continue the story of plant evolution, let us take a brief glimpse at the Pre-Cambrian landscape. It will raise some questions that we hope to answer in the next chapters. The most obvious difference between the Pre-Cambrian landscape and the one we see today is the total absence of land plants and animals at that time (Figure 1-3, pages 8 and 9). Clearly, sometime between the end of this early period and the present, the land was colonized by living things. All of the evidence at our disposal confirms the hypothesis that land plants and animals evolved from aquatic ancestors. If we accept this hypothesis, as most biologists do, we need to explain how plants and animals living in the seas could possibly become suited to survive in the bleak, desiccating land environment. What kinds of adaptations enabled plants to colonize the land without dehydrating? What were the primitive land plants like?

13-1 PLANT LIFE ON EARTH—A TIME SCALE

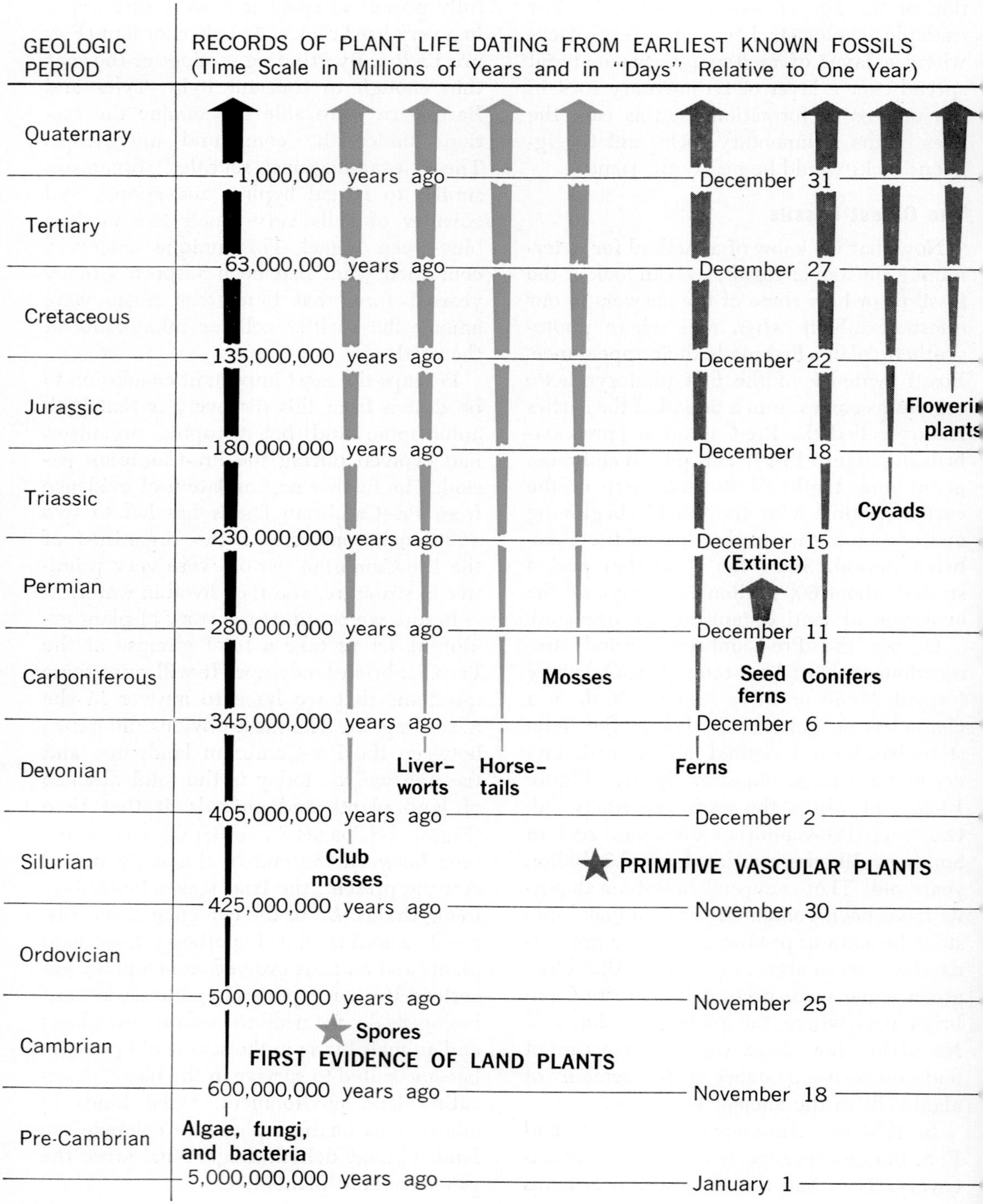

GEOLOGIC PERIOD	RECORDS OF PLANT LIFE DATING FROM EARLIEST KNOWN FOSSILS (Time Scale in Millions of Years and in "Days" Relative to One Year)

Quaternary

————1,000,000 years ago————————————December 31————

Tertiary

————63,000,000 years ago————————————December 27————

Cretaceous

————135,000,000 years ago————————————December 22————

Jurassic

————180,000,000 years ago————————————December 18————

Flowering plants

Triassic

Cycads

————230,000,000 years ago————————————December 15————
(Extinct)

Permian

————280,000,000 years ago————————————December 11————

Carboniferous

Mosses   **Seed ferns**   **Conifers**

————345,000,000 years ago————————————December 6————

Devonian

Liver-worts   **Horse-tails**   **Ferns**

————405,000,000 years ago————————————December 2————

Silurian

Club mosses   ★ **PRIMITIVE VASCULAR PLANTS**

————425,000,000 years ago————————————November 30————

Ordovician

————500,000,000 years ago————————————November 25————

Cambrian

★ **Spores**
FIRST EVIDENCE OF LAND PLANTS

————600,000,000 years ago————————————November 18————

Pre-Cambrian

Algae, fungi, and bacteria

————5,000,000,000 years ago————————————January 1————

a

New York State Museum and Science Service

13-2 **a** A Pre-Cambrian reef showing concentric layers of limestone. What indirect evidence leads biologists to believe that these limestone structures were formed by Pre-Cambrian organisms? **b** A microscopic view (190X) of fossil remains of organisms found in Pre-Cambrian rocks 1.6 billion years old. How does this evidence help substantiate the organic origin of ancient reefs like the one in **a**?

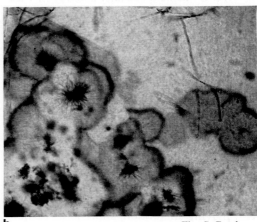

b

Elso S. Barghoorn

UNICELLULAR TO MULTICELLULAR— THE STORY OF ALGAE

One of the most obvious features of evolutionarily advanced organisms is their multicellular construction. The word *multicellular* literally means "of many cells," but multicellular organisms are more than just organisms with many cells. They are organisms with different kinds of cells, each kind performing specific functions. Thus, multicellular organisms have certain cells modified for movement of materials; there may be special cells for reproduction, and others with thick walls for support. There is a division of labor among the cells of multicellular organisms.

But where did multicellular organisms come from? Have they always existed? The evidence from comparative morphology, the fossil record, and experiments dealing with life's beginnings (Chapter 36) leaves little doubt that unicellular organisms were the ancestors of multicellular plants and animals.

Unicellular Origins

The unicellular level of organization should be familiar to you (Figure 9-1). You have studied unicellular bacteria and yeasts,

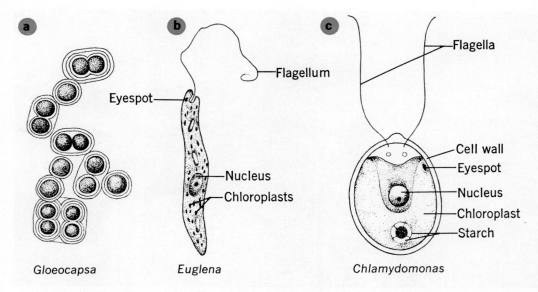

a   b   c

Gloeocapsa   Euglena   Chlamydomonas

13-3 Some unicellular autotrophs. These microscopic organisms are common inhabitants of freshwater ponds, lakes, and lagoons. **a** *Gloeocapsa* is one of the most primitive of all autotrophic organisms. **b** *Euglena* is very much like a protozoan except that it has chloroplasts. **c** *Chlamydomonas*, although motile, is very plantlike because it has a chloroplast, stores starch, and has a distinct cell wall. It may be very much like the ancestral unicellular organisms from which green plants evolved.

and you have examined a drop of pond water (Laboratory Exercise 3-7), in which you saw a variety of unicellular organisms—plant and animal. Some may have been blue-green in color and arranged in loose packets of cells called colonies (Figure 13-3a, *Gloeocapsa*—glee·o·ᴋᴀᴘ·sa). Others, green or colorless, may have been very active, moving in sudden, short jerks or darting across the field of the microscope. Many of the motile forms are propelled by flagella or cilia, while others are amoeboid.

The variety among unicellular types extends to differences in their methods of obtaining food. Many are colorless heterotrophs that ingest particles of food, including other unicellular organisms, either through a gullet at one end of the cell or by engulfing the particles with outthrust **pseudopods** (soo·doh·podz). Not all of the unicellular organisms are colorless, however. Some are brown and others are various shades of green, blue-green, or yellow-

green; all of these are photosynthetic organisms. They all contain chlorophyll and are capable of an autotrophic mode of existence.

Although the evidence from the fossil record tells us that blue-green algae were among the early photosynthetic organisms to inhabit the earth, there are many reasons to believe that other unicellular organisms such as *Euglena* (yoo·ɢʟᴇᴇ·na) may be more representative of the organisms that were ancestral to multicellular plants and animals. *Euglena* (Figure 13-3b) is a flagellated organism, with no cell wall. In contrast to the lack of a cell wall, in which they resemble animals, euglenas usually have well-defined chloroplasts and store a carbohydrate only slightly different from the starches of higher plants. It is now known that some of these autotrophs will, under some experimental conditions, lose their chlorophyll. This does not result in their death. They simply become heterotrophs and live by absorbing soluble nutrients. Thus *Euglena,* when treated with the antibiotic streptomycin, or with heat, can be converted from a "plant" into an "animal." A unicellular organism with the potentialities of *Euglena* deserves special attention when we are searching for the kind of organism that might represent the ancestral type from which plants and animals may have evolved at some time in the distant past.

Of all the unicellular autotrophs, those of greatest interest to us in our study of the evolution of land plants are those with bright green chloroplasts and well-defined cell walls. A common aquatic organism with those characteristics is the green alga *Chlamydomonas* (klam·ih·da·мoн·nas—Figure 13-3c). It is obvious that this unicellular organism is like some protozoans in having flagella. Yet when we examine its pigments and stored food we find them identical with those of green land plants. Both the green alga *Chlamydomonas* and green land plants contain two kinds of chlorophyll, which are designated chlorophylls *a* and *b.* Not only are the chlorophyll molecules the same in both types of organisms, but they are present in similar proportions. The biochemical similarity of the green alga *Chlamydomonas* and the green land plants extends even to their stored food, which is true starch. Because of these and other similarities, *Chlamydomonas* is believed to represent *the general type* of unicellular autotroph from which multicellular green plants may have evolved long ago.

At one stage in its life cycle, *Chlamydomonas* may do a rather unusual thing. The normally motile vegetative cells withdraw their flagella and become attached to some object in the water. Then they divide to form irregular masses of nonmotile green cells. This stage in the life cycle of *Chlamydomonas* is like an evolutionary "signpost" that points to the multicellular organization of nonmotile, green plants.

The same tendency of nonmotile, green cells to be intimately associated in packets or colonies can be seen in many other organisms (Figure 13-4). In fact, it may be very difficult for a casual observer to distinguish such clusters of cells from true multicellular organisms. To tell the difference between a packet of unicells and a multicellular organism, we must answer this question: Is there any "division of labor" here—any differentiation among the cells—

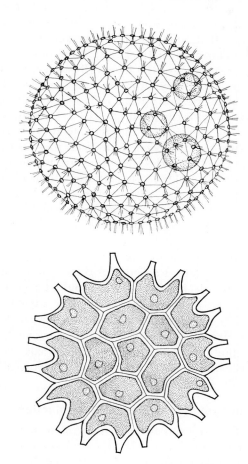

13-4 Two colonial autotrophs. *Volvox* (above) shows some division of labor, because only certain cells of the colony are potentially reproductive. *Pediastrum* (below) shows no division of labor. All of its cells are potentially reproductive. Which organism do you think most closely approximates a multicellular organization?

or are all the cells potentially self-sufficient, each one capable of carrying out all of the functions required for survival? If we can find some clear evidence of differentiation of cells, then we are looking at a multicellular organism.

Primitive Multicellular Organization

Primitive green plants living in aquatic environments *have* evolved a multicellular organization. One such alga is the common "sea lettuce," or *Ulva*, of our coastal tide pools (Figure 13-6). The bright green sheets that comprise this organism are usually two cells in thickness. Thus only the outer surfaces of the *Ulva* cells are exposed to the aquatic environment. At the base of the plant we find special cells differentiated into long threads. These cells are rootlike, in that they anchor the plant to rocks bordering the tide pools. Moreover, these cells are usually colorless, and they are never reproductive. They are differentiated cells that perform a specific function for the plant. Without these anchoring cells, *Ulva* would be unable to survive in the wave-washed tide pools.

Although many steps are missing from our generalized account of the evolution of the multicellular body, it should be clear that the direction has been from unicellular, to colonies of cells, to organisms showing differentiation of cells. (The evolution of multicellular organization in animals was basically the same as in plants, as we shall see in later chapters.)

The Evolution of Sexual Reproduction

The widespread occurrence of sexual reproduction among plants and animals testifies to its importance (review Chapter 9). We know of only two groups in which sexual reproduction has *not* been demonstrated. One of these is the blue-green algae. The other is a group of unicellular, flagellated organisms to which *Euglena* belongs.

In each instance of sexual reproduction that we have thus far described (in bacteria, slime mold, bread mold, and yeasts), the sex cells (gametes) were alike in structure. Sexual reproduction involving the fusion of gametes that are alike in structure is called **isogamy** (i·SOG·a·mee). *Chlamydomonas* has isogamous sexual reproduction (Figure 13-5a). Its gametes are tiny copies of the vegetative cells. This appears to be another evolutionary signpost; gametes probably have evolved from vegetative cells.

In many strains of *Chlamydomonas*, gametic fusion will not occur unless different mating strains are present. The genetically different strains are designated simply (+) and (−). The fusion of *Chlamydomonas* gametes occurs in water. The zygote that is formed is thick-walled and can withstand drying and other unfavorable environmental conditions. If the pond or rain barrel in which *Chlamydomonas* is growing should dry up, the chances of survival until more water is available are improved by the resistance of the zygote. Not all algae form thick-walled zygotes, however. Most marine algae, including the giant kelps, produce delicate, thin-walled zygotes. Can you explain why *Chlamydomonas* and the marine algae have structurally different zygotes?

Another sort of sexual reproduction is found in the green alga *Oedogonium* (ee-doh·GOH·nih·um). This organism produces two visibly different kinds of gametes (Figure 13-5b). It forms small, flagellated sperms and large, nonmotile eggs. The latter are retained in the protective covering of the egg-forming cell. Sexual reproduction such as that occurring in *Oedogonium*, involving the fusion of structurally different gametes, is called **heterogamy** (het·er·OG·a·mee). As an egg of *Oedogonium* develops, it becomes filled with starch grains and other stored food. Prior to fertilization, the cell containing the egg develops a pore on one side. The sperms will enter through this pore to reach the egg. Notice that the egg is *retained* inside the female structure

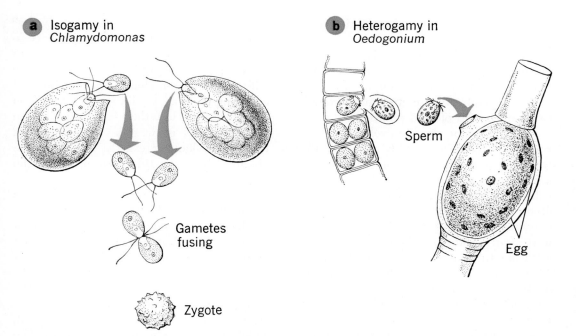

a Isogamy in *Chlamydomonas*

b Heterogamy in *Oedogonium*

Sperm

Gametes fusing

Egg

Zygote

13-5 Two patterns of sexual reproduction—isogamy and heterogamy. What features of heterogamy indicate that it is a more highly evolved kind of reproduction than isogamy? Of what importance are zygotes to survival?

until long after fertilization has occurred. Sooner or later, however, the thick-walled zygote is released into the water.

Heterogamous sexual reproduction, as in *Oedogonium* and many other algae, foreshadows the type of sexual reproduction of green land plants in at least three ways: (1) egg and sperm have been evolved; (2) the egg develops within the protective covering of a female reproductive structure; and (3) a tendency exists for the zygote to be retained in the female reproductive structure. As we will see, all of these characteristics are prerequisites to survival of green plants on land.

Spores

In Chapter 12 we stressed the importance of spore formation in the fungi as a means of asexual reproduction. The algae are also spore-formers. However, their spores are quite different from the thick-walled spores

of terrestrial fungi. Usually the spores of algae are thin-walled, and they may have flagella. Both *Chlamydomonas* and *Oedogonium* produce motile, flagellated spores, which are capable of reproducing the vegetative stage of the organism. Compared with the resistant spores of most fungi, the delicate spores of algae would have little chance to survive on dry land. If, as evidence indicates, green land plants evolved from algal ancestors, radical changes in spore structure must have occurred. This topic is discussed in the next chapter.

Alternation of Generations

Photosynthesis, the production of spores, the formation of cell walls, and alternation of generations are among the most universal characteristics of plants. There are exceptions, of course. The true fungi are not photosynthetic, and all plants do not have an alternation of generations—but taken together, these features characterize most plants.

Alternation of generations is of common occurrence among the algae and is more easily understood in the simple life cycles of these plants than in the more complicated life cycles of land plants.

Let us examine the life cycle of the marine alga *Ulva* (Figure 13-6). Imagine that we bring some specimens of *Ulva* into the laboratory, where we can study them critically. First we take fragments of the living green plants and look at them under the microscope. Not all the cells are the same in structure. Some may be in the process of releasing tiny, motile cells into the water. Almost as soon as these cells are deposited in the surrounding water, they start swimming about independently. If we are very patient we may see some of these cells pair and fuse with one another to form a single cell. If we remember what occurred in *Chlamydomonas,* we will recognize this as a stage in sexual reproduction, resulting in the formation of a zygote.

Let us isolate all of the zygotes we can find, so that we can see what they will produce. The zygotes of *Ulva,* like those of most marine plants, start to grow after a very short time. The rate of growth may be a bit slow to watch, but we can observe that the zygote is growing into a new *Ulva* plant, with the same structure as those we collected from the tide pool. At this point we might be inclined to conclude our observations, because we seem to be right back where we started in the life cycle.

But no—let us carry our experiment a little farther. Let the new plants mature. Perhaps with luck and patience we can see what kind of reproductive cells this generation will form. Except for the number of their flagella, the new reproductive cells (Figure 13-6) look very much like gametes, but they do not behave like gametes. No matter how long we look, they reveal no tendency to fuse in pairs. If these are

not gametes, what else could they be? Could they be spores such as algae commonly form? If so, they should grow into some kind of vegetative structure. So we will give them the chance by isolating and culturing them as we did the zygotes. Soon the motile cells lose their flagella and begin to divide and grow. They grow into an *Ulva* plant looking exactly like those we obtained from the tide pool and from the zygote.

We must have two generations of plants in this life cycle! Although they look alike, we have found one generation that produces nothing but gametes and one that produces only spores. We have seen that gametes fuse in pairs, and a zygote results. When the zygote grows it gives rise to the spore-producing plant. The spores that are produced each grow into an *Ulva* plant, which in turn produces more gametes. The cycle is complete. It is a life cycle in which there is an alternation of generations.

We should now try to define "alternation of generations" as it applies to plants. First, an alternation of generations occurs in those plants with *two multicellular stages* (the two *Ulva* plants in our example), one of which produces gametes and one of which produces spores. A multicellular gamete-producing generation, or **gametophyte** (ga-MEE-toh-fyt), alternates with a multicellular spore-producing generation, or **sporophyte** (SPOH-ro-fyt), in the life cycle of the plant.

Before we can draw any conclusions about why alternation of generations is important to plants, we must correlate the life cycle described for *Ulva* with chromosome number. Let us review the life cycle of *Ulva* again, but this time relate chromosome number to the two generations. We will start with the gametes and fertilization.

Each gamete of *Ulva lactuca* has a nucleus containing 13 chromosomes. This is the monoploid, or *n*, number. Two gametes fuse to form a zygote. Each gamete contributes 13 chromosomes to the fusion nucleus of the zygote, thus initiating the diploid, or *2n,* chromosome number of 26. Growth of the zygote is by mitotic divisions, so that each cell of the new *Ulva* plant derived from the zygote is diploid. Certain reproductive cells of this diploid plant (the sporophyte) divide by meiosis (Chapter 7) to form monoploid spores. The monoploid spores, each having the *n* number of chromosomes (13), grow as a result of mitotic divisions into a new monoploid *Ulva* plant (gametophyte). Some cells of this plant produce monoploid gametes. Now we have returned to the start of the cycle as introduced at the beginning of this paragraph. Read the paragraph again and compare the text with Figure 13-7.

There are several exceptions to this correlation. However, it is a generalization that applies to the majority of plants that show an alternation of generations.

Because of the universal occurrence of alternations of generations in green land plants, and its frequent occurrence among the algae, we can hardly avoid the conclusion that it must be of some selective advantage. That is, it must be a mechanism that promotes survival. Nevertheless, it is not at all obvious how an alternation of generations does promote survival.

A possible explanation, such as the following, might be offered. In the diploid sporophyte generation, meiosis occurs before the spores are formed. During this process there is a great shuffling of the genes and, as a consequence, a great variety of spores with different genetic makeups are produced. Some will have a genetic makeup that will give the possessors an improved chance of surviving in the particular environment where they occur. Others will have a genetic makeup that is not so good for survival.

The monoploid spores will develop into the monoploid gametophyte generation. The gametophytes with the better genetic makeup for survival in their environment will tend to be the ones that reach maturity. The gametophytes then produce the gametes. There is no meiosis at this time. The gametes are produced by mitotic divisions, and so will have exactly the same genetic makeup as the gametophyte. The gametophyte generation, therefore, can be looked upon as a mechanism for transmitting intact groups of genes that have been shown to be superior.

One might ask, therefore, why meiosis is necessary. When we have obtained a genetic makeup that is good for survival in a particular environment, why break it up by meiosis? The answer to this lies, at least in part, in the fact that the environment is often changing. What is genetically good for survival today may be genetically inadequate tomorrow. None but the simplest of animals or plants can survive for long if it reproduces without meiosis and genetic recombination. At least, there is no evidence that one ever has.

Thus many plants have evolved a mechanism for taking advantage of the desirable features of two ways of reproduction. The sporophyte generation produces a large variety of spores, which differ in their genetic makeup. The spores grow into the gametophytes, which "try out" the new genetic combinations. The gametophyte generation produces gametes with no further genetic changes. Therefore the gametophyte generation will reproduce intact the genetic system that has been tried and tested in the environment.

Different kinds of these selected gametes combine. This, of course, brings many more different genetic types into being:

n kinds of sperms $\times$ *n* kinds of eggs
$= n^2$ kinds of zygotes

Each zygote so formed develops into a sporophyte—in which genetic variability is once more increased by the process of meiosis that precedes spore formation. And that is where we started.

THE LIFE CYCLE OF *ULVA*

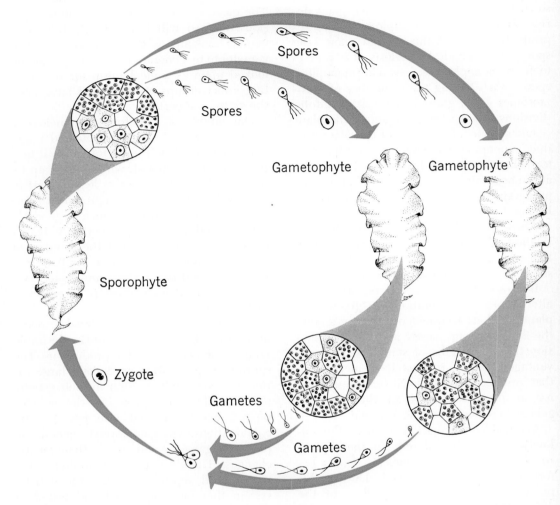

13-6 In the life cycle of *Ulva*, there is an alternation of generations—a sporophyte and a gametophyte that are identical in appearance. The sporophyte produces tiny motile spores with four flagella. The gametophyte produces even smaller motile gametes that fuse with one another to form zygotes. The changes in chromosome number from one generation to the other are shown in Figure 13-7.

ALGAE AND THE WORLD TODAY

The most obvious organisms are not always the most important, and so it is with the algae. Would you guess that the algae in salt and fresh water together account for 90 percent of the world's photosynthesis? This statistic may give you another partial answer to a question asked earlier: How are we going to increase our food supply as the population of the world increases? The seas hold a great reserve of food, more of

CHROMOSOME NUMBERS IN THE LIFE CYCLE OF *ULVA*

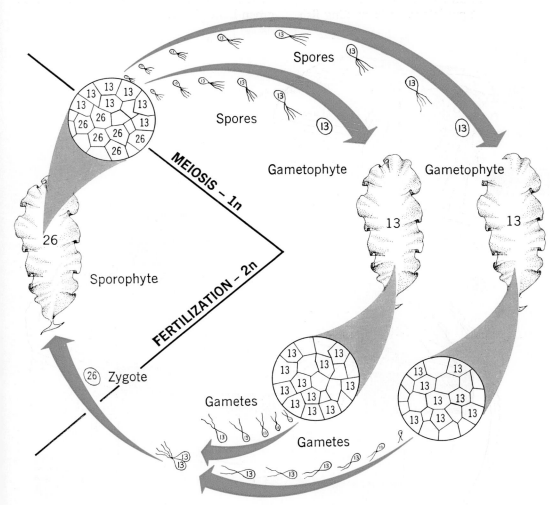

Spores

Spores

Gametophyte

Gametophyte

13

13

MEIOSIS – 1n

FERTILIZATION – 2n

26

Sporophyte

26 Zygote

Gametes

Gametes

13-7 The chromosome number of the gametophyte of this species of *Ulva* is 13. The gametes produced by the gametophyte also have 13 chromosomes. The zygote resulting from fusion of two gametes has what chromosome number? What is the chromosome number of the sporophyte? What occurs in spore-forming cells?

which could be shared by man with the heterotrophs in the sea.

Photosynthetic plants in aquatic environments supply most of the oxygen available to aquatic animals, from protozoans to fish. This explains why we include green plants in an aquarium with our tropical fish. The autotrophic algae are also an essential link in the food web (Chapter 8). As a matter of fact, they are the first link in this chain in aquatic environments. The algae make their food by photosynthesis. Heterotrophic protozoans then utilize the algae as a source of food. Other small animals may ingest the protozoans. Larger animals may eat the smaller ones, and so on up the line to the ocean's largest predators. In harvesting fish from the sea for his own use, man also plays a part in this food web. Clearly, without the algae there would be no life in the seas, just as there could be no life on land without green land plants.

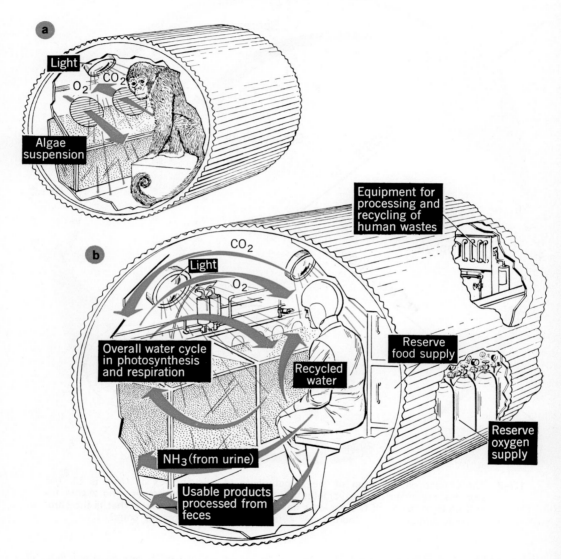

13-8 **a** A *Cebus* monkey in a temporarily closed environment. The monkey and the algae could survive for days—the algae longer—but not indefinitely. Can you guess why this experiment, unlike the one in **b**, would have to be terminated soon? (Would the monkey be able to feed himself and supply the algae with nutrients?) **b** Compare this hypothetical closed environment (for space travel exceeding thirty days) with the experiment shown in **a**. What are some of the factors that justify the longer-term, more complex environment for man?

Algae and Space Travel

"Thirty days out—everything A–OK." This well might be the message from space in the not-too-distant future as man attempts his first trip to the planet Venus. Not long ago such a trip seemed impossible, yet at the time of this writing many of the technological devices—the rockets, the space vehicles, the propellants—are available. It has been determined that such a trip, lasting over thirty days, would require "nonexpendable or regenerative life-supporting systems." What this means is that man will have to construct and maintain closed ecological systems within space vehicles, space platforms, or other structures used for extended habitation away from the earth.

What are some of the problems that must be considered in building such a closed system? Spacemen will need sources of oxygen and food. At the same time, some means of getting rid of CO_2 and other body wastes must be devised. Perhaps you will have some ideas about how this might be done when you recall the carbon-oxygen-hydrogen cycle and the nitrogen cycle and how they work on earth (Chapter 8).

In addition to the spacemen and their equipment, the spaceship could be supplied with some photosynthetic organism—one which can grow rapidly and supply food and sufficient oxygen. Certain microscopic, unicellular algae have been tested for possible use. Among these is the green alga *Chlorella pyrenoidosa* (klo·REL·a py·re·noy-DOH·sa). To simulate conditions that might be encountered in a space vehicle, investigators devised a closed system (Figure 13-8a) using the alga and a *Cebus* (SEE·bus) monkey. The closed system consisted of 55 liters of alga suspension connected to a 230-liter closed gas system containing the monkey. The alga delivered O_2 into the system at rates from 1.3 to 2.6 liters per hour, while the monkey consumed O_2 at rates between 1.0 and 2.1 liters per hour. The monkey produced CO_2 at rates from 1.4 to 2.6 liters per hour, and the alga absorbed it in photosynthesis at rates from 0.9 to 1.9 liters per hour.

At the end of fifty hours—the end of the experiment—the oxygen level had increased from 21 percent to 25 percent. At no time did the carbon dioxide content of the atmosphere exceed 1 percent. From the standpoint of gaseous exchange, the experiment could have run longer. However, the problem of food must be considered.

During the experiment the alga produced from 1.0 to 1.8 grams (dry weight) of energy-containing cells per hour. This represents a possible source of food in the closed system for a human being. (*Chlorella* is one of several unicellular algae that can be rendered palatable for human consumption.) To be an effective food producer in the closed system, the alga must have a source of nitrogen for the synthesis of protein. One obvious nitrogen source, as indicated in Figure 13-8b, is human wastes—urine and feces. Methods for utilization of both materials have been tested. One of the most promising methods resulted from the discovery that some species of algae can grow in diluted human urea. Hence this substance can be used as a nitrogen source for protein synthesis.

The algae have been harvested and fed to mice—they appear to have nutritive value for these animals, and there is no reason to believe that these algae could not be used as food for man.

The algae in these experiments are of particular interest in the investigation of space travel because they participate not only in the carbon-oxygen-hydrogen cycle but also in the nitrogen cycle. Bacteria are not required to recycle the nitrogen; everything necessary is accomplished by the one organism—the alga. Once again, we see how an understanding of certain basic principles of nature may help to solve technological problems—this time in the realm of space travel.

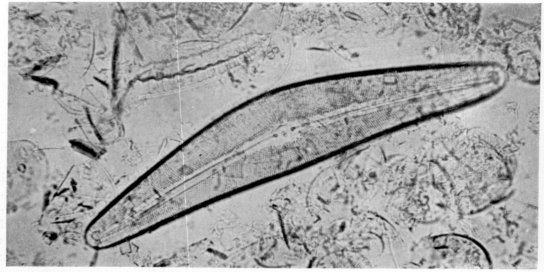

Hugh Spencer

13-9 The cell wall of a diatom, surrounded by fragments of other diatomaceous cell walls. This glasslike material accumulates in the debris at the bottom of the water in which diatoms live. As thousands of years pass, the accumulation continues to grow. Mixed with other sediment, it becomes diatomaceous ooze. What is the difference between the diatomaceous ooze on the ocean bottom and diatomaceous earth?

The Economic Importance of Algae

You might be surprised at the number of algae that are important in our daily living. For the most part, people living in the United States have an abundance of foods of a great variety, but the 180 million inhabitants of our country represent only a small fragment of the total population of the world. High concentrations of people are found in the countries of China and India. In these and some other countries famine has always been a problem. As a result, almost every possible source of food is utilized. With this understanding, it is not surprising to learn that a wide variety of algae supplies millions of people in the world with one of their staple foods. The algae usually used as food are the giant kelps. These fabulous brown algae are among the largest plants in the world! They grow in the seas of northern coastal regions, in the deeper waters beyond the tide zone. Here they may grow to be 60 or more meters in length.

Although they contain less available energy —pound for pound—than corn, wheat, rice, and other grains, they are high in mineral content and certain essential elements, such as iodine, potassium, and nitrogen. These elements make brown algae useful as fertilizers as well as food.

Substances obtained from brown and red algae are widely used. One of these substances is agar, used in preparation of media for the growth of bacteria and fungi. Another substance is **algin** (AL·jin), used in the manufacture of ice cream to give it a smooth texture, in brushless shaving cream and shampoos as a water-soluble base, and as a substance for taking impressions in making false teeth. Many foods, especially instant puddings, pie fillings, preserves, and candies, make use of these substances derived from marine algae.

Next to bacteria, the **diatoms** (DY·a·tomz— Figure 13-9) are the most abundant organisms in the world. In the seas and oceans they make up the largest part of the **plankton** (PLANK-ton—the floating organisms of a body of water) and are an important part of the food chain.

Most diatoms are unicellular. They have cell walls that are chemically nearly indestructible, because the wall is composed in part of silicon dioxide (SiO_2)—the compound used to make glass. We might say that diatoms "live in glass houses." Long ago great deposits of diatom cell walls were formed in the ancient seas. Later these deposits became elevated, and the seas drained. Some deposits of fossil diatoms (diatomaceous earth) are over 3,000 feet thick. The physical properties of the diatomaceous earth are the same as glass and explain why diatomaceous earth is used to insulate boilers and steam pipes, and as an abrasive in metal polishes and certain tooth powders. It is most widely used, however, to filter out foreign particles in the refining of sugar and gasoline. Thus, even the *fossil* algae are of importance to us.

CONCLUDING REMARKS

When considered as a group, the green algae show the following important characteristics in comparison with green land plants:

1. They are biochemically very similar to green land plants in their pigmentation and stored foods.
2. They have evolved a multicellular body plan characteristic of all green land plants.
3. They have evolved heterogamous sexual reproduction—the kind of sexual reproduction common to all green land plants.
4. Many members of the group have evolved an alternation of generations, which is a constant feature of *all green land plants*.

As a group, then, the green algae may have been ancestral to green land plants.

Thus we have identified the group from which we believe green land plants evolved long ago. We have answered one question: *from what?* We still must answer the questions of *when* and *how* green land plants evolved.

GUIDE QUESTIONS AND PROBLEMS

1. What discovery suggests that bacteria and blue-green algae were among the earliest cellular organisms?
2. What were the characteristics of the Pre-Cambrian landscape? How was it hostile to land plants?
3. How does *Chlamydomonas* represent the type of unicellular autotroph from which multicellular green plants evolved?
4. How can a colony composed of many single cells be distinguished from a true multicellular organism?
5. How did the evolution of sexual reproduction in the green algae help to make possible the colonization of land by green plants?
6. How do the sporophyte and gametophyte generations of *Ulva* compare?
7. What is the relation between alternation of generations in a life cycle, and chromosome number?
8. What is the evidence that the green algae are the most likely ancestors of green land plants?

SUGGESTIONS FOR ADDITIONAL READING

Books

Gibbs, R., *Botany: An Evolutionary Approach.* New York, McGraw-Hill, 1950.
A good general botany with a complete section on green water plants and their evolution.
Hylander, C. J., *The World of Plant Life*, 2nd ed. New York, Macmillan, 1956.
Smith, G. M., *Cryptogamic Botany*, Vol. I, *Algae and Fungi.* New York, McGraw-Hill, 1955.

14

THE LAND

TURNS GREEN

The land is *our* environment. Many of the characteristics we possess make it possible for us to live on land and only on land. For example, like all land animals, we have a system for obtaining the oxygen we need from the atmosphere. This same system is useless in an aquatic environment, where dissolved oxygen must be obtained from water. To us, the aquatic environment is hostile; it is an environment that we have learned to respect because we know that if we are submerged in it we cannot survive. Yet many kinds of organisms, from the microscopic diatoms to the largest sharks, are well adapted to live in this environment.

In a way, life for aquatic organisms is an easy life. There is little danger in the seas and oceans of any lack of water, so essential for the growth of all living things. There are abundant carbon-containing compounds in solution that are used by photosynthetic organisms which, in turn, provide a continual supply of oxygen for *all* the living things in the sea. The temperature in these vast bodies of water does not fluctu-

ate so much as the temperature on land. In short, the aquatic environment of the seas, oceans, or any large permanent body of water is much more uniform and much better supplied with some of the necessities of life, such as water, than is the rigorous land environment.

PLANTS BECOME ADAPTED TO LAND

Our first evidence that plants had invaded the land from the sea comes from fossils of the Cambrian period (Figure 13-1). These fossils are about half a billion years old. They are nothing more than spores, but these spores have thick walls with markings characteristic of the spores of various land plants. The first more complete land plant fossils are found in rocks approximately 400 to 425 million years old; these earliest preserved plants were **vascular** (vas·kyoo·ler) plants—plants with conducting vessels.

What problems faced the green plants of the seas as they evolved a morphology and physiology enabling them to live on land? The first great problem was that of water supply. Land plants are not bathed in water but must absorb it from the ground. The second problem was one of retention of water. Land plants must be so constructed as to reduce the loss of water to the air. The third problem was the absorption of CO_2 for photosynthesis from the atmosphere of the terrestrial environment. Compared with the environment of the seas, there is very little available carbon in the atmosphere. It is the purpose of this chapter to see what characteristics evolved that made possible the colonization of land by green plants, and to follow the major evolutionary pathways leading to those more complex land plants familiar to us.

We can divide green land plants into two distinct groups. One is the group which includes the **mosses** and **liverworts** (Figure 14-1); the other is the group of *vascular plants*. The vascular plants have special con-

a

Paul Knipping

b

Roche

14-1 **a** Liverworts of the genus *Marchantia*. These primitive green land plants are frequently found on rocks and soil of moist ravines. **b** Mosses of the genus *Polytrichum,* growing on a forest floor. In both photographs, the plants are shown from above, about natural size. Can you guess why they seldom get much larger?

ducting tissues called **xylem** (zy·lem) and **phloem** (floh·em). These special tissues are not a characteristic of the mosses and liverworts, which for that reason are often called *nonvascular.*

The Nonvascular Land Plants

The fossil record tells us that plants resembling the liverworts (Figure 14-1) were present at least 350 million years ago. Although we know very little about the struc-

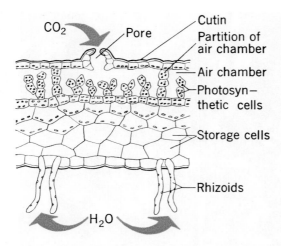

14-2 A drawing of part of a sectioned *Marchantia* thallus. How do the rhizoids and the cutin layer affect survival on land? Why is there no cutin on the rhizoids?

ture and reproduction of these ancient land plants, we can conclude, by observing the characteristics of their modern counterparts, how adaptation to land was accomplished. We will consider the following adaptive characters exhibited by mosses and liverworts:

1. A compact, multicellular plant body and the ability to conserve water
2. Some modification of photosynthetic tissues for the absorption of carbon dioxide
3. Special structures for the absorption of water
4. Heterogamy
5. Protection of reproductive cells
6. Formation of embryos
7. Alternation of generations

Of the seven characteristics in this list, the green algae (Chapter 13) show multicellular organization of the plant body, heterogamy, protection of reproductive cells, and alternation of generations. Thus, several features important for land plants had already evolved in the aquatic ancestors. The evolutionary step from water to land was not as big as might be anticipated.

The Multicellular Plant Body and the Conservation of Water

The plant body, or **thallus** (THAL·us), of all mosses and liverworts is multicellular (Figure 14-2). The advantages of this kind of organization in a land environment are best understood by going back to the unicellular vegetative cells of *Chlamydomonas* (Figure 13-3c). A *Chlamydomonas* cell has all of its surface exposed to the aquatic environment where it lives. Thus the whole cell surface of *Chlamydomonas* absorbs water, dissolved carbonates, and other minerals. But what would happen to *Chlamydomonas,* or other organisms with similar morphology, in a land environment? All the surfaces of the cell that absorb water and solutes in the aquatic environment would become surfaces of evaporation under terrestrial conditions. Since they would have no way of replacing the water lost as a result of drying, the vegetative cells would soon die.

If such single-celled organisms could not survive when exposed to the air, how can a multicellular organism such as a liverwort live on land? As we look at the cross section of this organism (Figure 14-2), we see that it is many cells thick. Of all of the cells comprising the thallus, only a small percentage have surfaces directly exposed to the drying effects of the atmosphere. When compared with *Chlamydomonas*, which has 100 percent of its cell surface exposed, the liverwort, although composed of hundreds of thousands of cells, has only a small percentage of its total cell surface exposed to the atmosphere. Thus *the relative amount* of cell surface from which evaporation can occur in a multicellular organism is less than in a unicellular one. Further reducing the rate of evaporation from surface cells is the formation of a waxlike substance, **cutin** (KYOO·tin), on the surfaces of some liverworts and mosses. (This same substance is also found covering leaves and some stems of more highly evolved green land plants.)

In spite of these adaptations, some liverworts and mosses that grow on exposed surfaces of rocks and trees become so dry that they are almost brittle in texture. Yet, within a short time after these plants become wet from rain or other water, they turn green again and proceed to carry out their normal life processes. What remarkable resistance to the destructive effects of drying!

Absorption of Carbon Dioxide

Ulva and all other algae growing in water can absorb their carbon for photosynthesis directly from the water in the form of dissolved CO_2 and ionized carbonates and bicarbonates. There is an abundant supply of these compounds in the seas and oceans. On land, however, the situation is quite different. Only about 0.03 to 0.04 percent of the atmosphere is CO_2. How can land plants absorb sufficient quantities of CO_2 for photosynthesis? We find that green land plants have evolved rather elaborate structures to do this. We can see an example of a CO_2-absorbing system in the liverwort *Marchantia* (mar·KAN·shih·a—Figure 14-2).

The upper surface of the *Marchantia* thallus has numerous pores. Each pore opens into an air chamber, which is partially filled with branching filaments of photosynthetic cells. The structure of the *Marchantia* thallus is remarkably like that of a leaf of a vascular land plant. The pores allow the inward diffusion of atmospheric gases, including CO_2. The CO_2 is absorbed by the wet surfaces of the photosynthetic cells in the air chambers and diffuses into the cytoplasm. Because of the branching nature of the inner structure of the thallus, the cells present a tremendous amount of surface available for the absorption of CO_2. At the same time, evaporation of water can occur from the wet surfaces of these cells. Thus, while absorbing CO_2 from the atmosphere, the green land plants will lose much

needed water. The evaporating water must be replaced or the *Marchantia* will soon wilt and die.

Absorption of Water

If we look at the underside of a *Marchantia* thallus, we will see water-absorbing structures. *Marchantia*, like other liverworts and mosses, has special structures called **rhizoids** (RY·zoidz). These are long, filamentous extensions of the cells of the lower surface of the thallus. They greatly increase the surface for absorption of water from the soil. Rhizoids perform the same functions as do the water-absorbing roots and root hairs of vascular plants.

Green land plants require large amounts of water. Most of the water they absorb through rhizoids and roots is unavoidably lost by evaporation from the photosynthetic organs while CO_2 is being absorbed from the atmosphere.

Heterogamy

The universal occurrence of sexual reproduction (involving eggs and sperms) in green land plants and in animals leaves little doubt that it is the most successful kind of reproduction to evolve. The large, nonmotile egg formed in heterogamy is full of stored food. After fertilization, this stored food is used to nourish the early stages in development of the new offspring. In other kinds of sexual reproduction—for example, isogamy in *Chlamydomonas*—the supply of stored food contributed even by both gametes together is very small. The food required for further development is manufactured by the zygote, which retains its photosynthetic capacity.

Protection of Reproductive Cells

At this point you should recall that certain algae retain the unfertilized egg in the protective confines of the female reproductive cell. The protection of sperms, eggs, and spores from drying and from mechanical injury is a very important characteristic of green land plants. To illustrate the point, let us see how a moss plant prevents its reproductive cells from drying.

The sex organs of a moss plant are produced at the tip of the green shoot. The shoot consists of an axis on which are radially arranged leaflike parts (Figure 14-1b). Since sexual reproduction is heterogamous, we can expect to find two kinds of sex organs, those that produce sperms (Figure 14-3a) and those that produce eggs (Figure 14-3b). Both kinds of sex organs are multicellular and differ in this respect from their unicellular counterparts in aquatic algae. Most of the cells of the moss sex organs are sterile and form a protective coat around the sperms or eggs. In addition, leaflike structures and sterile hairs produced at the tip of the shoot help to prevent drying of the sex organs.

The spores of this land plant are also well protected from drying. Spores are produced in a multicellular **sporangium** (spo·RAN·jih·um), or spore capsule, at the tip of a naked stalk (Figure 14-4). The capsule has a sterile jacket of cells surrounding the developing spores. As the spores mature in the capsule, each one forms a thick, waterproof layer which completely encloses the tiny bit of fluid cytoplasm and the nucleus in the center of the spore. As the capsule itself matures, it releases the spores to the external environment. Here the spores may survive for several months before germinating to produce new moss plants.

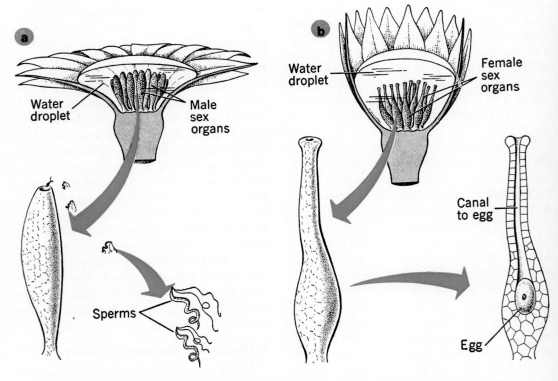

14-3   a A diagram of the sectioned tip of a male moss plant. The saclike male sex organs produce sperms with pairs of flagella. (What environmental substance must be present in order for fertilization to occur?) b The similarly sectioned tip of a female moss plant. Each of the flask-shaped female organs contains a single egg in the enlarged base. How does the sperm reach the egg?

Embryo Formation

In all green land plants that have sexual reproduction, the sperm is transported to the egg and unites with it inside the female reproductive structure. In mosses, liverworts, and primitive vascular plants, including ferns, the sperms are flagellated (Figure 14-3a), and a film of water is required for the sperm to swim to the egg. A zygote is formed inside the female structure when a sperm fertilizes the egg. An embryo develops from the zygote as it divides, still *inside* the protective coverings of the female reproductive structure. Thus the coverings formed by the female organism protect the growing embryo, as well as the egg and zygote, from drying out and from mechanical injury.

Among green plants, the mosses and liverworts are the first plants that form embryos. Some algae, *Oedogonium* for example, retain the zygote for a short time, but the subsequent development of the offspring takes place away from the female sex structure. Figure 14-5 contrasts the reproduction, especially in respect to this feature, in *Oedogonium* and in a moss plant (the female reproductive structure is shown). How does this part of the moss life cycle compare with that of human beings?

Alternation of Generations

The green alga *Ulva* has an alternation of generations in which both the gametophyte and the sporophyte are identical in appearance (Figure 13-6). Both plants are able to make their own food and thus are capable of an independent existence in the tide pools where they grow.

Although mosses and liverworts also have life cycles with alternating gametophyte and sporophyte generations, in the moss and liverwort these two generations are quite different in their structure and physiology. We have already discovered that the green shoot of a moss plant produces sex organs and sex cells (Figure 14-3). Thus the green

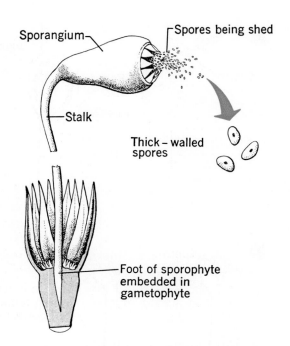

14-4 Which of the moss plant tips of Figure 14-3 is represented by this later stage in development? The stalk of the sporophyte grows from the tip of the gametophyte. After the spores are shed, what is to prevent them from drying out and dying?

shoot is the mature gametophyte (Figure 14-6). This shoot is autotrophic and is the structure we recognize at a glance as a moss plant. If the sporophyte (Figures 14-4 and 14-6) is present, it is attached to the top of the gametophyte. The sporophyte is composed of a **foot** which is embedded in the tissues of the gametophyte, and a **stalk** with a sporangium (spore capsule) on the upper end. The sporophyte bears little or no resemblance to the gametophyte to which it is attached. Evidence indicates that in the evolution of life on land, the gametophyte became the dominant generation, while the sporophyte became partially dependent on the gametophyte and greatly reduced in structure. Irrespective of how much it has become reduced, the sporophyte still forms large numbers of resistant spores in an elevated sporangium, from which the spores

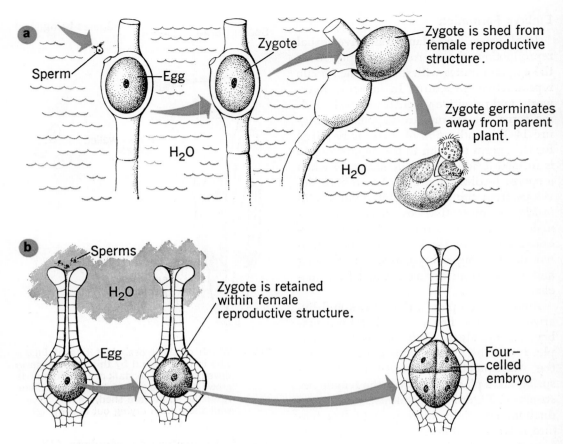

14-5 **a** Sexual reproduction in the alga *Oedogonium*. The female sex organ is unicellular and affords little protection for the egg. The thick-walled zygote is shed into the surrounding water. **b** By contrast, the female reproductive structure of a primitive green land plant (a moss in this case) is multicellular and protects the egg from drying. The zygote is not shed, but is retained within the female structure, where it develops into an embryo. The formation of protected embryos in this manner represented an important step in the evolution of green land plants.

are easily shed and dispersed. When the spores germinate, they produce more gametophytes, and the cycle is continued (Figure 14-6).

Changes in chromosome number occur at the time of fertilization and meiosis. These changes correspond to those in the life cycle of *Ulva* (Figures 13-6 and 13-7), where the fertilized egg represents the first cell of the sporophyte generation, and spores —the products of meiosis—represent the first cells of the gametophyte generation.

Although mosses and liverworts constitute only a very small percentage of all green land plants, a study and comparison of their characteristics and those of more primitive green algae gives us a good picture of the evolutionary steps that were required in the colonization of the land. Some of these steps are peculiar to plants, but many are applicable to the evolution of animals as well. For example, we find that the evolution of primitive animals in the ancient seas likewise resulted in the forma-

THE LIFE CYCLE OF A MOSS

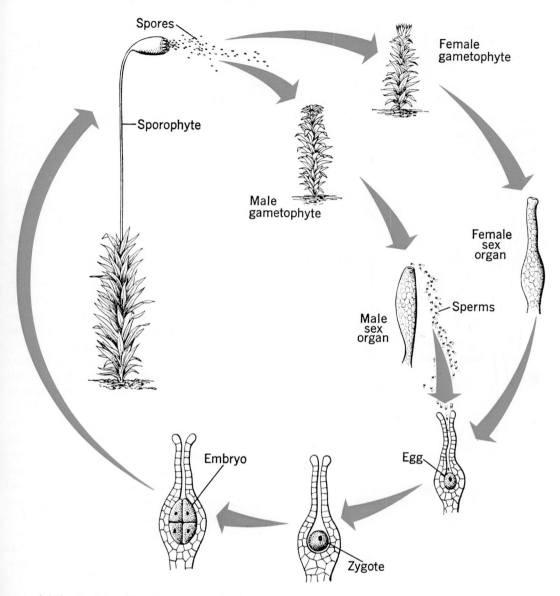

Spores

Female
gametophyte

Sporophyte

Male
gametophyte

Female
sex
organ

Sperms

Male
sex
organ

Egg

Embryo

Zygote

14-6 Compare this life cycle to that of *Ulva* in Figure 13-6. Does an alternation of generations occur in mosses? Where in the cycle does meiosis occur? fertilization?

tion of multicellular organisms that underwent heterogamous sexual reproduction and produced embryos. In their colonization of the land, animals, like plants, evolved structures for support and for prevention of excessive drying. Thus, in their early evolution in the seas and on the land, plants and animals show many parallels.

Evidence from fossils indicates that by the middle of the Devonian period, approximately 370 million years ago, green land plants (both vascular and nonvascular) were well established. Figure 13-1, page 246, indicates the groups of plants that were present at that time. Millions of years were to pass before plant-eating animals appeared on the lush, green land. Can you explain why green plants had to precede animals in the colonization of land?

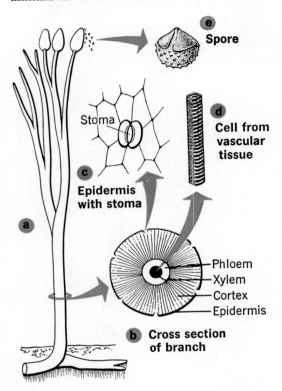

Spore
Cell from vascular tissue
Stoma
Epidermis with stoma
c
a
Phloem
Xylem
Cortex
Epidermis
b Cross section of branch

14-7 A reconstruction of the extinct Devonian plant *Rhynia*. **a** The plant had no leaves or roots and stood about 30 cm high. Sporangia were produced at the tips of the upper branches. **b** The branches had a core of xylem, with phloem around it. **c** Evidently the branches carried on photosynthesis, as evidenced by stomata in the epidermis. **d** The cells of vascular tissue were oblong, and in the case of xylem, hollow. **e** Thick-walled spores were produced *in fours* in the sporangia—an indication that the spores were the products of meiosis.

LAND PLANTS WITH VASCULAR TISSUE

Xylem and phloem are found in all green land plants other than the mosses and liverworts. These tissues have two functions; one is conduction and the other is support. Xylem (Figure 14-7b and d) is composed mostly of dead cells whose walls may be perforated, permitting the rapid movement of water. The direction of movement is usually upward from the roots to the leaves. The walls of the dead xylem cells are usually thickened to some extent and help support the parts of the plants above ground.

Phloem tissue is composed of both living and dead cells. Living cells of phloem conduct the soluble foods manufactured by the photosynthetic leaves. Here the direction of conduction is downward toward the stem and roots, where the food is stored. The dead, thick-walled cells of the phloem aid in support. More will be said about the vascular tissues in a later chapter.

We cannot stress the importance of vascular plants too much. They furnish us with the very necessities of life. We obtain nearly all of our food from vascular plants. The houses we live in are usually constructed of wood, which is a product of vascular plants. Clothes made of cotton or linen are products of vascular plants, and so are many medicines and most fuels, such as coal and peat. Vascular plants form an important and conspicuous part of the world we live in; over two thirds of all the plant species that inhabit the earth belong to this great group. The trees, shrubs, grasses, roses, ferns, pine trees, corn, wheat, rice—and a multitude of other plants we see every day —are vascular plants. Where did these organisms on which we are so dependent come from? How was it that they, rather than the mosses and liverworts, became so successful on land? When did they first appear? These are the questions we hope to answer in this part of the chapter.

The Primitive Type of Vascular Plant

In searching for the origin of vascular plants, we must turn our attention once again to the green algae and the mosses and liverworts. All of these plants are similar in their photosynthetic pigments and their stored food. Because of these similarities we must consider the alternative possibilities that vascular plants evolved from the group of mosses and liverworts or that they evolved directly from the green algae. Unfortunately the fossil record does not help us settle this point. It does, however, tell us what the primitive type of vascular plant was like. Thus we do have a starting point for our consideration of the origin of vascular plants.

Can you imagine a vascular plant without leaves or roots? This is rather difficult, because we are so used to seeing vascular plants with stems, leaves, and roots. Did vascular plants always have all of these parts? We think not. Again the fossil record provides us with the evidence. Back in the Devonian period (Figure 13-1), which started approximately 400 million years ago, vascular plants had made considerable progress in adapting to life on land. Among the invading plants were some curious species that had no leaves or roots. These plants consisted of a system of branches that forked repeatedly (Figure 14-7a). The pair of branches above each point of forking were of equal size; that is, one of them could not be called the stem and the other a branch. Some of the branches grew underground where they functioned much like roots, absorbing water and anchoring the plant. Some grew upright and were photosynthetic. How can we know this? The fossils of these plants are so well preserved that the pores (**stomata** [STOH·ma·ta], sing., **stoma** [STOH·ma]) for the exchange of gases in photosynthesis are still intact! (Figure 14-7c.) Because of their excellent preservation, it has been possible by special techniques to section these fossil plants and

use the compound microscope to get a clear idea of what they looked like inside.

In such a cross section (Figure 14-7b) of a branch, we can see cells of the **epidermis** (EP·ih·der·mis) and **cortex.** In the center there is a slender strand of vascular tissue composed of thick-walled xylem cells (Figure 14-7d), no doubt serving, as in plants today, for conduction and for support of the upright branches. At the tips of some of these branches we find sporangia containing thick-walled spores (Figure 14-7e) characteristic of land plants. Thus we know that these ancient plants with vascular tissue were sporophytes.

Because these ancient plants are so important to our understanding of vascular plant evolution, let us summarize their characteristics.

1. They had no roots and leaves.
2. They had forked branching systems. Branches were of equal size above a point of forking.
3. They had a simple, centrally located vascular strand in each branch.
4. They had sporangia at the tips of branches above ground.

We believe that these were the characteristics of the most primitive vascular plants; that from such plants all other vascular plants evolved at some time in the past, starting more than 400 million years ago.

A living plant that shows many of the primitive characteristics described above is the tropical genus *Psilotum* (sy·LOH·tum). It, too, has leafless green branches that fork. The arrangement of its vascular tissue is simple, like that of its ancient ancestors, and its sporangia are terminal, borne at the tips of short, lateral branches.

The primitive type of vascular plant described above provides a logical starting point for our consideration of the evolution of (1) the leaf, (2) the root, (3) arrangements of supporting and conducting tissues, and (4) protected sporangia.

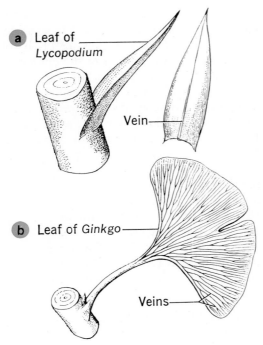

a Leaf of
Lycopodium

Vein

b Leaf of Ginkgo

Veins

14-8 These leaves illustrate the two principal leaf types among vascular plants: leaves with **a**, a single vein, and **b**, many veins.

Evolution of the Leaf

As we know, the leaf is the chief photosynthetic organ of a vascular plant. How did this important organ of plants arise, when none was present in the primitive

type? Before we answer this question, we must distinguish between two basic types of leaves occurring among vascular plants. One kind of leaf is usually quite small, almost scalelike, and has a single bundle of vascular tissue, a **vein,** in it (Figure 14-8a). The other type may be very large, with a conspicuous blade and two or more bundles of vascular tissue entering the blade (Figure 14-8b).

The interpretation of the fossil record does not permit a clear answer as to how the small one-veined leaf evolved. One possibility is that this leaf originated as an outgrowth, lacking vascular tissue, from the naked branches of the primitive plant (Figure 14-9a). With increase in size, a vascular strand was required to supply the leaf with water and to support it, and natural selection would bring about the change. Another possibility is that the single-veined leaf originated by a reduction in size of a part of the leafless branching system of the primitive vascular plant (Figure 14-9b).

In any event, this simple kind of leaf became well established in groups of primitive plants called club mosses and horsetails (Figure 14-10).

The fossilized remains of plants that lived during the Devonian and Carboniferous periods show us how the second type of leaf

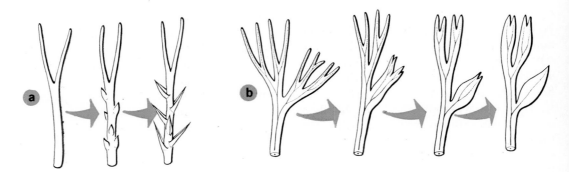

14-9 A diagrammatic summary of two theories of the evolution of single-veined leaves. Whether leaves emerged from naked branches, as in **a**, or resulted from a reduction of branches, as in **b**, tens or even hundreds of thousands of plant generations must have been required for the evolution to take place.

a   Hugh Spencer   **b**   Roche

14-10   Two living representatives of primitive vascular plants—**a** the club moss *Lycopodium,* and **b** the horsetail *Equisetum.* In *Lycopodium,* the small, scalelike leaves are on radially arranged branches. The candlelike structures at the tips of the branches are cones. The horsetail also has radially arranged branches and leaves. Of the three horsetail branches shown, the one on the left bears whorls of naked photosynthetic branches, and the two on the right have cones at the tips, with tight whorls of scalelike leaves farther down the branches below the cones.

(many-veined) evolved. Upon examining the photosynthetic organs of these ancient plants, we soon discover that the leaf, with its many bundles of vascular tissue, is nothing more than an evolutionary modification of the forked branching system we have seen already in the most primitive type of vascular plant. The first step in the evolution of this leaf type was **planation** (pla·NAY-sh'n). This evolutionary process involved a change from a three-dimensional system (Figure 14-11a) of forked branches to one in which all the branches were restricted to a single plane (Figure 14-11b). The branching system became flat.

Next in evolution, this flattened system became **webbed.** By webbed we mean that the space between the bundles and branches of vascular tissue became filled with photosynthetic tissue (Figure 14-11c). After this the organ, now a leaf, looked superficially like the webbed foot of a duck. The leaves of the majority of vascular plants had their evolutionary origin from a branching system of this kind.

Evolution of the Root

When we say that the primitive type of vascular plant had no leaves or roots, we do not mean that it lacked photosynthetic and

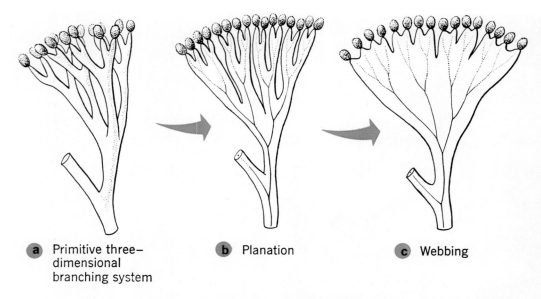

a Primitive three–
dimensional
branching system

b Planation

c Webbing

14-11 The principal steps in the evolution of a many-veined leaf. Much evidence from fossils of ancient vascular plants supports the steps illustrated here. The *Ginkgo* leaf (Figure 14-8b) is the product of planation and webbing.

water-absorbing organs. We have already discovered that its branches above ground were adapted for photosynthesis. The underground parts of the branching system were also adapted, but for the absorption of water. The amount of absorptive surface was greatly increased by many rhizoids that formed on the epidermis. *Functionally* the underground branches of the primitive type were roots, just as the aboveground parts functioned as leaves. *Structurally*, however, these branches were very much unlike the roots and leaves of bean plants, ferns, pine trees, and other more highly evolved plants.

One interesting structural similarity between the underground branches of the primitive type and the roots of more highly evolved vascular plants is the arrangement of the vascular tissue. Both have a central solid rod of xylem tissue (Figure 14-12a). This primitive arrangement of vascular tissue seems to have been retained in the roots of the more complex vascular plants of today.

Support in the Stem

We might say that those parts of the branching system of the primitive type that did not evolve into leaves or roots became the stem and branches of the more advanced vascular plants. As certain parts of the forked system were reduced or modified into roots and leaves, other parts became well supplied with vascular tissue serving not only for conduction, but for support as well.

The simple engineering principle that a hollow tube of supporting material is stronger than a solid rod composed of the same amount of material apparently was demonstrated in the evolution of the supporting vascular system of the stem. Would the plant ever have recognized this engineering principle? By no stretch of our imagination could we believe it. This was natural selection at work again.

In primitive small plants not more than 25 cm tall, the aboveground branches were supported by a vascular system that consisted of a central solid rod (Figure 14-12a). In larger, more complex, vascular plants we find stems supported by one or more rings of vascular tissue, often dissected into separate bundles functioning like supporting beams in the stem tissues (Figure 14-12b).

A second method of supporting the stems, leaves, and reproductive parts was introduced early in the evolution of vascular plants. This was the formation of a supporting tissue called *secondary wood*. We are all familiar with the tough wood in the trunks (stems) of trees. The introduction of this kind of supporting structure made possible the growth of plants of tremendous size. The largest living things in the world are the giant redwood and sequoia trees of our West Coast. One of these mammoths is 117 meters (385 feet) tall and more than 9 meters in diameter at the base. Nearly all of the bulk of these giant trees is secondary wood. From the standpoint of competition for sunlight and the distribution of reproductive spores, tall plants have proved most successful in the land environment!

The Protection of Sporangia

As we have seen, the primitive type of vascular plant (as represented today by *Psilotum*) had sporangia at the tips of upright branches (Figure 14-7a). Here the sporangia are well placed for dispersal of their spores. These sporangia are not protected in any way, however. Except in these few primitive vascular plants, and in the equally primitive mosses and liverworts, the sporangia of green land plants are well protected.

Many vascular plants, in addition to the pines and their relatives, form cones. The other cone-forming plants are the club mosses and the horsetails (Figure 14-10a and b). If we were to dissect the cone of a club moss, we would find its sporangia enveloped in a protective covering of leaves (Figure 14-13a), which make up the bulk

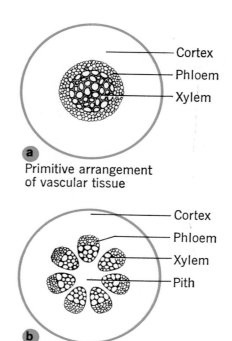

a Primitive arrangement of vascular tissue

b Advanced arrangement of vascular tissue (in stems)

14-12 The principal arrangements of vascular tissue in vascular plants. **a** The roots of most vascular plants, and the stems and branches of the more primitive vascular plants, have a central core of xylem, with phloem around it. **b** The stems of more advanced vascular plants usually have a central pith, surrounded by a ring of vascular tissue (often divided into bundles).

of the cone. The sporangia of the horsetail cone are produced on little branches. There are several sporangia on each branch and many branches in a cone. Each branch has a flattened end something like the six-sided head of a bolt (Figure 14-13b). The flattened ends of the branches fit together along their sides and form a protective layer over their sporangia, which are completely covered until the spores are mature.

These protected positions of the sporangia have come about through an evolutionary modification of the primitive type of arrangement in vascular plants. There is

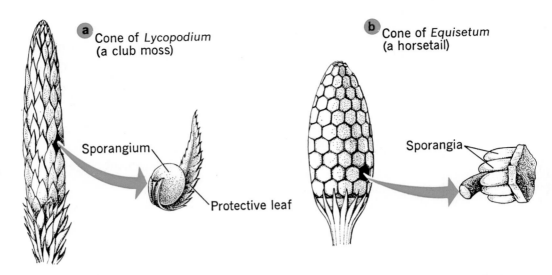

a Cone of *Lycopodium* (a club moss)

b Cone of *Equisetum* (a horsetail)

Sporangium

Protective leaf

Sporangia

14-13 The protected sporangia of a club moss and a horsetail. **a** The sporangia in a club moss cone are protected by overlapping leaves. **b** In a horsetail cone they are protected by the flattened ends of the sporangia-bearing branches.

ample evidence from fossil ferns, for example, to show that, step by step, the sporangia came to lie first at the margins of, and later on the underside of, the leaves.

The Evolution of the Seed

One thing we have all noticed about the plants around us is that they are not predominantly ferns, horsetails, club mosses, or true mosses. Instead they are seed plants (pines and their relatives, and flowering plants). There must be something about seed plants that has made them more successful. Could it be that the seed adapts these vascular plants to a wider variety of environments? We can hardly avoid this conclusion—but this does not tell us *why*.

To find an answer, we have to introduce a new idea. All of the green land plants we have described thus far produce only one kind of spore. That is to say, all spores from all sporangia of a species are nearly identical in size, structure, and function. There are, however, many vascular plants—all of the seed plants, for example—that form *two kinds of spores*. These plants are said to be

heterosporous (het-er-o-spor-us). Generally the spores are of different sizes, and they always have different functions. Instead of growing into gametophytes that are essentially similar in structure, heterosporous plants produce two different gametophytes. One of the two kinds of spores—let us call it the *male spore*—grows into a sperm-forming gametophyte; the other kind, the *female spore*, grows into an egg-forming gametophyte.

The two kinds of spores are formed in two different kinds of sporangia. These, like the sporangia of club mosses, horsetails, and ferns, have become protected as a result of the evolution of various enveloping structures. If we go back in the fossil records to the Carboniferous period (280 to 350 million years ago) we find some beautiful examples of the beginnings of seeds. Certain fernlike plants that were abundant during the Carboniferous period bore these seed-like structures. Each of their sporangia contained one or more female spores and were nearly surrounded by outgrowths from the sporophyte (Figure 14-14). These outgrowths appear to be little branchlike structures, which are fused along their sides to form an envelope or **integument** (in·TEG-yoo·ment) around the sporangium.

Instead of being shed from the sporangium to fend for themselves, like the spores of all other green land plants, the female spores of seed plants are retained and protected inside the integumented sporangium. Here the female spore develops into a tiny female gametophyte protected by the integument. Thus, the essential evolutionary steps in the production of this important reproductive structure—the seed—were: (1) the introduction of heterospory; (2) the formation of integuments around the sporangium that contains the female spores; and (3) retention of the mature female spores in the sporangium, where the female gametophyte develops.

When we examine a young seed (an **ovule** [OH·vyool]) we find, in addition to the protective covering of integuments, that it contains great quantities of food. Thus the ovule not only affords protection to the female gametophyte from the adverse effects of the environment; it also provides food for the new offspring that is produced when the seed matures and germinates. Clearly, seed production is one of the important characters that better adapts vascular plants to their environment and makes them the predominant form of vegetation on our earth.

A Vehicle for Sperms

Of equal importance to the production of seeds was the evolution of **pollen tubes** that transport sperms to eggs. For algae, plenty of water is available as a medium in which their flagellated gametes can move. With the evolution of primitive land plants, external water remained as a requirement for fertilization, since the sperm cells of these plants still move by swimming. The only way they can reach the large nonmotile egg is through water from rain, dew, or

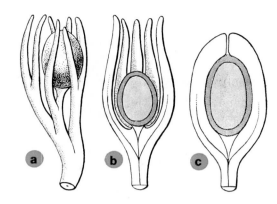

14-14 Steps in seed evolution. Fossil evidence for step **b** offers support for hypothetical step **a**. Step **c** shows the integumented seed of a modern plant.

splashings from nearby brooks or waterfalls.

Mosses, liverworts, primitive vascular plants, and ferns, all of which produce flagellated, motile sperms, are consequently somewhat restricted to moist land environments. They grow most abundantly in the tropical rain forests, deep shaded woods, damp ravines, or swamps.

The evolution of pollen tubes paralleled the evolution of seeds. The egg produced inside an ovule is very well protected in the sporangium (enclosed by its integuments and other tissues). It is so well protected that a flagellated sperm would not have the slightest chance of ever reaching an egg. This obstacle has been overcome by the development of pollen tubes. Once the pollen grain reaches the cone or flower, it germinates. The germinated **pollen grain** (look ahead to Figure 14-19b) is a tiny male gametophyte. It produces a long pollen tube, which grows to the ovule, and then digests its way through the protecting layers to the enclosed egg. The pollen tube forms a kind of living tunnel (as we will see shortly). Through its cytoplasm the nonflagellated sperms move to the egg.

The emancipation of vascular land plants from the requirement of external water for

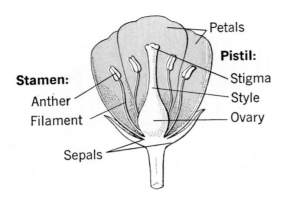

Stamen:
Anther
Filament

Petals

Pistil:
Stigma
Style
Ovary

Sepals

14-15 A diagram of a generalized flower. Some of the outer parts have been removed in order to show the internal reproductive structures clearly.

fertilization adds to our list of the characteristics that adapt seed plants to a wide variety of terrestrial environments. These environments range from the alpine environment of the mountains to the arid conditions of the desert.

The Importance of Flowers

With the evolution of the pollen tube, we might think that the last obstacle in adaptation to land had been overcome. Before we jump to this conclusion, however, let us survey the kinds of plants that have pollen tubes and produce seeds. Because of their abundance, we might suspect that flowering plants are the only plants with these two characteristics. That is not the case, however, for the pines and their relatives—the spruces, firs, and cedars—also have pollen tubes and seeds. Although pines, spruces, and fir trees are abundant in certain parts of the world, they are represented only by about 600 species. That is a very small number when compared with the 250,000 species of flowering plants, which certainly are the most abundant and the most successful vascular plants.

Although flowering plants comprise the largest group of vascular plants, we know very little about their evolutionary origin.

Many years ago it was said that "the origin of the flowering plants is an abominable mystery." Nothing has been added to our information in recent years to change this statement. The fossil record tells us that flowering plants made their appearance, in substantial variety, about 130 million years ago, early in the Cretaceous period (Figure 13-1). Almost from the beginning of their record, we find evidence that there were two kinds of flowering plants, those with wind-pollinated flowers and those with insect-pollinated flowers.

Pollination is the transfer of pollen grains from the **anthers** of the male parts of flowers to the **stigma** of the female flower part (Figure 14-15). Pollination by wind is haphazard. Thus it is not surprising to find that wind-pollinated flowering plants must produce large quantities of pollen and have large, feathery stigmas for straining the pollen from the air. Insect-pollinated flowers, on the other hand, have special floral parts that attract insects and insure pollination. The **petals** (Figure 14-15) of insect-pollinated flowers may be brightly colored, and the flowers may produce nectar and aromatic substances that attract bees, butterflies, moths, and many other kinds of insects. At the time an insect visits a flower to collect nectar or pollen, some of the pollen from the anthers is brushed off and sticks to the insect's body. The pollen is then carried to the next flower by the insect.

Many of the different types of flowers represent adaptations that increase the probability that pollination will occur. Unless pollination occurs, seeds will not develop in most flowering plants.

In many plants **self-pollination**, which is the transfer of pollen from an anther to the stigma of the same flower or that of another flower on the same plant, occurs regularly. Self-pollinated plants with which you may be familiar include the tomato, cotton, bean, and pea.

Much more common than self-pollination is **cross-pollination.** This involves the transfer of pollen from an anther of one plant to the stigma of another plant. It is here that insects and wind are most important.

In some species of insect-pollinated flowers, a single species of insect is responsible for the pollination. One of the most remarkable cases of interdependence between plant and insect is the example of the *Yucca* plant and the moth *Pronuba* (PRON-yoo·ba). *Yucca* is a native plant in the arid regions of our Southwest. Self-pollination of flowers in these plants is impossible because the anthers are in a position that isolates them from the stigmas. The flowers open in the evening, and the small white moths, attracted by the fragrance of the flowers, fly to them, and mate within the flower. The female moth then collects pollen from the anthers and rolls it into a ball. She flies to another *Yucca*, bores into the ovary of a flower, and deposits an egg within it. She then goes to the stigma of the same flower and presses part of the ball of pollen she has gathered into a deep chamber in the center of the stigma. This sequence is repeated until several eggs have been laid and the chamber is well stocked with pollen. Some of the seeds that develop later serve as food for the larvae of the moth, which by then have hatched from the eggs laid inside the plant's ovary. Eventually the larvae bore through the wall of the ovary, drop to the ground, and complete their development underground. Of several hundred seeds that form in each ovary, only a few are destroyed by the larvae. Neither moth nor plant is able to complete its life cycle without the other.

This is an extreme example of interdependence. Yet it shows us clearly how important the flowering plants have become to insects by providing food and protection, and how important the insects have become to the flowering plants. For, while obtaining its necessities of life, the insect insures the completion of pollination—the most critical step in the life cycles of flowering plants.

The Protection of Seeds

Perhaps you have observed a squirrel wrestling with a pine cone, biting away the scales of the cone to get at the seeds inside. The scales of the cone form a tough protective envelope around the seeds, one that squirrels and other rodents find difficult to penetrate. As the cones of most pines mature, the cone scales open outward. When this happens, the mature seeds are exposed and are gradually shed.

A few pines have cones with exceedingly tough scales. The cone scales may remain closed around the seeds for as much as 75 years before they finally open and release the seeds. If during this time there is a forest fire that heats and scorches these resistant cones, the cones will open in a short time and shed their seeds. This remarkable adaptation insures the seeding of a new crop of pines in the event of a fire, which may kill the parent trees.

In flowering plants the seeds are protected from mechanical injury and other unfavorable environmental conditions by the development of a **fruit.** The fruit is derived from the ovary of the female reproductive part of the flower (Figure 14-15). The ovary completely encloses the ovules, which later become the seeds. We all recognize a watermelon as a fruit that contains seeds. When we eat a slice of watermelon, we eat the pink flesh and throw the green rind away. Both of these parts are protective layers of the fruit and enclose the seeds. Tomatoes, pea pods, and bean pods are also examples of fruits that contain seeds. This may seem a bit strange, because we usually think of peas, beans, and tomatoes as vegetables. Like the watermelon, however, they are true fruits derived from the ovaries of flowers. Other familiar examples of the great variety of fruits produced by flowering plants are oranges, grapefruit, grapes, coconuts and other nuts in their husks, and grains of all kinds.

The fruits of some flowering plants, pea pods, for example (Figure 14-16a), both early in their development and at maturity resemble leaves in form and internal structure. Because of this and other evidence, we think that the protective ovary that develops into the fruit actually evolved from

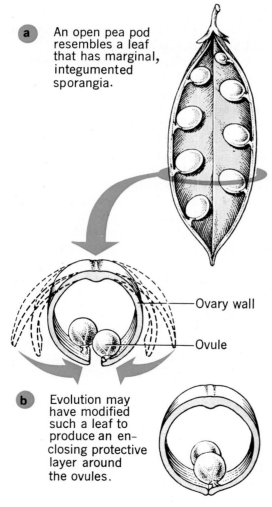

a An open pea pod resembles a leaf that has marginal, integumented sporangia.

Ovary wall

Ovule

b Evolution may have modified such a leaf to produce an enclosing protective layer around the ovules.

14-16 The evolution of a fruit around developing ovules. Most of the evidence for this theory is derived from study of modern vascular plants. To date, the fossil record has been of little help.

leaves. These were special leaves that had sporangia along the margins. The ovules, as they evolved, contained the sporangia (Figure 14-16b). To produce such a closed structure with the seeds inside, the margins of the reproductive leaf would have to fold until they touched. Finally, fusion, occurring along the line where the folded edges of the modified leaf touched each other, would completely seal in the ovules from the outside.

Fruits have almost every means of dispersal imaginable. The coconut floats from shore to shore and is often carried great distances by ocean currents. The fruit of the cocklebur has hooklike spines, which become tangled in the fur of passing animals. Many fleshy fruits, among them raspberries and mulberries, are eaten by birds, and the undigested seeds pass through the bird and fall to earth, perhaps miles from where they were eaten. One novel fruit has long hooks which catch in the nostrils of grazing animals. As the animal tries to dislodge this fruit, the seeds are scattered. The fruits of many plants, such as maple trees and elms, have "wings," which may transport the enclosed seed on the wind for some distance from the parent tree. These examples illustrate that it is not the fruit alone but also the means of dispersal of seed-containing fruits which helps explain the wide and successful distribution of the flowering plants.

The Lost Gametophyte

Alternation of generations was last discussed when the nature of the gametophyte and sporophyte of a moss plant was explained (Chapter 13). At this stage in the evolution of plant life cycles, the gametophyte was the predominant, photosynthetic structure—the familiar moss plant with its stem and leaves. By contrast, the sporophyte remained partially dependent on the gametophyte—a really inconspicuous part of the moss life history.

14-17 *Dryopteris,* a fern common in forests of a temperate climate. Large, much divided leaves such as these are characteristic of the sporophytes of many of the ferns.

Hugh Spencer

In all vascular plants, whether primitive examples or advanced flowering types, the sporophyte is the predominant generation and the gametophyte is subordinate. Thus, when we see grass plants, elm trees, pine trees, ferns, club mosses, or horsetails growing in nature, we are looking at sporophytes. The explanation of the predominance of the sporophyte seems to be that it is the generation in which vascular tissue originated.

Among the primitive vascular plants and ferns, the gametophyte generation is usually an independent, though inconspicuous, generation. Let us take the fern gametophyte as an example. The fern plants we see in the woods are fern sporophytes (Figure 14-17). Where are the gametophytes? The chances are that many more gametophytes than sporophytes are present, but we do not see the gametophytes because of their small size. You have to get down on your hands and knees and look carefully on the ground to find these tiny, green, heart-shaped structures (Figure 14-18). The largest is no bigger than a dime, and usually they are much smaller. These are the structures that produce the sex cells that complete the life cycle. Although photosynthetic and autotrophic, a simple, nonvascular fern

gametophyte hardly compares with the large, complex fern sporophyte.

Let us see what has happened to the gametophyte in a heterosporous plant. We will use a flowering plant as our example. To see the gametophytes of these plants, we need a microscope and some dissecting equipment. But where are we going to find these gametophytes? The male gametophyte of a flowering plant, you may remember, matures from a pollen grain. The pollen grain is deposited on the surface of the stigma (Figure 14-19a). The stigma supplies food for the growth of the pollen grain into the mature male gametophyte. When the pollen grain germinates, it produces its long pollen tube cell, which grows toward the female gametophyte. The germinating pollen grain also produces two sperms that move through the pollen tube to the female gametophyte. One sperm will fertilize the egg and the other will initiate the formation of the tissue known as the **endosperm** (EN-doh·sperm), which contains the stored food in the seed. Thus, the mature male gametophyte of a flowering plant consists of a pollen tube cell in which one can find two sperms (Figure 14-19b).

What and where is the female gametophyte generation? To find it, we must dissect out an ovule from within the ovary of the flower. Next we must cut through the integuments and the sporangium—the protective layers of the ovule. There in the well-protected recess, completely surrounded by tissue of the sporophyte, is the female gametophyte (Figure 14-19c). A careful examination, using special stains and a microscope, will show us that this female part of the gametophyte generation consists of seven cells (the two polar nuclei eventually fuse; they count as one cell). Only one of the seven cells is an egg. Together, the male and female gametophytes of most flowering plants are composed of only ten structures we can call cells! Is it possible that at some future time in evolution only egg and sperm will be produced and the gametophyte cells

will be entirely eliminated? If this were to happen, we would find that the generalized life cycle of a flowering plant would be essentially similar to our own. Can you explain why?

CONCLUDING REMARKS

As we look back and summarize the changes that have occurred in the evolution of the gametophyte generation of green land plants, we can see two distinct trends. However, before we can understand what these trends are, we must have a starting point. As the illustrated summary of plant evolution on pages 282 and 283 shows, we think that the ancestors of green land plants may have been green algae with a life cycle

Hugh Spencer

14-18   An ant's-eye view of a fern gametophyte. The whole structure is less than 15 mm in width. Looking upward from below the plant, we see the bottom surface with hairlike rhizoids extending downward. Just beneath the notch in the plant are the necks of female reproductive structures, glistening in the light.

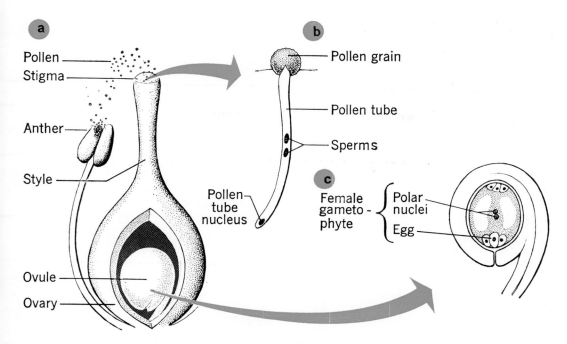

14-19 The gametophyte generation of a flowering plant. **a** The ovary of the pistil is shown cut open to reveal the position of the ovule. **b** A germinating pollen grain is the male gametophyte. Nearly all flowering plants have male gametophytes of the type shown. **c** Greater variability exists in the structure of the female gametophyte. Nonetheless, 70 to 80 percent of the flowering plants that have been studied have the type of female gametophyte shown here (the ovule has been cut open from top to bottom to reveal the protected gametophyte within).

similar to that of *Ulva*. You will recall that *Ulva* (Figure 13-6) has a life cycle with an alternation of generations. Both its gametophyte and its sporophyte are identical in their gross structure; both are green, photosynthetic plants capable of an independent existence.

When we compare the alternation of generations of this green alga with the alternation of generations of a green land plant, such as a moss or a liverwort, we find that the two generations of the moss or liverwort are *not alike* in structure and nutrition. In the moss, the gametophyte is the predominant, photosynthetic generation, while the sporophyte is small, short in its duration of life, and partially dependent on the gametophyte. What has happened to the sporophyte? We can conclude that in

the course of evolution from the algal ancestor, the sporophytes of mosses and liverworts became dependent on the gametophyte for some of their food and all of their water. Under these conditions the sporophyte became a "lazy freeloader" on the gametophyte. As a result, the sporophyte became reduced or simplified in structure.

Among the vascular plants we see that the sporophyte and the gametophyte are quite different from their counterparts in the mosses and liverworts. The sporophyte generation of vascular plants has become the predominant, complex, photosynthetic generation; the gametophyte has become greatly reduced in size. In ferns the gametophyte, although small, is still a photosynthetic, heart-shaped structure independent of the sporophyte. In seed plants, the ga-

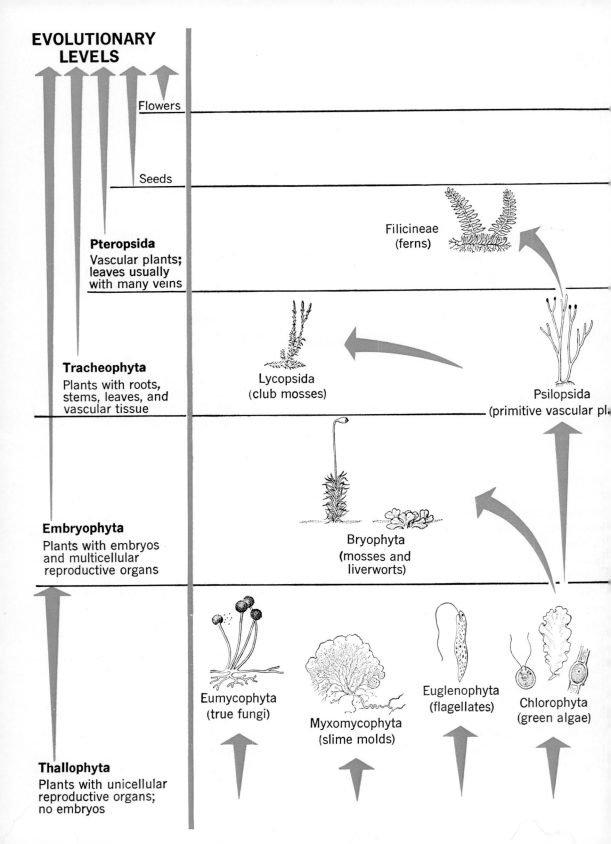

EVOLUTIONARY LEVELS

Flowers

Seeds

Pteropsida
Vascular plants;
leaves usually
with many veins

Filicineae
(ferns)

Tracheophyta
Plants with roots,
stems, leaves, and
vascular tissue

Lycopsida
(club mosses)

Psilopsida
(primitive vascular pl.

Embryophyta
Plants with embryos
and multicellular
reproductive organs

Bryophyta
**(mosses and
liverworts)**

Eumycophyta
(true fungi)

Myxomycophyta
(slime molds)

Euglenophyta
(flagellates)

Chlorophyta
(green algae)

Thallophyta
Plants with unicellular
reproductive organs;
no embryos

Angiospermae
(flowering plants)

Gymnospermae
(conifers, cycads, ginkgos)

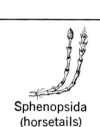

Sphenopsida
(horsetails)

PLANT KINGDOM

SUBKINGDOM— Thallophyta

Phylum	— Myxomycophyta
Phylum	— Eumycophyta
Phylum	— Cyanophyta
Phylum	— Rhodophyta
Phylum	— Chrysophyta
Phylum	— Phaeophyta
Phylum	— Euglenophyta
Phylum	— Chlorophyta

SUBKINGDOM— Embryophyta

Phylum	— Bryophyta
Phylum	— Tracheophyta
Subphylum —	Psilopsida
Subphylum —	Lycopsida
Subphylum —	Sphenopsida
Subphylum —	Pteropsida
Class	— Filicineae
Class	— Gymnospermae
Class	— Angiospermae

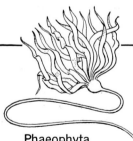

Phaeophyta
(brown algae)

Rhodophyta
(red algae)

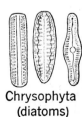

Chrysophyta
(diatoms)

Cyanophyta
(blue-green algae)

283

14-20 TRENDS IN THE EVOLUTION OF SPOROPHYTES AND GAMETOPHYTES

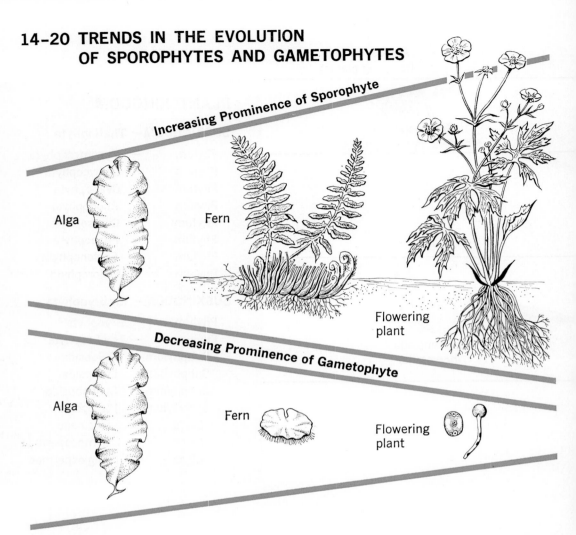

Increasing Prominence of Sporophyte

Alga · Fern · Flowering plant

Decreasing Prominence of Gametophyte

Alga · Fern · Flowering plant

metophyte is reduced even further. It has become completely dependent on the sporophyte. The evolution of the gametophyte and sporophyte in the vascular plants affords us an excellent example of *divergent evolution,* that is, two structures becoming increasingly different as a result of evolutionary changes (Figure 14-20). Thus, the sporophyte has evolved toward complexity, the gametophyte toward simplicity.

This is the end of our story of the evolution of vascular plants, and it ends with the most highly evolved of all—the flowering plants. No single characteristic places the

flowering plants at the top of the evolutionary ladder. Rather, they are the product of a combination of many characteristics. Some characteristics that have been discussed in this chapter are:

1. The evolution of roots, stems, and leaves
2. The evolution of vascular systems in stems and roots
3. The evolution of protected sporangia, including their enclosure by the seed and fruit
4. The evolution of the pollen tube

5. The evolution of the flower
6. The evolution of the alternation of generations

These characteristics, which include the development of complex vegetative and reproductive structures, did not come about suddenly. They are the result of long periods of successive evolutionary change, beginning with the primitive unicellular ancestors that lived hundreds of millions of years ago.

The illustrated summary of the classification of the green plants and fungi, pages 282–83, is based on the evolutionary relationships described in this and the two preceding chapters.

GUIDE QUESTIONS AND PROBLEMS

1. What are the advantages to aquatic organisms of their watery environment?
2. What problems faced plants in their colonization of the land?
3. What characteristics of the primitive green land plants insured their survival?
4. How are the simplest land plants adapted to conserve water?
5. What adaptations for CO_2 absorption are found in *Marchantia?*
6. What is the importance to a land plant of structures that protect the reproductive cells? How is protection of reproductive cells accomplished in the mosses?
7. What is the significance of embryo formation in the colonization of land by green plants?
8. What parallel adaptations to the land environment occurred in plants and animals?
9. What are the advantages to plants, in terms of survival, of having both asexual and sexual methods of reproduction?
10. What is the importance of vascular plants to man?
11. What was the structure of the most primitive vascular plants, according to the fossil evidence?
12. What explanations have been offered for the origin of leaves?

13. How does the fossil record clarify the origin of leaves with broad, flat blades and many veins?
14. What are the characteristics of the roots of vascular plants? What is their probable origin?
15. How do primitive vascular plants differ from the more advanced types in the structure of vascular supporting tissues?
16. What is the result of the development of secondary wood tissues in the vascular plants?
17. What is the importance of heterospory in the vascular plants?
18. How do the higher vascular plants escape the need for "free" water in fertilization?
19. What part did the development of a fruiting structure play in the evolution of green land plants?
20. How did insects play a role in the evolution of the green land plant?
21. What is meant by *divergent evolution?* How does the term apply to the sporophyte and gametophyte generations of land plants?

SUGGESTIONS FOR ADDITIONAL READING

Books

Barnett, L., and editors of *Life* Magazine, *The World We Live In.* New York, Golden Press, 1955.

> A beautifully illustrated account of the plants and animals of the world.

Benton, A. H., and W. E. Werner, *Principles of Field Biology and Ecology.* New York, McGraw-Hill, 1958.

> Contains an excellent and simple discussion of nomenclature.

Bold, H. C., *The Plant Kingdom.* Englewood Cliffs (N. J.), Prentice-Hall, 1960.

> One of the Foundations of Modern Biology Series, in paperback. A good general discussion of plant types; the evolutionary significance is stressed.

Foster, A. S., and E. M. Gifford, Jr., *Comparative Morphology of Vascular Plants.* San Francisco, Freeman, 1959.

> An advanced discussion of structure and reproduction in vascular plants.

15

PHOTOSYNTHESIS—

THE LINK BETWEEN

TWO WORLDS

"Therefore, 164 pounds of wood, bark, and root were formed of water only." Do you remember this statement? It was written by J. B. van Helmont (1577–1644) as his conclusion to his famous willow tree experiments (see Chapter 4, pages 68–70). Although we may be amused by his conclusion that all food for green plants comes from water, Van Helmont was one of the first to conduct a real experiment in the attempt to solve the mystery of plant nutrition. He was the first to test that old idea that green plants get their food from soil and water. Even though his conclusion was wrong, we can credit Van Helmont with starting the inquiry into that link in life's chain we now call photosynthesis.

The link was strengthened by the experiments of Joseph Priestley (1733–1804). A review of Chapter 4, pages 74–78, will help you to recall that it was Priestley who, in 1772, demonstrated the biological impor-

tance of atmospheric oxygen and its replenishment by green plants. At about the same time Priestley was conducting his experiments with oxygen, Jan Ingenhousz (1730–1799) found that sunlight was necessary for the production of oxygen by the green parts of plants. The link was strengthened further by Jean Senebier (1742–1809), who in 1782 discovered that under certain conditions green plants absorb carbon dioxide from the atmosphere. However, Senebier had no idea of the significance of his discovery—that is, the part that carbon dioxide plays in photosynthesis.

In 1804, Nicholas de Saussure (1767–1845) was able to show experimentally that water, too, is chemically involved in plant nutrition. In a little more than thirty years (between 1772 and 1804), the involvement of the three key factors in photosynthesis—water, carbon dioxide, and sunlight—had been experimentally demonstrated. It was not until the middle of the nineteenth century, however, that biologists were able to fit some of the pieces of the puzzle together. Two discoveries made this possible. One was the demonstration that green plants convert the energy of visible light into chemical energy, which is stored in compounds that the plants manufacture. The second was the identification of a sugar as the principal energy-containing compound produced in the plant's green cells.

The events described above serve as the foundation for our present understanding of the process of photosynthesis. Photosynthesis is a process that provides a link between two worlds—the living and the nonliving. Supplies of carbon dioxide, water, and energy from the sun are obtained from the nonliving world. No foods or fuels for the world of living things exist until green plants absorb and use these supplies to make sugar. We cannot overemphasize the importance of green plants and the part they play in maintaining life! With the exceptions of a few kinds of bacteria, *green plants are the only organisms that capture the energy in sunlight and use it to synthesize energy-rich compounds. These compounds are the only source of energy available to all the heterotrophic organisms.*

THE LEAF— A PHOTOSYNTHETIC ORGAN

We recognize the photosynthetic parts of plants because they are green. A very casual investigation of the plants that one might find in a garden or greenhouse shows us that different organs of the plants can be green. Their stems and some flower parts may be green. Some tropical plants, such as the vanilla plant and orchids, have roots that are green. As you might guess, such roots are not below the ground but are exposed to sunlight. Generally, however, we recognize the green leaves of plants as being the chief photosynthetic organs.

The leaves of many flowering plants—a bean plant, for example—are alike in having two main parts. One is a stalk, or **petiole** (PET·ee·ohl), which attaches the leaf to a branch. The other is the thin, flattened **blade** (Figure 15-1). If you hold the blade of a bean leaf up to a bright light, you will be able to see a network of **veins**. The veins extend from a **midrib**, which is a continuation of the petiole into the blade of the leaf.

The Cells of the Leaf

If we were to look only at the outside of a leaf we would certainly get the impression that the green pigment—the chlorophyll—is more or less evenly distributed through the leaf tissues. A microscopic examination of a thin section through the blade (Figure 15-2) will soon show us that this is not the case. Instead of being evenly dispersed in the cells and tissues, the chlorophyll is concentrated in discrete structures, the chloroplasts, within certain cells. Nearly all the chloroplasts are in living cells located in the middle layers of the blade. These layers are

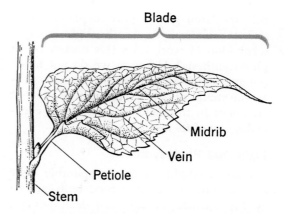

15-1 The external anatomy of a leaf. Of all plant organs, leaves show the greatest variability in form. Some may be several feet long, others are reduced to tiny scales. Many have smooth margins, others have such marginal irregularities as lobes, or the teeth shown in this drawing. Whatever their differences, however, most leaves are green (or contain chlorophyll in addition to another pigment).

sandwiched between the **upper** and **lower** **epidermis**. The cells of the layer next to the upper epidermis make up the **palisade** (PAL·ih·sayd) **layer**. Cells in this region are vertically elongated and differ in size, shape, and arrangement from those found lower in the leaf. Cells of the kind adjacent to the lower epidermis are less regular in shape, and there are large air spaces between them. Because of the numerous air spaces and the loose arrangement of cells, this layer is called the **spongy layer**. Both palisade and spongy layers are composed of living cells with numerous chloroplasts.

As we look at the distribution of chlorophyll in a leaf, we must be impressed by the fact that most of the living cells of the leaf contain some of this green stuff. Biologists discovered long ago that the green parts of plants had something to do with absorbing light and using its energy in the synthesis of carbohydrates. But how?

Sunlight is complex—a spectrum of light of many wavelengths. Do all portions of this spectrum play a part in photosynthesis? If chlorophyll absorbs light energy, what kind of work does this energy do in photosynthesis? Although we do not know the answers to all of these or the many other questions about photosynthesis, recent advances in this field of study have clarified many of its mysteries.

Light and Photosynthesis

When sunlight—or the comparable light from an ordinary electric light bulb—reaches the surface of a green leaf, several things happen to it. Part of the light is reflected from the leaf surface, while some continues through the tissues of the leaf and is said to be *transmitted* light. The light we are most interested in is neither

what is reflected nor what is transmitted, but that which is *absorbed* by the green pigments in the leaf. It is this light that provides the energy for photosynthesis.

With the understanding that a beam of light is really composed of a spectrum of light rays having different wavelengths, we can arrange to study that spectrum by passing a light beam through a prism (Figure 15-3, left). The prism separates the beam into bands of colors, deep red at one end of the spectrum and deep violet at the other. The red light waves are the longest waves of visible light, and they are bent the least when they pass through the prism. The short wavelengths of violet are bent the most. Wavelengths in the violet portion of the spectrum are about 400 millimicrons

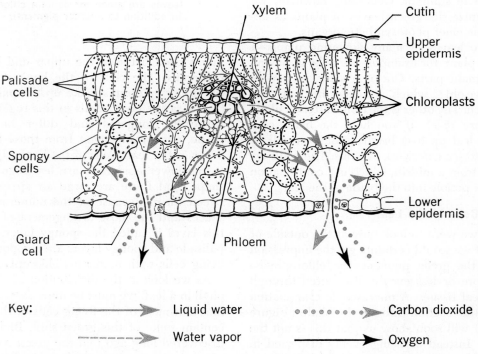

Key: —————▶ Liquid water   •••••••▶ Carbon dioxide

      – – – –▶ Water vapor   ————▶ Oxygen

15-2 Part of a leaf as it might appear in cross section under the microscope. The vein near the center is also in cross section. The arrows show the movement of carbon dioxide, oxygen, and water into or out of the leaf. What clues to the relationship of structure and function are evident in the drawing? (What is significant, for example, about the air spaces between the spongy cells? Or about the loss of water through the openings, or stomata, that admit carbon dioxide into the leaf?)

15-3 SELECTIVE ABSORPTION OF LIGHT BY CHLOROPHYLL

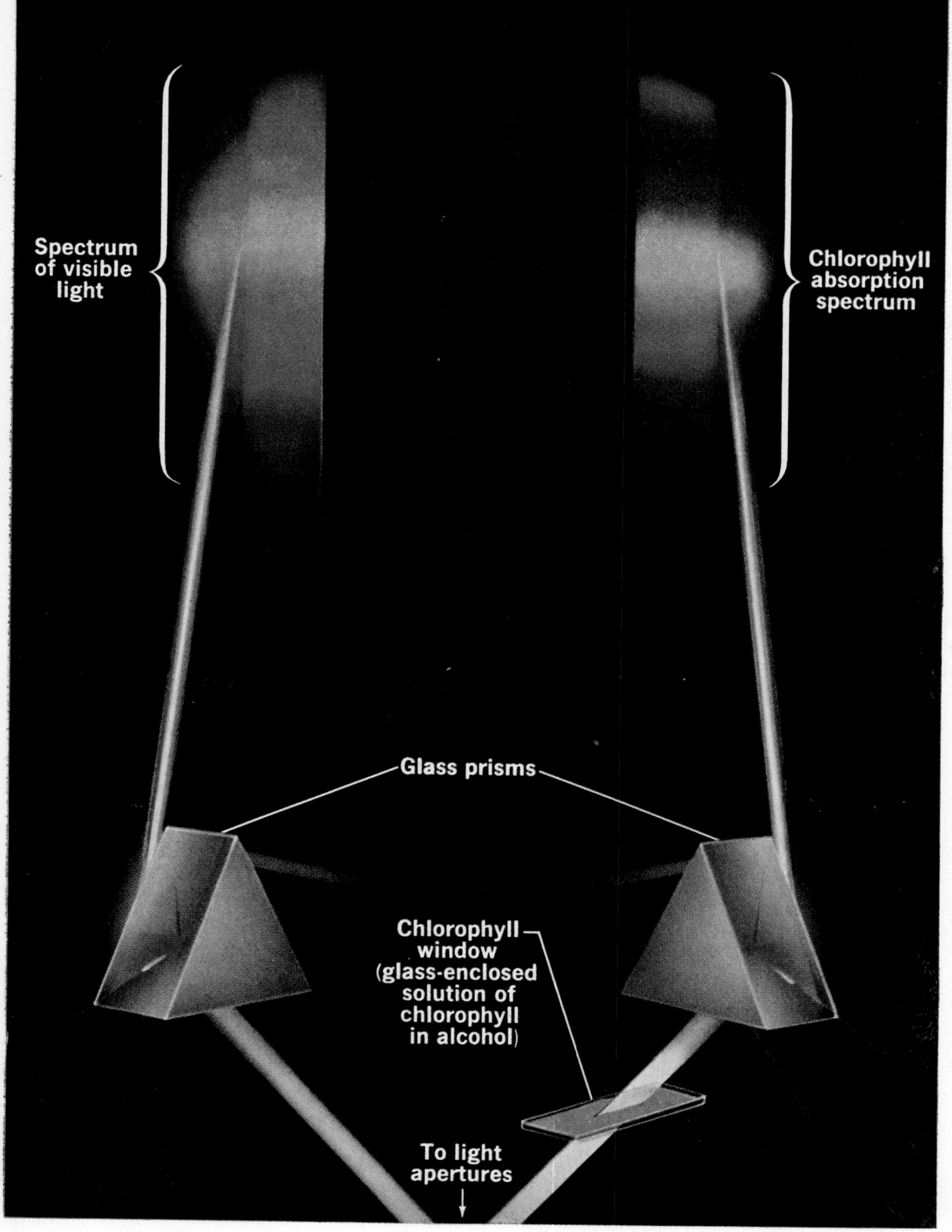
Spectrum of visible light
Chlorophyll absorption spectrum
Glass prisms
Chlorophyll window (glass-enclosed solution of chlorophyll in alcohol)
To light apertures

(mμ) in length, while those at the other end of the spectrum—the red portion—are much longer, about 730 mμ. (You will recall from an earlier part of your work that a milli-micron is equal to 1/1,000 of a micron or 1/1,000,000 of a millimeter.)

How can we find out what part of the spectrum is absorbed by the green substance in leaves—the molecules of chlorophyll? First we have to make an extract of chlorophyll. This can be done with such solvents as alcohol and carbon tetrachloride, as in Laboratory Exercise 15-1. Next we pour the purified extract into a clear glass container with flat, parallel sides and place the container with its contents between a source of white light and a prism (Figure 15-3, right). When we examine the spectrum of light that passes through the prism, we see that certain wavelengths are partly or completely absent, indicating that they have been absorbed more or less completely by the chlorophyll solution (as can be seen on the preceding page).

As a result, the original appearance of the spectrum is markedly changed. In regions where chlorophyll is an effective absorber, dark bands will be seen. In regions where little absorption occurs, changes in the spectrum will be slight. If we measure the percentage of light absorbed by the chlorophyll for the wavelengths running from 400 mμ to 700 mμ—that is, for violet, then blue, green, yellow, orange, and finally red light—we can prepare a graph showing the degree of light absorption by the chlorophyll solution (Figure 15-4).

We can now understand the relationship between the chlorophyll in the chloroplasts and the absorption of radiant energy necessary for photosynthesis. Only the light energy *absorbed* in the regions of violet, blue, orange, and red wavelengths can be used for synthesizing energy-rich compounds. What do you think happens to the other wavelengths of light—in the green region of the spectrum, for example?

Chlorophyll and Photosynthesis

What is chlorophyll like? The organic chemists who first attempted to determine the chemical composition of chlorophyll soon discovered that it was a complex substance consisting of a mixture of closely related substances. Today we know that there are at least six different kinds of chlorophyll —*a*, *b*, *c*, and *d* found in photosynthetic plants, and two others found only in photosynthetic bacteria.

Chlorophylls *a* and *b* are both present in most of the green land plants with which we are familiar. Their molecular formulas show that they are made up of five different kinds of atoms:

Chlorophyll *a*: $C_{55}H_{72}O_5N_4Mg$

Chlorophyll *b*: $C_{55}H_{70}O_6N_4Mg$

15-4 GRAPH OF ABSORPTION SPECTRUM OF CHLOROPHYLL (IN ALCOHOL)

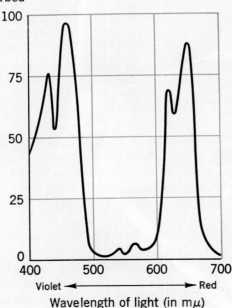

Percentage of light absorbed

Wavelength of light (in mμ)

Violet ← → Red

Each kind of chlorophyll is composed of large molecules containing well over one hundred atoms, but always including four atoms of nitrogen and one of magnesium. Interestingly enough, the chlorophylls are closely related chemically to the red pigment, hemoglobin, found in our own blood. A striking difference is that one molecule has iron, while the other has magnesium. Although we know that the iron molecule in hemoglobin is required in the transport of oxygen by the blood, we do not know what role magnesium plays in the chlorophyll molecule. How does the plant cell manufacture these complex chlorophyll molecules? Actually, we still know very little about their synthesis. We do know, however, that they are formed inside the chloroplast and are organized in layered, disk-shaped structures called **grana** (GRAY-na—Figure 15-5). Grana can be observed by using the electron microscope (Figure 15-6). Each of the layers, or **lamellae** (la-MEL·ee), of a single granum (Figure 15-5) is thought to consist of still smaller layers of protein, fatty substances, chlorophyll, and other pigments.

Chlorophyll is the special substance capable of trapping light energy and making it *available* for bringing about a whole series of reactions, which together constitute photosynthesis. The raw materials that are utilized are two relatively simple compounds, carbon dioxide (CO_2) and water (H_2O). Our next problem is to find out how the first of these, carbon dioxide, is obtained by the plant from its environment.

Carbon Dioxide and Photosynthesis

In the case of green land plants, carbon dioxide is absorbed from the atmosphere surrounding the leaves and stems. How much is normally present in an average sample of air? Analyses of air samples are indeed surprising in this respect, for they reveal that less than 1 percent of the atmosphere is carbon dioxide. This relatively

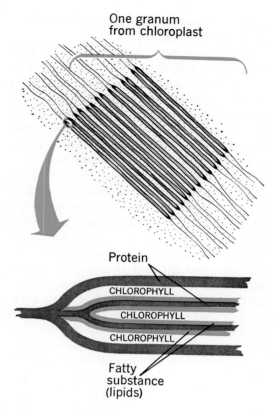

One granum from chloroplast

Protein

CHLOROPHYLL

CHLOROPHYLL

CHLOROPHYLL

Fatty substance (lipids)

15-5 A diagram of the structure of a granum from a chloroplast. A single chloroplast contains many such grana, as an electron micrograph (Figure 15-6) shows. Different investigators have different theories about the disposition of the protein, fatty substance, and chlorophyll in the lamellae (or layers) within a granum. One of the theories is illustrated here.

low concentration of carbon dioxide, 0.03 to 0.04 percent, is nevertheless the only known source from which green land plants obtain the carbon atoms that are later incorporated in each organic compound they manufacture. We must keep in mind, however, that green land plants account for only about 10 percent of the total photosynthesis occurring on earth. All of the rest goes on in the seas, oceans, rivers, and lakes, where in addition to dissolved carbon dioxide, large quantities of carbon-containing compounds such as bicarbonates and soluble carbonates are readily available.

In the section of this book dealing with the evolution of land plants (Chapter 14), it was explained that the land plants have evolved certain structures for the absorption of carbon dioxide from the atmosphere. Let us see what these structures are, and how they function in a leaf of a green plant. A review of Figure 15-2 will help us.

To absorb carbon dioxide, the green plant must have the wet surfaces of some of its cells exposed to the atmosphere. Within the leaf, these are cells of the spongy and palisade layers. The wet surfaces of these cells are exposed to the atmosphere in the air spaces of the leaf tissues. The carbon dioxide of the atmosphere, coming in contact with the water film that covers the spongy and palisade cells, dissolves in the water and is absorbed. As the carbon dioxide is absorbed from the air spaces by the cells of the leaf, its concentration in the air

spaces becomes lower than that present in the outside air. Under these conditions, carbon dioxide in the surrounding atmosphere will diffuse into the air spaces of the leaf.

As air diffuses into the leaf, it passes through stomata (pages 293–94)—pores in the epidermal layers. These pores are surrounded by paired guard cells. The size of the pores is regulated by changes in the water content of the guard cells. If stomata are closed by the action of the guard cells, the diffusion of carbon dioxide into the leaf will be halted. Without carbon dioxide, the process of photosynthesis will then cease, even though light energy and all the other factors required may be present. Hence it is important to understand how the guard cells function and how they affect the life processes of green land plants.

We may start our analysis by recalling that guard cells contain chloroplasts (Figures 15-7 and 15-8)—the guard cells are in fact the only photosynthesizing cells of the

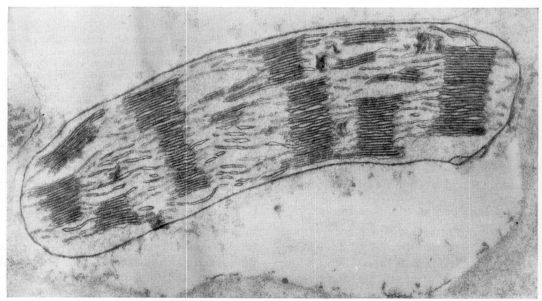

T. E. Weier

15-6 An electron micrograph of a chloroplast. The structures that look like stacks of coins (seen from the side) are the grana. The "coins" within each stack, or granum, are the lamellae. How does this photograph relate to Figure 15-5? (5,000 X)

epidermis. Like other photosynthetic cells, guard cells absorb carbon dioxide. Some of the carbon dioxide reacts with the water in which it is dissolved to form carbonic acid:

$$H_2O + CO_2 \rightleftarrows H_2CO_3$$
$$\text{carbonic acid}$$

In the presence of light energy, carbonic acid in the guard cells is decomposed again into carbon dioxide and water, which are rapidly used in the synthesis of sugar-phosphate compounds. Thus an analysis of the contents of illuminated guard cells reveals that their acid content is low (pH high) and their sugar content is high. During hours of illumination, the guard cells also absorb water from adjacent cells. They become turgid and bend apart like two sausages connected at each end (Figure 15-8). In this way they form a stoma, or pore, between them, through which the air, containing carbon dioxide, can pass to the photosynthetic tissues of the leaf.

Next, one might ask: Why do the guard cells absorb water that causes them to swell and bend apart? As sugar accumulates in the guard cells, the relative concentration of water in the cells decreases. Water molecules then diffuse from the adjacent, non-photosynthetic epidermal cells, where the H_2O concentration remains higher, through the cell membranes and into the guard cells. The principles of diffusion that regulate the action of the guard cells are plainly the same as those discussed in Chapter 6.

What do you suppose will happen to the guard cells if we turn off the light or put the plant in the dark? If we analyze the contents of the cells after a sufficient number of minutes in the dark, we will find that most of the sugar molecules have been removed by respiration or have been converted into insoluble starch. Accompanying this change is an increase in the acidity of the cell contents. Can you explain why? The water balance also changes. As sugar molecules are removed from the guard cells

and the relative concentration of water in the guard cells increases, water molecules diffuse out to the epidermal cells. This movement continues until a balance in the concentration of water molecules is established between the two kinds of cells.

As the guard cells lose water, they become less turgid. Their inner walls then move together until the pore between them is closed. The inner walls of the guard cells are thick, and act like straight leaf springs. When the guard cells are turgid, the spring-like walls become slightly bent and the stoma opens. With a decrease in turgidity, the walls straighten out and close the pore.

Stomata and the Loss of Water

When the stomata of the leaf are closed, carbon dioxide in the atmosphere cannot enter the leaf. But the stomata close when there is no light for photosynthesis; carbon dioxide would not be used by the plant even if it were available. Then what difference should it make if stomata were open through the night? Think about this question for a while. It ought to become clear to you that the presence of stomata that will open and close is really unnecessary just to admit carbon dioxide. But of course substances other than carbon dioxide diffuse. What is to prevent water vapor, present in high concentration in the air chambers of the leaf, from diffusing through the stomata and being lost to the drier atmosphere? Nothing, if the air spaces of the leaf are open to the outside air. In fact, green land plants, while absorbing carbon dioxide for photosynthesis, do lose large quantities of water vapor.

Water is precious to land plants. The excessive loss of water from a plant will result in wilting; that is, the living cells of the plant, including its guard cells, will lose their turgidity. As the guard cells lose turgidity, the stomata close and the rate of photosynthesis decreases sharply, even though plenty of light may be available.

The stomata will not open up again until the water deficit of the plant is made up by further absorption of water through the roots. Thus, to conserve water in a plant, the stomata must remain open only when all other factors necessary for photosynthesis are available. For example, if the stomata of a desert plant remained open at night, when it could not manufacture food anyway, it might lose enough water to kill it. Clearly the guard cell mechanism is of great importance. It admits carbon dioxide when it can be used, but conserves water as much as possible.

Water in the Leaf

In spite of the guard cell mechanism just described, plants lose great quantities of water from their leaves. A medium-sized elm tree for example, may release more

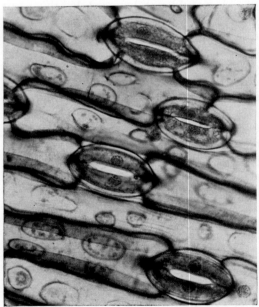

Harold V. Green

15-7 Part of the lower epidermis of a leaf, as seen through a compound microscope. The narrow opening between each pair of guard cells is a stoma. How do the guard cells function in conserving water in the leaf? In obtaining carbon dioxide from the atmosphere?

than a ton of water into the atmosphere in a single day. An acre of corn (about 200 feet square), the equivalent of about 3,600 square meters, has been estimated to use enough water during the growing season to cover the ground to a depth of 28 cm.

There is a wide variation in the number of stomata present in the upper epidermis, compared to the lower epidermis of the same leaf, as well as from one species of plants to another. A begonia, for example, may have an average of only 4,000 stomata per square centimeter of leaf surface, whereas a scarlet oak has 103,800 present in the corresponding area. In these two species, as in many others, the stomata are located only in the lower epidermis of the leaf; but this pattern of distribution is by no means universal. Corn plants have 5,200 stomata per square centimeter of upper epidermal surface, and 6,800 in the lower. The corresponding figures for pea plants are 10,100 (upper) and 21,600 (lower).

Of the great quantities of water lost from the leaves and stems of plants, more than 90 percent is lost through the stomata, and less than 10 percent from cells of the leaf epidermis. Why so great a difference? Look carefully at the upper and lower epidermis of the sectioned leaf (Figure 15-2). The cells of both layers are covered with a coating of the waxy material *cutin*, the same substance that coats liverworts (page 262). Cutin is very effective in preventing the passage of water.

We have already made it clear that in spite of mechanisms for the conservation of water in the stems and leaves of land plants, much water is unavoidably lost, especially when stomata are open. The water lost must be replaced through the roots, which absorb water from the soil. Once inside the root, the water is usually moved rapidly through the conducting system of root and stem into the leaf. The terminal portions of this conducting system can be seen in veins of the leaves (Figure 15-2).

Each vein is a complex structure composed of a group of dead tubular xylem cells in the upper part of the vein, and living phloem cells in the lower part of the vein. The cells of xylem are the pipes through which water moves into the leaves. The phloem cells move the sugars made in photosynthesis from the leaf to the stem and roots, where the sugars are converted into starch and stored. A sheath of photosynthetic cells, enveloping the xylem and the phloem, completes the vein's structure.

THE BIOCHEMISTRY OF PHOTOSYNTHESIS

We have seen that there are four essentials that a plant must have in order to carry on photosynthesis: carbon dioxide, water, light, and chlorophyll. In Chapter 6 there was a general discussion of the process of photosynthesis, but it was far from complete. Like respiration, photosynthesis consists of numerous steps, many of which are still not fully known. At the present time there are hundreds of scientists in all parts of the world working to clear up one or another of these areas of uncertainty.

The general equation for photosynthesis, now to be given, is a gross oversimplification. Nevertheless, it is a starting point.

$$6CO_2 + 6H_2O \xrightarrow[\substack{\text{chlorophyll} \\ \text{(in a living cell)}}]{\text{light energy}} C_6H_{12}O_6 + 6O_2$$

This equation indicates that photosynthesis involves 6 molecules of carbon dioxide and 6 molecules of water in forming 1 molecule of a carbohydrate (glucose) and 6 molecules of oxygen (which are released). Forming high-energy carbohydrates from comparatively low-energy raw materials obviously requires a source of energy. The source is light, absorbed by chlorophyll.

To pursue the matter further, suppose we now ask the following question: What is the origin of the free oxygen—the by-product of photosynthesis? It could come from

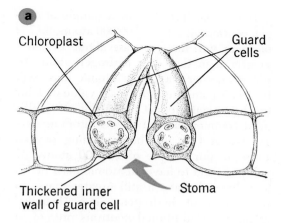

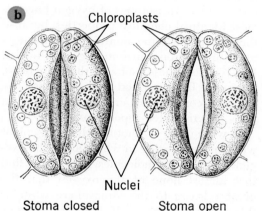

15-8 The structure of the stomatal apparatus. **a** In sectioned guard cells, the thickened inner walls show clearly. How do these inner walls function in the operation of the guard cells? **b** The regulation of a stoma by guard cells is one of the most spectacular mechanisms to be found in plants. On the left is a pair of guard cells as they might appear at night. On the right is the same pair as seen during the day (if plenty of water is available to the plant). How would the guard cells appear during a day of severe drought?

the carbon dioxide, or from the water, or perhaps partly from both. Until fairly recently it was almost impossible to find the answer to such a question. Only when supplies of isotopes (see Chapter 5) became available for experimental use could problems like this one be tackled.

If we take from the air a sample of oxygen containing exactly 100,000 atoms, 99,759 of them will have a mass about 16 times greater than that of a hydrogen atom. To put it another way, their atomic mass will be 16, as compared to a mass value of 1 for the hydrogen atom. Chemists identify this most common kind of oxygen atom as oxygen-16, or O^{16}. Of the remaining oxygen atoms in our sample of 100,000 atoms, 37 will be found to have an atomic mass of 17, and 204 will have a still greater mass, 18 times that of hydrogen. Such "heavier" atoms have additional neutrons present in their nuclei. All isotopes of oxygen have almost identical chemical properties, because they have the same number and arrangement of electrons surrounding their nuclei. But because these isotopes differ in mass, they can be separated and identified by using a complicated instrument called a **mass spectrometer** (spek·TROM·e·ter).

If we supply a photosynthesizing plant with carbon dioxide in which all of the oxygen of the CO_2 molecules is O^{18}, we find that almost none of the oxygen that the plant releases to the atmosphere contains this particular isotope. If, however, we give the plant *water* molecules in which the oxygen is O^{18}, we find O^{18} being released to the atmosphere. By using the heavy oxygen isotope, we have answered our question: the oxygen released in photosynthesis comes from the water that is used, not from the carbon dioxide.

Another problem now confronts us. According to our general equation for photosynthesis, 6 molecules (12 atoms) of oxygen are released for every 6 molecules of water taken up. Six molecules of water have, however, a total of only 6 atoms of oxygen present in them. If all the oxygen comes from the water, something is indeed amiss. The equation is not balanced. We must have more water available to supply the needed atoms. This leads us to formulate a new equation:

$$6CO_2 + 12H_2O^* \xrightarrow[\text{chlorophyll}]{\text{energy}}$$
$$C_6H_{12}O_6 + 6O_2^*\uparrow + 6H_2O$$

(O* indicates the heavy oxygen O^{18})

You will notice that we have had to add 6 more molecules of water on the right side of our equation so that the number of each different kind of atom is equal on both sides of the equation. Remember, matter and energy are neither created nor destroyed in ordinary chemical reactions.

Many isotopes are unstable or radioactive, having nuclei which disintegrate, releasing energy and particles, some of which may be charged. Some of these radioactive isotopes, like those of uranium and radium, occur in nature. Greater numbers of them are produced today by bombarding atoms of different elements with neutrons, protons, and other subatomic particles in a cyclotron or an atomic pile.

Radioactive isotopes of elements that occur in organisms are used to produce "tagged" molecules. For example, radioactive carbon-14 (or C^{14}) can be oxidized in a supply of nonradioactive oxygen to produce carbon-tagged carbon dioxide molecules. These, when taken in by the plant and used, can be detected in very low concentrations by employing instruments such as the Geiger-Müller counter.

By using radioactive isotopes and refined techniques of chemical analysis, it has been possible within the past twenty years to discover many of the intricate chemical transformations that take place during photosynthesis. We know now that the photosynthetic drama is a play in two acts. The main participants in Act I are chlorophyll, light, and water. The scene of the action is the chloroplast. As light energy is absorbed by the chlorophyll molecules, high-energy electrons are released from some of the atoms of these molecules. Some of the energy of the electrons is immediately used to change ADP to ATP, and a large amount is indirectly used to split molecules of water, releasing oxygen and producing high-energy compounds of hydrogen. There is evidence that one of the compounds that serves as a hydrogen acceptor is a nucleotide, TPN. The initials stand for **triphosphopyridine nucleotide** (try·fos·foh·PIHR·ih·deen NEW·kle·o·tide). TPN is very similar to the DPN that plays so prominent a role in electron transport in respiration (see Chapter 6). In fact, TPN and DPN are so closely related that TPN, instead of DPN, may at times take part in electron transport in respiration.

The electrons originally removed from the chlorophyll, having transferred their energy partly to ATP, and partly to TPN (now TPNH) and other high-energy hydrogen compounds, are eventually returned to the chlorophyll molecules. Thus chlorophyll is restored to its original state—ready to take part in a subsequent performance of the play. Act I is completed. The energy of light has been absorbed, and water molecules have been split by means of much of the absorbed energy. The reactions in Act I are therefore very appropriately entitled the **light reactions.**

Act II, the final part of the drama, follows almost immediately. Since the reactions involved here do not require light, they are referred to as the **dark reactions.** The ATP and the high-energy hydrogen compounds produced in Act I now react with new members of the cast, molecules of carbon dioxide. These become involved in a complex series of subplots. At the conclusion of the play, when all the complexities of plot and subplots have been resolved, we find the following situation. Half the hydrogen atoms originally split from the water have combined with half their number of oxygen atoms to form water again. (These oxygen atoms came from the carbon dioxide, each molecule contributing one of them.) The other half of the hydrogen atoms have become joined to the remaining parts of the

carbon dioxide molecules to construct molecules of glucose. The energy of the ATP molecules has contributed to the process, too.

Part of the original energy in the light is now locked up in the form of chemical energy within these molecules. A diagrammatic synopsis of this drama is presented in Figure 15-9.

The Amount of Photosynthesis

How much photosynthetic activity is carried on all over the world each year? Here is one estimate that has been made.

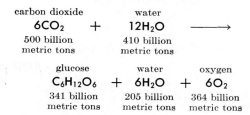

carbon dioxide   water

$$6CO_2 \quad + \quad 12H_2O \quad \longrightarrow$$

500 billion   410 billion
metric tons   metric tons

glucose   water   oxygen

$$C_6H_{12}O_6 \quad + \quad 6H_2O \quad + \quad 6O_2$$

341 billion   205 billion   364 billion
metric tons   metric tons   metric tons

The quantities of materials involved are obviously so large that they become almost incomprehensible on this worldwide basis. Yet each year, only about 1/2,000 of the total available energy received on earth from the sun is captured by plants through photosynthesis. There are, of course, many areas, such as deserts and the tops of high mountains, where lack of water, low temperatures, and other adverse environmental factors permit little or no plant growth. Even taking these areas into account, plants growing in more favorable regions are still estimated to fix only a relatively small proportion of the energy available. If we ask where in the world most photosynthesis takes place, the answer is indeed surprising—the oceans! Probably 85 percent of all the world's photosynthesis takes place in ocean waters, and another 5 percent in ponds, lakes, and rivers. As much as 90 percent of the total photosynthesis is thus attributable mainly to microscopic, aquatic algae. This estimate becomes more understandable when we remember that about

15-9 A SUMMARY OF PHOTOSYNTHESIS

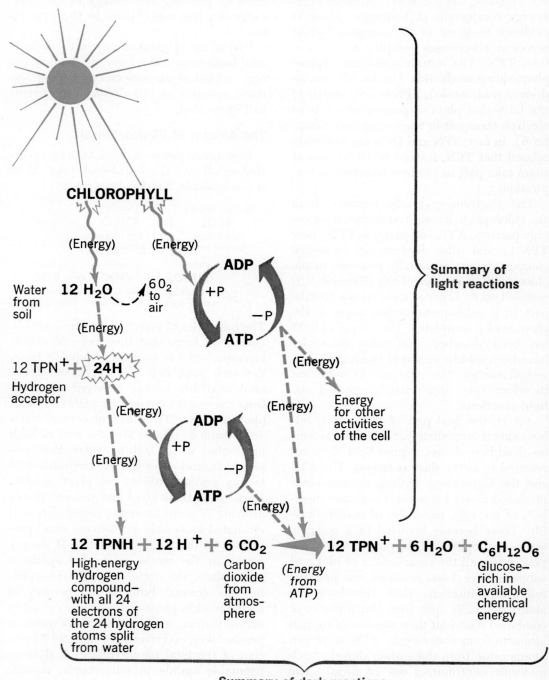

CHLOROPHYLL

(Energy)   (Energy)

ADP
+P
−P
ATP

Water from soil   **12 H$_2$O**   ⤴ 6 O$_2$ to air

(Energy)

12 TPN$^+$ + **24H**
Hydrogen acceptor

(Energy)

(Energy)   (Energy)

Energy for other activities of the cell

ADP
+P
−P
ATP

(Energy)

} Summary of light reactions

12 TPNH + **12 H$^+$** + **6 CO$_2$**

High-energy hydrogen compound— with all 24 electrons of the 24 hydrogen atoms split from water

Carbon dioxide from atmosphere

(Energy from ATP)

12 TPN$^+$ + **6 H$_2$O** + **C$_6$H$_{12}$O$_6$**

Glucose-rich in available chemical energy

Summary of dark reactions

70 percent of the earth's surface is covered with water. Can you think of any other reasons why an aquatic environment would be more favorable for photosynthesis than land?

CONCLUDING REMARKS

Although much progress has been made in disclosing the secrets of photosynthesis, no one has yet succeeded in duplicating the process for an extended period of time outside the green cells of living plants. In view of increasing human populations and shortages of food, it is important that scientists find out exactly how photosynthesis works. With this information it may be possible someday to add to the world's food supply by producing carbohydrates synthetically.

This problem is being attacked from many angles by scientists with many different backgrounds. For example:

1. Only certain wavelengths of light are important in photosynthesis, so we must call on the physicist to help us understand the energy relationships of photosynthesis.
2. We know that carbon dioxide and water are used by plants in the presence of chlorophyll to make glucose. The biochemists have already demonstrated that this is a complex process, which involves energy transfer in many steps. The molecular structure of the various chlorophylls, and their distribution in the chloroplast, are also problems for the biochemist.
3. But how can we be sure about the structure of the chloroplasts unless we see them in finest detail? The efforts of a cytologist, who studies cell structure and who knows how to use an electron microscope, are required.

Thus, the study of a complex process such as photosynthesis requires the combined talents of a great many people.

Although the story is incomplete, these and other kinds of scientists have already fashioned a remarkable story of how green plants manufacture carbohydrates. It is a story of the complementarity of structure and function. The structure is the photosynthetic organ—the leaf of the plant, and its chloroplasts. The leaf is well adapted in its structure to carry out the function of photosynthesis. There are special cells, guard cells, that regulate the exchange of gases between the leaf and the surrounding atmosphere, and that conserve the plant's water to the maximum extent possible. There are special cells within the leaf that

15-9 A summary of the light and dark reactions in photosynthesis. Sunlight, as it strikes the chlorophyll in a green leaf, activates two sequences of reactions. In one, water molecules are split, and in the other, ATP is made from ADP + P. (These two events are shown opposite one another, near the top of the page.) The splitting of the water then leads not only to the formation of high-energy hydrogen compounds (represented in the diagram by TPNH), but also to *more* ATP, produced as the "excited" hydrogen atoms from water are passed along to TPN+. (The 12 TPN+ shown in the diagram are converted to 12 TPNH by reaction with 12 hydrogen atoms and the 12 electrons from the remaining hydrogen atoms.) Energy from both TPNH and ATP is used during the dark reactions for the production of glucose (and other photosynthetic products). Actually, some of the steps in photosynthesis are not yet known in detail. No one yet knows, for example, whether two hydrogen atoms are split from each water molecule, or perhaps only one as an H^+ ion. In the latter case, the water (H_2O) would yield both H^+ and OH^- ions. Oxidation of OH^- ions to OH would lead to OH + OH reactions, yielding water and oxygen. The final result would be the general one you already know: the oxygen would be released to the atmosphere, and hydrogen (as H^+ ions) would react with carbon dioxide (and electrons from the cytoplasmic pool) to form glucose.

absorb carbon dioxide; these cells also are the ones that contain chloroplasts. The cells with the largest numbers of chloroplasts are oriented in the leaf so as to receive the maximum amount of light. The veins of the leaf are equipped with conducting cells through which water is supplied to the photosynthetic cells, or through which manufactured foods can be moved to other parts of the plant.

How did the leaves of plants become so well adapted to carrying out the function of photosynthesis? We know that the characteristics we find in the leaf of a vascular plant are the result of a long evolution from a primitive kind of vascular plant, which lacked leaves (Chapter 14). Thus really to understand photosynthesis in plants, we also have to understand the origin and structure of the leaf.

GUIDE QUESTIONS AND PROBLEMS

1. What tissues and cells of a leaf contain the chloroplasts?
2. What wavelengths of light are absorbed by the chloroplasts? How could this be demonstrated experimentally?
3. What wavelengths of light are transmitted by the chloroplasts? How is this fact interpreted?
4. Carbon dioxide diffuses into the leaf very rapidly during the daylight hours. Explain how the diffusion is brought about.
5. What is the function of the guard cells of the leaf? On what surface of the leaf of a water lily, which floats on the water, would you expect to find guard cells?
6. How do the guard cells regulate the opening and closing of the stomata? How does diffusion contribute to the functioning of the guard cells?
7. How are the stomata related to the loss of water from the leaves of plants?
8. How is the leaf adapted to getting the materials needed to carry on photosynthesis and to moving essential manufactured materials to other parts of a plant?

9. What is the source of the free oxygen that green plants give off as a by-product of photosynthesis? How was this demonstrated experimentally?
10. What are the major chemical events that occur in the light reactions of photosynthesis? What part does chlorophyll play in these reactions?
11. What are the major chemical events occurring in the dark reactions of photosynthesis? How do these events depend upon the results of the light reactions?

SUGGESTIONS FOR ADDITIONAL READING

Books

Galston, A. W., *The Life of the Green Plant.* Englewood Cliffs (N. J.), Prentice-Hall, 1961.

A brief, lucid account of plant functions.

Gabriel, M. L., and S. Fogel (eds.), *Great Experiments in Biology.* Englewood Cliffs (N. J.), Prentice-Hall, 1955.

Contains a number of classic papers describing experiments on photosynthesis.

Bonner, J., and A. W. Galston, *Principles of Plant Physiology.* San Francisco, Freeman, 1952.

A well-illustrated college-level text.

Machlis, L., and J. G. Torrey, *Plants in Action.* San Francisco, Freeman, 1956.

A fine laboratory manual in plant physiology, with many workable experiments that do not require elaborate equipment.

Magazines and Journals

Arnon, D., "The Role of Light in Photosynthesis." *Scientific American,* Vol. 203 (November 1960), pp. 104–09.

Bassham, J. A., "The Path of Carbon in Photosynthesis." *Scientific American,* Vol. 206 (June 1962), pp. 88–100.

Rabinowitch, E., "Photosynthesis." *Scientific American,* Vol. 179 (August 1948), pp. 25–35.

——— "Progress in Photosynthesis." *Scientific American,* Vol. 189 (November 1953), pp. 80–84.

Wald, G., "Life and Light." *Scientific American,* Vol. 201 (October 1959), pp. 92–100.

16

STEMS AND ROOTS

—A STUDY OF

COMPLEMENTARITY

OF STRUCTURE

AND FUNCTION

The time has come to re-emphasize one of our basic themes. It has been the "silent partner" of evolution (another of our basic themes) throughout our study of plant life, and in the last chapter it succeeded to the starring role again—but it was announced quietly. Did it escape your attention? Perhaps the *words* did, but the *idea* of complementarity of structure and function had to be uppermost in your mind as you read about the stomata and how they regulate gaseous exchange and water loss in the leaf —or as you read about the leaf epidermis, almost waterproof (precisely the characteristic most needed by the leaf for its outer cells).

With the stem and the root, we continue the study we have begun of complementarity in the structures and functions of the vascular plant and its parts.

THE STEM

The stem of a plant plays two different roles, both of major importance for plant survival. First, it provides support for the leaves and other photosynthetic tissues of the shoot. Second, it transports materials from regions where they are absorbed or produced to other parts of the plant where they are used, stored, or lost. Again we will focus our attention upon familiar plants.

First, let us consider the relationship of the supporting framework of stems and branches to the photosynthetic efficiency of a plant. To get a better idea of what this relationship is, imagine that you have just been asked to rake the leaves that have fallen from the maple tree in the front yard. By the time you are through, you have accumulated quite a pile of leaves. Now suppose you throw a large sheet of plastic film over the entire leafless maple tree and tie the ends of the sheet around the trunk. How does the volume of the space enclosed by the plastic compare with the volume of the pile of leaves? The difference is obviously very impressive. Next ask yourself this question: How does the surface area of the pile of fallen leaves, which is in contact with the air and light, compare with the surface area that was exposed when each leaf was attached to the tree? The point is clear. The structural framework of trunk and branches permits a much more effective interaction with a much larger volume of the environment *when the leaves are attached to the branches of the tree* than would be possible if the leaves grew in a compact mass. Unless leaves are well separated from one another, absorption of both light and, to a degree, carbon dioxide takes place less efficiently.

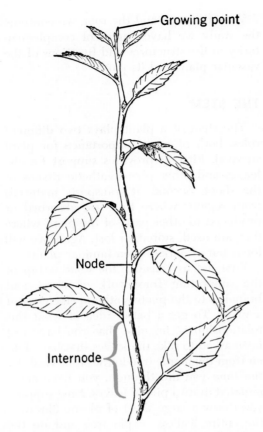

Growing point

Node

Internode

16-1 Part of the shoot of a flowering plant. Besides the growing point at the tip of the shoot, other growing points occur in the angles formed between leaf petioles and the stem.

The Stem Provides Support

Let us now see how the stems of both large and small plants are adapted to provide the support that makes this separation of leaves possible. But first, what are the forces which this supporting framework must withstand? In the case of land plants they are of two kinds: (1) the force of gravity, and (2) the forces imposed on the shoot by wind. How does the stem enable the plant to oppose them successfully?

Actually there are two fairly distinct types of stems. In the first kind, called a **herbaceous** (her·BAY·shus) stem, the tissues are relatively soft and easily crushed. Common examples are tomato, geranium, and milkweed. Plants having this kind of stem usually do not become very tall. If they are deprived of water the stem wilts, bends, and may even collapse entirely. We have seen earlier that the amount of water influences the turgidity of cells in the leaf (Chapter 15). In a similar way, water increases the cell turgidity, and hence the mechanical strength, of herbaceous stems.

The second kind of stem, the **woody stem,** derives its mechanical strength from cells that have stiff, thickened walls. Even when the cells completely dry out, the walls remain strong and maintain their shape. Older woody stems are composed mainly of xylem tissue. This, when sawed into boards, dried, and seasoned, is the wood sold in lumberyards.

Herbaceous Stems. The shoot of a herbaceous plant is made up of the stem and attached leaves (Figure 16-1). Leaves are attached at different levels along the stem. The points of leaf attachment are called **nodes.**

Let us examine a cross section of a sunflower stem (Figure 16-2), cut from the mid-region of an internode (part of the stem running between two successive nodes). The basic plan of organization is apparent at a glance. Strands of vascular or conducting tissue, which run up and down the stem parallel to its axis, are arranged in a circle. These are the **vascular bundles.** Outside the ring of bundles are cells that make up the **cortex** of the stem, and inside the ring of bundles are cells that make up the **pith** region. Cells of pith and cortex are usually thin-walled and living, although thick-walled, dead cells may be found in the outer cortex.

The outermost region of the stem as seen under higher magnification consists of a single layer of epidermal cells covered with a layer of cutin (Figure 16-2). Guard cells and their associated stomata are also present in the epidermis. The outermost *living* cells of the cortex have chloroplasts, which make the stem green in color. Photosynthesis can be carried on in this type of stem as well as in the leaf.

In a single vascular bundle, we can identify the xylem as a cluster of large, empty cells on the side of the bundle nearest the pith. These thick-walled cells provide support and a means for the conduction of water and soluble materials vertically through the stem. Additional support is provided by thick-walled cells that form a "cap" on each bundle. The xylem and the "caps" form vertical columns or rods of supporting tissue arranged in concentric rings.

Conduction of Materials in Stems

Stems of plants are also adapted to serve as efficient conductors of materials from leaves to roots, and vice versa. What kinds of materials must be transported? In general there are two: (1) water plus dissolved mineral salts, taken in by the roots, and (2) sugars, formed initially in leaves by photosynthesis. Usually the water and salts are transported in an upward direction from the roots, through the stem, and out into the leaves. In the summertime, the soluble sugars pass in the reverse direction. Early in the spring of the following year, however, when stored food in the roots and stem is mobilized for the resumption of growth, the sugars move upward. We say, "The sap is rising," and start to tap the sugar maples for syrup.

The structures primarily involved in conducting water and solutes (dissolved substances) are of two types. They are **tracheids** (TRAY-ke-idz) and **vessels**. These two structures, together with strong fiber cells and thin-walled storage cells, make up the xylem tissue of a vascular bundle (Figure 16-2). Tracheids are elongated single cells that in the course of their development have formed thickened walls and then died. Figure 16-3a shows in longitudinal section

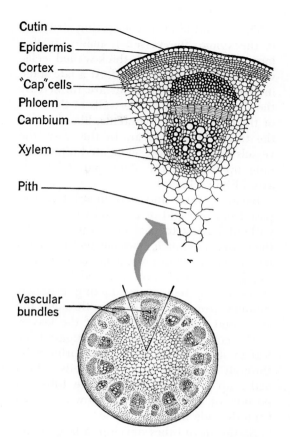

16-2 An internode of a sunflower stem, drawn in cross section. How does the vascular arrangement compare with that in a primitive type of stem (Figure 14-12a)?

a group of tracheids as they relate to one another in their arrangement.

The contents of tracheid cells eventually disappear, and their cellulose walls become freely permeable to both water and dissolved substances. Thus these substances can readily pass into, through, and out of the tracheids. Thin areas called **pits** occur at many points in the walls of these dead cells. In many cases the pits in two adjoining cells are exactly opposite each other, so that only a thin layer of wall material separates them. Water and dissolved salts can easily pass from one tracheid into another through these thin-walled areas.

The second kind of conducting structure in the xylem, the **vessel,** is made up of a long line of elongated, thick-walled cells, which are joined end to end. At a late stage in their development, holes are formed by the digesting away of the walls at the ends of the cells. The cell contents, like those of the tracheids, disappear. In this way, the vessels become hollow, elongated pipes running up through the stem, parallel to its axis (Figure 16-3b).

Because water and salts in solution can pass from one end of a vessel to the other without having to pass even through pits, the vessels are much more efficient conducting structures than are tracheids. Both tracheids and vessels are arranged to form a connected system of conducting channels running from the roots, up through the stem, and out into the veins of the leaves.

The conduction of dissolved sugars from leaf to stem to root takes place principally through long lines of phloem cells, which make up structures called **sieve tubes.** A portion of a sieve tube is shown as seen from the side in Figure 16-3c.

As the sieve tubes develop, a large number of small perforations appear in their end walls. Cytoplasmic connections run through the openings and thus make the cytoplasm continuous from cell to cell. In the final stages of development of a sieve tube, the nuclei in the individual cells disintegrate. The cytoplasm, however, remains alive as long as the sieve tube continues to function. The cells that make up a sieve tube are in close association with one or more smaller companion cells, which do have nuclei. These companion cells are believed to regulate the activity of the sieve tube cells adjacent to them.

The sieve tubes of the phloem form an interconnected system which, like the xylem, reaches all organs of the plant. Through it, sugars formed in the green tissues of the shoot are distributed to all the nongreen cells of shoot and root, which are totally dependent upon the sieve tubes for a supply of food.

Located between the xylem and phloem of the sunflower vascular bundle, there is a third kind of tissue, the **cambium** (KAM-bih·um—Figure 16-2). The cambium is made up of a zone of thin-walled cells, which continue to divide during the period when the stem is growing. The outermost of the new cells thus formed by the cambium develop into phloem cells (sieve tubes and companion cells); those formed toward the inside develop into additional tracheids and vessels of the xylem.

Woody stems. The shoots of herbaceous plants growing in temperate regions live for a relatively short period of time—usually less than a year. Their tissues remain fairly soft and are easily damaged. Quite different are the tissues of woody shrubs or trees, which develop thick, strong trunks and branches. These plants may live for years. Generally they become dormant during late fall and winter, and once more renew their growth in the following spring.

The stems of woody plants grow not only in height but also in diameter from year to year. The trunk, branches, and leaves of a mature maple or oak tree, after fifty years' growth, may weigh many tons. The development of a strong, massive, supporting framework is obviously required for adequate support of such a structure, well over 30 meters (100 feet) high and extending out from the trunk for perhaps 12 meters (40 feet) or more. A diagram of a cross section of a typical woody stem (Figure 16-4a) will show how it is constructed.

If we cut through the trunk of a large tree, at right angles to its axis, the exposed surfaces will be approximately circular in outline. The outermost layer in such a section is the **bark.** It is less compactly constructed than the inner parts of the trunk, which are made up of wood. A microscopically thin zone of small cells, the cambium, separates the bark from the wood. This layer cannot be seen with the unaided eye, but its location can be readily determined. Because the cells in this zone are mechanically weak, we can in most cases peel the bark from the wood. The outer region of the wood is light in color. Inside this region, and making up the central region of the trunk, is dark-colored wood. If we smooth the rough, cut surface of the trunk with fine sandpaper, and then apply water to it, we can see clearly that the wood is made up of many successive layers of cells, like a series of concentric rings.

This much we can see with the unaided eye—to learn more we must examine, with a microscope, thin sections taken from various regions of the trunk. You have already prepared and examined a thin section of cork (Figure 3-3) in the laboratory (Exercise 3-2), just as Robert Hooke did. In this case you used material obtained from the cork oak, in which very thick layers of bark are formed. The cells of cork have walls that are impregnated with a substance called **suberin** (soo·ber·in). Suberin is a fatty substance, a waterproofing material that forms a barrier which effectively limits water loss from inner tissues of the trunk.

Now let us examine a section that includes tissues from the inner bark, cambium, and the outer regions of the wood (Figure 16-4b). Here many different types of cells can be seen. The wood tissue, or xylem, is made up of cells having strong, resistant walls. Two of these types, tracheids and vessels, have already been described. In addition to these there are large numbers of fibers. These are elongated cells, small in cross section, which have particularly thick walls and contribute greatly to the strength of the wood. Running out from the center of the trunk are radially arranged thin-walled cells serving for storage and transverse conduction. All of these different kinds of cells are formed by divisions of the cells of the cambial zone.

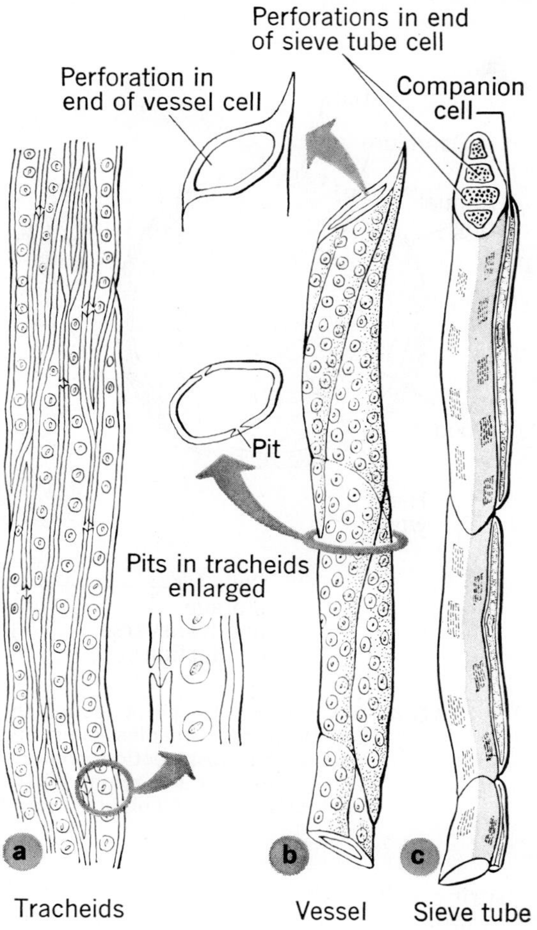

Perforation in end of vessel cell
Perforations in end of sieve tube cell
Companion cell
Pit
Pits in tracheids enlarged

a Tracheids   **b** Vessel   **c** Sieve tube

16-3 Some conducting cells of xylem and phloem. **a** The group of tracheids shown here is in longitudinal section. Conduction in these cells is facilitated by pits in the cell walls. (What other function besides conduction do tracheids perform?) **b** Two vessel cells (and part of a third) are shown from one side. Notice how the cells are situated on top of one another. In this arrangement, they make up a vessel. (What characteristics do vessels and tracheids have in common?) **c** Two kinds of phloem cells are shown from one side. Only one kind is a conducting tissue. Which kind conducts, and what does it conduct?

When trees are dormant, during the winter or periods of drought, very few, if any, new cells are formed by the cambium. When growth is again resumed in the

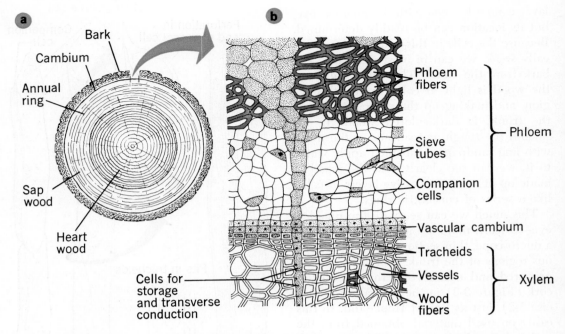

16-4 **a** A drawing of a cross section through a woody stem. This type of stem is characteristic of oaks, maples, elms, and many other familiar trees. **b** An enlargement of part of the cross section, showing the relationship between the vascular cambium and the phloem and xylem. What is the origin of the layer of living cells shown on each side of the cambium layer? What will happen to these layers of cells?

spring, cells in the cambium begin to divide rapidly, forming on the inside edge of the cambium the first cells of a new **annual ring.** These cells are larger than those produced later during the summer, which form the summer wood. This difference in size of cells results in the ringlike pattern that is characteristic of woody stems growing in temperate climates. Annual rings are not as evident in the wood of tropical plants that grow in regions where there is less annual variation in climate.

In the temperate regions of the world, a new ring of xylem tissue is produced by the cambium during each growing season. By counting the number of rings present in the stump of a tree, therefore, we can determine quite accurately the age of the tree at the time it was cut.

In some climates, particularly in the dry regions of our Southwest, trees produce rings that vary in width from one year to the next, depending upon the annual conditions of temperature and rainfall. Logs that are taken from houses built by Indians long before the discovery of the New World by Columbus, can be cut and polished to show their distinctive pattern of rings. The pattern of the outer rings can be matched with that of the inner rings of somewhat more recent trees. This matching procedure can be continued for trees of overlapping ages until an unbroken series of rings, one for each year, spans the period from the present back to the time when the oldest tree in the series was growing. In this way we can obtain information about ancient regional climatic changes, as well as determine with great accuracy the ages of some of the ancient Indian dwellings.

Division of cambium cells in a tree trunk proceeds in both directions. The outermost of the dividing cambium cells become transformed into the phloem tissues of the bark. Included here are sieve tubes with companion cells, groups of fibers, and thin-walled cells that form expanded extensions of the vascular rays running out from the xylem. Cells in the outer layer of the phloem divide and give rise to the layers of cork or bark, which you have already studied.

What happens when the bark of a tree is destroyed by fire or by one of the many different kinds of animals that use it for food? If the damage is not too extensive, a vigorous, healthy tree will repair itself relatively quickly by producing new bark at the edges of the wound. These new layers are gradually extended and will finally completely cover the exposed wood once more. Suppose, however, that we deliberately remove a band of bark several inches wide running completely around the trunk. This procedure, called **girdling** (Figure 16–5), was extensively used by pioneers to kill trees growing on lands needed for farming. Immediately after the operation the tree appears quite normal. Supplies of water can still move up through the outer wood to the leaves. Eventually the tree dies, however, for the simple reason that every living cell in the plant must be supplied with food if the plant is to continue living. The root system, living in darkness in the soil, cannot manufacture its own foods. The pathway for the transport of food from leaf to root—the phloem tissues of the bark—is completely interrupted by girdling. Therefore, the cells of the root system will die as soon as their own supplies of stored foods are exhausted. Dead roots cannot supply water and other essential substances to the rest of the plant, which soon dries out and dies. The dead tree can then be burned to clear the land. Thus the early settlers, by removing a small amount of

U.S. Forest Service

16-5 A power-driven machine for rapid girdling of trees. The girdling is done to kill trees that may be crowding the growth of other trees of greater economic importance.

bark, were able rather quickly to kill trees weighing many tons. By killing the roots they killed the tree. Obviously, we should proceed to find out something about the roots that are so necessary for the survival of vascular plants.

THE ROOT

All of us who have ever tried to pull up weeds in a garden, or remove dandelions from a lawn, know that roots anchor plants firmly in the soil. When we look at an uprooted plant, we may see a ball of dirt at its lower end composed of a tough system of roots plus attached soil. This is a **fibrous root system** (Figure 16–6a), typical of grasses, beans, clover, and many other kinds of plants. When we look at the roots of dandelions or carrots, however, we find a single, long, tapering **taproot** (Figure 16-6b), which has only a few small branch roots and very little soil adhering to it. What many persons are not aware of is that, in both cases, most of the root system has remained in the soil. If, instead of pulling up the plants, we had used a stream of water to wash the soil away gently, the smaller branch roots would have remained attached, and our picture of the root system would be entirely different. A small rye plant (60 cm, or 2 feet, high), with its root system carefully removed from the soil, was found to have about 14 million primary roots and branches with a total length of about 600 kilometers (380 miles). The to-

tal surface area of its root system was calculated at more than 600 square meters (6,500 square feet).

In addition to providing anchorage for the plant, root systems perform two other vital functions. First, they absorb water and soluble nutrient salts from the soil. Second, they provide conducting tissues for distributing these substances to the tissues of the shoot.

Unlike the stem of a herbaceous plant, the principal conducting and strengthening tissues of the root are grouped together at its center to form a rod-shaped core extending throughout its length. If we cut a cross section of a buttercup root and examine it under the microscope, this core of tissue in the center of the section is readily seen (Figure 16–7).

a   U.S.D.A. Photo   b   Hugh Spencer

16-6 Two principal types of root systems: **a** the fibrous root system of a common grass, and **b** the taproot of a beet. The beet itself is an enlarged portion of the taproot. (What are some other edible kinds of taproots?)

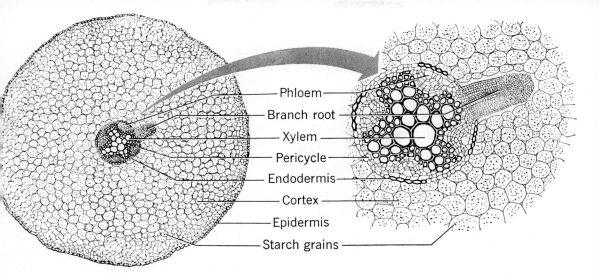

16-7 An enlarged cross section of a buttercup root, with the vascular core and a young branch root further enlarged at the right. Compare this arrangement of tissues with that of the stem in Figure 16-2. On the basis of the vascular structure, which do you think would be the most effective supporting organ—the root or the stem?

The xylem of this central core has the form of a fluted column, which in cross section may show three to five arms radiating from the center. Vertical strands of phloem tissue are located in concave regions of the flutings. In cross section, the strands of phloem alternate with the arms of xylem. In their arrangement, the tissues of the root present quite a different pattern from that found in stems (Figure 16-2). Outside the centrally located xylem and phloem, there is a narrow layer of thin-walled cells, the **pericycle** (PEHR·ih·sy·k'l). The branch roots originate from this tissue. A single layer of cells, the **endodermis** (en·doh·DER·mis) or "inner skin," with walls showing a distinctive pattern of thickening, surrounds the pericycle layer. The remaining tissues of the root consist of a broad zone of large thin-walled cells making up the cortex. The cortex is bounded on the outside by a single layer of smaller epidermal cells.

If we examine a root tip (Figure 16-8a) from which most of the soil particles have been removed, we can see two other features of roots. The root tip is covered with a layer of loosely attached, dead, or dying cells that form a **root cap.** These cells protect the underlying delicate cells of the root apex from injury as the tip is being forced through the soil by the elongation of cells located immediately behind the tip. As root-cap cells are sloughed off, they are replaced by dividing cells of the root tip. A little further back from the tip, large numbers of delicate *root hairs* extend out from the surface, giving the tip a fuzzy appearance. Under the microscope each of these root hairs is seen to be a thin-walled extension of a single epidermal cell (Figure 16-8b).

Absorption of Materials by Roots

The root hairs grow out into the spaces between soil particles. In a typical well-watered soil, each soil particle is surrounded by a thin layer of water containing a variety of salts in solution. These soluble substances are principally derived from the soil particles and the metabolic processes of other living organisms in the soil.

In soils that are not completely saturated with water, there are many air spaces between the irregularly shaped soil particles. The root hairs with their thin, pliable walls

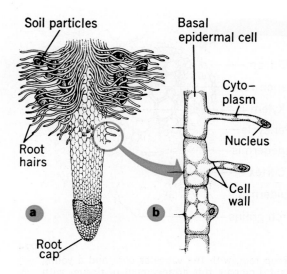

Soil particles

Basal
epidermal cell

Cyto-
plasm

Nucleus

Cell
wall

Root
hairs

Root
cap

a

b

16-8 **a** External features of a root. The root
cap protects the growing tip from injury.
Why is this protection needed? **b** Root
hairs on epidermal cells above the root
tip add greatly to the total cell surface
directly exposed to soil and water. How
does this benefit the plant?

come into direct contact with the soil water and the gases held in spaces between
the particles of soil. The thin walls and cytoplasmic membranes of the root hairs are
permeable to gases, water, and the ions
formed from the soluble salts. Oxygen that
has diffused into the air spaces from the atmosphere, or has been carried to the root
hair in solution in soil water, is readily
available. The oxygen diffuses into the root
hair, where it may either be used in respiration or be passed on to the living cells
deeper inside the root. Because of the respiratory activity in living root cells, the
concentration of oxygen is normally higher
outside the root than inside, and oxygen
therefore continues to diffuse from the surrounding soil into the root cells.

The ions of mineral salts are also taken
in and used to form a wide variety of compounds essential for the continuing existence of the plant. Plants, like animals, require compounds that contain a number of

different elements in addition to carbon,
hydrogen, and oxygen, which are fixed by
photosynthesis. As you already have
learned, nitrogen is essential for the synthesis of all proteins; sulfur is present in many
kinds of proteins. Phosphorus is needed for
nucleotides and nucleic acids. Calcium is
needed to form the compounds that serve
as a cement to hold the cells of the entire
plant body together. You will recall, too,
that each molecule of chlorophyll requires
one atom of magnesium. Iron atoms are not
incorporated in chlorophyll itself, but for
some reason plants cannot synthesize chlorophyll unless adequate amounts of iron-
containing compounds are present. Plants
growing in soils that are deficient in potassium salts may be stunted. Their leaves have
yellowed margins and spots of dead tissue.

In addition to the elements mentioned
above, traces of other elements must be
available. Copper, zinc, boron, manganese,
and molybdenum are all necessary for the
life of plants. These and other trace elements may serve as necessary components
of enzymes or coenzymes without which
the plant would die.

Conduction of Materials in Roots

After the ions of essential salts have been
absorbed by the root hairs, they diffuse
through the living cells of the cortex to the
central cylinder of conducting tissue. Here,
dissolved in water which is being moved
from the root up through the shoot, they
are finally distributed to all other living tissues of the plant.

As the root absorbs ions in soil water,
the concentration of ions inside the root
approaches that of the surrounding soil water. When this happens, the rate of uptake
of ions may slow down. Once absorbed and
transported to the various organs of the
plant, some of the ions are quickly incorporated into the structure of organic molecules. Such a synthesis of molecules requires energy from respiration (see Chap-

ters 6 and 8), and most plants, like animals, require oxygen for this process. Thus the rate at which ions are taken in by the roots depends upon the amount of oxygen that is available for respiration. Because roots are usually well supplied with oxygen, concentrations of ions many times greater than those present in the soil water may accumulate in the root cells. When this happens, the energy released from rapid respiration in the root cells is used to prevent diffusion of the accumulated ions back into the soil. Just how this energy-requiring mechanism operates is still not clear.

The movement of materials from one part of the plant to another involves forces affecting the entire plant. Associated with an understanding of the mechanisms involved, there are related problems concerned with the storage of various substances that are needed not only for the survival of the individual plant but also for the continuation of the species. Let us consider the mechanisms and the problems.

MOVEMENT AND STORAGE OF MATERIALS

As far as we know, the tallest living tree is a California redwood 117 meters (385 feet) high (Figure 16-9). The leaves growing at the tip of its highest branch are supplied with water absorbed through millions of root hairs buried in the ground several hundred feet below. During each growing season, tons of water move into, through, and out of this tremendous organism. From where does the energy come, and by what mechanism is it applied to so enormous a task? While there is still much to be learned about the processes involved, the main outlines of the story can be readily understood.

Let us start by recalling an experience familiar to all of us. When we go to the corner soda fountain to drink a glass of ginger ale or an ice cream soda, we are usually supplied with a straw for the purpose. We

Chicago Natural History Museum

16-9 The giant California redwood. These trees are the largest living things on earth. How does the water required for growth and maintenance reach the uppermost branches, hundreds of feet up?

insert the straw into the liquid, apply our lips to the straw's upper end, and suck. Immediately the level of the contents in the glass begins to drop.

Now let us try another, less familiar experiment (Figure 16-10a). This time let us place a container of water on the ground next to the wall of the school building. We can, if we wish, add dye to the water to make it more easily visible. We climb up to the roof, almost 14 meters (45 feet) above the ground, and using a long piece of plastic tubing we attempt to draw up some of the water. Try as we may, we find that we cannot. Next, we go down the hall to the physics laboratory, borrow a vacuum pump, connect it to the tubing, turn on the pump, and try again. This is also unsuccessful. If our school is located near sea level, we will find that the highest level to which we can draw the liquid is 1,036 cm (34 feet). In Denver, Colorado, where the altitude is approximately 5,000 feet, the vacuum pump could raise the water in the tube only about 850 cm (28 feet). There are definite limits, therefore, to the height that liquids can be lifted by pumps. How, then, does a tree ten or fifteen times higher than this limit manage to draw up the water it must have to survive?

Why could we not get the water to go any higher in the tube? Why did the water move up the tube in the first place? The answers are not difficult to discover. By removing air in the tube above the water by means of mouth or pump, we created a difference in air pressure. The surface of the liquid in the container was subjected to a higher pressure than that present in the tube. Thus the liquid in the tube rose.

The pressure of the atmosphere at sea level amounts to about 1.033 kg per square cm (14.7 pounds per square inch). In a plastic tube with a cross section of 1 square cm, with the air removed at the upper end, air pressure on the surface of the liquid at the lower end will force 1.033 kg of water up the tube, enough to make a column about 10.36 meters high.

Ascent of Water in a Plant

Suppose we try a new experiment (Figure 16-10b). This time we take a leafy shoot and insert the cut end into a piece of rubber tubing. We then connect the other end of the tubing to a slender piece of water-filled glass tubing 14 meters (or about 45 feet) long and only a fraction of a millime-

ter in diameter. We must make certain that there are no leaks in the system, and then, as our last step, dip the lower end of the tube into a container of boiled water in which some dye has been dissolved.

When completed, the apparatus consists of a continuous, connected system filled with water, beginning with the leaf cells, continuing down through the xylem vessels of the veins and branch, to the water in the long, thin glass tube, and ending with the water in the container on the ground. As we watch, the colored water from the container on the ground begins to rise rapidly. It reaches first the 3-, then the 6-, 9-, and finally the 14-meter level, more than 3 meters (10 feet) higher than we could raise the column in our experiment using a vacuum pump. How is this possible? The answer lies in an unusual property of water.

Under certain conditions water has a tensile strength similar to that of a good grade of steel wire. Here are the conditions:

1. The water must be held in a tube (or tubes) of small diameter.
2. The walls of the tube must be made of a material to which the water molecules will adhere.
3. The water under tension must not contain any appreciable amount of dissolved gases, which would come out of solution and form bubbles—causing breaks in the column.

Under these conditions, if water is pulled at the upper end of the column, the pull will be transmitted throughout the column. More water will move in at the bottom as it moves out at the top. Water in columns many times 10 meters in length can thus be moved upward, because it is literally pulled up, rather than being pushed up by atmospheric pressure.

In the living tree, a single column of cells in the network of xylem vessels corresponds to the thin-bore glass tubing of our experiment. The supplies of water in the soil in contact with the root surfaces correspond to the boiled water in the container on the ground. What force supplies the pull at the upper end of the column? Sugars produced by photosynthesizing leaf cells are at a higher level of concentration within these cells than in the rest of the plant. As water evaporates from the cells of the spongy and palisade layers of the leaf and passes out through the stomata, the concentration of soluble materials in the leaf cells increases. When this happens, water diffuses into the leaf cells from the xylem vessels and tracheids of the leaf. As this water moves in, cohesion between water molecules in the leaf cells and those in the xylem tissues makes possible the development of forces that pull water into the root, up the stem, and out into the leaves.

One additional necessary link needs to be explored before the picture of water movement in the plant is complete. How does water pass from the root hairs through the outer tissues of the root, to reach the xylem vessels and tracheids? The model shown in Figure 16-11 will help clear up this problem.

Take an L-shaped piece of large-bore glass tubing and pack one arm of it with short sections of **dialyzing** (DY·a·lyz·ing) tubing (made of a cellophanelike membrane), each section filled with sugar solution and tied at each end. We will assume that the dialyzing tubing is permeable to water and impermeable to sugar. We immerse the packed arm of the glass tube in water. Water will pass initially into the sections of dialyzing tubing by diffusion (see Laboratory Exercise 6-1). The sections of tubing will swell until they fit tightly inside the glass tube. If we now apply suction with a vacuum pump to the vertical arm of the tube, what will happen? The differences in air pressure at the two ends of the system will slowly force water to pass into the end of the horizontal tube, through the sections of dialyzing tubing, and up the vertical tube. How does this model compare with the situation in the plant? The following table will make this clear.

Model	*Plant*
1. Water in container	1. Soil water surrounding root
2. Sections of dialyzing tubing filled with sugar solution	2. Root cells of epidermis, cortex, endodermis, pericycle
3. Vertical tube	3. Xylem vessel

The model differs from the plant in one very important respect. In the model, water is forced by atmospheric pressure to pass through the series of cell-like containers. In the actual plant, water would move because of tension from above exerted on the water molecules extending throughout the system. The net result is the same.

Movement of Materials in Phloem

As previously mentioned, energy-rich sugars produced by photosynthesis are moved from the leaf through the sieve tubes of the phloem to other parts of the plant. At the present time there is no generally accepted explanation of the mechanism of such movement. We do know that the movement may be many thousands of times more rapid than could occur by simple diffusion. If the phloem tissues are killed by heat or chemicals, the movement is blocked. Although the direction of movement is usually from the leaf, down the stem, and into the root, movement in the reverse direction is not uncommonly observed. In many cases the direction of movement seems to be in contradiction to the laws of diffusion. In sugar beets, for example, the sugars are moved down the stem for storage in the enlarged roots, where the concentration of sugars is already far higher than in other regions of the plant. For this sugar transport to take place, energy derived from respiration is required. The exact mechanism involved, however, remains unknown.

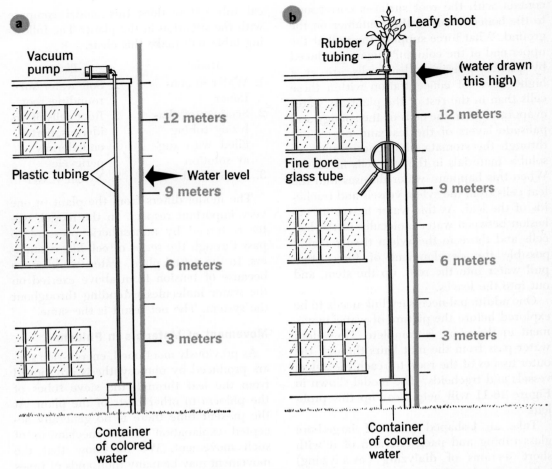

16-10 **a** An experiment to test the height to which water in a partial vacuum can be raised by atmospheric pressure. Why will the water not reach the vacuum pump? **b** Note the modifications in the experimental plan. The pump has been replaced by the shoot of a plant, and the plastic tubing has been replaced by a fine bore glass tube. How do these modifications affect the experiment and its outcome?

Energy and the Movement of Materials

What is the source of the energy needed to move tons of water dozens of meters or hundreds of feet against the force of gravity, or to cause sugars to accumulate contrary to the laws of diffusion? The answer should not really surprise you—directly or indirectly the energy comes from sunlight. The energy-rich substances present in the green leaf cells are all produced by photosynthesis.

Evaporation of water from the tissues of the leaf—the phenomenon bringing about the upward movement of water—requires heat, again representing energy originally absorbed by the leaf in the form of sunlight. The energy released by respiration and used in the transport of sugars in the phloem, if traced back through the biochemical pathways of energy transfer, will ultimately be found to be that originally trapped by light-absorbing chlorophyll molecules. Thus, the energy of the sun is the driving force responsible for the flow of water and of foods throughout the plant.

Storage of Materials

In order to survive, plants must have food and water. It is not surprising to find that many plants have specialized structures for storing these vital materials.

In a desert, rain may fall only a few times each year. A cactus plant must, however, have water continuously available if it is to survive, grow, and reproduce. The roots of the cactus extend out from the plant and cover a wide area, only a short distance below the soil surface. Water absorbed by this system is transported back to the main body of the plant, which is actually a very much thickened stem. Most of the volume of the cactus stem is made up of enlarged, thin-walled cells. Water is taken in by these cells and held in their vacuoles. Here it may be stored for long periods and be slowly released as it is needed for photosynthesis.

Foods produced by the plant in excess of what is needed for maintenance, growth, and repair are available for storage. In a corn plant, for example, the food budget can be estimated approximately as follows:

	Percentage of total foods manufactured
Foods used to supply energy	25%
Foods used for growth and repair	50%
Foods stored	25%

Stored foods are accumulated in the form of carbohydrates (starches and sugars), proteins, fats, and oils.

In the case of the vegetative parts of the plant—the roots, stems, and leaves—most of the food is stored in the form of carbohydrates. As you are no doubt well aware, Irish or white potatoes contain large quantities of starch (a carbohydrate). When you eat onions, you are obtaining food largely

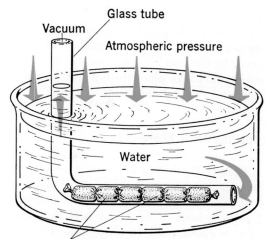

Glass tube
Vacuum
Atmospheric pressure
Water
Bags made of dialyzing membrane filled with sugar solution

16-11 A model for studying the lateral movement of water through root cells to the vascular core of the root. How do the parts of the model correspond to the parts of the root?

in the form of another carbohydrate, the sugar sucrose, which is stored in the thickened leaf bases of this fleshy bulb. Roots in which large amounts of stored sugars or starches are present include sugar beets, sweet potatoes, and turnips.

Proteins, fats, and oils, in addition to carbohydrates, are usually stored in seeds and fruits, the parts of the plant resulting from sexual reproduction. Human beings are so dependent upon these structures for a large proportion of their food that it is possible to classify various civilizations according to their dependence upon particular kinds of cereal grains (wheat, rice, corn, oats, barley), which have served as sources of food for thousands of years. We thus can recognize the rice civilizations of the Far East, the wheat civilizations of the lands bordering on the Mediterranean Sea, and the corn civilizations of the New World.

In these grains, the starches, sugars, proteins, and oils (an oil is simply a form of fat that is liquid at room temperatures) are present in abundance. These foods are thus available to the plant for growth and development of the embryonic parts within the seed. In the next chapter, we will study the events that take place during seed germination and early stages of growth.

CONCLUDING REMARKS

Clearly there is a very intimate interdependence between stem, roots, and leaves in their particular functions. For example, photosynthesis in the leaf would be impossible without roots to absorb the required water and a stem to support the leaves and move the water to them. Conversely, without photosynthesis to manufacture food for development of the plant, there would be no root cells to absorb water and no stem to conduct water to the leaves.

We have learned that stems of plants are well constructed for support, conduction, and storage. Some stems are even photosynthetic. The stem and its branches support the leaves and reproductive structures, giving the leaves maximum exposure to light and carbon dioxide, and giving the reproductive structures elevated positions from which seeds and fruits can be dispersed.

The supporting structures of a stem may be fibers found in the cortex and phloem, or wood cells of various kinds. Some support, especially in herbaceous stems, is derived from the turgidity of living cells. The supporting stems and branches, of course, are anchored in the ground by the roots.

Roots, stems, and leaves are all provided with conducting tissues. These tissues form a continuous system from near the tip of the root to the tip of the uppermost leaf. The principal conducting tissues are xylem and phloem. Tracheids and vessels are dead cells of the xylem that conduct water and soluble minerals, usually upward.

Excess soluble carbohydrate (glucose) manufactured in the leaves is conducted downward through the sieve tubes in the phloem of the leaves, stem, and roots. In the stem and roots the excess food is stored, usually in the living cells of the cortex. Here the sugars are converted into starch as reserve food supplies to be used later by the plant in repair and replacement of old cells, and in development of new cells, including those of reproductive structures such as flowers, seeds, and fruits.

GUIDE QUESTIONS AND PROBLEMS

1. What are the major functions of the stems of higher plants? How are the stems adapted to perform these functions?
2. How is the mechanical strength of herbaceous plants related to water?
3. How would you explain that the stems of aquatic plants are usually soft and weak?
4. What is the function of the xylem tissues in the vascular bundles of plants? Of the phloem elements?
5. How do tracheids differ from vessels in structure?
6. What cells in the vascular bundles transport dissolved sugars?
7. How can the rings of growth of woody plants be interpreted?
8. What are the functions of the root? How are roots adapted to perform their functions?
9. Why is atmospheric pressure alone not enough to raise water to the tops of tall trees? What other factors help to explain the rise of water?

SUGGESTIONS FOR ADDITIONAL READING

Books

See references at the end of Chapter 15.

Magazines and Journals

Biddulph, S., and Orlin Biddulph, "The Circulatory System in Plants." *Scientific American,* Vol. 200 (February 1959), pp. 44–49.
Greulach, V. A., "The Rise of Water in Plants." *Scientific American,* Vol. 187 (October 1952), pp. 78–80.

17

REPRODUCTION

AND DEVELOPMENT

IN FLOWERING

PLANTS

Many kinds of plants and animals are capable of producing offspring by asexual as well as by sexual methods of reproduction. The primary distinction between the two kinds of reproduction is that sexual reproduction involves an alternation of meiosis and a fusion of gametes; asexual reproduction involves no meiosis and no fusion of gametes, but rather the formation of offspring from vegetative organs of the parent organism. Let us consider some examples of asexual reproduction in flowering plants.

ASEXUAL REPRODUCTION

Each spring, when farmers prepare "seed" potatoes for planting, they cut each potato into several pieces, each of which includes

one or more "eyes." The eyes are easy to see on the surface of the potato, since each one lies in a slight depression.

When the pieces of potato are planted, the eyes develop into leafy shoots, drawing upon the water, starch, and other nutrients stored in the piece of potato.

Soon roots appear at the lower end of each shoot, and before long the new plants are well established (Figure 17-1a). From one potato, quite a number of new plants can be propagated in this way.

In the mature banana plant, shoots (or "sword suckers") grow up to the surface of the ground from the underground stem (Figure 17-1b). These can be detached and planted. After a year or more they, too, will have developed into treelike plants bearing a large cluster of fruits.

In pineapple culture in Hawaii, "slips" and "suckers," which are shoots that develop below the fruit-bearing stalk, are similarly used for planting the next season's crop of pineapples.

Branches of raspberry bushes and many other kinds of shrubs may be bent and covered with soil—leaving only the ends of the branches exposed to air and light (Figure 17-1c). Soon roots form on the buried portions of the branches. When these become well established, the branches can be cut from the parent plants, and the new plants will continue to grow independently.

A leaf of *Bryophyllum* (bry·o·FIL·um), the so-called "life plant," has small indentations or notches around its edge. Older leaves of this plant may develop small plants, complete with roots, stem, and leaves, at every notch. If the leaves are placed on moist soil in a flowerpot, many of the tiny plants become established. During the early stages of growth they draw upon food and water stored in the thick, fleshy leaf (Figure 17-1d).

All of the examples we have described have two things in common. First, each of a number of single mature plants has pro-

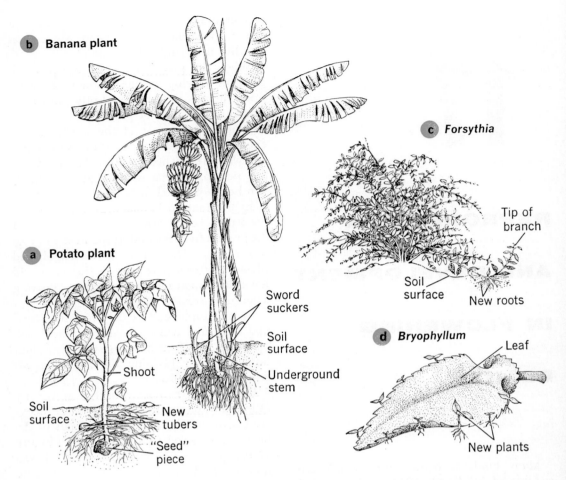

b Banana plant

c *Forsythia*

Tip of
branch

Soil
surface

New roots

a Potato plant

Sword
suckers

Soil
surface

Underground
stem

Shoot

Soil
surface

New
tubers

"Seed"
piece

d *Bryophyllum*

Leaf

New plants

17-1 Asexual reproduction in four flowering plants. **a** Potato growers prefer to plant pieces of potatoes, rather than seeds, from a good crop of the year before. Why? **b** Banana culture is based upon transplanting the "sword suckers" produced at the base of the stem. The seeds of the fruit are useless—nonfunctional—as you can demonstrate by trying to produce new plants from seeds of the next banana you eat. **c** Many plants, like *Forsythia*, take root at points where branches are in contact with the soil. Can you name other such plants? **d** Few people can name another plant like *Bryophyllum*, which produces new plants at notches in its leaves! Until they become established, the plants draw on the food supply of the leaf.

duced new plants genetically identical with the parent. Second, the new individuals came from plant parts produced solely by cell division (mitotic) and subsequent cell specialization. There was no meiosis and no fusion of gametes.

This type of asexual reproduction, called **vegetative propagation,** is extensively used in multiplying a wide variety of ornamental and crop plants. It has several advantages. Perhaps the most important one is that the offspring resemble the parent plant exactly, or nearly so. A farmer using a certain variety of seed potatoes finds that the new potatoes that he grows are almost identical to those which were used for seed. If he used seeds produced by potato flowers, his crop would show great variation, although all would be potatoes. Many would be of poor quality, and there would be marked differences in their size, thus reducing the value of the crop. The reasons for this will be clear to you when you have studied genetics (Chapters 30–33).

Vegetative propagation is used also for producing plants that for a variety of reasons are very difficult to grow from seed, or for which the time required to produce seed may be excessive. Some plants, such as bananas, certain kinds of grapes, and navel oranges, either never form fertile seeds or form no seeds at all. These plants must, therefore, be reproduced asexually.

SEXUAL REPRODUCTION

The story of the evolution of sexual reproduction in the Plant Kingdom has been considered in Chapters 12–14, where we have emphasized sexual reproduction as it occurs in fungi, algae, and primitive green land plants. Now let us examine the essentials of this process as it takes place in flowering plants.

There are approximately 250,000 species of flowering plants. With few exceptions, all of them give rise to seeds enclosed in fruits. Most of the plants with which you are familiar are flowering plants. Their variety is quite remarkable. They range in size from trees weighing many tons to tiny water plants about the size of a grain of rice. A stunted willow growing in the wastes of the Arctic, a giant cactus in the Arizona desert, an orchid plant perched high up on the branch of a jungle tree—all are flowering plants.

The Structure of a Flower

What is a flower, the characteristic structure possessed by all these plants? Most botanists interpret it as a specialized branch or stalk of the plant bearing groups of highly modified leaves at its tip. Variations in floral structure are almost endless. Indeed, it is impossible to speak of a typical flower. We can, however, imagine an idealized or generalized flower, which will illustrate basic features common, in one form or another, to many diverse groups of plants. In such a flower there are four different kinds of structures attached at successively higher levels of the flower stalk (Figure 17-2a). The lower and outermost parts, enclosing other floral parts, are the **sepals** (SEE·p'lz). They are usually green and closely resemble leaves. Attached just above these—and often extending at their upper ends beyond all the other flowering parts—are the **petals,** white or variously colored, and also usually leaflike in shape. Attached above the bases of the petals is a third group of highly modified structures, the **stamens** (STAY·menz), which in most cases hardly resemble leaves at all. Each stamen, a male reproductive structure, consists of a slender elongated stalk, the **filament,** and an expanded lobed structure at its tip, the **anther.** The anthers, as you will recall from Chapter 14, contain sacs in which large numbers of small pollen grains are formed. The uppermost point of attachment at the tip of the flower stalk, and in the center of the flower, is that of the **pistil.** This is the female reproductive structure. It is usually composed of three easily recognizable regions—an expanded tip, the **stigma;** an elongated **style;** and an enlarged base, the **ovary.** Within the ovary are one or more small structures, the **ovules,** which are attached by short stalks to the ovary wall.

How a Flower Functions

Let us trace the series of events beginning with a newly opened flower and ending with the development of mature fruits containing seeds. Although we have discussed some of the reproductive parts of flowers (see Chapter 14), we have not thus far described the steps in the sexual reproduction of a flowering plant.

An anther, when fully developed, usually consists of two elongated sacs containing pollen grains. As we learned in Chapter 14, these grains develop from uninucleate cells, which are monoploid spores produced by meiosis. As development proceeds, the nucleus in each one of these cells divides to form two daughter nuclei. At this stage in

THE LIFE CYCLE OF A FLOWERING PLANT

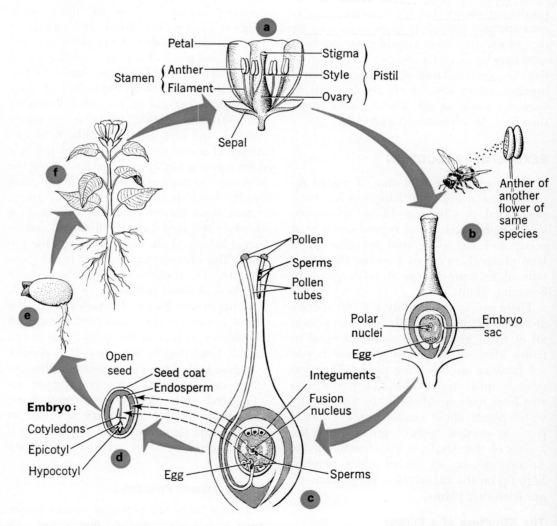

17-2 Shown in sequence for a generalized flowering plant are: **a** the flower; **b** pollination by an insect; **c** the interior of the pistil at the time of fertilization (a pollen tube has grown to the ovule, and double fertilization is about to take place); **d** the seed (the black arrows indicate that the seed coat is produced by the integuments of the ovule, the endosperm in the seed by the fertilized fusion nucleus, and the embryo by the fertilized egg); **e** the seedling; and **f** the mature plant, with flower.

pollen grain formation, the wall of each anther splits, forming openings through which the pollen grains can be shed (Figure 17-2b). Pollination is completed when pollen is then transferred to a stigma, by wind, water, or insect.

Cells on the surface of the stigma secrete a sticky nutrient fluid containing sugars and other substances. As pollen grains germinate on the stigma, each one produces a slender, thin-walled pollen tube (Figure 17-2c). This grows down through the tissues of the stigma, style, and ovary until it reaches the ovule. As the pollen tube develops, the two nuclei of the pollen grain move down into it. One of these nuclei divides again to form two somewhat elongated sperms (Figure 17-2c). The other nucleus is usually located near the tip of the pollen tube, with the two sperms following along behind. The pollen tube, as it reaches the ovule, grows through a small channel leading into the interior of the ovule (Figure 17-2c). What happens then? In order to find out, we must look into the structure of the ovule.

An ovule is an egg-shaped structure attached by a stalk to the inside of the ovary. Depending upon the species of plant involved, an ovary may have one, two, several, or even thousands of ovules. At the center of each ovule is a microscopic **embryo sac** (Figure 17-2b), filled with food and water. The embryo sac, composed of gametophyte cells, is the female gametophyte described in Chapter 14.

The majority of flowering plants have an embryo sac consisting of seven cells, two of which are important to our discussion. One is a large central cell containing two nuclei. These are called the **polar nuclei.** The other cell is the egg. It is located at the end of the embryo sac closest to the opening through which the pollen tube enters (Figure 17-2c).

Soon after the tip of the pollen tube enters the embryo sac, the end of the tube ruptures and releases the two sperms into the sac. One of the two sperms fuses with the egg to form a zygote. The zygote will develop into an embryonic plant within the ovule.

By the time the egg cell has been fertilized, the two polar nuclei have combined to form a single **fusion nucleus** (Figure 17-2c). Now the *second* sperm deposited in the embryo sac by the pollen tube moves to the center of the embryo sac and unites with the fusion nucleus. Fertilization of the fusion nucleus stimulates the formation of a new tissue—the endosperm—in which foods are stored as development of the ovule proceeds.

Union of one sperm with the egg, and the second sperm with the fusion nucleus, is called **double fertilization.** As far as we know, double fertilization occurs only in flowering plants.

After double fertilization, the ovule increases rapidly in size as a result of the formation of endosperm tissue and the development of the new embryo. The embryo consists of one or more **cotyledons** (kot·ih-LEE·dunz), an **epicotyl** (EP·ih·kot·'l), and a **hypocotyl** (HY·po·kot·'l) (see Figure 17-2d). Both the epicotyl and hypocotyl are parts of a rodlike axis attached to the cotyledons. The cotyledons digest and absorb the endosperm and make the stored food it contains available for the growth of the epicotyl and hypocotyl. The cotyledons of some flowering plants, beans for example, digest, absorb, and store the foods from the endosperm as the ovule is maturing into a seed. As a consequence, the cotyledons become greatly enlarged (full of stored food), as in Figure 17-3a, and the endosperm disappears more or less completely. In many other flowering plants (such as corn or castor bean), the endosperm tissue continues to grow as the ovule matures into a seed. Thus, in a corn grain, most of the seed is endosperm, and the embryo is located at one side (Figure 17-3b).

As an ovule matures into a seed, there are other changes in addition to the formation of an embryo and the accumulation of stored foods. The protective coverings (the integuments and sporangium), which surround the embryo sac, are transformed into a **seed coat.** The seed coats of many seed plants are tough, and they protect the enclosed embryonic plant from injury.

Depending upon the plant species involved, the walls of the fully formed fruit may be dry, resistant structures, or soft and fleshy. The outer covering of the corn grain, for example, is made up of the tough ovary wall fused to the seed coat of the single seed of the grain (Figure 17-3b). Examples of familiar fleshy fruits include the tomato,

orange, and peach. In the tomato, the ovary wall and the central tissues to which the seeds are attached are juicy and edible. In the case of the orange—typical of citrus fruits including the lime, lemon, and grapefruit—the outer wall of the fruit becomes leathery. The edible part, the pulp, is made up of juicy multicellular outgrowths of the inner layer of the ovary wall. The cell sap squeezed from these structures is orange juice, a rich source of sugars and vitamin C. In the peach, the inner layers of the ovary wall become transformed into hard stony tissues, the stone. The outer layers, by contrast, remain soft and juicy.

Variety Among Flowers

Our account of the structure of a flower and of the events leading to the development of fruits and seeds has been presented in a very general and abbreviated way. There are actually several thousand different types of flowers, many of which would seem to bear only a limited resemblance to the one shown in Figure 17-2a. Many of our common trees—maples, oaks, and hickories —have flowers in which the sepals and petals are either very inconspicuous or have disappeared entirely. In some plants, such as corn, there are *two* kinds of flowers. The flowers that develop in the tassels have stamens but no pistils. Those of the ears, borne lower down on the plant, are just the opposite, with pistils and no stamens.

Corn (maize) is a species of grass. Like all grasses, corn has its flowers modified for wind pollination (see Chapter 14). That is, the flowers do not have the attractive petals and nectar that guide insects to them. Instead, they have large feathery stigmas (the silks) and anthers (in the tassels) that produce abundant pollen. These characteristics help to insure pollination by wind. (Figure 17-4a shows pollen-producing flowers of another wind-pollinated plant.)

Insects and even birds, especially hummingbirds, are attracted by the showy

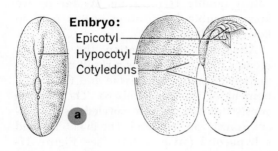

Embryo:
Epicotyl
Hypocotyl
Cotyledons

a

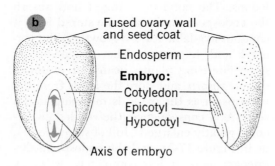

b

Fused ovary wall
and seed coat

Endosperm

Embryo:
Cotyledon
Epicotyl
Hypocotyl

Axis of embryo

17-3 **a** A bean seed and its parts. What is the origin of the thin seed coat? the stored food in the cotyledons? the embryo? **b** A corn grain and its parts. The endosperm (the stored food) is not a part of the embryo. The corn grain is really a fruit with a single seed inside. The seed has a single cotyledon.

All photos by Roche

a

b

c

d

17-4 Several kinds of flowers. **a** These flowers have stamens but no pistil. They are the pollen-producing flowers of a shrub closely related to witch hazel. Note the many anthers exposed to air currents. The wind carries the pollen to pistils of other flowers of the plant (or other plants of the species). **b** These insect-pollinated flowers of the butterfly bush are part of an inflorescence of many small flowers on a single stalk. **c** The Easter lily is an example of the flower of a *monocotyledonous* plant. There are 3 sepals and 3 petals, all of which look very much alike in the mature flower. There are 6 stamens and a 3-part compound pistil. **d** The passion flower is an example of the flower of a *dicotyledonous* plant. There are 5 sepals and 5 petals. Here, too, sepals and petals look very much alike in the mature flower. Five stamens and a compound pistil occupy the center of the flower.

17-5 COMPARISON OF DICOTS AND MONOCOTS

Dicot	**Monocot**

Two cotyledons	One cotyledon

Leaves with network of veins	Leaves with parallel veins

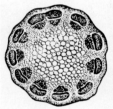 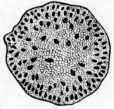

Stems with vascular cambium and with vascular bundles in a ring	Stems without vascular cambium and with scattered vascular bundles

Flower parts in 4's or 5's or multiples of 4 or 5	Flower parts in 3's or multiples of 3

parts of many flowers (Figure 17-4b). In one species of orchid, the pollen-producing anthers bear a superficial resemblance to the female of a species of bee. Male bees of this species, seeing these "reasonable facsimiles," fly to the flower and try to mate with it. In the process the bees pick up pollen from the flower, and then carry it to the next orchid.

The reproductive structures of flowering plants are an aid in their identification and classification. For example, we find that many flowers resemble a lily or an iris in having their floral parts in threes or multiples of three (Figure 17-4c), and in having a single cotyledon in their seeds. All flowering plants with these characteristics are placed in a group called the **monocotyledons** (mon·o·kot·ih·LEE·dunz). We call them the **monocots** (MON·o·kots) for short.

The majority of flowering plants have their floral parts in twos or fives or some multiple of these numbers (Figure 17-4d). Their seeds have two cotyledons, and for this reason they are called the **dicotyledons** (dy·kot·ih·LEE·dunz) or **dicots** (DY·kots).

A summary of these and other differences between monocots and dicots is presented in Figure 17-5.

DEVELOPMENT

A hundred seeds taken from the cones of a giant California redwood can be held in the palm of your hand. Each, under favorable circumstances, may develop into a tremendous tree—the largest living thing the world has ever known. Each of these small seeds contains a hereditary pattern that, when translated through processes of development, results in a huge plant with hundreds of branches bearing millions of leaves. Extending into the soil from the base of the massive trunk are large woody roots, which branch and rebranch, finally ending in many millions of slender, pointed root tips.

Key:

I Parts derived from hypocotyl of embryo

II Parts derived from epicotyl of embryo

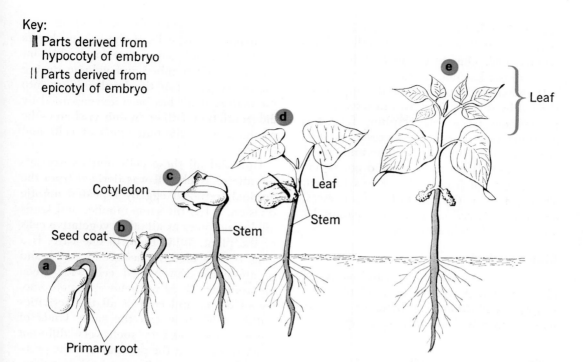

Cotyledon

Leaf

Seed coat

Stem

Stem

Leaf

Primary root

17-6 Stages in germination of a bean seed. In sequence, the stages are: **a** establishment of the root system in the soil; **b** elevation of the remainder of the seedling above ground; **c** shedding of the seed coat; **d** enlargement of the first true leaves of the epicotyl; and **e** establishment of the plant as a completely autotrophic individual, after the stored food of the cotyledons has been consumed.

Growth

How does so much growth and development come about? The answer in terms of growth can be stated, in a general way, very simply—but the search for a *complete* answer is the major concern of thousands of biologists working in laboratories all over the world. Let us consider the simple answer to our question by observing what happens when a bean seed germinates. If you wish, you can take the opportunity in the laboratory or at home to grow seeds of many kinds of plants. In each case you can see that growth starts with the formation of a slender primary root (Figure 17-6), which breaks through the seed coat. If we look for the origin of this primary root, we can see that it has been formed by the enlargement and elongation of the hypocotyl of the

seed. But why has there been an increase in size? How has *growth* of the root occurred? The answer is twofold.

All of the tissues of the embryo of a bean —the epicotyl, hypocotyl, and cotyledons— are made up of cells. These cells originated by repeated divisions, starting with the first division of the zygote. When the bean seed matured and became dry, the cell divisions ceased. If the seed is supplied with water, however, the cell divisions will begin again. With renewal of cell divisions, we might expect growth to occur—but stop and think for a moment. Does it necessarily follow that if cells divide and increase in number there will be any increase in size?

A cell, by repeated division, may give rise to 2, 4, 8, 16, and even more descendant cells. If each one remains the same size as it was after division, the combined volume of the cells will be equal only to that of the original cell. One brick divided into four smaller ones has not increased in volume.

If, however, each one of the new cells formed by division increases in size, the total volume of the cells resulting from the divisions will necessarily increase. A full-grown bean plant has a volume millions of times greater than that of the original fertilized egg cell from which it was formed. Thus, growth is the result of two processes, *an increase in cell number* accompanied by *an increase in volume of cells.*

Differentiation

Now let us consider a further aspect of development. A mature bean plant is not simply a collection of millions of cells, all like the zygote. Instead it is composed of

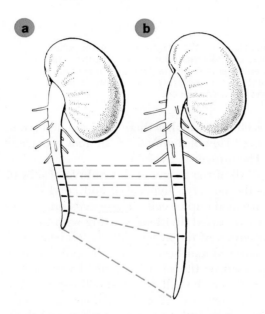

17-7 An experiment on comparative regions of growth in the root of a bean seedling. **a** India ink marks are placed on the root at equal intervals. **b** As the root grows, rapid changes appear in the spacing of some of the ink marks. Why do the lines marked near the tip become so much more widely separated than those farther removed from the tip?

many different types of cells—tracheids and companion cells, cells of the spongy layers of the leaf, and many more kinds. The increase in cell number and volume during the development of the fertilized egg into the mature plant has been accompanied by **differentiation** (dif·er·en·shih·AY·shun)—the production of different *kinds* of cells and tissues.

How did all these cells and tissues differentiate? Each cell was derived from the original fertilized egg by repeated mitotic division; it has the same number and kinds of chromosomes as all other vegetative cells of the plant. Why, then, in one case, is a long, thick-walled tracheid cell formed, and in another a thin-walled cell with green chloroplasts? If, as we believe, the chromosomes direct and control all the activities within cells, how can the same kinds of chromosomes lead to such very different kinds of cells? At the present time the problem remains essentially unsolved, but thousands of research workers are seeking an answer.

Development of the Root

Let us examine the development of a root in the light of what we know about growth and differentiation. Suppose we take a germinating bean and, using India ink, place a series of equally spaced marks along its root (Figure 17-7a). We then place it, root tip down, between layers of moist cotton. After a day or two we again examine it. Changes in the spacing of the ink marks (Figure 17-7b) tell us that most of the increase in length has taken place close to the tip.

If growing roots are examined, three distinct regions can be distinguished (Figure 17-8a). The first of these is covered by the root cap, which protects a group of thin-walled, small cells having relatively large nuclei and small vacuoles. Cells in this region divide rapidly. Immediately above this region is a zone in which the cells are in-

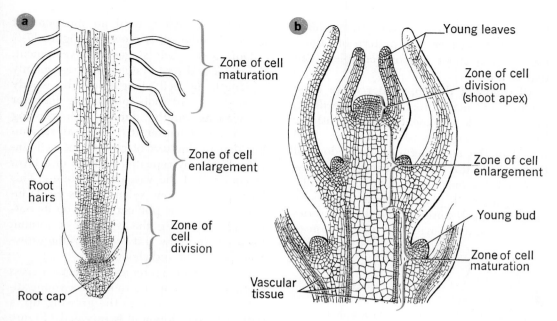

17-8 **a** A longitudinal section of a root tip. How well do the zones of growth and differentiation correlate with the changes in spacing of India ink marks on the root of Figure 17-7b? **b** A longitudinal section of a stem tip. Notice the correspondence between the zones here and in the root at the left. The differentiation of vascular tissue appears to take place independently in the stem and in the young leaves.

creasing in size, primarily as a result of elongation. In a third region, lying farthest from the root tip, cells are reaching their maximum size and undergoing differentiation into the various cell types of the epidermis, cortex, and central conducting cylinder (see Chapter 16). Thus, as we "read" what we see in the root from the tip upward, we see the processes of cell division, cell enlargement, and cell differentiation producing the tissues that the seedling root will have as a mature root.

Shortly after the primary root becomes well established, branch roots make their appearance from older portions of the primary root. Branch roots originate from cells deep within the primary root (Figure 16-7, page 309).

When a seed germinates, the seedling root system develops rapidly and precedes the growth of the shoot (stem and leaves). From the standpoint of survival, the root system *must* be established first to supply water for growth and to anchor the plant. But what determines that the root system will develop before the shoot? What coordinates this and other events in the growth of a plant? These questions, like others we have raised, remain unanswered for the present.

Development of the Shoot

After the root system of a seedling has become established, the epicotyl of the embryo grows rapidly to form a stem on which leaves and branches are produced. A growing region, basically similar to that at the tip of a root, is found at the tip of the developing stem. In addition to forming cells of the stem, the growing tip forms cells which become differentiated into cells of leaves and branches (Figure 17-8b). Unlike the internally produced branch roots, the branches and leaves of a stem originate from superficial cells of the young shoot. Thus, at its surface, the pattern of organization of a shoot is more complex than that of a root.

All stages of development require large amounts of energy. In the young seedling, prior to the development of photosynthetic structure, energy is derived from food stored in the endosperm or cotyledons of the seed. By the time this energy supply is depleted, the first leaves have usually fully developed, and photosynthesis has commenced. This beautifully coordinated series of events, starting with the germination of a seed and lasting until an independent plant is produced, is shown in Figure 17-6.

During the early stages of development, the shoot and root systems increase mainly in length, by cell elongation. The woody dicot stems and roots increase in diameter (as well as length) during each growing season (see Chapter 16). You may remember that in this sort of growth the cells involved arise by repeated division of a layer of cells called the vascular cambium. This layer produces new xylem tissues on its inner side and new phloem tissues on its outer side. How is the vascular cambium formed? And how is it related to the growing tips of root and shoot?

If we examine under a microscope a cross section through an internode of a young dicot stem, made close to the growing tip, a pattern of development is revealed (Figure 17-9a). Strands of elongated but incompletely differentiated cells are arranged in a circle embedded in tissues of cortex and pith. At this level in the stem, all tissues are *primary tissues* formed by the differentiation of cells that originate from the growing tip of the stem. As development continues, the strands of elongated cells differentiate into vascular tissue. Cells of the outer region of each strand become primary phloem, and inner cells differentiate into primary xylem (Figure 17-9b). Between the primary xylem and phloem of each strand there remains a thin layer of cells that retain their capacity to divide and produce new cells. This layer is the vascular cambium. It gradually extends laterally between the adjacent vascular bundles, until it eventually forms a continuous ring of cambium (Figure 17-9c). Tissues derived from the vascular cambium are called *secondary tissues*. Thus, the layer of new xylem formed just inside the vascular cambium is *secondary xylem*, and the layer of phloem formed just outside the cambium is *secondary phloem*. The accumulation of secondary tissues, especially the secondary xylem, results in

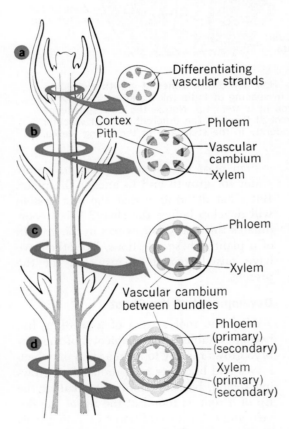

Differentiating vascular strands

Cortex
Pith

Phloem

Vascular cambium

Xylem

Phloem

Xylem

Vascular cambium between bundles

Phloem
(primary)
(secondary)

Xylem
(primary)
(secondary)

17-9 Part of a stem diagramed in longitudinal section and in four cross sections. At intervals from the tip, note the increasing complexity as the vascular cambium develops into a complete ring of cells producing secondary xylem and phloem.

an increase in the diameter of the dicot stem (Figure 17-9d).

The stems of monocots usually do not have cambium. In these plants all tissues of the root and the shoot are primary tissues, formed from cells produced at the growing tips, or from dividing cells located at the nodes.

Although we have not offered any explanation of factors regulating the development of a plant from a seed, we have shown that the stages in development of a plant are coordinated. If the coordinated events occur where there is plenty of water, oxygen, carbon dioxide, light, and a suitable temperature, then we can expect the plant to grow and finally reproduce. Like all living things, plants adjust to their environment. Thus their leaves may become oriented more favorably to the sunlight, or their roots may grow toward a greater supply of water and salts. If we understand the factors that help plants adjust themselves to their environment, we will have some insight into factors that regulate growth.

Plants Respond to Their Environment

A farmer planting a field of soy beans pours the bean seeds into the hopper of a machine called a drill. The drill digs shallow furrows, distributes the seeds along them, and then covers the seeds with a thin layer of soil. A week or two later, the first plants appear above the ground. Although the seeds, when dropped into the furrow, were buried in every conceivable position, only the shoots and never the roots appear above the ground.

Why do shoots grow up and roots grow down? To ask the question sounds a bit silly, for everyone knows that this is the way things are! But science advances when scientists wonder why—and investigate why —the obvious things happen. As a result of a large number of experiments conducted long ago—experiments some of which may

be repeated by you in the laboratory—it was demonstrated that a plant is oriented with respect to gravitational attraction. Roots of young plants tend to grow down toward the earth's center. Their shoots, by contrast, grow upward, or away from gravity. The force of gravity provides a stimulus that acts from one direction. It is a "one-sided," or unilateral, stimulus. How could this be determined by experiment? Obviously, since the earth's gravity cannot be eliminated, some way of equalizing it, or producing still bigger forces like those of gravity, must have been used. Can you think of one? Yes, rotation would do. Try to devise such an experiment.

The response that a plant makes to a stimulus is called a **tropism** (TROH.piz'm). Because gravity is the stimulus in this case, the responses of the bean seedlings are termed **geotropisms** (jee.oh.TROH.piz'mz— Figure 17-10a). The roots growing toward the stimulus are said to be *positively* geotropic, and the shoots growing away from it are *negatively* geotropic.

If we take a young plant growing in a pot and put it in a completely dark room, its stem will continue to grow straight up. Now, if we place the plant at one end of the room and an electric light at the other, the region of the stem just below the growing tip will begin to grow in such a way that the tip of the stem is directed toward the light. In this case the stimulus is light. We say that the shoot is positively **phototropic** (foh.toh.TROH.pic—Figure 17-10b).

Mechanisms of Plant Responses

Although geotropic and phototropic responses were recognized and described well over a hundred years ago, the mechanisms involved are still being investigated. As long ago as 1880, Charles Darwin, together with his son Francis, performed a series of experiments on the growth curvature of grass seedlings. These seedlings, like our potted plant, were placed in a dark room and exposed to a single source of light placed some distance to one side of them. If the tips of the seedlings were protected from the light by covering them with tiny caps made of tin foil, there was no curvature. If the tips were exposed but other parts of the seedlings were shaded, curvature toward the light resulted. These observations, together with other experiments that involved *removing* the tips rather than shading them, indicated that the tips of the stems were the regions that reacted to the light, that is, received the stimulus. The actual curvature, however, occurred some distance below the tips.

In attempting to explain these observations, Darwin hypothesized that some kind of an excitation was produced in the tip of the seedling and then transferred to the tissues below it, where the growth response was observed. We now have conclusive experimental evidence that a chemical substance is actually involved. The first part of a young grass seedling to appear above the ground is a slender, pointed sheath, the **coleoptile** (koh·le·OP·til), which surrounds

and protects the young leaves curled up within it. If the tip of the coleoptile is cut off, further elongation ceases in 15 to 20 minutes. If the tip is cut off and then subsequently replaced, growth is once more resumed (Figure 17-11a). If a decapitated coleoptile is exposed to light from one side only, no curvature toward the light occurs. If the tip, which has been removed, is again placed on top of the coleoptile, the coleoptile will grow in the direction of the light (Figure 17-11b).

A Danish biologist, Boysen Jensen, in 1910 described a series of experiments which showed that the stimulus causing these growth responses would pass through a layer of gelatin placed between the restored tip and the rest of the coleoptile. Gelatin is a material through which substances dissolved in water will diffuse read-

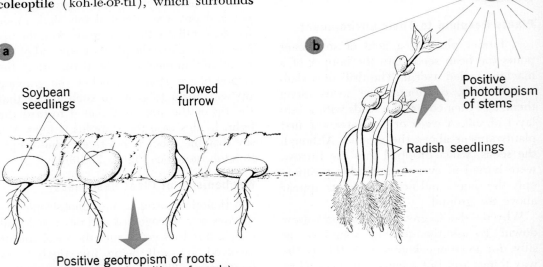

Light source

a

Soybean seedlings

Plowed furrow

Positive geotropism of roots (independent of position of seeds)

b

Positive phototropism of stems

Radish seedlings

17-10 **a** Bean seedlings showing a response to gravity. No matter what the positions of the seeds, the roots always grow downward. Why? **b** Radish seedlings showing a response to light. If the illumination is from one side only, the seedlings all grow toward that side. How do the stems manage to change position so readily?

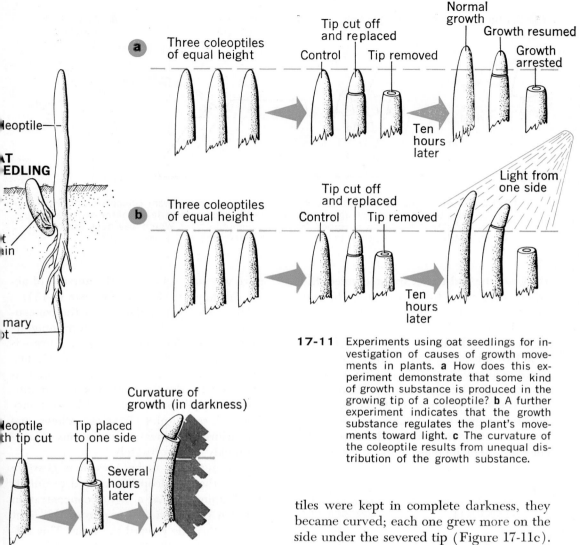

a Three coleoptiles of equal height

Tip cut off and replaced

Control | Tip removed

Normal growth

Growth resumed

Growth arrested

Ten hours later

b Three coleoptiles of equal height

Tip cut off and replaced

Control | Tip removed

Ten hours later

Light from one side

Curvature of growth (in darkness)

Coleoptile with tip cut | Tip placed to one side

Several hours later

Coleoptile

WHEAT SEEDLING

Grain

Primary root

17-11 Experiments using oat seedlings for investigation of causes of growth movements in plants. **a** How does this experiment demonstrate that some kind of growth substance is produced in the growing tip of a coleoptile? **b** A further experiment indicates that the growth substance regulates the plant's movements toward light. **c** The curvature of the coleoptile results from unequal distribution of the growth substance.

ily. If, however, the experiment was repeated with a thin layer of impervious mica substituted for the gelatin, all growth responses ceased. Apparently a substance causing cells to elongate was produced in the tip, from which it diffused to the growth regions directly below the tip.

Somewhat later, in 1919, another biologist experimented with decapitated coleoptiles. In this case, the tip of each coleoptile was replaced in lopsided fashion, toward one side of the base. Although the coleop-

tiles were kept in complete darkness, they became curved; each one grew more on the side under the severed tip (Figure 17-11c).

Finally, in 1928, F. W. Went, an American botanist of Dutch origin, developed experimental methods for obtaining the substance responsible for these growth reactions. He also developed methods for measuring the concentration of the growth substance. He did this by cutting off a number of tips and placing them on a thin layer of solid agar (Figure 17-12a and b). Gradually the substance produced by the tips diffused into the agar. The tips were then removed and the agar cut up into small blocks (Figure 17-12c). These blocks could

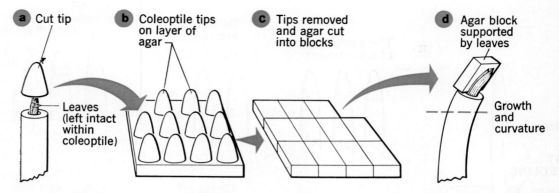

a Cut tip

b Coleoptile tips on layer of agar

c Tips removed and agar cut into blocks

d Agar block supported by leaves

Leaves (left intact within coleoptile)

Growth and curvature

17-12 An experimental method for obtaining growth substance from coleoptile tips. How does the final test—an agar block on a decapitated coleoptile—confirm that growth substance has been absorbed from the coleoptile tips? Which way does the coleoptile grow in response to the one-sided placement of the agar block?

then be attached to decapitated coleoptiles, where they were found to cause the same kinds of growth responses as the original tips (Figure 17-12d).

What would happen if the concentration of active substance was doubled by placing twice as many coleoptile tips on a layer of agar? Again the agar was cut into blocks, and Went discovered that the increased amount of growth substance caused an increase in the curvature of the decapitated coleoptile. The increase in the angle of curv-

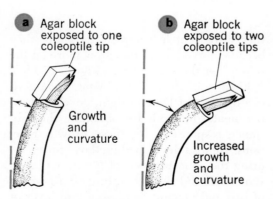

a Agar block exposed to one coleoptile tip

Growth and curvature

b Agar block exposed to two coleoptile tips

Increased growth and curvature

17-13 An experiment for measuring relative concentration of growth substance. The observed angle of curvature is proportional to the amount of growth substance in the agar blocks. Of what value is a bioassay such as this?

ature was proportional to the amount of active substance in the agar (Figure 17-13).

This technique of measuring the concentration of a substance—by determining its quantitative effect on a living organism—is an example of a **bioassay** (by·o·a·SAY). The active substance, called **auxin** (AUK·sin), is produced by the tip in very small quantities, too small to be measured by ordinary chemical techniques. Bioassay allows one to measure very low concentrations of auxin quickly and accurately.

By using these techniques, it is possible to show that a coleoptile exposed to unilateral illumination has a higher concentration of auxin on the side *away* from the light than on the side toward the light. This difference in the distribution of auxin is responsible for the greater rate of elongation of cells on the darker side, which causes curvature toward the light (Figure 17-14).

The geotropic responses of the root and shoot have also been shown to be caused by differences in auxin distribution. If a young seedling is placed in a horizontal position, auxin will accumulate in the cells located on its lower side. This results in a greater elongation of the cells of the shoot on that side, and causes an upward curvature of the shoot. The root cells show just the opposite reaction. In this case, cells of the upper side of the root elongate more rapidly and cause the root to curve downward. How can this difference be explained? If we compare the growth of root and shoot tissues exposed to different concentrations of auxin, we find that root cells are much more sensitive than shoot cells to this substance. Concentrations of auxin, which stimulate elongation in the shoot, actually inhibit it in the root. Thus, the root shows a positive geotropic curvature, while the shoot shows just the opposite response.

Growth Substances

It has been conclusively demonstrated that auxin is **indole** (IN·dohl) **acetic acid** (IAA). There are several suggestions about how IAA acts in the plant to regulate the elongation of cells. Certain concentrations of IAA are known to affect the plasticity of the cell wall. Cells with more plastic cell walls will elongate more than those with less plastic walls. Thus IAA, by affecting plasticity, affects elongation. IAA may also regulate the degree of permeability of cell membranes to water.

IAA is of practical importance. It is used to stimulate the formation of roots in cuttings that are difficult to propagate. The IAA is applied in low concentrations to the lower end of the cutting. The auxin stimulates the production of root-forming tissues from the cut surface. By this method it is possible to "root" cuttings of yew, holly, and many other valuable ornamental plants that are otherwise difficult to propagate.

Within the last thirty or so years, a number of different compounds have been discovered which can bring about plant growth. These substances, which are of considerable practical importance, can be synthesized at relatively low cost, and like the naturally occurring IAA, they are effective when used in very low concentrations.

One such compound is **naphthalene acetic acid** (NAA). It is extensively used to

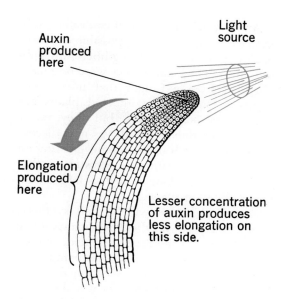

17-14 The nature of the growth response in a stem or coleoptile. Unequal elongation of cells results from unequal concentration of auxin. The auxin content is higher on the shaded side. As a result, the cells on that side elongate more than the cells on the illuminated side.

prevent sprouting of potatoes during storage. Whereas untreated potatoes frequently begin to sprout after several months' storage, NAA inhibits the development of the eyes, or buds, so that the treated potatoes may in some cases be kept in good condition for as long as three years.

Some varieties of apple trees lose a sizable proportion of their developing fruits because of premature development of the separation layer, a zone of thin-walled cells at the base of the stem which attaches each apple to a branch. Fruits that fall from the tree early are bruised as they hit the ground and are of little value. Spraying the trees with NAA avoids most of this loss.

Flowering in pineapples can also be controlled by applying NAA to the growing plants in low concentrations. This treatment causes the plants to produce flowers and fruit several weeks early.

The image caption within the figure reads:

Light source

Auxin produced here

Elongation produced here

Lesser concentration of auxin produces less elongation on this side.

Another group of growth-controlling substances being studied for possible extensive use in agriculture are the **gibberellins** (jib-er·EL·inz). These substances were originally obtained from a fungus that infects rice plants in Japan. The infected plants are taller than normal ones, but they rarely flower or produce seed. It was next discovered that cultures of the fungus growing on artificial media contained substances that stimulate stem elongation in a large number of different plants.

One of the most widely used synthetic compounds is **2,4-dichlorophenoxyacetic** (dy·klo·ro·fe·nok·see·a·SEE·tic) **acid,** mercifully abbreviated to 2,4-D. This compound, in contrast to the others mentioned above, is employed to kill plants, for it makes their growth wildly abnormal. It is highly poisonous to a wide variety of broad-leaved plants, including many common weeds. Proper concentrations of this substance added to lawns or cornfields will kill unwanted weeds without harming the grasses. 2,4-D is poisonous to animals and human beings when sufficiently concentrated, so it must be used with care!

Today, through the use of auxin or another appropriate growth substance, it is possible to control the patterns of growth and development of many of our most important food plants and to eliminate unwanted plants that compete with them for light, water, and mineral nutrients.

As we have seen, the development of a flowering plant, from the first step of seed germination to the final production of a mature, reproductive organism that produces more seeds, involves many factors and mechanisms about which we know very little. It has been discovered, however, that some growth responses and patterns of development are controlled by auxin or other growth-regulating substances. These substances are responsible for bringing about coordinated development of the plant as a whole.

CONCLUDING REMARKS

Before we leave our study of plants, let us look backward, in a very general way, at what we have covered. In Chapters 12 through 17, emphasis has been placed on the structures of flowering plants (their leaves, stems, roots, and flowers) as well as the functions these structures perform. We have discussed the remarkable adaptations of these structures to the special features of the environments in which they perform their functions. For example, green leaves have stomata and spongy cells that admit carbon dioxide from the atmosphere; roots have root hairs that absorb water from the soil; roots, stems, and leaves have vascular tissue that transports needed materials throughout the plant; and flowers may have colorful petals that attract insects from the surrounding environment.

The world around us, the environment, is constantly changing. Consequently, the plants must continually readjust and readapt to their environments in order to survive. Plants have not always inhabited the land. In the early stages of their evolution they were confined to water. Over long periods of time, they have evolved and become adapted to a wide variety of environments on land as well as in the seas. We have followed their evolution (Chapters 12 through 14), emphasizing only the major steps, from the primitive aquatic ancestors to the most highly evolved land plants—the flowering plants.

As evolution proceeded, the delicate balance between organisms and their environment had to be maintained if there was to be survival. An excellent example of this was seen in the evolution of guard cells surrounding stomata in the leaves of green plants (Chapter 15). In the manufacture of food, green plants take carbon dioxide from the atmosphere through their stomata. However, stomata are normally open only during the day, when light is available as the energy for photosynthesis. At night, the guard cells close the stomata and reduce the rate of water loss from the plant.

In the balance of organisms and their environment, we have stressed the importance of plants and the dependence of animals on them for food and shelter. Not infrequently, however, we find that plants and animals are actually **interdependent.** In these cases, neither can live, or live so well, without the other. For example, we have seen how essential the insects, especially bees, are to pollination. At the same time, the flowering plants are essential to the bees, which use the nectar and pollen for food. How did this "togetherness" between members of the Plant Kingdom and Animal Kingdom come about? Certainly in the case of bees and flowers, evolution did not proceed independently in the two organisms.

First there must have been flying insects —perhaps the remote ancestors of bees. Next, plants with parts in some way attractive to flying insects must have evolved. These would have been the first steps in the evolution of the insect-flower relationship. Subsequently, some insects evolved to the point of becoming completely dependent on nectar and pollen for their food. The advantages of cross-pollination then led to the selection of floral structures that "directed" the insect from the male part of one flower to the female part of another. The result of this coordinated evolution of certain plants and animals is seen in many flowers, which only certain insects can pollinate. It is seen in the bees with their highly specialized structures and behavior for collecting and processing pollen and nectar.

We have purposely picked this extreme example of the interdependence of plants and animals in order to remind you forcefully of the meaning of biology. Biology is not merely the study of plants or the study of animals. *Biology is the science of life in all of its forms and relationships.*

GUIDE QUESTIONS AND PROBLEMS

1. What are the advantages of vegetative propagation:
   a. to the plants that reproduce in this way?
   b. to man in the cultivation of plants that can be propagated in this way?
2. What is the role of the pollen tube in the reproduction of flowering plants?
3. What are the results of the double fertilization that occurs in the ovule?
4. What is a seed? a fruit?
5. What are the advantages of cross-pollination? the disadvantages?
6. What facts are revealed about growth and differentiation through observation of the growth of a young bean plant?
7. What is the source of the energy required for the growth and development of a young plant?
8. What is vascular cambium tissue? How is it related to the growth and differentiation of the plant stem?
9. How did Charles Darwin use controlled experiments in his study of the sensitivity of plants to light?
10. What was Went's technique for measuring the relative amount of auxin?
11. What are some of the practical uses of auxin and synthetic growth substances in farming and in horticulture?

SUGGESTIONS FOR ADDITIONAL READING

Books

Galston, A. W., *Life of the Green Plant.* Foundations of Modern Biology Series. Englewood Cliffs (N. J.), Prentice-Hall, 1961.
   A concise account of plant growth and differentiation.

Magazines and Journals

Biale, J. B., "The Ripening of Fruit." *Scientific American,* Vol. 190 (May 1954), pp. 40–44.
Naylor, A. W., "The Control of Flowering." *Scientific American,* Vol. 186 (May 1952), pp. 49–56.
Salisbury, F. B., "Plant Growth Substances." *Scientific American,* Vol. 196 (April 1957), pp. 125–30.

DIVERSITY

18

THE WORLD

OF ANIMALS

We have now reached the point where we can begin a meaningful discussion of the Animal Kingdom. This is *our* kingdom. It was advisable, however, to postpone our consideration of animals until we had learned about bacteria, fungi, and green plants, for without these organisms there could be no animal life. It is the green plants that synthesize the organic compounds that are necessary for the maintenance and growth of animals. It is the bacteria that are essential in keeping the nitrogen cycle in operation. Bacteria and fungi are the decomposers.

Thus the bacteria, fungi, and green plants are essential for animal life. We, and all other animals, are here, so to speak, "by courtesy of the bacteria, fungi, and green plants." The plants, our silent companions of the living world, are more important than we may generally think.

Before we begin our detailed study of the Animal Kingdom, let us look at some of the ways animals and plants are alike—and different.

Where Animals and Plants Live

We learned that plants are found nearly everywhere. This is true also of animals. Wherever it is neither too hot nor too cold, and wherever moisture and the proper chemicals are found, there you can find animals and plants. Most of the surface of the earth—land, water, and air—is inhabited by plants and animals (Figure 18-1).

But there are some spots where we find very little life. In the south polar regions, which are covered largely by ice, there is not much life. Although we can find species of both plants and animals that live exposed to the hot noonday sun in Death Valley, their number and variety are quite limited.

The farther we travel from the warm and shallow seas in which we suspect life once originated, or from the warm and moist areas of tropical rain forests, the fewer living forms we find.

In the depths of the oceans, the absence of light makes it difficult for animals and plants to survive. Of course, there can be no green plants there because darkness makes photosynthesis impossible. Almost no green plants are found in water deeper than 100 meters. Bacteria and fungi, however, have been recorded from the deepest parts of the ocean. The same is true of animals.

Biologists using specially designed ships have explored many parts of the oceans. They have used nets and dredges to collect organisms from various depths as well as from the bottom. An astounding assortment of marine animals have been discovered in this way, and they live in an astounding environment. Here there is no light, save for an occasional flash of a luminous fish, darting around like a firefly of the ocean's depths. Here there are no seasons. At great depths the water is always near freezing, even in the tropics.

Perpetual darkness and perpetual cold—how is life possible there? What is the

18-1 The world of life. The forces of evolution have perfected species that live almost everywhere on land and in the oceans. Life is most abundant in the upper 100 meters of the oceans, and on land from sea level to an altitude of 3,000 meters. But even

source of energy? There can be no energy of the sun's rays to be used in synthesizing the energy-rich glucose molecule. Yet there are animals that live in these depths (Figure 18-2) and bacteria that decompose them when they are dead. The animals survive in a strange way. They are, so to speak, garbage feeders. Their food chain begins in the surface waters, where the sun's light permits the growth of algae. The small animals of the surface layers feed on the algae. Larger animals eat the smaller animals. Eventually the animals of the surface layers die. Some are eaten on the spot, but a few drift down into the world of darkness. It is this slow rain of corpses that provides food for the animals of the depths.

No organisms live solely in the air. Some animals of today, as of the past, such as insects, extinct flying reptiles, bats, and birds, may invade the air for varying lengths of time. But these flying animals return to the earth's surface to feed or to rest. No plant lives solely in the air, though the seeds and spores of some of them are blown from place to place.

Man can escape from his normal environment and travel into the stratosphere or into the depths of the sea only within a strong capsule containing air of nearly the same pressure, temperature, and chemical composition as that to which he is accustomed. He has to take his environment with him.

Some think that man's great success as an animal stems from his ability to use this idea. Cave shelters, fires for warmth, clothes, huts, houses, submarines, and jet planes are all used or designed in such a way as to make a small part of the environment more suitable for human existence.

Some Conditions for Life

Although plants and animals inhabit extensive areas of the surface of the earth, they evidently thrive best where the physi-

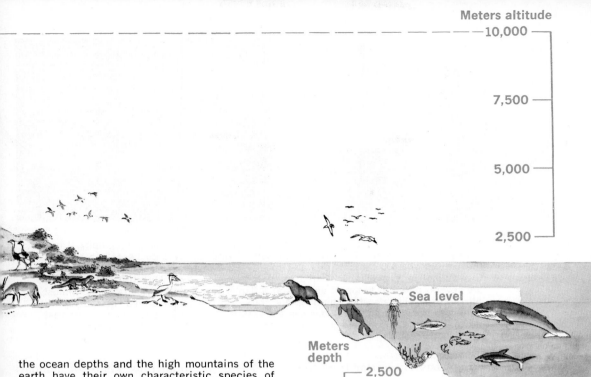

Meters altitude

10,000

7,500

5,000

2,500

Sea level

Meters depth

2,500

5,000

7,500

10,000

12,500

the ocean depths and the high mountains of the earth have their own characteristic species of microorganisms, plants, and animals.

cal environment provides certain things. It must offer a constant and sufficient supply of water. Oxygen, too, must be plentiful. In addition, plants must have supplies of carbon dioxide and nitrogen compounds in order to manufacture glucose, amino acids, and all other organic compounds necessary for their existence. And animals must have plants or other animals to feed upon.

Oxygen and carbon dioxide can be found in the air and dissolved in water. Partly because of this, animals and plants may live either surrounded by air or surrounded by water. In the air, however, they face the problem of losing water. In terrestrial plants and animals the loss of water is controlled in part by the nature of the outer layer of the organism. This layer, of which our own skin is an example, is always partly or completely impermeable to water. Organisms living in water itself avoid this problem. Their outer coverings are often freely permeable to water.

Other conditions of the environment must remain fairly constant for life to exist. These are conditions that tend to keep constant the chemical reactions upon which living things depend. Most of these reactions occur at temperatures between 0° and

THE WORLD OF ANIMALS **339**

Lamont Geological Observatory of Columbia University

18-2 Life in the depths of the oceans. The light was supplied for photography; these animals live in total darkness. On the left is what appears to be a "tea bag" at the bottom of 2,600 fathoms of water (nearly 4,800 meters, or 15,600 feet). Probably this animal is a sponge, anchored to the ocean floor by a long tuft. On the right are several different kinds of animals at a depth approaching 2,900 fathoms. Almost all of these animals—the small brittle stars and the larger animal at the right— belong to the group that includes sea stars (starfish). (In both photographs note that all the animals shown have a means of "standing" above the soft, deep sediments.)

40° C. We do not have to go far from the surface of the earth to encounter temperatures that living things cannot endure. To some extent, changes in air pressure also affect the rates at which chemical reactions occur. In man, for example, if the air pressure is very low, sufficient hemoglobin does not combine with oxygen to allow a person to live. This becomes a problem for individuals climbing mountains. Most persons feel the effects of insufficient oxygen at altitudes above 4000 meters (13,000–14,000 feet).

Thus, living things can remain alive only if they can obtain the necessary chemical substances as sources of energy and for the synthesis of their living substance. They must have a fairly uniform range of temperature and air pressure. Is there, then, life on planets other than earth? We do not really know, but many scientists believe that the answer is Yes. The astronomers tell us that the number of celestial bodies is tremendous. Some of these may be like our earth. If so, perhaps life could have started on one of these remote worlds.

There are numerous kinds of animals and plants occupying the many habitats of the earth's surface. Algae, bacteria, fungi, fishes, whales, seals, shellfish, worms, and many other types of animals are found in the oceans. Trees, mushrooms, mosses, ferns, flowering plants, birds, mammals, salamanders, snakes, insects, spiders, and other organisms occur in the forests. The prairies have numerous grasses and other plants as well as distinctive kinds of animals. Lakes, rivers, and ponds have their own species of animals and plants.

It has been estimated that there are somewhere between two million and ten million species of plants and animals on the earth today. Biologists believe they have a reasonably satisfactory explanation for this diversity. Over the course of time, natural selection, acting on gene mutations, has given rise to the many species, all similar in some ways (Figure 18-3), but each adapted for a particular way of life. We have referred to this process of evolution before, and we shall return to consider it more fully in Chapters 34–38.

18-3 PLANTS AND ANIMALS—LIKE OR UNLIKE?

SIMILARITIES	DIFFERENCES	
Plant and animal	Plant	Animal
Both types of organisms are made of cells, with nuclei, nucleoli, chromosomes, mitochondria, ribosomes, Golgi bodies, enzymes, and cell membranes.	But most plant cells have cell walls . . . 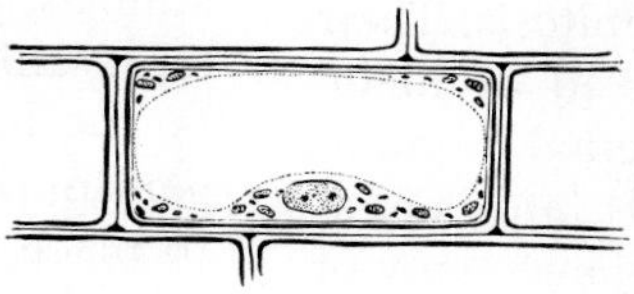	. . . while animal cells do not. 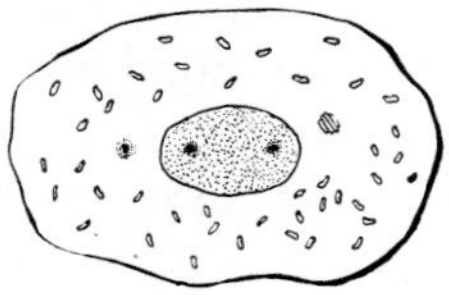
Both plants and animals grow by means of cell growth and cell division.	But cell division in plants 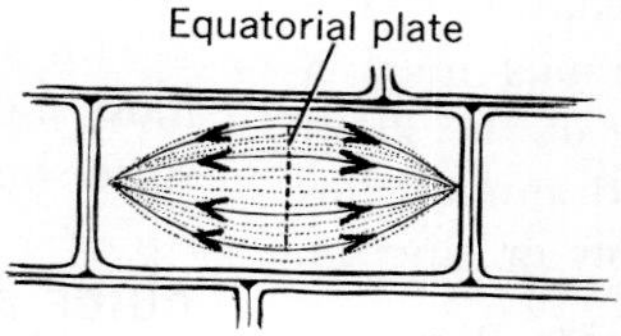 . . . Equatorial plate	. . . is not identical to that in animals. 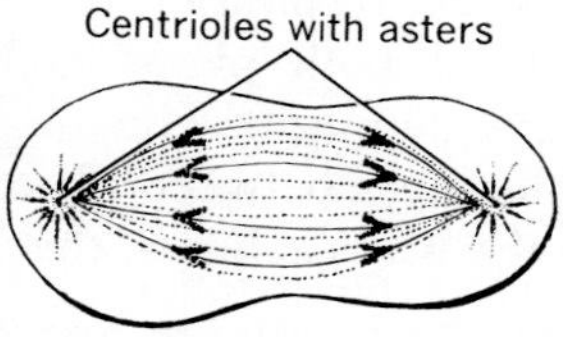 Centrioles with asters
Both plants and animals require food with carbon, hydrogen, oxygen, nitrogen, and other elements necessary for growth and maintenance.	But plants usually *make* their food . . . 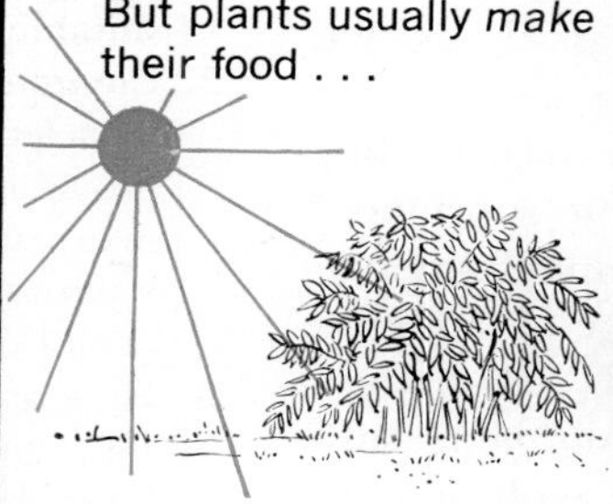	. . . while animals *take* it. 
Both plants and animals digest food, excrete wastes, grow, respond to stimuli, and reproduce.	But plants usually carry on these life processes as *sessile* organisms . . . 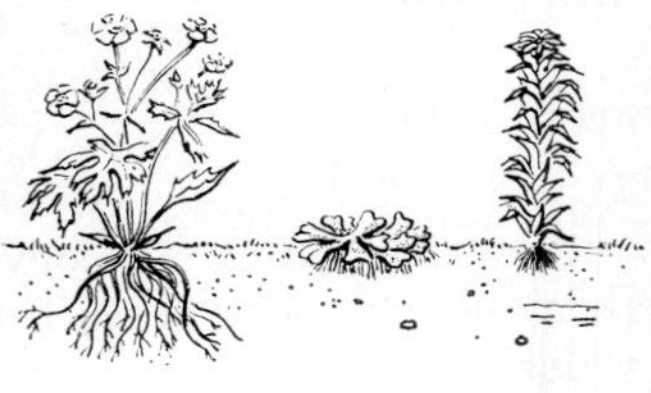	. . . while animals usually are *motile*—free to move about their environments. 

How Animals and Plants Are Alike

If animals and plants have evolved from the same ancestors, as biologists believe, it is not surprising that they should have many features in common (Figure 18-3).

Both animals and plants are composed of cells. The cells of both have nuclei, chromosomes, nucleoli, mitochondria, Golgi bodies, ribosomes, and cell membranes. The nuclei of both are divided by mitosis. Their chromosome numbers are halved by meiosis, and restored to the original number through the fusion of two cells into one, at fertilization. The cells of both have many of the same enzymes. Both transfer the energy from glucose to ATP in similar cellular processes called respiration.

You have already learned that in order to carry on respiration and to make ATP, the cells of both plants and animals need a ready supply of glucose. One of the great differences between plants and animals lies in the way each gets this supply of glucose.

How Green Plants and Animals Differ

Green plants and animals differ in several important ways. In Chapter 15, we learned that green plants are autotrophic and photosynthetic organisms. That is, they can synthesize all their living substances from CO_2, H_2O, and other simple inorganic molecules, by using the energy of sunlight. Animals, on the other hand, are heterotrophic. They require both inorganic substances and complex organic molecules to synthesize their living substance. Their energy comes from the oxidation of glucose and similar molecules. These differences are illustrated in the carbon-hydrogen-oxygen cycle (Figure 8-6).

Two other important differences between green plants and animals were examined earlier when we studied cells. Plant and animal cells both possess a cell membrane, but only in plant cells is this generally surrounded with a stiff cell wall. The other difference has to do with the fact that plants are usually green. Some plant cells possess chloroplasts, which are situated in the cytoplasm. The chloroplasts contain enzymes that help plants absorb the energy of the sun and use it to synthesize glucose.

The Problem of Defining Animals

Now that we have examined the similarities and differences between plants and animals, we should attempt to define the term "animal." A definition for animal might be the following: An animal is a living organism that can generally move from place to place and that depends on other organisms for the glucose and the amino acids and other organic molecules that it needs for life. We should add that its cells possess a thin, pliable cell membrane but no stiff outer cell wall and no chloroplasts.

This definition will distinguish between most, but not all, plants and animals. Despite shortcomings, it will suit our purposes.

GUIDE QUESTIONS AND PROBLEMS

1. What environmental conditions are most suitable for supporting life?
2. Environment directs the course of evolution by selecting individuals with mutations that provide better chances for survival. Since man can modify his environment and "take it with him," how might this power affect the evolution of man?
3. How are plants and animals alike? What is the significance of these resemblances?
4. How do green plants and animals differ?

SUGGESTIONS FOR ADDITIONAL READING

Books

Simpson, G. G., C. S. Pittendrigh, and L. H. Tiffany, *Life: An Introduction to Biology.* New York, Harcourt, Brace & World, 1957.
    A comprehensive, unified approach to biology, with evolution the unifying factor.
Storer, T. I., and R. L. Usinger, *General Zoology*, 3rd ed. New York, McGraw-Hill, 1957.
    A college textbook with specific and detailed information about animals.

19

PARAMECIUM

AND THE ANIMAL

WAY OF LIFE

In some of the previous chapters that dealt with cells and plants, problems of the animal way of life have been briefly described. Animals are heterotrophic creatures. What does that mean? In a broad sense, they are parasites among living organisms. They cannot use inorganic materials to synthesize carbohydrates, fats, proteins, and nucleic acids. They cannot use free energy from any physical source to maintain or build up their complex cellular structure. They depend absolutely on the biochemical proficiencies of other creatures for their existence.

Cells require an intake of substances in order to maintain themselves and grow. To grow, they must produce more of their own matter, and yet they cannot *create* matter— that is, they cannot operate in defiance of the Law of Conservation of Mass (page 79). Therefore, any increase in the quantity of living matter can be brought about only by a *transformation* of other matter. The "other matter" is the food that comes from the environment.

Animals are food gatherers. Somehow they must obtain the food substances they need and make these substances available as molecules or ions to all of their cells. Let us determine what kinds of molecules and ions are required and how they are brought into animal cells.

Variations in the Animal Way

Animals cannot, as green plants do, make their carbohydrates and fats from carbon dioxide (CO_2) and water (H_2O); they must have organic molecules such as glucose, fatty acids, amino acids, and glycerol. They also cannot combine CO_2, H_2O, and nitrogen-containing salts to make proteins; they must have about 20 amino acids. Similarly, to synthesize nucleic acids, animal cells must have both amino acids and simple sugars. In these various syntheses, vitamins are also required.

What all this means is that there must be available to the *interior* of animal cells the following: glucose, glycerol, fatty acids, amino acids, vitamins, water, and mineral substances. The water and mineral substances (salts of calcium, phosphorus, sodium, and so on) are usually available in the nonliving environment. They can pass across cell membranes and hence reach the interiors of cells.

On the other hand, glucose, glycerol, fatty acids, amino acids, and vitamins are not ordinarily available from the nonliving environment. They are formed only by living cells, and even here they are rarely available in their "free" (uncombined) form. The meat you eat, for example, contains only traces of *free* amino acids. Nearly all of the amino acids in the meat are chemically bonded to one another to form the proteins characteristic of the animal from which the meat came. Most of these proteins would be useless as such to your

19-1 INTRACELLULAR vs. EXTRACELLULAR DIGESTION

INTRACELLULAR

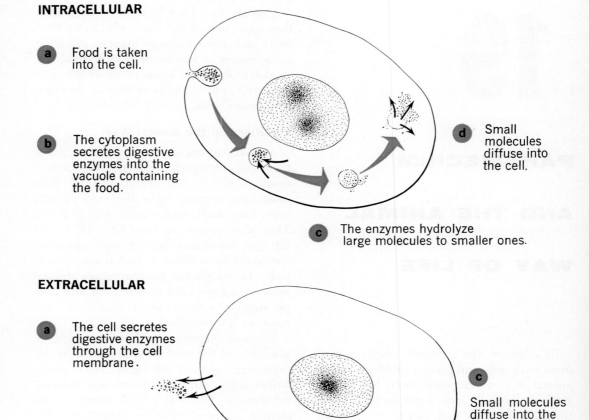

a Food is taken into the cell.

b The cytoplasm secretes digestive enzymes into the vacuole containing the food.

d Small molecules diffuse into the cell.

c The enzymes hydrolyze large molecules to smaller ones.

EXTRACELLULAR

a The cell secretes digestive enzymes through the cell membrane.

c Small molecules diffuse into the cytoplasm.

b The enzymes hydrolyze large molecules to smaller ones.

cells. Similarly, there is almost no free glucose in food. Most of it is part of starch molecules from plants and glycogen molecules from other animals.

Somehow, then, animal cells must obtain and break down the complex protein, starch, and other molecules formed by plant cells or the cells of other animals to get the foodstuffs that are essential to animal maintenance and growth. And here is a further complication. With few exceptions, large molecules like proteins and starches are too big to diffuse across cell membranes.

What a problem it is to be an animal! Not only are the organic substances required by animal cells almost always "locked up" in larger molecules, but these larger molecules cannot diffuse across cell membranes.

The difficulties are overcome by the cells of different animals in one of two ways (Figure 19-1):

1. If the large molecules can be taken into the cells by some means other than diffusion, they may be broken down chemically within the cells.
2. If the large molecules can be broken down into smaller molecules outside of the cells, the small molecules can diffuse into the cells.

Both of these processes are called digestion. The first is called **intracellular digestion** because it occurs inside cells. The second is called **extracellular digestion** because it occurs outside of cells. Both intracellular and extracellular digestion consist of the hydrolysis (see Chapter 5) of large molecules.

Different species of animals may use one method, or the other, or even both. In man, extracellular digestion is the rule.

Once the smaller molecules are inside a cell, they can be used either to synthesize more of the living material of the cell or to liberate energy. We saw in Chapter 5 that synthesis proceeds by dehydration processes, and we learned in Chapter 6 that energy liberation is a complex process involving ATP. We can summarize the reactions that liberate energy by two equations:

$$\underset{\text{glucose}}{C_6H_{12}O_6} + \underset{\text{water}}{6H_2O} \rightarrow \underset{\substack{\text{hydro-}\\\text{gen}}}{24H} + \underset{\substack{\text{carbon}\\\text{dioxide}}}{6CO_2}$$

$$\underset{\text{hydrogen}}{24H} + \underset{\text{oxygen}}{6O_2} \rightarrow \underset{\text{water}}{12H_2O}$$

The net result is that oxygen is used in the cell, and carbon dioxide and water are produced. The oxidation of fats also requires oxygen and has as its end products carbon dioxide and water. When proteins are oxidized, they, too, produce carbon dioxide and water. Recall, however, that proteins also contain nitrogen. The nitrogen leaves the cell in a nitrogen-containing molecule such as urea. Thus, the total movement of substances into animal cells and out can be summarized as in Figure 19-2.

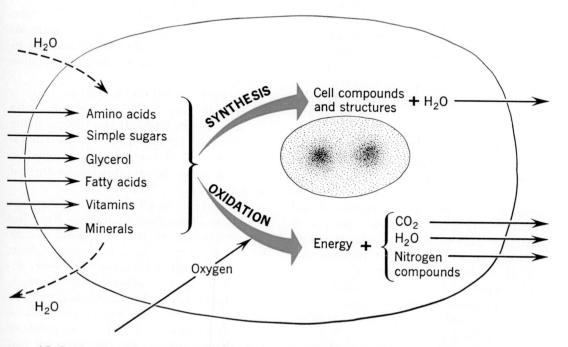

19-2 A summary of the metabolism of an animal cell. All animal cells require similar substances, utilize them in similar ways, and eliminate similar waste products.

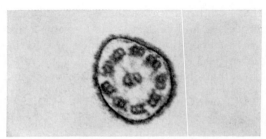

Delbert E. Philpott

19-3 An electron micrograph of a single cilium in cross section. The example is a cilium of *Paramecium*, but it has the same structure found in cilia elsewhere—for example, the cilia of cells that line the inside of your windpipe. (110,000 X)

All cells in all animals have these same basic problems of obtaining the molecules they require and eliminating those in excess. But even a moment's reflection will show you that different animals must have different ways of handling these problems.

Recall the microscopic animals that Leeuwenhoek saw when he examined drops of water with his crude microscope (Chapter 2). Some of these were protozoans, that is, single-celled animals. The cell membrane is in immediate contact with the surrounding environment—the primary source of the chemical substances required by the cells. Such are the conditions existing for single-celled animals.

Another set of conditions exists for many-celled animals. There are no living cells of your body exposed to the environment—except for those of the mucous membranes lining the eyeballs and the respiratory and digestive passages. The outer portion of your skin consists of dead cells. Hair and nails are made by cells but they are not cells themselves. The living cells are generally far removed from the food and oxygen of your surrounding environment. Yet each of your living cells must have these supplies, as with the protozoan.

Certain other many-celled animals have a layer of living cells covering their bodies.

Even in these organisms, however, most of the total number of body cells are within the body and remote from the primary source of food and oxygen.

Our study of animals will be an exploration of the many ways in which different animals solve the problem of keeping their cells, and hence themselves, alive. Our first example will be the protozoan *Paramecium*. It will give us an insight into the way of life of an animal whose body consists of a single cell. In later chapters we will study life in more complex animals.

PARAMECIUM—THE ANIMAL WAY OF LIFE IN ONE CELL

One of the commonest animals found in ponds is the protozoan *Paramecium*. In fact, even a small pond may have more individual paramecia than the earth has human beings. Paramecia are so small that they can just be seen with the unaided eye. We should qualify this statement, however; some species are larger or smaller than others, so that the length of the mature individual may be as little as 100 microns or as much as 300 microns, depending upon the species.

The entire outer surface of the body is covered by tiny hairlike projections, **cilia** (SIL·ih·a—Figure 19-3). If you study a living *Paramecium* (Figure 19-4) in the laboratory, you will observe that its locomotion depends upon the coordinated beating of its many cilia.

A cilium is so small that one might expect it to have little internal structure. Even the highest power of the compound microscope fails to reveal anything complex about it. The electron microscope, however, reveals a complex structure. Each cilium is now known to be a bundle of long rods. In cross section, one can see the cut ends of the rods (Figure 19-3). There is a circle of nine double rods on the outside, with two single rods in the center. This characteristic structure is observed in all cilia, whether in *Paramecium* or man, animal or plant.

At the time this book is being written, no one understands very clearly the mechanism of ciliary movement. One can easily observe it under the microscope, but so far no one knows how the cilium bends, or what the eleven rods do.

Cilia are used not only for locomotion but for the capture of food, as we shall now see.

Feeding

Paramecia feed on bacteria and other tiny organisms that live with the paramecia in ponds and puddles. On one side of the body of *Paramecium* there is an **oral groove** lined by cilia. Food is carried down the groove by the beating of these cilia. A **food vacuole** forms at the lower end of the oral groove (Figure 19-5). This can be observed in a living *Paramecium*. The vacuole begins to form like a tiny bubble, and the food particles are swept into it. After a short time the food vacuole breaks off and is carried around the body. Another food vacuole then begins to form.

Obviously *Paramecium* is an example of an organism that carries on *intracellular* digestion. Food, such as bacteria, that is too large to diffuse into the cell gets there by way of the oral groove and food vacuoles. Now let us see what happens to the food.

Digestion and Transport

The food that *Paramecium* encloses in its food vacuoles is composed of proteins, carbohydrates, and fats. As in all animals, these large organic molecules must be digested before they can be used. The enzymes involved are synthesized in the cyto-

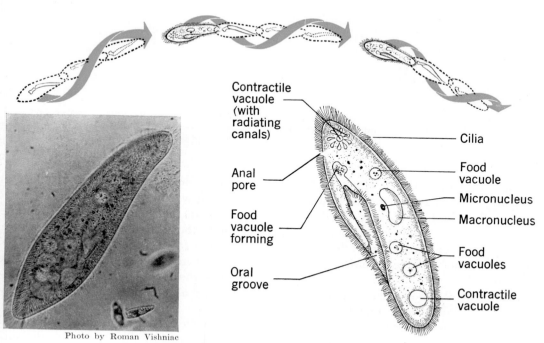

Contractile vacuole (with radiating canals)

Anal pore

Food vacuole forming

Oral groove

Cilia

Food vacuole

Micronucleus

Macronucleus

Food vacuoles

Contractile vacuole

Photo by Roman Vishniac

19-4 *Paramecium caudatum,* an example of a species that you may study in the laboratory. The photograph was taken through a compound microscope. Above the photograph, the animal swims, with its spiral motion, to the position shown in the drawing on the right. (The anterior end is up in the photograph, down in the drawing.)

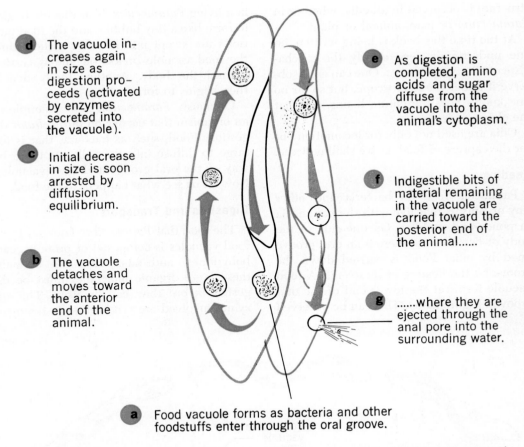

d The vacuole increases again in size as digestion proceeds (activated by enzymes secreted into the vacuole).

c Initial decrease in size is soon arrested by diffusion equilibrium.

b The vacuole detaches and moves toward the anterior end of the animal.

e As digestion is completed, amino acids and sugar diffuse from the vacuole into the animal's cytoplasm.

f Indigestible bits of material remaining in the vacuole are carried toward the posterior end of the animal......

g ......where they are ejected through the anal pore into the surrounding water.

a Food vacuole forms as bacteria and other foodstuffs enter through the oral groove.

19-5 Digestion in *Paramecium*. The events shown are for a single individual; the second body outline permits a clearer view of several of the events that would otherwise be obscured by the schematic depiction of food intake through the oral groove.

plasm, and they enter the food vacuoles. Like digestive enzymes in other animals, those within the food vacuoles of *Paramecium* hydrolyze proteins to amino acids and carbohydrates to glucose and other simple sugars. It is not definitely known that fats are digested.

Meanwhile, the food vacuoles move to all parts of the cellular body, thus transporting digested foods wherever they may be used. Food transport is quite simple in this single-celled animal, for the cytoplasm is always in motion. Currents sweep the freshly formed food vacuoles from the site where

they are formed, at the end of the oral groove, forward toward the anterior end of the animal, then back along the opposite side until they arrive finally at a point near where the food vacuole first formed. This movement may take more than an hour. By this time the food is almost completely digested and absorbed by the cytoplasm. Any indigestible substances remaining in the food vacuole are expelled through the **anal pore** (Figures 19-4 and 19-5) into the surrounding water of the animal's habitat (Figure 19-6). The old vacuole disappears at this point.

John A. Moore

19-6 A typical habitat of *Paramecium*. From the water of the pond, the animal takes food and oxygen, and into the water go the indigestible remains of food plus all the wastes generated by the busy operation of living. This one pond probably contains billions of paramecia—more than the human population of the entire earth.

Assimilation

Utilization of the products of digestion in the synthesis of cellular structures is known as **assimilation** (a·sim·ih·LAY·sh'n).

The movement of food vacuoles, plus diffusion of digested foodstuffs, supplies amino acids, sugars, and other food molecules to all parts of the cytoplasm. Within the confines of its single cell, *Paramecium* builds its living substance from the amino acids, simple sugars, and other substances that diffuse out of the food vacuoles. Its fats can be synthesized from molecules formed during the breakdown of carbohydrates.

Nucleic acids in paramecia are synthesized from amino acids and simple sugars. The proteins, carbohydrates, fats, and nucleic acids synthesized by these one-celled animals differ from those of bacteria and other organisms that paramecia eat. For example, bacterial proteins are digested to amino acids and then used to synthesize "paramecium-type" proteins. Highly specific nucleic acids (the hereditary basis for the animals being paramecia) are synthesized from substances that an hour before were equally highly specific for bacteria.

Energy-releasing Reactions

The synthesis of structural materials such as proteins and nucleic acids in *Paramecium* is an energy-consuming process. To obtain the required energy, the animal oxidizes glucose and other organic molecules. The chemical energy released is used to synthesize ATP from ADP (see Chapter 6). The energy of ATP is then used for all the energy-requiring activities of the cell.

If you will remember, the distinctive feature of adenosine triphosphate (ATP) molecules is a row of three phosphate groups attached at one end of each molecule (Figure 6-7, page 131). Most of the energy transferred in changing ADP to ATP during respiration is stored in the bond between the last two phosphate groups. The energy is not transferred from glucose to ATP in a single, sudden reaction. Rather, you will remember, there are many steps, and the energy of one glucose molecule is transferred to no less than 36 ATP molecules, with the help of a whole series of respiratory enzymes. In paramecia, many of these reactions occur in the mitochondria, as they do in other animals and plants.

The energy-releasing reactions require oxygen. This is obtained from the pond water in which paramecia live. The cell membrane is freely permeable to oxygen, which enters by simple diffusion.

Getting Rid of Wastes

As a result of the biochemical reactions going on in paramecia, waste products are formed. These are molecules that are present in a concentration greater than the animals can use. Thus, during respiration, carbon dioxide and water are produced:

$$C_6H_{12}O_6 + 6O_2 \rightarrow 6CO_2 + 6H_2O + energy$$

Water is always needed in the cell, but if more is formed by respiration than can be used, the excess water is a waste product. Animal cells also can use small amounts of carbon dioxide, but most of what is formed during respiration is more than can be used. The excess is a waste product.

Carbon dioxide and water are the main waste products formed when carbohydrates, fats, and proteins are broken down. In the case of proteins, there is always an additional waste product, one containing nitrogen. In paramecia, the chief nitrogenous waste product is ammonia (NH_3).

The process of getting rid of the waste products formed by the biochemical reactions occurring within the body is known as **excretion.** *Paramecium* has no structure for getting rid of two of the excretory products, namely, carbon dioxide and ammonia. It needs none, for these wastes simply diffuse from the cell into the surrounding pond water (Figure 19-7a).

Diffusion in paramecia is very effective, since the organisms are so small. And being small, they have a relatively large surface compared to their volume. That is, every part of *Paramecium* is close to the outside. Diffusion, aided by the fact that the cytoplasm of *Paramecium* is in constant motion, is sufficient to allow carbon dioxide and ammonia to pass from the cell to the surrounding water. Getting rid of excess water, however, is a special problem, as we shall learn shortly.

Paramecium also has solid wastes that must be removed. These are the indigestible remnants of the animal's food, which, as we have learned, are expelled through the anal pore (see Figure 19-5).

Paramecium and Water: A Lesson in Homeostasis

Paramecia not only produce water as a waste product, but they live surrounded by water. Their living substance contains more molecules of water than of anything else. Getting enough water is not a problem, but getting rid of *excess* water is. There is just too much water!

The cell membrane of *Paramecium* is freely permeable to water, but not to many of the substances in the cytoplasm. So far as relative concentration is concerned, the cytoplasm of *Paramecium* has less water than the surrounding pond (which will be more than 99.5% water). With a greater concentration of water on the outside than on the inside, and with a permeable membrane between, the result is inevitable. The net movement of water is from the pond

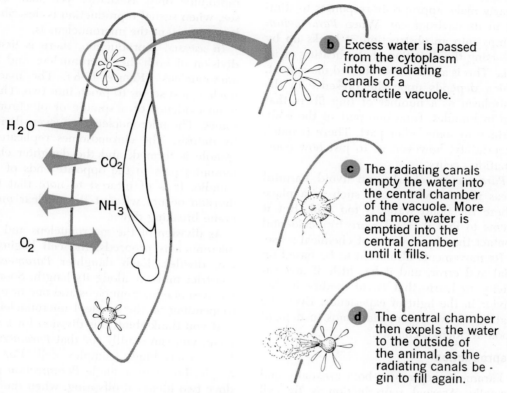

a Diffusion serves *Paramecium* to maintain a balance between respiration and excretion, but it also creates a water surplus. To get rid of the excess water, special mechanisms are required.

b Excess water is passed from the cytoplasm into the radiating canals of a contractile vacuole.

c The radiating canals empty the water into the central chamber of the vacuole. More and more water is emptied into the central chamber until it fills.

d The central chamber then expels the water to the outside of the animal, as the radiating canals be - gin to fill again.

H_2O

CO_2

NH_3

O_2

19-7 Diffusion and a problem it causes in *Paramecium*. Diffusion of each of the four indicated substances takes place in both directions across the cell membrane— but not in equal amounts. The net result is directional, as shown here.

into the cytoplasm. Water is constantly diffusing into the body of *Paramecium* more rapidly than it is diffusing out. If no other factors were involved, the body would swell and, in a short time, burst.

To survive, *Paramecium* must be able to bail itself out! It does this by means of two structures known as **contractile** (kon·TRAK-til) **vacuoles** (Figure 19-7).

This is only one of the many illustrations of a great principle in biology termed **homeostasis** (hoh·me·o·STAY·sis)—the capacity of living things to maintain constant or

nearly constant internal conditions. Water diffuses into *Paramecium*. The contractile vacuoles pump it out again. The concentration of water in the cell, therefore, is kept constant.

Notice that the homeostasis in this case involves the transfer of water from a region of lower concentration (the cell) to a region of higher concentration (the pond). Energy must be provided for this to be done. The energy for the activities of the contractile vacuoles comes, as you might guess, from ATP.

Coordination and Behavior

Paramecium has no nervous system—it is, after all, unicellular in organization. Nevertheless, its behavior is coordinated: it can clearly make appropriate responses to stimuli in its environment. When *Paramecium* bumps into an obstruction, it backs up by reversing the direction of the beating of its cilia. This is a finely coordinated movement, which depends upon the presence in the cytoplasm of a number of tiny fibers that run in bundles, from one part of the body surface to some other part. There is much uncertainty, however, as to just how coordination occurs.

Paramecium clearly can avoid harmful areas in its environment, such as a place where the pond water is too acid. But it seems to find its food more by accidental contact than by any sort of chemical sense.

Its movements also seem to be based on trial and error, and it has little if any capacity to learn—that is, to modify its behavior in the light of experience. Even the mating of two paramecia seems to depend upon accidental contact.

Reproduction

Paramecia reproduce both asexually and sexually. Asexual reproduction is by cell division, with an animal dividing across its length to produce two individuals. The internal events are made somewhat complex by the fact that there are two kinds of nuclei: a small **micronucleus** (my·kro·NOO-kle·us) and a large **macronucleus** (mak·ro-NOO·kle·us). (In some species there may be two, or even more, micronuclei). At the time this book is being written, the data are not sufficient for one to say precisely what is the function of each type of nucleus. Generally speaking, the macronucleus seems to be concerned with the general metabolism of the cell, and the micronucleus with reproduction. The story is more complicated than this, however. It is known that some strains of paramecia are wholly

without micronuclei. One might conclude from this that micronuclei are not very important. This is clearly not the case, because the strains without micronuclei can reproduce only asexually. We shall soon see, when sexual reproduction is described, how important the micronucleus is.

In asexual reproduction, there is first a division of both the macronucleus and the micronucleus (Figure 19-8). The macronucleus just seems to pinch into two. There is no evidence of a spindle or of chromosomes. The micronucleus, however, divides by mitosis. The chromosomes replicate, a spindle is formed, and the daughter chromosomes pass to the opposite ends of the spindle. It is of interest to note that this division occurs without the nuclear membrane breaking down.

As division of the macronucleus and the micronucleus proceeds, the cell begins to constrict midway along its length. Soon it, too, divides. Each daughter *Paramecium* receives one macronucleus and one or more (depending on the species) micronuclei.

If you think about this division for a moment, you can readily see that *Paramecium* is an exceedingly complex cell. For example, how can a single *Paramecium* produce two identical offspring, when the two ends of the animal are so different? Most of the oral groove is in the anterior end of the individual. Does only one of the daughter cells get it? Furthermore, there are two contractile vacuoles. Does each of the daughter cells get but one? If one studies individuals before, during, and after they divide, a striking series of changes is observed. The oral groove becomes fainter and fainter and then disappears (Figure 19-8). Later two new oral grooves begin to form—one in the anterior half and the other in the posterior half. By the time the individual is dividing into two, the new oral grooves are nearly formed. The two contractile vacuoles of the original individual remain, one in each half of the dividing

ASEXUAL REPRODUCTION IN *PARAMECIUM*

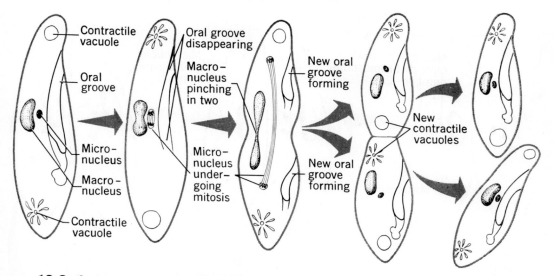

Contractile vacuole

Oral groove

Micro-nucleus

Macro-nucleus

Contractile vacuole

Oral groove disappearing

Macro-nucleus pinching in two

Micro-nucleus under-going mitosis

New oral groove forming

New oral groove forming

New contractile vacuoles

19-8 Contrast this method of reproduction with that in Figure 19-9. Which of the two types of nuclei is essential to both methods?

Paramecium. Two new ones are formed, one in each of the daughter individuals. So the process goes, until two *complete* new individuals are formed.

Sexual reproduction, as opposed to asexual reproduction, involves a temporary fusion of two cells. We can think of the two cells as male and female even though they look identical. The two fused cells form a little bridge of cytoplasm that connects them (Figure 19-9). The macronucleus in each cell disintegrates. The micronucleus in each undergoes meiosis, producing four micronuclear products, three of which disintegrate. Thus the original nucleus begins as diploid and then becomes monoploid. The monoploid nucleus then divides by mitosis to produce two monoploid nuclei in each individual. One of these remains in the individual, but the other moves across the cytoplasmic bridge into the other individual. After this has occurred, each individual will have two monoploid nuclei, one of its own and one from the individual with which it

is mating. These two nuclei fuse and produce the diploid chromosome number again; thus, we see that a true fertilization process occurs.

After the exchange of micronuclei, the two individuals separate. The newly fused micronucleus in each individual then divides twice or several times, depending on the species. Some of the daughter nuclei become macronuclei and others micronuclei. One or more divisions of each one-celled parent result in new individuals, to each of which a macronucleus and one or more micronuclei (again depending on the species) are contributed by the dividing parent. The whole process of sexual reproduction is summarized in Figure 19-9.

When *Paramecium* reproduces *asexually* the micronucleus divides by mitosis. Both new individuals possess sets of chromosomes identical with those of the parent individual. In other words, the daughter individuals will be identical insofar as their heredity is concerned. Whatever life the

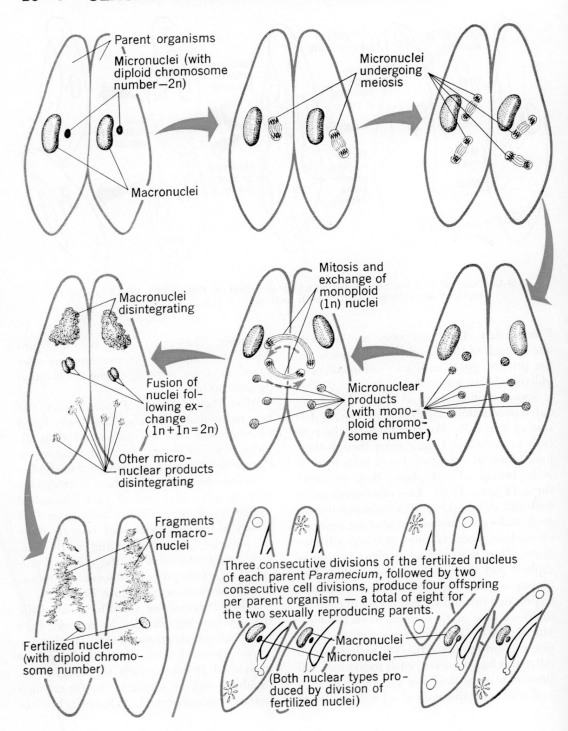

Parent organisms

Micronuclei (with diploid chromosome number—2n)

Macronuclei

Micronuclei undergoing meiosis

Macronuclei disintegrating

Mitosis and exchange of monoploid (1n) nuclei

Fusion of nuclei following exchange (1n + 1n = 2n)

Other micronuclear products disintegrating

Micronuclear products (with monoploid chromosome number)

Fragments of macronuclei

Three consecutive divisions of the fertilized nucleus of each parent *Paramecium*, followed by two consecutive cell divisions, produce four offspring per parent organism — a total of eight for the two sexually reproducing parents.

Macronuclei

Micronuclei

Fertilized nuclei (with diploid chromosome number)

(Both nuclear types produced by division of fertilized nuclei)

19-10 GROWTH OF A LABORATORY POPULATION OF *PARAMECIUM*

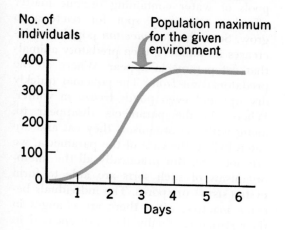

No. of individuals

Population maximum for the given environment

400
300
200
100
0

1 2 3 4 5 6
Days

parent was fit for, the offspring will be fit for. Whatever conditions the parent could not endure will be unendurable for the offspring, too.

On the other hand, when paramecia reproduce *sexually* each new individual is to some degree different from either parent. It receives a monoploid nucleus from each one. If the hereditary elements, the genes, are at all different in the two lines of ancestry that are brought together in the mating, then the combination of genes will be a new one. Sexual mating, in other words, introduces *variety* into the hereditary constitution of new individuals. Natural selection proceeds to sift the different gene combinations according to their fitness in each particular environment—a puddle being unlike a pond, a life of abundance being unlike one of scarcity, and so on. The evolution of new species of paramecia is closely related to the production of new varieties through sexual mating.

The *Paramecium* Population and Its Community

The animal way of life includes the place of the individual in the population and community of which it is a part. Our treatment

of paramecia would not be balanced if we considered only the life of an individual. If the conditions for life are favorable, individuals multiply and soon form a population of vast numbers. The number in any given environment depends upon several factors, such as the time since the population began to grow, the amount of food, the available space, and the presence or absence of predatory creatures that eat paramecia. Studies of the growth of *Paramecium* populations in the laboratory have provided some interesting general principles about population increase. Whether one studies yeast cells, bacteria, fruit flies, mice, or men, the same relationships appear.

Suppose we start with a single *Paramecium* in a culture vessel with plenty of food. It divides to make two, the two make four, the four make eight, and so on. In a few days there will very likely be more than one hundred individuals (Figure 19-10). At first the growth is rapid, until the population becomes crowded in its living space. Then the rate of increase becomes less and less, until finally there is no increase in numbers. We say that the population, in this stage of its history, has reached a maximum.

19-11 FLUCTUATIONS IN POPULATIONS OF *PARAMECIUM* AND YEAST

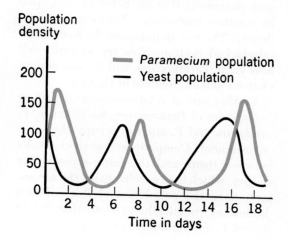

Population density

▬▬ *Paramecium* population
— Yeast population

200
150
100
50
0

2 4 6 8 10 12 14 16 18
Time in days

Thereafter one of several things may happen. If the food supply is continually replenished (but not increased), the population may remain at a constant size. If the food supply diminishes, the population will actually decrease. Under certain conditions the population size will fluctuate.

We must remember that the food of paramecia is itself most likely to be some form of living organism. Suppose our culture of paramecia is feeding upon a pure culture of growing yeast cells, which are themselves growing in a sugar solution. What will happen? First the yeast cells will reach a maximum number, depending on the food supply. When the first *Paramecium* is introduced into this environment, it will multiply rapidly. But as the *Paramecium* population increases and eats the yeast cells, the growth of the yeast population will be checked. As the yeast population declines until it reaches a minimum, the *Paramecium* population will begin to starve. The individuals first stop multiplying and then diminish in number. When very few are left, the yeast cells will multiply faster than the *Paramecium* population and soon reach a maximum number again. But this encouragement to the *Paramecium* population to multiply sets the cycle in motion again (Figure 19-11).

Exactly the same phenomenon occurs with paramecia that are being preyed upon by another protozoan, *Didinium* (dih·DIN·ih·um). The two populations fluctuate in an interlocked rhythm. Now try to figure out how yeast, *Paramecium*, and *Didinium* populations will all oscillate in rhythm.

Another sort of relationship occurs when two species of *Paramecium*, for instance, *P. caudatum* and *P. aurelia*, occupy the same environment. Competition for food results between them, and the faster-reproducing species, which is *P. aurelia*, gains the advantage. Soon the population of *P. caudatum* diminishes practically to extinction, while that of *P. aurelia* flourishes alone.

The natural environment of paramecia is a variable and impermanent one. Little pools of water containing organic matter afford a temporary spot for bacteria to grow. Soon the *Paramecium* population increases in numbers, then predatory animals that eat paramecia appear. Where do the predators come from? The pool may quickly dry up; and even ponds freeze in winter. Where do the paramecia disappear to, along with the organisms they eat and are eaten by? In the case of the paramecia, we are not sure. But practically all the microorganisms of such sorts are able to form **cysts** (SISTS) or spores. The individuals become inactive; often there are changes in their structure; finally they are encased in tough-walled, drought-resistant capsules. Tiny living organisms, in cyst or spore form, can endure great extremes of heat and cold and drought, adverse pH, low oxygen concentration, and a variety of other environmental conditions that would make active life impossible for them. It is an interesting and mysterious fact that, while biologists have observed cysts of a great many microorganisms, there is no evidence that paramecia encyst under natural conditions.

CONCLUDING REMARKS

Paramecium has served to show us how one kind of animal lives. It has the same general problems as do all animals. To survive, it must:

Procure food composed of proteins, carbohydrates, fats, vitamins, and inorganic substances

Digest food, that is, break it down into smaller molecules such as amino acids and simple sugars

Transport the molecules of digested food through all parts of the body

Assimilate the molecules of digested food to form parts and structures of the cell

Respire, or transfer some of the energy in the molecules of digested food to ATP, which acts as a storehouse for energy

Exchange gases with the environment—absorb oxygen and expel carbon dioxide

Excrete wastes, including excess water and nitrogen compounds

Coordinate behavior in obtaining food, avoiding enemies, and avoiding situations in the environment that are harmful

Reproduce, that is, produce offspring like the parents

Grow and *develop*

Paramecium does all of this within the confines of a single cell. But is it truly a single cell? Let us consider this question.

If we wish to decide whether or not *Paramecium* is a cell, we must first decide on an acceptable definition of a cell. In the morphological sense, we might say that a cell is a structure containing a nucleus, cytoplasm with a variety of particles (such as mitochondria, Golgi bodies, ribosomes, and centrioles), and an enclosing cell membrane. In a general sense, *Paramecium* fits this definition. It resembles in many ways the single cells of our own bodies.

In other ways, *Paramecium* also resembles our entire body. That is, we are both *organisms* that must obtain food, digest it, respond to stimuli, reproduce, grow, and so on. Without doubt, we must admit that *Paramecium* is an organism. It carries on an independent life that is in marked contrast to the dependent existence of each of our body cells. Looking at *Paramecium* this way, we might say that it is an organism whose body is not divided into cells (it could not be, of course, if it consisted of only one cell!).

So *Paramecium* can be thought of either as a single cell that carries out all of the basic functions of an organism, or as an organism whose body is not divided into cells. In short, cell and organism are one in *Paramecium,* and in most other Protozoa.

GUIDE QUESTIONS AND PROBLEMS

1. What materials are necessary for the life of animal cells?
2. In what way can animals be regarded as parasites?
3. How do animals change large protein, carbohydrate, and fat molecules in digestion?
4. What happens to the molecules of food that reach the cells by diffusion?
5. How do the problems of one-celled animals, such as *Paramecium,* differ from those of many-celled animals?
6. How does *Paramecium* obtain its food? How does it digest the food?
7. How are digested foods distributed to all parts of the cell of *Paramecium?*
8. How is energy release in *Paramecium* the same as in all higher organisms? How is the oxygen needed for energy release obtained?
9. What are the waste products of the biochemical activities of *Paramecium?* How are they removed from the body?
10. How do the contractile vacuoles function as homeostatic structures?
11. Would you expect a protozoan that lives in salt water to have contractile vacuoles? Why or why not?
12. On what evidence can we conclude that *Paramecium* must have some kind of coordinating mechanism?
13. How does *Paramecium* reproduce asexually?
14. What is the long-term significance of sexual reproduction in *Paramecium?*
15. What changes in the growth of a population of *Paramecium* occur as a result of introducing a living food organism such as yeast? a predator of *Paramecium* such as *Didinium?* another species of *Paramecium?*

SUGGESTIONS FOR ADDITIONAL READING

Buchsbaum, R., *Animals Without Backbones.* Chicago, University of Chicago Press, 1948. Easy to read and extremely well illustrated.

Moore, J. A., *Principles of Zoology.* New York, Oxford University Press, 1957. The biology of animals, with emphasis on general principles.

20

THE DIVERSITY

AMONG ANIMALS—

VARIATIONS ON

A THEME

Paramecium has one way of life—that of a particular kind of animal that lives in ponds. There are many other ways of life in the Animal Kingdom—that of an earthworm, fly, shark, sparrow, and man—to name just a few. Each species of animal alive today has its own way of doing things—securing food, avoiding enemies and unfavorable environments, finding a place to live, and reproducing its kind.

When we realize that there may be as many as two million species of animals, it becomes clear that no one can learn about the way of life of each. Even if it were possible or desirable to do so, it would be unnecessary for this reason: although each species has its own way of living, these ways of living are not equally different. For

example, a bullfrog and a green frog are different species, yet their ways of life have many features in common. Both spend most of their lives along the edges of ponds and lakes. Both eat insects. They digest their food, breathe, excrete, and reproduce in almost identical ways. Their nuclei contain the same number of chromosomes. They respond in similar ways to heat or cold and enemies such as snakes or man. Thus, if one knows about the life of a bullfrog, much of the knowledge would also apply to the green frog. And, as a matter of fact, it would apply to most kinds of frogs.

CLASSIFICATION

We might say, therefore, that there is a "frog way of life"—just as there is a "green-frog way of life" and a "bullfrog way of life." That is, there are groups of animals that do similar things in similar ways. Biologists have realized this for a very long time, and so did man long before there were any biologists. This concept of groups of animals is a concept of classification. Biological classification, therefore, is the arrangement of living organisms into groups of similar species. There are many different groupings beginning with *species* and ending with *kingdom*. Thus, you and all other human beings belong to a group known as the species *Homo sapiens* (HOH-mo SAY·pih·enz). In addition, you and all other animals belong to the group **Kingdom Animalia** (an·ih·MAY·lih·a).

Species

The system of classifying organisms has developed gradually over the past 300 years. It was not until the late seventeenth century that an Englishman, John Ray (1627–1705), developed a clear concept of species. To him a species consisted of offspring of similar parents. The concept has been modified since the time of Ray. We now look upon a species as a group of individuals that can breed with one another. At the same time individuals of one species do not usually breed with individuals of other species in nature.

It was left to the great Swedish biologist, Carolus Linnaeus (1707–1778), to establish the rules that are used for naming organisms. Linnaeus gave every species that he knew a name consisting of two words. Hence his system is known as **binomial nomenclature** (by·NOH·mih·al NOH·men·klay·tyoor). The first word of the species name is the name of the **genus** (pl., *genera*) to which it belongs. The second name is the so-called descriptive or trivial name. Both words are Latin or Latinized Greek (later systematists have not always used classical words in naming organisms). The genus and descriptive name together constitute the species name of the organism concerned. For example, the large group of cats was given the generic (genus) name *Felis* (FEE·lis). A particular group of cats was given the trivial name *leo*. These words together, *Felis leo*, are used for the lion, which is one species of cat. The scientific name of the common house cat is *Felis domesticus* (doh·MES·tih·kus); of the tiger, *Felis tigris* (TY·gris). All are cats, but each is a different species of cat.

Linnaeus listed 4,236 species of animals in his *Systema Naturae* of 1758. The total that has been described by now is almost a million. We are sure there are just as many, and probably even more, that have not been named. Most of the species known to Linnaeus were from Europe. They were also the larger and more conspicuous forms. Since the time of Linnaeus, biologists have explored all regions of the world, and they have studied very small and microscopic forms as well as big ones. In these ways they have greatly increased the number of described species.

In order to ensure that no two groups of animals get the same specific name, a very elaborate system has been set up for classifying animals. There is even an international court of biologists that will decide any disputed cases of naming!

The Need for Binomial Nomenclature

Many students question the need of giving animals scientific names based on Latin. Many times a student will ask, "Why does a robin need a scientific name? Everybody knows what a robin is." However, while everyone knows a robin in his particular area by that common name, in other areas the name may be used for a different kind of bird. The "robin" in England is a very different species from the "robin" of North America. It is not even in the same genus.

Let us take another example. The word "gopher" is known to people in many parts of the United States. In California a gopher is a small burrowing rodent. Its scientific name is *Thomomys bottae* (THOH·mo·mis BOT·ee). In the midwest a gopher is a 13-lined ground squirrel—the lines are on its back—whose scientific name is *Spermophilus tridecimlineatus* (sper·MOF·ih·lus try·des·im·lin·e·AY·tus). In Florida a gopher is not a rodent at all, but a kind of turtle, or tortoise, whose scientific name is *Gopherus polyphemus* (GO·fer·us pol·ih·FEE·mus).

Can you imagine the confusion that would result if a biologist from California, one from Iowa, and one from Florida got together and the topic of gophers was brought up? No confusion would result if these biologists used the scientific names.

A scientific name has the advantage of standing for a single kind of animal, plant, or microorganism throughout the scientific world. It reveals in a small way what great advantages a universal language would confer! Each man could understand his fellowman.

The Classification of Species

The group *species* is the starting point for classification. Sometimes smaller groups, *subspecies*, are recognized, but these will not concern us until we discuss evolution. There are many larger groups: genus, family, order, class, phylum, and kingdom. These groups are successively more inclusive. The relation of the various groups is shown in Table 20-1, which shows the classification of the species we have been discussing.

Let us begin with the first seven species. We belong to the genus *Homo* and to more inclusive groups: (1) the family **Hominidae** (hoh·MIN·ih·dee), which includes, in addition to *Homo,* extinct men *not* of the genus *Homo,* and (2) the order **Primates** (pry-MAY·teez), which includes also the lemurs, monkeys, and apes. The three cats—lion, house cat, and tiger—belong to the genus *Felis.* In general we can think of a **genus** as a group of closely related species. The three cats also belong to the family **Felidae** (FEE-lih·dee). Generally a family includes related genera (in the table, this is shown only in the case of the two genera of robins). The dog, on the other hand, belongs to a different genus, *Canis* (KAY·nis), which also includes the wolves and coyotes, and to a different family, **Canidae** (KAN·ih·dee). The dogs and cats, however, do resemble one another in many ways. You will agree that they look more similar to one another than to a man or a horse. On the basis of their resemblances, the families Felidae and Canidae are put in a common order, **Carnivora** (kar·NIV·o·ra). Generally an **order** includes related families.

In a similar way, two of the "gophers" (excluding the tortoise) are not enough alike to be included in the same genus, or even in the same family, but they are alike enough to be put in a still more inclusive group, the order **Rodentia** (ro·DEN·shih·a).

The first seven species, different enough to be put in three orders, are yet alike in many ways. All are covered with hair, they nurse their young with milk, and their red blood cells are without nuclei. Because of these and other resemblances they are combined in a still more inclusive group, the class **Mammalia** (ma·MAY·lih·a). A **class,** therefore, is composed of related orders.

What is the relation of these first seven species, which we classify as Mammalia, to the other species in the list? A close study would show that all, with the exception of *Paramecium,* have certain points of resemblance. For example, all have a backbone. Their internal organs are also alike in many ways. All have gills, or structures like gills, in their embryonic stages. These general resemblances are sufficient for us to recognize a still more inclusive group, the phylum **Chordata** (kor·DAY·ta). A **phylum,** then, includes similar classes.

Paramecium, on the other hand, is so different from the other species listed that it, together with other single-celled animals, is put in the phylum Protozoa.

Finally, the Chordata, the Protozoa, and the many other animal phyla not represented in Table 20-1 are grouped together as the Animal Kingdom. The Animal Kingdom and the Plant Kingdom are all-inclusive for our purposes. Some biologists, however, prefer to put viruses, bacteria, unicellular plants, and unicellular animals in a third kingdom, the Protista (proh·TISS·ta).

Biologists have classified all of the known animals in the way just described. Their system of classification not only shows how organisms are related to one another, but it also conveys much information about the animals themselves. This can be brought out by the following analogy. Suppose you are told that object X belongs to a group "vehicles." Even if you have never seen this particular X you would be able to make some very general predictions about its structure and function. It would probably have wheels or runners, be used for carrying objects or people, and so on. If you were then told that X belongs to a more specific group "vehicles with internal combustion engines," you could make more specific predictions. It would probably have spark plugs and pistons and use a fuel derived from petroleum. If you were told that X is an "automobile" you would be able to make still more specific predictions. Finally, if you were told that X is a "Ford automobile" you would know a great deal more about it. The group, Ford, might be thought to correspond to the group, genus, in biological classification. The many kinds of Fords would correspond to the various biological species within a genus.

Biological classification, then, is one way of systematizing biological knowledge. It is a tremendously important concept. Just as the word "automobile" carries certain connotations, so does the word "Mammalia." When a biologist is told that Y is a mammal, he immediately knows a great deal about its structure and way of life. Not only will he know that Y has hair, nurses its young, and has no nuclei in its red blood cells, but a host of other things as well.

Think of the case of a biologist who has just collected a new species of small mammal in some faraway land. He would immediately recognize it as a mammal because of its hairy coat. And because of the presence of hair, he would know a great deal else. He would know this because he, and generations of biologists, have studied animals with hair and found many common features in their anatomy and physiology. As he holds the animal in his hand, you could ask him many questions about the internal structure of his specimen. He would be able to tell you many details about it that you would find true if you looked. He could make predictions about the brain and nerves, the numbers and positions of the main blood vessels, what the kidneys are like, the structure of the heart, how its embryo develops, and so on. If you then checked to see if he were correct, you would find that in nearly every case he would have been. The word "Mammalia," then, carries a tremendous amount of information.

Homology, the Major Basis of Classification

We might well ask what criteria are used to classify animals into groups. Briefly, the animals placed in a particular group all have many fundamental similarities in their structure. It is not always easy to recognize these basic similarities in structure, however. At first sight, the flipper of a whale, the wing of a bat, and the arm of a man do not seem to have much in common. The first is used for swimming, the second for flying, and the third, with its hand, for grasping. Yet if one examines their internal structure—the bones and muscles—it can be seen that the three are very much alike (Figure 20-1). The flipper, wing, and arm are all built on the same pattern. During the course of evolution, each has been modified from the basic pattern to serve a particular function.

The flipper, wing, and arm are believed to resemble one another because they originated from the same structure in a common ancestor, and thus were once controlled by the same genes. Structures that are similar because of their common origin are said to be **homologous** (ho·MOL·o·gus). It is principally the homologous structures that one considers in relating animals to one another in a classification scheme.

Figure 20-1 should not be misconstrued to mean that homology refers to gross structures alone. Nowadays cellular structures, especially chromosome number and type, are considered, too. Then there are physiological homologies, and even biochemical homologies. Moderate revision of animal groupings may occur as more is learned about cellular and biochemical similarities.

Analogy

There is another type of similarity between the structures of different animals. For example, the leg of an insect and the leg of a cat are both *legs*, which are used

TABLE 20-1 EXAMPLES OF ANIMAL CLASSIFICATION

Common Name	Species Name
Man	Homo sapiens
Lion	Felis leo
House cat	Felis domesticus
Tiger	Felis tigris
Dog	Canis familiaris
Gopher	Thomomys bottae
Gopher	Spermophilus tridecimlineatus
American robin	Turdus migratorius
European robin	Erithacus rubecula
Gopher turtle	Gopherus polyphemus
Green frog	Rana clamitans
Bullfrog	Rana catesbeiana
Paramecium	Paramecium caudatum

for walking. Also the wing of a fly and the wing of a bat are both *wings,* which are used for flying. A careful study of the two legs would reveal that they are constructed on totally different plans. The leg of the cat has the bones of the skeleton in the center of the leg. These are covered by muscles. The insect leg is the reverse: the muscles are *inside* and the skeleton is a hard case surrounding them.

A careful study of the bat's wing and the fly's wing would show that the two wings are likewise built on totally different patterns.

Therefore, the legs of the insect and the legs of the cat are not homologous. Neither are the wings of a fly homologous with the wings of a bat. Moreover, from fossil records we know that there was no common structure in any common ancestor of both insect and cat that evolved one way into the cat's leg and another way into the insect's leg.

The legs of a cat and of an insect do have a superficial resemblance. Both are long ap-

pendages that are used for walking. We speak of structures having a superficial resemblance and serving roughly the same function, as being **analogous** (a·NAL·o·gus).

Evolution has a role in the origin of both homologous and analogous structures. Homologous structures have an evolutionary origin in the same structure of a common ancestor. During the course of time the homologous structures of different animals evolve in different ways—and the result is the flipper of a whale, the wing of a bat, and the arm of man. Thus, one structure is modified into several.

The formation of analogous structures is just the opposite. In this case evolution begins with two different structures, and in the course of evolution they change until they resemble one another.

Physiology and Biochemistry as Bases of Classification

Although structural homology is the principal basis of classification today, it is not the only one. There are studies of relation-

Genus	Family	Order	Class	Phylum	Kingdom
Homo	Hominidae	Primates			
Felis	Felidae				
		Carnivora	Mammalia		
Canis	Canidae				
Thomomys	Geomyidae			Chordata	
Spermophilus	Sciuridae	Rodentia			
					Animalia
Turdus					
Erithacus	Turdidae	Passeriformes	Aves		
Gopherus	Testudinidae	Chelonia	Reptilia		
Rana	Ranidae	Salientia	Amphibia		
Paramecium	Parameciidae	Holotricha	Ciliata	Protozoa	

ships in physiology and biochemistry, too. Usually these add more evidence for the relationships suggested by structure, but this is not always the case. For example, there have always been some species of birds that could not be classified easily into families. Some characteristics might suggest that they belonged to family A while other characteristics suggested that they belonged to family B. How could one decide? Recently, Charles Sibley, a biologist at Cornell University, has been studying the egg-

20-1 Homologous bones in the forelimbs of seven vertebrates—from left to right, the foreleg of a frog, the flipper of a whale, the foreleg of a horse and of a lion, the arm of man, and the wing of a bat and of a bird. One set of homologous bones is shown in color. Can you find others? Many other bones of the skeletons of these and other vertebrates also show homologous relations.

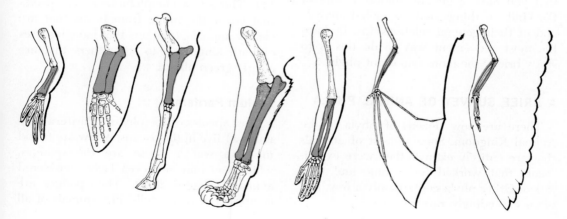

white proteins of birds from the entire world. He has found that the chemical characteristics of proteins can give clues to relationships. Clear evidence obtained from the proteins of some of these "problem" birds has permitted a more accurate classification.

Thus, while organisms are classified in the same group because they resemble one another, their resemblances may be based either wholly on homologous structures or partly on key physiological processes. Structures are homologous because they are derived, in evolution, from the same structure in a common ancestor. Homologous physiological processes are related for the same reason. We are now at the point where we can identify the fundamental basis of the similarity of organisms included in the same group: the different species of a particular genus or family or order or larger group resemble one another because they have been derived from the same ancestral source. Thus, every species in Phylum Chordata is believed to have evolved from a common ancestor. The same is true of all species in Class Mammalia or the genus *Felis*.

We will make no attempt to survey in detail the Animal Kingdom. The system of classification is almost always in revision at some level, as it is in several respects today, making an extensive coverage of questionable value. Nevertheless, it is important that you have a general understanding of the kinds of things that are called animals and of their general relationships. Perhaps the most convenient way to do this is to study briefly the more important phyla.

A BRIEF SURVEY OF ANIMAL PHYLA

There are now dozens of phyla in the Animal Kingdom. Some consist of animals that are entirely extinct—they were experiments that worked for a time and then failed. Other phyla contain only a few, and often exceedingly rare, species.

The ten phyla that we will describe contain nearly all (probably more than 98%) of the species of living animals. The phyla are listed here roughly in order of their structural and functional complexities, beginning with the least complex. The sequence is probably *not* a precise evolutionary one. Nevertheless we may suppose that simpler animals preceded more complex ones in evolutionary history. (Our knowledge of the evolutionary interrelationships of the phyla is so incomplete that it is not possible to make a correct evolutionary sequence at this time.)

Phylum Protozoa

We have already been introduced to this phylum. *Paramecium* is a protozoan, and so is *Plasmodium*, which causes malaria (Chapter 1). Several other protozoans are pictured in Figure 20-2.

The body of a typical protozoan can be thought of as a single cell (but recall the argument on page 357). Some species consist of colonies, or groups of cells. Protozoa are found in freshwater and saltwater habitats. The soil contains many species of protozoans, and many others are parasites. In man not only malaria is caused by a protozoan, but also amoebic dysentery and African sleeping sickness.

The Animal and Plant kingdoms meet in the Protozoa and the Algae (see Chapter 13). There is a complete series of species that cover the range from forms that are clearly animals, to others that have features of both kingdoms, to still others that are clearly green plants.

Phylum Porifera

Most species of the phylum **Porifera** (po-RIF·er·a) live in the oceans. A few are found in fresh water. These are the sponges, which you may not even have considered animals (Figure 20-3). The sponges are composed of many cells, like animals of all

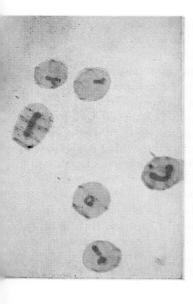

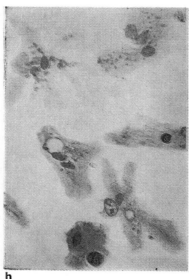

b

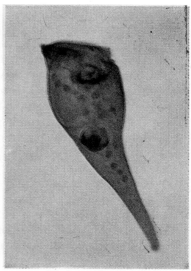

c

All photos, Gen. Biological Supply House, Inc., Chicago

20-2 Phylum Protozoa. Three freshwater protozoans (**a** *Didinium,* **b** *Amoeba,* **c** *Stentor*) are seen above (all three are fixed and stained). Paramecium (Figure 19-4) is another protozoan. Even certain organisms classified on pages 282–83 as algae (*Euglena,* for example) are also classified as protozoans. Why?

Both photos, D. P. Wilson

20-3 Phylum Porifera. The nature of sponges is apparent in these photographs of marine sponges. In the close-up of part of a sponge below, pores for the exit of water show clearly. Inside the body, water is constantly circulated; food organisms are taken from the circulating water.

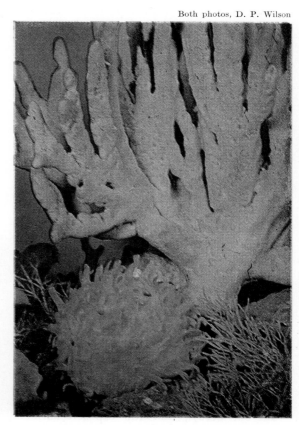

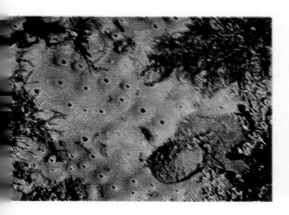

phyla except the Protozoa. The cells, however, are not very highly specialized. There are no true organs. There is a single cavity (or many cavities) inside the body. The cells lining these cavities have flagella. The beating of the flagella creates a current of water that flows through the body. A sponge lives on small animals and plants that are brought to it in this current of water.

Until recently, we had always assumed that sponges were without nerves. Now there is some evidence, as yet not convincing, that sponges may have nerve cells.

The bath sponge has a skeleton of fibers. This skeleton is the "sponge" formerly widely used in kitchens and bathrooms (most "sponges" used today are synthetic).

Phylum Coelenterata

If you have ever visited the seacoast, you may have seen **coelenterates** (se·LEN·ter-ayts—members of Phylum **Coelenterata**—se·len·ter·AY·ta).

By the time we reach this level of organization, the structure of the animal is becoming fairly complex. Jellyfish, sea anemones, corals, and sea fans all belong to this phylum. Some representatives, such as *Hydra* (Figure 20-4), are found in fresh water. *Hydra* will be one of the animal types that we will use in our discussion of functions in the chapters to come, so we should mention something about it here.

Hydras are about 5 mm in length. Frequently they are found on water plants in ponds and streams. The body of a hydra is constructed much like a tall vase with a narrow opening at the top. The body wall, corresponding to the walls of the vase, is fairly thin. It encloses a central cavity, the digestive cavity (Figure 20-4). There is a single opening, the mouth, leading into the digestive cavity. A circle of tentacles surrounds the mouth. There is no right or left side to the body, anymore than a tall, round vase has a right or left side. The body could be cut across, and the exposed surface

would resemble a doughnut. Such a body arrangement is known as **radial symmetry** (RAY·dih·al SIM·e·trih).

A microscopic examination of the body wall shows it to be composed of an outer layer of cells, a thin jellylike layer, and an inner layer of cells (Figure 20-4, right).

A hydra attaches itself to some object, such as a water plant, with the basal end of its body. It can move, though very slowly, from place to place. Generally it stays in one position waiting for food to come to it. It feeds on other small animals in the pond water; it captures them with its tentacles. The outer layer of cells on the tentacles, and other parts of the body as well, contain stinging cells. These, too, aid hydras in capturing food.

Hydras consist essentially of two layers of cells. They have no circulatory system, no respiratory system, and no excretory system. Nerves extend all over their bodies, but there is no concentration of them that could be called a brain.

In some species of hydras, male and female reproductive organs occur in the same individual. In most species, however, there are separate males and females.

Several other coelenterates are shown in Figure 20-5.

Phylum Platyhelminthes

When the name of Phylum **Platyhelminthes** (plat·ih·hel·MIN·theez) is translated it becomes "flatworm." Nearly all of the species that belong to this phylum are small worms with flattened bodies. They are found principally in freshwater and marine habitats. Some are parasites in the bodies of other animals. For example, the tapeworms, liver flukes, and blood flukes, which are all flatworms, may cause diseases of man. These parasites are usually more common in the tropics than in the temperate zones. A few species of flatworms live on land, but always in a place where there is considerable moisture.

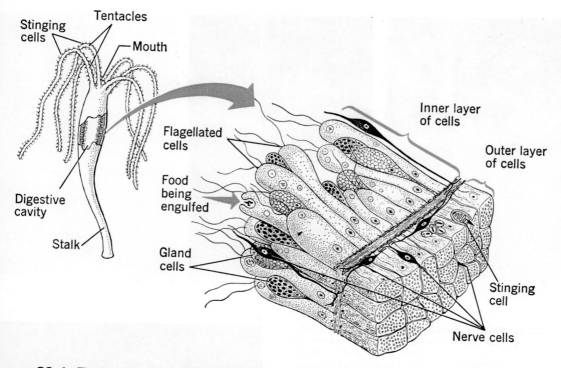

20-4 The body plan of *Hydra*. The interior of the body consists of a single, central cavity, as shown in the drawing at the left, where part of the body wall has been cut away. Food enters the cavity through the mouth, which also serves as an exit for undigested remnants of the food. The drawing at the right shows a section of the body wall enlarged. The outer layer of cells is primarily for protection; it includes stinging cells, which can shoot out barbs into food or foe. The inner layer of cells is primarily digestive in function. The gland cells of the inner layer are enzyme-secreting cells; many other of the inner cells engulf and digest food particles.

We learned that the bodies of coelenterates are composed of two main layers of cells—one layer on the outside and one on the inside. The flatworms have these two layers plus one in the middle. In this and all the more complex phyla of the Animal Kingdom, these three layers are present and play similar roles. In general, the outer layer forms the skin, the inner layer the digestive system, and the middle layer everything else.

The bodies of hydras and most other coelenterates are radial. In the flatworms and nearly all more complex animals, however, the body has a right and a left side. We speak of this as **bilateral** (by·LAT·er·al) sym-

metry. One can also recognize anterior (head) and posterior ends (Figure 20-6).

One group of flatworms, the planarians, will be used in discussions of functions in the chapters to come. Planarians are generally about 10 mm in length (Figure 20-7). They live in freshwater ponds and streams, frequently occurring on the undersides of rocks and dead leaves.

Planarians move about freely. The outer cells on the undersides of their bodies have tiny, hairlike structures, cilia, like those of *Paramecium*. The cilia beat in unison and move the animal over surfaces of rocks and leaves, in a film of mucus that the flatworm secretes from cells on the lower side of its

a R. Koch

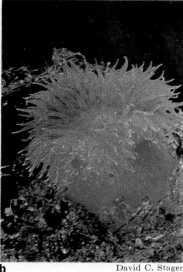
b David C. Stager

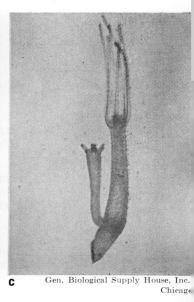
c Gen. Biological Supply House, Inc.
Chicago

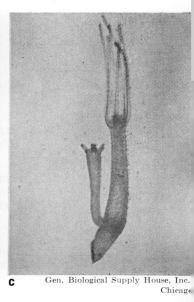
d D. P. Wilso

20-5 Phylum Coelenterata. Among the marine coelenterates are sea anemones (of which two kinds are shown in **a** and **b**) and jellyfish (**d**). The other photograph (**c**) is of *Hydra*, a freshwater coelenterate, shown reproducing by budding.

body. Planarians have muscles that enable them to change direction.

Planarians feed on small animals that live in the ponds, and on the bodies of dead and decaying animals.

Much of the body space is taken up by a branching digestive system. This digestive system has a single opening, as in a hydra. There is a simple excretory system, but no respiratory or circulatory systems. In the head end there are two concentrations of nerve cells that can be called brains. Above these brains are two dark eyespots, sensitive to light. The eyespots represent a very primitive type of eye.

A cross section of the body of a planarian reveals that it is more complicated than a hydra (Figure 20-7). In addition to an outer layer of cells forming the skin, and an inner layer forming the wall of the digestive system, there is the third layer between. Pla-

narians have male and female reproductive organs. Both planarians and some hydras are **hermaphroditic** (her·maf·ro·DIT·ik)—that is, a single individual produces both eggs and sperms.

Phylum Nematoda

Phylum Nematoda (nem·a·TOH·da) is also composed of wormlike species (Figure 20-8). These species, however, have cylindrical rather than flattened bodies. Usually the body is sharply pointed at each end. One end is definitely anterior, but this is usually difficult to tell externally. There are, for example, no special sense organs such as eyes, and no clearly marked head. There is a huge number of species of nematode worms. Some species are found in freshwater habitats, others in the oceans; there are tremendous numbers in the soil, where they may cause diseases of plants, including man's food plants. In fact, most of the species of parasites both of animals and of plants are nematodes. The more common nematode parasites of man are hookworms, pinworms, *Trichinella* (trik·ih·NEL·a—which causes the disease **trichinosis** [trik·ih·NOH·sis], acquired by eating poorly cooked pork containing the worms), and **filaria** (fi·LAY·rih·a) **worms** (which live in the blood and cause **filariasis** [fil·a·RY·a·sis], a disease of tropical regions of the earth).

Phylum Annelida

Most of the "worms" with which you are familiar belong to Phylum **Annelida** (a·NEL-ih·da); they are commonly called **annelids** (AN·eh·lidz). The earthworm (Figure 20-9) is a common example. Other species are abundant in the oceans, especially along the coast. Compared to the phyla already considered, the annelid worms show many advances. They have a circulatory system, which was not present in lower forms. All of their other organ systems are more complex in organization. The body is segmented—that is, divided into similar sections. If you have ever looked at an earthworm closely, you will have noticed that the body seems to have lines cutting across it. These are the divisions between the segments.

The earthworm will be one of the forms that we will discuss frequently in the next few chapters to come. Earthworms may be 20 cm or even more in length. They live in burrows in moist, rich soil. Earthworms feed on decaying matter in the soil. In order to obtain their food they pass large amounts of soil through the digestive system. The undigested parts are the "castings," which you may have seen near an earthworm's burrow.

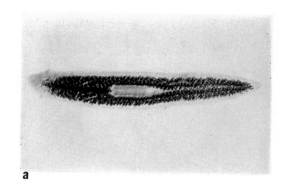

a

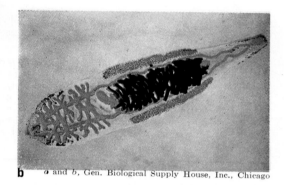

b   *a* and *b*, Gen. Biological Supply House, Inc., Chicago

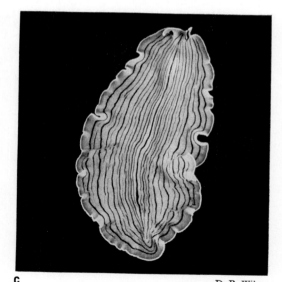

c   D. P. Wilson

20-6 Phylum Platyhelminthes. Example **a** is one of the free-living planarians found in ponds and streams. An example of a parasitic flatworm is **b**, *Clonorchis,* the Chinese liver fluke. Example **c** is another, more spectacular free-living flatworm.

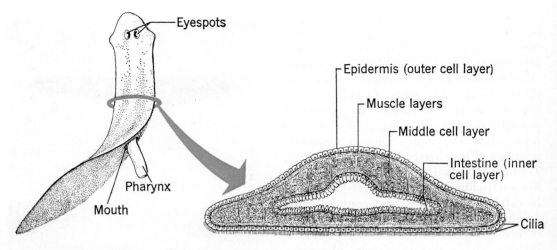

Eyespots

Epidermis (outer cell layer)

Muscle layers

Middle cell layer

Intestine (inner cell layer)

Pharynx

Mouth

Cilia

20-7 A diagram of a planarian. At the left is an entire individual, with its pharynx extended as in feeding. (At other times the pharynx is withdrawn into the body.) At the right is a cross section of the body. Three main layers of cells can be seen. The muscle layers that are shown, and other types of cells not shown, are parts of the three main cell layers—that is, the muscle cells were derived from cells of the middle layer. Planarians of this general type are common inhabitants of many ponds and streams. A small chunk of raw liver will often attract them by the dozens.

20-8 Phylum Nematoda. In photograph **a** are dozens of vinegar eels. In **b** are two parasites with sharp, anterior projections by which they attach themselves to the intestinal wall of their host. Shown in **c** is a *Trichinella* encysted in muscle.

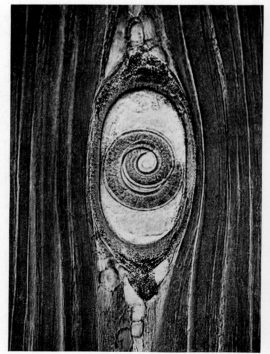

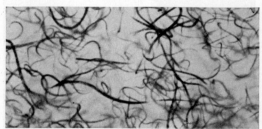

a   Both, Gen. Biological Supply House, Inc., Chicago

b

c   Carl Strüwe from Monkmeyer

Earthworms die quickly if they are in a dry place. You have probably noticed what happens to them after a rain. During heavy rains the burrows of earthworms are often flooded and the worms come out. They crawl about on the ground. When the rains are over and the ground begins to dry, the worms begin to dry up. Their skins are permeable and cannot prevent loss of water.

An earthworm is far more complex than a planarian. It has a digestive system with two openings, a mouth and an anus. It also has well-developed circulatory, excretory, and nervous systems. It is hermaphroditic —that is, it has male *and* female reproductive organs. In fact, it has all systems found in man except a breathing system.

Figure 20-10 shows two other annelids.

Phylum Mollusca

Snails, slugs, clams, oysters, octopuses, and squids belong to Phylum **Mollusca** (mo·lus·ka—Figure 20-11). The bodies of most **mollusks** (mol·usks) are covered by shells. In spite of the rather shapeless forms of the soft parts of many species, the body is highly organized. There are complex systems for digestion, respiration, circulation, reproduction, and excretion. The nervous system is also well developed, especially in active forms like the squid.

Phylum Arthropoda

More described species of animals belong to Phylum **Arthropoda** (ar·throp·o·da) than to any other (Figure 20-12). In fact, most

20-9 An earthworm and a cross section of its body. Outwardly, an earthworm may not appear to be more complex than a hydra (Figure 20-4) or a planarian (Figure 20-7). In fact, identifying the anterior end of the earthworm is much more difficult than in hydras and planarians. (In the photograph, the anterior end is at the extreme right.) Yet the cross section of the earthworm's body shows considerably more specialization than is found in hydras or planarians. Notice the well-developed muscles, the blood vessels, the nerve cord, and the different types of cells in the intestinal wall. Notice also the large body cavity.

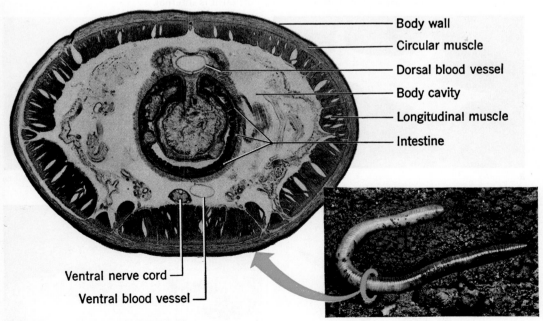

Body wall
Circular muscle
Dorsal blood vessel
Body cavity
Longitudinal muscle
Intestine

Ventral nerve cord
Ventral blood vessel

Photos by John A. Moore and John Markham

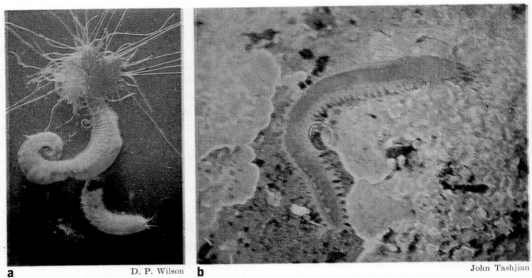

D. P. Wilson

John Tashjian

20-10 Phylum Annelida. Two marine annelids are shown above. Species **a** lives mostly buried in the ocean floor. Its tentacles aid in the capture of food. Species **b** is a clam worm. The earthworm of Figure 20-9 is also an annelid.

20-11 Phylum Mollusca. Species **a** is a colorful marine nudibranch, **b** an octopus, **c** a whelk, and **d** a cuttlefish. Most mollusks have shells, as in **c**, but some (including nudibranchs) do not. The shell of the cuttlefish is internal.

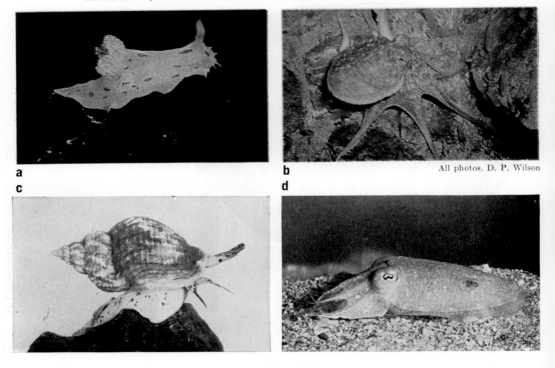

All photos, D. P. Wilson

a

Constance Warner

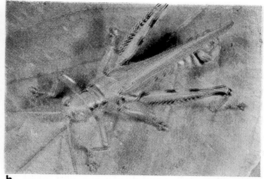

b

Constance Warner

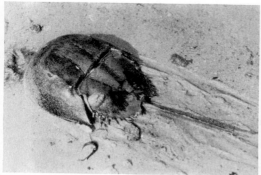

c

D. P. Wilson

d

John Tashjian

f

Constance Warner

e

D. P. Wilson

20-12 Phylum Arthropoda. The majority of animals on land, in the air, and in the oceans are arthropods (see Figure 20-14). This phylum alone accounts for most of the known animal species. Shown here are: **a** a black scorpion; **b** a grasshopper; **c** a horseshoe crab; **d** a butterfly; **e** a barnacle; and **f** a crab spider. Some other examples of arthropods are flies, lobsters, shrimps, beetles, centipedes, bees, and ants.

of the living creatures that one comes in contact with are **arthropods** (AR·thro·podz). Possibly a more impressive fact is this: there are more described species of beetles alone than there are species of all the nonarthropod animals in the world.

In addition to beetles, the grasshoppers (Figure 20-13), butterflies, and all other insects are arthropods—so are the lobsters, shrimps, spiders, scorpions, centipedes, millipedes, ticks, mites, and crabs (Figure 20-14). The arthropod body is segmented, as is the case with the annelid worms. The *skeleton* is on the *outside* of the body, and the muscles are attached to the *inside* of it. The skeleton is rich in a chemical substance, **chitin** (KY·tin). The skeleton in forms like lobsters, crabs, and beetles is

very rigid. Most arthropods have appendages, and these are jointed.

In later chapters we will deal with the functioning of grasshoppers, and so a word about them here seems necessary. The grasshopper, and all other insects, belong to the class Insecta. In the grasshoppers (Figure 20-13), the power of locomotion is far greater than in hydras, planarians, or earthworms. Like insects in general, grasshoppers have three pairs of legs with which they walk and jump. Most species also have wings.

The body wall, or skeleton, of a grasshopper is tough and resistant, in contrast to the soft body walls of the hydra, planarian, and earthworm. The body wall not only provides support and makes better lever-

20-13 A grasshopper. The three pairs of jointed legs are characteristic not only of the grasshopper, but of other insects. Notice the well-developed external morphology of the body—the eyes, the antennae, the wings, the segmented body, and the highly specialized legs. What resemblance to the annelids do you see? What differences between the grasshopper and hydras or flatworms are obvious? Do you see any evidence of a specialized body system not found in earthworms?

Charles Halgren

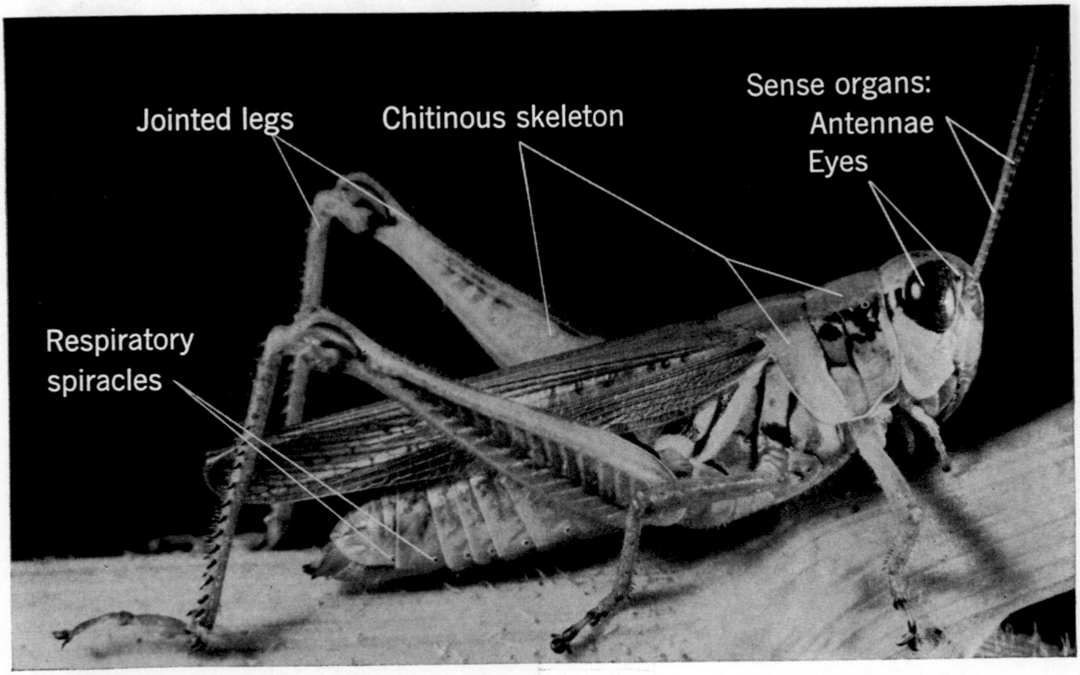

Jointed legs   Chitinous skeleton   Sense organs:
Antennae
Eyes

Respiratory spiracles

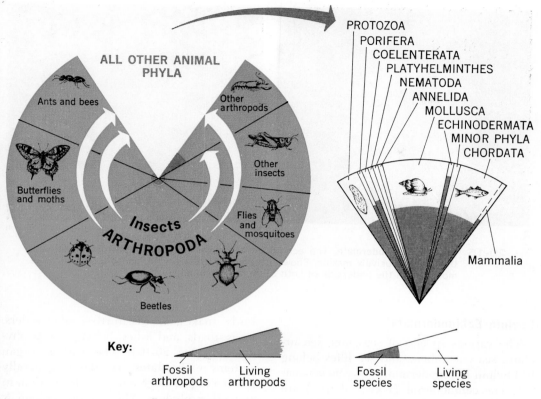

ALL OTHER ANIMAL PHYLA

Ants and bees

Other arthropods

Butterflies and moths

Other insects

Insects

ARTHROPODA

Flies and mosquitoes

Beetles

PROTOZOA
PORIFERA
COELENTERATA
PLATYHELMINTHES
NEMATODA
ANNELIDA
MOLLUSCA
ECHINODERMATA
MINOR PHYLA
CHORDATA

Mammalia

Key:

Fossil arthropods Living arthropods

Fossil species Living species

Redrawn after Siemon Wm. Muller and Alison Campbell, *Systematic Zoology*, 3:168–170

20-14 A visual comparison of the relative number of species in each of the ten principal animal phyla. How does your impression of this graph tally with other impressions you may have of relative degrees of biological success among the phyla?

age possible in movement of the jointed appendages, but it also protects the grasshopper from losing water. The animal can, therefore, live in very dry air.

Grasshoppers feed on plant materials. Sometimes they are so numerous as to become agricultural pests. Locusts are grasshoppers. Perhaps you have heard that sometimes they fly in swarms that look like huge clouds; they descend to the earth to consume every leaf and blade of grass. Then they fly on to devastate another area. These plague locusts are found in some of the drier areas of the earth, such as the interior of North America, North Africa, and parts of Asia. (You should not confuse these true locusts with the cicadas, which sing in the trees and are sometimes called "locusts" too. They belong to a different order of the class Insecta.)

A grasshopper is generally more complex than the earthworm in all of its body parts. The major advances in organization that it shows, however, are a breathing system and well-developed sense organs such as eyes. Also, unlike some hydras, and the planarians and earthworms, its sexes are distinct. That is, male and female reproductive organs do not occur in the same individual. In this respect, the grasshopper resembles man more closely than it does the other animals so far discussed.

a   b   Both photos, D. P. Wilson

20-15 **Phylum Echinodermata.** The echinoderms are the only major phylum of animals that are exclusively marine. Shown here are: **a** a sea urchin, and **b** a sea star. The mouth is on the underside of both of these individuals.

Phylum Echinodermata

The various species of sea stars, sea urchins, sea cucumbers, and sea lilies belong to Phylum **Echinodermata** (e·ky·no·DER·ma-ta). The **echinoderms** (e·KY·no·dermz) are the only major animal phylum that is exclusively marine. Sometimes the body is shaped like a biscuit or a disk. More frequently, however, there is a central disk from which arms radiate (Figure 20-15). In fact, the animals are generally radial in their symmetry. There are specialized organs for digestion and reproduction, but by and large these animals exhibit a rather low degree of organization. There are usually no specialized organ systems for respiration or excretion. The nervous system is also poorly developed: there is no brain. There is only a poorly organized circulatory system. You may be surprised to learn that our own phylum, the Chordata, seems more closely related to the echinoderms than to any other phylum.

Phylum Chordata

Here we are! Our own species, *Homo sapiens,* together with all other mammals, birds, snakes, lizards, turtles, salamanders, frogs, toads, and fishes, belong to this phylum (Figure 20-16). The various organ systems in **chordates** (KOR·dayts) generally reach a higher degree of complexity than in any other phylum. The nervous system is more highly developed. Our bodies are bilateral. The skeleton is on the inside of the body (in contrast to the arthropods).

The three most distinctive features of the chordates are a **notochord** (NO·toh·kord), dorsal nerve tube, and paired slits in the **pharynx** (FAIR·inks). You are a chordate, but the chances are none of these structures is familiar to you. The notochord is usually a structure found only in the embryo. It is a long rod that extends down the back. The dorsal nerve tube is modified as the brain and spinal cord in man. The paired slits in the pharynx are associated with the gills in fish and are involved in respiration. There are only traces of these pouches in our bodies. All but a few chordates are also **vertebrates;** that is, they have a vertebral column or backbone. The vertebral column replaces the embryonic notochord. Both are supporting structures.

a   D. P. Wilson   b   John Tashjian

c   Constance Warner   d   John Markham

e   John Tashjian   f   John Tashjian

20-16 Phylum Chordata. Of the chordates shown here, probably the least familiar to you are those in **a**—five tunicates. These primitive marine chordates have no vertebral column. The other illustrated species are vertebrates: **b** a fish, the Garibaldi; **c** a tropical frog; **d** the bearded lizard; **e** a night heron; and **f** a wallaby.

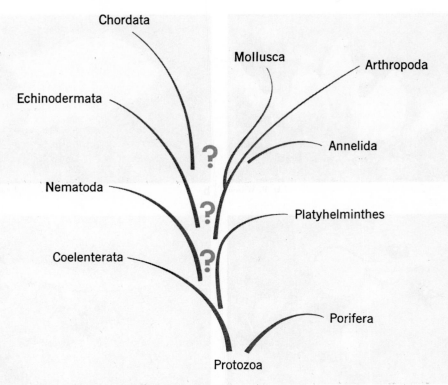

20-17 Evolutionary interrelationships of the major animal phyla. There is considerable evidence that the arrangement as shown may be correct, but until more fossils are discovered and studied, it remains a hypothesis.

CONCLUDING REMARKS

These ten phyla include most of the species of animals, and also the ones most frequently encountered. There are many other phyla, however.

It is believed that all the animals in a single phylum have evolved from a common ancestor. Little is known, however, of the interrelationships among the various phyla. There are a few *probable* instances of relationship. For example, there is much evidence that the annelids, mollusks, and arthropods are related. Many biologists believe that both the mollusks and arthropods evolved from the ancestors of the annelid worms. There is also some evidence that the echinoderms and the chordates had a common ancestor. These relationships are suggested in Figure 20-17.

There is tremendous variety in the Animal Kingdom. Yet paramecia, hydras, planarians, earthworms, grasshoppers, and man are all faced with similar problems. They must obtain food, digest it, transport the digested products throughout the body, respire, excrete, reproduce, act in a coordinated way, and so on. Now, problem by problem and chapter by chapter, let us see how these problems are solved.

GUIDE QUESTIONS AND PROBLEMS

1. What are the advantages to biologists of using scientific names for animals?

2. What was John Ray's concept of a species? How has this concept been modified?
3. What is meant by binomial nomenclature? How has it simplified the naming of animals?
4. What purpose is served by using increasingly larger categories such as genus, family, order, and class in classifying animals?
5. How may we interpret the fact that two animals belong to the same family? the same order? the same class?
6. How is homology used in classification?
7. What interpretation is given to the formation of analogous structures such as the legs of a mammal and an insect?
8. What is the basic body plan of the coelenterates?
9. How are the many types of flatworms similar? the nematodes? How do these worm groups differ from the earthworms?

SUGGESTIONS FOR ADDITIONAL READING

Books

Buchsbaum, R., *Animals Without Backbones*, 2nd ed. Chicago, University of Chicago Press, 1948.

Also available in paperback edition. Easy to read, extremely well illustrated introduction to the invertebrates.

Collins, H. H., *Complete Field Guide to American Wildlife*. New York, Harper & Row, 1959.

A handbook of the animals of most of America, with over two thousand illustrations.

Moore, J. A., *Principles of Zoology*. New York, Oxford University Press, 1957.

The biology of animals, with emphasis on general principles.

Simpson, G. G., C. S. Pittendrigh, and L. H. Tiffany, *Life: An Introduction to Biology*. New York, Harcourt, Brace & World, 1957.

A comprehensive, unified approach to biology, written for college students.

Storer, T. I., and R. L. Usinger, *General Zoology*. New York, McGraw-Hill, 1957.

A traditional college text of zoology, which can be used to obtain specific and detailed information about animals.

Weisz, Paul B., *The Science of Biology*. New York, McGraw-Hill, 1959.

An effective general biology text for college freshmen.

Zim, H. S., et al., in Golden Nature Series, New York, Golden Press. *Birds* (1949), *Fish* (1959), *Insects* (1951), *Mammals* (1955), *Reptiles and Amphibians* (1953), *Seashores* (1955).

Inexpensive, well-illustrated guides to the native animals of the United States.

The following series of works portrays a wide variety of animal types, beautifully illustrated with accompanying descriptive text.

Buchsbaum, R., and L. Milne, *The Lower Animals, Living Invertebrates of the World*. New York, Doubleday, 1960.

Cochran, Doris M., *Living Amphibians of the World*. New York, Doubleday, 1958.

Gilliard, E., *Living Birds of the World*. New York, Doubleday, 1958.

Herald, E. S., *Living Fishes of the World*. New York, Doubleday, 1961.

Klots, A., and Elsie Klots, *Living Insects of the World*. New York, Doubleday, 1959.

Sanderson, I., *Living Mammals of the World*. New York, Doubleday, 1955.

Schmidt, K. P., and R. F. Inger, *Living Reptiles of the World*. New York, Doubleday, 1957.

21

DIGESTION IN

MULTICELLULAR

ANIMALS

The animal way of life involves a great dependence on the environment. We have seen that *Paramecium* depends on its environment for food and oxygen. The environment serves also as a place for it to dump its wastes—carbon dioxide, water, nitrogen compounds such as ammonia, and the indigestible contents of the food vacuoles.

For *Paramecium* these problems are simplified to some extent by virtue of the fact that the body is very small—it is a single cell. Every part of this cell is close to the environment on which it depends (Figure 21-1a).

Similar Requirements Among Animals

All animal cells have similar requirements. They must have a supply of such things as water, amino acids, simple sugars, fatty acids, glycerol, vitamins, oxygen, and many other organic and inorganic substances. They must also be able to dispose

of their waste products, principally carbon dioxide, water, and nitrogen compounds such as ammonia, urea, or uric acid.

Most species of animals have bodies composed of many cells. This introduces an enormous problem in the larger multicellular animals. Whereas every part of *Paramecium* is close to the outside, most of the cells of multicellular animals are far from the outside environment (Figure 21-1b). A cell in the interior of a large animal cannot capture and ingest bacteria, as *Paramecium* does. If it dumps its wastes, they are dumped not into the surrounding environment but among other cells. The interior cells, therefore, are unable to obtain the substances they require directly from the environment and unable to dispose of their wastes directly into it.

Animals overcome the problems associated with size and with being composed of many cells in two ways.

First, there is a *division of labor among the cells*. The single cell of *Paramecium* does everything: it captures food, digests food, obtains oxygen from the environment, disposes of wastes, moves, and reproduces. In animals composed of many cells, there has been an evolutionary trend toward the specialization of cells. Different groups of cells have become specialized for capturing food, digesting food, obtaining oxygen, getting rid of wastes, movement, support, reproduction, receiving stimuli, and coordinating the various activities of the whole organism.

Second, the multicellular animals have *systems for transport* within the body. The transport systems carry food and other materials to every cell and remove waste substances.

In both these respects, multicellular animals resemble multicellular plants, which solved the same problems in the same general ways. As you will recall, plants have also undergone differentiation of their cells and a division of labor (see Chapters 13

21-1 THE MULTICELLULAR PROBLEM

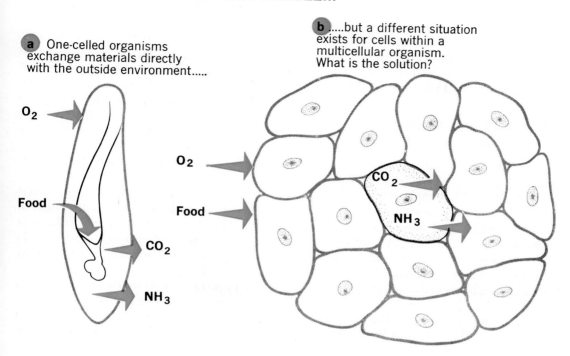

a One-celled organisms exchange materials directly with the outside environment.....

O_2

Food

CO_2

NH_3

b ....but a different situation exists for cells within a multicellular organism. What is the solution?

O_2

Food

CO_2

NH_3

and 17). They, too, have evolved transport systems (Chapter 16).

No matter how specialized a cell becomes, it still has the same basic requirements for staying alive. Yet as a cell becomes specialized, it becomes increasingly less able to provide for all its own needs. It becomes more and more dependent on its fellow cells.

Let us consider a human muscle cell. The function of a muscle cell is to contract. When it contracts it moves, but that is about all it can do. The muscle cell depends on the cells of the digestive tract for its supply of digested food materials. It depends on the cells of the lungs for obtaining oxygen from the environment. It depends on the cells of the kidneys and the lungs for ultimately casting out most of its waste products from its intercellular environment. It depends on the cells forming the vessels of the circulatory system for car-

rying digested food substances and oxygen to it and for removing its waste products from its immediate vicinity. It depends on the cells of the nervous system, in part, to coordinate all these complex activities, including its own contraction.

Every cell in the body, in its own specialized way, contributes to the functioning of the whole. Conversely, we can think of the whole body as functioning to keep every individual cell alive.

The organization of a human community is much like the organization of a complex animal. The farmers raise the food, the carpenters build the houses, the physicians strive to maintain health, the railroad men and truckers transport what we need, and the community government attempts to regulate all these activities. The individual depends upon the community and the community depends upon the individual. The more specialized the members of the community, the more dependent they become on all their fellow specialists. Life in our society today furnishes many examples.

This chapter is the first of several that will deal with cell specialization. The specialty to be considered here, in animals selected from several phyla, is digestion.

PROBLEMS AND METHODS OF DIGESTION

The substances that animal cells require, such as oxygen, water, various inorganic salts, amino acids, simple sugars, vitamins, glycerol, and fatty acids, can pass across cell membranes and enter the cells of all animals.

Supplies of oxygen, water, and inorganic salts are usually readily available in the environment. The molecules and ions are all in a form that can enter cells and be used. All that is required is that the oxygen and inorganic salts become dissolved in the watery film of body fluid on cell surfaces. Then they will diffuse through the cell membranes.

Amino acids, simple sugars, vitamins, glycerol, and fatty acids, as such, are rare in the natural environment. Organisms almost never have these substances *directly* available to them. In nature, all but the vitamins (and sometimes these, too) are usually parts of much larger molecules—proteins, complex sugars, starch, glycogen, and fats. Generally these larger organic molecules cannot pass through cell membranes. *Paramecium* solves the problem by taking in these larger molecules, which are present in its food, through its oral groove. Some animal cells can take in limited quantities by **pinocytosis** (pin·o·sy-TOH·sis), as we learned in Chapter 6 (page 126). However, for most multicellular animals, a sufficient rate of supply depends upon *extracellular* digestion (page 345). Large organic molecules must be changed to kinds that can cross cell membranes.

Why is it that so few proteins and other large molecules pass through the cell membrane? The answer is entirely logical, in terms of evolution. Since the cell is made largely of proteins, RNA, and DNA, and since it stores glycogen, starch, and fats, it could not survive if these essential components diffused away. Therefore the cell must have evolved—a very long time ago—a differentially permeable membrane *that would keep essential things in.* Consequently, only the smaller molecules could be permitted to diffuse back and forth.

The function of digestion is to convert large organic molecules, which are found in foods, into the small organic molecules that can pass across cell membranes. Not only must the molecules be small, but they must be of certain specific types. Thus the proteins must be broken down into amino acids, not into other types of molecules.

Amino acids, simple sugars, fatty acids, and glycerol are a biochemical "common currency" in living creatures. These small organic molecules are used by each species to synthesize its own specific cellular structures. Man eats beef. The beef protein is digested to amino acids. These amino acids are used to synthesize human proteins. No matter how much beef you eat, your proteins will never become more bovine.

The changes from large to small molecules are, of course, chemical changes. All these changes are hydrolytic reactions controlled by enzymes (page 119).

Apart from varying dependence on intracellular as against extracellular digestion, all other general features of digestion are the same in paramecia, hydras, planarians, earthworms, and man. This is another example of the fact that all animals face the same problems and solve them in much the same way.

Paramecium takes food into its food vacuoles by way of the oral groove. This food cannot be absorbed until it is converted to amino acids and simple sugars. Enzymes

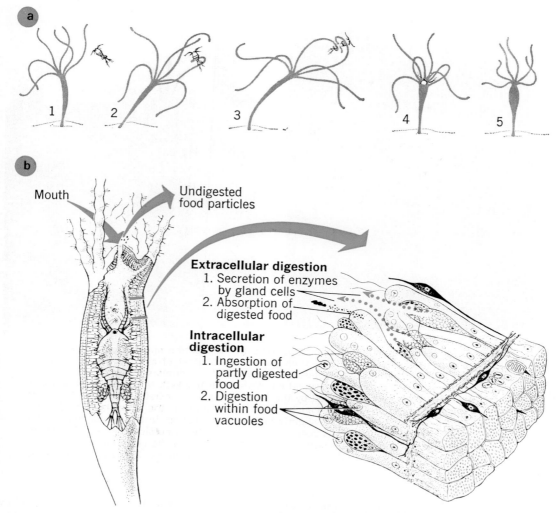

a

1 2 3 4 5

b

Mouth

Undigested food particles

Extracellular digestion
1. Secretion of enzymes by gland cells
2. Absorption of digested food

Intracellular digestion
1. Ingestion of partly digested food
2. Digestion within food vacuoles

Part *a* redrawn from Buchsbaum's *Animals Without Backbones*

21-2 Food-getting and digestion in *Hydra*. **a** The animal normally is attached at the foot of its body to an underwater leaf or twig. The hydra shown here is capturing and ingesting a very small freshwater animal, *Cyclops*. **b** The food organism, now within the digestive cavity, is attacked by enzymes secreted by gland cells. The enlargement at the right indicates that digestion is both extracellular and intracellular.

are secreted by the cytoplasm into the food vacuoles. Slowly the food is digested, and the products are absorbed and assimilated.

Digestion in *Hydra*

Small aquatic animals are paralyzed by the stinging cells and caught by the tentacles of hydras. The tentacles slowly move the food to the mouth. The food is then pushed into the digestive cavity (Figure 21-2). The cells that line the digestive cavity secrete enzymes into this cavity, much as substances are secreted by certain cells of man and other animals (Figure 21-3). The enzymes begin the hydrolysis of the proteins and fats that are in the body of

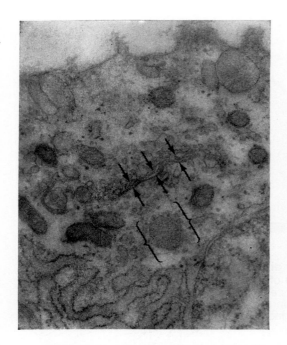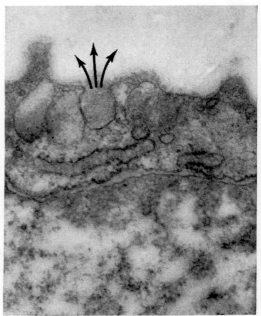

Lee D. Peachy

21-3 Evidence of secretion, as photographed with the electron microscope. At the left is a portion of one kind of cell from the urinary bladder of a toad. The two rows of arrows identify the Golgi bodies, the site at which materials synthesized in the cytoplasm are concentrated for secretion. Within the brackets in the same photograph is a secretion droplet, formed by the fusion of smaller secretion vesicles. (Some of the tiny secretion vesicles can be seen dimly between the Golgi bodies and the larger secretion droplet.) At slightly higher magnification, in the photograph at the right, a secretion droplet is seen emptying its contents outside the cell. The membrane of the droplet fuses with the cell membrane, and the secretion is released—in this case, into the interior of the bladder. Magnifications: 25,000 X and 47,000 X.

the prey. (Hydras apparently cannot digest carbohydrates.)

This is only a small part of the digestive process in *Hydra*. Most digestion takes place *not* in the digestive cavity but inside body cells, in the manner of paramecia. As the body of the prey is broken down into smaller and smaller chunks in the digestive cavity, some of these tiny chunks are taken into the cells lining the digestive cavity. When a chunk of food is adjacent to the cell, the cell membrane bulges out and encloses it. As a result, the food becomes enclosed in a vacuole within the cell. The big organic molecules in this food vacuole are no more useful to the cell than when they were still in the body of the prey. They must still be hydrolyzed to amino acids, fatty acids, and glycerol. Enzymes inside the cells bring these changes about. Outside, in the digestive cavity, the same changes are going on with the remainder of the prey.

Digestion in *Hydra* is thus both extracellular and intracellular. It occurs in the digestive cavity and within the cells, converting the prey to amino acids, fatty acids, glycerol, vitamins, and inorganic substances. Those products of digestion formed in the digestive cavity are absorbed by the cells lining the cavity. The small organic molecules are used for energy and for the synthesis of the living substance of *Hydra*.

Any undigested material is ejected from the digestive cavity. Since there is only one opening, it serves as both a mouth and an anus (Figure 21-2).

Digestion in a Planarian

A planarian, like *Hydra*, has a saclike digestive cavity. There is only a single opening, which must, therefore, serve both as a mouth and an anus. In the planarian the opening is a tubelike projection on the underside of the body, almost midway between the anterior and posterior ends (Figure 21-4).

A planarian can capture small live aquatic animals, but most of its food seems to consist of the bodies of dead aquatic animals. Digestion is not very different from that in *Hydra*, so there is no need to describe it in detail. Some digestion occurs in the digestive cavity. In addition, the cells lining the digestive cavity engulf and digest small particles of food.

Digestion in the Earthworm

Compared to hydras and planarians, the digestive system of earthworms is greatly advanced. Instead of being a sac with a single opening, the digestive system of the earthworm is a tube with two openings—a mouth at one end (Figure 21-5), an anus at the other.

There is one important advantage of the tube type of digestive system over the sac type. In the sac type, food enters a single cavity, where it is digested. Any undigested remains go out through the same portal through which the food entered. In the tube type of digestive system, food passes in one direction only. The food enters at the mouth and passes along the tube to the anus. Thus, with a one-way digestive tube, *it becomes possible for different parts of the tube to do different jobs in succession.* There can be, consequently, an assembly-line *division of labor* along the way.

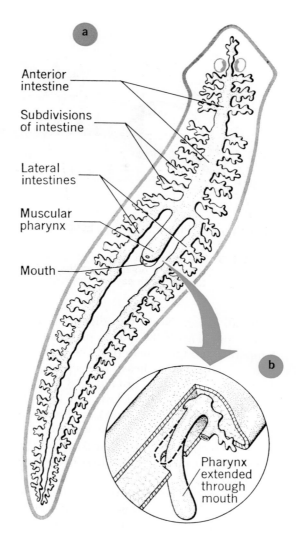

Anterior intestine

Subdivisions of intestine

Lateral intestines

Muscular pharynx

Mouth

Pharynx extended through mouth

21-4 The digestive system of a planarian. Like *Hydra*, a planarian has a single opening in its digestive system. Through this opening (the pharynx), food is ingested, and indigestible materials eliminated.

We can illustrate this by examining the parts of the digestive tube of the earthworm. The first section of the earthworm's digestive tract, the **pharynx** (FAIR·inks), has strong muscular walls. It pumps the soil containing decaying organic matter, the earthworm's food, into the **esophagus** (e·SOF·a·gus), which continues to push the ingested

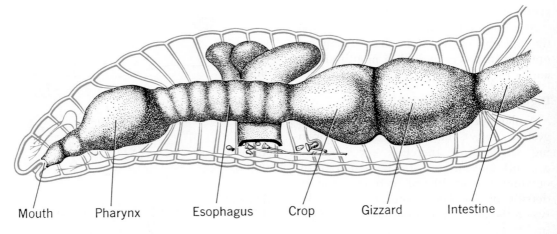

Mouth   Pharynx   Esophagus   Crop   Gizzard   Intestine

21-5 The digestive system of an earthworm. Traffic is one-way, with division of labor among the organs along the route from mouth to anus. Can you associate a specific function with each of the specified organs of the digestive tract?

material along. Next, the digestive tract widens out. This is the **crop,** a place for the temporary storage of material. The next section, the **gizzard,** has heavy muscular walls. Here the material is ground and broken into small particles. The last, and longest, section of the digestive tract is the intestine. The cells that form the walls of the intestine secrete enzymes that work on the food in the cavity of the intestine. When the food has been entirely digested, end products are absorbed by the cells that line the intestine. The undigested material is pushed along through the intestine and out the anus.

A similar, one-way, tubular digestive system is found in most groups of complex animals. The grasshopper (Figure 21-6) and man have digestive systems of this general type. There is consequently little need to discuss the digestive tract of the grasshopper or man as far as general principles are concerned. We must, however, say something about the digestive process and how it occurs in our bodies, and in so doing we will need to be familiar with the layout of the digestive tract and the functions of the organs it includes.

DIGESTION IN MAN

The digestive system in man consists of a long tube that extends from the mouth to the anus (Figure 21-7). The main sections, in the direction of the passage of food, are the oral cavity, esophagus, stomach, small intestine, large intestine, and rectum. In addition there are many glands, the most important being the three pairs of salivary glands, the pancreas, and the liver. The salivary glands and the pancreas secrete juices that contain enzymes. The liver secretes bile, which aids digestion but does not contain enzymes.

We can learn about digestion in man by describing how a hamburger on a bun, for example, is converted to amino acids, simple sugars, glycerol, fatty acids, vitamins, salts, and water.

Digestion in the Oral Cavity

There are several specific functions of the oral cavity. Food selection is one of them. When food enters the oral cavity it is tasted, smelled, and felt. If the taste or smell of the hamburger suggests that it is old, we reject it. If the teeth or tongue de-

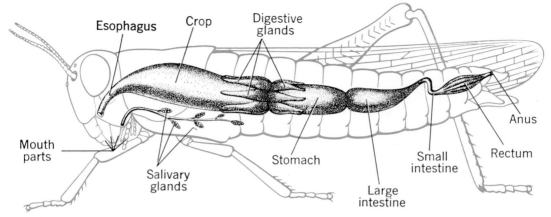

21-6 The digestive system of a grasshopper. Here again, as in the earthworm, traffic is one-way, with a succession of specialized functions performed by the organs between the mouth and the anus. What are some of these functions?

tect hard objects, such as pieces of bone or dirt, we also reject the hamburger. The oral cavity is aided in selecting food by the senses of smell and sight.

A second function of the oral cavity is the grinding of food into small particles. This is useful first because the esophagus can pass only relatively small pieces. (You can bite off a much bigger piece of a hamburger than you can swallow whole.) Also, food is easier to digest when it is in small particles. Enzymes must be in contact with the food molecules they digest. In a solid mass of food, the enzymes would penetrate slowly from the exposed surface inward and only gradually would convert the food to soluble molecules. With food in small particles, there is much more surface for the enzymes to attack and much less solid interior to penetrate.

The third and fourth major functions of the oral cavity are the digestion and lubrication accomplished by saliva. Under the tongue, behind the jaw, and in front of the ear are the salivary glands, which pour their material into the oral cavity (Figure 21-7). Saliva has two main functions. First, it adds water and mucus to the food.

The water dissolves some substances. Water and mucus act as a lubricant and ease the passage of food through the esophagus. Second, saliva contains an enzyme that begins the conversion of starch to the double sugar maltose.

Within the oral cavity, therefore, the food is selected, ground, lubricated, and its digestion begun. The food is then swallowed and passed into the esophagus, which conveys it quickly to the stomach.

This quick conveyance is achieved by a process called **peristalsis** (pehr·ih·STAL·sis —Figure 21-8). Immediately in front of a mass of food, the muscles of the esophagus wall relax and the esophagus widens. Behind the mass of food the muscles contract and squeeze the food along. The area of contraction moves as a wave from the throat to the stomach. These peristaltic waves are responsible for moving food not only through the esophagus but also through the entire alimentary canal. To demonstrate that this is so, and that it is not gravity alone that makes the food go down, you might try chewing and swallowing a cracker, or even drinking water, while hanging from a horizontal bar.

21-7 THE DIGESTIVE SYSTEM IN MAN

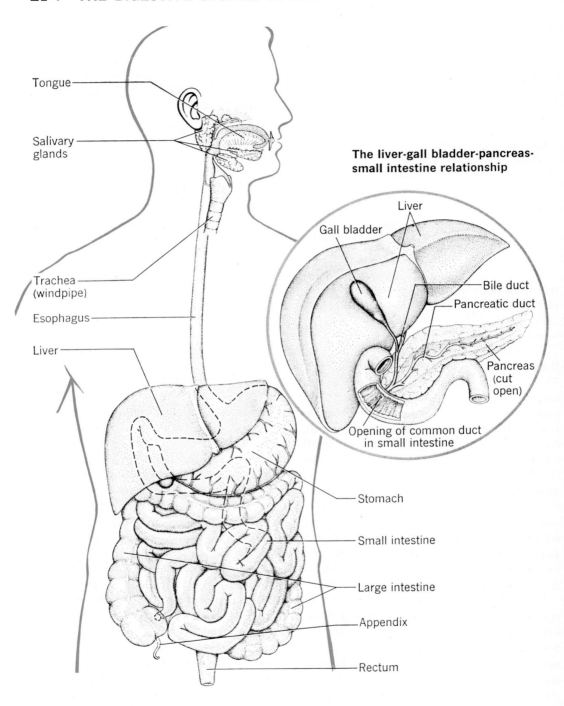

Tongue

Salivary glands

The liver-gall bladder-pancreas-small intestine relationship

Liver

Gall bladder

Bile duct

Pancreatic duct

Trachea (windpipe)

Esophagus

Liver

Pancreas (cut open)

Opening of common duct in small intestine

Stomach

Small intestine

Large intestine

Appendix

Rectum

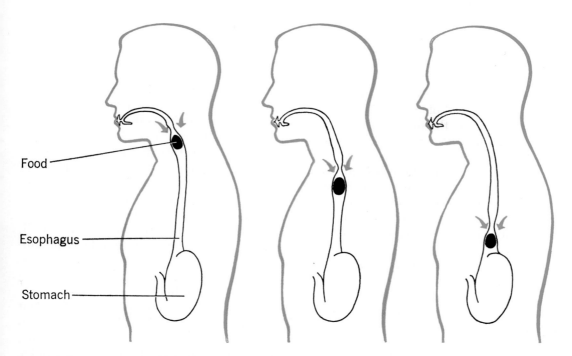

Food

Esophagus

Stomach

21-8 Movement of food through the alimentary canal. A wave of constriction of the wall of the esophagus, preceded by a wave of relaxation, forces the food through the esophagus and into the stomach. The same process of peristalsis carries the food (or the indigestible remains, following absorption of the digested food) through each of the other organs of the digestive system.

Digestion in the Stomach

A considerable amount of digestion occurs in the stomach, in contrast to the small amount that takes place in the oral cavity. The cells lining the stomach secrete gastric juice, which contains an enzyme, **pepsin,** and hydrochloric acid. The hydrochloric acid provides the pH that is necessary for the protein-digesting work of the pepsin.

A nice problem is raised here. Since gastric juice is a powerful protein-digesting fluid, why does it not digest the stomach itself, which is made mostly of protein? The answer to the question is not fully known. Certainly one of the factors involved is that certain cells of the lining of the stomach secrete mucus. This coats the inside of the stomach and makes it difficult for the gastric juice to attack the wall cells (including the cells that produced the gastric juice!).

Strong emotions at meal times can inhibit the secretion of mucus, as motion pictures of stomach action have shown. (Would you like to speculate on how such pictures might be taken?)

Unhappily, the protective mechanisms do not always work; the stomach does digest itself at times—a small portion of the lining may be eaten away. The result is an ulcer. If the ulcer is small in size and properly treated, it will heal. Large ulcers may have to be removed by surgery.

The chemical work of the stomach is facilitated by its muscular activity. Its walls contract and relax, and these movements help to mix the gastric juice and the food, thus helping enzymatic digestion.

But our story of digestion in the stomach is not complete. What causes gastric juice to be secreted? Let us return to our hamburger and bun. If we bite off a piece of the hamburger and bun, chew it, and then swallow it, there will be some gastric juice ready for the food by the time it reaches the stomach. How is the stomach able to prepare for the arrival of food? When food is in the oral cavity, the nerves in the cheeks and tongue are stimulated. These carry messages—in the form of nerve impulses—to the brain. From the brain these messages then pass to nerves that extend to the wall of the stomach, where they stimulate the gastric glands. As a consequence, there is some gastric juice in the stomach when the food arrives.

When the food touches the lining of the stomach, more gastric juice is secreted, but only a moderate amount. If you eat only a bun, which has little protein in it, the stomach does not secrete much gastric juice. On the other hand, if meat is eaten there is a need for abundant gastric juice—and there is an abundant secretion of it in response. What accounts for this neat efficiency?

The way in which proteins stimulate secretion of gastric juice is elaborate. The small amount of gastric juice that is on hand when food reaches the stomach begins the digestion of any proteins that may be present. The huge protein molecules are hydrolyzed to smaller molecules. These smaller molecules have a specific stimulating effect on some of the cells lining the stomach. They stimulate these cells to secrete a substance called **gastrin**. Gastrin enters the blood system and is distributed to all parts of the body, including the stomach. Here it has the specific effect of stimulating the cells of the stomach to secrete more gastric juice.

The economy of this mechanism is obvious. If there is protein in the stomach contents, a large amount of gastric juice is secreted. If only fats and carbohydrates are present, there will be no gastrin and no increased secretion of gastric juice.

Gastrin is a **hormone** (HOR·mohn). As such it belongs to a class of complex organic molecules that have the following characteristics: first, hormones are secreted by cells; second, they are carried by the circulatory system; third, they have very specific effects on other cells—often in different parts of the body than where they are secreted.

Gastric juice, then, is secreted in response to three types of stimuli: first, in response to messages (nerve impulses) evoked by stimuli in the mouth; second, in response to similar messages evoked by the stimulus of food in contact with the stomach wall; third, in response to the products of protein digestion, which cause a liberation of gastrin that in turn stimulates the secretion of more gastric juice.

What have we accomplished so far? Our hamburger and bun have been chewed into small bits by the teeth. The starch-digesting enzyme of saliva has begun the conversion of starch into smaller molecules. Digestion of proteins has begun in the stomach but cannot be completed there. The contractions of the stomach walls mix the food with digestive enzymes and also help break the food into smaller particles. By the time the food leaves the stomach it is a souplike mixture, thanks to partial digestion and to the water from saliva and gastric juice.

An Aside on Alexis St. Martin's Stomach

For a great many years the interior of the human body was a puzzle to investigators. Air and food went in and waste products came out. The beating of the heart could be detected. At times strange noises, gurglings, and rumblings could be heard from within.

Observations of this sort told little regarding what occurs within the body of a living individual. The only direct way of finding out what happens would be to open the body and look. The difficulties with *this* approach are rather obvious.

Major surgery was uncommon, because it was nearly always fatal, until late in the nineteenth century. Direct observations of the functioning of the parts of the body, therefore, were exceedingly rare until recently. Only as a result of the strangest of circumstances could one see inside a living human body. But this was the opportunity that came to William Beaumont (1785–1853), a physician in the United States Army.

In 1822 a badly wounded man, Alexis St. Martin, was brought to Beaumont. The accidental discharge of a shotgun had blown a large hole in St. Martin's left side. Parts of the ribs, muscles, and wall of the stomach had been shot away. Beaumont patched up his patient as well as he could, but the wound never closed properly. The wall of the stomach healed by growing to the skin and muscles of the body wall. As a result, there was a hole in the left side of the body that led to the interior of the stomach (Figure 21-9). Bandages had to be kept over the hole to prevent food from falling out.

Beaumont realized that he had a wonderful opportunity to study the function of the stomach. Alexis St. Martin cooperated, and the interior of his stomach was studied for eleven years.

Beaumont made many observations. He observed that the stomach secreted a fluid, gastric juice. He put gastric juice on meat and found that the meat was digested. He observed that the stomach moved and churned when food was in it. These and many other observations helped to lay the basis for our understanding of the stomach in man.

As a result of Beaumont's investigation, later research could be undertaken on a much more intelligent basis. Gradually, more and more was learned of stomach functioning, and gastric juice was analyzed to discover its chemical nature and activity. Eventually, the facts as we know them today emerged. Nevertheless, there is still much to be learned about the physiology of the stomach.

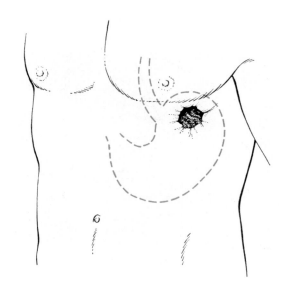

21-9 A diagram of Alexis St. Martin's shotgun wound. The wound healed, but improperly. The ruptured stomach wall and the body wall grew together around the edges of the wound, leaving a permanent hole. Through this "window," digestion in St. Martin's stomach was observed and studied for eleven years.

Digestion in the Small Intestine

Food is a souplike mixture when it leaves the stomach and enters the small intestine. Within the intestinal cavity the food is mixed with three secretions: pancreatic juice, intestinal juice, and bile. These are the secretions that complete the process of digestion.

Pancreatic juice is secreted by the pancreas (Figure 21-10), a large gland in the abdominal cavity just below the stomach. The juice reaches the intestine through small ducts that connect the pancreas to the first portion of the small intestine.

Pancreatic juice contains enzymes that act on the three main classes of foods. One of its enzymes is similar to the enzyme in saliva. It acts on starch (Figure 21-11) and converts it to the double sugar maltose. Another enzyme acts on fats, changing them to fatty acids and glycerol. Pancreatic juice

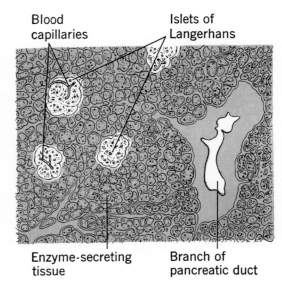

Blood capillaries

Islets of Langerhans

Enzyme-secreting tissue

Branch of pancreatic duct

21-10 A diagram of part of the pancreas, as seen under the compound microscope. Two kinds of secretions are produced. The islets of Langerhans secrete a hormone, insulin (see Figure 5-7, page 106). The remaining cells (making up most of the pancreas) secrete digestive enzymes that are delivered to the small intestine by the pancreatic duct.

also contains several enzymes that act in specific ways on proteins, changing them into smaller molecules (Figure 21-12).

Intestinal juice is secreted by the cells of the inner lining of the small intestine. This, too, contains enzymes that act on all three classes of food. Several enzymes convert double sugars, such as maltose and sucrose, into glucose and other 6-carbon sugars. One enzyme acts on fats and changes them to glycerol and fatty acids. Several enzymes, each acting in a specific way on the partially digested proteins, convert them to amino acids.

Bile, secreted by the liver, contains no enzymes, but it has an important role in the digestion of fats. Fats are insoluble in water and, therefore, are not easily attacked by digestive enzymes, which must be dissolved in water to act. Bile contains substances, the bile salts, that emulsify fats, breaking them up into small globules. This increases the surface area of the fats and speeds up enzyme action.

Absorption in the Small Intestine

The end products of digestion enter the body through cells of the small intestine. The surfaces of cells that face the cavity of the intestine absorb the food. The food is then moved across the cell to the opposite surface. There it is moved into one of two transport systems. The amino acids, simple sugars, some of the glycerol, and some vitamins and salts are transferred to the bloodstream. Some of the fatty acids, and also some vitamins, go into other less familiar transport vessels called the **lymphatics** (lim-FAT-iks). The remainder of the glycerol and fatty acids combine (again, by the active work of the intestinal cells) to form fats, which also go into the lymphatics.

These processes of active transport and combination take time, and the volume of food to be transported and combined is considerable. If the interior of the intestinal wall were a smooth cylinder, there would be relatively few cell surfaces to do the work of transport and combination. Hence absorption would be very slow—too slow, indeed, to serve the needs of a large body such as man's. A very simple expedient solves this problem. The inner surface of the intestine is wrinkled into thousands of small "fingers," called **villi** (VIL-i—Figure 21-13), which project into the intestinal cavity, thus vastly increasing the available surface.

Absorption in the Large Intestine

Where the small intestine enters the large intestine there is a blind sac, and off this is a little fingerlike projection called the **appendix** (Figure 21-7). Sometimes food becomes trapped in its cavity and an infection results—called **appendicitis**. In such cases it may be necessary to remove the appendix.

1-11 SPECIFICITY OF ENZYMES IN DIGESTION OF STARCH

a Digestion of starch begins with the action of amylase, an enzyme that occurs in saliva and in pancreatic juice. Amylase works upon starch in the mouth and in the small intestine, hydrolyzing it to molecules of the double sugar maltose.

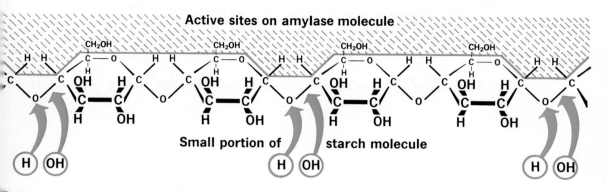

The process is completed by the intestinal enzyme maltase, which hydrolyzes the maltose molecules to molecules of glucose.

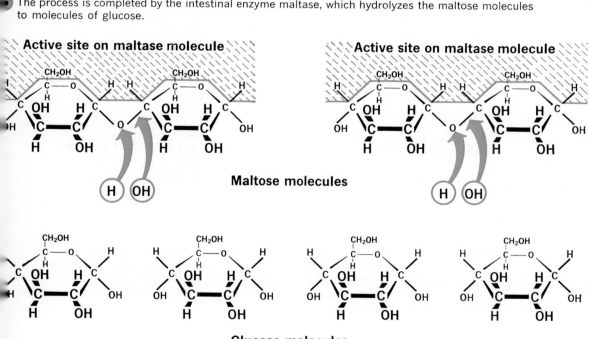

The material that passes from the small intestine to the large intestine contains a large amount of water. One of the main functions of the large intestine is to extract most of this water, which is accompanied by some salts, and return it to the bloodstream.

The body periodically rejects the remaining water and solid matter. These rejected materials are the feces. A large part, but not all, of the fecal material consists of undigested food. A considerable proportion consists of bacteria and worn-out cells sloughed

21-12 SPECIFICITY OF ENZYMES IN DIGESTION OF PROTEINS

a Protein digestion begins in the stomach. The gastric enzyme pepsin hydrolyzes bonds adjacent to tyrosine (**Tyr** below) and phenylalanine (**Phe** below).

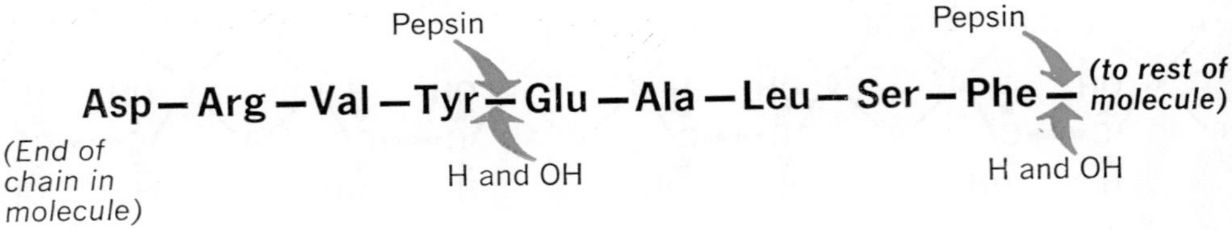

Pepsin
Pepsin
Asp — Arg — Val — Tyr — Glu — Ala — Leu — Ser — Phe —
(to rest of molecule)
(End of chain in molecule)
H and OH
H and OH

b The partly digested protein passes on to the small intestine, where pancreatic enzymes and intestinal enzymes work upon other bonds between the amino acid subunits. One of the pancreatic enzymes, trypsin, hydrolyzes bonds adjacent to arginine (**Arg** below) and lysine (not shown below). Another pancreatic enzyme, chymotrypsin, hydrolyzes the tyrosine and phenylalanine bonds *opposite the corresponding bonds already hydrolyzed by pepsin.* The same enzyme also hydrolyzes bonds adjacent to leucine (**Leu** below) and tryptophan (not shown below).

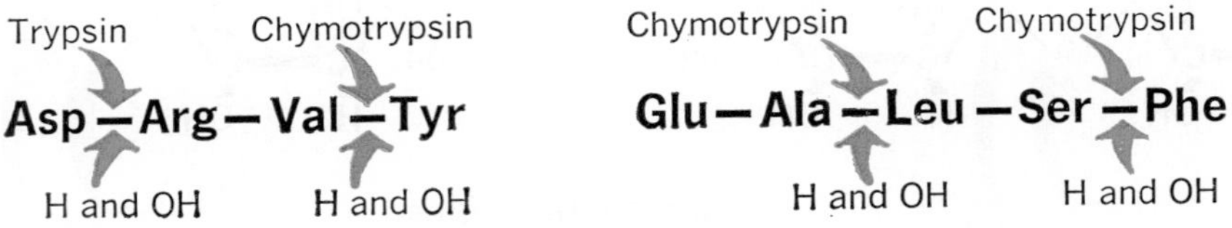

Trypsin
Chymotrypsin
Chymotrypsin
Chymotrypsin
Asp — Arg — Val — Tyr
Glu — Ala — Leu — Ser — Phe
H and OH
H and OH
H and OH
H and OH

c The process is completed by another pancreatic enzyme and by intestinal enzymes. Two of these enzymes hydrolyze bonds of amino acids *at the ends* of remaining chain fragments. Another kind of enzyme hydrolyzes bonds between *triplet* amino residues, and still another kind (shown below) hydrolyzes bonds between *doublet* amino residues.

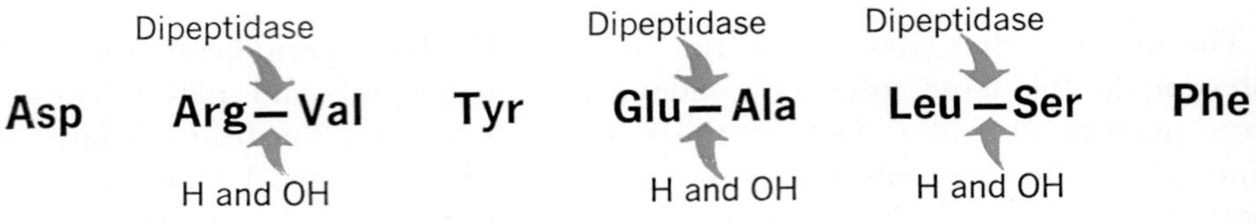

Dipeptidase
Dipeptidase
Dipeptidase
Asp
Arg — Val
Tyr
Glu — Ala
Leu — Ser
Phe
H and OH
H and OH
H and OH

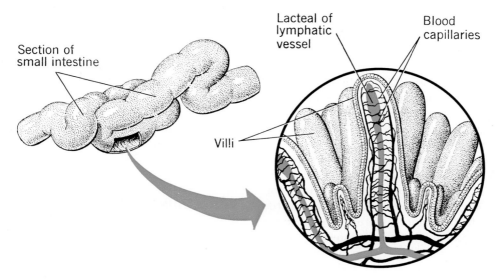

21-13 A diagram of a portion of the inner wall of the small intestine, enlarged to show several villi. Each villus contains a branch (lacteal) of a lymph vessel and a network of blood capillaries. What is the function of the lacteal? of the capillaries?

off from the walls of the digestive tract. These cells need not concern us, but the bacteria do, for they have contributed to another important function that takes place in the large intestine.

In effect, the bacteria of the large intestine are a source of additional useful substances for *our* body: they synthesize some of the vitamins necessary for our normal body function. The vitamins are absorbed into the bloodstream along with water.

An Aside on Secretin

In our brief coverage of digestion in man, we indicated what happens in each organ of the alimentary canal. Only for the secretion of gastric juice, however, did we explain what causes the secretion to occur. We could have carried the question of *cause* to other organs as well. For example, when food enters the small intestine, the pancreas secretes pancreatic juice. The pancreatic juice flows along the pancreatic duct and into the small intestine. Here it helps to digest the food, as we have learned.

The pancreas does not secrete all the time, however. In fact, there is almost no secretion unless food is in the small intestine. This is obviously an economical arrangement; when there is no food to be digested, no pancreatic juice is secreted. But what is the control?

The answer came in 1902 from the work of two English physiologists, Bayliss and Starling. At the time they did their experiments, it was well known that nerve impulses can stimulate glands to secrete. This can be shown for the pancreas as well. If the nerves to the pancreas are stimulated, pancreatic juice is secreted. There is even a reasonable mechanism to account for the result. It had been observed previously that when food enters the first portion of the intestine, pancreatic juice begins to flow. The food itself is not necessary as a stimulus, for if a weak acid is placed in the intestine, this also stimulates the flow of pancreatic juice. (Acid was tried experimentally for good reason. Food is very acid when it leaves the stomach and enters the intestine.)

A reasonable hypothesis to account for these events is as follows: Acid food, or acid alone, stimulates the nerves in the small intestine. These nerves carry messages to the brain. Connections are made in the brain, and other nerves carry the message to the pancreas: "Secrete!" All of the data are accounted for, but is the hypothesis correct? Perhaps. Let us try to prove the hypothesis in the usual way.

We first assume our hypothesis to be true. If it is true, certain deductions follow. One of the most obvious is this: if the nerves to the pancreas are cut, and if we place acid in the small intestine, there should be no secretion of pancreatic juice. Bayliss and Starling did indeed cut the nerves to the pancreas and put acid in the small intestine. When this was done, *the pancreas secreted pancreatic juice.* Clearly the hypothesis is inadequate. There must be some mechanism, in addition to nerves, that causes the pancreas to secrete.

After much experimentation they discovered the cause. They ground up the lining of the small intestine and extracted it with a weak acid. The extract was injected into the blood vessels of an experimental animal. The result was a voluminous secretion of pancreatic juice.

Their extract, therefore, contained a substance that stimulated the pancreas to secrete. They named the substance **secretin** (se·KREE·tin). This was the first real proof of the existence of chemical substances secreted by one class of cells but active upon other cells. Such substances, as we have already discussed in the case of gastrin, are known as hormones.

The cells of the small intestine secrete the hormone secretin. In man and other animals that have a circulatory system, hormones are carried throughout the body in the blood. When secretin is liberated by the cells of the intestine, therefore, it is carried all over the body by the circulatory system. Hormones have specific ef-fects. Secretin specifically affects the pancreas. It has no known effect on any organ except the pancreas.

There are some organs that secrete hormones as well as other substances. Thus, the pancreas itself has two types of secretions (Figure 21-10). One is the digestive juice known as pancreatic juice. The other is the hormone insulin, which we will discuss in Chapter 25.

CONCLUDING REMARKS—DIGESTION

The large protein molecules of a hamburger and a bun are hydrolyzed into successively smaller molecules by the protein-digesting enzymes in gastric juice, pancreatic juice, and intestinal juice (Figure 21-12). The end products of these chemical reactions are *amino acids.*

The starch of the bun is acted on by starch-digesting enzymes of saliva, pancreatic juice, and intestinal juice (Figure 21-11). The first product is the double sugar maltose. This double sugar and two other double sugars, which are common in our food, are converted by enzymes of the intestinal juice into *simple sugars.* Simple sugars contain 6 carbon atoms. The most common simple sugar is *glucose.*

The fats in the hamburger and the bun are digested in a single step. The fat-digesting enzymes of pancreatic juice and intestinal juice both act in the same way. The end products of their action are *glycerol* and *fatty acids.*

At the end of digestion, therefore, our hamburger and bun have been reduced to a soup of small molecules in the cavity of the small intestine. We began with a tremendous number of different sorts of molecules. At the end we have comparatively few: about 20 different kinds of amino acids; two or three kinds of simple sugars; glycerol; a few kinds of fatty acids; water; dissolved salts; and traces of special compounds of great importance to the life of cells, the vitamins.

These end products of digestion have three features in common: they are small molecules that can pass through cell membranes; they are molecules that cells can use for energy; and they are the kinds of molecules that the cell can use to make its own specific structure. This last point should be stressed. The proteins of the hamburger were beef proteins. They were digested to about twenty different kinds of amino acids. The amino acids are the same whether they come from beef, lamb, pork, or beans. These different amino acids enter the cells of our own bodies and are built into the proteins characteristic of man.

GUIDE QUESTIONS AND PROBLEMS

1. How do the problems of specialized cells in a multicellular animal differ from those of a single-celled animal such as *Paramecium*? How are they similar?
2. What chemical substances must all animals obtain from their environment?
3. Which of the molecules taken in by animals must be broken down chemically into smaller molecules? Why?
4. Compare digestion in *Paramecium* with digestion in *Hydra*. How is it the same? How is it different?
5. What are the advantages of a tube-type digestive system, with openings at both ends, over a saclike system with a single opening?
6. What is the advantage to animals of chewing food and breaking it up into smaller particles?
7. Why is the action of bile on fats not considered to be an enzymatic action?
8. What structures in the digestive system of land vertebrates would be least important to a freshwater fish? Why?
9. What is the relation of hormones to digestion in man? Give specific examples.

10. What are the end products of digestion? What characteristics do they have in common?
11. How is the small intestine adapted for the absorption of the products of digestion? How is absorption accomplished?
12. What is the role of the large intestine in the digestive process?

SUGGESTIONS FOR ADDITIONAL READING

Books

Best, C. H., and N. B. Taylor, *The Living Body*, 4th ed. New York, Holt, Rinehart & Winston, 1958.
    A well-written introductory account of mammalian physiology.
Buchsbaum, R., *Animals Without Backbones*, 2nd ed. Chicago, University of Chicago Press, 1948.
    Easy to read, extremely well written introduction to the invertebrates. Particularly good simplified diagrams.
Carlson, A., V. Johnson, and H. M. Cavert, *The Machinery of the Body*, 5th ed. Chicago, University of Chicago Press, 1961.
    One of the best college-level texts on principles of human physiology.
Moore, J. A., *Principles of Zoology*. New York, Oxford University Press, 1957.
    The biology of animals, with emphasis on general principles.
Schmidt-Nielsen, K., *Animal Physiology*. Englewood Cliffs (N. J.), Prentice-Hall, 1960.
    A relatively simple account of animal processes, including a good section on digestion.
Simpson, G. G., C. S. Pittendrigh, and L. H. Tiffany, *Life: An Introduction to Biology*. New York, Harcourt, Brace & World, 1957.
    A comprehensive, unified approach to biology, with evolution as the unifying theme.
Storer, T. I., and R. L. Usinger, *General Zoology*, 3rd ed. New York, McGraw-Hill, 1957.
    A traditional college textbook of zoology that can be used to obtain specific and detailed information about animals.

22

TRANSPORTATION

WITHIN MULTI-

CELLULAR ANIMALS

The processes of digestion make available molecules of amino acids, glucose, fatty acids, and glycerol. Our next problem is to see how these molecules, together with vitamins, salts, and water, are transported to where they are used.

One way that molecules move is by diffusion (page 103). The molecules and ions of substances dissolved in body fluid or a cell's cytoplasm are continually in motion, bombarding and being bombarded by other molecules, chiefly the water molecules of the fluid or the cytoplasm itself. The net result is diffusion; the dissolved substances are spread around.

The unfailing restlessness of all these molecules and ions is not enough, however. Animals require additional means for transporting the essential materials of life. Diffusion alone cannot supply the need, for it takes a great deal of time for materials in solution to diffuse even a few inches.

PROBLEMS AND METHODS OF TRANSPORTATION

Suppose we were to enlarge one specimen of *Paramecium* to the size of a man. Let us then place some molecules of glucose or amino acids at one end of our gigantic *Paramecium*. How long would it take some of these molecules to reach the other end *by diffusion alone?*

Diffusion of dissolved substances is so slow a process that at least half a year would be required for molecules to diffuse the length of our man-sized *Paramecium*. With only diffusion to distribute materials, the giant *Paramecium* would die almost immediately. Some more effective means of transporting materials from one part of the body to another would be required if the animal was to survive. Even a normal-sized *Paramecium* could not be as active as it is if it relied solely upon diffusion to transport materials throughout its one-celled body. We have already seen that the cytoplasm of *Paramecium* circulates and so helps to distribute materials.

As a generalization, we can say that no animal or animal cell large enough to be seen by the unaided eye can rely solely upon diffusion as a means of transporting molecules.

Transportation Within *Hydra*

A hydra is, of course, large enough to be seen. In fact, the body may be half a millimeter in diameter. Yet it has no specialized transportation system. How can this be?

Very little of the half-millimeter diameter of the body is occupied by cells (Figure 22-1). Most of the interior of a hydra is occupied by the digestive cavity. The body wall itself is composed of only two main layers of cells. Therefore, nearly every cell is adjacent either to the outside pond water or to the water in the digestive cavity.

The amino acids, glycerol, and fatty acids that are made available in the digestive

cavity are absorbed by the cells lining this cavity. Additional amino acids, glycerol, and fatty acids are made available by digestion within these cells themselves. Some of the molecules resulting from digestion diffuse from this inner cell layer to the cells of the outer layer. The cells of the outer layer, therefore, depend entirely on the inner cells for their organic food substances.

There is a second aspect of transportation in hydras. Some of the cells lining the digestive cavity have long hairlike projections known as flagella. The beating of these flagella stirs up the contents of the digestive cavity. In this way food particles, as well as digested food molecules, are brought into contact with the cells lining the cavity.

Transportation Within a Planarian

A planarian seems to be near the maximum size and complexity that animals can attain without a general transport system. They are very sluggish in their movements. Animals larger and more active than planarians have circulatory systems.

A planarian shows many adjustments to the absence of a general transport system. For one thing, the body is greatly flattened, as shown in Figures 20-7 and 21-4. Actually, the body is considerably more flattened than either drawing shows; both drawings have been made in a way to show the internal structure more clearly. Because the body is so flat, every cell is close to the outside, and hence in a position to absorb oxygen and to eliminate carbon dioxide.

The distribution of digested food materials is taken care of largely by the digestive sac itself, which occupies much of the interior. No part of the body is far from some branch of the digestive sac.

A planarian does have one special transport system. All over the body there are tiny tubes that arise in specialized cells and carry liquid wastes to the outside. These are parts of the excretory system, and they will be discussed in Chapter 24.

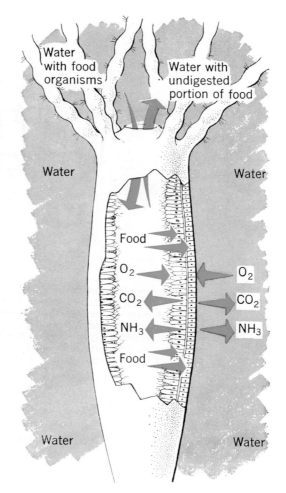

22-1 A diagram of the transportation of water, food, oxygen, and wastes in *Hydra*. No special transport system is needed. Why?

Transportation Within the Earthworm

The segmented worms are the least complex animals to possess a general system for transporting materials throughout the body. They have a circulatory system.

The circulatory system of the earthworm is similar in its basic structure to that of man and many other complex animals. It consists of a series of tubes, the blood vessels, which contain a fluid, the blood. Some of the blood vessels have walls that pulsate,

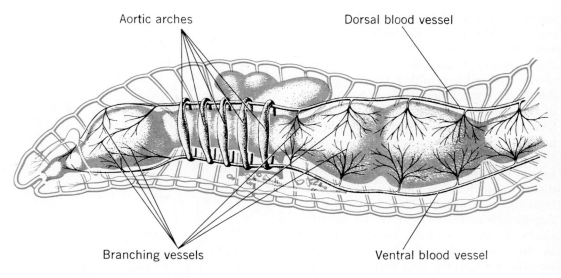

Aortic arches   Dorsal blood vessel

Branching vessels   Ventral blood vessel

22-2 The circulatory system of an earthworm. Blood is circulated through the body in a series of tubes, the blood vessels. In the skin, the blood picks up oxygen and loses carbon dioxide. In the intestine, digested foods enter the blood and are delivered to body cells everywhere. Wastes from the body cells also are transported by the blood —to the excretory organs and, in the case of carbon dioxide, to the skin. For what reasons does the earthworm need a more specialized system of transportation than the simple arrangement that is found in *Hydra* (Figure 22-1)?

and this moves the blood. Blood vessels reach every part of the body—hence every cell in the earthworm is adjacent to or at least very near a blood vessel.

The essential features of a circulatory system are shown in Figure 22-2, where a few of the blood vessels of the earthworm are drawn in a diagrammatic way.

In the anterior part of the worm there are blood vessels known as **aortic arches.** There are five of these on each side. These vessels pulsate and pump the blood toward the lower side of the worm. The lower ends of the aortic arches join a blood vessel, the **ventral vessel,** that runs along just below the digestive tract. The ventral vessel carries blood from the arches toward the anterior and posterior ends of the worm. Many small vessels branch off the ventral vessel. These go to all parts of the body. (The ones that go to the digestive tract are indicated in the diagram.) Each small vessel branches into

even smaller vessels as it enters the tissues. Eventually the smaller vessels branch into **capillaries.**

Capillaries are exceedingly small; in fact, they are microscopic in size. They are also so numerous that every cell is next to—or very near—a capillary. The branches of the ventral vessels that enter the walls of the digestive tract break up into innumerable capillaries. These capillaries have very thin walls, and diffusion across these walls occurs quite rapidly. The end products of digestion, such as amino acids and fatty acids, diffuse into the cells lining the intestine, then into the blood within the capillaries. Once in the bloodstream, these end products of digestion are distributed to all parts of the body.

The capillaries play a unique role in the circulatory system. Only these vessels have walls thin enough for molecules to diffuse across readily. Consequently, all the impor-

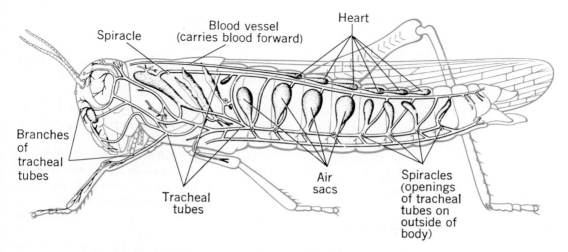

22-3 The circulatory and respiratory systems of a grasshopper. Unlike most other kinds of animals, grasshoppers and other insects have a separate transportation system that carries oxygen to the body cells, and carbon dioxide from these cells to the outside of the body. In association with this complex respiratory system, the circulatory system is simpler than in the earthworm or in man. There is a heart and a single blood vessel that carries blood forward from the heart; elsewhere the blood circulates through spaces between body organs. (Would you say that this system is less efficient than the circulatory systems of the earthworm and of man? Before reaching a decision, recall [see Figure 20-14] the abundance of insects on the earth today.)

tant exchanges that occur between blood and the environment or between blood and cells occur in capillaries. This is true for all animals with a blood circulation system.

The capillaries of the intestinal wall join one another and eventually form larger vessels. These carry blood to a vessel, the dorsal vessel, that runs along the top of the digestive tract. The dorsal vessel is contractile. It helps force the blood forward to the aortic arches, where it is pumped back into the ventral vessel.

The blood of the earthworm is a circulating fluid that is always in tubes—the blood vessels. This type of circulatory system is known as a **closed circulatory system**, since the blood is always within tubes. This is the kind of circulatory system we have.

Transportation Within the Grasshopper

The grasshopper has two main systems for transporting materials—one for gases and the other for foods and nitrogenous waste products.

Gases are transported in a series of tubes known as **tracheal** (TRAY-ke-al) **tubes.** These open to the outside of the body (Figure 22-3). From these openings the tracheal tubes extend to the interior of the body. They branch repeatedly, and the branches reach every part of the body. (The tracheal tubes will be discussed again in the next chapter when we consider respiration.)

The grasshopper's second transporting system is a blood system. This consists of a fluid that moves throughout the body carrying digested food materials and waste products, as is the case in the earthworm. However, the blood system of the grasshopper is built on quite a different plan from the closed circulatory system of the earthworm.

The grasshopper has an **open circulatory system.** That is, its blood is not always enclosed in tubes; much of the time it flows in large spaces that bathe the tissues.

The grasshopper has a small heart located in the upper portion of its body. The heart pumps blood out toward the head in a single vessel. This vessel ends in the head region, where the blood flows out of the vessel and into large spaces among the body tissues. The blood moves back through the cavities of the body. Eventually the blood returns to the heart to be pumped forward once again.

TRANSPORTATION WITHIN MAN

In man there is a single system of transport, the circulatory system. It is of the closed type, as in the earthworm. The general way in which it functions is the same as in the earthworm.

Of course, there are many differences. A single portion of man's circulatory system, the heart, serves as a pump. In the earthworm the five pairs of aortic arches, the dorsal vessel, and probably some other vessels, all contract and pump the blood.

In the earthworm, the major blood vessels are not usually differentiated as "arteries" or "veins." In man a distinction is made. **Arteries** carry blood away from the heart. They branch repeatedly and end in capillaries. **Veins** carry blood from the capillaries toward the heart.

The main pathways of circulation in the human body are shown in Figure 22-4. Let us go over some of them, beginning with the artery leading from the left side of the heart, the **aorta** (ay·OR·ta). The aorta is the chief distributing vessel of the body. Smaller arteries branch from the aorta and carry blood to capillaries of the head, arms, liver, stomach, intestine, kidneys, and legs.

The capillaries connect with tiny veins, which join to form larger veins. The veins carrying blood back from the head and arms join to form the **superior vena cava** (VEE·na KAY·va). Blood from the posterior part of the body is carried toward the heart by the **inferior vena cava.**

The superior vena cava and the inferior vena cava both carry blood to the **right atrium** (AY·trih·um), one of the four chambers of the heart. Blood next passes into the **right ventricle.** The right ventricle and the **left ventricle** are the main pumping portions of the heart.

The right ventricle contracts and forces blood into the **pulmonary** (PUL·mo·nehr·ee) **artery.** The pulmonary artery divides and carries blood to the capillaries of each lung, where, as we will see in the chapter on respiration, oxygen enters blood and carbon dioxide leaves it. Next the blood passes in the **pulmonary veins** to the **left atrium** and then to the left ventricle. The left ventricle contracts and forces blood into the aorta. This is where we began the story of circulation.

The human heart is a double pump. The left ventricle pumps blood to all parts of the body except the lungs. This blood supplies the cells with digested food substances and oxygen. It also collects carbon dioxide and nitrogenous wastes. This blood returns to the right side of the heart and then is pumped to the lungs. Thus the blood must pass through lung capillaries, gaining oxygen and losing carbon dioxide, before it is pumped around the body once again.

The blood always flows through the chambers of the heart in one direction. The direction of flow is controlled by valves (Figure 22-5). There are valves between the right atrium and right ventricle as well as between the left atrium and left ventricle. When the ventricles begin to contract, these valves close the openings into the atria. As a result, the blood passes into the pulmonary artery and into the aorta, not back into the atria.

There are also valves in the base of the aorta and the pulmonary artery. After the ventricles have contracted and forced the blood into the aorta and the pulmonary artery, the ventricles relax. If there were

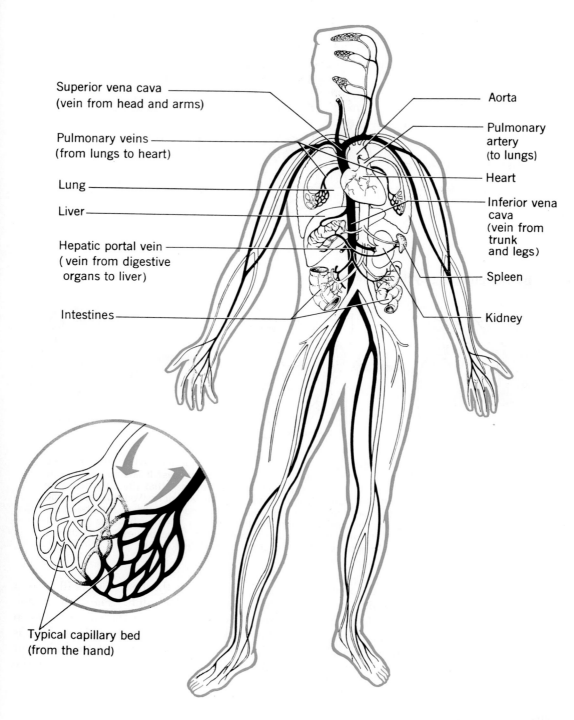

Superior vena cava
(vein from head and arms)

Pulmonary veins
(from lungs to heart)

Lung

Liver

Hepatic portal vein
(vein from digestive
organs to liver)

Intestines

Aorta

Pulmonary
artery
(to lungs)

Heart

Inferior vena
cava
(vein from
trunk
and legs)

Spleen

Kidney

Typical capillary bed
(from the hand)

a The human heart

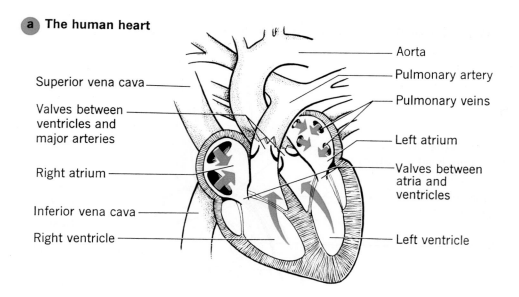

Superior vena cava

Valves between ventricles and major arteries

Right atrium

Inferior vena cava

Right ventricle

Aorta

Pulmonary artery

Pulmonary veins

Left atrium

Valves between atria and ventricles

Left ventricle

b The pumping cycle of the heart

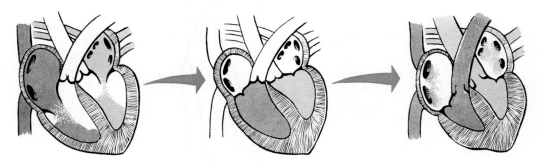

22-5 The heart and its pumping cycle. **a** In longitudinal section, the parts of the heart are shown in this diagram. What is the function of the four valves? **b** The pumping cycle reveals that the heart is really two pumps in one. Suppose that the situation were otherwise—that the heart had only one atrium and one ventricle. Would it really matter if blood from the lungs mixed in the heart with blood from the rest of the body? (Sometimes at birth, the wall between the two atria in the tiny heart is not completely closed. Infants with this irregularity are called "blue babies." What do you suppose the major symptoms of this developmental defect are?)

nothing to hold the blood in the aorta and the pulmonary artery, it would flow back into the relaxed ventricles. However, the valves at the base of the aorta and the pulmonary artery close and prevent backflow.

The abrupt closing of the valves is responsible for the sounds made by the heart.

If you listen to the heart you will hear a double sound: "lub-dub." The "lub" is due to the snapping shut of the valves between the atria and the ventricles. The "dub" is due to the snapping shut of the valves at the base of the aorta and the base of the pulmonary artery.

An individual's heart is about the size of his fist. This muscular organ must continue to contract as long as life continues. Its activity is staggering; during a normal lifetime, it contracts 3 billion times or more. Often it carries on its work even following the damage of a "heart attack." Such malfunctions are of numerous types, one of the more common of which is illustrated below in Figure 22-6.

Arteries, Veins, and Capillaries

Arteries carry blood away from the heart toward the capillaries that supply food and oxygen to the body cells. Veins carry blood from the capillaries toward the heart.

The blood leaving the ventricles and entering the aorta and the pulmonary artery is under considerable pressure; it moves rapidly. The pressure is maintained by the repeated contractions of the ventricles,

22-6 THE MECHANISM OF A "HEART ATTACK" (CORONARY THROMBOSIS)

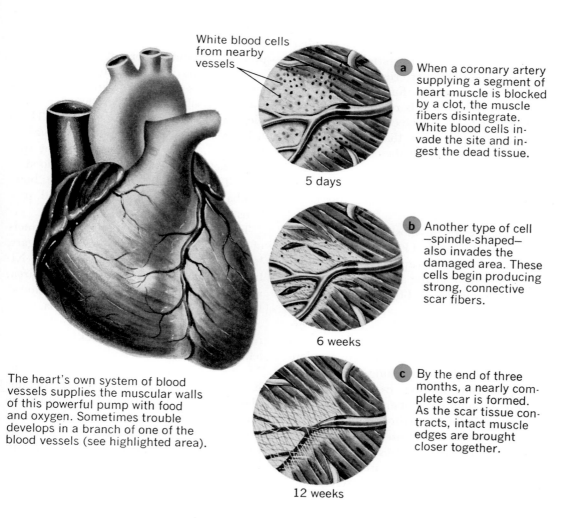

White blood cells from nearby vessels

a When a coronary artery supplying a segment of heart muscle is blocked by a clot, the muscle fibers disintegrate. White blood cells invade the site and ingest the dead tissue.

5 days

b Another type of cell —spindle-shaped— also invades the damaged area. These cells begin producing strong, connective scar fibers.

6 weeks

The heart's own system of blood vessels supplies the muscular walls of this powerful pump with food and oxygen. Sometimes trouble develops in a branch of one of the blood vessels (see highlighted area).

c By the end of three months, a nearly complete scar is formed. As the scar tissue contracts, intact muscle edges are brought closer together.

12 weeks

which force more blood into the two major arteries. It is also maintained by the elastic nature of the walls of these arteries, which expand with each heartbeat and then gradually contract between heartbeats. The pressure is sufficient to send the blood through branching arteries, capillaries, and veins, and back to the heart.

If one compares the artery leading to a particular body organ with the vein that receives the blood from the organ, two main differences will be apparent. The artery has a smaller bore and a thicker wall than the vein. The thicker-walled artery must withstand greater blood pressures than the vein. Furthermore, the artery's elasticity helps change the *pulsing* flow of blood as it leaves the heart into the *steadier* flow seen in the smaller arteries. The smaller size of the branch arteries does not indicate a lower capacity, for the *total* cross-sectional area (which is related to the volume of blood that can be carried) is greater for the branch arteries than for the main arteries, and greater for the capillaries than for the branch arteries.

The major veins have valves that serve to keep the blood flowing in one direction only—toward the heart.

Capillaries are the most numerous blood vessels in the body (Figure 22-7). Cells are always close to a capillary. It is through the capillaries that the actual exchange occurs between blood and the individual cells. Blood flow through the capillaries is regulated by tiny muscles in the walls of the arteries that open into each branching bed of capillaries. It is thus possible to regulate the amount of blood reaching any organ at any given time. During strenuous exercise, such as running or swimming, a great deal of blood is in the capillaries of the muscular system, and very little is in the capillaries of the digestive system. (Does this suggest to you the reason why you are told not to swim or indulge in excessive exercise immediately after a meal?)

Capillaries immediately under the skin contain more blood when the body is warm and thus serve to radiate heat away from the body through the skin. Conversely, when outside temperatures are low and the body is in danger of losing too much heat, these capillaries are partially shut off and contain far less blood. This is a good example of a homeostatic mechanism (page 6), one of the many ways an organism maintains constancy—in this case constancy of body temperature.

Blood

The circulatory fluid within the blood vessels is a complex substance. It consists of a fluid portion, the **plasma** (about 55 percent of the volume), and various cells and cell products (about 45 percent of the volume).

The plasma is principally water with a large number of inorganic and organic substances dissolved in it. There are, for example, several types of blood proteins. These help to maintain the osmotic pressure of the blood. They also have important special functions, such as helping the blood to clot. The antibodies that help the body combat disease organisms are blood proteins.

The plasma also contains the products of digestion—amino acids, simple sugars, fats, and other supplies used by cells. Nitrogenous waste substances, such as urea, and some of the carbon dioxide produced by cells are also found in the plasma.

Three sorts of cells or cell-like bodies—red blood cells, white blood cells, and platelets—are found in blood (Figure 22-8). The most numerous are the red blood cells. Each cubic millimeter of blood contains about five million of them. In the adult, the red blood cells are produced in bone marrow. During their formation the nucleus is cast out of each cell. Red blood cells contain large amounts of **hemoglobin** (HEE·mo·glow-b'n), a protein of great importance for carrying oxygen and to a lesser extent for carry-

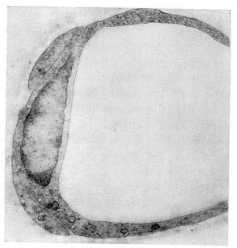

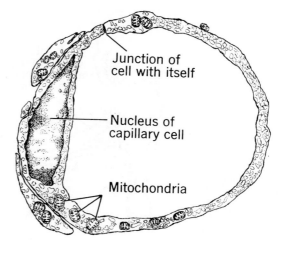

Junction of
cell with itself

Nucleus of
capillary cell

Mitochondria

Lee D. Peachy

22-7 A cross section through a capillary. On the left is an electron micrograph, and on the right a drawing, showing a section of the circular wall of a capillary as a single cell. The capillary is made up of a series of such cells (Photograph: 92,500 X).

ing carbon dioxide. More will be said about red blood cells when we discuss respiration.

White blood cells, of which there are several kinds, are produced in bone marrow, lymph nodes, and in the spleen. A cubic millimeter of blood usually contains 7,000 to 8,000 of them. All have a nucleus. The chief function of white blood cells is to protect the body against bacteria. Some of these cells can actually engulf bacteria; they push their cell membrane around the bacteria. The bacteria are then used as food by the cells. (This behavior may remind you of the manner in which some of the protozoans, or the cells of hydras, feed.) Other white blood cells form antibodies.

In an infection, such as pneumonia, the white blood cells greatly increase in number. They help to combat the disease by destroying the bacteria. The pus that forms in an infected wound is largely white blood cells that have died fighting bacteria.

The platelets are much smaller than either red blood cells or white blood cells. They contain a substance that plays a key role in the clotting of blood.

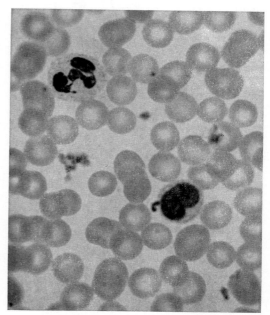

F. W. Maynard

22-8 A stained smear of human blood, as seen under the compound microscope. The doughnutlike structures are red blood cells. The two larger cells with dark nuclei are white blood cells. Small, irregularly shaped platelets can also be seen in the spaces between red blood cells.

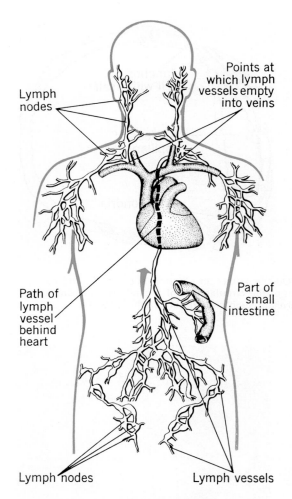

Lymph nodes

Points at which lymph vessels empty into veins

Path of lymph vessel behind heart

Part of small intestine

Lymph nodes

Lymph vessels

22-9 The lymph system in man. Lymph escapes from the bloodstream and bathes the body cells, then enters tiny branches of lymph vessels. Traffic in lymph vessels is one-way—leading through lymph nodes back to the circulatory system. Most of the lymph re-enters the circulatory system at a point on the large vein that carries blood from the left arm toward the heart. Some lymph enters the corresponding vein on the body's right side.

The Lymphatic System

Some of the fluid of blood is constantly passing through the capillary walls and entering the spaces between the cells. This fluid is called **lymph** (LIMF). The walls of the capillaries prevent the blood cells and most of the proteins of the plasma from leaving the bloodstream. (Some white blood cells leave the capillaries by forcing their way out between the cells that make up the capillary walls.) Except for these components, the composition of lymph is much the same as blood.

Lymph bathes the cells and then returns in very irregular channels known as **lymph vessels** to the veins (Figure 22-9).

Located along the lymph vessels are **lymph nodes,** which act as filters to remove harmful substances, such as bacteria, from the lymph. These lymph nodes are located at various places in the body, such as around the major organs, in the limbs, and in the neck. Frequently those in the neck become swollen during infections.

An Aside on William Harvey

It seems safe to say that man's written intellectual history goes back at least 5,000 years. During the first 4,700 of these years a most elementary fact about blood—namely, that it circulates—was unknown or unproved. (Early Chinese physicians related the pulse to a movement of the blood.)

The fact that blood does circulate was demonstrated by William Harvey (1578–1657) and Marcello Malpighi (first mentioned on page 31) in the seventeenth century. In order to understand their achievement, we must know some of the theories about blood that were held in the sixteenth and early seventeenth centuries.

Aristotle believed blood to be produced in the liver. From there, according to belief, it flowed to the heart and then out in the veins to all parts of the body. Yes, veins—not arteries. In Aristotle's day it was believed that arteries contained air. The very term "artery" is based on this belief. Artery is derived from the Greek *arteria*, which means "windpipe."

This was a perfectly justifiable error. After death, blood flows out of the arteries and accumulates in the veins of the corpse. If one examines the arteries after death, they are empty; hence it was easy to think of them as full of air.

About 500 years after Aristotle's time, Galen (A.D. 130–200), a Greek physician and author of important books on medicine, found that arteries contain blood.

In the sixteenth century it was believed that blood moves, though in a slow and irregular way. Generally it was believed that blood flowed out from the heart and back in the same vessel. There was no understanding that the heart is a pump. People generally believed what Aristotle and Galen had said so many years before.

Harvey (Figure 22-10) *almost* proved that blood circulates. He studied the hearts of pigs, dogs, snakes, frogs, fish, chick embryos, and even some of the invertebrates, such as mollusks and water fleas. In many instances he examined the heart and blood vessels of living animals. As a result of his observations, Harvey came to realize that the heart is a pump. He believed that blood circulates; that is, the heart pumps it into arteries, the arteries then carry the blood to the organs, and the veins carry it back to the heart. Harvey would have found our Figure 22-4 a good representation of his views. Why, then, is the statement made that "Harvey *almost* proved that blood circulates"?

There is an important distinction. Harvey *believed* that blood circulates; he did not *prove* it. This he realized. He knew that blood is carried to a given organ by an artery and brought back to the heart by veins. He did not know how the blood manages to get from arteries to veins. He could see that the arteries branch and become smaller and smaller. He also knew that small veins join to become larger and larger. A connection between the ends of the tiny arteries and the beginnings of the veins must exist, but he could not find it.

Malpighi did. If one examines with a mi-

© 1959, Parke, Davis & Co.

22-10 A reproduction of a painting of William Harvey, shown demonstrating evidence for his theory of blood circulation. Was his theory correct? In what way did his evidence fail to constitute proof?

croscope a small portion of the lung or urinary bladder of a living frog, the tiny capillary connections between arteries and veins can be seen (see also Laboratory Exercise 22-2). Malpighi saw that blood flows through the small arteries, into the even smaller capillaries, and then into the veins. Harvey's theory of the *circulation of blood* had been demonstrated beyond a reasonable doubt.

Harvey, without using a microscope, had done as much as he could. He knew that a connection must exist. But in science, strong belief is not fact. Harvey could never have proved his theory of circulation with the methods he used. No amount of genius enables one to see capillaries without the aid of a microscope! Malpighi and a new tool proved the theory. The circulation of blood was then fact, not theory.

Harvey's work was one of the intellectual triumphs of man. That being the case, you may wish to repeat one of the experiments that led to his theory of circulation. His

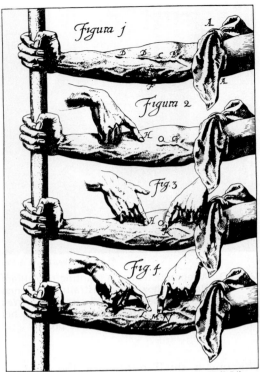

Linda Hall Library

22-11 You can duplicate Harvey's demonstration (Figure 22-10) by following these directions (in his own words): "Let an arm be tied above the elbow as (A, A, Figure 1). In the course of the veins, certain large knots or elevations (B, C, D, E, F) will be perceived . . . ; these are all formed by valves. If you press the blood [through] . . . a valve, from H to O (Figure 2), you will see no [new] influx of blood [from below, leading to the valve] . . . ; yet will the vessel continue sufficiently distended above that valve (O, G). If you now apply a finger of the other hand upon the distended part of the vein above the valve O (Figure 3), and press downwards, you will find that you cannot force the blood through or beyond the valve. If you press at one part in the course of a vein with the point of a finger (L, Figure 4), and then with another finger streak the blood upwards beyond the next valve (N), you will perceive that this portion of the vein continues empty (L, N). That blood in the veins therefore proceeds from inferior to superior parts of the heart appears most obviously."

teacher, Fabricius (1537–1619), who was a professor at the University of Padua, in Italy, had discovered that there are valves in the veins. Harvey realized that the valves made it possible for the blood in veins to move in one direction only—there could be no ebb and flow. You can repeat for yourself one of the experiments on valves (Figure 22-11).

CONCLUDING REMARKS

Some system of transporting materials throughout the body is present in all the more highly developed animals. Even the earthworm has a complicated circulatory system with distributing and collecting vessels, capillaries, and specialized vessels that pump the blood. No animals that are large in size and active in movement are without a transportation system. In some animals, such as the earthworm and man, the blood remains in the arteries, veins, and capillaries. These animals are said to have a closed circulatory system. Other animals, such as the grasshopper, have a different arrangement. The blood leaves the arteries and enters large cavities and bathes the organs. The blood continues through these cavities until it reaches the heart. This arrangement is known as an open circulatory system.

The circulatory system of man transports chemical substances throughout the body. Everything that the individual cells must receive and eliminate is moved by blood and lymph, the fluids of the circulatory system. The blood is pumped by the ventricles of the heart through the arteries—the distributing vessels of the blood system. Next the blood enters the capillaries, and it is here that exchanges are made with the cells. Some of the plasma, minus most of its blood proteins, leaves the capillaries and passes into the spaces around the cells. This fluid is called lymph. The blood that remains in the capillaries continues into the veins. The lymph passes through lymph vessels and eventually returns to large veins near the heart. The veins are the collecting vessels that return blood and lymph to the heart.

Other sorts of transporting systems are found in planarians (for transporting water and nitrogenous wastes) and in grasshoppers (for transporting gases—see Figure 22-3). What the gas-transport system does for a grasshopper will be the next topic we investigate in other animals.

GUIDE QUESTIONS AND PROBLEMS

1. What are the limitations of diffusion as a means of transporting dissolved substances in living animals?
2. What structures make up a simple but complete transport system?
3. What is the relation between the blood fluid and tissue fluid?
4. Distinguish between an open circulatory system and a closed circulatory system. Which would you expect to be more efficient? Why?
5. What are the major functions of any transport system?
6. How did Harvey approach the problem of the motion of blood through the body?
7. What essential fact about circulation was not directly known to Harvey?
8. What is the significance of the enormous surface area of the capillaries of the body?
9. What is the function of the plasma proteins?
10. What is the origin of the chemical substances normally found in the blood plasma? What function does each perform?
11. What are the cellular elements of the blood? What are their major functions?
12. What is the major difference between plasma and lymph? What is the significance of this difference?

SUGGESTIONS FOR ADDITIONAL READING

Books

Best, C. H., and N. B. Taylor, *The Living Body*, 4th ed. New York, Holt, Rinehart & Winston, 1958.
   A well-written introductory account of human physiology.
Buchsbaum, R., *Animals Without Backbones*. Chicago, University of Chicago Press, 1948.
   Easy to read, unusually well illustrated introduction to invertebrate structure and function.
Schmidt-Nielsen, K., *Animal Physiology*. Englewood Cliffs (N. J.), Prentice-Hall, 1960.
   A relatively simple account of animal physiology.
Walker, K., *Human Physiology*. Baltimore, Penguin Books, 1956.
   A well-written introduction. A paperback book.

Magazines and Journals

Bing, R. J., "Heart Metabolism." *Scientific American*, Vol. 196 (February 1957), pp. 50–54.
DeBakey, M. E., and L. H. Engel, "Blood Vessel Surgery." *Scientific American*, Vol. 204 (April 1961), pp. 88–98.
Ebert, J. D., "The First Heartbeats." *Scientific American*, Vol. 200 (March 1959), pp. 87–92.
Kilgour, F. G., "William Harvey." *Scientific American*, Vol. 186 (June 1952), pp. 56–60.
McKusick, V. A., "Heart Sounds." *Scientific American*, Vol. 194 (May 1956), pp. 120–22.
Ponder, E. W., "The Red Blood Cell." *Scientific American*, Vol. 196 (January 1957), pp. 95–98.
Slaughter, F. G., "Heart Surgery." *Scientific American*, Vol. 182 (January 1950), pp. 14–17.
Surgenor, D. M., "Blood." *Scientific American*, Vol. 190 (February 1954), pp. 54–62.
Zweifach, B. W., "The Microcirculation of the Blood." *Scientific American*, Vol. 200 (January 1959), pp. 54–60.

23

RESPIRATION IN

MULTICELLULAR

ANIMALS

With the exception of some microorganisms, all living cells require oxygen to carry out their vital activities. The cells of animals, fungi, most species of bacteria, and green plants use the energy of glucose to make ATP. A summary of the many reactions involved in making the energy of the glucose molecules available is:

$$C_6H_{12}O_6 + 6O_2 \rightarrow$$
$$6CO_2 + 6H_2O + energy$$

This is the general reaction of respiration. (In green plants during the hours of illumination, there is more photosynthesis than respiration. Hence, the net reaction for a green plant in light is photosynthesis, the reverse of what has just been given.)

Thus, two gases are involved in respiration. Oxygen is used and carbon dioxide is produced. Small amounts of carbon dioxide are used in animal cells, but so much is produced that most of it is a waste product.

Respiring cells must have some means, therefore, of obtaining oxygen and getting rid of carbon dioxide.

Respiration is the sum of all the processes involved in the equation given in the first paragraph. Respiration includes not only the processes occurring within the cell as described in Chapter 6, but *all* the events concerned with getting oxygen to the cell and disposing of carbon dioxide.

METHODS OF RESPIRATION

Respiration in *Paramecium* is relatively simple (Chapter 19). The oxygen molecules in pond water diffuse across the cell membrane and into the cytoplasm. Diffusion and the movements of the cytoplasm carry the oxygen to the mitochondria (Chapter 6). Here the oxygen is combined with hydrogen to form water. The carbon dioxide molecules move in the reverse direction. Diffusion and movements of the cytoplasm carry them to the cell membrane. They diffuse across the cell membrane and into the surrounding pond water. *Paramecium* swims on, leaving its wastes behind.

The source of oxygen for animals that live on land is the air that surrounds them. The supply of oxygen for aquatic animals is what is dissolved in the water.

Oxygen and carbon dioxide molecules cross living cell membranes readily. They can do this because living membranes are moist. They cannot cross dry membranes. Frogs are able to respire through their skins, which are moist. This is not possible for animals with dry skins, such as insects, reptiles, birds, and mammals.

Animals with dry skins, therefore, have the problem of obtaining oxygen and disposing of carbon dioxide in other ways. Even the frog has this problem, too, for its body is too large to be supplied with oxygen solely (or even largely) through the skin. The solution to the problem is roughly the same for all these animals. Thin, moist

23·1 RESPIRATION IN THE EARTHWORM

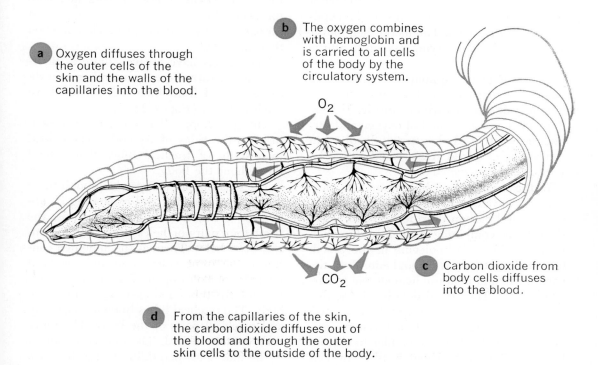

a Oxygen diffuses through the outer cells of the skin and the walls of the capillaries into the blood.

b The oxygen combines with hemoglobin and is carried to all cells of the body by the circulatory system.

O_2

c Carbon dioxide from body cells diffuses into the blood.

CO_2

d From the capillaries of the skin, the carbon dioxide diffuses out of the blood and through the outer skin cells to the outside of the body.

membranes, which are essential for respiration, are situated in the interior of the body, as the linings of lungs, tracheal tubes, and gills.

Respiration in *Hydra* and a Planarian

Neither a hydra nor a planarian has organs specialized solely for respiration. As we have learned before, both have their cells in thin layers. Both live in water. Oxygen diffuses into their bodies across the membranes of the outermost cells. In the case of hydras, oxygen also diffuses from the water in the digestive cavity into the adjacent cells.

Carbon dioxide leaves hydras and planarians by simple diffusion.

Respiration in the Earthworm

The earthworm has a moist skin. Oxygen diffuses across the outermost cells. Carbon

dioxide leaves by diffusing out from the same cells. In these respects earthworms resemble hydras and planarians.

If the earthworm relied only on diffusion to supply its cells with oxygen and to remove the carbon dioxide, it would have been extinct long ago. Or, rather, it never could have existed at all. Its body is too big. The oxygen that diffuses in would move too slowly to be used by any except the outermost layers of cells. Cells in the interior would die from want of oxygen (see the argument at beginning of Chapter 22).

The solution to this problem is a system of transportation. In the last chapter we learned that the earthworm has a circulatory system. The blood in the circulatory system transports oxygen to the cells and carries carbon dioxide away (Figure 23-1).

Blood, then, forms the link between the cells and the outside environment. The skin of the earthworm is richly supplied with capillaries. Oxygen diffuses across the outer cells of the skin and the walls of the capillaries into the blood. The blood then moves around the body, carrying oxygen to all the cells.

The cells of active animals require large amounts of oxygen, and they produce large amounts of excess carbon dioxide. If they depended on the amount of oxygen and carbon dioxide that can be carried dissolved in the water of blood, they could never be very active or very large.

In the course of evolution, animals have evolved ways of carrying large amounts of oxygen and carbon dioxide in blood. They do this by combining oxygen and carbon dioxide with some molecule in the blood. One such molecule is hemoglobin. Both the earthworm and man use hemoglobin to carry oxygen. (The actual details will be discussed in the section on respiration in man.)

The advantages of a blood system containing hemoglobin can be understood from the following data. About 5 ml of oxygen can dissolve in a liter of water (at room temperature). The same amount of blood from the earthworm, which has hemoglobin in solution, can hold about 65 ml of oxygen. Man has an even better arrangement, with large amounts of hemoglobin in his red blood cells. A liter of his blood will hold 250 ml of oxygen. Thus, earthworm blood can carry about 13 times as much oxygen as can water. Human blood can carry about 50 times as much as water.

Respiration in the Grasshopper

It is probable that the ancestors of the grasshopper and of other arthropods had a circulatory system with hemoglobin (since they are believed to have been annelidlike ancestors—see page 378). As the primitive arthropods evolved, however, blood became increasingly less important for land-dwelling forms in the transport of oxygen and carbon dioxide. Some insect larvae have hemoglobin in their blood, but apart from these, the blood of insects lacks hemoglobin. Their blood, therefore, is unimportant for carrying respiratory gases. Then how do they manage?

The insects have evolved quite a different way of carrying oxygen and carbon dioxide to and from their cells. They have tracheal tubes (Figure 22-3).

The grasshopper has ten pairs of openings on the sides of its body. These lead to a series of tracheal tubes that extend throughout the body.

The grasshopper pumps air through these tubes by contracting and expanding its abdomen. When the abdomen expands, the front four pairs of holes are open. Air enters these holes. Then, as the abdomen contracts, the front holes close and the hind six pairs of holes open. This forces the air through the tubes and eventually out of the body. The tracheal tubes branch repeatedly and reach all parts of the body. The inner ends contain a fluid. The oxygen dissolves in the fluid and then diffuses into the cells. Carbon dioxide moves in the reverse direction—also by diffusion and the movement of the air through the tracheal tubes.

RESPIRATION IN MAN

Man faces the same general problems of obtaining oxygen and getting rid of carbon dioxide as do all other large and complex animals. He must have moist and thin respiratory membranes across which gaseous exchanges with the environment can occur. In addition, he must have some means of transporting oxygen and carbon dioxide to and from the cells.

The respiratory membranes through which exchange of gases with the environment occurs are the linings of the lungs. The linings are much folded, and so their total surface is enormous. If flattened out, they would cover an area of about 93 square meters (1,000 square feet). How

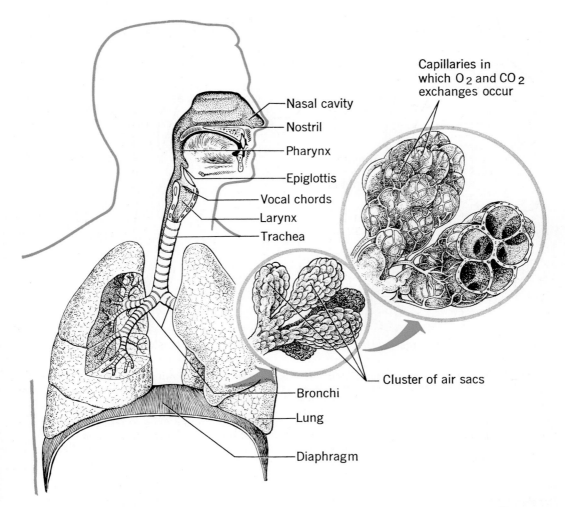

23-2 The respiratory system of man. Part of one lung has been cut away to expose the branching system of bronchial tubes. In the successive enlargements of lung tissue in the drawings extending to the right, the extremely small structures (or air sacs) responsible for bringing fresh air into contact with the capillaries are shown.

does this compare with the area of the floor of your biology classroom?

The transport of oxygen and carbon dioxide between lungs and cells is taken care of by the circulatory system. Our first problem, therefore, will be to bring some portion of the circulatory system close enough to the air for diffusion of the respiratory gases to occur. The lining of the lungs is richly supplied with capillaries. In some parts of the lungs, moreover, the capillary walls themselves form the lining of the lungs. Thus, blood is as close to air as possible.

The lungs are closed sacs that connect to the outside by way of the trachea and the nostrils or mouth (Figure 23-2). Diffusion alone is not enough to keep the air in the lungs "pure." It is necessary to pump air in and out.

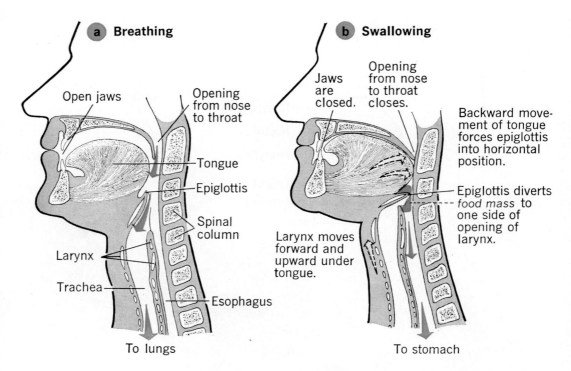

a Breathing

Open jaws

Opening from nose to throat

Tongue

Epiglottis

Spinal column

Larynx

Trachea

Esophagus

To lungs

b Swallowing

Jaws are closed.

Opening from nose to throat closes.

Backward movement of tongue forces epiglottis into horizontal position.

Epiglottis diverts *food mass* to one side of opening of larynx.

Larynx moves forward and upward under tongue.

To stomach

23-3 Events in the throat associated with breathing (**a**) and swallowing (**b**). The commonly held belief that the epiglottis closes downward upon the larynx when food is swallowed is not quite true. The closure is probably never effectively completed; whatever degree of closure exists is determined partly by the backward movement of the tongue during swallowing (which forces the epiglottis into a more or less horizontal position) and partly by the upward movement of the larynx (which brings it up under the epiglottis). Food does not enter the partly open larynx and obstruct breathing primarily because the epiglottis diverts the food mass to one side of the opening.

Breathing

The events concerned with pumping air in and out of the lungs are called breathing.

The structures directly concerned with channeling air into contact with capillaries containing blood are the **nostrils, nasal cavity, pharynx, larynx** (LAR·inks), **trachea** (TRAY·ke·a), **bronchi** (BRONG·ky), and **lungs** (Figure 23-2). Air enters the body through the nostrils (or, instead, the mouth) and passes into the nasal cavity. Here it is filtered. The moist surfaces of the lining of the nasal cavity, and the hairs growing from its sides, remove some of the tiny particles of dirt in the air. In addition, as the inhaled air passes through the nasal cavity, its tem-

perature is brought close to that of the body, and it is humidified.

From the nasal cavity the air goes into the pharynx. There is a tricky problem here. At the back of the pharynx there are two passageways, one to the lungs and one to the stomach. It is important that air go in one and food in the other. (Try to swallow and breathe at the same time. It cannot be done.) We do not want food to enter the tube to the lungs, nor is it particularly desirable that air should go to the stomach. The traffic is kept properly channeled by a flaplike valve (the **epiglottis**—ep·ih·GLOT·iss) that protects the tube to the lungs. This valve is partly closed when we swallow; it deflects food down to the stomach and keeps it out of the route to the lungs. The epiglottis opens more widely when we take a breath, and air enters the lungs (Figure 23-3).

The passageway to the lungs goes first through the larynx. This stiff box contains our **vocal cords.** When air passes out of the lungs and over the vocal cords, it causes them to vibrate. This produces sounds—the basis of our speech and song.

The larynx is at the upper end of the trachea. You can feel both larynx and trachea by pressing gently on your throat. At its lower end the trachea divides into two bronchi—one leading to each lung.

The lungs are spongy organs. Their interior is divided into many small chambers, thus tremendously increasing the moist surface available for transfer of gases between air and blood.

Breathing is the process of inhaling and exhaling. The lungs themselves neither draw in air nor push it out. Instead, the chest wall and the **diaphragm** (DY·a·fram) act as a large pump in moving air into and out of the lungs (Figure 23-4).

The chest wall is made up of the ribs, their muscles, and the skin. The ribs are attached at an angle to the spine (if you run your finger along one rib, you will notice that it extends downward from the spine). When we inhale, the chest wall moves up and out. This increases the volume of the chest cavity.

The diaphragm is a sheet of muscle that extends across the body cavity. It may be thought of as the floor of the chest cavity. When the diaphragm is relaxed, it is in the shape of a dome—with the convex side of the dome extending into the chest cavity. When the diaphragm contracts it flattens out a bit. That is, the dome moves downward. As a result, the volume of the chest cavity is still further increased.

There are two ways, therefore, for the volume of the chest cavity to increase: by elevation of the chest wall and by lowering of

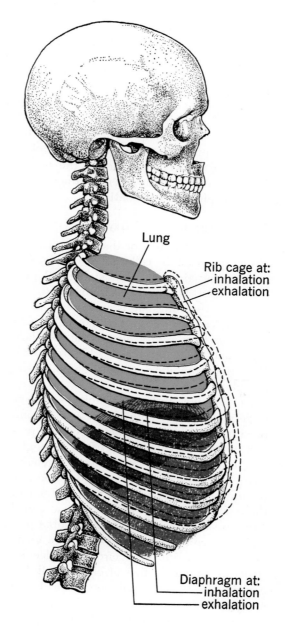

Lung

Rib cage at:
inhalation
exhalation

Diaphragm at:
inhalation
exhalation

23-4 Movements of the thorax during inhalation and exhalation. The positions of the rib cage and of the diaphragm as shown represent a degree of movement that is characteristic of moderately deep breathing. During periods of rest or of quiet activity, the diaphragm contracts to this extent only occasionally; thus, the type of breathing used most of the time by most people is chiefly "rib breathing."

RESPIRATION IN MULTICELLULAR ANIMALS **417**

the diaphragm. When the volume of the chest cavity is increased, its internal pressure decreases and the air from the outside rushes into the lungs. This is **inspiration** (inhalation).

Then the reverse occurs. The chest wall is lowered and the diaphragm relaxes and assumes its dome shape. These changes increase the pressure on the lungs; their elastic tissue contracts and squeezes the air out through the nose to the external atmosphere. This is **expiration** (exhalation).

The Transportation of Oxygen

The original source of the oxygen that is ultimately used in cells is, of course, the surrounding air. Air contains about 21 percent oxygen. When air is brought into the cavity of the lungs, it is in close contact with the capillaries. Oxygen molecules pass from the lung cavity across the capillary walls and into the blood (Figure 23-2). Here they combine with hemoglobin in the red blood cells.

Hemoglobin, being a protein, is a very large molecule. In spite of its size and complexity, we know the structure of few protein molecules better than that of hemoglobin. It consists of four component chains (see Chapter 5) loosely bound together, two of one sort and two of another. Each of these four chains is folded into a coiled structure very similar to the myoglobin protein molecule (Figure 5-9). Each chain bears a **heme** group, a circular molecular structure similar to that of chlorophyll, but carrying in its center an iron, instead of a magnesium, atom.

When oxygen combines with hemoglobin it attaches to the iron atoms. One molecule of oxygen, O_2, combines with each iron atom. The combination of oxygen and hemoglobin is called **oxyhemoglobin** (ok-sih·HEE·mo·glow·b'n). We can express the reaction as:

$$Hb + O_2 \rightarrow HbO_2$$

(The symbols Hb and HbO_2 are abbreviations for hemoglobin and oxyhemoglobin. They are not true chemical symbols.)

There are some important things to learn about this reaction between hemoglobin and oxygen. One is that the reaction is reversible.

$$Hb + O_2 \rightleftarrows HbO_2$$

Not only can hemoglobin combine with oxygen, but oxyhemoglobin can break up into hemoglobin and oxygen.

Another important feature of the reaction is its dependence on the *concentration* of oxygen. If hemoglobin is exposed to air at sea level, nearly every molecule combines with oxygen to form oxyhemoglobin (Figure 23-5). At a height of 13 km (about 8 miles) above sea level, the concentration of oxygen is much lower—about one fifth as great as at sea level. Under these conditions only about half the molecules of hemoglobin combine with the gas to form oxyhemoglobin. In fact, human life is impossible at such an altitude without a supplementary supply of oxygen.

The air in our lungs is not the same as the surrounding air. When we are at rest, or exercising moderately, our breathing exchanges only a small portion of the air in the lungs. The concentration of oxygen in the lung cavity is about two thirds of that in fresh air. Nevertheless, this is sufficient for about 95 percent of the hemoglobin molecules to form oxyhemoglobin.

In the capillaries of the tissues, the red blood cells meet a very different environment. The tissue cells are continually using oxygen; hence, the concentration of oxygen is quite low in them. It might be only one third of that in the lungs. When the concentration of oxygen is so low, only about half of the hemoglobin can be HbO_2. The other half is Hb. This means that when the blood reaches these tissues, about half the HbO_2 molecules break down and form Hb and O_2. The oxygen enters the cells.

In other words, the hemoglobin molecule forms a loose compound, oxyhemoglobin, with oxygen when there is a great amount of oxygen available, as in the lungs. The oxyhemoglobin gives up its oxygen when it comes to an area poor in oxygen, as in the tissues of the body.

When man is exposed to high altitudes, either as a mountain climber or as an aviator in an unpressurized airplane, he has the problem of obtaining oxygen. When the concentration of oxygen is low, as it is at high altitudes, the proportion of hemoglobin that forms oxyhemoglobin in the lung capillaries is lower than that at sea level. The blood moves throughout the body with an inadequate amount of oxyhemoglobin. The cells, therefore, do not receive as much oxygen as they need.

The Transportation of Carbon Dioxide

In the reactions that occur within cells, an excess of carbon dioxide is produced. The excess carbon dioxide diffuses into the capillaries. Carbon dioxide is carried in blood in two forms: some is combined with hemoglobin, but most is carried as the bicarbonate ion.

The formation of the bicarbonate ion occurs in the following way. First, carbonic acid is formed:

$$CO_2 + H_2O \rightarrow H_2CO_3$$

The carbonic acid then ionizes to form hydrogen ions and bicarbonate ions:

$$H_2CO_3 \rightarrow H^+ + HCO_3^-$$

When blood leaves the capillary beds in the tissues of the body, therefore, the carbon dioxide is mostly in the form of HCO_3^-.

In the capillaries of the lungs the reverse reactions occur:

$$HCO_3^- + H^+ \rightarrow H_2CO_3 \rightarrow H_2O + CO_2$$

Carbon dioxide passes out of the capillaries, by diffusion, into the cavity of the lungs, from which it is exhaled.

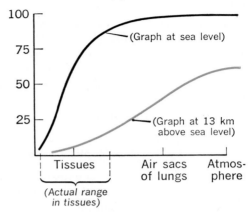

Relative saturation with oxygen — or — Percent of hemoglobin that combines with oxygen

23-5 The relative oxygen saturation of human blood in various parts of the body, at sea level and at 13 kilometers above sea level. The atmospheric concentration of oxygen is also shown in both instances. The difference in oxygen concentration of blood in the lungs and blood in the tissues is an indication that the blood releases its oxygen when it is in the tissues (where the relative oxygen concentration is always low—why?). At high altitudes, such as 13 km shown here, the concentration of oxygen in the atmosphere is so low that even in the lungs no more than 50 to 60 percent of the hemoglobin molecules combine with oxygen.

The blood, therefore, serves as a carrier of the respiratory gases, oxygen and carbon dioxide. The mechanisms involved are noteworthy in that those occurring in the capillaries of the lungs are the exact opposite of those occurring in the capillaries of other tissues. This is a most economical situation, because the hemoglobin and the water are not used up. All of the hemoglobin molecules of the body's millions of red blood cells can be used over and over again in the transport of oxygen.

CONCLUDING REMARKS

Before we discuss the next organ system of the animal body, we should pause and take stock. What have we learned so far?

Reactions are constantly going on in the cells of animals. Some of the most important involve the oxidation of glucose to liberate energy. The end products of these reactions are carbon dioxide and water. The details are complex but the total picture can be expressed as follows:

$$C_6H_{12}O_6 + 6O_2 \rightarrow$$
$$6CO_2 + 6H_2O + energy$$

Glucose and oxygen are being used up. Carbon dioxide and water are being produced. There must be mechanisms to provide a constant supply of the things being used and to dispose of those being produced.

We have already learned how the digestive system supplies glucose, which is transported to all cells, either by diffusion or by the circulatory system.

In some animals, such as hydras and planarians, oxygen is supplied by diffusion. In some other animals the combined efforts of the respiratory and circulatory systems make oxygen available to the cells. The grasshopper has a tracheal system.

The two items on the left side of our equation, therefore, have been accounted for. There are two kinds of molecules on the right side, carbon dioxide and water. There is no problem with the products of a reaction if they can be used by the cell. If they cannot be used, or are overabundant, they must be removed.

A small amount of carbon dioxide is used in animal cells, but so much more is produced than is needed that most is a waste product. In hydras and planarians, the carbon dioxide diffuses out. In earthworms and man, the circulatory and respiratory systems eliminate the excess carbon dioxide. Grasshoppers dispose of carbon dioxide via the tracheal tubes.

Water is usually not a waste product in man and other animals that live on land. In our own case, water is constantly lost by evaporation from the moist lining of our lungs and in perspiration, so it must be replaced. Water is also necessary to us for removal of wastes by the kidneys. Insects also use the water produced in their cells.

In planarians and hydras, water is a waste product and must be removed.

The mechanisms described so far account in a general way for what happens, not only to glucose, but to all carbohydrates and fats. They contain carbon, hydrogen, and oxygen, and the end products of their oxidation are carbon dioxide and water.

The proteins represent a special situation because they contain nitrogen as well as carbon, hydrogen, and oxygen. The nitrogen presents a special problem—one handled by the excretory system.

GUIDE QUESTIONS AND PROBLEMS

1. How do gills function in gas exchanges?
2. What are the advantages of tracheal tubes and lungs for respiration on land?
3. How is the circulatory system related to the respiratory system in complex animals?
4. What is the role of respiratory molecules, such as hemoglobin, in oxygen transport?
5. What are some important properties of the respiratory molecules in blood?
6. How is carbon dioxide carried in the blood?
7. Distinguish between tissue respiration and pulmonary respiration in man.
8. How are breathing and gas transport affected during ascent to high altitudes?

SUGGESTIONS FOR ADDITIONAL READING

Books   (See references at end of Chapter 22.)

Magazines and Journals

Fox, H. M., "Blood Pigments." *Scientific American*, Vol. 182 (March 1950), pp. 20–22.
Williams, C. M., "Insect Breathing." *Scientific American*, Vol. 188 (Feb. 1953), pp. 28–32.

24

EXCRETION IN

MULTICELLULAR

ANIMALS

More kinds of chemical reactions go on in every animal cell than in the largest of chemical factories. Chromosomes, mitochondria, ribosomes, contractile vacuoles, cell membranes, and all other cell structures are constructed within the cell.

The chemical reactions that occur within cells produce substances or release energy that the cell uses to remain alive. For example, the complete oxidation of glucose results in energy being made available. This is necessary for the cell to live. However, molecules of carbon dioxide and water remain. For the most part, the cell has no way of chemically using either. They are waste products.

Considering the tremendous numbers of chemical reactions that occur in cells, it is surprising that so few of the molecules produced are waste products. As we learned before, the chief waste products are carbon dioxide, water, and nitrogen-containing

compounds (such as ammonia, urea, and uric acid). The removal of these, as well as all other waste products resulting from the cell's activities, is **excretion.** The removal of carbon dioxide is part of excretion, but it is also part of respiration. The unified body of a complex organism does not always recognize the arbitrary divisions we attempt to make in its activities. In this chapter our main concern will be with nitrogen excretion. When we refer to an excretory system we will mean the structures responsible for removing the wastes of cellular metabolism, with the exception of carbon dioxide.

METHODS OF EXCRETION

In Chapter 19 we learned how *Paramecium* excretes. The carbon dioxide and ammonia diffuse out of the cell. Water is more of a problem. The cell obtains some as a consequence of oxidation. Much more is constantly diffusing in from the surrounding pond. The surplus water in the cell is pumped out by the contractile vacuoles.

Excretion in *Hydra*

Hydras have no structures specialized for excretion. Carbon dioxide and the principal nitrogenous waste product, ammonia, leave the cells by diffusion. Nearly every cell is either adjacent to the outside pond water or to the digestive cavity, so there is a ready place to pass the wastes.

Hydras are freshwater organisms. Their cells have a lower concentration of water than does the surrounding pond. Hydra cells, therefore, face the same problem as *Paramecium* does. Water is probably entering constantly. The mechanism by which the surplus water is cast out is not fully known.

Since the normal physical situation is for the water to diffuse in, each cell must do work to remove the water and get it back into the pond. Energy is required. We speak

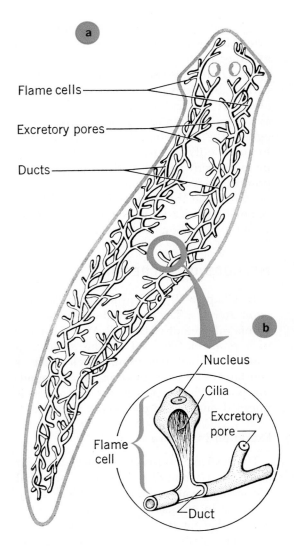

Flame cells

Excretory pores

Ducts

a

b

Nucleus

Cilia

Excretory pore

Flame cell

Duct

24-1 The excretory system of a planarian. Shown enlarged are a flame cell and an excretory pore. Flame cells remove wastes (mainly excess water) from within the body; the wastes are then eliminated through the pores in the body wall.

of this as **active transport.** The active transport of water across the cell membrane to the outside balances the diffusion of water into the cell. Thus, the concentration of water remains relatively constant within the cells—but at the cost of energy expenditure.

Excretion in the Planarian

In flatworms the excretion of carbon dioxide and much of the chief nitrogenous waste substance, ammonia, is simply a matter of diffusion.

A planarian, however, has an excretory system. This consists of a series of branching tubes. The outer ends of the tubes open to the outside through small pores. The inner ends of the tubes end in **flame cells** (Figure 24-1).

Each flame cell contains a space that connects with an excretory duct. A tuft of cilia projects into the space within the cell. In a living animal, the movement of the cilia reminded the early observers of a flickering candle flame—hence the name "flame cell."

The main function of the excretory system of a planarian is probably the removal of excess water. Planarians must cope with the same problem that faces paramecia and hydras. Water constantly diffuses into the cell and must be removed. It is probable that the flame cells remove the excess water from the spaces around the cells.

Excretion in the Earthworm

Once again, in earthworms, our understanding of excretion is most incomplete. The earthworm has a circulatory system, and this is the chief route for the removal of carbon dioxide.

The earthworm has excretory tubes (Figure 24-2), two for nearly every segment of the body. The inner end of each tube is in the body cavity. The body cavity contains a fluid, and within this fluid many waste substances collect. Some of these are removed by the excretory tubes, which have openings encircled with cilia. The cilia propel fluid into each excretory tube, and contractions of the muscular wall of the excretory tube force the fluid through it to the outside of the body.

The earthworm also has some specialized waste-absorbing cells. These are found in various parts of the body. There are many,

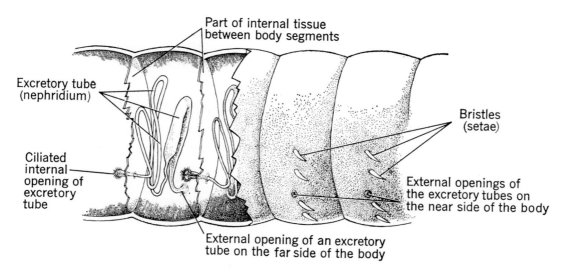

Labels on figure:
Part of internal tissue between body segments

Excretory tube (nephridium)

Ciliated internal opening of excretory tube

Bristles (setae)

External openings of the excretory tubes on the near side of the body

External opening of an excretory tube on the far side of the body

24-2 Excretory tubes in the earthworm. The near side of the body, including the alimentary canal and the circulatory system, has been cut away in the left-hand portion of the drawing. Each excretory tube has its internal opening in one body segment and its external opening in the next segment to the rear.

for example, on the wall of the intestine facing the body cavity. These waste-absorbing cells remove waste products from the blood. Eventually they break off from the outer wall of the intestine and become free in the fluid of the body cavity. After this, the waste-absorbing cells move to the outer part of the skin. There they disintegrate, leaving the wastes as pigments in the skin. This is a strange process.

Ammonia and urea are the chief nitrogen-containing wastes that are excreted.

Excretion in the Grasshopper

The grasshopper has specialized excretory tubes. These are often called **Malpighian** (mal·PIG·ih·an) **tubules** (Figure 24-3). (They were discovered by Malpighi, who, you may recall, made many contributions to biological science.) They are long, fine tubes. One end of each tube opens into the digestive canal. The other end floats freely in the large blood cavities. The excretory tubes extract waste products from the blood and pass these into the digestive canal.

Eventually the wastes pass out through the anus, along with undigested food remnants.

The chief nitrogenous waste product of the grasshopper is uric acid. The fact that uric acid, rather than ammonia or urea, is excreted is one of the grasshopper's evolutionary adaptations for life on land. Ammonia is very poisonous to cells. If the ammonia concentration in the blood of a rabbit reaches as much as one part in 20,000, the rabbit dies. Urea is less toxic. Uric acid is hardly poisonous at all. Ammonia can be the chief nitrogenous waste product only in very small animals, where it can leave cells rapidly by diffusion, and if there is plenty of water to wash the wastes away. Thus, *Paramecium, Hydra,* and the planarian can excrete ammonia.

Urea is excreted only if the animal lives in an environment where there is plenty of water. Man excretes urea—but with so much water that the urea concentration is always low. We require at least a liter of water each day just to carry away the urea produced by our cells.

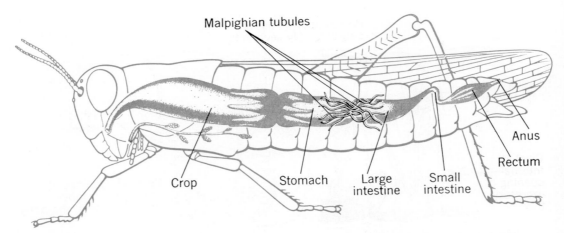

24-3 The excretory system of a grasshopper. The Malpighian tubules are the excretory organs. They remove nitrogen-containing wastes from blood in the cavities between body organs. The wastes are dumped into the alimentary canal and eliminated through the anus. (In what ways other than excretion have you found the grasshopper's solution to problems of life different from that of man? Recall, for example, the manner in which the grasshopper supplies its body cells with oxygen.)

The grasshopper excretes its nitrogenous wastes in the form of nontoxic uric acid. Little water is used to carry away the uric acid. In fact, the grasshopper deposits solid uric acid crystals in the cavities of its excretory tubes. These crystals then pass into the digestive tract and out with the undigested food materials.

The grasshopper disposes of its carbon dioxide via the tracheal tubes (Chapter 23).

EXCRETION IN MAN

In man, most nitrogen waste is excreted as urea, $CO(NH_2)_2$. Urea, as you may remember from Chapter 5, is formed by combining two amino groups with carbon and oxygen. A small amount of uric acid is also excreted by man.

Most of the urea is formed in the liver. It is here that the amino groups are removed from the amino acids. Figure 24-4 shows one way in which this is accomplished. We will begin with two molecules of an amino acid. In a reaction controlled by an enzyme, two amino acid molecules combine with a molecule of oxygen. Two molecules of ammonia are split off. The rest of the molecule is now pyruvic acid, or some related organic acid.

You may recall that pyruvic acid is a key substance in the oxidation reactions that occur in cells (page 132). The pyruvic acid formed, therefore, is oxidized, and energy is released to the synthesis of ATP from ADP. The other acids can be converted to fat or carbohydrate, or into pyruvic acid itself.

Now back to the ammonia molecules, which we have learned are toxic in high concentration. They are rapidly removed by being combined with carbon dioxide to form urea. Cells have a special way of doing this—involving three organic molecules: **ornithine** (OR·nih·theen), **citrulline** (sih-TRUL·een), and **arginine** (AR·jih·neen). Figure 24-4 explains the process.

First, one of the molecules of ammonia and a molecule of carbon dioxide combine with ornithine. This forms citrulline. Citrulline combines with another molecule of

24-4 THE FORMATION OF UREA

Alanine

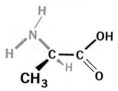

a If the CH_3 group were replaced by $CH(CH_3)_2$, the example would be valine, a different amino acid. Any of numerous amino acids could serve as the example, with a corresponding substitution for the CH_3 group that characterizes this example as alanine.

Alanine

b Here the example of an amino acid (alanine again) is presumed to be in the liver. Shown in yellow are the amino group (NH_2) and a single H, both bonded to the central carbon atom. If these two single bonds are broken . . . .

Pyruvic acid

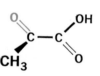

c . . . . and replaced by a double bond to oxygen, the resulting compound is pyruvic acid, which may be used to make a different amino acid or oxidized to provide energy (to make ATP, just as when glucose is split to produce two molecules of pyruvic acid).

d What happens to the nitrogen wastes of an amino acid *deaminized* by the liver can be shown in several steps (again using alanine as the example).

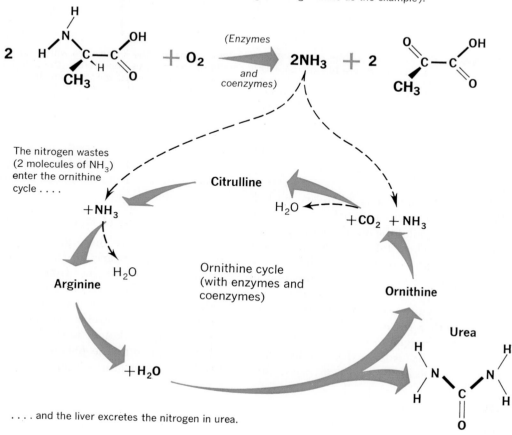

$$2 \; \text{[alanine]} + O_2 \xrightarrow{\text{(Enzymes and coenzymes)}} 2NH_3 + 2 \; \text{[pyruvic acid]}$$

The nitrogen wastes (2 molecules of NH_3) enter the ornithine cycle . . . .

Citrulline

$+NH_3$

$H_2O \leftarrow +CO_2 + NH_3$

H_2O

Arginine

Ornithine cycle (with enzymes and coenzymes)

Ornithine

Urea

$+H_2O$

. . . . and the liver excretes the nitrogen in urea.

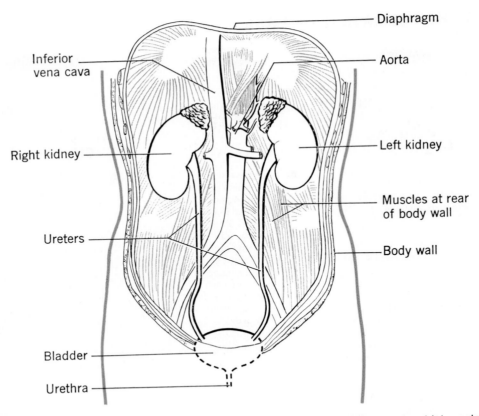

24-5 The excretory system of man. The excretory organs are the kidneys, to which wastes are brought by the bloodstream. Other parts of the system—the ureters, the bladder, and the urethra—are responsible for eliminating the excreted wastes from the body. Excretion of certain waste substances takes place also in the lungs and in the skin. (What substance, for example, is excreted through the skin? In the lungs?)

ammonia, and this forms arginine. Arginine combines with water and splits into urea plus ornithine.

Of course, ornithine is where we started. We have here a sort of biochemical wheel, or cycle. We call it the **ornithine cycle.** Each turn of the wheel takes up two molecules of ammonia and one of carbon dioxide and forms one molecule of urea (and one of water). No molecules of ornithine are destroyed—they are used over and over again.

Many other substances behave in a cyclic way. Hemoglobin is one (Chapter 23).

The urea that is formed in the liver, and in lesser amounts in other cells, passes into

capillaries. It is carried in the blood throughout the body. The next step is the removal of urea from the blood. This occurs in the kidneys.

Excretory Organs of Man

The kidneys are the organs that remove urea, as well as nearly all waste substances except carbon dioxide, from the blood. There are two kidneys, one located on each side of the spine and just above the hipbone. A duct, the **ureter** (yoo-REE-ter), extends from each kidney to the **bladder.** The bladder opens to the outside through the **urethra** (yoo-REE-thra—Figure 24-5).

Each kidney is composed of about a million tiny tubes, the **nephrons** (NEF·ronz), that do the work of extracting urea and other waste materials from the blood. Each nephron is a long, coiled tube of microscopic size (Figure 24-6). One end opens into a duct that collects urine. The other end is closed. The closed end is like a cup in shape, and the cavity so formed contains a network of capillaries.

There is a flow of materials from blood in the capillaries into the cup-shaped cavity of the closed end of the nephron. A percentage of all the materials of blood, except the red blood cells, white blood cells, platelets, and large protein molecules, next moves into the cavity of the nephron. In short, the fluid in the cavity of the first part of the nephron is blood plasma minus its proteins. Naturally there are many substances of vital importance to cells in this fluid. Glucose is one of these substances.

As the fluid moves along the cavity of the nephron, the cells of the nephron remove the substances that are useful. Thus, the glucose is extracted and passed back into the bloodstream. These same cells remove other substances from the blood and pass them into the cavity of the nephron. Thus, there is a two-way traffic of molecules through these cells.

It is especially interesting that the glucose continues to be reabsorbed from the nephron and restored to the blood long after the concentration of glucose in the blood is higher than that in the tubule. Obviously, simple diffusion cannot account for this. Here is another example of *active transport* (see page 421), which involves a great expenditure of energy. The transfer of glucose continues until, under normal circumstances, virtually *none* is left in the

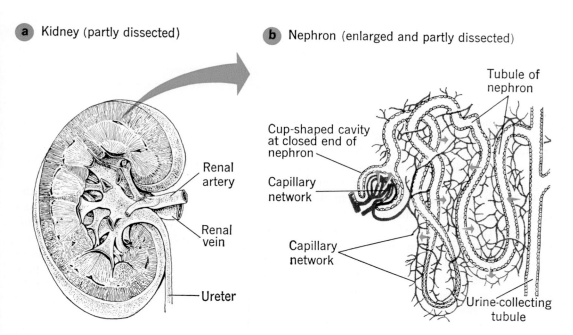

a Kidney (partly dissected)

Renal artery

Renal vein

Ureter

b Nephron (enlarged and partly dissected)

Tubule of nephron

Cup-shaped cavity at closed end of nephron

Capillary network

Capillary network

Urine-collecting tubule

24-6 A drawing of a kidney in longitudinal section, with an enlargement of a single nephron. What kinds of substances are transferred from the blood to the cup-shaped cavity at the closed end of the nephron? What transfers between the blood and the nephron take place farther along the way in the nephron tubule?

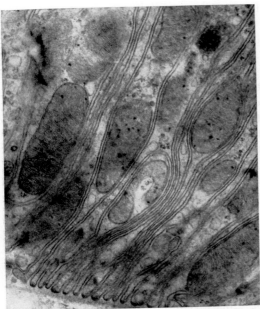

Lee D. Peachy

24-7 An electron micrograph of part of a kidney tubule cell in a rat. (17,000 X) Evidence of the energy expenditure required for active transport is seen in the number of mitochondria near the long, slender nephrons. Can you explain what the mitochondria do? (You may wish to look back to Chapter 6, page 134.)

There are few better examples, in all physiology, of the regulation of the internal environment—the homeostatic control, within narrow limits, of certain states of the body—than that carried out by the functioning kidney.

By the time the fluid reaches the lower part of the nephron, it is urine. Urine, therefore, is highly modified blood. It is a fluid from which nearly all the substances useful to cells have been removed and returned to the blood.

The nephrons remove all substances that are wastes—substances in excessive concentrations—from the blood, with the exception of carbon dioxide. Thus, if you drink a large amount of water, it will pass across the lining of the alimentary canal and enter the blood. The excess water will be removed rapidly by the nephrons. Similarly, if a large amount of salt is eaten, this also enters the blood, and the excess is removed by the nephrons.

The nephrons have a vital role in maintaining the constancy of the blood. They do this by the selective removal of different kinds of molecules (except carbon dioxide) that are in excessive quantities.

tubule. Other substances that are similarly removed from the tubule and restored to the blood include amino acids, fatty acids, glycerol, vitamins, and hormones. A similar process applies to water. Water is reabsorbed in the lower part of the nephron until the concentration of the dissolved substances in the urine is far higher than in the blood. Certain waste substances, such as urea and uric acid, are actively transported from the blood into the fluid in the tubule. Once again, these substances are moved against the normal direction of diffusion. Hence, work is done. It has been estimated that a very large part of the total expenditure of energy by the body is used in carrying on this active transport by the kidney (Figure 24-7).

CONCLUDING REMARKS— THE MAINTENANCE OF A CONSTANT ENVIRONMENT

The life of a multicellular individual depends on the life of its cells. We learned earlier that the various activities of multicellular animals can be thought of as ways of keeping the cells alive. The organism as a whole obtains food and oxygen. But these are used by individual cells (Figure 24-8). The organism removes the wastes produced by the cells—or the cells will die.

As we progress from simple to complex animals, there is a trend toward the specialization of groups of cells to serve specific functions. For example, hydra has no excre-

24-8 A SUMMARY OF CIRCULATION, RESPIRATION, DIGESTION, AND EXCRETION

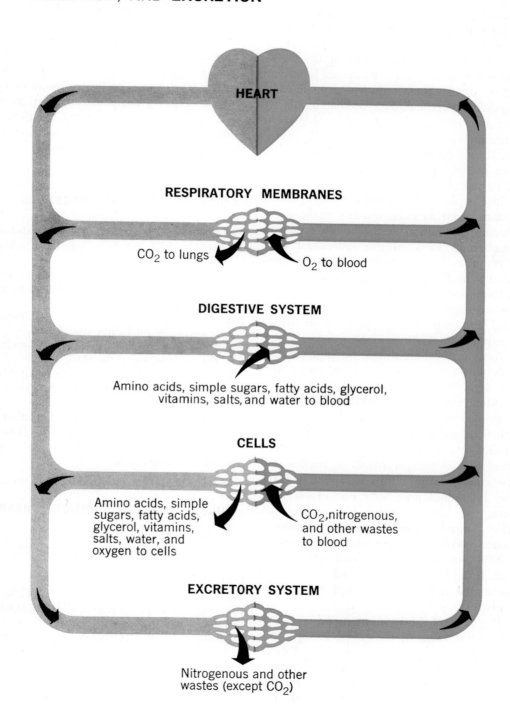

HEART

RESPIRATORY MEMBRANES

CO_2 to lungs O_2 to blood

DIGESTIVE SYSTEM

Amino acids, simple sugars, fatty acids, glycerol, vitamins, salts, and water to blood

CELLS

Amino acids, simple sugars, fatty acids, glycerol, vitamins, salts, water, and oxygen to cells

CO_2, nitrogenous, and other wastes to blood

EXCRETORY SYSTEM

Nitrogenous and other wastes (except CO_2)

tory system; planarians and earthworms have simple excretory systems; the human excretory system is more complex.

As cells become more specialized, they lose some of their abilities to perform a variety of functions. A cell lining the digestive cavity of a hydra can capture food particles, digest them, absorb oxygen, and eliminate carbon dioxide and ammonia. It can even contract like a muscle, though in a rather feeble way. It can divide by mitosis. It can do everything that *Paramecium* does except reproduce by sexual means and move rapidly.

In complex animals with a closed blood system, such as man, we can make more specific this notion of the whole organism functioning to keep the individual cells alive. The substances that must be supplied to and removed from cells are carried in the blood. Therefore, we can say that the various organ systems function in ways that tend to keep the composition of blood nearly constant.

In man, the blood must be kept remarkably constant. If the concentration of oxygen is only slightly below normal, the individual becomes unconscious. As another example, we may note that there is only a trace of calcium ions (Ca^{++}) in blood plasma—the concentration is about 0.0001 (that is, one part in 10,000 of plasma). If the concentration drops to about 0.00005, the individual goes into convulsions and dies. The blood supplies glucose to cells. The normal concentration of glucose is about 0.0007. If the concentration drops to 0.0003, convulsions and death are the result. If the level rises to 0.0012 and remains there, the individual develops the disease diabetes.

Figure 24-8 shows in a general way how the composition of the blood is kept constant. Various groups of specialized cells, such as those of the digestive, respiratory, and excretory systems, add to and remove chemical substances from the blood. You may regard this figure as a summary of the material covered in Chapters 21–24. All systems function in maintaining the constancy of blood, and hence the life of cells.

There is one important thing missing in Figure 24-8. There is no provision for coordinating all the activities. Any physiological enterprise as complex as a multicellular animal requires coordination. Such an animal possesses two interrelated means of coordination—nerves and hormones—which we will discuss in the next chapter.

GUIDE QUESTIONS AND PROBLEMS

1. What are the important waste substances produced by metabolic activity in complex animals?
2. What is the relation between the excretory system and the circulatory system in complex animals?
3. What is the evidence that active transport is necessary for kidney function?
4. What is the role of the kidney in regulating the composition of the blood fluid?
5. How can we interpret the fact that hydras do not have an excretory system, while planarians do?
6. A wide variety of excretory structures has evolved in invertebrate animals. How are they basically alike? How do they contribute to homeostasis?

SUGGESTIONS FOR ADDITIONAL READING

Books
See references at the end of Chapter 22.

Magazines and Journals
Merrill, J. P., "The Transplantation of the Kidney." *Scientific American*, Vol. 201 (October 1959), pp. 57–63.
Salisbury, P. F., "Artificial Internal Organs." *Scientific American*, Vol. 191 (August 1954), pp. 24–27.
Smith, H., "The Kidney." *Scientific American*, Vol. 189 (December 1953), p. 40.

25

COORDINATION

IN MULTICELLULAR

ANIMALS

In multicellular animals there is a division of labor among cells. Some groups of cells are specialized for securing food, others for digesting it, some for excreting wastes, others for respiring. There is one important consequence of specialization: as a cell becomes more specialized, it also becomes more dependent.

The Need for Coordination

One might regard a multicellular animal, therefore, as being composed of many different kinds of specialized cells—each type having comparatively specific functions but being incapable of completely independent existence. Such being the case, there must be another consequence of specialization: coordinating mechanisms are required. No organism could consist of many specialized cell types with each type carrying on its activities independently. Or-

ganisms are organized, and part of the organization consists of coordination.

If there is to be coordination of parts, three basic conditions must be met: first, there must be a coordinator; second, information must pass from the parts to the coordinator; third, information must pass from the coordinator to the parts.

Breathing—An Example of Coordination

Let us take as an example the coordination of the parts of the human body that are involved in supplying oxygen to the cells. We have already learned the principal parts. The lungs provide the moist membranes where the oxygen of the atmosphere comes into contact with blood. The diaphragm and the muscles of the ribs change the size of the chest cavity, making possible the movement of air into and out of the lungs. The blood, with its hemoglobin molecules, carries oxygen throughout the body to all cells.

Everything seems to be accounted for—but it is not. The independent functioning of these parts could not sustain life. We must add another factor: coordination. Let us see why. At this moment you are probably breathing at a rate of about fourteen times a minute and are taking shallow breaths. This rate and depth of breathing are sufficient to supply the cells with all the oxygen required for their activities. Now let us suppose that you begin a game of tennis or walk upstairs rapidly. Under these conditions your muscle cells become much more active. ATP changes to ADP, and energy is transferred. Glucose is oxidized, changing the ADP back to ATP. Oxygen combines with all the extra hydrogen atoms produced. As a result, the muscle cells require more oxygen than when at rest.

You are well aware of what happens. Your rate and depth of breathing greatly increase. More oxygen is made available to the blood capillaries in the lungs. Furthermore, the heart beats faster and the blood is forced around the body more rapidly. The result of these various changes is that more oxygen is made available to the muscle cells.

That is fine; when more oxygen is needed, more is provided. But what is responsible for this ideal solution of the problem?

The first point to be made is that the blood does not carry a *higher concentration* of oxygen when we are exercising. As a matter of fact, even when we are at rest nearly all the hemoglobin molecules combine with oxygen when they are in the capillaries of the lungs. In periods of increased metabolic activity in the cells, more oxygen *leaves* the blood. As a consequence, the concentration of oxygen in the blood decreases. The concentration cannot be allowed to drop very much, however. In fact, if it drops to even 90 percent of the normal amount, the brain cells cannot function properly and we become unconscious. The problem of coordination, then, is to keep the concentration of oxygen in the blood at or near the maximum amount that can be carried.

But still we have not solved the problem. Any coordinating mechanism for maintaining the constancy of oxygen in the blood can operate only if there is accurate information about the concentration of oxygen at a given time. There must be some way of knowing if there is too much, too little, or the proper amount.

Physiologists now know the main outlines of the answer to this problem. The chief coordinating structure for controlling the amount of oxygen in the blood is found to be a small area in the brain, known as the **breathing center.** The breathing center is located in the part of the brain called the **medulla** (meh·DUL·a). Careful experimentation has shown that the cells of the breathing center indeed detect the concentration of oxygen in the blood—though in a very indirect way. They actually respond *not* to the concentration of oxygen but to that of

carbon dioxide. You may regard this as a backward way of doing things, and of course it is. The fact remains, it works.

Experiments have revealed a very close relation between the concentration of oxygen and that of carbon dioxide in the blood. For any given concentration of oxygen, there is a corresponding concentration of carbon dioxide. For example, the blood in the lung capillaries picks up all of the oxygen that it can carry; it then can hold only a minimum amount of carbon dioxide (Figure 25-1). Conversely, blood in the capillaries near very active cells picks up a large amount of carbon dioxide by way of diffusion from these active cells. The chemical changes that result from the entrance of this carbon dioxide into the blood lead to a release of oxygen from the hemoglobin. Thus you can see that when the concentration of carbon dioxide is 40 to 50 ml per 100 ml of blood, the concentration of oxygen in the blood will be between 97 and 98 percent. By measuring the concentration of carbon dioxide in the blood, one also has a measure of the oxygen concentration.

The activity of the breathing center keeps the concentrations of carbon dioxide and oxygen within certain limits, as shown in Figure 25-1. It does this by controlling the rate and depth of breathing. This introduces us to another aspect of coordination: the methods used by the coordinator (in this example the breathing center) to convey information to the parts involved. We have already learned what the parts are— the rib muscles, the diaphragm, and the lungs (Figure 23-4). The breathing center in the medulla (Figure 25-2) is connected with the diaphragm and rib muscles by nerves. The breathing center stimulates these nerves to carry nerve impulses to the diaphragm and rib muscles.

Let us put all of this together. Cells function normally only if the capillaries near them contain blood with a sufficiently high concentration of oxygen and a sufficiently low concentration of carbon dioxide. These are not really two separate problems, for the process that maintains the concentration of oxygen at a high level also maintains the concentration of carbon dioxide at a low level. The process, of course, is the rate and depth of breathing.

Coordination involves, first, information passing from the parts to the coordinator. In our example, the part is the blood. The information that reaches the coordinator (breathing center) is the concentration of carbon dioxide in the blood. If the concentration is too high, information passes from the coordinator to the parts (diaphragm and rib muscles) that results in greater activity of the parts—a quicker rhythm and an increase of muscle contraction. Breathing becomes more rapid and deeper; more carbon dioxide is "thrown off" in the lung capillaries, and thus its amount is reduced in the blood; more oxygen is taken in, and thus its amount is increased in the blood. The information is carried from the coordinator to the parts, in this case, by nerves. Conversely, if the concentration of carbon dioxide is below the normal range, the coordinator responds to this information by controlling a decrease in the rate and depth of breathing. (Check this on yourself as follows: Breathe rapidly and as deeply as possible for seventeen inspirations; then relax and breathe naturally. How does the rate and depth of breathing compare to your normal rate and depth when at rest?)

As a consequence of this coordination, the activities of the lungs, blood, diaphragm, and rib muscles are so regulated and interrelated that the concentrations of oxygen and carbon dioxide in the vicinity of the cells remain nearly constant. This constancy could not be maintained if each part acted in an independent and unregulated way.

The example of coordination just given is for a multicellular animal. All organisms, however, are coordinated in some way.

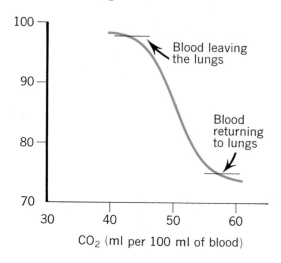

O_2 (as percent of hemoglobin combined with O_2)

Blood leaving the lungs

Blood returning to lungs

CO_2 (ml per 100 ml of blood)

This is true even of the single-celled forms such as *Paramecium*. Individual paramecia respond to changes in temperature, the concentrations of various chemicals, and to electric currents. The response usually involves movement. The movement, in turn, depends on the coordinated motions of the cilia.

In most multicellular organisms, there are two distinct, though related, systems of coordination: the **nervous system** and the **endocrine** (EN·doh·kryn) **system**. Although these two coordinating systems work together and in many ways are not separate, for convenience we will study them one at a time.

NERVOUS SYSTEMS

Before we discuss the nervous systems of specific animals, we need some general understanding of how animals receive stimuli and respond to them. Even in the simple

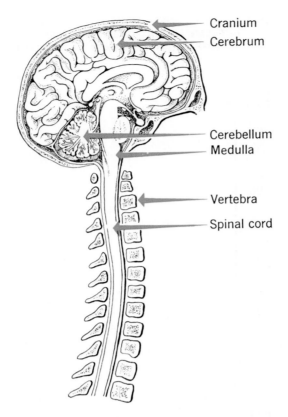

Cranium
Cerebrum
Cerebellum
Medulla
Vertebra
Spinal cord

25-2 The central nervous system of man. The medulla, in which the breathing center is located, is one part of the brain. Some nerves originate directly from the brain. Most nerve pathways, however, lead from the brain into the spinal cord, from which numerous nerves branch to the parts of the body.

multicellular animals we can recognize three main types of structures related to stimuli and responses. Each has a specific function. The three structures are **receptors, neurons** (NYOO·ronz), and **effectors.**

Receptors may be neurons themselves, or they may be organs that are specialized for detecting stimuli. We have many receptors, among which are those for touch, taste, smell, temperature, light, and sound.

The unit of structure and function in the nervous system is the neuron (Figure 25-3), which is a single cell. Neurons are often

very long. The longest of those in the human body reach from the ends of the fingers or toes to the spinal cord.

The neurons are specialized for transmitting **nerve impulses.** A nerve impulse is an electrochemical change, along the cell membrane, that begins at one end of the neuron and travels rapidly to the other. In some neurons of man, the nerve impulse has a speed of approximately 100 meters per second. In many of the lower animals, the speed is much less.

Generally, several or more neurons are involved in any behavioral activity. One neuron carries an impulse along its length. When the impulse reaches the end of the first neuron, it stimulates the next neuron. The gap between the end of one neuron and the beginning of another is called the **synapse** (SIN·aps—Figure 25-3).

In those animals that have **central nervous systems**—concentrations of neurons that amount to a brain at some point in the body—it is convenient to recognize different classes of neurons. **Sensory neurons** (Figure 25-3, left) carry impulses from receptors to the central nervous system (Figure 25-2). **Motor neurons** (Figure 25-3, right) carry impulses from the central nervous system to effectors.

Effectors are structures that respond when they are stimulated by nerve impulses. In the more complex animals, the principal effectors are muscles and glands. Muscles respond by contracting; glands respond by secreting (Figure 21-3).

The way in which receptors, neurons, and effectors are all involved can be understood from the following. Let us pretend that you are walking without shoes and you step on a sharp rock. You feel pain and rapidly lift your foot (Figure 25-4). What really happens?

The skin of the foot contains a number of receptors. Some of these are stimulated by strong pressure. Some (which are actually naked nerve endings) respond to any suf-

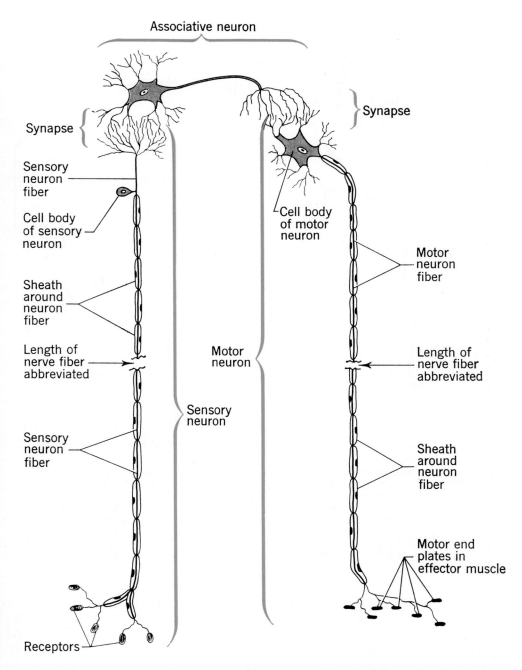

Associative neuron

Synapse

Sensory neuron fiber

Cell body of sensory neuron

Sheath around neuron fiber

Length of nerve fiber abbreviated

Sensory neuron fiber

Receptors

Synapse

Cell body of motor neuron

Motor neuron

Sensory neuron

Motor neuron fiber

Length of nerve fiber abbreviated

Sheath around neuron fiber

Motor end plates in effector muscle

25-3 Three types of neurons in man—associative, sensory, and motor. (Another type is shown in Figure 3-11b, page 62.) Basic similarities in types of neurons occur in animals that are closely related in evolution; thus, in a cow, for example, neurons almost identical to these can be found. In *Hydra*, on the other hand, the neuron structure is different (Figure 25-5). The functional association of the three types of neurons shown here is diagramed in Figure 25-4.

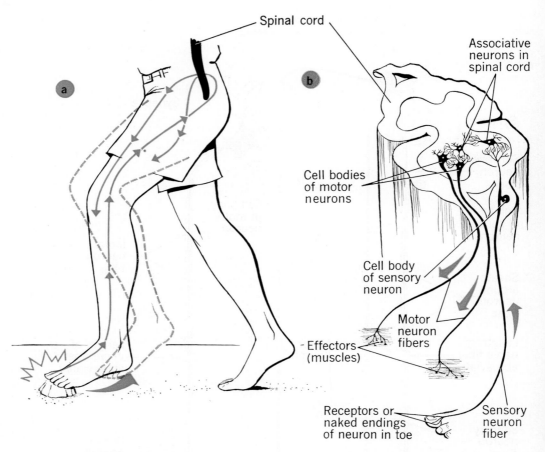

25-4 A diagram of a reflex arc. Stepping upon the sharp rock stimulates receptors in the affected toe (or the sole of the foot, as the case may be). Impulses travel along one or more sensory neurons to the spinal cord, where associative neurons are stimulated. The impulses are "switched" to other neurons—among them motor neurons that stimulate leg muscles to contract and move the foot away from the rock. Nor is this the end (although in a sense it is for the initial reflex arc). Other neurons carry impulses from the spinal cord to the brain. More "switching" occurs; you feel pain, and you may cry out. The brain takes over, and you decide what to do next.

ficiently intense stimulation; these are associated with pain. When you step on a sharp rock, the receptors are stimulated.

The receptors, in turn, initiate nerve impulses in the neurons. Neurons extend from these receptors up the leg to the spinal cord, where they end. Their endings are in close association with the ends of other neurons. Some of these other neurons extend up the spinal cord to the brain. Others extend to

the muscles of the leg. Thus, there are two routes that the nerve impulses can take. Some go back over other neurons to the muscles of the leg and cause these muscles to contract, which moves the foot from the stone. This relatively simple pathway, shown in Figure 25-4, is termed a **reflex arc.** Other nerve impulses travel along the neurons to the brain. When the impulses reach the brain, you become aware of what has occurred. It is not until this time that you feel pain in the toe or the foot.

The brain now takes control of the situation. Perhaps you wish to move farther away from the stone or to see if the foot has been injured. In order to do either of these things, the brain must send nerve impulses along the neurons of the spinal cord and out to the appropriate muscles.

The muscles are the effectors in this example. When stimulated by nerve impulses, they contract, and movement occurs—in this case away from the stone.

The Nervous System of *Hydra*

Let us now investigate the nervous system of a hydra. As you can see from Figure 25-5, its nervous system looks like a net of threads that extends throughout the animal.

This netlike structure is made up of neurons, which have synapses between them. Since each neuron makes synaptic connections to another or to several others, it is possible for communication to occur from any point in the animal to any other point. In the hydra there is no definite pathway that messages follow. The nerve impulses move in either direction along the neuron.

How does this nerve net function in hydras? Primarily, it seems, for local contractions. That is, if one area of the organism receives a stimulus, impulses in a neuron will cause the local cells to contract. There are no specialized muscle cells in hydras. However, most of the cells of the inner and outer layers can contract. With a strong stimulus the impulses may spread to other neurons, and the whole organism may react.

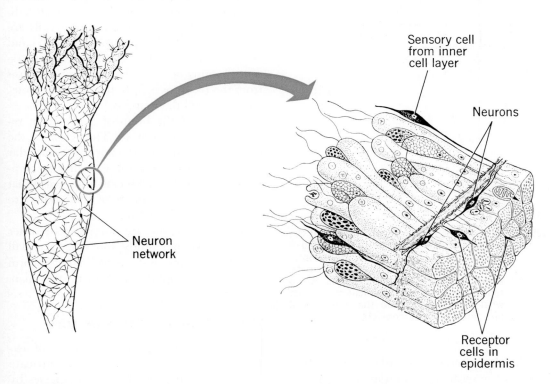

Sensory cell from inner cell layer

Neurons

Neuron network

Receptor cells in epidermis

25-5 The nervous system of *Hydra*. A neuron network extends throughout the body and tentacles. There is no brain, however. The drawing of some of the body cells (much enlarged) indicates the relationship of the network of neurons to other specialized cells in the outer and inner cell layers.

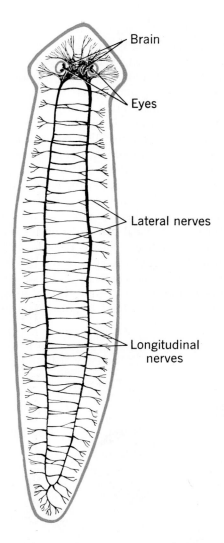

are directly connected to the network of neurons and thus initiate nerve impulses to all parts of the body. Although a hydra does possess receptor cells, neurons, and contractile cells, the movements it can make are very limited. It can bend and shorten its body and move its tentacles. There is nothing resembling a brain or any other center of nervous coordination.

The Nervous System of a Planarian

Planarians have the beginnings of a central nervous system, that is, a concentration of neurons in some part of the body. There is a concentration of neurons in the head region that can be called a brain (Figure 25-6). There are also two main longitudinal nerves. (Nerves are bundles of neurons.)

Also in the head end of a planarian is a concentration of receptor cells connected directly to the brain. These receptor cells are sensitive to light, pressure, touch, and chemical stimuli. The central nervous system contains neurons that transfer impulses from the receptor cells to the motor neurons, which lead to the muscles.

Removal of the brain of a planarian reduces its ability to move. The action of the cilia is not disturbed, but the muscular movement necessary for crawling is completely stopped. This seems to indicate that the muscular movements of planarians are controlled by the brain.

Nervous systems are complex. In order not to make our study too long, we will omit the nervous systems of the earthworm and the grasshopper and turn next to man.

25-6 The nervous system of a planarian. At the anterior end is what might be called a brain. Connected to the brain are receptor cells—those of the eyes or eyespots, sensitive to light, and others sensitive to touch, pressure, and chemical stimuli. Of what types of cells do the longitudinal and lateral nerves consist?

The hydra receives some information about its environment from another kind of receptor cell. These are special cells that are very sensitive to stimuli such as chemical substances or pressure. The receptor cells

THE NERVOUS SYSTEM OF MAN

The brain of man is a triumph of evolution. Man alone can convey intricate thoughts to other members of his species by means of language. Man alone can preserve his understanding of himself and the world about him in written records. Man alone is skilled in the use of tools. Man alone can transmit adequately the knowledge he gains to succeeding generations.

In spite of the unique intelligence of man, his nervous system is essentially like that of other mammals. Even the most primitive of vertebrates have receptors, neurons, brains, and effectors constructed on the same general pattern as ours. Even hydras have the rudimentary beginnings of a nervous system, with receptor cells, neurons, and effector cells.

Receptors in Man

Information about the external world is received through receptors, the sense organs. Each sense organ is specialized to receive a specific type of stimulus. Our ears are stimulated by air vibrations, our eyes by electromagnetic radiation of specific wavelength, our taste buds and organs of smell by chemical substances.

Any one type of sense organ receives only a small portion of possible stimuli. The eyes are stimulated by electromagnetic radiation that varies from the short-wave violet to the long-wave red. These wavelengths are only a small portion of the total range of wavelengths that actually occur in the world around us. The waves shorter than violet, the ultraviolet for example, do not stimulate our eyes in such a way that we see. There are also waves that are longer than red—the infrared and radio waves. We know of their existence only when we use special instruments to detect them.

Have you ever thought of the ceaseless activity that is going on around you and is undetected by your sense organs? Imagine that you go into a closet and close the door. Let us also suppose that the door and the walls shut out all air vibrations that you could "pick up" with your ears, and all electromagnetic radiation lying between the short-wave violet and long-wave red. You stand in the closet seeing nothing and hearing nothing—but all around there are messages from the environment. If you carried a powerful radio into the closet you would find the closet full of these messages. Hundreds or thousands (depending on the excellence of your equipment) of broadcasting stations throughout the world would be transmitting electromagnetic radiation undetected by your sense organs, yet detected by the radio. A television set would reveal other sorts of messages. Other instruments would show that you are constantly bombarded by cosmic rays.

Clearly, our eyes and ears tell us very little of the many events going on around us. We are blind and deaf to most changes in the environment.

Sensory Neurons

When you stepped on that sharp rock early in the chapter, neurons carried impulses from your foot to your spinal cord. These and other neurons that carry impulses to the brain and spinal cord are sensory neurons. They carry impulses from the ears, eyes, taste buds, nose, and skin.

The sensory neurons also carry impulses from all the internal parts of the body. We are aware of some of these messages but not all. Even with your eyes closed, you know the position of your arms—whether they are outstretched or at your sides. You know because sensory neurons associated with muscles are carrying impulses to the brain, informing it about the position and degree of contraction of the muscles.

There are other sensory neurons that function without our awareness, bringing to the brain or spinal cord nerve impulses from the heart, liver, digestive tube, blood vessels, kidneys, and other internal organs.

The Brain and the Spinal Cord

The brain and spinal cord are the coordinating centers of the nervous system. Their functional units are neurons. Sometimes the brain and spinal cord are compared to the central switchboard of a telephone system.

The comparison is not too apt, for the brain operates on a much higher level. It makes judgments; it directs. A switchboard merely connects.

The impulses that reach the brain over the sensory neurons are all the same. Those from the eyes, the ears, and the receptors of pain are identical. Neurons can be stimulated to carry impulses by touching them in an appropriate way. If you were to touch a neuron from the eye you would have the sensation of light. If you were to touch a neuron from the ear you would have the sensation of sound. If the receptor cells of your ear were made to attach to the stump of the nerve leading from your eye to your brain, and you "listened" to a Beethoven symphony, you would have the sensation of seeing—not hearing.

You can convince yourself that some of this is true by the following experiment. Move your eyes so that you are looking upward and to the left. Close your lids. Now tap with your finger on the outer side of the right upper eyelid. Usually you will see a flash of light. There was no light, of course, but you stimulated the neurons from the eye by the tap with your finger. The brain interprets all impulses coming over these neurons as "light."

It is in the brain that we have the sensations of seeing, hearing, tasting, smelling, and feeling. The sensory neurons from each type of sense organ end in a special place in the brain. Thus the neurons from the eye, for example, end in one specific region of vision and two regions of eye-adjustment in the **cerebrum** (SEHR·e·brum).

Man's superior intelligence seems to be due largely to the great development of the cerebrum. Specific areas of the cerebrum are associated with specific functions (Figure 25-7).

The brain not only receives impulses but it also originates them and sends them out. In this way it controls the responses that the organism makes.

The Motor Neurons

The motor neurons carry impulses from the brain and spinal cord to the effectors in all parts of the body. The impulses, once again, are the same as in all other neurons.

The Effectors

We are now nearing the end of the story. The organism is stimulated by some event in the environment. The stimulus is received by a sense organ; it is transmitted as a train of nonspecific nerve impulses along the sensory neurons to the brain; the brain analyzes the impulses and relates them in some way to its past experiences (we have no sure knowledge of what this involves); the brain then sends messages (again, nerve impulses), by way of the motor neurons, to the parts of the body that respond —the muscles and glands.

All our responses are due to contraction by muscles or secretion by glands, as in *Hydra* and planarians—or else to cerebral activity that does not involve muscles or glands. Thus many of our responses are thoughts that we do not translate into body activity. More often than not, however, thoughts lead us to make some other response, which if barely perceptible, is enough to lead someone to say, "A penny for your thoughts . . ."

Conscious and Unconscious Activity

Most of the examples of the functioning nervous system that we have given are for activities we are aware of and to which we can consciously respond. In addition to these, there is a whole group of activities that are controlled by the brain without our conscious participation.

We discussed one such example at the beginning of this chapter. During exercise our cells use glucose and oxygen in increased amounts and produce more carbon dioxide. The body as a whole responds by increasing the rate and depth of breathing and the speed of movement of the blood.

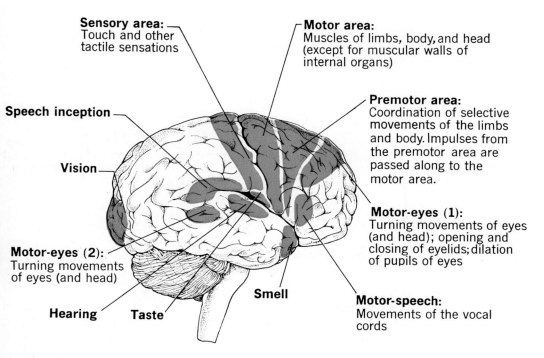

Sensory area:
Touch and other
tactile sensations

Motor area:
Muscles of limbs, body, and head
(except for muscular walls of
internal organs)

Premotor area:
Coordination of selective
movements of the limbs
and body. Impulses from
the premotor area are
passed along to the
motor area.

Speech inception

Vision

Motor-eyes (1):
Turning movements of eyes
(and head); opening and
closing of eyelids; dilation
of pupils of eyes

Motor-eyes (2):
Turning movements
of eyes (and head)

Hearing   **Taste**

Smell

Motor-speech:
Movements of the vocal
cords

25-7 Some functional areas of the human cerebrum. What do you suppose would happen
if you could stimulate one of these specialized areas directly? Regions not marked
and labeled with highly specific functions seem to have the most complex functions
of all—thinking, planning, associating, directing, learning, remembering, and other
remarkable things that collectively characterize man's unique intelligence.

This is controlled by nerve impulses, transmitted at a greater than normal frequency
from the brain along the motor neurons to
the rib muscles and diaphragm. The brain
also initiates impulses at a greater rate
along certain neurons to the heart. All these
things occur without conscious effort on
our part—no thinking is involved. Wouldn't
life be difficult if we had to think about
each of these things before doing them?

Much is known about the physiology of
the nervous system, but we have almost no
understanding of what functions of the
brain are responsible for such complex
things as memory, thinking, joy, sadness,
and the like. There are specific centers
in the brain concerned with sleep, rage,
simple pleasure, and sexual feelings. They
have been pinpointed by using needlelike

electrodes, which can be pushed into an animal's brain without damage to it, and then
used to stimulate the region. The responses
are amazing to watch in a cat or rat.

Delicate operations on the brain to remove certain diseased parts have also revealed the locations of centers of certain activities. But in respect to consciousness itself, or the more complex functions mentioned previously, the human brain has had
limited success in understanding itself.

An Aside on Nerve Physiology—
Loewi and the Frog's Heart

Scientists are among the most inquisitive
of human beings—but they are rarely satisfied with the answers they obtain. It was
quite an accomplishment to discover the
basis of nervous control of behavior—that

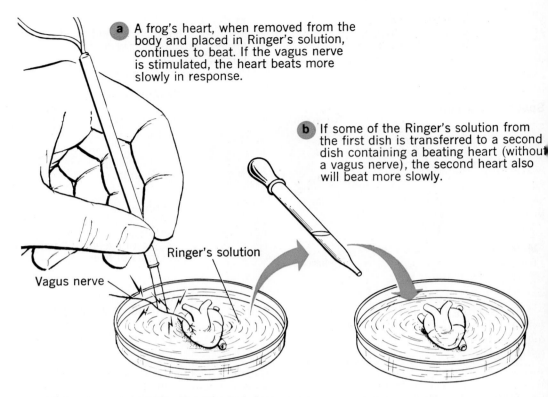

a A frog's heart, when removed from the body and placed in Ringer's solution, continues to beat. If the vagus nerve is stimulated, the heart beats more slowly in response.

b If some of the Ringer's solution from the first dish is transferred to a second dish containing a beating heart (without a vagus nerve), the second heart also will beat more slowly.

Vagus nerve

Ringer's solution

25-8 Loewi's experiment with frogs' hearts. The stimulus to the nerve stump was electrical. Was the stimulus to the heart muscle also electrical? Given a control in which these events do not occur without a stimulus, what does the experiment prove?

receptors, neurons, and effectors are stimulated successively. But this knowledge only raises more questions.

A nerve impulse travels down a motor neuron to an effector—say a muscle. The muscle contracts. What causes the muscle to contract? Is it the electrochemical message that we call the nerve impulse?

Perhaps we could look at the junction between the neuron and muscle with a microscope and obtain some hint. If we did look, we would see that the neuron ends with tiny branches (Figure 25-3). These branches are adjacent to a specialized area of the muscle cell. That is all we would find out.

As is so often the case in science, the answer to one question may come from trying to answer an entirely different question.

This was certainly the case in one impor tant experiment that helps us understan how neurons function.

The heart of a frog beats in a rhythmi fashion like all other vertebrate hearts. I has been known for a long time that nerve extend from the central nervous system t the heart. One of the nerves is the vagu (VAY·gus). When nerve impulses pass alon the vagus nerve, the heart slows its rate o contraction. Nerve impulses passing alon; another nerve, the accelerator nerve, spee up the rate of contraction of the heart.

There is nothing very surprising abou this, but the next bit of information *is* su prising: the frog's heart can be remove from the body and it will continue to bea If properly cared for—that is, kept mois with a solution containing inorganic salts and glucose—it will live and beat for days. Of course, since its nerves have been cut, there can be no control by the brain.

The frog's heart, then, must have its own internal mechanism that stimulates contraction. There is no escaping this conclusion, since the isolated heart can continue to beat. A little biological detective work revealed that a special area in the heart, named the **pacemaker,** is involved. The pacemaker sends out rhythmic impulses that cause the heart muscles to contract. What do the nerves to the heart do, then?

Otto Loewi in 1921 began the experiment that is shown in Figure 25-8. There are two dishes, each with a living and contracting frog's heart. Heart **a** has its vagus nerve attached. Each dish contains a fluid (Ringer's solution) that has small amounts of inorganic salts—in the correct proportions to keep the heart alive for days.

When Loewi stimulated the vagus nerve of heart **a,** which he could do with a very weak electric current, the heart slowed down. This was the expected result. Now came the key step in his experiment. Loewi took some of the Ringer's solution from dish **a** and put it into dish **b.** The result was astounding: the heart in dish **b** slowed its rate of contraction!

This key observation was the beginning of a long series of experiments by Loewi and many others. First it was found that the experiment can be repeated, always with the same result. The vagus-stimulated heart releases into the solution some chemical substance that causes other hearts to slow down their rate of contraction.

Loewi had no idea what the chemical substance was. He just called it "vagus material." Later it was identified as an organic compound, **acetylcholine** (a·see·til-KOH·leen).

More research showed that acetylcholine is secreted by the ends of the neurons of the vagus nerve. Each time a nerve impulse comes to the ends of the neurons, acetylcholine is liberated. In the case of the heart, acetylcholine acts on the pacemaker. The pacemaker then sends out its impulses less rapidly, and the heartbeat slows down.

But what about the accelerator nerve? It increases the rate of the heart's contraction. It, too, was found to secrete a substance, **adrenaline** (ad·REN·al·in). Adrenaline stimulates the pacemaker, causing it to send out impulses more rapidly.

Acetylcholine and adrenaline were found to have other functions as well. Either acetylcholine or adrenaline (or the related noradrenaline) is secreted by the ends of all neurons. This means that there are two kinds of neurons in terms of their effects. For example, the intestine receives two types of motor neurons. One type secretes acetylcholine. This increases peristalsis in the intestine. The other type secretes adrenaline or noradrenaline. This decreases peristalsis in the intestine.

Acetylcholine is also responsible for the nerve impulse crossing the synapse. It happens in this way. An impulse travels down one neuron, and when it reaches the end, acetylcholine is secreted. Acetylcholine then stimulates the next neuron.

Loewi and his frog hearts gave us a lot of important information.

ENDOCRINE SYSTEMS

Loewi's observations and those of others have broken down the distinction that was formerly made between the nervous system and the endocrine system. It was thought that the nervous system worked because of neurons and the electrochemical messages they carry. The endocrine system worked by secreting chemical substances, the hormones. The nervous system was the fast worker—nerve impulses traveled as much as 100 meters a second. The hormones were distributed by the bloodstream—a slower process. There seemed little in common.

These neat distinctions vanished when it was discovered that nerves control the effectors (muscles and glands) by secreting acetylcholine or adrenaline. The latter is identical to the hormone adrenaline, secreted by the adrenal gland. And to cap the story, that part of the adrenal gland that secretes adrenaline is just a modified group of neurons.

Thus, in controlling body functions, the nervous system and the endocrine system both really function in the same way—by secreting substances. However, we can make an anatomical distinction that is useful in most cases. *Neurons do the secreting in the nervous system. Endocrine glands do the secreting in the endocrine system.* In man the hormones are distributed almost entirely by the circulatory system. In a few instances, however, they have local effects near the place where they are secreted.

Endocrine Glands of Man

The principal structures that secrete hormones in the human body will now be listed to give you an idea of the variety of hormones and their effects (Figure 25-9).

The **thyroid gland** is in the throat. It secretes **thyroxin** (thy·ROK·sin), which regulates the general rate of metabolism (the sum of the body's biochemical activities).

The **parathyroid** (par·a·THY·roid) **glands** are embedded in the thyroid gland. Their hormone controls body use of calcium.

The **thymus gland,** also in the throat, secretes a hormone important in fetal, infant, and childhood development. Later the thymus gland degenerates. (The thymus has another, nonendocrine function: the production of antibodies.)

The **adrenal cortex** is the outer part of the adrenal gland, which is located on top of each kidney. It secretes several hormones, one of which is **cortisone** (KOR·tih·sohn). These hormones influence the concentrations of the blood salts and the way in which glucose is used in the body.

The **adrenal medulla** is the central portion of the adrenal gland. It secretes adrenaline, which increases the rate of breathing and heartbeat, increases the concentration of glucose in the blood, and causes the pupils of the eyes to enlarge and the hair to stand on end. It prepares the body for emergency situations.

The **islets of Langerhans** (I·lets [of] LAHNG·er·hahns), which are located in the pancreas, secrete **insulin** (IN·suh·lin). This hormone has an important role in controlling the way glucose is used in the body. The familiar disease **diabetes mellitus** (dy·a·BEE·teez meh·LY·tus) is a result of abnormal functioning of the islets of Langerhans.

The **pituitary** (pih·TOO·ih·tehr·ee) secretes a number of hormones. Some of these have effects on other endocrine glands. Thus, the pituitary secretes a hormone that affects the secretion of thyroxin by the thyroid gland. Other pituitary hormones influence the rate of bone growth, the secretion of milk by the mammary glands, the development of the ovary and testis, the activity of the adrenal cortex, the removal of water from the nephrons of the kidney, and the contraction of the muscles of the uterus.

The **testes** (TES·teez) of the male, in addition to producing sperms, secrete **testosterone** (tes·TOS·ter·ohn). After fetal life, testosterone is first secreted in appreciable amounts at the time of puberty. It influences the change of voice and other events involved in the maturing of the male. The hormone will be discussed in Chapter 27.

The **ovaries** (OH·va·reez) of the female secrete several hormones that influence the maturing of the female and are necessary for the prenatal development of the human infant. The ovarian hormones will be discussed in Chapter 27.

Remember, too, the production of secretin, gastrin, and other hormones by parts of the digestive system. The *stomach* and first portion of the *small intestine* are endocrine structures to be added to the list. Hor-

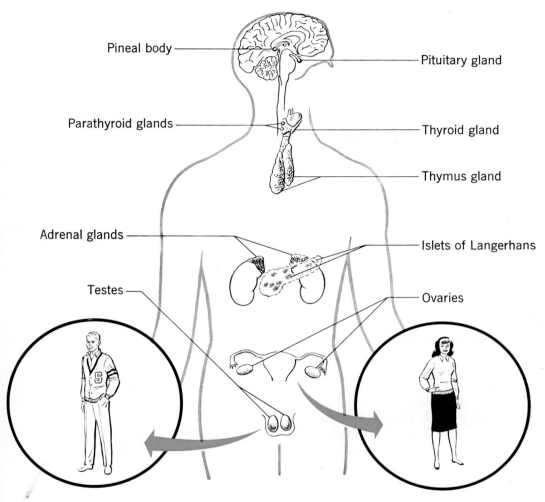

25-9 Some of the endocrine glands of the body. The stomach and part of the small intestine are also endocrine structures, in addition to their roles as digestive organs. All of the structures illustrated, except one, can be associated with known hormones (see text). The exception is the pineal body. Biologists suspect that it is an endocrine gland, but they have not yet discovered its function or its hormone(s).

mones are known to be important substances for controlling biological processes in many kinds of animals. Most of our knowledge of them is restricted to man and other animals with backbones. In recent years, however, hormones have been found in insects and many other animals. Plants, too, have hormones that are important in controlling their growth (see Chapter 17).

In species with circulatory systems, the hormones are generally distributed in the blood. In other animals the hormones may diffuse from cell to cell.

An example of the way hormones work will be given now. It involves the body's use of glucose. In Chapter 27 we will supply additional examples of the way hormones are involved in human reproduction.

Diabetes Mellitus

The blood of man contains only a trace of glucose—about 0.07–0.12 percent. This trace, however, is vital for the life of all the cells. Earlier we learned that if the amount drops to about 0.03 percent, convulsions and death will result. In the disease diabetes mellitus, the concentration of glucose in the blood reaches a level above 0.14 percent, and again death may result. The control of glucose concentration, then, is a problem of great importance.

Diabetes mellitus has been recognized as a specific disease since the days of the Romans. The very name reveals two features of the disease. *Diabetes* comes from two Greek words meaning "to go through." *Mellitus* is the Latin word for "honey." In diabetes mellitus, "the honey goes through"— that is, the patient passes a large amount of urine containing sugar.

Although the story goes back far, we can begin in 1889 with two German physiologists, Von Mering and Minkowski. They were interested in the function of the pancreas. They used dogs in their studies.

One way to study the effect of an organ is to remove it. It was not anticipated that this would be too serious in the case of the pancreas. Although this gland secretes pancreatic juice, it was thought that the enzymes in gastric juice and intestinal juice would enable the dogs to digest their food.

This prediction was incorrect. When the pancreas was removed, all the dogs died. Von Mering and Minkowski might have advanced the hypothesis that the enzymes secreted by the pancreas are necessary for life. Perhaps they would have but for an apparently trivial observation: ants were attracted to the kennels where the dogs that had no pancreases were kept; there was no gathering of ants in the kennels of the dogs not operated upon.

Great discoveries in science often result from chance observations of this sort. Most scientists probably would not have noticed the ants. After all, the experiment was on dogs, not ants. Even if they had noticed the ants, it is unlikely that they would have thought much about their presence.

Yet this was the key—why were ants so much more numerous in the kennels with the experimental animals? Were they everywhere in these kennels? As a matter of fact, they were not. The ants went to the places where the dogs had urinated. On the other hand, ants were not attracted to the urine of the normal dogs.

There must be something strange about the urine of dogs without pancreases. Chemical analysis showed this to be so: the urine contained a large amount of glucose. The glucose had attracted the ants.

It was also noticed that the experimental dogs passed much more urine than did the normal dogs—more urine, *and* glucose in this urine. Von Mering and Minkowski then realized what had happened: their dogs without pancreases had diabetes mellitus!

A pancreas was necessary, therefore, to keep a dog from developing diabetes mellitus. We spoke earlier of scientists as persons never satisfied with one answer. Now that they knew the pancreas was necessary to prevent diabetes, they wanted to know more: Is all or only some part of the pancreas necessary?

The pancreas is composed of two main types of cells. One type, by far the more abundant, was thought to secrete pancreatic juice. The other consists of little clusters of cells—the islets of Langerhans (Figure 21-10). No one knew their function, so they were named for their discoverer.

When it was found that the pancreas was important in preventing diabetes, the next step was obvious. What would the pancreas look like in human patients who had died of diabetes? When the pancreases of these patients were examined, it was found that the cells that secrete pancreatic juice were normal. On the other hand, the cells of the islets of Langerhans were definitely abnormal. This observation suggested that some abnormality of the islet cells might be the cause of diabetes.

The islet cells are not connected to the pancreatic ducts. Their only contact with the rest of the body is by way of the blood-stream. A likely hypothesis, then, was the following: The islet cells secrete a hormone that regulates the amount of glucose in the blood. This hypothetical hormone was given the name *insuline*—the insulin we know today.

The next step was to try to isolate the hormone. Many investigators tried to do it. They ground up the pancreases of cows, sheep, and other mammals, and made extracts. All early attempts failed. We now know why. Insulin is a protein. When a whole pancreas is ground, the material liberated contains the enzymes of pancreatic juice. Some of these enzymes can digest proteins, and so digest the hormone!

The problem of how to obtain insulin was solved in 1922 by a Canadian physician, F. G. Banting, and his assistant, C. H. Best. They succeeded where others had failed, because they were able to put two and two together, so to speak. Twenty years earlier another physiologist, Ssobolew, had been working on the pancreas. He observed that if he tied off the pancreatic ducts, the pancreas would begin to degenerate. After a time all enzyme-secreting cells would degenerate, while islet cells remained normal.

Banting knew of Ssobolew's work and realized it was a solution to his problem. He would tie off the ducts and wait for the enzyme-secreting cells to degenerate. Then he would extract the pancreases without fear that the hypothetical hormone would be destroyed by enzymes.

The experiment succeeded. Banting obtained an extract that would maintain life in dogs from which he had removed the pancreas.

The extract was soon tried on humans. The first subject was so ill from diabetes that life was nearly gone. But he recovered! The experiments on a few dogs have saved the lives of thousands of human beings.

The hormone insulin promotes the utilization of glucose in the body and thus lowers its concentration in blood. Insulin does not *cure* diabetes. A cure could be made only if it were possible to return the cells of the islets of Langerhans to a normal state. There is no known way to do this. But a diabetic person can control the level of glucose in his blood by receiving definite amounts of insulin at regular times.

Other hormones are also involved in regulating the concentration of blood glucose. For example, adrenaline increases the glucose level. Cortisone, from the adrenal cortex, and another hormone from the pituitary likewise increase the amount of glucose in the blood. Can you suggest why so many hormones control glucose concentration?

Clearly the control of the concentration of glucose in the bloodstream is a complex affair. Part of the control comes from the balanced secretion of insulin, adrenaline, cortisone, and a pituitary hormone.

We answered one question and are left with dozens more.

CONCLUDING REMARKS—COORDINATION

Coordination, as we have seen, involves receiving information and doing something about it. The information may be of many sorts: the words you are now reading, the odor of a skunk, the hot air near a flame, the noise of an automobile horn, the concentration of carbon dioxide in the blood, the presence of acid food in the first portion of the small intestine, a nerve impulse, or glucose in the blood. These various sorts of information (or stimuli) can lead to a variety of responses: a feeling of pleasure that you have nearly finished reading the chapter, holding your nose, moving from the flame, turning to look at the automobile, breathing more rapidly, the release of secretin, the contraction of a muscle, or the release of insulin.

In multicellular animals, there is nearly always a division of labor among structures that detect, transmit, coordinate, and respond to information. Detection is generally done by some part of the nervous system or a sense organ. Transmission is by way of neurons (with their nerve impulses) or the blood (with hormones). Coordination usually occurs in the central nervous system. Body response is through contraction by muscles or secretion by glands.

The ultimate purpose of coordination is survival—by maintaining the normal homeostatic conditions for the life of cells and by responding to the environment in such a way as to make further homeostatic control more probable. But for man, and possibly a few other animals, there is an extra something. A large part of our relation to the environment results in intellectual activity or in what can be described, inadequately to be sure, as a feeling of pleasure.

GUIDE QUESTIONS AND PROBLEMS

1. What are the consequences of division of labor for cells in multicellular animals?
2. Under what circumstances could carbon dioxide be considered a hormone?
3. How does the regulation of the oxygen content of blood show the mechanisms of coordination in the human body?
4. How does the breathing center function in respiration and breathing?
5. How is the nervous system of a planarian an advance over the nerve net type of organization found in *Hydra*?
6. What structural characteristics of the neuron make it well adapted as a conductor of stimuli?
7. What evidence supports the idea that nerve impulses stimulate muscles, glands, and other nerve cells by chemical means?
8. What are the major functions of the cerebrum?
9. What are the functions of the thyroid hormones?
10. What is the relation between the thyroid and the pituitary gland?
11. How could it be shown experimentally that a particular gland produced a hormone?
12. What hormones are involved in the control and regulation of the growth of the body?
13. How is the body's use of glucose regulated?
14. What are the functions of the adrenal hormones? the parathyroid hormones?

SUGGESTIONS FOR ADDITIONAL READING

Books

See references at the end of Chapter 22.

Magazines and Journals

Aird, R. B., "Barriers in the Brain." *Scientific American*, Vol. 194 (February 1956), pp. 101–02.

Benzinger, T. H., "The Human Thermostat." *Scientific American*, Vol. 204 (January 1961), pp. 134–40.

Gerard, R. W., "What Is Memory?" *Scientific American*, Vol. 189 (September 1953), pp. 118–24.

Gray, G. W., " 'The Great Ravelled Knot.' " *Scientific American*, Vol. 179 (October 1948), p. 26.

——— "Cortisone and ACTH." *Scientific American*, Vol. 182 (March 1950), p. 30.

Katz, B., "The Nerve Impulse." *Scientific American*, Vol. 187 (November 1952), p. 55.

Keynes, R. D., "The Nerve Impulse and the Squid." *Scientific American*, Vol. 199 (December 1958), pp. 83–90.

Li, C. H., "The Pituitary." *Scientific American*, Vol. 183 (October 1950), p. 18.

Marrazzi, A. S., "Messengers of the Nervous System." *Scientific American*, Vol. 196 (February 1957), pp. 86–90.

Snider, R. S., "The Cerebellum." *Scientific American*, Vol. 199 (August 1958), pp. 84–90.

Walter, W. G., "The Electrical Activity of the Brain." *Scientific American*, Vol. 190 (June 1954), pp. 54–63.

26

ANIMAL SUPPORT

AND LOCOMOTION

Among the vast array of animals on earth, there are two major ways to solve the problem of getting food. The first way—the solution adopted by most animals—is to go where the food is. This requires some means of locomotion. The second solution is to become attached to a surface and depend upon the food that comes to the animal. An animal that attaches itself to one place and remains there is called a **sessile** (SES·il) animal (Figure 26-1).

Most sessile animals live in the shallow areas of seas where microscopic plants and animals are abundant in the water. Some of these sessile animals, such as the sponges and sea squirts, feed by passing water through their bodies and filtering out the tiny animals and plants. Other sessile forms, such as corals and sea anemones, capture food organisms by using specialized arm-like structures called **tentacles** (TEN·ta·k'lz). Hydras feed in this manner (Chapter 21). In either case, a sessile existence depends upon a constant, abundant food supply in the vicinity of the animal.

As we have mentioned, most animals do not stay attached to one spot but move from one place to another in search of food. Animals capable of such locomotion are said to be **motile** (MOH·til).

Locomotion in animals is accomplished in a variety of ways (Figure 26-2). Horses, on long legs that can be alternately flexed and extended, cover swiftly the great distances of flat grassland. Porpoises and fishes move swiftly through the water by undulations of the body and vigorous action of the tail. Birds, bats, and bees fly by means of wings, which push against air. Snakes crawl on their bellies. Monkeys, squirrels, and opossums climb trees.

D. P. Wilson

26-1 A group of sea anemones. These coelenterates are an example of sessile animals with radial symmetry. *Hydra* (Figure 20-4) is another example. Other radially symmetrical animals that are not sessile, but motile instead, include jellyfish and sea stars. (Some biologists classify sea stars as bilaterally symmetrical, since part of their water-circulating system is slightly off center in their bodies.) All the radially symmetrical animals are aquatic.

a   D. P. Wilson

b   Marcel Cognac

26-2
Four motile animals with bilateral symmetry. All four are vertebrates. One lives and travels underwater (the ray in **a**), two fly (the duck in **b** and the chaffinch in **c**), and the fourth depends solely on its legs (the field mouse in **c**). Yet all accomplish their locomotion in the same way—by muscle contraction and its effect upon bones of the skeleton (see Figure 26-7b).

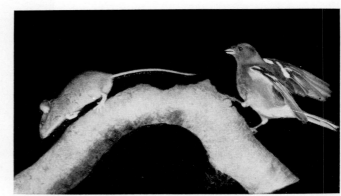

c   Eric Hosking

The Body Form of Animals

If you were to survey all the animals that move on the surface of the earth, you would find that most of them have similar body plans. Perhaps the most significant feature of most moving animals is that one end generally moves forward first. This is the head. Heads explore the environment: they always contain sense organs and the main nerve centers, or brain. The sense organs receive information from the environment and pass it to the brain. The brain then controls what kind of response will be made.

An animal that possesses a head always has two similar sides. That is, an imaginary line drawn down the center of the organism from head to tail divides the animal into two similar halves (Figure 26-2). An animal with this kind of body plan shows bilateral symmetry (as we learned in Chapter 20).

Some kinds of animals, such as the corals, jellyfish, or adult sea stars, do not have heads. Instead of having a head and a tail end and being bilaterally symmetrical, these animals have bodies arranged like a wheel, around a single central point. All sides of their bodies seem to be equally sensitive. The hub or center of the circular body has an opening, the mouth, through which the food passes. We learned in Chapter 20 that animals with this kind of construction show radial symmetry (Figure 26-1).

Among the radially symmetrical animals some, such as corals and sea anemones, are sessile forms. Others, such as jellyfish, move about slowly.

METHODS OF ANIMAL LOCOMOTION

Animals with bilateral symmetry and others with radial symmetry have existed in the seas for more than 500 million years. But only the animals with bilateral symmetry have invaded the land. Most of the animals that move rapidly are bilateral and often have a streamlined shape that meets with little resistance from water or air. This is true of animals living in sea, lake, pond, river, or on land. The bilateral body plan, therefore, has played a more important role in evolution than has the radial body plan.

Locomotion in the Protozoa

Biologists currently believe that the first protozoans to evolve were flagellated forms. That is, they moved themselves through the primordial seas by whipping their flagella against the water (Figure 26-3).

Other protozoans are adapted to crawling. One of these, for example, *Amoeba proteus* (a·MEE·ba PROH·te·us), moves about by extending false feet called **pseudopodia** (soo·doh·POH·dih·a). This kind of locomotion results from a flowing movement. That is, the cytoplasm moves into the gradually extending pseudopodia (Figure 26-4).

Still other kinds of protozoa, such as *Paramecium*, swim through the water by the beating of hundreds of small cilia.

In summary, there are three main ways by which protozoans move: with flagella, with pseudopodia, and with cilia. The fact

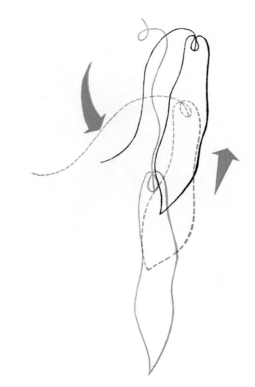

26-3 Locomotion in *Euglena*. As the flagellum is whipped backward, the organism moves forward. Can you explain how this or any other kind of locomotion is, in principle, related to your own walking? (A basic law of physics states that every action is accompanied by an equal and opposite reaction; does this help you in your explanation?)

that protozoans can move at all shows that these single-celled organisms are coordinated.

Locomotion in Multicellular Animals

Within a multicellular animal, cells, tissues, and organs work together to move the individual. One type of locomotion is demonstrated by the radially symmetrical jellyfish (Figure 26-5). This animal moves by a kind of jet propulsion. You could imagine it to be like the opening and closing of an umbrella under water. When the umbrella is closing, water is forced out. This pushes

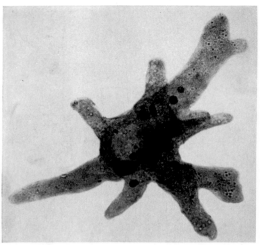

Bildarchiv Croy

26-4 Which way will it go? The question is difficult to answer, since this amoeba has pseudopodia extended all around.

ing to 3–4 kilograms (7–8 pounds). This eventually opens the shells of the mollusk slightly. The sea star then turns its stomach inside out and inserts it through the narrow opening between the mollusk's shells. The stomach is then wrapped around the body of the mollusk. The sea star's stomach begins to digest the mollusk's body. Before very long the mollusk dies and its shells open wide. Then the sea star withdraws its stomach, together with the partially digested mollusk.

Planarians move along on underwater surfaces with a kind of gliding locomotion. This movement is accomplished by cilia on the lower surface of the animal. It is supplemented by muscular contractions of the body.

the jellyfish through the sea. Although the jellyfish floats largely at the mercy of wind and wave, its slow pulsation provides some control over its movement.

The sea stars and sea cucumbers, which are echinoderms, have another interesting pattern of locomotion (Figure 26-6). If you examine carefully the surface on which the mouth of a sea star opens, you will see that each arm has a groove extending from the mouth to the tip. In this groove there are hundreds of soft tube feet. The sea star uses its tube feet to hold objects or to walk. Each individual tube foot acts as a suction cup and is under muscular control. The tube feet are extended by water being pumped into them. Contraction of muscles in the tube feet shortens them. The tube feet can also be moved laterally.

The food of a sea star includes clams, scallops (Figure 26-6), and oysters, the shells of which the sea star opens by use of its tube feet. First, the sea star fits its body over the edge of the shells opposite the hinge and attaches its tube feet to both shells at once. Then it exerts a pull amount-

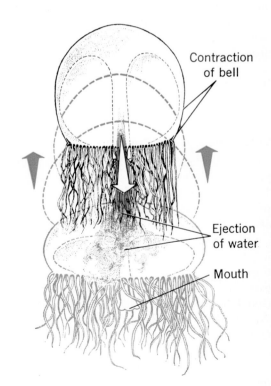

Contraction
of bell

Ejection
of water

Mouth

26-5 Another type of locomotion. Any jellyfish can demonstrate that jet propulsion is new only to man. Can you relate this means of travel to the two discussed in the caption for Figure 26-3?

D. P. Wilson

26-6 Mealtime in a marine aquarium. The meal will be scallops, and the chase is virtually over, since the imbalance in means of locomotion favors the sea stars (one of which already is demonstrating a "boardinghouse reach").

The gliding locomotion of the planarian can be contrasted with the accordionlike motion of the earthworm. The earthworm first becomes long and thin. Then little bristles, which are on the lower side of the body, dig into the soil and hold the front end steady while the tail end is pulled forward. The bristles of the rear end then serve as anchors as the front end is extended. This accordion type of locomotion is familiar if you have watched earthworms.

Skeletons and Locomotion

The multicellular animals discussed thus far are incapable of rapid locomotion. We can get a clue to one of the major reasons why the earthworm, for example, cannot move rapidly, by comparing its structure with that of a grasshopper or a rabbit.

The earthworm, using muscles and bristles, moves itself slowly. The grasshopper and the rabbit are capable of much more rapid motion (Figure 26-7). Both of them have appendages (legs) that are moved by muscles. The appendages act as levers; the muscles move the levers. Levers work only if stiff, and the bones of the rabbit's skeleton possess this necessary mechanical property. The grasshopper also has a skeleton that makes its legs stiff.

The rabbit has an internal skeleton, or **endoskeleton.** The grasshopper has an external skeleton, or **exoskeleton.**

Skeletal Muscle

There are several kinds of muscles in the human body. These include the **cardiac muscle** of the heart and the **smooth muscle**

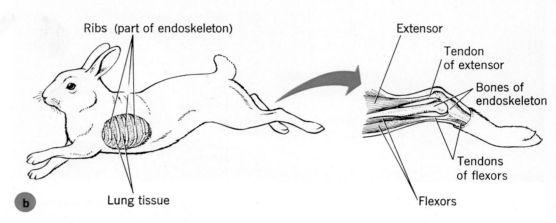

26-7 The relationship of locomotion, support, and protection of vital tissues in an insect and in a mammal. The insect has a supporting exoskeleton; the mammal a supporting endoskeleton. Locomotion in both is basically the same. Muscles are attached to the skeleton in such a way that one end of a muscle (or its tendon) is attached to one bone or skeletal part, and the other end (or its tendon) to a different bone or part. Contraction of the muscle then produces skeletal movement. How does a skeleton serve a protective role in addition to its roles in locomotion and support?

of the blood vessels, digestive tract, and many other organs. Cardiac muscle and smooth muscle are entirely independent of voluntary control. You cannot voluntarily make your heart beat faster, or slow down peristalsis in the intestine.

There is another type of muscle, **skeletal muscle,** which is usually associated with the movements of bones. The action of skeletal muscles is under conscious control, so we say that they are voluntary muscles.

Many skeletal muscles work in pairs. That is, one muscle pulls a bone in one direction, and the companion muscle pulls the bone in the opposite direction. This arrangement of skeletal muscles is known as **antagonism** (an·TAG·o·niz′m). A muscle's action is antagonistic, so to speak, to that of its companion muscle. Most of the skeletal muscles are arranged in such antagonistic pairs. A good example is the combination of a **flexor** muscle and an **extensor** muscle. A flexor bends a joint, while an extensor straightens it out again. The knee movement used in walking involves such a flexor-extensor antagonism. Raising and lowering the foot, as in standing on tiptoe, then normally, is much the same. What are other examples?

Figure 26-7 shows a diagram of part of an insect limb and part of a vertebrate limb. Notice how the muscles must be attached to endoskeletons and exoskeletons. Also notice that each muscle requires an antagonistic muscle in order to function effectively. Why do you suppose this is so?

Contractility

Contractility, the ability to contract, is a fundamental characteristic of living substance. So far as we know, it is essential to all kinds of movements except growth and cytoplasmic streaming. It looks very simple, but the simpler it looks the harder it is to explain. What is it that keeps the filaments of the blue-green alga *Oscillatoria* and some of its relatives ceaselessly waving in perfectly still water? What makes a flagellum or a cilium wave so vigorously and so rhythmically (see Chapter 19)? When we watch an amoeba pull itself in here and protrude its pseudopodia there, how does it do this? Are these simple forms of motion related structurally or chemically to the contraction of an animal's muscles?

Much work has gone into efforts to discover the mechanism of flow in an amoeba. Many observations and experiments reveal that the inside of an amoeba is more fluid than the external layer, which is a rather firm gel. Fluid cytoplasm, flowing up the center of a pseudopod, appears to burst through the tip, flow out a little way, and then congeal as it reacts with the surrounding water. The tube of solidified, or gelled, substance remains relatively stationary as the rest of the amoeba flows through it. At the same time that the fluid cytoplasm becomes gel at the advancing end, the solid gel at the rear seems to be drawn into the interior of the body and rendered fluid again. As the fluid cytoplasm is transformed into a gel, it contracts; it is very interesting that the amoeba possesses a protein quite similar to the contractile proteins of animal muscles. To contract requires energy, and

this is probably supplied by ATP, for the amoeba is very sensitive to ATP. When ATP is added to the medium in which the amoeba is living, or when it is injected into the amoeba, the protozoan responds by local contractions.

Most of what we know about contraction comes at present from studies of vertebrate muscle cells, especially those that form the skeletal muscles, also called **striated** (STRY-ayt-ed) muscles. Striated means striped, and this term is used because the fibers of a skeletal muscle, when examined under the microscope, show numerous cross bands of alternating dark and light stripes (Figure 26-8a). When the muscle fiber contracts, the pattern of cross bands shifts. By a combination of observations with the electron microscope and the methods of the biochemist, the meaning of these shifts in the appearance of the fiber when it contracts has been revealed.

A muscle is made up of a great many individual muscle fibers. Nuclei and mitochondria lie on the outside of each fiber, and the body of the fiber consists largely of special contractile proteins, the two most abundant ones being **myosin** (MY-o-sin) and **actin**. In a cross section of a fiber seen under the electron microscope (Figure 26-8b) one observes dark spots that represent dozens of filaments running lengthwise along the fiber. The filaments are of two sizes, the thicker ones being about 10 millimicrons in diameter, and the thinner ones about 5 millimicrons in diameter. They are arranged in a very regular hexagonal pattern, six thin filaments surrounding each thick one (see inset, Figure 26-8b). It has recently been determined that the thick filaments are myosin filaments and the thin ones are actin.

The cross bands of the striated muscle fiber change in width when the muscle fiber contracts. Certain thin cross bands, known as **Z bands**, get closer together when the fiber contracts. But the filaments of myosin

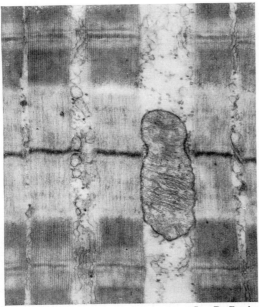

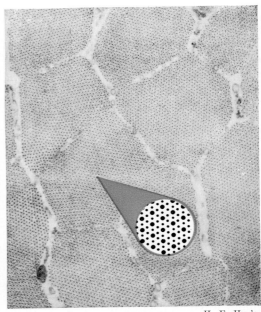

Lee D. Peachy

H. E. Huxley

26-8 **a** An electron micrograph of a longitudinal section through several skeletal muscle fibers. A region of Z bands shows as a dark, broken stripe that runs across the fibers near the center of the photograph. The broad, dark areas near the top and bottom are the regions in which actin and myosin filaments overlap (see Figure 26-9). Note also a mitochondrium. (20,000 X) **b** Another electron micrograph of skeletal muscle fibers, this time in cross section. The inset drawing shows the difference in size of the two types of contractile proteins, the larger being myosin, the smaller, actin.

and of actin, we now discover, do not contract at all—at least not in the sense that the muscle fiber as a whole does. What kind of model will explain these observations? Clearly, the actin and myosin filaments must slide over each other. This is possible if the actin filaments are attached to the Z bands by one end, and if the myosin filaments lie free at each end, in between the Z bands (Figure 26-9a).

The energy for the contraction comes from ATP that is stored in the muscle fiber. When a nerve impulse passes along a motor neuron to its terminal (which branches out over the surface of the fiber in a sort of brushlike ending), the stimulus to the muscle fiber leads to a release or activation of an enzyme that acts on ATP. The ATP is converted to ADP. The energy released is

expressed in the contraction of the muscle fiber. The actin and myosin filaments slide past each other, and the distance between Z bands shortens; thus the muscle fiber as a whole contracts, and work is done on the masses that are attached by tough, inelastic tendons to the ends of the muscle (Figure 26-7).

It is very interesting, and perhaps it will surprise you, that the contraction of each muscle fiber is "all-or-none." If it contracts at all, it does so to the fullest of its capacity at any existing moment—no halfhearted action here! The reason a *muscle* can contract to varying degrees is because it has many hundreds of separate muscle fibers; the contraction of the muscle as a whole may involve several dozens, or many hundreds of fibers.

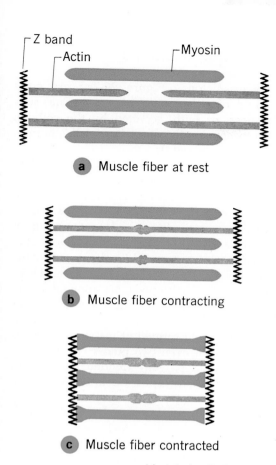

Z band
Actin
Myosin

a Muscle fiber at rest

b Muscle fiber contracting

c Muscle fiber contracted

Adapted after H. E. Huxley,
Scientific American, Nov. 1958 (p. 76)

26-9 A diagram of the contraction of a muscle fiber. The energy for the contraction is supplied by ATP. Do you suppose some contractions would stop at stage **b**? Or would they all proceed to stage **c**? If the contractions always are "all the way," how can you explain varying degrees of muscle activity?

In the contraction of a skeletal muscle, it would not serve at all well if a long interval of time had to elapse between the arrival of a nerve impulse and the responding contraction of the muscle fiber. One's very life may depend upon an instant response. In other words, the muscle must be ready to contract immediately upon command, and this means that, like a gun ready for use, it must

be "loaded and cocked." Since each muscle fiber, once it has contracted, must be restored to its original state of readiness (and that takes time), the entire muscle must be made of many independent fibers, some of which are always kept in reserve.

Meanwhile the used fibers must recover. It is a complicated business, since the reserve supply of ATP must be replaced in the fiber from the ADP that is formed when the contraction occurs. This process, you may recall, requires the breakdown of glucose to pyruvic acid through many steps, the breakdown of pyruvic acid, again through many steps, and the flow of electrons along the electron transport chain of the mitochondria until they combine with free oxygen. But a muscle fiber does not have room for many mitochondria; to supply additional oxygen to a muscle requires *time.*

Have you ever noticed that when you exercise vigorously—say by running quickly up a flight of steps—you do not begin to breathe deeply or to pant until a considerable time after the effort is begun? You can actually run up an "oxygen debt" in your muscles before the relatively slow mechanisms that speed up your rate of breathing begin to operate. How is this possible?

Essentially what happens is as follows. In the muscle cell there is a store of another kind of energy-rich phosphate compound, known as **creatine** (KREE·a·teen) **phosphate.** (In crustaceans and other invertebrates this is substituted by arginine phosphate or some related compound.) Creatine phosphate will donate its phosphate groups to ADP:

Creatine P + ADP → ATP + Creatine

Obviously the muscle cell will then be short of creatine phosphate, and the supply of that reserve energy-rich substance must also be replaced. Glucose is brought to the muscle fiber during its rest and recovery periods, by the blood. It is converted into glycogen and stored in large amounts in muscle, just as in the liver. When the muscle fiber has contracted and is recovering, glycogen is reconverted into glucose and the glucose is oxidized, although not to pyruvic acid as you might suppose, but to lactic acid ($CH_3 \cdot CHOH \cdot COOH$). These oxidative steps yield a small amount of ATP, sufficient to replenish the supply of creatine phosphate and ATP used up.

But now the cell has a load of lactic acid. It has often been supposed that muscle fatigue is produced by this accumulation of lactic acid. Maybe not, but in any case it is harmful to the cell and must be eliminated. Lactic acid, oxidized in steps like those in which pyruvic acid is oxidized, supplies electrons for the transport chain in the mitochondria, whereby an abundance of ATP is generated.

In 1922 Otto Meyerhof of Germany and A. V. Hill of Great Britain shared a Nobel prize for their magnificent work on muscle contraction and muscle physiology. One of the important and very surprising discoveries Meyerhof had made was that only about one fifth of the lactic acid produced because of a muscle contraction is actually oxidized to carbon dioxide and water. What happens to the rest of it? A beautiful arrangement of nature, truly, for it turns out that the energy released from the fraction of the lactic acid that is oxidized is used to "push" the remaining four fifths "uphill" to return it to glycogen and replenish the store of that substance in the muscle.

This remarkable story of the contraction and recovery mechanisms of striated muscle once again offers an example of the homeostatic capacity of living systems. It seems likely that similar mechanisms, if not so refined, are operating in the contraction and recovery of smooth, involuntary muscle cells. Indeed, this story may point to the fundamental nature of all contractility, for glucose, ATP, and muscle proteins such as myosin and actin almost undoubtedly play a universal role from amoeba to man.

EXOSKELETONS AND ENDOSKELETONS

Exoskeletons (Figure 26-7a) are composed of either inorganic or organic substances, or both, secreted by the cell (in protozoans) or by specialized cells (in multicellular animals).

In many cases exoskeletons are very rigid and heavy. They restrict an animal's movements to the extent that the animal must lead a very slow-moving life (clams, snails) or even a sessile life (corals). One group of animals, however, has attained a very successful solution to the difficulty posed by the rigidity and weight of an exoskeleton. These animals, the arthropods, are completely encased in a very light substance known as chitin. In addition, their exoskeletons, instead of being formed of just one piece (as in snails) or even two pieces (as in clams, oysters, scallops), are divided into several distinct sections. Thus, the arthropods have combined relative ease of motion with a protective outer covering. No doubt this is a factor in the biological success of this group. But, successful as this type of exoskeleton seems to be, it presents at least one great disadvantage—if the animal is to grow at all, it must rid itself of its restricting armor. Arthropods do this by molting. As they grow they periodically shed their skeletons and grow larger ones. Many do not grow after becoming adult.

"Soft-shelled" crabs are those caught just after molting. They have cast off their former tough exoskeletons, and the new ones have not yet hardened. Among insects, molting occurs only in the immature stages. An adult beetle, for example, has reached its maximum size.

The largest of animals, both living and extinct, have been those with endoskeletons. The blue whale, the elephant, and the extinct giant reptiles are good examples. A rigid framework sheathed in layers of muscle, in addition to providing a means of locomotion, is apparently a good design for supporting and for holding an animal together.

In addition to its role in locomotion and support, the skeleton serves also to protect parts of the animal. An internal skeleton, such as we have, may protect some internal organs (Figure 26-7b). For example, heavy bone protects such important structures as the brain, the internal ears, and parts of the eyes. The backbone encloses the spinal cord. The ribs protect the lungs and heart.

The bony skeleton of vertebrates, in contrast to the inert exoskeleton of insects, contains living tissue. Thus, bones contain bone cells, which form the fibers and deposit the minerals that make up the bone.

Evolution, Internal Skeletons, and Locomotion

The fossil record gives a clear and fairly detailed picture of the development of the skeleton in various groups of vertebrates. The earliest vertebrates were fish, in which several adaptations for swimming are to be seen. The jawless fish, which are the oldest vertebrates found in the rocks, were animals that swam by undulating their bodies. Usually there were no paired fins of the sort characteristic of most living species of fish. The body moved by alternating waves, or ripples, of muscle contractions passing along the muscles on either side of the animal. This caused the body to undulate from side to side. These undulations were transmitted through the back part of the body and the tail as a series of backward pushes against the dense water. This is the primary type of locomotion among vertebrates.

This type of locomotion, with many variations, is retained in a great majority of fish for the simple reason that it is the most efficient way of getting through the water. For such swimming animals it is generally advantageous that the vertebral column, the "backbone," be quite flexible. This can be seen in fish whose vertebrae commonly lack articulations or processes for locking the individual bones together (Figure 26-10).

The lobe-finned fish, a group of early fish, differed from the other fish of their time in that (among other things) their paired fins were supported by a series of bones arranged in a particular way. A single long bone was at the base of each fin, and its attached, or **proximal,** end joined and rotated on the bones of the shoulder girdle, or of the hip girdle. At the other end of this bone, the **distal** end, there were two more rather long bones, side by side. And at the distal end of these two bones were several bones, all side by side. Here was the beginning of the skeleton of the **tetrapod** (TET-ra·pod) or four-legged vertebrate's limb: a single bone in the upper part of the leg (or arm), the two lower bones of the leg (or arm), and the several bones of the feet (or hands).

Lobe-finned fish were the ancestors of the four-legged amphibians. As the amphibians evolved, they faced the problem of gravity, heretofore of little consequence to the water-living vertebrates. At an early stage in amphibian evolution, the vertebrae became rather complex, linked together by interlocking articulations (see Figure 26-10). Thus the backbone became a strong, but reasonably flexible, girder that supported the weight of the body.

With the land-living vertebrates the basic method of locomotion has been that of walking on all four legs (Figure 26-11). In the early amphibians the legs sprawled out from the body, so that the animal probably dragged itself over the ground. This type of locomotion also characterized the first reptiles. Most of their muscular energy would have been spent just in holding up the weight of the trunk, if it did not rest on the ground. In an early stage in reptilian evolution, however, there were trends toward bringing the feet in beneath the body and raising the body clear of the ground.

This more efficient method of walking and running has been characteristic of most reptiles since the beginning of the Age of Dinosaurs, and of nearly all mammals. As a specialized departure from the four-footed means of locomotion, many reptiles and mammals have, through the ages, become bipedal—walking, running, or hopping on their hind limbs. Such a method of locomotion commonly releases the forelimbs for feeding or other activity.

One very special type of locomotion found among most of the primates—the monkeys and apes—is **brachiation** (bray-kih·AY·sh'n). By this method, a primate can swing through the trees by using its grasping hands and long arms.

Many animals that climb trees are too small to brachiate; consequently they jump from branch to branch. Some small animals that jump through the trees flatten the body as they jump, thus making of themselves a sort of primitive glider. It is but a short and obvious step from this adaptation to one in which there is a large gliding membrane, usually between the front and hind legs, such as typifies the flying squirrels.

Of course, the ultimate development in aerial locomotion is true flight. This evolved simultaneously during the Jurassic period of earth history, about 175 million years ago, in the flying reptiles and in the first birds, which were descended from reptiles. With these animals, the forelimbs were transformed into wings. At the end of the Age of Dinosaurs, the flying reptiles became extinct, but the birds continued and became highly varied.

One should not suppose any of these advantages in locomotion were purposefully acquired. As we will see in Chapters 34 and 35, natural selection is sufficient to account for all adaptations of living beings, through the more successful reproduction of some, and the less successful reproduction of other hereditary types.

VERTEBRAE AND BODY SUPPORT

a Primitive fish

b Alligator

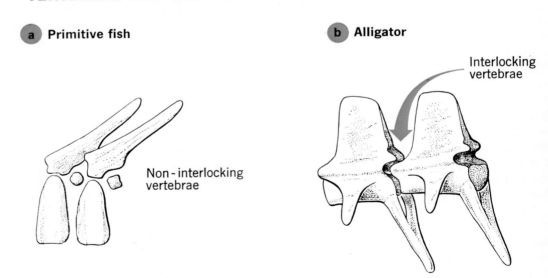

Interlocking vertebrae

Non-interlocking vertebrae

26-10 What is the most noticeable difference between these two patterns of vertebrae? In what way is pattern **a** not adequate for a land-inhabiting vertebrate? How does pattern **b** restrict the movements of the animals in which it is found?

THE EVOLUTION OF BODY SUPPORT IN LAND VERTEBRATES

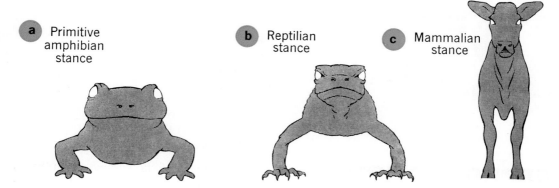

a Primitive amphibian stance

b Reptilian stance

c Mammalian stance

26-11   One trend in the evolution of land-inhabiting vertebrates consisted of getting up off the ground. A few vertebrates, however, interrupted and reversed the process. What do you suppose one result would be? (See Figure 34-12a, page 608.)

GUIDE QUESTIONS AND PROBLEMS

1. What are the differences between bilateral and radial symmetry? Why do you suppose that only animals with bilateral symmetry have colonized the land?
2. How is the presence of a skeleton related to locomotion?
3. How does the structure of striated muscle help explain the contraction of a muscle?
4. How does the chemistry of muscle action show homeostatic capacity?
5. What is the major limiting factor of an exoskeleton? If exoskeletons contained living cells, does it seem plausible that the limiting factor might no longer exist?
6. What are opposing muscles? What do they oppose? Why are they necessary to efficient locomotion in the animals that possess them?

SUGGESTIONS FOR ADDITIONAL READING

Books

Buchsbaum, R., *Animals Without Backbones*, rev. ed. Chicago, University of Chicago Press, 1948.
    Includes clear descriptions and diagrams of invertebrate locomotion.

Gray, J., *How Animals Move*, rev. ed. New York, Cambridge University Press, 1959.
    A beautifully written, well-illustrated description of many methods of animal locomotion.

Schmidt-Nielsen, K., *Animal Physiology*. Foundations of Modern Biology Series. Englewood Cliffs (N. J.), Prentice-Hall, 1960.
    A relatively simple account of animal processes, including locomotion.

Magazines and Journals

Gray, Sir James, "How Fishes Swim." *Scientific American*, Vol. 197 (August 1957), pp. 48–54.

Hayashi, T., and G. A. W. Boehm, "Artificial Muscle." *Scientific American*, Vol. 187 (December 1952), pp. 18–21.

Huxley, H. E., "The Contraction of Muscle." *Scientific American*, Vol. 199 (November 1958), pp. 66–72.

Katchalsky, A., and S. Lifson, "Muscle as a Machine." *Scientific American*, Vol. 190 (March 1954), pp. 72–74.

McLean, F. C., "Bone." *Scientific American*, Vol. 192 (February 1955), pp. 84–86.

Szent-Györgyi, A., "Muscle Research." *Scientific American*, Vol. 180 (June 1949), pp. 23–24.

27

REPRODUCTION

IN ANIMALS

In one respect reproduction differs from all other functions in living things. It is not necessary for the well-being of the individual! Any one of the reproductive organs—even the whole system—can be removed, and yet the individual may continue in good health.

Without a reproductive system the individual may enjoy well-being, but the species, of course, will not. If the reproductive systems in all members of a species were suddenly to stop functioning, the species would be doomed. These existing individuals would live out their life spans and die, and the species would die with them.

In some species of animals, reproduction is carried out for the species by only a very few of its members in every generation. Bees are an example. The vast majority of hive members are sterile females, called workers, that have no part in reproduction, but do take care of the developing young. Only the queen bee of the hive produces eggs. A few individuals of the hive are fertile males, which produce sperms.

PATTERNS OF REPRODUCTION

Many ways of reproduction have arisen independently in the evolution of the invertebrates and vertebrates. There are two main patterns: sexual reproduction and asexual reproduction.

Sexual reproduction is any method of producing new individuals that involves a fusion of nuclei from different sources, either from different individuals or from different organs in the same individual. There are three common patterns:

1. The fusion of the nucleus of an ovum, produced by a female, with the nucleus of a sperm, produced by a male (man and most other familiar species)
2. The fusion of the nucleus of an ovum produced by a **hermaphroditic** (her-maf·ro·DIT·ik) animal, with the nucleus of a sperm produced by (a) the same hermaphroditic individual (as in the tapeworm) or by (b) another hermaphroditic individual of the same species (as in earthworms)
3. The fusion of nuclei produced by individuals of different mating types (paramecia)

Whatever the method of fertilization, there must also always be meiosis. Meiosis and fertilization alternate in the life cycle. In animals meiosis characteristically comes just before fertilization, during the formation of the reproductive cells.

Asexual reproduction is any method of producing new individuals that does not involve the fusion of the nuclei of two cells, and does not involve meiosis.

We will consider the two main patterns of reproduction, beginning with asexual.

Asexual Reproduction

Mitotic cell division in the Protozoa is a simple type of asexual reproduction. In *Amoeba* and *Paramecium* a parent cell gives rise to two daughter cells (Figure 27-1). In most amoebas this is the only type

27-1 EXAMPLES OF ASEXUAL AND SEXUAL REPRODUCTION

Organism	Asexual reproduction	Sexual reproduction
Amoeba	Mitosis and cell division	None
Paramecium	Mitosis and cell division	Conjugation and fusion of micronuclei
Hydra	Bud Budding	Sperms Ovary (with eggs) Testis The embryos are shed in the water, where they develop into new individuals.
Tapeworm	None	Sperms travel to eggs — Testes — Zygotes develop here until liberated. Ovaries — Fertilization occurs here. Internal self-fertilization
Earthworm	None	Exchange of sperms Sperms are produced and exchanged. Then each worm fertilizes its own eggs with sperms from the other worm.
Man	Identical twins from one egg	Egg Sperms Internal fertilization and development of offspring

of reproduction known to occur, but in *Paramecium* there is sexual reproduction as well (Figure 27-1; or in more detail, Figure 19-9, page 354).

Recall that a slightly different type of asexual reproduction in a protozoan occurs in *Plasmodium* (Figure 1-10). After the parasite enters a red blood cell, it divides by mitosis, producing a dozen or more new individuals.

Budding is a type of asexual reproduction in which a new animal is produced as a bud, or outgrowth, on an older animal. The process is somewhat like branching in plants. The bud eventually breaks off and becomes a new individual. You may have observed this process of budding in your laboratory study of hydras. You will remember that in this coelenterate some cells form an outgrowth from the body of the animal, and the outgrowth eventually separates as a new individual (Figure 27-1; also, Figure 20-5c, page 368). Similar reproduction occurs in other coelenterates.

Many flatworms reproduce asexually by constricting into two halves, each of which becomes a new individual. Among the annelid worms there are groups living in fresh water that regularly reproduce by dividing into two pieces. The anterior piece regenerates a new posterior part and the posterior piece regenerates a new anterior part. This is somewhat like the division of a protozoan, but on a multicellular scale.

While asexual reproduction does occur in animals, most species do not depend exclusively on asexual methods. Asexual reproduction occurs even in man, though in very special circumstances, namely, in the formation of identical twins from one zygote.

The exact details of the formation of identical twins are unknown for man. From what is known of early development in other species, a highly probable hypothesis can be constructed. In normal human development the fertilized egg divides repeatedly to form the embryo and finally the adult.

All of the cells remain a part of the same individual. Identical twins may be thought of as resulting from an error in normal development. The fertilized egg divides into two cells. Somehow these two cells come apart, and then each continues *separately* to undergo division and eventually produce an embryo and later an adult. It is possible that the separation of the embryo into two parts may come about somewhat later than the two-cell stage. Whenever the separation does occur, the development of identical twins is asexual reproduction because the two individuals are formed from one zygote by an asexual process. The process is essentially the same as asexual reproduction in *Paramecium* and *Amoeba*—cell division. Identical triplets, quadruplets, and quintuplets, such as Canada's celebrated Dionne quintuplets, form in a similar way.

Parthenogenesis (par-the-no-JEN-e-sis) is yet another type of asexual reproduction. Generally, the egg develops without meiosis and fertilization ever occurring. The offspring are diploid. Parthenogenesis may occur in species that also show sexual reproduction. In addition there are some species of insects, and of microscopic animals known as rotifers, in which all reproduction is parthenogenetic. There are no males known in these species.

There is a type of parthenogenesis in which meiosis does occur, and the egg (monoploid) can develop whether fertilized or not. The monoploid offspring develop into males, the diploid offspring into females. This strange kind of reproduction occurs in bees, ants, and wasps and their insect relatives. Here one finds asexual and sexual reproduction going on almost simultaneously.

Sexual Reproduction

In the great majority of animals, as in sexually reproducing plants, we recognize two kinds of individuals that produce sex cells, or gametes. The males produce

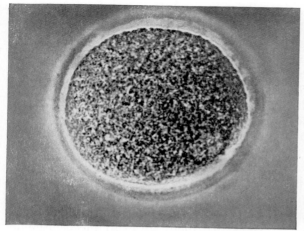
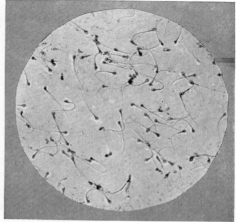

Left, Dr. L. B. Shettles; *right*, Dr. Seymour F. Wilhelm

27-2 A human ovum (left) and numerous human sperms (right), as seen under the compound microscope. The enlargement is approximately the same in both photographs (200 X); the egg is many times larger than a sperm. What kind of substance stored in the egg accounts for most of the difference in size?

sperms, the females produce ova (eggs). Reproduction depends upon the union of a sperm and an ovum to form the cell from which a new individual develops. This is sexual reproduction, the most common pattern of reproduction in the Animal Kingdom.

Most of the animals that reproduce sexually (other than some protozoans and sponges) have specialized organs, the **gonads** (GO·nadz), for the production of gametes. Gonads are of two types: ovaries, which form ova, and testes (sing., testis), which form sperms.

The gametes from the two sexes of a species are quite different. The ovum is usually spherical or oval and is immotile (Figure 27-2). Ova of different species carry varying amounts of yolk, which nourishes the newly developing individual. The largest single cells in the world are the ova (the "yolks") of birds' or reptiles' eggs.

Sperms are generally very small and motile. They usually have a single flagellum, a long whiplike tail (Figure 27-2). The movement of a sperm is made possible by the beating of its flagellum.

The great advantage of sexual reproduction is the *variation* in individuals that it produces—a variation that serves as the raw material of evolution. In asexual reproduction, there are no gametes. In sexual reproduction, each parent individual produces a variety of gametes. These gametes differ in the kinds of hereditary units, or genes, that they contain. When ova and sperms combine at fertilization, many different variations in offspring subsequently develop. Natural selection screens these many variations and preserves those best able to survive and reproduce. Sexual reproduction is consequently of enormous importance in evolution. No wonder it is so common among living organisms.

In many species belonging to various phyla, the same individual possesses both ovaries and testes. Examples are planarians and earthworms. Animals with both ovaries and testes in the same individual are called **hermaphrodites** (her·MAF·ro·dyts). Even among vertebrates, hermaphroditic *individuals* occasionally occur; hermaphroditic *species,* however, are rare among the vertebrates.

There are two main patterns of reproduction in hermaphrodites. First, two hermaphroditic individuals may mate and exchange sperms. An example of this is observed in the earthworm. Second, a sperm and ovum of the same individual may unite and produce a zygote. The tapeworm (one of the flatworms, and a parasite of man and other chordates) provides an example of this pattern of reproduction (Figure 27-1).

In most hermaphroditic species, the great advantage of sexual reproduction—the shuffling and recombining of genes—is maintained. There is some shuffling and recombining of genes even when ova and sperms of the same individual unite. There is more when two hermaphroditic individuals mate and exchange sperms.

In most animals there are two sexes—male and female. The difference between male and female is genetic (the evidence will be presented in Chapter 21). Male and female are defined on the basis of the type of gamete they produce—sperms by a male, ova by a female. The presence of testes or ovaries, therefore, can be said to be a primary sex characteristic.

In many species there are other differences between male and female. These are known as the secondary sex characteristics (Figure 27-3). Frequently the secondary sex characteristics develop in response to hormones produced by the testes or ovaries (to be discussed later in this chapter).

To summarize, the ways in which animals reproduce are varied. Basically, *the function is the same in all—reproduction ensures the continuance of the species; and sexual reproduction ensures a variety of genetic types in the population, the variety upon which evolution depends.*

External Fertilization

The ovum, with its food supply for the new organism, does not have any device for locomotion. The sperm can move, but its swimming motion requires a liquid. For animals that live in water, there is no problem. In some species, ova and sperms may simply be shed into the water.

But there may be another problem. Gametes have no way of nourishing themselves. Hence, they cannot exist long when shed from the the parent animal. Furthermore, sperm cells cannot travel far. So, if there is to be any reasonable chance of a sperm finding an ovum, both must be shed at approximately the same time and place. Individuals of some aquatic species do just this; they shed their sperms and ova *into the water* at the same time and same place. We know that there are many mechanisms by which this simultaneous spawning is accomplished, but we are far from fully understanding how they operate.

Internal Fertilization

Internal fertilization, a method characteristic of many species, further insures the meeting of sperm and ovum. The male places the sperm within the tube that the ova must traverse in their journey from the ovary to the outside of the body. This method of internal fertilization takes place even among animals living in the water. Many crustaceans have it; so do some fish, such as dogfish (certain sharks).

For animals living on land, internal fertilization is nearly always a necessity. Sperms are quickly killed by drying. Since terrestrial animals are all motile, they need not depend on thin films of dew or rain to transport the sperms from male to female, as some land plants do (see Chapter 14); hence internal fertilization is the rule.

Internal fertilization does not solve all the problems of efficient transport of sperms to ova, however. There is still a problem of timing. In most cases, the tiny sperm, which lacks any quantity of stored food to support its active swimming, lives only a short time. Furthermore, ova can be fertilized only when they reach a proper stage of development and are released from the ovary.

a

Philip Gendreau

27-3 Secondary sex characteristics in three species of vertebrates. **a** The antlers of a buck immediately distinguish him from a doe. **b** Of these two white leghorns, which is the hen and which the rooster? **c** The chief difference between a lion and a lioness is the mane of the male.

b

Caru Studios and Philip Gendreau

c

Philip Gendreau and Lightfoot from Nat. Audubon Assoc.

In many insects this timing problem is solved by storage of the sperms. Once the sperms are deposited within the reproductive system of the female, they are maintained in a special pouch and released as the ova are laid. In bees, for example, sperms may be stored for several years. In many mammals, the timing problem is solved by means of a complex control system of hormones. We shall turn to this problem very soon.

PATTERNS FOR NOURISHING AND PROTECTING THE EMBRYO

Fertilization is only one part of reproduction. Once this is achieved, there is still the problem of nourishing the developing embryo, providing a suitable environment for it, and protecting it against danger. There are many ways whereby fertilization is achieved and care for the developing young is provided. We will describe a few of the important ones.

Insurance by Numbers

With many animals, continuation of the species is assured mainly by reliance on numbers. For example, a single codfish can produce 5 million ova! Many are eaten or otherwise destroyed, but even the survival of a small percentage of the total is enough to maintain the species. Generally the number of ova produced by each female of any species is correlated with the average chance of a single offspring developing to maturity.

There are many other variations and additional safeguards. In the first place, the ova of many living organisms are supplied with stored food, which nourishes the developing young until they are able to feed. In many cases a proper temperature is assured by the fact that production and fertilization of the ova occur at a definite season of the year. In other cases, such as that of birds, few eggs may be laid, but each de-

veloping offspring is warmed and protected by a parent, or parents, both before and after hatching.

Protective Coats for the Embryo

Amphibians, such as frogs, lay their eggs in water. Each ovum is surrounded by layers of jelly, which afford some degree of protection for the developing embryo. The ovum contains enough stored food for the early development of the embryo. Oxygen diffuses in from the surrounding pond; wastes diffuse out.

Animals belonging to the next class of vertebrates, the reptiles, lay eggs on land, although many of them, as adults, live in water. The reptiles were the first vertebrates to lay their eggs on land. Of interest to us now are the changes in egg structure that made possible life on land. You are familiar with two necessary structures in the hen's egg—a porous shell, and just inside it, a tough but thin shell membrane.

The outer shell and membrane are not the only protective structures of the land egg evolved by reptiles and birds. If we study an early chick embryo we are likely to notice first that the embryonic digestive tract swells, about midway along its length, into a large sac. This is the **yolk sac**, a membrane filled with stored food (Figure 27-4). Just how much food there may be we can judge from the yolk of the hen's egg we ate for breakfast.

If we look closely we will find another membrane that extends from the embryo's body wall and encloses the entire embryo within a sac. This sac, called the **amnion** (AM·nih·on), is filled with fluid. So you see, even though the adult animal lays its eggs on land, the young are supplied with adequate food, and development takes place in a fluid environment.

The **allantois** (a·LAN·toh·is), the third membrane, is an outgrowth from the digestive tract of the embryo and becomes a large saclike structure, well supplied with blood

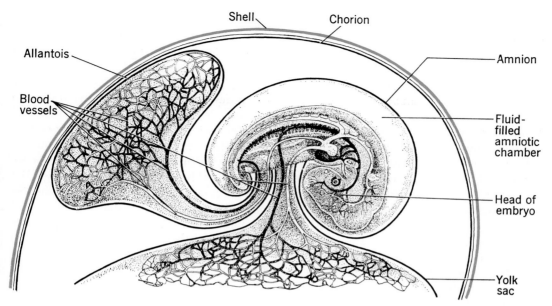

Shell

Chorion

Allantois

Amnion

Blood vessels

Fluid-filled amniotic chamber

Head of embryo

Yolk sac

Redrawn from Patten, *Foundations in Embryology*

27-4 A developing chick embryo. The embryo is enclosed in fluid within one of four membranes—the amnion. The food supply, and associated blood vessels leading to the embryo, are enclosed within another membrane—the yolk sac. Carbon dioxide-oxygen exchange takes place in blood vessels enclosed by a third membrane—the allantois. All these membranes and their enclosures are contained within still another membrane—the chorion. (There is also a shell membrane inside the shell.)

vessels. The outer portion of the allantois joins with the fourth embryonic membrane, the **chorion** (KOH·rih·on). The chorion completely encloses the embryo and all other membranes. It lies very close to the egg shell, which is porous and readily permits gases to diffuse through it. The allantois, fused in part with the chorion, acts as a respiratory organ for the embryo. Its blood vessels allow for the exchange of oxygen and carbon dioxide with the atmosphere. (What do you suppose would happen to the embryo if you coated the eggshell with wax?) In addition, the allantois serves as a storage "tank," because nitrogenous wastes are deposited here—outside the body of the embryo. The arrangement is like that of a house with a remote septic tank.

In summary, reptiles and birds have evolved reproductive systems that make it

possible for them to lay their eggs on land. The egg usually has a firm shell that keeps the embryo from being crushed and protects it from drying out. In addition, there are embryonic membranes that protect, aid in respiration, provide a liquid environment, serve in storing nitrogenous wastes, and aid in the nourishment of the embryo.

Protection by Internal Development

In some animals with internal fertilization, the embryo develops within the body of the female. There, within its own membranes and using its own stored food, the fertilized egg develops. Eventually the developed offspring reaches a stage at which it can fend for itself; then it is born. We find this kind of protection—internal development, but *without* food being supplied by the mother—in some sharks and reptiles.

Food from the Female—
The Egg-laying Mammals

Our own group of animals, the mammals, make an important new contribution to the feeding of the young—the secretion of milk. Mammals have also elaborated in various ways the family system of care for the offspring. In other respects mammals, for the most part, rely on a combination of methods evolved by more primitive vertebrates.

The duckbill platypus (Figure 27-5a) is a member of the most primitive group of living mammals. It produces an egg very much like the egg of a reptile. The egg is not laid immediately after it is formed. Instead, it is retained for a time in the body of the female. Then it is laid in a nest and hatched.

Once the embryos hatch, the female secretes milk from glands on her belly, and the young lick it off the fur. The glands that secrete milk, which nourishes the newborn mammals, are called **mammary glands.** Mammary glands are characteristic of the chordate class Mammalia.

Food from the Female—
The Pouched Mammals

The American opossum, and the many pouched mammals of Australia, belong to another group of primitive mammals, the pouched mammals. They have evolved a unique pattern of caring for the young (Figure 27-5b). Their small eggs have but little yolk—enough to provide for the development of only very small and immature individuals. Early development occurs within the body of the female. Then the tiny, almost helpless infants emerge from the female's body. They crawl up the female's belly and slip into the pouch, from which this group of mammals gets its name. Here the infants are sheltered and kept warm; also, they find food, for the female's mammary glands open here in the pouch. Each infant opossum, or the baby kangaroo, slips a nipple into its mouth and lives on the female's milk as it develops.

Maximum Care of the Embryo—
The Placental Mammals

No animals go farther than the placental mammals in the care and protection of their young. Fertilization is internal, and the early development of the young occurs in the female's body (Figure 27-6). The female supplies the embryo with oxygen and food while it is within her body, and she disposes of the embryo's metabolic wastes by means of her own kidneys and lungs. We will see how special tissues, which form the **placenta** (pla·SEN·ta), make possible these exchanges of oxygen, food, and wastes between the embryo and female. After birth the young individual is nourished by the female's milk.

REPRODUCTION OF
A PLACENTAL MAMMAL—MAN

We will study human reproduction as an example of reproduction in the placental mammals. We shall see how development with regard to protection of the offspring reaches its peak with the internal development, birth, and later care and feeding of the young. The process begins, as with other animals that reproduce sexually, with the sperms of the male and an egg of the female.

In the male human the two testes are located in an outpocketing of the body wall called the **scrotum** (SKROH·tum). The male reproductive cells, the sperms, are produced in very large numbers (hundreds of millions) in a series of small, highly coiled tubes in each of the two testes. Most other parts of the male reproductive system (Figure 27-7) are essential for the transport of the sperm cells.

The development of the male reproductive organs is regulated by the male sex hormones. Usually during early teens the voice of the male becomes lower in pitch, and hair grows on his face. These events are controlled by the male sex hormones, which are secreted by the testes.

27-5 REPRODUCTION IN THE PLATYPUS AND THE OPOSSUM

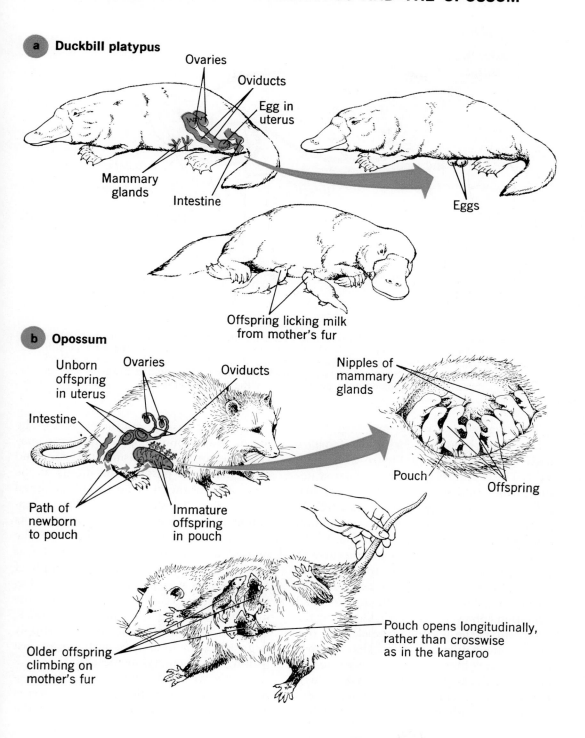

a Duckbill platypus

Ovaries

Oviducts

Egg in uterus

Mammary glands

Intestine

Eggs

Offspring licking milk from mother's fur

b Opossum

Unborn offspring in uterus

Ovaries

Oviducts

Intestine

Nipples of mammary glands

Pouch

Offspring

Path of newborn to pouch

Immature offspring in pouch

Older offspring climbing on mother's fur

Pouch opens longitudinally, rather than crosswise as in the kangaroo

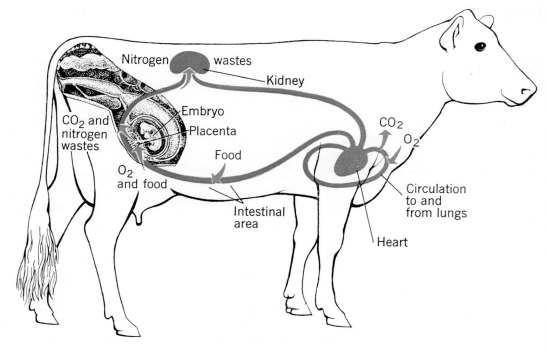

27-6 Internal development of the young in a placental mammal. Part of the circulatory system of the female is adjacent to the placental blood supply of the embryo. Diffusion does the rest. From the mother's bloodstream, food and oxygen are supplied by diffusion to the circulatory system of the embryo. The embryo's wastes are removed from its bloodstream by diffusion in the reverse direction.

The two ovaries, where ova (eggs) are formed, are located deep in the female's body (Figure 27-8 and Figure 25-9, page 445). The ova develop in tiny cellular structures called **follicles,** which at first look like cellular bubbles (Figure 27-8). As a follicle grows, it develops a cavity filled with fluid. Each follicle contains a single ovum. When an ovum is mature, the follicle ruptures at the surface of the ovary and the tiny ovum (almost the size of a period in newsprint) is flushed out. This release of the egg is called **ovulation** (oh·vyoo·LAY·shun). Generally the ovum enters the widened funnel of an **oviduct** (OH·vih·dukt), a tube that extends from the neighborhood of an ovary to the muscular, thick-walled **uterus** (YOO·ter·us). Fertilization occurs as the ovum passes through the oviduct; thus begins a new life.

As the egg passes from the oviduct to the uterus, we encounter one of the most marvelous control mechanisms that man and other mammals possess: the uterus at the time of fertilization is beautifully adapted to receiving the developing embryo, providing it with food, and disposing of its wastes. A few days prior to this time, the uterus was in no such condition. Then it was small, its tissues were thin, and its supply of blood vessels was poor. Now that the fertilized egg, or zygote, is about to enter, the uterus is much larger. Its inner wall is thick, soft, and moist with fluid; its blood supply is greatly increased. It is, so to speak, just waiting for an embryonic occupant.

Shortly we shall return to this transformation and see something of how it occurs and how it is timed for the arrival of the fertilized ovum. But now let us see what the transformation does for the developing embryo.

The human fertilized ovum undergoes mitotic cell division as it moves down the oviduct and finally attaches to the soft tissues of the uterus. Once attached, the embryo sinks into the soft inner uterine wall. Then certain cells of the embryo develop into the four membranes (the same as those of the bird's or reptile's egg) that help to nourish, protect, and support it.

The chorion, the outer membrane surrounding the embryo and all its other membranes, is the first to form. During the development of the embryo, tiny fingerlike projections grow from the surface of the chorion into the soft tissues of the uterus. Gradually, small pools of blood in the uterine wall form around these fingerlike projections. These tissues of the chorion and the adjacent part of the uterine tissue make up the placenta.

Under normal conditions there is never a direct blood flow between mother and young. The blood systems of the two are separated by thin membranes made up of cells that allow an exchange, by diffusion, of oxygen, carbon dioxide, nutrients, and waste materials.

Another embryonic membrane, the amnion, grows around the embryo itself. The cavity within the amnion becomes filled with fluid. The embryo develops in this fluid-filled cavity, which keeps it moist and protects it from minor mechanical injury. In man, as in reptiles and birds, a yolk sac develops, even though in man it does not contain yolk.

The last of the four membranes to form is the allantois, which originates from the digestive canal of the embryo. Together with the chorion, the allantois helps form the placenta.

The edges of the amniotic folds come together around the stalks of the allantois

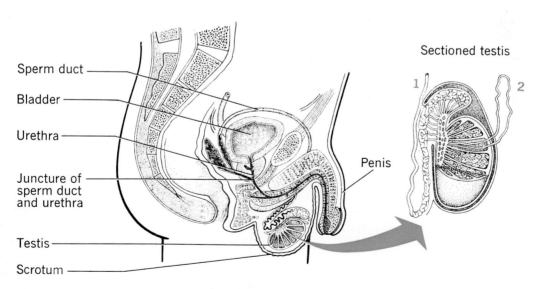

Sectioned testis

Sperm duct

Bladder

Urethra

Juncture of sperm duct and urethra

Testis

Scrotum

Penis

1

2

27-7 The reproductive system of a human male, viewed as if cut along a midline between the left and right sides of the body. One testis and sperm duct (from the near side of the body, not shown) are omitted. The other testis and sperm duct are shown and labeled. To the right is an enlargement of a sectioned testis, showing at **1** the sperm duct and at **2** one of the numerous sperm-producing tubes, uncoiled and extended from its normal position inside a chamber of the testis.

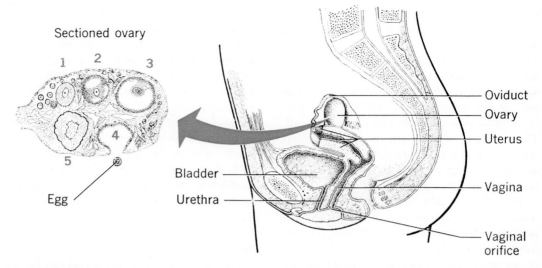

Sectioned ovary

1 2 3

4

5

Egg

Bladder
Urethra

Oviduct
Ovary
Uterus

Vagina

Vaginal
orifice

27-8 The reproductive system of a human female. The uterus has been cut along its length and at an angle across the top, revealing the entrance of one oviduct into the uterus. The other oviduct (from the near side) and the corresponding ovary are not included in the drawing. To the left is a composite view of events that take place (not all at the same time) in an ovary. The egg is forming at **1,** and it leaves the ovary at **4.** In **5,** the empty follicle forms a corpus luteum.

and yolk sac and form a tube, which leads from the embryo to the placenta. This tube is called the **umbilical cord.** It contains the very important blood vessels that connect the developing embryo with the placenta, and contains, in addition, the remnants of the yolk sac and allantois.

Thus the embryo (three isolated stages are shown in Figure 27-9) develops until it is ready to be born. Pregnancy lasts, on the average, 9 months, or 280 days, in the human female. The average length of pregnancy varies by species: it is 63 days for the domestic cat and dog, 330 days for the horse, 280 days for the cow, and 20–22 days for the rat and mouse.

BIRTH

As pregnancy progresses, the **fetus,** which is the name we give an embryo after it has taken on a characteristic form, grows and the uterus increases in diameter. Usually, at

about the ninth month after fertilization, near the end of human pregnancy, the head is turned down toward the opening of the uterus. At birth the head usually comes out first (Figure 27-10). Sometimes the feet come first; this makes the delivery more difficult.

We still do not understand how the child-birth mechanism, or labor, is triggered. This is a complex problem. Childbirth begins when the muscle layers of the uterus start to contract and relax—these actions are felt as "labor pains." At first, muscular activity of the uterus is just strong enough to move the baby slowly toward the **vagina** (va·jy-na), the outer canal of the female reproductive tract. Generally, at this stage, the sac (amnion) around the baby breaks, and its fluid contents are released. This is a good sign that labor is well on its way.

Then the contractions of the muscles become stronger and more frequent, and the baby is pushed through the vagina and into the outer world. The umbilical cord (containing blood vessels), leading from the baby to the placenta, is tied off and cut by the doctor. (The small piece of cord remaining attached to the baby shrivels and falls off within a few days. The navel marks the place where it once entered the body.) After the birth of the baby, the muscular contractions of the uterus continue until they push out the tissues of the placenta, which are commonly called the "afterbirth."

During the last part of pregnancy a watery lymphlike fluid called **colostrum** (ko·LOS·trum) accumulates in the mammary glands, which have gradually been enlarging and undergoing a transformation. For the first few days after the baby is born, the mammary glands secrete only colostrum. Following this, milk is secreted.

Each mammary gland of the human female is composed of sixteen to twenty-five lobes. Each lobe is connected to the nipple by a duct. The duct, as it travels back to the individual lobes, becomes highly branched. When the gland is not secreting milk, it consists mostly of an extensive duct system and cells filled with fat.

A characteristic change occurs during pregnancy. The duct system becomes even more highly branched. At the end of each tiny branch lie cells that secrete milk.

If the newborn baby does not feed from the mammary glands of its mother, they soon stop secreting and return to normal size. After childbirth, and when milk secretion has stopped, the female reproductive cycle (see below) begins again. However, ovulation, fertilization, and a new pregnancy sometimes start during the period of milk secretion.

HORMONE CONTROL OF THE FEMALE REPRODUCTIVE CYCLE

The Role of the Ovary

One hint about how the female reproductive cycle is controlled is provided by closer observation of what happens in the ovary. We note two things. First, the cells of the follicle (Figure 27-8) in which the egg ripens secrete one or more female sex hormones called **estrogens** (ES·tro·jenz). Their action after passing through the bloodstream to the uterus may have to do with

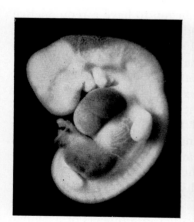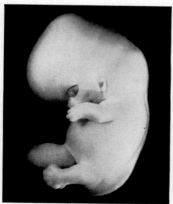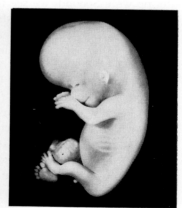

Chester F. Reather, FBPA, Johns Hopkins U. School of Medicine

27-9 Human embryos (without enclosing membranes) at three stages of development. From left to right are a four-week, a six-week, and an eight-week embryo. The first of the body organs to fulfill its function is the heart (the dark bean-shaped structure on the chest region of the four-week-old embryo). Well before the end of the first month of development it begins circulating the blood. By eight weeks of development, the eyes, ears, mouth, ribs, fingers, and toes are evident.

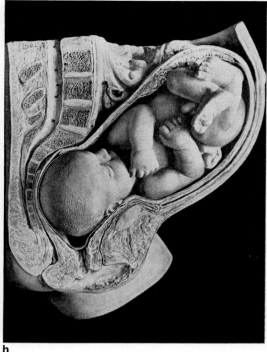

a   b

27-10 The normal position of a baby near the end of pregnancy (**a**) and at the beginning of birth (**b** on this page and **c** and **d** on the facing page). The head of the baby

starting the renewed development of the uterine wall. Second, we see that when the ripe follicle on the ovary bursts and releases the egg, the follicle "heals over" in a special way. The cavity of the follicle fills up with cells that have a good supply of blood capillaries. The structure formed by these cells is called the **corpus luteum** (KOR·pus LOO-te·um) because of its yellow color. There is ample evidence that this structure, too, is an endocrine gland, and that it secretes a hormone (**progesterone**—pro·JES·ter·ohn) into the blood. Can you conceive of just what kinds of experimental tests would prove these statements?

The hint that the ovary is somehow responsible for timing the cycle of development and deterioration of the inner wall of the uterus is made stronger by a simple experiment. Suppose we remove the ovaries

from young female rats, so young that they have not yet begun to have a reproductive cycle. We find that the cycle does not start (Figure 27-11), nor does the uterus develop into its normal adult condition. Instead, it remains infantile.

What this experiment suggests is strengthened by further experiments. Let us now inject material from the follicles of mature rats into young rats from which the ovaries have been removed. Very soon after, we see the cells of the inner tissues of the uterus of each injected young female begin to divide and grow.

Through further experiments of a similar nature we can now be reasonably sure that the two kinds of hormones produced by the ovary, estrogens and progesterone, are primarily responsible for the changes in the uterus. One of these changes is produced

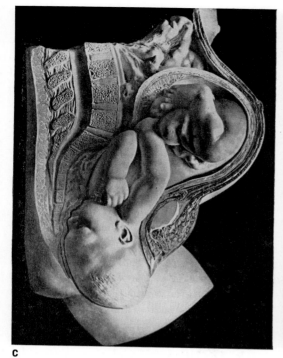

c

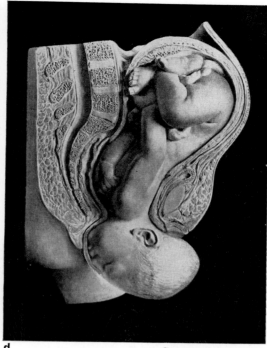

d

Courtesy of *Birth Atlas*,
published by Maternity Center Assoc., New York

emerges first. The mother's last previous medical examination before the onset of labor will have confirmed the baby's position relative to its forthcoming birth.

by one or more follicular hormones (estrogens) during the ripening of the egg. Estrogens are responsible for the commencement and continuation of the growth of the uterine wall. The other kind of hormone that effects a change comes from the corpus luteum. This hormone is progesterone, which serves to bring on further development of the uterine wall—additional thickening of the wall and added development of blood vessels and glands.

Reproductive Cycles

What do we mean by a cycle? The passing of day and night or the seasons of the year are common examples of cycles. We may define a cycle as a succession of events repeated regularly within a given period of time. A simple alternation of two phases, such as an alternation of generations, is a cycle. But the cycle may be more complex, containing several phases before returning to the first one. The periodic repeating of structural and physiological changes in the female reproductive system is a complex reproductive cycle. The cycle has been studied extensively in laboratory animals.

The female laboratory rat goes through a short period of increased mating desire, which has been called **estrus**, or heat. The physiological changes occurring from one period of estrus to the next are called the **estrous cycle**. Ovulation, or the release of the eggs from the ovary, generally occurs during the period of estrus. Rats, mice, dogs, sheep, and many other mammals exhibit estrous cycles. The cycles of these animals vary in length and frequency. The laboratory rat has an average estrous cycle of five days. With the dog the cycles occur

27-11 DETERMINATION OF THE CAUSE OF CYCLIC CHANGES IN THE UTERUS OF THE FEMALE RAT

Subjects: Young female rats of pre-reproductive age

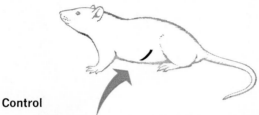

Control

Body wall opened and closed but ovaries not removed.

Reproductive cycle begins at age of expected maturation.

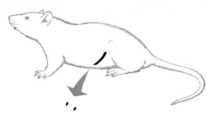

Experimental No. 1:

Body wall opened and ovaries removed.

Reproductive cycle fails to start.

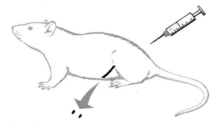

Experimental No. 2:

Body wall opened and ovaries removed.

Reproductive cycle fails to start.

Injections of extract from follicles of mature rats result in changes in the uterus. Reproductive cycle begins.

only twice a year: thus the female will mate and can conceive only twice a year.

The reproductive cycle of the human female (and of some other primates) is quite different from the estrous cycle. It is called the **menstrual** (MEN·stroo·al) **cycle.** The outward indication of the human cycle is **menstruation** (men·stroo·AY·shun). Menstruation, which is a discharge of blood, mucus, and cellular debris, is brought about by a breakdown of the soft tissues lining the uterus, which pass to the outside by way of the vagina.

Changes in Ovary and Uterus During the Menstrual Cycle

The human menstrual cycle takes about twenty-eight days. There is, however, much individual variation in the length of cycle and time of ovulation. What events take place during this cycle? Let the first day of menstruation represent the first day of the cycle. Ovulation takes place sometime between two periods of menstruation, usually around the middle of the cycle.

To simplify the description, the human menstrual cycle will be divided into three stages. *Stage F* (for follicle stage) covers the period of time from the end of the menstrual flow to ovulation. *Stage L* (for corpus luteum stage) is from ovulation to the beginning of menstruation. *Stage M* (for menstrual flow stage) represents the period of menstruation.

During *stage F* only a single egg follicle enlarges, except in the rare cases that may lead to twin or other multiple births. An estrogen is released from the ovarian follicle and stimulates a considerable increase in the size of the uterus. The growth of the soft tissues of the uterus is due primarily to three effects of the estrogen: mitotic activity is stimulated; blood supply is increased; and tissue fluid accumulates.

After ovulation and during *stage L*, progesterone secreted from the corpus luteum acts on the already estrogen-prepared uterus. Progesterone stimulates the thickening of the uterus, affecting gland and blood vessel development until the soft tissues form a rich spongy layer suitable for the attachment of a fertilized ovum. These changes in the uterus must take place before the fertilized ovum can become attached and develop normally.

If fertilization and the attachment of the embryo do not occur, menstruation will start. Normally the onset of menstruation, *stage M*, is closely associated with a decrease of progesterone. The cycle is now complete, returning once again to the beginning.

In the United States, human females usually start to menstruate at the age of thirteen or fourteen, but there is a great deal of variation. It is not uncommon for menstruation to start as early as nine or as late as twenty-one years of age. Generally some time during the forties, the menstrual cycle of the human female ceases—this is referred to as the **menopause** (MEN·o·pauz).

The Role of the Pituitary Hormones

Of course, this story of the hormonal control of the reproductive cycle raises certain further questions. First, granted that ovarian hormones regulate the uterus, what regulates the ovary? What sets an ovum and follicle developing and later the follicle forming a corpus luteum? Second, what is it that makes the difference between the corpus luteum stage (*stage L*) and pregnancy; that is, what maintains the high development of the uterus for the 280 days when an embryo is present?

Our first insight into these questions begins with the experimental evidence that removal of the pituitary gland, a small body near the base of the brain, interferes with reproduction. If the pituitary is removed from an immature male or female rat, there is no normal development of either testes or ovaries. If the pituitary is removed from a mature female rat, the ovaries as well as the

uterus stop their cycles. With the adult male, the testes, which are not so cyclic in activity, are not so strongly affected.

It is clear that the pituitary gland influences both the ovary and the uterus. Adding what we already know about the influence of the ovary on the uterus, we can tentatively summarize the relationships among pituitary, ovary, and uterus in this way:

$$\text{Pituitary} \xrightarrow{\text{influences}} \text{Ovarian activity}$$
$$\xrightarrow{\text{influences}} \text{Uterine activity}$$

Many experiments indicate that there are three different hormones of the pituitary that affect the reproductive system.

When one of the pituitary hormones is given to an experimental female animal whose pituitary has been removed, the ovaries increase in weight. This increase in weight is due to the development of many follicles. The pituitary hormone having this action is called the **follicle-stimulating hormone,** commonly abbreviated FSH. Even though this compound stimulates the follicles to grow, the uterus remains small. This fact shows that effective amounts of estrogen are not being secreted.

The second pituitary hormone is called the **luteinizing** (LOO·te·ny·zing) **hormone,** or LH. It brings about very little change in the ovary if the ovary has only small follicles. When LH is given to an animal that has well-developed follicles, ovulation occurs and the follicles change to corpora lutea (plural for corpus luteum).

Only when FSH is given at the same time as LH do the developing follicles secrete detectable amounts of estrogen. With certain combinations of FSH and LH there is maximum development of follicles, secretion of estrogen, and ovulation.

The third pituitary hormone is called LTH, or the **luteotropic** (LOO·te·o·TROP·ic) **hormone** (it is also called **prolactin** [pro-LAK·tin] because it stimulates the development of and secretion by the mammary glands). The corpora lutea secrete progesterone in response to LTH.

Especially noteworthy is the *feedback* control exerted by the ovary on the pituitary. The amounts of estrogen being secreted by the ovary, in the several phases of its cycle, inhibit the secretion of one hormone by the pituitary but trigger, or stimulate, the secretion of another. Thus a rising concentration of estrogen inhibits pituitary production of FSH and stimulates the production of LH.

Very much more could be said about the control of the reproductive cycle. But some of the evidence is still conflicting, and too many details may prevent one from seeing the main relations clearly.

Hormonal Control by the Placenta

How is the uterus maintained through the duration of pregnancy? There is good evidence that the placenta in some mammals (rats, mice, rabbits, man, monkeys, horses, and a few others) secretes hormones that function somewhat like those of the pituitary. These chemicals differ in structure and function from the pituitary hormones and are not the same from one mammal group to another. With the human embryo, the chorion has become specialized to produce a hormone that acts somewhat like LH but also has LTH activity. This placental hormone takes over the job of stimulating the corpus luteum to secrete progesterone until the placenta has developed to a stage where it is able to begin secreting progesterone and estrogen.

For some mammals, the ovaries are essential for the continuance of pregnancy. If the ovaries of female rats, mice, opossums, or rabbits, for example, are removed at any period during pregnancy (except, perhaps at the very end), pregnancy stops, and the young usually die. With other mammals, such as guinea pigs, the ovaries can be removed in the latter part of pregnancy without serious effect. Pregnancy usually contin-

ues, and birth of the young takes place at the same time as in the normal animals. In female mammals with the highest reproductive specialization (horses, monkeys, man), the ovaries can be removed even during the early stages of pregnancy without affecting the development of the young.

What is the explanation for these peculiar differences in the three groups? It seems that only in certain mammals has the placenta evolved the ability to secrete ovarian hormones as well as pituitarylike hormones. Thus with man, monkeys, and some other mammals, when the ovaries are removed the placenta takes over and carries the pregnancy to completion. Of course, the prolonged reproductive cycle comes to an end after the birth of the young and the ejection of the placenta.

CONCLUDING REMARKS

The main methods that animals have developed to insure the effectiveness of reproduction may be listed in a sequence leading up to placental mammals. Many of these methods are regulated by complicated hormonal interactions.

The sequence of reproductive specializations is as follows: (1) some means to insure internal fertilization; (2) a reduction in number of eggs produced; (3) storage (in the egg cell) of yolk, a reserve food supply for the nourishment of the developing embryo; (4) retention of the developing embryo in the reproductive tract of the female, affording the embryo greater protection during development; (5) development of a placenta (with the loss of yolk), which protects the embryo and brings to it a constant food supply; and finally (6) development of mammary glands, which supply the immature or newborn young with a source of nourishment (and along with the nourishment, a corresponding increase in maternal protection).

GUIDE QUESTIONS AND PROBLEMS

1. In what sense are binary fission, spore formation, and budding basically the same methods of reproduction?
2. How would the traits of any individuals that arose by asexual reproduction compare with those of their parents?
3. What are the two basic cellular events of sexual reproduction?
4. How does fertilization combine the genetic contributions of the two parents?
5. How may sexual reproduction contribute to variations in characteristics of the offspring?
6. How do the sperm and egg resemble one another in respect to the contribution each makes to the potential new individual? How do they differ in their contribution?
7. How is internal fertilization advantageous to those organisms in which it occurs?
8. How do the various ways by which embryos are nourished and protected help maintain the species?
9. How has the development of such membranes as the allantois, yolk sac, and amnion made possible embryos that do not require a marine environment?
10. What are the advantages of internal development of the embryo (a) to the embryo itself and (b) to the species to which it belongs?
11. What are the possible evolutionary steps by which placental mammals may have attained internal development of offspring?
12. In mammals, how is the uterus adapted to receive and retain the fertilized ovum?
13. What is the role of the embryonic membranes in human development?
14. What is the role of the ovary in the hormonal control of the reproductive cycle?
15. What part do the pituitary hormones play in the female reproductive cycle in mammals?

SUGGESTIONS FOR ADDITIONAL READING

Books

Buchsbaum, R., *Animals Without Backbones*, rev. ed. Chicago, University of Chicago Press, 1948.
  Includes good, clear descriptions of reproductive cycles and life histories of many invertebrates.
Corner, G. W., *Ourselves Unborn*. New Haven, Yale University Press, 1944.
  A well-written description of human reproduction and development.
Young, J. Z., *The Life of Vertebrates*, rev. ed. New York, Oxford University Press, 1962.
  Interesting accounts of vertebrate reproduction. A reference text primarily for college students.

Magazines and Journals

Allen, R. D., "The Moment of Fertilization." *Scientific American*, Vol. 201 (July 1959), pp. 124–30.
Csapo, A. I., "Progesterone." *Scientific American*, Vol. 198 (April 1958), pp. 40–46.
Li, C. H., "The Pituitary." *Scientific American*, Vol. 183 (October 1950), p. 18.
Monroy, A., "Fertilization of the Egg." *Scientific American*, Vol. 183 (December 1950), p. 48.
Pincus, G., "Fertilization in Mammals." *Scientific American*, Vol. 184 (March 1951), p. 44.
Reynolds, H. C., "The Opossum." *Scientific American*, Vol. 188 (June 1953), pp. 88–90.
Zahl, P. A., "The Evolution of Sex." *Scientific American*, Vol. 180 (April 1949), p. 52.

28

THE

DEVELOPMENT

OF ANIMALS

Animals and plants are exceedingly complex. This we have learned. An oak tree and a man are both composed of billions of cells, but they are not just masses of cells. Their cells are organized. In man, the cells are organized into a creature who lives, thinks, speaks, and in many ways controls his environment. How does this amazingly organized complexity develop from a single cell?

Development comprises the events that begin with fertilization and end with the formation of the adult body. The study of development is called embryology. Many things occur during development. All are interrelated, but for convenience we can think of development as being composed of four main processes.

The Processes of Development

First, there is an *increase in the number of cells*. The fertilized egg is a single cell. Its diploid nucleus contains the chromo-somes of the sperm plus those originally in the ovum. The single cell divides into two cells by mitosis (Chapter 7). Cell division continues, and slowly the adult body forms. This may take a few days, weeks, months, or years—depending upon the species of animal or plant.

Cell division usually continues throughout life in some parts of the body. In our own bodies, the cells of the lower layers of the skin and of the lining of the intestine, and those giving rise to the blood cells, divide frequently. Cells in many other parts of our bodies (for example, the brain) divide rarely or not at all.

Second, development entails *growth*. Each of us began as a tiny cell, so small as to be just visible to the unaided eye. Now look at us! A fertilized frog's egg is a sphere about 1.5 mm in diameter. From this minute beginning a large bullfrog may develop. A human fertilized egg is even smaller than a frog's egg, and the product of its growth is many times bigger than the bullfrog.

Third, many different kinds of cells are produced in the course of development. We call this process *cellular differentiation*. The many cells that have arisen from the fertilized egg are not mere fragments or duplicates of the egg. Instead, they have changed in many different directions. Some have become muscle cells and others have become skin cells; some have become gland cells, which produce hormones and other secretions; others have become ova or sperms.

Fourth, the many kinds of different cells become *organized* into various structures. That is, in the course of development, the cells become arranged and grouped in such a way that they can perform their specialized functions in an efficient manner. These arrangements of cells are the tissues and organs of the adult organism.

We have divided the large problem of development into four smaller problems. Cells divide. As they divide, they begin to differentiate. Growth generally begins when the cells are just starting to differentiate. With differentiation comes organization into tissues and organs. If we remember, then, that development is the sum of all these processes, we may continue to study them as separate problems.

You already know something about two of these problems. Cell multiplication, with nuclear mitosis, was discussed in Chapter 7. The nutrition of cells was discussed in Chapter 6. There is nothing special about cell division or the general features of cell metabolism in embryonic cells. Hence, we need not reconsider cell division and cell physiology here. The *special* problems of embryology are those concerned with differentiation and organization. These are the problems we will talk about now, using the amphibian embryo as our example.

DEVELOPMENT OF
THE AMPHIBIAN EMBRYO

Why do embryologists spend their time studying the development of frogs and salamanders? Would it not seem more appropriate to study the development of man? By now you should be able to give an answer. Biologists tend to investigate problems in those situations that are most likely to yield answers. A biologist would be more likely to study the problems of inheritance in some small, rapidly breeding animal or plant than in the much slower breeding elephant or oak tree! Embryologists have found the embryos of amphibians, chickens, sea stars, sea urchins, and some other animals far more useful than embryos of man.

Advantages of Studying
Amphibian Embryos

What are the advantages of using amphibian embryos over those of man? Briefly, they are easier to get, easier to maintain, and easier to use in experiments. As you might imagine, very young human embryos are exceedingly difficult to obtain. Further-more, they require special conditions for growth. The normal conditions, present in the uterus, have so far not been duplicated in the laboratory. The day of the "test-tube baby" is still a long way off.

If embryologists had been forced to restrict their studies to the embryos of man, our present knowledge of development would be scanty. But we have seen repeatedly that fundamental biological processes are very much alike in similar organisms. As a matter of fact, we do know a great deal about the development of the human embryo; but this knowledge is based on the far better data obtained from experimental studies of development of frogs, salamanders, chicks, and sea stars and from some glances at the embryos of monkeys. Of all of these, it is probable that investigations of amphibian embryos have provided the best understanding of fundamental processes in development.

To begin with, amphibian embryos can easily be kept in the laboratory. A dish of pond water and a relatively cool room (15–20° C) suffice. No food is needed; the egg, when it leaves the body of the female, has a large supply of yolk granules.

The yolk of an amphibian egg is much like that of a hen's egg. It consists largely of protein. In the hen's egg there is enough stored food to supply the needs of the embryo during its entire development from zygote to hatched chick. A frog's egg, or a salamander's egg, has enough stored food material to supply the embryo's needs up to the time it becomes a swimming larva able to obtain its own food. The egg of the human being, and of all other placental mammals for that matter, contains only a small amount of stored food. The embryo of a placental mammal receives nearly all of the raw materials it needs for maintenance, growth, and development from the female, by way of the placenta (Chapter 27).

It is easy, therefore, to raise the embryos of frogs and salamanders in the laboratory.

John A. Moore (Figs. 28-1 through 28-17)

28-1 A marbled salamander, *Ambystoma opacum*. As a female of the species, she is of additional interest as the mother of the embryo (actually several at different stages) that you will watch develop from a fertilized egg, in Figures 28-2 through 28-17.

Another advantage is that in most parts of the world, amphibian embryos are easy to collect. Salamanders are common in many parts of North America, Europe, and Asia. Frogs are found on all the continents except Antarctica. The egg masses of amphibians are often familiar sights in ponds and streams. In many parts of the United States, the croaking and peeping of frogs and toads, when they are at their breeding sites, is a familiar sound of spring and summer nights.

The modern embryologist, however, does not have to wait for spring to carry out his experiments! Many species of frogs can be stimulated by hormones to ovulate. The technique is simple. A mature healthy female is injected with about four to six mashed pituitary glands from other frogs. After an interval of two or three days, the eggs are released from the ovary and collect in the uterus. If the female is squeezed gently, the eggs can be forced from its body into a dish containing a suspension of sperms. The sperm suspension is prepared by removing the testes from a mature male frog and cutting them into small pieces in about 10 ml of clean pond or aquarium water. This procedure liberates the sperms into the water. The embryologist can fertilize the eggs as needed for his experiments.

Thus, amphibian embryos are readily available, in contrast to the inaccessible embryos of man and many other mammals.

Amphibian embryos have another tremendous advantage—they are extremely hardy. In fact, they can be cut into pieces, and the pieces will survive. Possibly such an operation seems pointless to you. You will soon learn, however, that answers to some of the most basic problems in development have been obtained by cutting embryos into various pieces and observing what happens to the pieces.

The Pattern of Development of a Salamander

The general pattern of development in the common species of salamanders and frogs that are found in the temperate regions of the northern hemisphere is much the same. We will use as an example the development of the marbled salamander, which has the scientific name *Ambystoma opacum* (am·BIS·toh·ma oh·PAY·cum—Figure 28-1). Fertilization is internal, and fertilized eggs are laid in the autumn. The females make little burrows near the edge of a pond, and in these the eggs are laid. The embryos shown in the photographs that follow were collected, brought into the laboratory, and kept at 20° C.

Figure 28-2. The fertilized egg, when laid, is a sphere about 2.88 mm in diameter. The outer portion is pigmented, but not uniformly. Approximately one half is pale brown and the other half almost white. The darker half is called the **animal hemisphere,** and the paler half is the **vegetal hemisphere.** The vegetal hemisphere is heavier than the animal hemisphere. As a consequence, the embryo becomes oriented vegetal hemisphere down. In the photograph, we are looking down onto the animal hemisphere.

Figure 28-3. About 9 hours after the egg leaves the body of the female, a dramatic event occurs—the egg divides, or cleaves, into two cells. The first evidence that this is about to occur is the appearance of a thin pigmented line across the animal hemisphere. This line quickly becomes a deep groove, which cuts the single cell into two cells. The internal events are equally dramatic but are, of course, invisible. Each of the two cells formed has a diploid nucleus produced by mitosis.

Figure 28-4. About 2 hours and 20 minutes later, the embryo divides again. In each of the two cells the nucleus undergoes mitosis and the cell as a whole divides. Thus the two-celled embryo is converted into a four-celled embryo. Notice that the first two cleavages cut through the center of the animal hemisphere. The four cells are equal in size. Each contains a portion of the animal hemisphere and of the vegetal hemisphere. (In the photograph, we are still looking down on the animal hemisphere.)

Figure 28-5. After another interval of approximately 2 hours and 20 minutes, or about 13 hours and 40 minutes after the egg is laid, the third cleavage divides the embryo into four small and four large cells. The plane of this cleavage is at a right angle to the first two. The first two cleavages produced cells equal in all respects. The third cleavage is different. Not only are the two quartets of cells unequal in size, but they differ in the materials they contain.

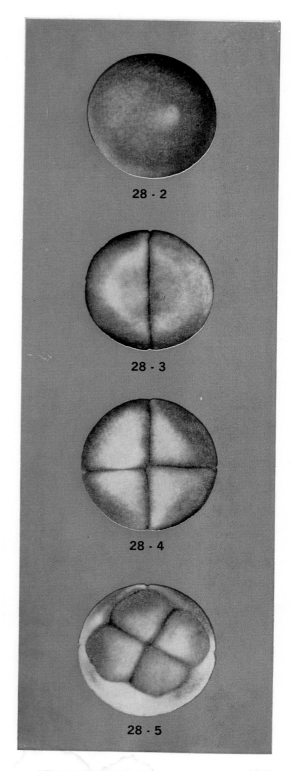

28 · 2

28 · 3

28 · 4

28 · 5

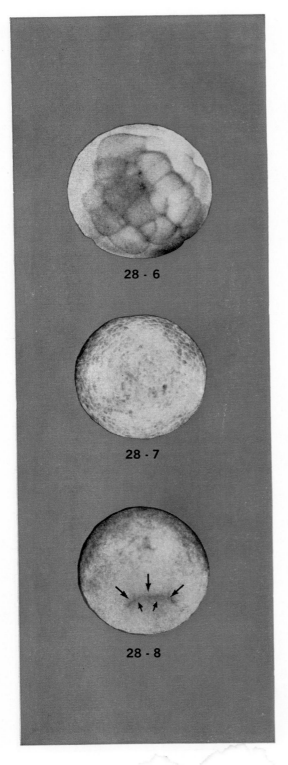

28 - 6

28 - 7

28 - 8

Figure 28-6. The process of cell division continues, and the original material in the one-celled zygote becomes apportioned among many cells. More than thirty cells are visible in this photograph, which shows only the animal hemisphere side of the embryo. Nineteen hours have passed since the egg left the body of the female. Cell division is slightly more rapid in the cells of the animal hemisphere than in those of the vegetal hemisphere. As a result, the cells of the animal hemisphere are smaller. There is no over-all growth of the embryo yet, but only cell division with some degree of cellular differentiation. Growth will occur in later stages.

Figure 28-7. Now the embryo is 29 hours old. The cells of the animal hemisphere are quite small, and there are many hundreds of them. If one were to cut this embryo in half, a large cavity would be revealed (Figure 28-18a). This cavity occupies much of the interior of the animal hemisphere. It is filled with a fluid, largely water but with some dissolved salts and proteins. An embryo consisting of many cells and with a cavity of this sort is called a **blastula** (BLAS-tyoo-la). The cells are nearly alike, except in size and presence of pigment. Chemically, they may be more different than they appear.

Figure 28-8. When the embryo is about 50 hours old, an event of profound importance begins—there is a rearrangement of cells. The embryo shown here has been rolled over so that we are looking at the vegetal hemisphere. A curved groove has formed, which is known as the **blastopore** (BLAS-toh-pohr). The cells on the outside of the embryo, both above and below the blastopore, move slowly toward the blastopore. Here, as shown by the arrows, they disappear into the interior of the embryo. This process of rearrangement of the cells by the movement of some of them into the interior is known as **gastrulation** (gas-troo-LAY-shun).

Figure 28-9. Five hours later the blastopore increases in size; that is, the groove becomes deeper and extends farther around the sides. In fact, it now forms an arc of about 180°—halfway around the circle it will soon complete. The surface cells continue to move into the interior through the blastopore. (Before gastrulation begins, the cells that are to form the **ectodermal** (EK-toh·der·mal), **mesodermal** (MES·o·der·mal), and **endodermal** (EN·doh·der·mal) structures (Figure 28-21) form a continuous layer upon the outside of the embryo. During gastrulation the cells that will form the mesodermal and endodermal structures are the cells that move to the interior.)

Figure 28-10. Eighty hours have passed since egg laying, and the blastoporal groove now forms a complete circle. The cells that will form the mesodermal and endodermal structures continue moving through the blastoporal groove to the interior of the embryo. The cells that remain on the outside are now largely those that will form ectodermal structures. Most of the cells that pass, or have already passed, to the interior do so through the first part of the blastopore that took form, namely, that which was evident in the 50-hour-old embryo (Figure 28-8). This first part of the blastopore is known as the **dorsal lip.**

Figure 28-11. In this 90-hour-old embryo, the blastopore is reduced to a mere slit (seen vertically in the lower half of the photograph). Eventually it disappears entirely; but not too long after this happens the posterior end of the digestive tube breaks through in nearly the same place. In the 90-hour embryo the entire outer layer of cells is the **ectoderm.** This is the layer of cells that will form the nervous system and the outer part of the skin. The **mesoderm,** which is now inside, will form the muscles, skeleton, kidneys, circulatory system, and gonads. The **endoderm,** which is also inside now, contains the cells that will form the digestive tract, lungs, liver, and pancreas.

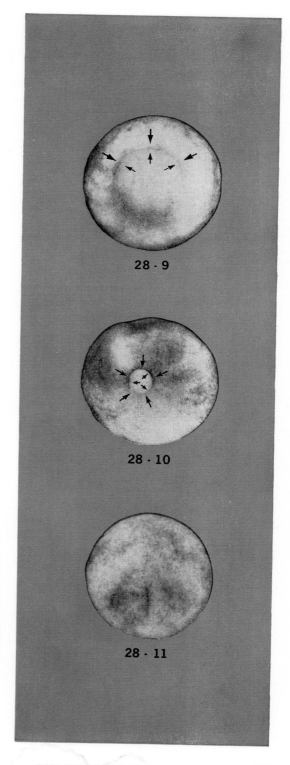

28 · 9

28 · 10

28 · 11

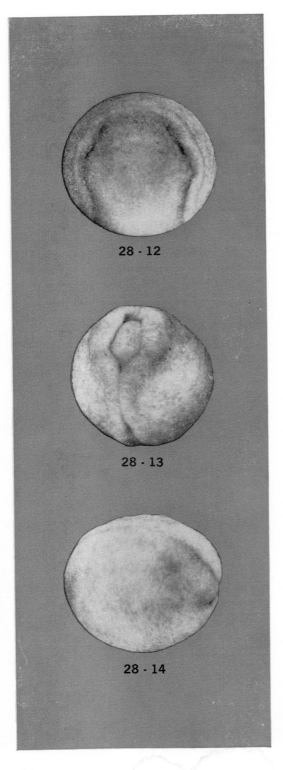

28 · 12

28 · 13

28 · 14

Figure 28-12. When the embryo is 95 hours old, it is no longer merely a spherical ball of cells. The nervous system begins to differentiate from the rest of the ectoderm. The beginnings of this are shown in the photograph. The closed blastopore is on the underside of the embryo, on the side toward the bottom of the photograph. Extending from the region of the blastopore up the side and over the top of the embryo are two lateral ridges. These are known as the **neural ridges.** The neural ridges are connected at their anterior ends, as can be seen in the photograph (where the neural ridges and the anterior connection have roughly the shape of an inverted "u").

Figure 28-13. This embryo is 10 hours older than the one in the preceding photograph. During this interval of time, the neural ridges become larger and also move together. Where the ridges meet, they fuse at their top edges. As a result, an internal tube is formed immediately beneath the fused edges. (This process can be more easily followed in the diagrams of Figure 28-19.) The ridges are farthest apart near their anterior ends. It is this region that will form the brain. In the embryo pictured, the ridges have not closed in the anterior (brain) region. The part that has already closed will form the spinal cord.

Figure 28-14. By 110 hours the neural ridges have come together along their entire lengths. We are looking at the embryo from the side (slightly toward what is becoming its back) and from above. The enlarged portion of the neural ridges at the right will form the walls of the brain. One can still distinguish a line that runs along the back (in the upper portion of the photograph), marking the place where the neural ridges came together. This is the midline of the back in the developing embryo. Now the embryo begins to elongate slightly and acquire a new form. At this stage cilia begin to form in the cells of the outer ectoderm. Their beating slowly moves the embryo.

Figure 28-15. More than a day later, at 140 hours of age, the embryo is much elongated. We are looking at it from the right side, more or less the same perspective from which we viewed it in Figure 28-14. The bump at the right is the head, which bends downward. If you look closely about ⅛ inch below the top of the embryo and about halfway from front to rear, you can see a tiny ridge. This ridge marks the presence of an excretory organ, one of the embryo's kidneys, which form on either side from the mesoderm under the skin. Many other changes take place inside. For example, the digestive canal forms, though as yet it does not open at either end to the outside.

Figure 28-16. At 160 hours one can see a few more external developments of form. The head, which is still to the right in the photograph, has a bump on the near side of it (and also on the far side). This is caused by a bulging out of a part of the brain that forms the eye cup. Some cells of the ectoderm over the eye cup will differentiate as the lens. The eye, then, is formed in part as an outgrowth of the brain (which is derived from the ectoderm) and in part directly from the ectoderm that covers the embryo. The ears and nostrils also form as an ingrowth of the outer ectodermal layer, but they cannot be seen at this time.

Figure 28-17. The embryo pictured here has been developing for nearly 9 days—for 209 hours to be exact. These times, you will recall, are for development at 20°C. (If we had kept the embryo at 10°C, it would have taken it about three times as long to reach this stage. If the embryo had been kept at 25°C it would have developed a little faster than at 20°C.) The dark spot near the front end is a nostril. The big bump, about one quarter of the distance from the front end, is where gills are forming. The tail is now fairly well developed. Internally, all of the organ systems are differentiating.

Now we have seen how the embryo changes as it develops from a spherical egg

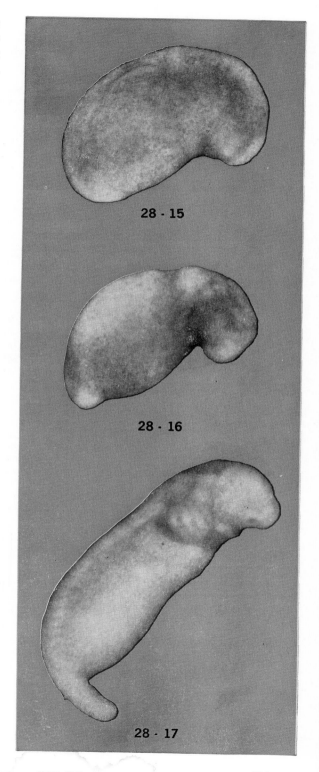

28 - 15

28 - 16

28 - 17

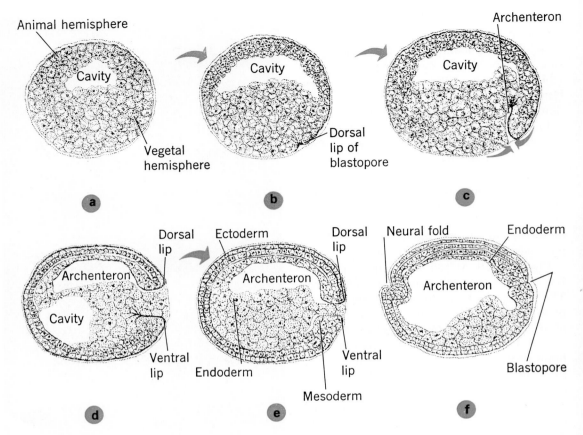

28-18 Early steps in the formation of a salamander embryo, as seen in sectioned embryos. A complex series of movements converts the blastula into a gastrula. Notice the gradual growth of the archenteron, which will form the alimentary canal. Can you relate these diagrams to the photographs of the developing embryo in Figures 28-2 through 28-17? (Note especially the stages from Figure 28-7 through 28-11.)

into a young larva. Let us go back and study some of the events that take place *inside* the embryo. We have been aware of a few of these from the ridges and bumps that appear on the surface. Any detailed understanding of what goes on inside, however, can be gained only from making sections of the embryos and studying them under a microscope.

By a series of cell divisions, the fertilized egg becomes converted into a blastula (Figure 28-18), which is a hollow ball of cells. At gastrulation the cells become rearranged. Roughly speaking, those of the

vegetal hemisphere and equatorial region move to the inside through the blastopore. The cells of these areas form the mesoderm and endoderm. These movements are shown diagrammatically in Figure 28-18. The small pocket that first forms at the dorsal lip of the blastopore gradually expands into a large cavity known as the **archenteron** (ar-KEN·ter·on). The archenteron in later development forms the digestive canal. The lungs, liver, and pancreas grow out from its walls. The cells lining the archenteron are endodermal, so all of the structures just mentioned have their origin in this layer.

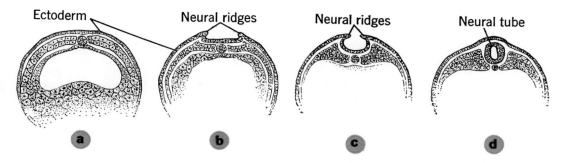

Ectoderm   Neural ridges   Neural ridges   Neural tube

a   b   c   d

28-19 The formation of the neural tube in a salamander embryo. Dorsal parts of four stages are shown in cross section. Beginning with a fold in the ectoderm (**a**), the tube that is to become the brain and spinal cord takes shape (**b, c, d**).

The photographs of the developing embryo show that the nervous system begins as a pair of ridges forming on the dorsal side (Figure 28-12). The processes involved become clearer if we supplement our observations of external development with a study of sectioned embryos (Figure 28-19). Here we see how the neural ridges are elevated, and how they move together and then fuse to form the **neural tube.** The anterior part of this tube becomes the brain; the middle and posterior parts, the spinal cord. All of the nerves develop from the neural tube and the ectoderm adjacent to it.

The eyes, which we noticed as mere bumps on the side of the head of the early embryo, develop from the brain region of the neural tube. The process is shown in Figure 28-20. The ears and nose are also formed from the ectoderm that covers the embryo.

Basic Features of Vertebrate Development

The basic features of development are much the same in all vertebrates. A three-layered embryo forms, the nerve tube rounds up from the ectoderm in much the same way, and so on. The early embryos of fish, amphibians, reptiles, birds, and mammals resemble one another in many ways. It is only in later development that the different species become distinguished.

This similarity of early developmental stages suggests that the "theme" of development is shared by most animals. The comparative study of early development of species that are really quite unlike as adults often provides strong evidence of descent from a common ancestor. From such studies we can even trace certain common features shared by the very primitive vertebrates with some of the invertebrates.

The Embryonic Layers

As we might expect, the formation of three layers of cells is a process shared by the embryos of all vertebrates. We call these three layers the **embryonic layers,** meaning that they are distinctive areas in the embryo that give rise to all the organs and systems of the adult. Some organs are made up primarily of cells that come originally from two layers. The stomach, for instance, as well as the rest of the digestive system, is a kind of hollow tube. Its inner lining cells come from endoderm, but its muscular walls are made up of cells that come from mesoderm. The skin likewise has two components, the outer, tough epidermis (from ectoderm), and the inner layers (from mesoderm).

Figure 28-21 is a cross section of a salamander embryo. It shows the fundamental positions of the three embryonic layers and the main structures formed from each layer.

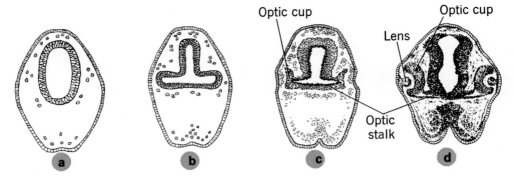

28-20 The formation of the eyes in a salamander embryo. From the anterior end of the embryo, four stages of development are shown in cross section. The optic cups can be seen growing out from the ventral portion of the embryonic brain. Simultaneously, the lenses of the eyes develop from the ectoderm that covers the embryo.

The same embryonic layer may produce different structures in different animals. For instance, in many animals ectoderm gives rise to the epidermis of the skin and to hair, as in mammals. In other vertebrates, however, the structures that emerge from and protect the surface of the body may be feathers (in birds) or scales (in birds, reptiles, and some mammals). Yet all of these surface structures arise from the same embryonic layer, the ectoderm.

CONCLUDING REMARKS

The problems of development, from fertilized egg to adult, are much the same in all organisms, and the solutions are also similar.

The fertilized egg is a single diploid cell. The adult may consist of many billions of cells, nearly all of which will be diploid. This increase in cell number is brought about by cell division.

Not only is there an increase in cell number, but ultimately there is also growth. Some fertilized eggs contain their own food supply—yolk—which makes growth possible. The hen's egg has a large amount of yolk— enough to carry the embryo to the chick stage. The amphibian egg generally has

less—just enough to produce a swimming larva that can capture its own food. The egg of a placental mammal has little or none— it relies on its mother for food.

As the cells increase in number, they also differentiate; that is, they change in structure and function. The cells of the upper portion of the animal hemisphere of a blastula are much alike (Figure 28-7). They are all part of the embryonic layer known as the ectoderm. In the course of development, however, some differentiate into the cells of the neural tube or into the outer layer of the skin; others form the cell types found in the eyes; still others, the ears and nose. All neurons are differentiated from these cells.

The various cell types become organized into the specialized tissues and organs of the older embryo and the adult. They are organized to form stomach, kidneys, bones, muscles, testes, a pituitary gland, and so on.

What is responsible for the differentiation of cells and their organization into the parts of the adult? These are fascinating, though largely unanswered, questions. Nevertheless, in the next chapter we will review some of the observations and experiments that contribute to the answers that can be given today. Someday we will know more about these processes.

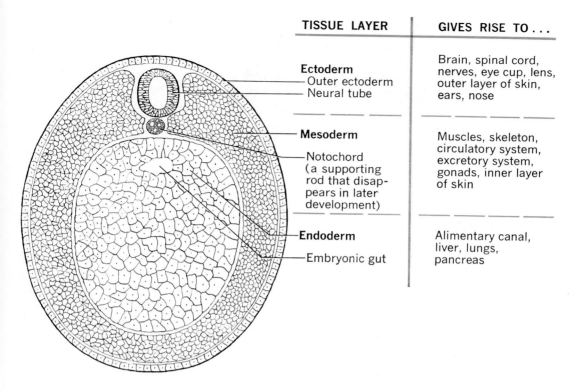

TISSUE LAYER	GIVES RISE TO . . .
Ectoderm Outer ectoderm Neural tube	Brain, spinal cord, nerves, eye cup, lens, outer layer of skin, ears, nose
Mesoderm Notochord (a supporting rod that disappears in later development)	Muscles, skeleton, circulatory system, excretory system, gonads, inner layer of skin
Endoderm Embryonic gut	Alimentary canal, liver, lungs, pancreas

28-21 A diagram of a salamander embryo in cross section, with indications of major body structures that originate from each of the three embryonic cell layers. Can you see the relation between this diagram and one of the kind shown in Figure 20-7?

GUIDE QUESTIONS AND PROBLEMS

1. What are the initial events that occur in the development of the fertilized egg?
2. What four processes are involved in the embryonic development of all complex organisms?
3. What are the advantages of studying the development of salamander embryos?
4. What changes occur in the development of a fertilized egg of the marbled salamander during the first 29 hours of development?
5. What major changes in development have occurred by the 50th hour? by the 80th hour? by the 105th hour?
6. How can we interpret the fact that the basic features of all vertebrates are the same?
7. What structures in the mature animal develop from each embryonic layer?

SUGGESTIONS FOR ADDITIONAL READING

Books

Barth, L., *Embryology*, rev. ed. New York, Holt, Rinehart & Winston, 1953.
    A good general embryology text.
Sussman, M., *Animal Growth and Development*. Englewood Cliffs (N. J.), Prentice-Hall, 1960.
    An excellent, brief, and up-to-date treatment of the growth and development of animals.

Magazines and Journals

Moog, F., "Up from the Embryo." *Scientific American*, Vol. 182 (February 1950), p. 52.
Waddington, C. H., "How Do Cells Differentiate?" *Scientific American*, Vol. 189 (September 1953), pp. 108–14.

29

THE ANALYSIS

OF DEVELOPMENT

Look again at the series of photographs in Chapter 28 showing the gradual development of a salamander egg into a larva. Is this not an almost incredible series of events? (Or perhaps you would feel more at home pondering the development of a living chick from an egg of the type of your breakfast egg this morning. Of course, the egg you ate probably was not fertilized.) A fertilized egg of a salamander seems to be a rather ordinary cell. In fact, it appears to be far less specialized than almost any cell in the adult. It is, seemingly, just a large spherical cell, with a lot of yolk granules in it. How does a larva that can swim, respond to stimuli, respire, excrete, and develop into an adult salamander arise from such a formless beginning? Variations of this question have been asked for at least 2,500 years. Today there is reason to hope for a solution to this fundamental biological problem within the next decade.

Now let us survey some of the questions man has asked about his own beginnings and those of other animals.

DEVELOPMENT—BY PREFORMATION OR EPIGENESIS?

Centuries ago, Aristotle proposed two different hypotheses to account for development. He pointed out that there are only two ways of explaining how an embryo arises from an egg. Either the embryo is already present in the egg, though not visible; or it is not in the egg but somehow appears during development.

Aristotle's first idea has been called **preformation.** Preformation implies that an egg or sperm is not as simple as it looks, but that it actually contains the new individual already formed (Figure 29-1).

Aristotle's other proposal is called **epigenesis** (ep·ih·JEN·e·sis). The idea is that the egg or sperm contains no preformed structures; rather, these structures somehow develop in their proper positions later, constructed from material in the egg.

For two thousand years after Aristotle's time, men argued whether preformation or epigenesis was the correct explanation for development. Scholars who believed in preformation thought that the animal was present in either the egg *or* the sperm (Figure 29-1). Of course, a preformed body could not be in both (if it were, think of the confusion at fertilization!).

Those who believed in epigenesis claimed that the idea of an animal in miniature inside an egg or sperm is false. They said that the egg *develops* into an animal—though they were at a loss to explain how.

During the past fifty to one hundred years, these arguments have been resolved, at least in part, by careful experimentation. One of the most important experiments was done in 1888 by the German scientist Wilhelm Roux.

Evidence for Preformation

Roux's experiment was so simple that we may do it in the school laboratory. He fertilized frog eggs and let them divide once.

Then he poked a needle into one of the two cells produced by each egg to kill that cell. The other cell was not injured. Roux then found that the healthy cell developed into a *half* embryo—sometimes a head end, sometimes a tail end, sometimes a left half, and sometimes a right half, but always a half embryo, never whole (Figure 29-2).

Let us think about Roux's experiment. It *seems* to be evidence for some sort of pre-formation—not preformation of a body, but preformation of a pattern that controls development. If one of the first two cells develops into a left half of an embryo, that cell must have had only the pattern for this one side. The surviving cell is not able to change its organization and produce a whole embryo. Figure 29-2 summarizes this situation, from which Roux concluded that preformation is nearer the truth than epigenesis.

Evidence for Epigenesis

Roux's experiment was so interesting that many people began doing similar experiments, poking eggs with needles or separating the first two cells in some way. One of these investigators was Hans Driesch. He did an experiment similar to Roux's but with a different animal. He used sea urchin eggs that were at the two-cell stage, and completely removed one of the cells instead of killing it. The result was very different from that of Roux: the remaining cell gave rise to an *entire* embryo. This result led Driesch to believe epigenesis is nearer the truth than preformation. If a half egg, which according to preformationist theory would normally contribute to only half an embryo, could actually produce a whole embryo, then the embryo is not preformed in the egg.

Roux and Driesch began a long argument. They wrote articles in scientific magazines, each saying the other was wrong. We now know they were both partly right. Modern biologists have repeated Roux's ex-

From Nicolaas Hartsoeker, *Essai de Droptrique*, Paris, 1694

29-1 An early idea of the structure of the human sperm. If you look closely, you will see the presumptive offspring, already formed—awaiting an opportunity to grow. What hypothesis does the diagram illustrate—epigenesis or preformation?

periment and have discovered that half frog eggs do sometimes develop into whole embryos. Whether one gets a half embryo or a whole embryo depends on how the experiment is done. Thus if one actually removes one of the first two cells instead of killing it, the remaining cell usually gives rise to an entire embryo. In Roux's original experiment, apparently the mere presence of the dead cell prevented the formation of a whole embryo.

Driesch's experiments with the sea urchin have also been repeated and the same results obtained. However, sometimes a half sea urchin egg forms only a half embryo rather than a whole embryo. If the two

29-2 ROUX'S EXPERIMENT

a A fertilized frog egg is allowed to divide into two cells.

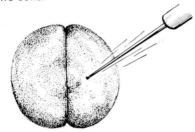

b One of the cells is killed with a needle.

c The living cell divides to produce half a blastula.

d The half-blastula may continue to develop and form half of the neural ridge.

cells formed *at the first division* are separated, either one can give rise to an entire embryo (Figure 29-3a). But, if the egg cell is cut through along the equator, *thus separating the animal hemisphere from the vegetal hemisphere,* neither half gives rise to a whole embryo (Figure 29-3b).

A whole series of experiments shows that most eggs behave this way. The results depend upon the way the experiments are done. The old debate of preformation versus epigenesis is essentially over. The basic answer is known—as a careful study of a developing embryo in the school laboratory will show (or a study of the series of photographs in Chapter 28).

Development is largely epigenetic. There is no preformed tadpole in a frog egg or sperm. There is no tiny human being, such as was described long ago (Figure 29-1), in a gamete of man. New structures do make their appearance in development. The ectoderm is originally a sheet of cells on the outside of the embryo. In the course of development some of these cells curl up to form a tube (Figure 28-19). Later the tube differentiates into a brain and a spinal cord. Still later the eye cup grows out from the brain (Figure 28-20). The brain and eye cups are not preformed as minute structures in the egg (or sperm). Their development is epigenetic.

But there is an element of truth in preformation—though not in the way it was first conceived. In a sense one can say that the embryo is preformed, because it receives genes from the parents. Its development will depend on the action of these genes. Thus, an embryo inherits a preformed genetic makeup. But this is very different from the theory of preformation that was believed for so long. The organization of the embryo arises by epigenesis, a process controlled by the genes.

THE PROBLEM OF DIFFERENTIATION

Roux and Driesch have left us a difficult problem. It would be easy to explain the "how" of development if preformation were correct: development would be just the enlargement of an organism already present

29-3 WHOLE OR HALF?
—AN EXPERIMENT WITH SEA URCHIN EGGS

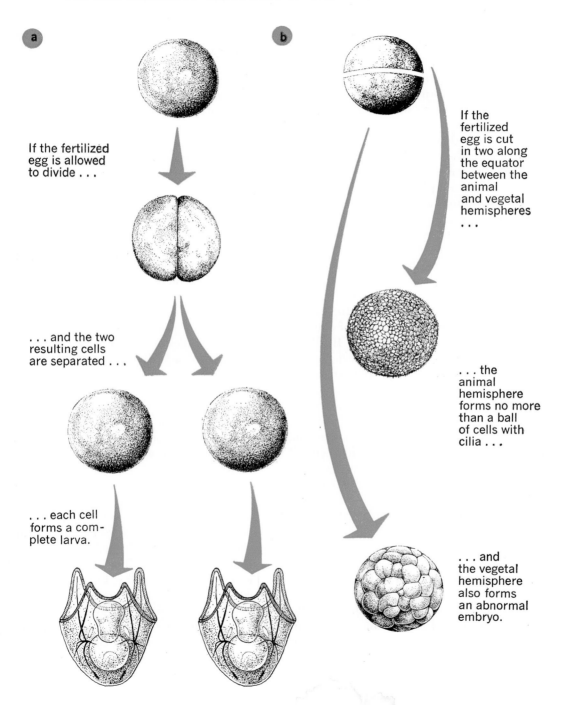

a

If the fertilized egg is allowed to divide . . .

. . . and the two resulting cells are separated . . .

. . . each cell forms a complete larva.

b

If the fertilized egg is cut in two along the equator between the animal and vegetal hemispheres . . .

. . . the animal hemisphere forms no more than a ball of cells with cilia . . .

. . . and the vegetal hemisphere also forms an abnormal embryo.

in the egg. There would be only growth and cell multiplication, no differentiation or organization. Since preformation is not the explanation, we have a harder task. We must explain how a preformed genetic pattern, combined with epigenetic development, produces the adult organism.

Obviously epigenesis is more difficult to explain than preformation. Many biologists thought it was so mysterious that it could not be explained strictly in mechanical, or physical and chemical, terms. (See Chapter 4, where the debates of the mechanists and vitalists were discussed.) Believers in epigenesis were often vitalists, while believers in preformation prided themselves on their rejection of mysterious vitalistic principles in interpreting life processes. This is worth remembering, because so many students (and biologists) think that mechanists are always right.

How does a simple egg develop into a complicated organism? How do the organs of the tadpole form from parts of the egg that are just like any other part? If all the parts of the egg cell are alike, it is hard to see how differences in the organism's cells can arise. Why isn't the tadpole made up of cells all of the same kind? From where do the differences come?

These are the questions of differentiation, one of the four aspects of development. It is quite easy to see how a cell can grow by taking up food; it is quite easy to see how a cell can divide by mitosis. It is more difficult to see how these cells differentiate into specific types.

One of the most revealing series of experiments on differentiation was carried out by Hans Spemann in 1924. Spemann was a student of a student of Roux's, and he continued the work of his "scientific grandfather" by inventing ways of doing more complicated surgery on frog embryos. Using very fine scalpels he was able to cut embryos into small pieces. He then made careful studies of how the pieces developed.

Spemann's Work on Development of the Neural Tube

Spemann's most famous experiments dealt with the differentiation of the embryonic nervous system. We have already described how the ectoderm folds up to form a tube and how the cells of the tube go on to form the nervous system. Spemann chose to investigate this act of differentiation and organization. From embryos he cut out the ectoderm that normally becomes the nerve tube and put the piece of ectoderm in a separate dish. An embryo from which the piece was taken healed and lived, but it had either a defective nervous system or none at all. Moreover, the isolated piece of ectoderm did not form a nervous system, though it remained alive and healthy. Why did the piece form a nervous system if left in the embryo, but not by itself?

Possibly something about the relation of the ectoderm to the rest of the embryo was necessary to start development of a nervous system. Spemann concluded that the piece of ectoderm needed to be attached to the embryo in order to develop properly. If you think back to the early structure of the embryo, you will remember that there is a layer of mesoderm underneath the ectoderm. Spemann thought that perhaps the mesoderm stimulates the ectoderm to develop into the nervous system. So he did a second experiment.

He cut a flap of ectoderm from the top of an embryo. He did not remove the piece of ectoderm but just folded it back. Then he cut out the mesoderm underneath and discarded it. Finally, he folded the flap of ectoderm back in place. The ectoderm healed and looked quite healthy, but it did not develop into a nervous system.

Spemann's hypothesis appeared to be proved. When the mesoderm is removed, the ectoderm does not differentiate into nerve tissue. The mesoderm must influence the ectoderm somehow to cause the differentiation of nervous tissue.

Spemann did a third experiment that substantiated more conclusively the hypothesis that the mesoderm stimulates the ectoderm to form a neural tube. To understand this experiment, we must know that the mesoderm of an early gastrula forms a band extending around the equator of the embryo—in the zone connecting the animal and vegetal hemispheres (Figure 29-4). Spemann used two embryos, both in the early gastrula stage. From one he removed a piece of mesoderm from immediately in front of the dorsal lip of the blastopore. From the second embryo, he removed a similar-sized piece from the mesodermal area 180° from (or exactly opposite) the dorsal lip. In its place he put the piece of mesoderm from the first embryo. The transplanted mesoderm formed a blastopore and moved inside the embryo. Neural ridges, and later a brain and spinal cord, formed normally in front of the embryo's *original* dorsal lip. Of much greater interest was *the same occurrence in front of the blastopore that developed where the transplant was made* (Figure 29-4).

So a sort of Siamese-twin embryo was produced. From the belly of an otherwise normal tadpole protruded part of another with a brain and spinal cord (Figure 29-5 is a photograph of a tadpole produced by a similar experiment.)

Obviously there is something very interesting about the mesoderm of the dorsal lip region. If it is removed, the animal produces no nervous system in the normal place. If it is put in a strange place, the animal develops an extra nervous system. This area of mesoderm seems to control the differentiation of nerve tissue.

Spemann's experiment was considered so important that he was given a Nobel prize in 1935.

Embryonic Induction

The effect of mesoderm in stimulating ectoderm to become nerve tube was called **embryonic induction** by Spemann. Embryonic induction remains one of the very important mechanisms by which we explain differentiation. Basically it means that cells of one kind direct the development of other

29-4 SPEMANN'S EMBRYO TRANSPLANT

a

A late blastula is shown from the left side. The dorsal lip of the blastopore is just forming. Cells that will form mesodermal structures are those immediately below the equator.

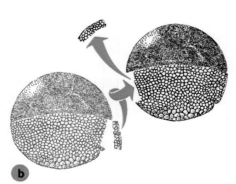

b

A piece of mesoderm from the area opposite the dorsal lip is removed from the embryo and replaced by mesoderm from *above* the dorsal lip of another embryo.

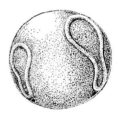

c

Later, neural ridges form in front of the normal blastopore in the embryo with the transplant. Neural ridges also form "in front of" a secondary blastopore that develops where the transplant was placed. Eventually the embryo develops two heads, as shown in Figure 29-5.

John A. Moore

29-5 A salamander tadpole following an experiment similar to the one in Figure 29-4. Notice the induced second head protruding from the belly of the tadpole.

cells. In this case, mesodermal cells of the dorsal lip region *induce* the ectoderm to form a nerve tube.

Since the time of Spemann, induction has been discovered in other tissues of the frog embryo. Induction has also been discovered in many other kinds of animal embryos. Therefore, induction seems to be important for differentiation in all animals.

One of the most exciting recent experiments is that of another embryologist, J. Holtfreter, who used the technique of tissue culture to study induction. He changed Spemann's experiment in the following way: He cut a piece of the ectoderm from an early frog embryo and put it in a small dish of special salt solution. Then he cut a piece of the mesoderm and put it in the same dish. He pressed the two pieces together so that the mesoderm healed in contact with the ectoderm.

You might expect from Spemann's experiment that this would cause the ectoderm to form a nervous system. So it did. It was not a very well shaped nervous system, be-

cause the pieces curled up in tissue culture, but it was obviously brain and spinal cord. This demonstration was the first example of induction of a tissue outside of the embryo. In control experiments, where the ectoderm alone was cut out and cultured, no brain or spinal cord formed.

Many other experiments on this same problem have shown that interaction between the parts of the embryo is common and highly important in bringing about differentiation.

For example, it is possible to mark out with stains certain areas on the blastula that are exactly the same in appearance but are destined to form ectoderm leading eventually to two different tissues—skin and nerve. If bits of tissue are exchanged between the two regions, their development is influenced by their new locations. Thus cells from the skin area develop into nerve tissue when placed in the area of nerve ectoderm. Similarly, cells from the nerve area develop into skin when placed in the area of skin ectoderm. The same seems to hold true for exchanges of tissue during the early gastrula stage.

But by about the end of gastrulation, these two areas are fixed so far as their future development is concerned. That is, cells from the skin area will develop into skin even when placed in the area of nerve ectoderm. And, cells from the nerve area will develop into nervous tissue when placed in the area of skin ectoderm. This is so because the underlying cells by the end of gastrulation have induced the ectoderm cells to differentiate in specific ways.

Still later in development, other changes occur that further restrict the sort of thing particular cells can do. It is as if each cell passes along a series of ever-branching pathways, and at each fork it must take one path or the other. Its possible goals are constantly more and more narrowly restricted. Thus a cell in the ectodermal area of an *early gastrula* is able to develop into skin, or any part of the brain or spinal cord, or part of the eye, nose, or ear. As time goes on, an ectodermal cell is no longer able to develop into *any one* of these parts; it can give rise to *only* skin cells, or *only* part of the nervous system, or *only* a part of the eye, and so on. These changes are apparently brought about by the interaction of one tissue layer with an adjacent one in which the process of induction is important. Such an interaction causes a tissue to develop in a particular way. The developed tissue then interacts with another one in turn. Thus, one tissue is a stimulus for the differentiation of the next. This seems to account for the orderly, properly timed, and properly spaced differentiation of body parts.

You can see that embryonic tissues are influenced to differentiate in certain ways by other tissues. What kind of "message" is sent by the mesoderm to the ectoderm? How does the mesoderm "tell" the ectoderm to form nerve tissue? We suppose that the "messenger" the mesoderm sends to the ectoderm is a chemical substance. Recently a substance has been found that may be this "messenger."

The substance was found by an American embryologist, M. Niu, who took a piece of mesoderm from the dorsal lip area and let it stand in a salt solution for a few hours. Then he removed the piece of mesoderm and put in a piece of ectoderm. In the culture dish, the ectoderm formed nervous tissue. Niu did a control experiment in which he put a piece of ectoderm into plain salt solution that had not been exposed to mesoderm. The control piece of ectoderm did not form a nervous system. Does this experiment remind you of another famous experiment we have described? (Refer to Chapter 25, pages 441–43.)

Obviously the mesoderm leaves something behind in the salt solution, and this something stimulates the ectoderm to differentiate into nerve tissue. What is this something? Chemical analysis of the solution shows that it contains *nucleic acid*.

This exciting experiment tells us that perhaps induction occurs by the transfer of a nucleic acid from mesoderm to ectoderm. Perhaps substances other than nucleic acids are active as well. We cannot tell until more experiments have been done.

POST–EMBRYONIC DEVELOPMENT IN ANIMALS

Development does not stop when an adult animal has been formed from the egg. It continues, in a sense, from "cradle to grave."

Two examples of processes that resemble development in some respects are (1) regeneration and (2) abnormal differentiation of cells, such as those of cancer and those caused by glandular defects.

Regeneration

If one (or more) of the arms of a sea star is removed, a new arm begins to regenerate shortly (Figure 29-6). The regenerating arm continues to develop until it has the same size, form, and function as the arm it replaces. Similarly a lobster, after it loses one of its larger pincer claws, begins to grow a new one. In the lower animals we find even more dramatic instances of ability to form new structures. With planarians (flatworms) a variety of experiments can be done. If one splits the head end of a planarian between the eyespots, two new heads will develop. (Figure 29-7 shows the result of a similar experiment upon the tail end.) If one cuts a planarian in two halfway between the head and the tail, two new individuals will develop: the head end forms a new tail, and the tail end forms a new head.

In plants, regeneration is very common; the removal of large portions of a plant is offset by a new development that duplicates the missing structures.

Among the animals, even some vertebrates display a remarkable capacity for regeneration. If one removes a leg from a salamander, for instance, the salamander will form a new leg. The leg is a duplicate of the one that was amputated. Every bone, every muscle, every nerve, every blood vessel is replaced accurately. The proper connections to the rest of the body are made in such a way that the leg functions perfectly. In every way it is a fully normal replacement for the lost leg.

In such cases of regeneration we have all the biological problems of embryonic development: cell division, growth, differentiation, and organization. Since the development involved in regeneration occurs at a later stage in the life of the organism, and becomes correlated with the structures and functions that have already developed, the problems are even more complicated.

There is still a great deal to be learned about regeneration, but the main conclusions are clear. The regeneration of lost parts involves the same kinds of processes that are characteristic of the initial development of an organism. It would seem that some cells of the adult retain their embryonic abilities to differentiate into a variety of cell types. These nonspecialized cells are more abundant in some species than in others—more abundant in salamanders than in frogs, for example, even though both are amphibians. If one amputates a frog's leg, the wound heals, but no new limb develops. Even man has some regenerative powers, although he cannot regenerate a limb, or even a finger. Skin wounds heal by a regeneration of the various cell types we find in the epidermis and dermis. In the case of severe loss of tissue, the wound heals somewhat imperfectly, leaving a scar. Some but not many of man's internal organs can also regenerate to some degree. The tongue, when injured, has good regenerative capacity. The liver will regenerate to its normal size when large portions have been removed surgically.

Abnormal Development

Although the processes of development are repeated with remarkable accuracy generation after generation, sometimes mistakes occur. These mistakes may have their origins in gene mutations, of which we will learn more later. If the genes that control developmental processes do not function properly, abnormal development may result. Outstanding examples are some kinds of dwarfism and giantism. Usually these patterns can be traced to a malfunctioning pituitary gland (Figure 25-9).

We know also of gross physical defects, which are sometimes found in both animal and plant development. The four-legged chicken, the two-headed calf, the Siamese twins joined together in various ways, are all examples of such abnormal development.

D. P. Wilson

29-6 Regeneration in a sea star. Two of its arms have been lost; two new ones are growing in their place. For another example of regeneration, see Figure 29-7.

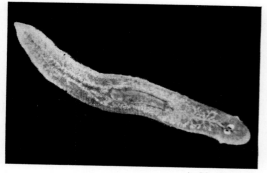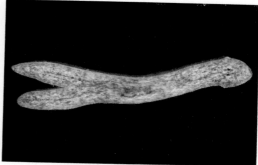

A. M. Winchester, from *Biology and Its Relation to Mankind*, D. Van Nostrand

29-7 Regeneration in a planarian. At the left is a normal individual. If its tail end is split, each half will regenerate the "missing" tissues, and an individual of the type at the right will be produced. What do you suppose will happen if the tail end is split into three parts? if the head end is similarly split into two or more parts?

In most cases the unfortunate individuals do not survive, or at best are able to survive only with special care.

Cancer is another kind of abnormal development. Ordinarily cells continue to divide by mitosis and to differentiate until the organism reaches its adult form. The rate of cell division then drops off gradually, and new cells are produced only as replacements for those that wear out in normal life activities. Red blood cells, for instance, are destroyed at a very fast rate, and the body must manufacture about 7 to 10 million new red blood cells a second, just to keep the number of these cells in the blood constant.

If the rate of cell division in an organ suddenly and abnormally increases, more cells are produced than are needed by the body. These rapidly developing cells get their raw materials for division and growth from the cells of organs that are already formed. Such cancerous growth may lead to the formation of tumors or to abnormal numbers of certain kinds of cells that upset the balance of function in the body. The word "cancer" really refers to a large variety of different types of abnormal development. Leukemia, for example, is a condition in which large numbers of excess white blood cells are produced and released into the bloodstream. To complicate the example further, not even all cases of leukemia are identical. Some are obviously no more than "generally" like others. Apparently, there is not a single cause.

A great deal of progress has been made, but the problem of cancerous development is still a long way from solution. This is because the many kinds of cancer may each have a variety of causes. Although we are still uncertain about many of these causes, the techniques for detection of cancerous growth, and for its treatment, are being improved each year. We can be confident that our knowledge about cancer will continue to increase, and that eventually we shall be able to control such abnormal development effectively.

GUIDE QUESTIONS AND PROBLEMS

1. Why was epigenesis a difficult hypothesis to reconcile with what was known of mitosis and the division of a fertilized egg?
2. Has preformation been disproved? If so, why do animals produce offspring only of their own species? Why, for example, does a cat never give birth to anything but kittens?

THE ANALYSIS OF DEVELOPMENT　**503**

3. How may the experiments of Roux and Driesch best be interpreted?
4. What was Spemann's hypothesis about the differentiation of the embryonic cells that give rise to the nervous system? How did his experimental work with embryos support his hypothesis?
5. What evidence suggests that chemical influences are a basic factor in cell differentiation?
6. In what way is the regeneration of a lost part by an adult organism similar to the developmental problem in embryos?
7. Generally speaking, the capacity for regeneration decreases as complexity and specialization in animals increases. Can you suggest a reason why?
8. In what way is the problem of cancer related to an understanding of developmental processes? Can you suggest how increased knowledge of the mechanisms of embryonic development may help lead to more successful treatment of many types of cancer?

SUGGESTIONS FOR ADDITIONAL READING

Books

Gabriel, M., and S. Fogel (eds.), *Great Experiments in Biology*. Englewood Cliffs (N. J.), Prentice-Hall, 1955.

> Original documents of experiments by Hans Driesch, Hans Spemann, and O. Mangold.

(See also the references to Barth and Sussman at the end of Chapter 28.)

Magazines and Journals

Dahlberg, G., "An Explanation of Twins." *Scientific American*, Vol. 184 (January 1951), p. 48.

Gray, G. W., "The Organizer." *Scientific American*, Vol. 197 (November 1957), pp. 79–88.

Wigglesworth, V. B., "Metamorphosis, Polymorphism, Differentiation." *Scientific American*, Vol. 200 (February 1959), pp. 100–02.

3

CONTINUITY

In the world of life, success is measured by survival. The failures can only be fossils. The survival is never of individuals—only of life itself. Individuals reproduce and are replaced by another generation. In the course of time, even the types of organisms change. Continuity of life, then, is a reflection of reproduction and evolution.

CONTINUITY

30

PATTERNS

OF HEREDITY

You have already studied (in Chapters 17 and 27) some of the fascinating processes of reproduction displayed by different kinds of living organisms. The essential point of reproduction in plants or animals, whether it is sexual or asexual, is that a new generation of living organisms results.

But the members of the next generation do not commonly burst forth from the parents, full-sized and completely able to care for themselves. Usually there is a period of development during which the individuals both *grow* (increase in size) and *differentiate* (become specialized for their own particular life activities), as we saw in the preceding chapters. After this period of development, which may be short or long, the organisms become able to reproduce and to give rise to another generation.

This is the story of life—a long "chain" of living forms, generation after generation, stretching forward in time from the mists of prehistory. One by one the strands of living substance have emerged from other strands until we can indeed recognize a "tree of life," which spans the centuries and the eons, with roots nurtured in the primitive, organic seas of the young earth.

What Is Genetics?

As we have seen, in sexual reproduction the bridge that connects one generation to the next is microscopic. It consists of an egg cell, produced by the female parent, and a sperm cell, produced by the male parent. Within these tiny bits of living matter are preserved the contributions of the ancestors to the next generation. The sperm fertilizes the egg, and each fertilized egg will develop in accordance with a set of chemical instructions contained chiefly in the nucleus of the cell. The instructions in the fertilized human egg control the development of the embryo into a human being rather than into an elephant or a mouse. So, too, for every other species of animal, every plant, and every sexually reproducing microorganism. These instructions control development. They set limits to it. But the development can be affected also by a variety of external conditions, which may shape the path followed by the embryo and the adult.

The chemical instructions received from the parents, and transmitted by the reproductive cells, are the new individual's **heredity** (heh·RED·ih·tee). All the external materials, forces, and organisms that affect the growing and developing individual, and which indeed affect its entire life, make up its *environment*. What a human being, or any organism, becomes depends upon the *complex interaction of both heredity and environment.*

Every generation of every species resembles its ancestors. There has been an inheritance of a basic plan, which is distinctive of the species. And yet we all know there are differences between parents and their offspring. These differences are summarized in the term **variation.** The branch of biology called **genetics** (je·NET·iks) is concerned with both the heredity and variation of the successive generations of organisms. Geneticists are interested in both the similarities and the differences between individuals and their parents, relatives, and ancestors.

HEREDITY AND ENVIRONMENT

If all offspring were exactly like their parents in every detail, there would be no science of genetics. All our methods in genetics depend on our ability to recognize differences between parents and offspring over successive generations.

Some of these differences are of vital importance. In green plants, for example, the presence or absence of chlorophyll is a difference that has a hereditary basis; in mammals the females typically produce milk, but some individuals cannot. Albino plants and the offspring of "dry" mothers die.

There are also inherited traits that apparently are not very important in life. In man, for instance, some individuals have small hairs on the middle joints of their fingers, and others do not. Some have ear lobes that are closely attached to the head, and others possess free lobes. These traits are inherited but certainly are not as important as blood type, which also is inherited (as you will learn in Chapter 33).

So, we begin to compile a list of traits that are inherited. As our list grows, we begin to see that many, if not most, aspects of the life of an organism, both important and unimportant, have a hereditary basis. The hereditary picture becomes more complex, and the geneticist quickly realizes that he cannot possibly analyze all heritable traits at once. Instead he selects one or a few traits out of the thousands that are under genetic control and studies only these. The geneticist never forgets, however, that there is a large hereditary background always present, always functioning, and always affecting his experiments and observations.

As the geneticist works out the influences of an organism's heredity, patiently gathering clues and forming his hypotheses, he must not allow his attention to become so concentrated on the *heredity* of the organism that he forgets that all organisms live in a complex environment. For the environment often strikingly affects the degree to which a hereditary trait is expressed.

Heredity determines what an organism *may* become, not what it *will* become. What an organism will become depends on both its heredity and its environment. It is these two causes working together that determine the final outcome. Let us look at a few examples of the relationship between heredity and environment.

1. In the fruit fly, *Drosophila,* there is a hereditary condition that causes the wings to curl up sharply. If flies so afflicted are raised in a temperature of 25° C, the wings curl. On the other hand, if the flies are raised in a lower temperature, say 16° C, the trait appears but rarely; most of the wings appear straight, just like those of flies that do not have the curly-wings trait. The hereditary basis of the trait is still present in these apparently normal flies, however, and will be expressed in the next generation if the temperature is suitable (Figure 30-1).

2. Most plants inherit the ability to produce chlorophyll. But even in those plants that do so, the chlorophyll cannot be synthesized in the absence of light. If corn, or bean, or tobacco seeds are germinated and allowed to grow in the dark, all the young plants appear to be albinos. It is not until these same plants are exposed to light that they begin to manufacture chlorophyll and turn green. Only under the proper environmental conditions can we know the genetic potential of these plants. A few flowering plants, such

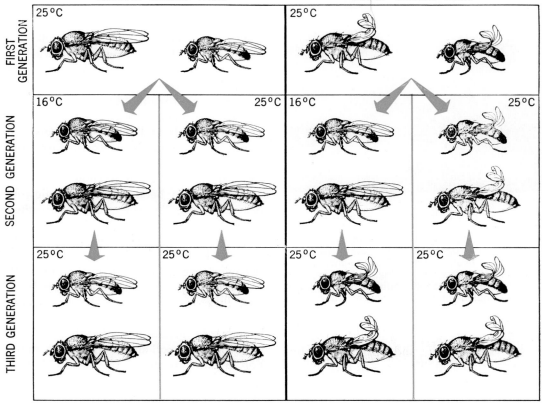

NORMAL - WINGED FLIES   CURLY - WINGED FLIES

FIRST GENERATION
SECOND GENERATION
THIRD GENERATION

25°C   25°C   16°C   25°C   16°C   25°C   25°C   25°C   25°C   25°C

30-1 A diagram showing the effect of temperature, during development, on the expression of the curly-wings trait in *Drosophila*. Normal-winged flies have normal-winged offspring, no matter what the temperature. Curly-winged flies have normal-winged offspring if the offspring are raised at 16° C—but the genes are not altered. The offspring, if raised at 25° C, all have curly wings.

as Indian pipe and dodder, can exist without chlorophyll, and they are colorless or pale yellow. They live as parasites on other plants, or as saprophytes (see page 200). They do not have the proper hereditary makeup to produce chlorophyll, even when light, the required environmental factor, is present.

3. Identical twins in man provide another opportunity to study the interactions of heredity and environment. These individuals arise from the same fertilized egg and hence have the same

heredity. The embryos become separated very early in development, but they are genetically identical. Sometimes, after birth, identical twins are brought up by different families in different environments. In such cases geneticists can study the effects of different environments on the same hereditary material. A number of studies have shown that even when identical twins are reared apart, they still bear a remarkable resemblance to one another (Figure 30-2). They seem to be

Reprinted by special permission of *The Journal of Heredity*

30-2 This pair of identical twins grew up separated from the time of birth. George (left) grew up in New York City, while Millan (right) lived in Salt Lake City. They lived in different environments and had different schooling, but in appearance and mental abilities they still resembled each other closely. They were reunited when 19 years of age.

physiologically and psychologically very similar. Differences in their intellectual ability are sometimes found, however, as measured by tests. Evidently environmental influences definitely affect the development of what we call intelligence.

EXPERIMENTS IN SELECTIVE BREEDING

For thousands of years the selected pedigreed animal—the animal whose ancestry is known for many generations—has been prized above all others. The dairyman wants selected pedigreed cattle from which to breed his milk cows. The hunter wants a pedigreed dog. Similarly, pure lines of selected cultivated plants are prized by the farmer. These breeds and pure lines are the result of having carefully selected and mated desirable types over many generations. Inferior individuals were discarded for breeding purposes. The best male hunting

dogs were bred with the best female hunting dogs; cows that gave more milk than the average were selected and bred with bulls whose mothers gave much milk; the best-yielding, best-milling wheat was selected for seed; and so on. As a result of this selective breeding, the inherited characteristics most wanted by man were much improved in many cases.

Such animals and plants are prized for two major reasons: their offspring are more likely to resemble the parents than are the offspring of animals of unknown ancestry, and they have been selected for desired characteristics. The cows can be depended upon to produce more milk. The sheep will yield more wool. The dog will probably have the body build and display the kind of behavior that are desired by the hunter.

In other cases of selective breeding, however, little or no success has been obtained. Breeders of Dalmatian dogs (coach hounds), for instance, wanted their animals to have many small and distinct black spots. For breeding purposes they selected dogs with the desired coat pattern. But, generation after generation, regardless of the coats of the parents, the pups showed coats with widely different kinds of spotting.

In short, men knew that selective breeding sometimes gives the results they want, and sometimes it does not. They knew that heredity is involved, but they did not know *how* it operates. It was not until 1865 that a little-known Augustinian monk, Gregor Mendel, set forth the first principles governing the way in which traits are inherited. For his great contributions to this field of biology, he is often called the "father of genetics" (Figure 30-3).

The Work of Mendel

Mendel grew up in an agricultural district of what is today Czechoslovakia. Quite early he was attracted to the monastic life and was ordained a priest at the age of twenty-five. Later he took additional training at the University of Vienna, and taught in the high school in the town of Brünn for some years. It was during these years that he kept a small garden plot at the monastery and carried out his experiments with garden peas—experiments that threw the first clear light on the nature of heredity.

Although he performed very few experiments that had not been done before, Mendel succeeded where others had failed. His success stemmed in part from the unusual combination of talents he brought to the task: he was trained in mathematics as well as in biology. With this background, he planned experiments that at the time were novel in three important respects.

First of all, instead of studying only the relatively small number of offspring one obtains from a single mating, Mendel used many identical matings. Hence he was justified in pooling the offspring of these matings, just as if they were one very large family of a single mating. As a result, he had large numbers of offspring to study. You will appreciate the importance of this when you perform Laboratory Exercise 30-2.

Because he could study large numbers of offspring, he was able to introduce his second innovation—the use of mathematics, especially the mathematics of probability. He used it in two ways: first to analyze his data, and then to arrive at a theory explaining his results. Again, Laboratory Exercise 30-2 will show you how important this is.

Third, in order to concentrate on particular traits, and to deal with them mathematically, Mendel made no attempt to study everything about all the offspring at once. Instead, he limited each cross to a single difference, a single pair of alternative traits at a time. In other words, the cross was between two types contrasted in just one respect, such as tall and dwarf. He ignored other characteristics for the time being.

One additional point we must keep in mind: Mendel knew nothing of chromo-

Linda Hall Library

30-3 Gregor Mendel. The photograph was made at about the time he began his famous experiments with garden peas.

somes or the processes of cell division—nor even of the union of gametes. Several decades were to pass before these biological phenomena were recognized and even partially understood. The principles he established were based solely on the evidence from his breeding experiments. They did not depend in any way on knowledge of what changes were taking place in the cells. It was not until many years later that knowledge about the cell was successfully related to the hereditary principles established by Mendel (as you will see in Chapter 31).

Mendel selected garden peas for his experiments because he knew they possess many desirable features. The plants are easy to cultivate and cross, and the generation time is reasonably short. Numerous varieties were available to him, and the offspring of crosses between these different varieties are fertile. Finally, and of great

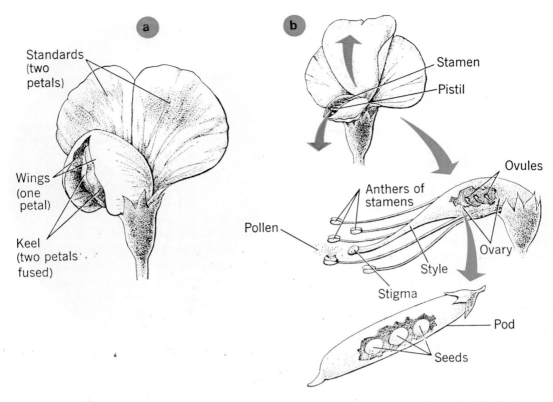

30-4 The flower and the fruit of the garden pea. How do the wings and the keel indicate that the flower is normally self-pollinating? Why was Mendel's choice of a self-pollinating flower an advantage in his experiments? At the right the petals are shown opened, then removed in an enlarged view of the reproductive structures of the flower. At the lower right is a pea pod, partly cut away to show the seeds.

importance, the structure of the pea flower is such that Mendel knew it to be usually self-pollinating, and not cross-pollinated by bees or other insects.

The importance of this last point needs explanation. Let us look briefly at the structure of the flower of the pea and see how fertilization usually occurs (Figure 30-4). It is like what takes place in other flowering plants, as described earlier in Chapter 17.

You will recall that the ovules are formed in the ovary. The pollen grains, which give rise to the male gametes, are formed in the anthers. Pollen from a pea flower's own anthers falls on the stigma above the ovary. From the pollen grains develop pollen

tubes that grow down through the style; one of the two male gametes in each pollen tube fertilizes an egg within an ovule. In the pea flower, the stigma and the anthers are completely enclosed by the petals. This means that egg cells within the ovules are normally fertilized by gametes from the anthers of the same flower. The male and female gametes arise from parent cells that have *the same heredity.*

Now, if you want to pollinate one pea flower with the pollen from another plant, you must remove the anthers from the flower before its own pollen is mature. Later, when the stigma is ready to receive pollen, you can dust it with pollen taken from some other flower of your choice. In this way the parentage of the next generation can be controlled by the experimenter.

Mendel, having selected this favorable material and made his plans, was ready for his experimental work. First he made sure that his plants were pure-bred for the single traits he wanted to study. He did this by letting the plants fertilize themselves (self-pollinate) for a number of generations. The offspring of each generation were studied to make sure they were all like one another and like the parent plant.

Then Mendel made hundreds of crosses by dusting the pollen of one kind of plant on stigmas of plants of another kind. For instance, he pollinated plants from a strain whose seeds were always *round*, with pollen from a strain whose seeds were always *wrinkled*.

In every case of this kind of cross, Mendel found that all the offspring resembled *one* of the parents and showed no sign of the trait of the other parent. Thus, all the crosses between plants with round seeds and plants with wrinkled seeds produced offspring whose seeds were always *round*. Moreover, this held true whether the pollen came from the plants with round seeds or the plants with wrinkled seeds. One trait seemed to "dominate" the alternative trait. Mendel, therefore, called a trait **dominant** that appeared without exception in the offspring of parents with contrasting traits.

Let us now look at a summary of the results that Mendel found in this first major experiment. He used seven different pairs of contrasting traits. What he discovered about their dominance is recorded in Table 30-1.

When a cross is made between two plants of tested pure varieties, the parent generation is called the P_1 generation. The offspring of the P_1 cross are the "first filial generation," or F_1 generation. (The word *filial* refers to offspring.) These symbols will help us as we follow Mendel's work.

Mendel next performed the second major step in his experiments. He let the F_1 plants pollinate themselves. In the generation of plants that resulted (the F_2 generation), the dominant trait appeared in 75 percent of the offspring, while in 25 percent the other trait *reappeared*. Since the other trait had receded into the background for a generation, Mendel called it **recessive,** thus contrasting such traits with their *dominant* alternatives. He also noted no "in between" forms. The new seeds were either round or wrinkled, yellow or green, and each of the other traits was likewise one way or the other, as in the P_1 generation.

In Table 30-2 are some of the results Mendel obtained when he permitted members of the F_1 generation to produce an F_2 generation by self-fertilization. You can see that the ratios of plants with the dominant trait to those with the recessive trait are

TABLE 30-1   DOMINANCE IN SEVEN PAIRS OF TRAITS IN GARDEN PEAS

1. Seed shape	**Round** seed dominant to wrinkled seed
2. Seed color	**Yellow** seed dominant to green seed
3. Seed-coat color	**Colored** seed coat dominant to white seed coat
4. Pod shape	**Inflated** pod dominant to wrinkled pod
5. Pod color	**Green** pod dominant to yellow pod
6. Flower position	**Axial** flowers dominant to terminal flowers
7. Stem length	**Long** stem dominant to short stem

TABLE 30-2 MENDEL'S RESULTS WITH TWO GENERATIONS OF GARDEN PEAS

Traits Selected for P₁ Cross	F₁ Plants	F₁ Self-pollination	F₂ Plants	Actual F₂ Ratio
1. Round X wrinkled seeds	all round seeds	round X round	5,474 round seeds 1,850 wrinkled seeds 7,324 Total	2.96:1
2. Yellow X green seeds	all yellow seeds	yellow X yellow	6,022 yellow seeds 2,001 green seeds 8,023 Total	3.01:1
3. Colored X white seed coats	all colored seed coats	colored X colored	705 colored seed coats 224 white seed coats 929 Total	3.15:1
4. Inflated X wrinkled pods	all inflated pods	inflated X inflated	882 inflated pods 299 wrinkled pods 1,181 Total	2.95:1
5. Green X yellow pods	all green pods	green X green	428 green pods 152 yellow pods 580 Total	2.82:1
6. Axial X terminal flowers	all axial flowers	axial X axial	651 axial flowers 207 terminal flowers 858 Total	3.14:1
7. Long X short stems	all long stems	long X long	787 long stems 277 short stems 1,064 Total	2.84:1

roughly the same, regardless of whether seed shape, length of stem, or any of the other traits is considered.

Inheritance of a Single Trait

Perhaps these results seem puzzling to you, as well they might. It was in explaining them that Mendel made his great contribution to genetics. He began by assigning symbols—letters of the alphabet—to represent each trait. Simple symbols permitted Mendel to think about patterns of inheritance much more easily than if a written description had been used.

Mendel assumed that the *trait* of round seeds was caused by a *dominant element*. He used a capital R to symbolize this ele-

ment. The *trait* of wrinkled seeds, the alternative to round seeds, was caused by a *recessive element*, symbolized by a small *r*. Basically we use the same symbols today. Around 1910, however, well after Mendel's work, the genetic element, whether dominant or recessive, was given the name **gene**. We will use that term hereafter.

Next, Mendel assumed that every plant had a *pair* of genes for each trait. He was forced to this assumption, since some parent plants (and all the F₁ generation) with a dominant trait produced some offspring with the recessive trait. These parents could hardly have a dominant trait without having the dominant gene. And they could hardly produce offspring with the recessive trait without also having the recessive gene. Therefore, every F_1 plant must have had each sort of gene. The F_1 plant, in other words, was Rr, for the trait of round seeds.

Of course, Mendel was forced to assume a *pair* of genes—one recessive to the other—only in those cases where the offspring produced were different from the parents. However, following an old rule of logic, he also assigned a pair of genes per trait even to plants which are true-breeding. The old rule is, "In constructing explanations, be as simple and consistent as possible until forced by the data to make the explanation more complicated."

A plant from parents that bred true for round seeds could therefore be symbolized by RR, meaning that it received two identical genes for round seeds, one from each parent. Likewise, a plant from parents that bred true for wrinkled seeds could be symbolized by rr, indicating that it had received one r gene from each parent plant. The genes of an organism can be designated by these paired symbols, which for the trait being studied indicate the organism's **genotype** (JEE·no·type).

With the genotype thus assigned, Mendel was able to *test assumptions* about genes. If he knew the genotype of each parent, he could predict the kinds and proportions of *gametes* each parent could produce. Then he could, in turn, predict the kinds and proportions of offspring.

If every pea plant had a pair of genes for each trait, was there any rule about how these genes were passed on to the next generation? Mendel thought about the meaning of the wrinkled seeds and the other recessive types that appeared in the F_2 generation. To be what they were, the wrinkled seeds could not carry the dominant gene, R. They must therefore have received the recessive r gene from the F_1 parent (remember, the F_2 generation was produced by self-fertilization in the F_1 generation). The next question was the following: How frequently do gametes that carry r occur among all the gametes produced by the F_1 (Rr) parents? Mendel reasoned back from the proportions of rr wrinkled seeds in the F_2. These amounted to one fourth of the entire F_2 generation. Then this fraction (one fourth) should be the *product* of the frequencies of eggs carrying r and male gametes carrying r; and if these frequencies are equal, they could be discovered by taking the square root of one fourth. (Mendel deduced this relationship on the basis of his knowledge of the simple laws of probability, which we will work out for ourselves in Laboratory Exercise 30-2.) In other words, the frequency of r in the eggs and male gametes produced by the F_1 generation should be one half, since $\frac{1}{2} \times \frac{1}{2} = \frac{1}{4}$. This means that half the gametes of an Rr plant would carry R; the other half r.

Mendel thus arrived at a general rule: *The two members of each pair of genes must separate when gametes are formed, and only one of each pair can go to a gamete.* This **law of segregation**, as it is often called, applies also to the paired genes when they are identical. The genes separate so that only one gene from a pair enters any particular gamete. If the parent is RR, its gametes will all carry one R gene, not two. If the parent is rr, its gametes will all carry a single r gene. If the parent is Rr, half the gametes will carry R, and half will carry r. (Notice that according to this reasoning, the r gene apparently is unaltered by being coupled with a R gene for one, or even many, generations.)

Three new words will make our further discussion easier. Two of them are **homozygous** (HOH·mo·zy·gus) and **heterozygous** (HET·er·o·zy·gus). The prefix *homo* means "the same"; *hetero* means "different." *Zygo* means "a pair." So homozygous refers to a pair of the same, while heterozygous refers to a pair of different units or elements. In this case, we mean a pair of the same *genes* and a pair of different *genes*. In short, an organism with the genotype AA is a **homo-zygote**. So is one with the genotype aa. An organism with the genotype Aa, on the other hand, is a **heterozygote**.

The third new word is **allele** (a·LEEL). It is a Greek word meaning "belonging to one another." We use it to refer to the individual members of a gene pair. With the gene pair Bb, B is an allele of b, and vice versa. For the gene pair AA, A is an allele of A. But A is *not* an allele of B—they are members of different pairs entirely, hence they cannot "belong to one another." Alleles always separate as they go into the gametes.

PROBABILITY IN GENETICS

The simpler problems in genetics are exactly like the problem of calculating the expected results of tossing two pennies, or rolling two dice and tallying odd and even. Nothing new is added except that we are using gametes instead of pennies or dice. And we get zygotes instead of combinations of pennies or dice.

Let us take a problem in genetics in which one of the parents is the homozygote AA, while the other parent is the heterozygote Aa. What kind of offspring might we expect? Algebraic multiplication will really help us here.

Gametes of Aa parent: $\frac{1}{2} A + \frac{1}{2} a$
Gametes of AA parent: $\frac{1}{1} A$

(Notice that we are shortening the statement of gametes for the homozygous parent. There is no need to say $\frac{1}{2} A + \frac{1}{2} A$ when it is quicker and easier to say $\frac{1}{1} A$.)
We multiply:

$$\frac{1}{2} A + \frac{1}{2} a$$
$$\times \frac{1}{1} A$$
$$\overline{\frac{1}{2} AA + \frac{1}{2} Aa}$$

(the probabilities among the zygotes)

So half the zygotes are expected to be homozygous AA, while the other half are expected to be heterozygous Aa.

Now let us take a problem in which both parents are heterozygous. Again, we begin by separating the alleles in the gametes:

Gametes of Aa
parent: $\frac{1}{2} A + \frac{1}{2} a$
Gametes of other
Aa parent: $\times \frac{1}{2} A + \frac{1}{2} a$
$\overline{\frac{1}{4} AA + \frac{1}{4} Aa}$
$+ \frac{1}{4} Aa + \frac{1}{4} aa$
$\overline{\frac{1}{4} AA + \frac{1}{2} Aa + \frac{1}{4} aa}$

Thus, we discover that with a cross between two heterozygotes, the *probabilities* are that $\frac{1}{4}$ of the offspring will be *homozygous dominant* (both genes alike and dominant); $\frac{1}{2}$ will be *heterozygous;* and $\frac{1}{4}$ will be *homozygous recessive.*

A graphic way of performing this algebraic multiplication is shown in Figure 30-5. The kinds of gametes contributed by one parent are placed along one side of a "checkerboard," those contributed by the second parent along an adjacent side. The squares are then filled in with the combinations, and identical types are added together to obtain the ratio.

THE INTERPRETATION OF MENDEL'S RESULTS

We have now laid most of the basis for interpreting Mendel's results. We need one more concept, that of **phenotype** (FEE-no-type). Where *genotype* refers to the "gene formula" of an organism for a particular trait (AA, or Rr, or aa), *phenotype* refers to the trait itself—in other words, what an organism with a particular genotype looks like.

In the case of Mendel's peas, the genotype RR produces the phenotype *round seed.* So does the genotype Rr (since the R is dominant to r). But the genotype rr produces the phenotype *wrinkled seed.*

With this idea in mind, we can now return to Mendel's experimental results and arrive at a plausible explanation. If R stands for the gene for *round seeds* and r

stands for the gene for *wrinkled seeds*, then Mendel's original pure-breeding lines were evidently *RR* and *rr* in genotype. In the parental cross:

P₁ phenotypes: round × wrinkled
P₁ genotypes: *RR* × *rr*
P₁ gametes: ⅟₁ *R* × ⅟₁ *r*
F₁ genotypes: all *Rr* zygotes
F₁ phenotypes: all round

Now, you will recall that Mendel permitted the F₁ plants to self-fertilize, so next is the heterozygote × heterozygote cross. We would therefore obtain the following kinds of zygotes from such a cross:

¼ *RR*
½ *Rr*
¼ *rr*

If we translate these genotypes into phenotypes:

¼ *RR* = ¼ round
½ *Rr* = ½ round
¼ *rr* = ¼ wrinkled

We get: ¾ round + ¼ wrinkled

These are approximately the ratios Mendel actually obtained by using very large numbers of individuals in his experiments. Check Mendel's results again in Table 30-2. Notice that the actual data deviate slightly from the "ideal," or expected, ratio, even when the number of offspring is very large.

Using the rules of probability, Mendel was able to draw his conclusions. We can summarize them as follows:

1. There are definite elements, or genes, that determine the inheritance of traits.
2. For any particular hereditary trait, a plant possesses two genes (alleles) that may be alike or different.
3. When the two alleles are different, one will be expressed (dominant) while the other will remain hidden (recessive).
4. The alleles, unchanged in nature, are separated into the gametes, and each

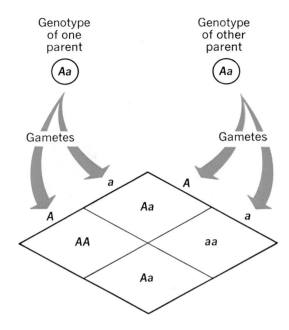

Genotype of one parent · Aa

Genotype of other parent · Aa

Gametes

Gametes

30-5 Determination of expected genotypes in offspring, when the parents are heterozygous for the same trait. With respect to that trait, each parent produces only two types of gametes. The symbols (*A* and *a*) for the gametes are placed along two sides of a "checkerboard," and the indicated combination is made for each square in the board. The results: ¼ *AA*, ½ *Aa*, and ¼ *aa*.

gamete carries only one allele of each pair. (This is known as Mendel's law of segregation.)

5. At fertilization there is a random uniting of gametes, which results in a predictable ratio of the alternative traits among the offspring.

Look at Figure 30-6 for a diagrammatic summary of one of Mendel's crosses.

OTHER EXAMPLES OF SINGLE TRAIT INHERITANCE

Mendel's principles were worked out in one kind of plant, the garden pea. Without doing the same kinds of experiments with

30-6 INHERITANCE OF TERMINAL AND AXIAL FLOWERING IN PEA PLANTS

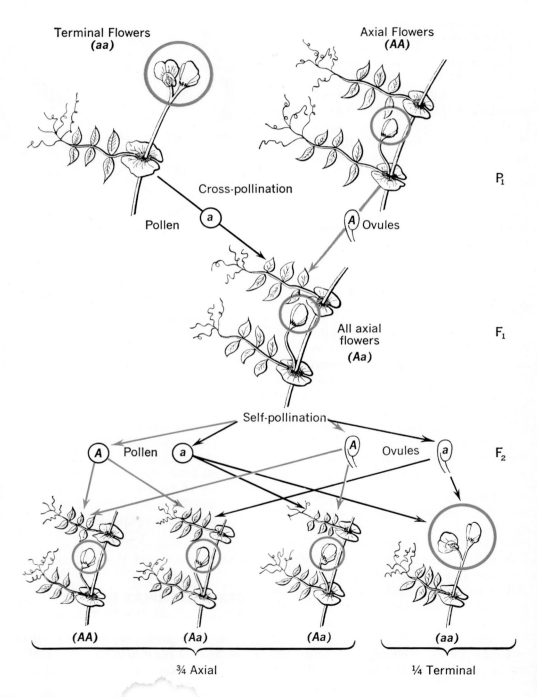

Terminal Flowers
(aa)

Axial Flowers
(AA)

Cross-pollination

Pollen

a

A Ovules

P₁

All axial flowers
(Aa)

F₁

Self-pollination

A Pollen *a*

A Ovules *a*

F₂

(AA)

(Aa)

(Aa)

(aa)

¾ Axial

¼ Terminal

many different kinds of organisms, both plant and animal, we cannot be sure whether these principles apply *in general* to the inheritance of traits.

Let us take an example from animal heredity. If we cross a homozygous (pure stock) black male guinea pig with a homozygous (pure stock) white female guinea pig, all the F_1 offspring are black, and presumably heterozygous for the gene for white color. So we can conclude that the black trait is dominant to white in the guinea pig. When the cells within the ovaries and within the testes of the F_1 individuals form ova and sperms, $\frac{1}{2}$ of the ova will carry the gene for black, and $\frac{1}{2}$ will carry the gene for white; the same is true of the sperms. The expected ratios of the F_2 generation would be $\frac{1}{4}$ homozygous black, $\frac{1}{2}$ heterozygous black, and $\frac{1}{4}$ homozygous white—the same ratios Mendel got in his peas. These are the results we actually get in such an experiment. Mendel's principles apply in guinea pigs as well as in peas.

Let us turn the experiment around and see another way in which this sort of genetic analysis can be used. Suppose you had a black guinea pig whose parents were not known to you, and you wanted to know whether the guinea pig was homozygous or heterozygous for black. How would you go about finding out? One way is to make a *test cross*. We mate the organism we wish to test with one that has the *homozygous recessive* genotype for this trait. Each offspring from such a mating would receive one recessive gene from the homozygous recessive parent; the offspring's phenotype would therefore depend on whatever it received from the parent being tested. For example, we would mate the unknown black guinea pig with a white (homozygous recessive) guinea pig. If, among all the offspring, there is even a single white guinea pig (homozygous recessive), the tested black guinea pig must be a carrier of the recessive allele, and therefore heterozygous.

PROBLEM: Assign symbols for black and white, and diagram the crosses just described. Show why the test cross works, using a round-seeded pea of uncertain genotype.

PROBLEM: In sheep, white coat is dominant to black. Occasionally a black sheep appears in the flock. How can a farmer eliminate the genes for black coat from his flock? (The wool is worth less.)

PROBLEM: In man the gene for nonblue eyes (brown, hazel, or gray) is dominant over the gene for blue eyes. If two non-blue-eyed parents have four children, two nonblue-eyed and two blue-eyed, what are the genotypes of the parents? How could you explain this ratio?

We have spoken of alleles as being dominant or recessive as if there were no other possibilities. But sometimes one allele of a pair is *not* completely dominant over the other. In shorthorn cattle, for instance, when a red bull (RR) is crossed with a white cow (rr), the heterozygous offspring (Rr) are neither red nor white, but *roan* (having intermingled red and white hairs). If a roan bull (Rr) is crossed with a roan cow (Rr), the calf has one chance in four of being white (rr), two chances in four of being roan (Rr), and one chance in four of being red (RR). (See Figure 30-7.)

PROBLEM: Using symbols, work out a cross of roan with red.

PROBLEM: A farmer wants to establish a pure strain of roan cattle that breeds true. Why is this impossible?

PROBLEM: If a four-o'clock plant having red flowers is crossed with a white-flowered four-o'clock, the F_1 plants are all *pink*-flowered. What kinds and ratios of plants will occur in the F_2 generation in regard to flower color if: red is crossed with red? red $\times$ pink? pink $\times$ white? white $\times$ white?

30-7 INHERITANCE OF COAT COLOR IN SHORTHORN CATTLE

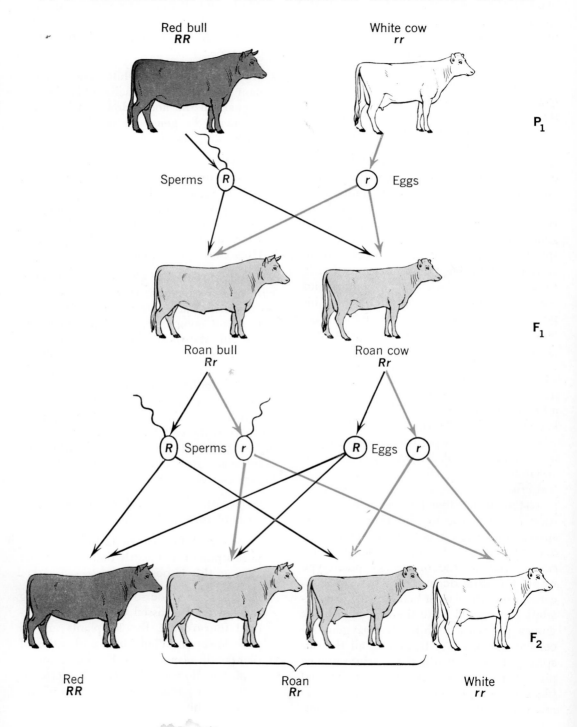

Red bull
RR

White cow
rr

P₁

Sperms ⓇR   ⓡr Eggs

F₁

Roan bull
Rr

Roan cow
Rr

ⓇR Sperms ⓡr   ⓇR Eggs ⓡr

Red
RR

Roan
Rr

White
rr

F₂

Multiple Alleles

We have now learned how to deal with genetic problems in which there are two unlike members of a gene pair—A and a, for instance. These members of the same gene pair are called alleles, as we know. For many traits there may exist more than two different alleles of the gene that affects the trait; in other words, there may be **multiple alleles**. These are all alleles of one another —any two may occur together in the same cell, and in any combination. The important thing to remember is that *only* two alleles of a given gene are normally present in the genotype at the same time. As always, one allele is contributed by the male parent, the other by the female parent.

A well-known example will illustrate what we mean. Whether a person has type A, type B, type AB, or type O blood depends on the presence or absence of specific substances on the red blood cells. There are two of these substances—**antigens** (AN·tih·jenz) A and B. Thus, a person with antigen A is considered to be type A, a person who is type O has neither of the antigens, and so on. It is interesting and important to know that a person's blood type is under genetic control.

In what way do the blood-type genes determine which blood type a person has? We now know that there are three alleles in this particular series: I^A, I^B, and i. (The I of each symbol indicates the allelic relation of one to another. B could not very well be used as a symbol for an allele of A, for you would be likely to forget that they form a pair and must separate as they go into the gametes.) The three alleles may be paired in any combination, but as we said earlier, only two of them can be present in a single individual. The dominance relationships of these three alleles are interesting, too. Both I^A and I^B are fully expressed in the presence of the other. On the other hand, both I^A and I^B are dominant to i, and it is only when both I^A and I^B are absent (when the genotype is ii) that a person is type O. Let us summarize these relationships in a chart:

Phenotype	Genotype	Antigen on cells
Type A	$I^A I^A$ or $I^A i$	A
Type B	$I^B I^B$ or $I^B i$	B
Type AB	$I^A I^B$	A and B
Type O	ii	none

Because of the dominance relationships in this set of multiple alleles, it is possible to deduce immediately the genotype of persons who are type AB or type O. Type A and type B persons may have either of two genotypes, however, and which one they possess must be determined from the blood types of their offspring or by sensitive laboratory tests.

We can best become acquainted with the inheritance of blood types by working out an example:

PROBLEM: Suppose a man with type A blood marries a woman who has type AB blood. What blood types would you expect to find among their children? In this problem we have no way of knowing whether the man is homozygous or heterozygous for the I^A allele. What would tell you which of the genotypes he has?

PROBLEM: Suppose two newborn babies were accidentally mixed up in the hospital, and there was a question of which baby belonged to which parents. From the following blood types, determine which baby belongs to which parents:

Baby 1	Type O
Baby 2	Type A
Mrs. Brown	Type B
Mr. Brown	Type AB
Mrs. Smith	Type B
Mr. Smith	Type B

Now calculate the genotype of each of the six persons.

INHERITANCE OF TWO TRAITS

Geneticists are sometimes interested in following the pattern of inheritance of *two* different traits. Mendel performed such experiments and crossed plants that varied in two traits. He was therefore able to follow two pairs of genes simultaneously. We can take an example from the guinea pig.

In guinea pigs with colored hair, the hair color may be black (*B*) or brown (*b*). This difference is not the same as the difference between black and white, mentioned earlier. That was really a difference between colored (black) and *colorless* (white). But in the present case, too, black is dominant. Also the hair may be short (S) or long (*s*). What is dominant according to these symbols? Suppose we intend to cross an animal that is *Bbss* with one that is *bb*SS. What are the parental phenotypes?

We can easily see what to expect from such a cross by using our method of algebraic multiplication. First, we make our computation for one gene pair at a time, doing each one exactly as before. To begin, we ignore the S's, and concentrate on the *B*'s.

$$\begin{array}{lrl} \text{Gametes of } Bb \text{ parent:} & & \tfrac{1}{2}\,B + \tfrac{1}{2}\,b \\ \text{Gametes of } bb \text{ parent:} & \times & \tfrac{1}{1}\,b \\ \hline & & \tfrac{1}{2}\,Bb + \tfrac{1}{2}\,bb \end{array}$$

Now we work out the S cross, ignoring the *B*'s:

$$\begin{array}{lrl} \text{Gametes of } ss \text{ parent:} & & \tfrac{1}{1}\,s \\ \text{Gametes of } SS \text{ parent:} & \times & \tfrac{1}{1}\,S \\ \hline & & \tfrac{1}{1}\,Ss \end{array}$$

Now for the next step. Let us assume (as did Mendel) that the events that separate the *B* genes from one another are entirely independent of the events that separate the S genes from one another. If so, we can use our "product rule" (see Laboratory Exercise 30-2) that combinations of independent events have a probability that is the product of the probabilities of each of the events. We merely need to multiply the results of the *B* cross by the results of the S cross:

$$\begin{array}{rl} & \tfrac{1}{2}\,Bb + \tfrac{1}{2}\,bb \\ \times & \tfrac{1}{1}\,Ss \\ \hline & \tfrac{1}{2}\,BbSs + \tfrac{1}{2}\,bbSs \end{array}$$

What are the phenotypes?

A bit more complicated is one of the F_1 crosses we could go on to make. Suppose we pick one male and one female double heterozygote (*BbSs* and *BbSs*) and cross them. We perform the *B* cross first while ignoring the S's. Then we do the S cross and ignore the *B*'s.

For the *B* cross we have *Bb* × *Bb*. This gives us results as follows:

$$\tfrac{1}{4}\,BB + \tfrac{1}{2}\,Bb + \tfrac{1}{4}\,bb$$

For the S cross we have S*s* × S*s*. This gives:

$$\tfrac{1}{4}\,SS + \tfrac{1}{2}\,Ss + \tfrac{1}{4}\,ss$$

Now we combine the results of the two by algebraic multiplication:

$$\begin{array}{l} \tfrac{1}{4}\,BB + \tfrac{1}{2}\,Bb + \tfrac{1}{4}\,bb \\ \tfrac{1}{4}\,SS + \tfrac{1}{2}\,Ss + \tfrac{1}{4}\,ss \\ \hline \end{array}$$

Multiply these carefully, just as we have done before. If done correctly, you will get nine different genotypes, but only four different phenotypes, as follows:

	Genotype	*Phenotype*
1/16	BBSS	black short
1/8	BbSS	black short
1/16	bbSS	brown short
1/8	BBSs	black short
1/4	BbSs	black short
1/8	bbSs	brown short
1/16	BBss	black long
1/8	Bbss	black long
1/16	bbss	brown long

If we collect all similar phenotypes in the above list, we will find that we have a ratio that Mendel made famous. It has been called the 9 : 3 : 3 : 1 ratio. This ratio is short for:

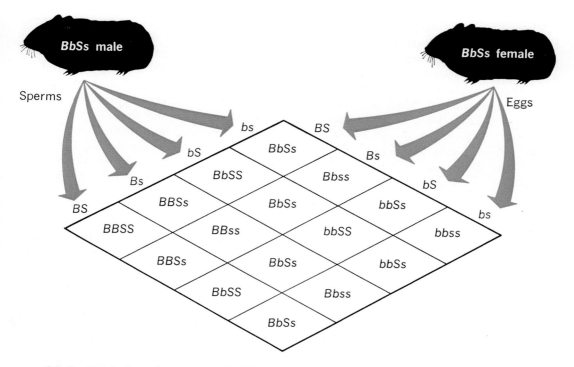

30-8 Checkerboard calculation of expected genotypes in offspring, when the parents both are heterozygous for the same two traits. In this case, the parents are two guinea pigs, heterozygous for black hair and for short hair. Four kinds of gametes will be produced by each parent. Can you complete the calculations by adding together the identical genotypes wherever they occur in the checkerboard? How many different genotypes will there be among the offspring? How many different phenotypes?

$9/16$ **dominant dominant**
$3/16$ **dominant recessive**
$3/16$ **recessive dominant** } **phenotypes**
$1/16$ **recessive recessive**

Another way of predicting the results of this cross is to calculate the kinds of gametes the F_1 parents can produce and then to combine these by algebraic multiplication. A *BbSs* guinea pig can pass on to its gametes either *B* or *b* and either *S* or *s*. Either kind of color allele can be present with either allele for hair length; that is, we might have *BS*, *Bs*, *bS*, or *bs*. These four kinds of gametes should occur with equal frequency, in both ova and sperms of the F_1 parents. We can combine the kinds of gametes with the aid of the checkerboard, which is simply a graphic means of carry-ing out an algebraic multiplication. Compare the result, shown in Figure 30-8, with the result obtained by treating the two kinds of traits as separate crosses and then combining them by multiplication afterward. Is the outcome the same?

Mendel did crosses of this kind, too. In a cross involving both seed shape and seed color, he found in a total of 556 F_2 seeds the following:

> 315 round yellow
> 108 round green
> 101 wrinkled yellow
> 32 wrinkled green

Is this a good 9 : 3 : 3 : 1 ratio? You may test it by the chi-square method you have learned in the laboratory.

These 9 : 3 : 3 : 1 ratios for two pairs of traits in the F_2 generation demonstrate that the traits are independent of one another and that combinations turn up as expected according to chance. This is often called Mendel's **law of independent assortment.** It may be stated as follows: *When two pairs of traits are followed in the same crosses, they assort independently.* Mendel found this to be true for all the combinations of the seven pairs of hereditary traits he used in his pea crosses. Yet, as we shall see, there are important exceptions.

CONTINUOUSLY VARYING TRAITS

Quite deliberately, in order to simplify his experimental design, Mendel chose to work with traits that showed only sharply distinct alternatives: wrinkled as against round seeds, yellow as against green seeds, axial flowers as against terminal flowers, for example. But what about such traits as length of a giraffe's neck, or color of the human skin? In such cases as these, there may be dozens or even thousands of degrees of variation. These can hardly be accounted for by a single pair of Mendel's factors, for even with nondominance, one pair can yield only three genotypes. Some cases of varying traits are certainly due to multiple alleles. But even this phenomenon does not account for many characteristics that seem to have a *quite continuous* variability—as height in man, for example.

To account for such continuously varying traits as human height, human skin color, and human intelligence, we have developed the hypothesis that several different pairs of genes may affect the same trait. An example will illustrate this idea better than abstract discussion. Suppose, for example, that gene X produces a certain degree of red coloring, and that XX is redder than Xx. Suppose that gene Y also does the same thing, as does gene Z. In addition, suppose that x, y, and z produce no color. In such a

case, an organism with the genotype $xxyyzz$ would be pure white. The genotype $XXYYZZ$ would have 6 doses of color-forming genes and would be very dark red indeed. $Xxyyzz$ with only 1 dose of red pigment would be a very light shade of pink. $XXyyzz$, $xxYYzz$, and $xxyyZZ$ would each have 2 doses and be a shade darker and so on up through 6 possible shades. This is actually the way seed color is inherited in wheat, as a Swedish geneticist, Nilsson-Ehle, showed in 1908.

Out of this hypothesis grew a great technological triumph—the first gift of the new science of genetics to the welfare of mankind. The American geneticists E. M. East, George H. Shull, and Donald F. Jones were responsible. The achievement was the development of hybrid corn, which has enormously increased the corn yield for the same input of acreage, fertilizer, and farm labor. The reasoning of these geneticists went as follows. Hybrids are often more vigorous than the parent types that produce them. This, according to the theory, might be because one pure parent strain is $WWXXyyzz$ and the other is $wwxxYYZZ$. Cross them, and you should get $WwXxYyZz$. If any of these genes are dominant, the hybrid should then be better, in terms of the desired characteristic, than either parent type.

Pure strains of maize were selected and crossed. The hypothesis was indeed proved true. The F_1 hybrid plants were vastly better in yield than either of the pure parent strains. The F_2 generation, however, showed enormous diversity, ranging from the very best-yielding to quite worthless types.

Jones then worked out what he called a "double cross," although he meant something still better by this term, and not the usual implication of it. He combined four pure lines to get his productive hybrid. Line A was crossed with line B, and line C was crossed with line D. Then, in the next generation, came the "double cross" between the hybrid A/B and the hybrid C/D. In this way all the recessive, poor-yielding genes become masked in effect. Only the high-yielding, dominant genes remain effective (Figure 30-9).

Different sorts of hybrid corn have been developed for different areas. A type of hybrid corn good for Iowa will not do well in Mexico or the U.S.S.R. Local pure lines, adapted to the climate, must be chosen for the purpose. But when hybrid corn is produced properly, the increase in yield is phenomenal. During the years 1942–45 alone, the increased yield in the United States, from the *same* acreage and with *less* labor than had been expended before World War II began, amounted to nearly 2 billion bushels of corn. And, in the days of peace that followed, throughout the devastated and war-stricken countries of Europe, it was food supplied by the United States—made possible largely by increased production of corn—that prevented widespread famine and political disorder.

One may truly say that insofar as our food supply is concerned, the American standard of living, so much higher than that elsewhere in the world, rests solidly on a foundation of hybrid corn (remember that most of the corn raised is used to feed hogs and cattle, which in turn, become our food as meat, milk, and butter).

In the next chapter we shall try to find out more about the genes and where they are actually located in living cells.

GUIDE QUESTIONS AND PROBLEMS

1. In what way do a sperm and an ovum contribute equally to a potential new individual?
2. In what way is the contribution of the ovum to a new individual different from that of the sperm?
3. Show how both heredity and environment contribute to the expression of a trait in animals, in plants, and in man.

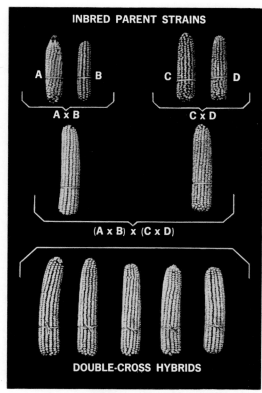

INBRED PARENT STRAINS

A   B   C   D

A x B   C x D

(A x B) x (C x D)

DOUBLE-CROSS HYBRIDS

USDA photos

30-9 Hybrid vigor in corn. The four inbred lines at the top were crossed, *A* with *B* and *C* with *D,* giving rise to the hybrid ears in the center. When kernels from these ears were planted, the resulting hybrid types of corn plants were again crossed, as indicated, giving rise to the large ears in the lower row.

4. Mendel planned his experiments with great perception. What features of his planning were important factors in his success?
5. Why did Mendel choose to perform his experiments with garden peas?
6. How did Mendel insure that his parent pea plants were pure for the traits he was observing?
7. What precautions must Mendel have taken to eliminate the variable effects of environment on the inheritance of the traits of the garden pea?
8. What would the results be if *RR* plants were used to provide eggs while *rr* plants

were used as pollen sources in a cross of two individuals homozygous for the given traits? Suppose this were reversed and the *RR* plants provided the pollen and *rr* plants the eggs? What is the significance of these two sets of results?

9. Why do experiments in genetics require large numbers of individuals for conclusions to be reasonably valid?

10. Among the following genotypes, which ones are heterozygous and which are homozygous? Which of the genotypes have the same phenotype (the capital letter stands for dominance)? Pick out from the list one or more genes for which only two alleles are given. Also pick out a series of multiple alleles.

$AA, I^A I^B, ss, Bb, I^B i, Aa, BB, rr, ii$

11. What is a test cross? How is it used to determine the genotype of an animal or plant of unknown gene makeup?

12. Describe three different ways in which two alleles may contribute to the phenotype of a heterozygote.

13. How can there be multiple allelic genes for a hereditary trait when a single individual can carry only two alleles of a gene? How do multiple alleles operate in the inheritance of blood type in man?

14. What would be the results of a cross of $AaBbCc \times AaBbCc$ in which three inherited traits were observed? Let *A* represent the dominant gene for short and *a*, the recessive for tall; *B*, the dominant gene for black and *b*, the recessive gene for white; *C*, the dominant gene for curly and *c*, the recessive gene for straight.

SUGGESTIONS FOR ADDITIONAL READING

Books

Bonner, D., *Heredity*. Englewood Cliffs (N. J.), Prentice-Hall, 1961.

A short, up-to-date account of the biochemical side of genetics, emphasizing the heredity of the microorganisms.

Goldstein, P., *Genetics Is Easy*, 2nd ed. New York, Viking, 1961.

A clearly written, brief but authoritative introduction to genetics.

Moore, J. A., *Heredity and Development*. New York, Oxford University Press, 1963.

A concise treatment of heredity and embryology, with recent research on DNA.

Scheinfeld, A., *The New You and Heredity*. Philadelphia, Lippincott, 1950.

Well-written, interestingly illustrated introduction to human heredity.

Sinnott, E. W., L. C. Dunn, and T. Dobzhansky, *Principles of Genetics*, 5th ed. New York, McGraw-Hill, 1958.

Standard complete textbook of genetics. Excellent as a single reference.

Srb, A. M., and R. D. Owen, *General Genetics*. San Francisco, Freeman, 1952.

Excellent but rather out-of-date textbook for more detailed formal development of the principles of genetics.

Magazines

Allison, A. C., "Sickle Cells and Evolution." *Scientific American*, Vol. 195 (August 1956), pp. 87–88.

Beadle, G. W., "Genes of Molds and Men." *Scientific American*, Vol. 179 (September 1948), pp. 30–39.

Bearn, A. G., "The Chemistry of Hereditary Disease." *Scientific American*, Vol. 195 (December 1956), pp. 126–36.

Bearn, A. G., and J. L. German, "Chromosomes and Disease." *Scientific American*, Vol. 205 (November 1961), pp. 66–76.

Dobzhansky, T., "Genetics." *Scientific American*, Vol. 183 (September 1950), pp. 55–58.

Gray, G. W., "Sickle-Cell Anemia." *Scientific American*, Vol. 185 (August 1951), pp. 56–59.

Horowitz, N. H., "The Gene." *Scientific American*, Vol. 195 (October 1956), pp. 78–86.

Hotchkiss, R. D., and Esther Weiss, "Transformed Bacteria." *Scientific American*, Vol. 195 (November 1956), pp. 48–53.

Hurwitz, J., and J. J. Furth, "Messenger RNA." *Scientific American*, Vol. 206 (February 1962), pp. 41–49.

Mirsky, A. E., "The Chemistry of Heredity." *Scientific American*, Vol. 188 (February 1953), pp. 47–57.

Taylor, J. H., "The Duplication of Chromosomes." *Scientific American*, Vol. 198 (June 1958), pp. 36–42.

31

THE CHROMOSOME

THEORY

OF HEREDITY

The paper in which Mendel reported his studies with the garden pea lay unnoticed for a long time. During the years following 1865, many breeding experiments were performed with different plants and animals. Biologists attempted to make sense of the results they obtained, but these efforts were not successful. It was not until the year 1900, thirty-five years after Mendel presented his results, and some years after his death, that his paper was "discovered" by three biologists. All three were working independently on the same kind of problem that Mendel had investigated. These men, Carl Correns, H. de Vries, and E. Tschermak, each working in a different country in Europe, obtained results that agreed with those of Mendel. The modern science of genetics was born with the recognition by each of these men that Mendel's work established the foundation upon which hereditary studies could build.

Where Is the Gene?

You will recall that the experiments with garden pea plants led Mendel to the view that heredity is controlled by a number of independent elements that we now call genes. Each inherited trait, such as seed shape, or flower position, or height of plants, is supposedly controlled, as we now express it, by a *pair* of genes. One member of each pair—one allele—comes from the male parent (in the pea plant, from the male part of the flower, or anther), while the other allele comes from the female parent (the ovule in the pea plant).

The new zygotes (in the seeds), resulting from the P_1 cross, develop into mature plants, and each in turn produces gametes. During the production of gametes, members of the gene pair again separate, and again only one of the two alleles enters any one sperm or egg cell. This segregation of the members of gene pairs to the gametes, and their pairing with new alleles in the zygote, we recognize as the rule in sexual reproduction.

Mendel assumed that the members of a gene pair are in no way modified by being associated with one another in the cells of a heterozygous organism. He believed this because when the recessive genes are present in homozygous offspring of heterozygous plants, their normal effects can be observed. The gene for white seed coat, for instance, remains the same "determiner" of whiteness, in spite of being associated with a gene for colored seed coat in a heterozygous plant.

This theory of Mendel's is all very well as far as it goes. It accounts beautifully for the experimental data obtained from breeding pea plants. Further investigation of the heredity of a variety of plants and animals shows that Mendel's principles can also account for the results in many different kinds of organisms. But an important question looms unanswered. If there are really such things as the elements, or genes, that

Mendel postulated, where are they? Shouldn't we see them behaving after the manner postulated for them; that is, pairing in each zygote, and separating before being assorted to the gametes?

The answer to these questions is found in the behavior of the chromosomes, the rod-shaped structures so conspicuous in dividing cells. Specifically, the behavior of the chromosomes during the cell divisions that produce gametes does parallel the behavior of the genes.

CHROMOSOMES AND GENETIC CONTINUITY

At this time we must recall some of the things that we have learned about chromosomes and cell division.

First, we learned that all cells come from pre-existing cells (Chapter 3). One cell divides into two, the two divide into four, and so on.

The events that occur during cell division are complex (consult Chapter 7). Some of the cell's contents seem to be passively divided when the one cell divides into two. The chromosomes, however, are always divided exactly, by mitosis. Some time before the cell is to divide, each chromosome replicates. Thus, there come to be two of every original kind of chromosome. During the mitotic division, one chromosome of each and every kind goes into each daughter cell. The two daughter cells, therefore, have identical chromosomes; and these chromosomes are identical to the chromosomes of the parent cell from which they are derived.

We have also learned that all individuals of the same species have the same number of chromosomes (later in this chapter we will consider a few exceptions to this generalization). The normal number for man is 46, for the potato, 48; hydras and cherry trees have 32; garden peas have 14, the fruit fly, 8; and so on.

Meiosis

We have learned that most of the cells in an individual animal or plant have the same number of chromosomes. We call this the diploid number. But not all cells can have the diploid number; and we saw in Chapter 7 that the process of meiosis reduces the chromosome number by half during the formation of eggs and sperms. (In plants, meiosis occurs during the formation of spores; but sooner or later the spores produce eggs and sperms, so these gametes have the reduced number of chromosomes.)

There is much more to meiosis than a simple reduction of the chromosome number. Let us remind ourselves that Chapter 7 ended with a question, a very important question: If the daughter cells—the eggs and sperms—have only half the number of chromosomes present in the parent cells, how can they have *all* of the instructions of heredity? How can it be that all the kinds of DNA in the 46 chromosomes characteristic of the human cell are present in only 23 chromosomes of an egg or a sperm?

There is another puzzling thing. To reduce their number by half, chromosomes should have to pass—without replicating—through only one cell division. Yet meiosis, in every one of the hundreds of species of sexually reproducing plants and animals that have been studied, seems always to require *two* successive divisions. Consequently the eggs and sperms, or in plants the spores, are always formed in quartets. Now why should this be necessary?

The answer becomes apparent when we see how the mechanism of meiosis differs from ordinary mitosis. Let us begin by thinking of the significance of the diploid ($2n$) chromosome number present in most of the cells of the individual, including the immature reproductive cells that undergo meiosis. This number clearly arises in the first place because of fertilization—because the egg and the sperm, which unite, each carry the monoploid (n) number of chromosomes. Now if every chromosome carried by the egg is matched by a very similar or identical chromosome contributed by the sperm, we could say that the monoploid number represents a set of chromosomes (one of every kind), and the diploid number two sets of chromosomes (two of every kind). Is there any evidence of this?

There is indeed. It was one of the first important things discovered about meiosis, back in 1902. In meiosis, just as in mitosis, the chromosomes shorten and thicken and the spindle begins to form. But while this is going on, something very extraordinary takes place. Every chromosome finds a matching chromosome of its own size and shape, and, we may suspect, with corresponding genes. Each pair of chromosomes is made up of one chromosome that is paternal in origin and a corresponding one that is maternal in origin. In other words, these chromosomes that make up a pair are truly *homologous* structures (see Chapter 20). They not only correspond in size and shape and in the genes they carry, but somewhere back in time they had a common ancestral chromosome.

The homologous chromosomes pair, side by side, starting at one point and continuing in both directions like a closing zipper. At the end of this process, the nucleus of the cell contains just as many pairs of closely matched chromosomes as the monoploid number, that is, just half as many as there were visibly separate chromosomes to start with. While this pairing of chromosomes, or **synapsis** (sih·NAP·sis) as it is called, is going on, it also becomes evident that each chromosome has undergone a replication, just as it usually does in mitosis. Consequently, each pair of chromosomes actually consists of *four* threads, or **chromatids** (KROH·ma-tidz—Figure 31-1).

When the chromosomes line up on the equator of the spindle, each pair of chromosomes (group of four chromatids) remains intact. Then a second unique feature

of meiosis occurs. In a usual cell division, of course, the centromere holding the duplicate chromatids together splits, and the two new centromeres go toward opposite poles of the spindle. But in meiosis this does not occur during the first cell division. Instead, the centromeres of each pair of maternal and paternal chromosomes pull away and draw the homologous chromosomes toward opposite poles. Thus a *segregation* of homologous chromosomes occurs.

Note that now, unlike the case of mitosis, each chromosome of each new cell is still made up of *two* chromatids, held together at the centromere. These new cells now undergo another division, but one with *no replication* of chromosome strands. Instead, the two chromatids of each chromosome separate, one to each daughter cell.

The result of the two divisions in meiosis is four cells, each with a *single* member of each pair of chromosomes. In Figure 31-1, the process is illustrated diagrammatically. Contrast it to the result of two mitotic divisions—namely, four cells each with *two* of every kind of chromosome.

Next we should notice what happens to the chromosomes of *different* pairs during meiosis. Do all the paternal chromosomes line up on one side of the equator of the spindle, and all the maternal chromosomes on the other? That would indeed lead to an extraordinary result, for then each sperm would contribute chromosomes from the paternal grandfather only or the paternal grandmother only, and never some chromosomes from each grandparent. The same extraordinary restriction of inheritance would apply to each egg in the female line. But surely we know from observation that an individual may inherit traits from any or all of its four grandparents, not just two!

Independent Assortment

What happens has already been referred to as the great discovery of 1902. Actually the different pairs of homologous chromo-

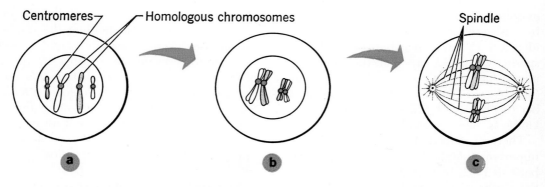

Centromeres — Homologous chromosomes — Spindle

a   b   c

31-1 A summary of the events of meiosis, shown for a cell in which the diploid (2*n*) chromosome number is 4. Before following through the entire sequence, look first at stages **a**, **e**, and **h**, in the three corners of the diagram. These are the one-, two-, and four-cell stages. In **a**, the diploid cell has one each of the four chromosomes; two of these are homologous to the other two. In **e**, each of the two new cells has only half the original variety—two of the four chromosomes (one of each homologous pair),

somes, in lining up on the spindle during the first meiotic division, pay no attention to each other. They line up purely by chance. The paternal chromosome of a particular pair can head toward either pole with equal probability—like a coin that has an equal chance of landing heads or tails. Two pairs of chromosomes behave like two coins flipped together, or two dice on which one notes only odd or even (see Laboratory Exercise 30-2). Let us refer to the maternal chromosome and the paternal chromosome of a particular homologous pair as 1^m and 1^p. Those of another homologous pair could be designated 2^m and 2^p. A possible combination of chromosomes in a gamete would then be 1^m2^m, 1^m2^p, 1^p2^m, or 1^p2^p. There is an *independent assortment* of the pairs of chromosomes, according to the laws of chance.

Chromosomal Exchanges During Synapsis

There is still another vastly important event that takes place during the first meiotic division. If, during synapsis, we look very closely at the four chromatids of a side-by-side pair of homologous chromo-

somes, we find that the strands do not stay neatly straight and separate. On the contrary, they twist about one another. Furthermore, when they begin to separate, they do not always merely uncoil and straighten out. Instead, when separation occurs, the upper part of one chromatid may be united with the lower part of a homologous chromatid. That is, the two chromatids will have exchanged exactly equal parts. The effect of this exchange is to put material from two corresponding (homologous) chromosomes into new combinations. These new combinations persist and lead to the formation of gametes of many kinds.

The Formation of Gametes

Each potential germ cell gives rise, by meiosis, to four new cells. These cells in a male animal complete their development by condensing the nuclear material into a "head" and by developing a small middle piece and a long tail, which functions in locomotion. The cells are now mature sperm cells. In seed plants, the pollen (spore) mother cell gives rise to pollen grains, within which are produced the male gametes.

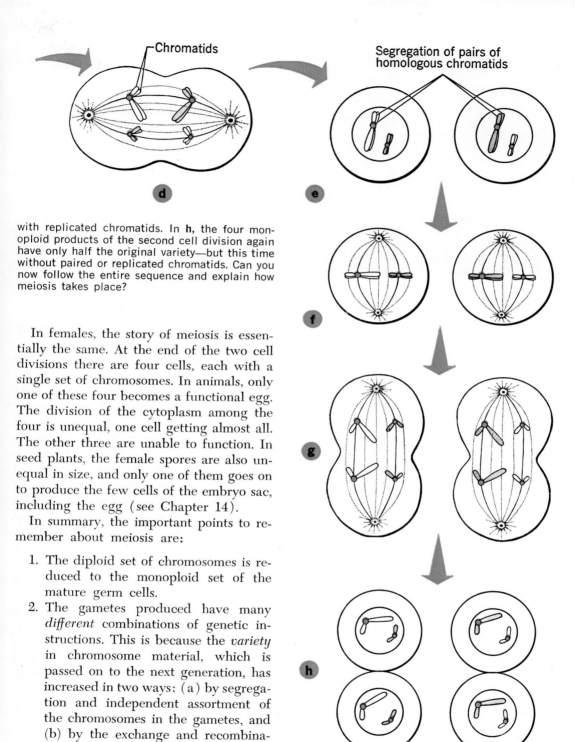

Chromatids

Segregation of pairs of homologous chromatids

d

e

f

g

h

with replicated chromatids. In **h,** the four monoploid products of the second cell division again have only half the original variety—but this time without paired or replicated chromatids. Can you now follow the entire sequence and explain how meiosis takes place?

In females, the story of meiosis is essentially the same. At the end of the two cell divisions there are four cells, each with a single set of chromosomes. In animals, only one of these four becomes a functional egg. The division of the cytoplasm among the four is unequal, one cell getting almost all. The other three are unable to function. In seed plants, the female spores are also unequal in size, and only one of them goes on to produce the few cells of the embryo sac, including the egg (see Chapter 14).

In summary, the important points to remember about meiosis are:

1. The diploid set of chromosomes is reduced to the monoploid set of the mature germ cells.

2. The gametes produced have many *different* combinations of genetic instructions. This is because the *variety* in chromosome material, which is passed on to the next generation, has increased in two ways: (a) by segregation and independent assortment of the chromosomes in the gametes, and (b) by the exchange and recombination of parts of chromatids when the chromosomes were in synapsis.

Victor A. McKusick

31-2 Walter S. Sutton (1876–1916). Sutton made his important contributions to genetics in 1902 and 1903. He subsequently studied and practiced medicine.

THE CHROMOSOME THEORY OF HEREDITY

Sutton's Hypothesis

Walter S. Sutton (Figure 31-2), a young graduate student working at Columbia University, provided one of the first leads to the solution of the problem "Where are the genes?" Sutton's contribution was his recognition of certain *similarities* between the assumed behavior of Mendel's genetic units and the visible behavior of the chromosomes during meiosis. Sutton argued that these parallels between the behavior of chromosomes and of Mendel's genetic units are too striking to be accidental. Let us follow some of the evidence and arguments, of Sutton and others before him, that convinced biologists that the genes are definite, physical bodies located at predictable places on the chromosomes.

One step in the early argument ran as follows. The biological link between generations of multicellular organisms is physically minute. It consists typically of two tiny cells—a microscopic sperm cell from the male and a somewhat larger egg cell from the female. Therefore, the genes that control heredity must necessarily be contained within these two reproductive cells.

A second step in the argument is the fact that the egg and sperm cell, although differing in many ways, especially in size, appear to make precisely the same genetic contribution to the organism that develops from their union. Mendel himself supplied the evidence for this equal genetic contribution from the two gametes. He made reciprocal crosses in which first the male and then the female plant carried the dominant trait he was studying. And yet, these crosses produced *exactly the same kind of offspring*. It made no difference which parent had the dominant trait.

Now, the argument ran, if the genetic contribution of the sperm and the egg are essentially the same, the *location* of the genes ought to be in the same place in the two gametes. There is a single conspicuous candidate for this honor—the nucleus; for many sperm cells consist of a nucleus and little else. The nucleus of the egg is, in nearly all respects, a duplicate of the nucleus of the sperm. But the cytoplasm of the egg differs vastly in both amount and nature from that in the sperm. On this basis, therefore, we might conclude that the *nucleus* is the seat of heredity.

Within the nucleus lie the chromosomes. A careful study reveals that they seem to behave much as the hypothetical Mendelian factors are supposed to behave. The individual chromosome retains its structure throughout the various cell divisions of meiosis, and indeed throughout the numberless cell divisions in the **somatic** (so-MAT-ik) tissues—the body tissues of each generation. Clearly, this preservation of the individuality of each chromosome is required if the chromosomes are to serve as the carriers of heredity.

Sutton drew up a precise list of these parallel types of behavior:

1. At the conclusion of meiosis, the number of chromosomes found in each sperm and each egg is just one half the number found in the cells of the body. Each pair of separating chromosomes is found to be made up of one chromosome inherited from the male parent and one derived from the female parent. This corresponds to Mendel's requirement that one and only one of each pair of genetic elements be present in each germ cell.

2. The union of sperm and egg, each with its single set of chromosomes, re-establishes for the new organism the whole number (two sets) of chromosomes previously seen in the body cells of the parent organisms. This corresponds to the requirement that the genes be contributed equally by each parent.

3. Next, it can be observed that each pair of homologous chromosomes segregates quite independently of every other pair during meiosis. The four possible combinations of two pairs of chromosomes, described on page 530, correspond exactly to what Mendel had found to hold true for different pairs of traits, such as round versus wrinkled, or yellow versus green, when they were followed together. In other words, Mendel's law of independent assortment corresponds exactly to the behavior of the different pairs of chromosomes, which likewise assort independently of each other.

Sutton carefully calculated the *number* of combinations that would be possible in gametes and in zygotes with different numbers of pairs of chromosomes in the diploid cells. He found that the number of possible chromosome combinations is just the same as the number of combinations of genetic elements Mendel postulated in explaining the results of his crosses with pea plants.

After considering all these striking parallels, Sutton proposed in effect the following:

Let us assume that the genes are actual physical units located on the chromosomes, one member of each pair of genes being located on each member of a chromosome pair. Then the behavior of the chromosomes in meiosis and fertilization will account for the results of the breeding experiments.

In Figure 31-3, two pairs of genes located on two pairs of chromosomes are indicated in a diagrammatic fashion. Follow the various genes through meiosis, and see how they provide a plausible explanation for the Mendelian ratios.

Sutton realized, of course, that there must be *more* than one gene pair to a pair of chromosomes. If this were not so, the number of traits under genetic control in an organism would be limited to the number of its pairs of chromosomes. Since some organisms have only one or two pairs of chromosomes and man has but 23, the number of hereditary traits would be very limited indeed. Sutton therefore assumed that many different genes are located on a single chromosome. This conclusion led him to a brilliant prediction. If several genes are linked together on a single chromosome, they can scarcely be transmitted independently of each other. It follows that in any species there should be groups of hereditary elements that do not assort independently, and the number of these **linkage groups** of genes should correspond to the number of pairs of chromosomes.

Mendel did not find any linkage group in the pea, but in his experiments he tested only seven pairs of alternative traits. Perhaps if he had tested more, he would have found an exception to the independent assortment of different pairs of genes. (As a matter of fact, the pea has just seven pairs of chromosomes.) Sutton predicted that

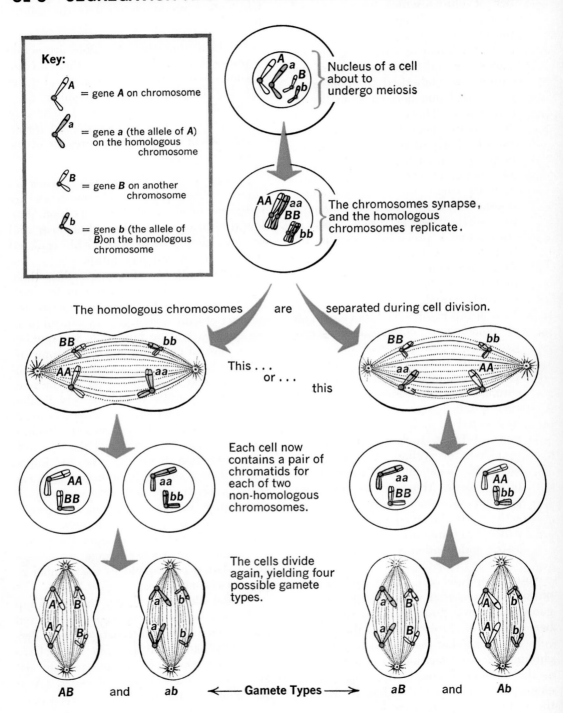

Key:

= gene **A** on chromosome

= gene **a** (the allele of **A**) on the homologous chromosome

= gene **B** on another chromosome

= gene **b** (the allele of **B**)on the homologous chromosome

Nucleus of a cell about to undergo meiosis

The chromosomes synapse, and the homologous chromosomes replicate.

The homologous chromosomes are separated during cell division.

This . . . or . . . this

Each cell now contains a pair of chromatids for each of two non-homologous chromosomes.

The cells divide again, yielding four possible gamete types.

AB and **ab** ←— **Gamete Types** —→ **aB** and **Ab**

when the monoploid chromosome number of a species has been determined, it will correspond to the number of linkage groups in that same species. He was unable to confirm this idea himself. More than a decade was to pass before geneticists knew enough about the chromosome number and inheritance in any species to test the hypothesis. The fruit fly, soon to be discussed in the text and used in your laboratory exercises, was the first species for which the data were available. Yet today, for quite a number of species—in fact, for every species about which we have enough information about its heredity and chromosome number—Sutton's prediction has been verified, with convincing evidence.

The Nature of Scientific Proof

What do we mean by "convincing evidence"? What does it mean to "prove" a hypothesis in biology? Is it something like proving a theorem in geometry? Proof in geometry starts with axioms and postulates and moves by a series of logical steps to a conclusion. This conclusion is *unquestionable* if the assumptions (axioms and postulates) are granted, and if the steps of the proof are logical. A "proof" in any science is quite different. The biologist gradually and haltingly accumulates data—by many steps and with many doubts. At intervals he tries to interpret his data. He seeks to find some pattern that will relate them to one another, and thus organize them into a reasonable whole, which we call a theory.

A theory can do no more than take account of all the available data. If it does so, without any omissions or distortions, it is a very good theory indeed. One effect of a good theory is to spur scientists to search for new data, to advance hypotheses, and to test the hypotheses. The very surest test is to make a prediction (hypothesis) on the basis of the theory—just as Sutton did—and then check the old and new data to see whether the prediction holds true or can be shown to be false. Whenever new data are found, the theory must be re-examined. If the new data do not support the theory, then the theory must be revised to take them into account, or abandoned if the new data contradict it entirely.

So in biology, as in all science, no theory is ever proved once and for all. However, if a theory continues to account for all new data as they appear over the years, then it is said to be established.

DISCOVERY OF THE SEX CHROMOSOMES

Let us return to the mounting evidence for the chromosome theory of heredity. Most of it came from the study of the small fruit fly, which you have doubtless seen hovering around overripe fruit. Its scientific name is *Drosophila melanogaster* (dro·SOF·il·a mel·a·no·GAS·ter), meaning "black-bellied dew-lover."

Drosophila was first studied intensively in the laboratories of Columbia University in New York City, where Walter Sutton had earlier been a graduate student. Here T. H. Morgan (Figure 31-4), around 1910, raised thousands of the red-eyed flies in bottles, supplying mashed bananas as food. In the course of examining these flies, Morgan found one fly that had *white* eyes instead of red eyes. What was the basis of this variation? Could it be due to genetic differences, such as Mendel had found in peas?

This fly was a male and was mated with a normal red-eyed female. The F_1 generation consisted entirely of red-eyed flies. This meant, if one used Mendel's scheme, that the gene for white eyes is recessive to the gene for red eyes. Next, the members of the F_1 generation were mated to produce an F_2 generation. Among these offspring a ratio of ¾ red-eyed flies to ¼ white-eyed flies was obtained. This, too, agreed with Mendel's F_2 results for single trait inheritance—until Morgan noticed that *all the white-eyed*

California Institute of Technology

31-4 Thomas Hunt Morgan (1866–1945). Morgan's discovery of sex-linked traits in *Drosophila* led to experiments that collectively yielded chromosome "maps"—identification of the genes carried by each chromosome, and the approximate location of each gene on a chromosome.

flies were males! The eye color is a trait inherited in some direct relationship to sex. White eye color is a **sex-linked trait.** Similar phenomena had been discovered a short time before, in a moth and in the canary.

Here is a new problem. Might we get a clue by looking at the chromosomes of *Drosophila?* Just before Morgan's discovery of the white-eyed male fly, some careful work on the cells of *Drosophila* had shown that there is a difference between the chromosomes of males and females. Of the four pairs of chromosomes in each cell, three pairs are identical in males and females. But one pair is not (Figure 31-5). The straight, rod-shaped chromosomes of this pair are named **X chromosomes.** The hook-shaped member of this pair (found in the male only) is named the **Y chromosome.**

These observations, and the knowledge of meiosis, led to the conclusion that males must produce *two* different kinds of sperms so far as these chromosomes are concerned: half the sperms would carry an X chromosome, the other half a Y chromosome. Females, on the other hand, produce only one kind of egg with respect to these chromosomes: every egg carries an X chromosome. (Both eggs and sperms of course also contain one chromosome of each of the other pairs of chromosomes.) Because of their connection with the sex of the flies, the X and Y chromosomes are called the **sex chromosomes,** and all the remaining chromosomes are called **autosomes.**

Sex Determination

The discovery of two kinds of sex chromosomes suggested that perhaps they would provide an explanation for the determination of sex. Flies with two X chromosomes are always females, and those with an X and a Y chromosome are always males. Then, with respect to the X chromosome, all egg cells are alike, containing a single X chromosome. The sex of a fly therefore depends on whether the egg is fertilized by a sperm with an X chromosome or one with a Y chromosome. It is thus apparently the male fly's gamete that determines the sex of the offspring, since it carries either an X or Y chromosome. Figure 31-6 shows a diagram of this theory of sex determination.

In later years, when techniques were improved, it became possible to show that a similar difference in one pair of the chromosomes of males and females is common among animals. With most plants there are no individuals of separate sex; but in plant species that do have separate male and female individuals, sex chromosomes can be distinguished (in mosses and liverworts, the ginkgo tree, and some flowering plants, for example). The study of human cells has revealed that man's pattern of sex chromosomes is similar to that of *Drosophila.*

Man has 23 pairs of chromosomes in all. Twenty-two pairs of these are the autosomes ("non-sex chromosomes"); and one pair, the sex chromosomes. In man, the Y chromosome is very small in size, compared to the X chromosome. By applying our rule of keeping explanations as simple as possible, we can explain sex determination in humans the same way we do in fruit flies. The male produces two kinds of sperms, half carrying an X chromosome, the other half carrying a Y chromosome. All eggs carry an X chromosome. If an egg is fertilized by a sperm bearing a Y chromosome, the offspring is a male. But if an egg is fertilized by an X-bearing sperm, the offspring is a female. Figure 31-7 depicts the human chromosomes.

Not all kinds of animals have sex-determining sperms. In some, such as birds,

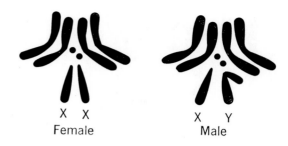

X   X
Female

X   Y
Male

31-5   The four pairs of chromosomes of female and male *Drosophila* in diploid cells.

butterflies, and moths, it is the *female* that has two kinds of sex chromosomes, and hence produces two kinds of gametes. In these organisms all sperm cells are alike in respect to the kinds of sex chromosomes they possess. It is the kind of egg cell that is fertilized that determines the sex of the

SEX DETERMINATION IN *DROSOPHILA*

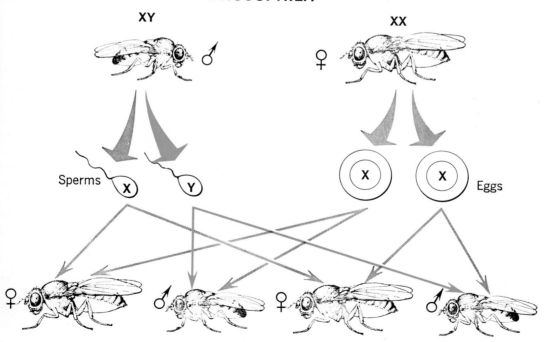

XY

XX

Sperms X   Y

X   X   Eggs

31-6   A diagram of the apparent means of sex determination in fruit flies. Which of the parents—male or female—contributes the sex-determining chromosome to each offspring? (Later on you will qualify your answer, as you read page 544.)

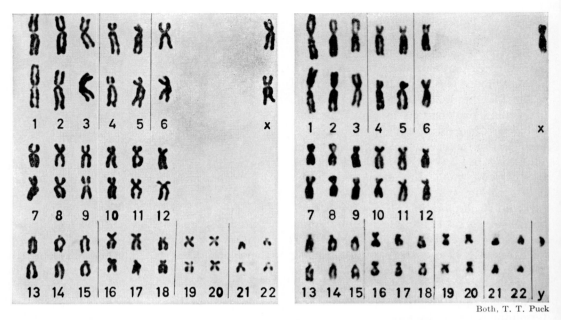

Both, T. T. Puck

31-7 The chromosomes of the human female (left) and male (right), arranged according to size. Cytologists have perfected techniques for arresting mitosis in the paired-chromatid stage, when each chromosome appears double, as above. The easily visible chromosomes can then be measured, described, and identified by number, as shown.

offspring. In other species one of the sex chromosomes is missing entirely. In some grasshoppers, for instance, males have 23 chromosomes, but females have 24. In this case half the sperm cells have 11 chromosomes, the other half have 12. The sex of the young grasshopper depends on the kind of sperm that fertilizes the egg.

Sex-linked Inheritance

The sex chromosomes carry not only some of the genes that determine sex but other genes, too. The heredity of traits whose genes are located on the sex chromosomes is different from that of traits whose genes are on the autosomes. This pattern of heredity differs from that found by Mendel, for his results require us to assume the presence of pairs of similar genes in *both* sexes. With this new chromosome picture in the male fruit fly, there is reason to doubt that all the X chromosome genes have correspond-

ing partners (alleles). In fact, Morgan's case of white-eye inheritance in *Drosophila* can be most easily explained by assuming that the gene for white eye color is carried on the X chromosome and that the Y chromosome has no allele of this gene. Since this proves to be true of many other genes on the X chromosome, the Y chromosome in *Drosophila* may be said to be "inert" in inheritance. Consequently even a recessive gene on the X chromosome always affects the phenotype and is recognizable in the male fly, since there is no corresponding allele on the Y chromosome.

Figure 31-8 shows two generations of sex-linked inheritance in Morgan's cross involving a white-eyed male.

We can now expand our chromosome theory of heredity to include the data from sex-linked inheritance. Morgan found evidence of a *direct relation* between a particular hereditary trait and a particular chromosome. It was a dramatic confirmation of Sutton's theory. Further work showed that sex-linked traits are not limited to *Drosophila* but occur in a number of species, including man. Let us consider two of these sex-linked traits in man, color blindness and **hemophilia** (hee·mo·FIL·ih·a).

1. *Color blindness*. Sex-linked color blindness is a rather common trait. Persons

afflicted have difficulty in distinguishing red from green. This type of color blindness can be detected by using special charts made up of a number of colored dots so arranged that color-blind persons see a different pattern (or word) than other persons do.

PROBLEM: There are eight or ten times as many color-blind men as color-

SEX-LINKED INHERITANCE IN *DROSOPHILA*

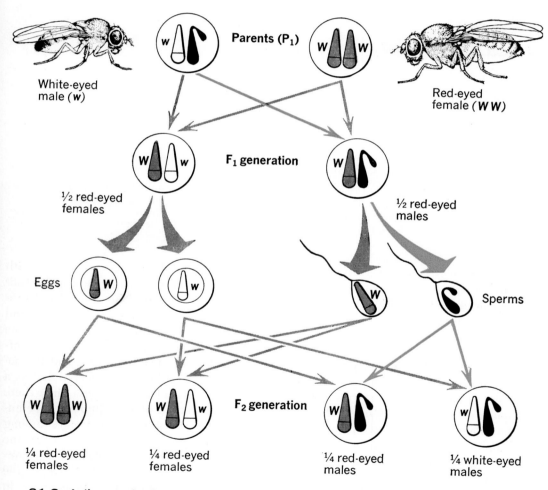

31-8 A diagram showing two generations of the inheritance of a trait controlled by a gene located on the X chromosome of *Drosophila*. The gene in this case controls the production of white eye color; its normal allele results in red eye color.

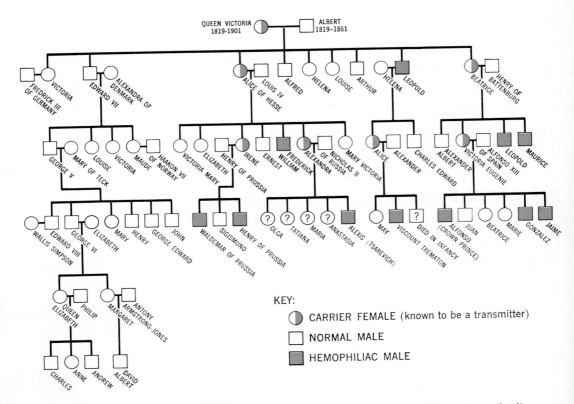

31-9 A pedigree of some of Queen Victoria's descendants, showing the hereditary distribution of hemophilia. The present British royal line descended through Edward VII, who did not have hemophilia and therefore did not inherit from his mother, Queen Victoria, the X chromosome carrying the recessive gene for hemophilia.

KEY:

◑ CARRIER FEMALE (known to be a transmitter)

☐ NORMAL MALE

■ HEMOPHILIAC MALE

blind women. Use the model worked out for white-eye inheritance in *Drosophila* and show why you would expect more color blindness among men than among women.

2. *Hemophilia.* Genetic hemophilia is a much more serious human defect than color blindness, and fortunately a much rarer one. (How might this fact be related to natural selection?) Hemophilia is a condition in which the blood fails to clot after a surface or internal injury, or else clots very slowly. Persons with extreme cases of hemophilia can bleed to death from even a small cut.

Hemophilia is a genetic defect with a royal history. The gene for the trait became so widely distributed in European royalty during the nineteenth and early twentieth centuries that the course of history was profoundly affected, especially in Spain and Russia. The gene probably appeared first as a mutation in Queen Victoria, since there is no record of hemophilia in her ancestry. Because of marriages among the royalty of Europe, the gene became distributed in a number of royal families. Figure 31-9 shows the pedigree of the distribution of hemophilia in Queen Victoria's descendants. Note that the present royal family of Great

Britain is free of the gene. How can one be positive about this?

You will note in the pedigree that there are no female hemophiliacs. In order for a female to have hemophilia she would have to receive one X chromosome from her mother, the other from her father, both of the chromosomes carrying the hemophilia gene. This occurs very rarely, partly because the gene itself is rare, and partly because few male hemophiliacs survive until maturity and marriage.

PROBLEM: If you had a red-eyed female fly, but did not know whether it carried a gene for white eye color, how would you find out?

PROBLEM: What would be the result of each of the following *Drosophila* crosses: white-eyed male × white-eyed female? white-eyed female × red-eyed male?

PROBLEM: If a blue-eyed, color-blind woman marries a normal-visioned man who is homozygous for brown eye color, what kind of children might they expect with respect to these two traits? If one of the sons in turn marries a brown-eyed, normal-visioned woman, what kinds of children might they expect with respect to these traits? (Consider several possibilities in this last case.) Remember, human eye color is *not* sex-linked.

PROBLEM: Determine what kind of inheritance is shown by each of the following human pedigrees:

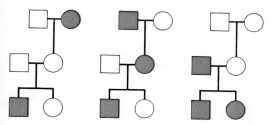

Can two different hypotheses account for any of the preceding pedigrees? If so, what are they?

LINKAGE AND CROSSING–OVER

All the sex-linked genes on the X chromosome of *Drosophila* are linked in their inheritance, just as hemophilia and color blindness are linked in human families in which both have been observed. But linkage is not restricted to sex-linked traits. In fact, it was discovered in sweet peas even before Morgan began observing the linkage of white eye color and other sex-linked traits in the fruit fly.

You will recall that Mendel found that each of the genetic differences he followed in his pea experiments is inherited independently. A heterozygous mating involving two different traits gave him a $9 : 3 : 3 : 1$ ratio of the phenotypes in the F_2 generation. But shortly after Sutton's statement of the chromosome theory, F_2 ratios were found that were far from being the expected $9 : 3 : 3 : 1$. Morgan explained these "exceptions" to Mendel's rule of independent assortment by supposing that genes located on the same pair of chromosomes behave as if linked. It was what Sutton had predicted!

Yet surprisingly, the linkage is not perfect, as you might expect it to be if two genes were riding together on the same chromosome and could not separate. If this were the case, then two dominant traits, if linked, would always be passed on together; and we might suppose that we actually have a single gene with two different effects. Or, if one dominant gene is on one chromosome and another dominant gene on the homologous chromosome, they should always segregate. Instead, what Morgan and others observed was that although the combinations of linked traits in the original parents tend to be preserved in most of the descendants, there are also *recombinations*. And what is more, these recombinations always occur *with the same frequency* between particular linked traits. It does not matter at all whether the F_1 has received both dominant traits together from a single parent, or has obtained one from one parent and the other from the other parent. The percentage of recombinations in the F_2 generation is the same. Thus, if the F_1 individual has inherited both *A* and *B* from one parent, and *a* and *b* from the other, the percentage of recombinations (*Ab* and *aB*) in the F_2 is, say, 10 percent. But if the F_1 has obtained *Ab* from one parent and *aB* from the other, the percentage of recombinations (*AB* and *ab* this time) in the F_2 is still 10 percent.

If two genes are located on the same chromosome, why do they not *always* stay together? In discussing meiosis (page 530) we pointed out that when chromosomes unite in synapsis, the chromatids of the homologous chromosomes may break and exchange parts in the process. New recombinations of linked genes result from this process. It is called **crossing-over.** Figure 31-10 shows how crossing-over in 20 percent of the meiotic divisions modifies the proportions of gametes (50 percent *AB* + 50 percent *ab*) that would be expected if genes *A* and *B* were always inseparable.

In this case the break is close to the middle of the chromosome, and the two genes *A* and *B* (or the recessive alleles *a* and *b*) are at opposite ends. If *A* and *B* were closer together, we might suppose that a break between them would not occur as frequently. In fact, the farther apart two genes are on the same chromosome the more likely they are to be separated by crossing-over. This simple principle, pointed out by Morgan, has enabled geneticists to construct maps of chromosomes locating the genes in relation to one another. Of course, this can be done only for organisms that have been used in hundreds of genetic experiments involving many thousands of offspring. For the fruit fly, for corn (maize),

and for a few other species, this has been done quite thoroughly. Mapping of the human chromosomes in this way is just beginning. Can you suggest why?

BRIDGES' PROOF OF THE CHROMOSOME THEORY

In 1916, C. B. Bridges, who was one of Morgan's graduate students at Columbia University, published a paper entitled "Nondisjunction as Proof of the Chromosome Theory of Heredity." In this and later studies, he presented detailed evidence that established beyond question the conclusion that genes are physically associated with chromosomes.

Bridges had worked with genes located on the X chromosome—and therefore sex-linked. In particular he investigated a gene called "vermilion," which is responsible for the development of very bright-red eyes, as contrasted with the dark-red eyes of the normal flies. Vermilion is recessive and is normally inherited just like white eye color (see Figure 31-8). From your knowledge of sex-linked inheritance you can see that a vermilion-eyed female crossed with a normal male should give rise to females that appear normal and to vermilion-eyed males.

Figure 31-11 is a diagram of this cross, showing the X and Y chromosomes, and having *v* stand for the gene for vermilion eyes while *V* symbolizes its partner allele for normal red eye color.

In the early days of breeding *Drosophila*, it was noticed occasionally in a cross between a vermilion-eyed female and a normal male that an *F_1 female* was produced with vermilion eyes, or an *F_1 male* was produced having the normal red eyes (this does not happen more than once in every 2,000 flies). Such F_1 offspring are clearly exceptions to the rule and raise some doubts about the chromosome theory of heredity. How can we possibly explain these exceptions without giving up the theory?

31-10 CROSSING-OVER DURING MEIOSIS

Linkage of genes on the same chromosome does not altogether prevent recombination of the linked genes. A certain percentage of cells (shown as 20% in this diagram) may undergo crossing-over during meiosis.

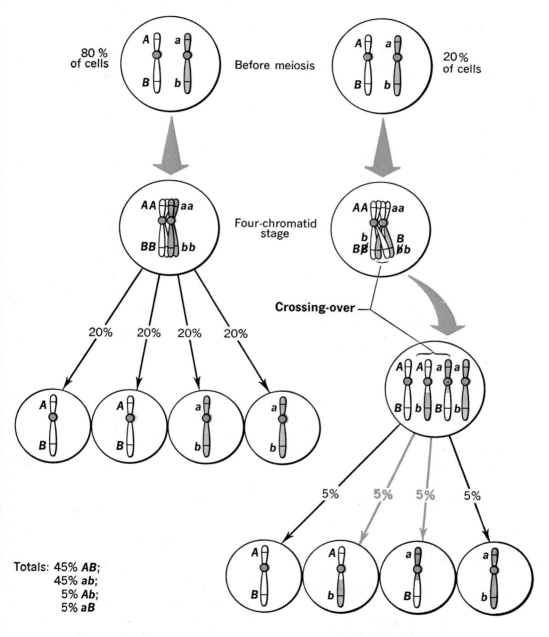

Totals: 45% **AB**;
   45% **ab**;
   5% **Ab**;
   5% **aB**

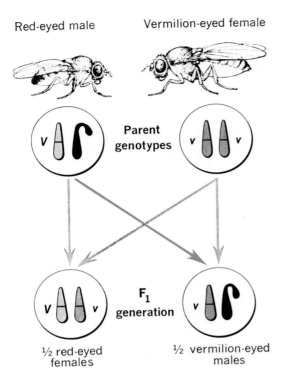

Red-eyed male   Vermilion-eyed female

Parent genotypes

F_1 generation

½ red-eyed females   ½ vermilion-eyed males

31-11 A diagram showing the normal inheritance of a sex-linked trait, vermilion eye color, in a cross of a vermilion-eyed female with a red-eyed male. Occasionally this normal pattern of sex-linked inheritance is upset, with results as shown in Figure 31-12.

One deduction from the theory is that a vermilion-eyed female can be produced only if *two* vermilion alleles are present. One of these alleles is definitely contributed by the vermilion-eyed female parent, but where does the other vermilion allele come from? In the cross diagramed in Figure 31-11, the only other vermilion allele available is also in the female parent! Perhaps we can account for these *exceptional* F_1 males and females by assuming that in the female parent *the two X chromosomes fail to separate in meiosis*, so *both* X chromosomes occasionally pass into a single egg. This failure of the two X chromosomes to separate (or to disjoin) as they and other

chromosomes normally do during meiosis is called **nondisjunction.**

In Figure 31-12 we see the consequences of nondisjunction of the X chromosomes for the phenotypes of the offspring. By nondisjunction, two kinds of exceptional eggs can be produced: eggs with two X chromosomes (and hence two vermilion alleles), and eggs with *no* X chromosomes at all. When these two kinds of eggs are fertilized by normal sperms, half of which carry an X chromosome, the other half a Y chromosome, we obtain the combinations of sex chromosomes shown in the diagram. Note that the individuals with either three X chromosomes or no X chromosomes do not live a normal life span—their genetic disturbance is too great.

By now you have probably begun to suspect that the determination of sex is not as simple as we may have thought. If a fly with two X chromosomes and a Y chromosome is a female, what role does the Y chromosome play? The clues are to be found in Figure 31-12. If a fruit fly has an X chromosome but no Y chromosome, then it is a male, but is sterile. We conclude that the Y chromosome is responsible for male fertility, even if otherwise it is inert genetically. The observation that an XXY individual is a female, in spite of the presence of the Y chromosome, suggests that *the number of X chromosomes* determines sex: one X chromosome, a male; two X chromosomes, a female. We can now revise and improve our original hypothesis of sex determination without affecting our first approximation. It is still a good general rule to say that XX results in a female, and XY in a male. But now we explain the generalization on the basis of the *number of X chromosomes*, rather than on the presence or absence of the Y chromosome.

Let us return to Bridges' hypothesis for one final check. We have *assumed* that these exceptional flies result from the presence or absence of certain sex chromosomes.

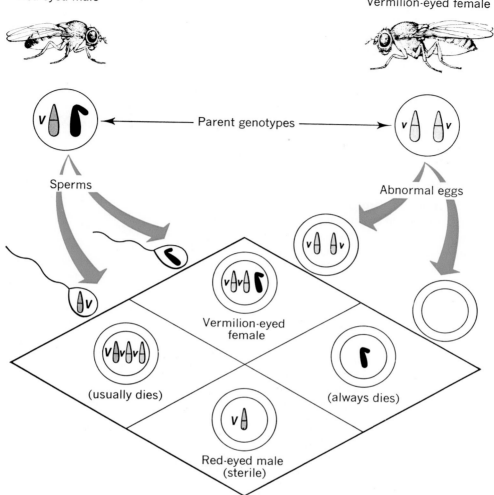

Red-eyed male

Vermilion-eyed female

Parent genotypes

Sperms

Abnormal eggs

Vermilion-eyed
female

(usually dies)

(always dies)

Red-eyed male
(sterile)

31-12 A diagram showing the kinds of offspring that would be produced if the two X chromosomes of a vermilion-eyed female failed to segregate (disjoin). The vermilion-eyed females and red-eyed males that result from such combinations of nondisjunctional eggs and normal sperms are called *exceptional,* since obviously they are exceptions to the rule that we expect to get all red-eyed females and vermilion-eyed males from a mating of vermilion-eyed females and red-eyed males.

Now the final and convincing test of this hypothesis would be to see if these flies actually have these particular chromosomes in their cells. Bridges examined the cells of these flies and found perfect agreement among (1) the inheritance of vermilion, (2) the sex of the fly, and (3) the chromo-

somes of the fly, according to the nondisjunction hypothesis.

The exceptional vermilion-eyed females, for instance, which are supposed to have the genotype *vvY*, do in fact have two X chromosomes and one Y chromosome. Figure 31-13 shows the actual appearance of the chromosomes under the microscope. The series of experiments carried out by Bridges was a dramatic and convincing demonstration that the genes are indeed located on the chromosomes. The chromosome theory of heredity was established. Occasionally traits are found that depend on hereditary factors located in the cytoplasm instead of in the chromosomes. But there is now no doubt that the great majority of typical genes are located on the chromosomes.

Nondisjunction in Humans

From the time of Bridges' work until 1959, the occasional nondisjunction of chromosomes in reproductive cells was thought to be an interesting scientific curiosity, probably occurring mostly in fruit flies. Its study was extremely valuable in helping to provide proof for the chromosome theory of heredity, but knowledge of nondisjunction was not thought to be of any practical value to man.

Then, as so often happens, it was discovered that this odd piece of knowledge about inheritance in an insect helped us to understand a new discovery in human biology. With the new techniques for studying human chromosomes, it became possible to count them accurately and to identify the individual chromosomes (Figure 31-7). Normal human cells contain 46 chromosomes. In the process of examining and counting the chromosomes from many persons, it was discovered in 1959 that the cells from *some* individuals contain 47 chromosomes. Some other persons have only 45 chromosomes in each cell.

Are these variations in human chromosome number unimportant, or are they related to some physical condition? The extra or missing chromosomes very often turned out to be sex chromosomes, X's or Y's. And the number of sex chromosomes an individual has is related to modifications in the normal sex characteristics, and sometimes in normal mental abilities as well. Some of the unusual combinations of sex chromosomes that have been found are X, XXX, XXY, XXXY, XXXX, and even XXXXY instead of the usual XX and XY. Contrary to the situation in the fruit fly, where the number of X chromosomes determines the sex and the Y chromosome has a minor role, in humans the presence of a single Y chromosome always produces a male, no matter how many X chromosomes may be present. And a human female who is XXX, instead of being fatally affected as in *Drosophila*, is normal and fertile.

Extra autosomes have also been found in human cells. When the body cells of "Mongoloid" idiots are examined, the cells are found to contain a small extra autosome. Figure 31-14 shows the chromosomes, including the extra autosome, of such a cell. Here the consequence of nondisjunction is indeed tragic.

We now realize that nondisjunction of human chromosomes in the reproductive cells of parents can have very severe and unfortunate consequences for the offspring. Even before it was definitely proved that high-energy radiation causes gene mutations, it was known that radiation can cause an increase in the proportion of nondisjunction among the chromosomes in the gametes of the fruit fly. In our concern for the possible mutations radiation may cause in humans, we have perhaps forgotten that radiation may also result in grosser kinds of

31-13 Chromosomes of a normal female *Drosophila* (left), and an exceptional vermilion-eyed female with two X chromosomes and one Y chromosome.

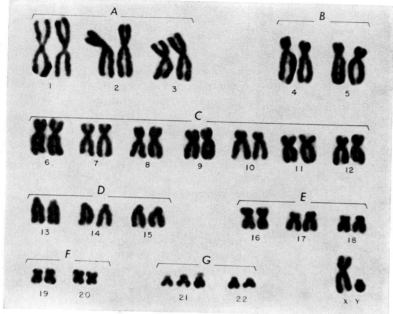

D. H. Carr and M. L. Barr

31-14 The chromosomes of a "Mongoloid" idiot, arranged according to the usual manner of numbering them. Observe that there are *three* of the No. 21 autosomes, resulting in a total of 47 chromosomes. Compare this count with the two of Figure 31-7.

cell defects, such as nondisjunction of chromosomes. One extra chromosome, or one less chromosome, in an individual's cells can have a drastic effect. This knowledge gives us additional reason to avoid unnecessary exposure of the reproductive cells to radiation.

GUIDE QUESTIONS

1. Why was Mendel unable to provide direct evidence for the existence of genes?
2. What did Mendel mean by the "principle of independent assortment"?
3. How does the behavior of chromosomes in mitosis and meiosis relate to Mendel's conclusions?
4. Why would it have been necessary to postulate a process such as meiosis even if no evidence that it occurs was available?

5. How does the inheritance of red and white eye color in *Drosophila* convincingly link the inheritance of a particular trait with a specific chromosome?
6. Suppose crossing-over between genes *A* and *B*, in a pair of homologous chromosomes, occurs in 20 percent of the gametes in an individual heterozygous for *Aa*, *Bb*, and *Cc*, and that it occurs between *A* and *C* in 8 percent of the gametes. How often would you expect crossing-over between *B* and *C*?
7. What additional evidence for the chromosome theory of inheritance is provided by nondisjunction? How does cytological evidence support this?
8. How does sex determination in man differ from sex determination in *Drosophila*?

SUGGESTIONS FOR ADDITIONAL READING

See references at the end of Chapter 30.

32

GENES AND

HOW THEY ACT

Mendel's experiments, important as they are, do not tell us very much about the gene. They did establish that genes behave in heredity as if they are separate particles that remain unchanged from generation to generation. The study of genic effects revealed a variety of patterns of heredity that could be analyzed from a mathematical standpoint.

Later, under the stimulus of Sutton's clear ideas about the relationship of genes to chromosomes, conclusive evidence was collected that showed, beyond any reasonable doubt, that genes are physical units located on chromosomes. Chemical studies of chromosomes and of microorganisms eventually led to the current belief that the gene is made up of DNA. We shall now seek the basis for this belief.

THE CHEMICAL NATURE OF GENES

One type of pneumonia in man is caused by the bacterium **pneumococcus** (nyoo·mo·кок·us). The cells of some strains of pneu-

mococcus are surrounded by a capsule. These strains are the ones that cause pneumonia. The capsule protects the bacterial cells from being engulfed by white blood cells (Chapter 22). Other strains of pneumococcus do not have a capsule. These can be destroyed by the white blood cells.

With rare exceptions, the cells with capsules divide, and their daughter cells also have capsules. Similarly, the descendants of cells lacking capsules also lack capsules. The presence or absence of capsules, therefore, can be said to be inherited.

Transformation in Pneumococcus

In 1928, an investigator named F. Griffith inoculated mice with a pneumococcus strain that does not develop capsules. Ordinarily, this would not have harmed the mice. But at the same time, Griffith inoculated them with dead pneumococcus of the sort that does make capsules. In a short time the mice were dead or dying. Griffith examined their blood and made cultures of the pneumococcus present; he found live pneumococcus that *had capsules!* What could have happened?

Sixteen years later, in hope of finding an explanation for Griffith's discovery, investigators carried out new experiments. First, they made an extract of pneumococcus cells that had capsules. The extract, of course, did not contain any living cells. Second, they mixed this extract with pneumococcus cells lacking capsules. A small proportion of the bacteria then began to form capsules (Figure 32-1). This means that cells previously unable to form capsules had been transformed into cells that could form capsules. Something in the extract evidently caused the transformation.

Once a cell has been transformed, the new ability is inherited. Thus, the descendants of the transformed cells continued to form capsules; an extract, devoid of living organisms, had altered their heredity. What is this transforming principle?

32-1 TRANSFORMATION IN PNEUMOCOCCUS

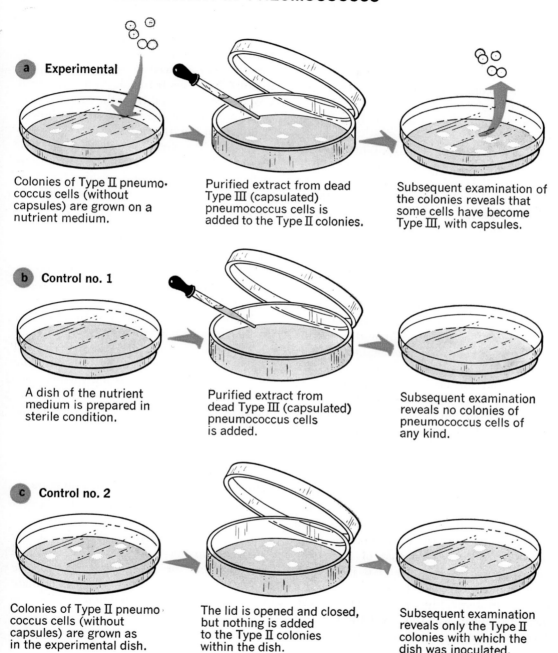

a **Experimental**

Colonies of Type II pneumo-coccus cells (without capsules) are grown on a nutrient medium.

Purified extract from dead Type III (capsulated) pneumococcus cells is added to the Type II colonies.

Subsequent examination of the colonies reveals that some cells have become Type III, with capsules.

b **Control no. 1**

A dish of the nutrient medium is prepared in sterile condition.

Purified extract from dead Type III (capsulated) pneumococcus cells is added.

Subsequent examination reveals no colonies of pneumococcus cells of any kind.

c **Control no. 2**

Colonies of Type II pneumo-coccus cells (without capsules) are grown as in the experimental dish.

The lid is opened and closed, but nothing is added to the Type II colonies within the dish.

Subsequent examination reveals only the Type II colonies with which the dish was inoculated.

Conclusion: Genetic transformation of Type II pneumococcus cells into Type III pneumococcus cells has occurred.

After much very careful preliminary work, O. T. Avery, C. M. MacLeod, and M. McCarty, of the Rockefeller Institute for Medical Research, New York City, discovered that this active principle is *deoxyribonucleic acid*. We should be fairly familiar with this compound by now (see pages 115, 136, and 146).

The DNA in the extract was from pneumococcus cells having capsules. This DNA had been responsible for the ability of these cells to make capsules. When this DNA was extracted and placed in contact with the capsuleless bacteria, it entered them. This foreign DNA actually became part of the hereditary mechanism of capsuleless cells. From then on, cells previously unable to form capsules could do so.

This experiment is of enormous importance. It shows that hereditary elements—genes—can be extracted from one organism and be made to enter another. But even more important, it shows that the gene is DNA. The genes, of tremendous importance in the life of the cell, organism, and species, had now been identified chemically.

Further work showed that this kind of transformation can occur in many varieties of bacteria, for a number of traits.

The Hereditary Substances of Viruses

Certain viruses, called bacteriophages, attack bacteria. When they do so, they commandeer the chemical processes of the bacteria, and divert these processes from their normal activity of producing more bacterial substances to that of producing new virus particles (Figure 9-6, page 187).

A virus consists of a core of DNA and a coat of protein (Figure 9-4). The experimental problem was this: Is it the DNA of a virus, the protein of its coat, or both that enter a bacterium and act to control the chemical activity of the bacterium?

Alfred Hershey and Martha Chase, working at Cold Spring Harbor, New York, "labeled" a bacteriophage with isotopes of sulfur and phosphorus in two separate experiments. The radioactive sulfur was incorporated into the protein coats of the virus particles; the radioactive phosphorus was incorporated into their DNA. After the viruses were allowed to infect bacteria, the mixture was centrifuged, and the virus coats were separated from the infected bacteria. Analyses of the two fractions showed that almost all the radioactive sulfur remained in the virus coats and never entered the bacteria, while all the phosphorus radioactivity was found inside the bacterial cells. This was conclusive evidence, then, that it is only the DNA of a virus that enters a host cell and commandeers the materials of the bacterium to make more virus DNA and protein. The conclusion was that DNA carries the genetic instructions on how to make more viruses, thus *is* the genetic material of the virus.

There is other evidence pointing to DNA as the substance of inheritance. In fact, all the evidence so far accumulated, for all organisms from bacteria and viruses to the most complicated animals and plants, supports the view that the hereditary instructions in the cell are carried in the nucleic acid molecules. In most instances the hereditary nucleic acid is DNA, but in a few viruses it is RNA.

The Parts of a Nucleic Acid Molecule

The nucleic acids are among the largest of all molecules found in living organisms, and yet they are composed of just a few kinds of smaller molecules. First, we find a compound of phosphorus, *phosphoric acid*, which is usually called phosphate when in chemical combination.

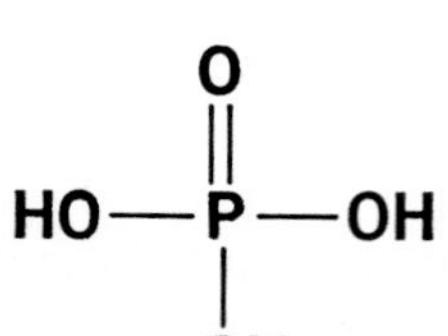

Phosphoric acid

We also find a form of the 5-carbon sugar ribose. Ribose itself, the structure of which is drawn in the form of a ring, has a hydrogen (H) atom and a hydroxyl group (OH) attached to the No. 2 carbon. (Chemists assign numbers to the carbon atoms in a molecule in order to describe related compounds accurately.)

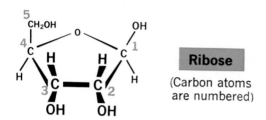

Ribose

(Carbon atoms are numbered)

Another form of ribose has a hydrogen (H) atom *instead* of the hydroxyl group (OH) at the No. 2 carbon. One oxygen atom is therefore missing (compared to ribose), and this molecule is therefore called "de-oxy-ribose," or *deoxyribose.*

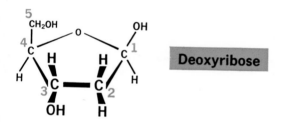

Deoxyribose

The nucleic acid containing ribose is RNA, while the nucleic acid with one fewer oxygen atoms in the ribose is DNA (the "D" stands for deoxyribose, in which the final –se is dropped when the name is combined with *nucleic acid,* so that we get the name with which we are familiar, *de-oxyribonucleic acid*).

The two other kinds of molecules we find in nucleic acids are also ring compounds. One of these kinds is a type of **pyrimidine** (pih·RIM·ih·deen), while the other is a type of **purine** (PYOOR·een). A pyrimidine has a basic skeleton of four carbon and two nitrogen atoms in a ring:

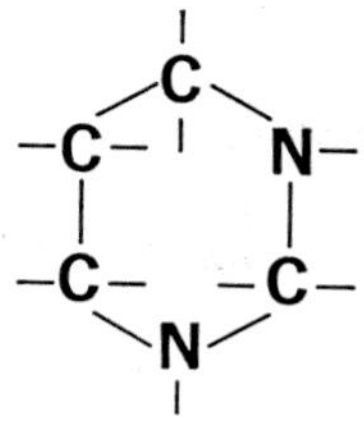

Pyrimidine "skeleton"

The free chemical bonds may attach various atoms and chemical groups, as you will see later.

Purine compounds have a basic skeleton that is actually a double ring of carbon and nitrogen atoms, as shown:

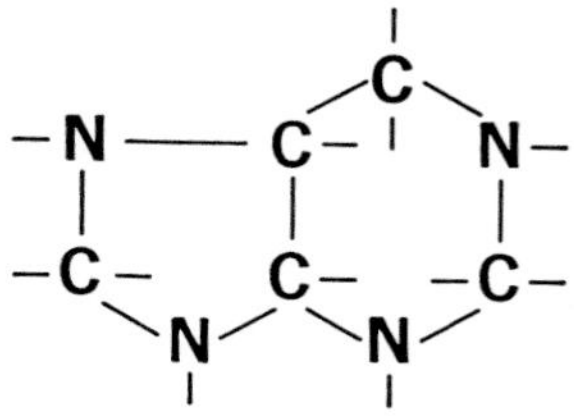

Purine "skeleton"

The types of purines and pyrimidines that we find in DNA, for instance, are diagramed in Figures 32-2 and 32-3.

If one of these purines or pyrimidines becomes attached to a sugar (ribose or deoxyribose), and the sugar in turn becomes attached to phosphoric acid, then the new molecule, made of these *three parts,* is called a **nucleotide** (NEW·kle·o·tyd). Only

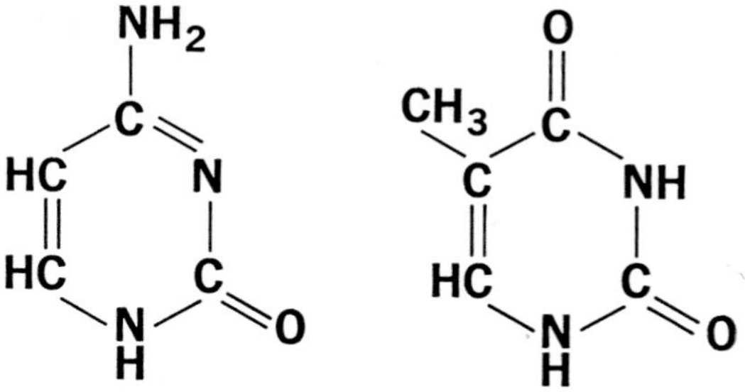

Cytosine

Thymine

32-2 Cytosine and thymine, the two types of pyrimidines that are found in DNA.

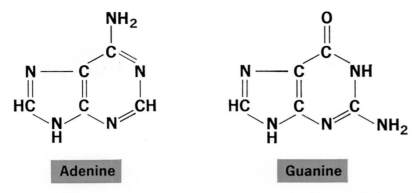

Adenine   **Guanine**

32-3 Adenine and guanine, the two types of purines found in DNA. These two compounds, and the pyrimidines of Figure 32-2, form parts of nucleotides (see Figure 32-4).

a few kinds of nucleotides are possible. One of them is diagramed in Figure 32-4. This single molecule is made by bonding together one molecule each of adenine (AD-e-neen), deoxyribose, and phosphoric acid. We call it an **adenine nucleotide.**

There are only three other nucleotides formed from the components found in DNA. All four of these nuleotides are very similar—*they differ only in the kind of purine or pyrimidine they contain.* This fact is important to understand. It provides the

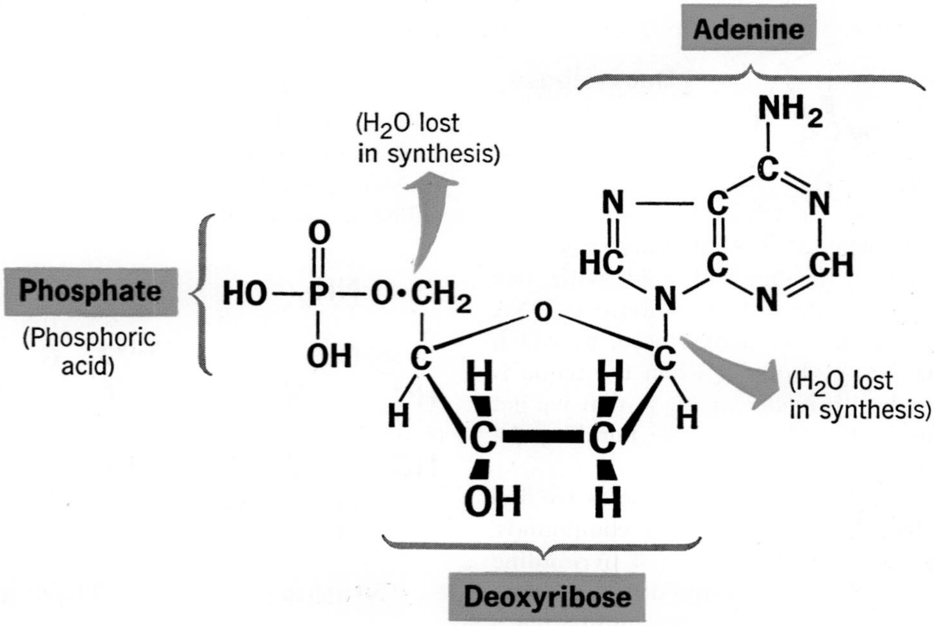

Adenine

(H₂O lost in synthesis)

NH₂

Phosphate

(Phosphoric acid)

HO—P—O·CH₂

(H₂O lost in synthesis)

Deoxyribose

32-4 A diagram of a nucleotide containing adenine. This and three other kinds of nucleotides (with guanine, cytosine, and thymine, respectively) are the components of DNA.

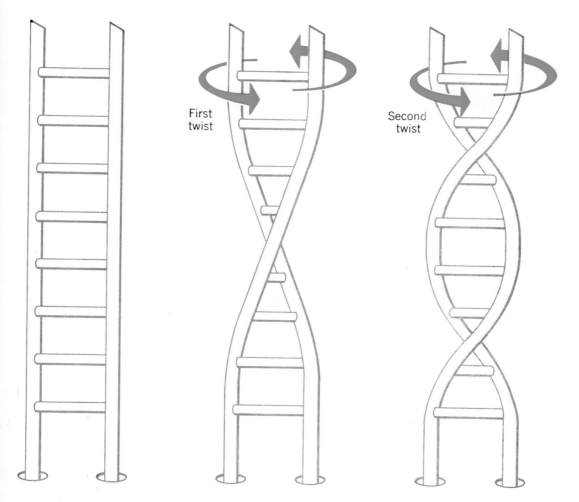

32-5 A symbolic representation of the shape of a small part of a DNA molecule. Visualized as a flexible ladder, the molecular fragment assumes its shape with two twists.

basis for one of the most impressive biological theories advanced in years.

The chemical constituents of DNA were known before 1900. But not until 1953, when J. D. Watson and F. H. C. Crick arrived at a plausible scheme of arrangement for these constituents, was a satisfactory "model" of a DNA molecule presented. By "model" we mean a hypothetical construction based upon the available experimental evidence. It is used to help visualize data that previously were not well correlated. It also serves to suggest further investigations on the general problem it illuminates.

Watson and Crick, working at Cambridge University, in England, used evidence gained by studying the DNA molecule with *X rays*. This kind of study (called X-ray diffraction) suggests something about the *shape* of the molecule (Figure 32-5). A leader in this work with X rays was M. H. F. Wilkins, who shared with Watson and Crick a 1962 Nobel prize for elucidating the structure of DNA.

Key to symbols for
the four nucleotides:

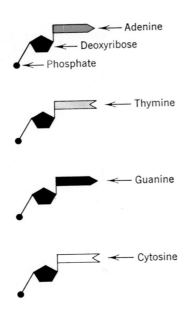

← Adenine
← Deoxyribose
← Phosphate

← Thymine

← Guanine

← Cytosine

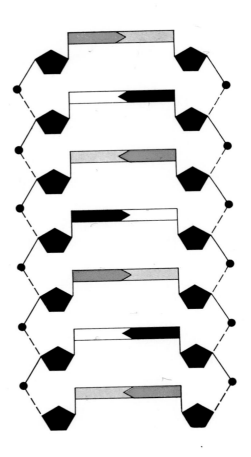

32-6 Another symbolic representation of a small part of a DNA molecule, unwound for ease of study. The ladder of Figure 32-5 has been converted to a nucleotide ladder. (The dash lines represent bonds between the individual nucleotides.)

Watson and Crick also used the evidence that, in all kinds of DNA, the amount of *adenine* present is the same as the amount of *thymine* (THY-meen) present. Similarly, the amount of *guanine* (GWAH-neen) always equals that of *cytosine* (SY-toh-seen). This information suggests a constant relationship between nucleotides containing adenine and those containing thymine, and between nucleotides containing guanine and those containing cytosine.

The Watson-Crick Model of DNA

Taking into account all the facts known at the time, Watson and Crick proposed the following model for the structure of DNA.

The X-ray analysis strongly suggests that the DNA molecule consists of two strands twisted about one another in the form of a *double helix* (HEE-lix). (A helix is a coil like a wire spring; in technical terms, a spiral, often confused with a helix, is flat.) A double helix can best be pictured by imagining a ladder as shown in Figure 32-5.

Now let us unwind our ladder and take a closer look at its parts, to see what it is made of. In Figure 32-6, the key shows us that the uprights of such a ladder are made entirely of the phosphate and ribose portions of the nucleotides. The "rungs" are made only of the purines and pyrimidines. Each rung consists of a purine matched with a pyrimidine. Adenine is always paired with thymine; guanine is always paired with cytosine. Each rung has a weak spot right in the middle where each purine is attached to its pyrimidine partner.

Along one side of the ladder, the nucleotides are arranged in any order, and are repeated as often as desired. But once that order is established, the other strand or side of the ladder is also determined: an adenine nucleotide must *always* pair with a thymine nucleotide, according to the model, and a guanine nucleotide must *always* pair with a cytosine nucleotide. Notice, too, that the uprights of the ladder, the backbone of the molecule, are nowhere any different from anywhere else. The uprights are simply an almost endless repetition of: . . . sugar-phosphate-sugar-phosphate. . . . The *distinctive* part of each DNA molecule lies in the center, where the particular sequence of purine and pyrimidine groups along a sugar-phosphate strand forms a code, like a language in which all the words are made up of the same four letters.

According to the Watson-Crick model, then, the DNA molecule is made of two strands wound about one another. Each strand is believed to be made up of a chain of nucleotides. The phosphate groups link the nucleotides together. Each phosphate serves as a link between two deoxyribose groups; and a purine or pyrimidine is attached to each deoxyribose. The two strands are held together by weak bonds between each purine and its partner pyrimidine. Even though each of these bonds is weak, there may be 20,000 such purine-pyrimidine pairs holding the two strands together in a single DNA molecule; so the total force of these weak bonds holds the two strands quite firmly together. Figure 32-7 shows how a small part of such a molecule looks when the individual atoms are represented by spheres. It also shows the ladder structure and the various parts of the nucleotides.

Joseph Morsello for the Franklin Inst.

32-7 A model of a small part of a DNA molecule, with the individual atoms of the nucleotides represented by spheres.

The Self-duplication of DNA

From careful measurements we know that both the chemical nature and the total amount of DNA in similar kinds of cells remain constant from generation to generation. This means that both the *quantity* and the *quality* of the DNA must remain the same in cells derived from the same parent cells. Our theory for the duplication of DNA molecules must therefore account for *both* of these requirements. The puzzle is this: How can we get two identical DNA

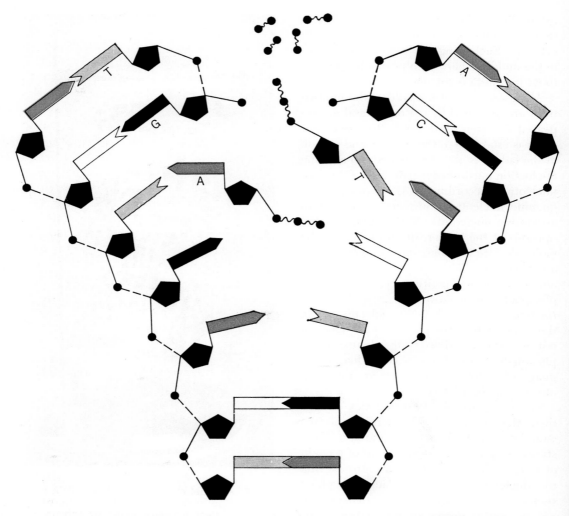

32-8 A diagram of replication of DNA, shown again as a nucleotide ladder (see Figure 32-6). The two strands of the DNA molecule begin to "unzip," and new nucleotides of the proper kind fall into place. Each new nucleotide initially has *three* phosphate groups and two high-energy bonds. The extra phosphate groups are split off, and the energy derived from a broken high-energy bond in each nucleotide is used in bonding the individual nucleotides to one another in the two new sequences.

molecules, each one a double helix, if we must start with only one such molecule that contains its distinctive part virtually hidden away in the center?

It is very hard to imagine how it can happen unless first the two coils of the DNA molecule somehow come apart. Suppose the weak forces that hold together the dou-

ble helix of DNA are released, starting from one end like a zipper. One by one, each purine separates from its pyrimidine partner. Each separation leaves an unmatched purine and pyrimidine, which can be "satisfied," or complemented, only by the addition of the proper partner of the same kind as before. This process is shown in Figure 32-8. An adenine group makes a new bond only with a new thymine group, and a guanine is complemented only by a cytosine. In the cell's storehouse of raw materials, there are a variety of nucleotides, each like ATP with *three* phosphate groups and two high-energy bonds. *A new* nucleotide of the proper kind falls into place. Thymine bonds to an adenine nucleotide in the complementary matching of the pairs; and cytosine bonds to a guanine nucleotide.

Little by little the double spiral "unzips" along its length, and new nucleotides of the proper kind—the only kind able to make the proper bonding—are added to the separated chains (Figure 32-8). The extra phosphate groups on the nucleotides being added are split off, and the energy of the high-energy bond is used in attaching the sugar group of one nucleotide to the phosphate group of the next nucleotide. Thus a new upright is supplied for each ladder.

By the time the end of the spiral has been reached, the two *original* strands of the DNA have separated. Each original strand has replaced the nucleotide partners it has lost with new partners (complements) of exactly the same kind (Figure 32-9), and the new nucleotides are bonded together.

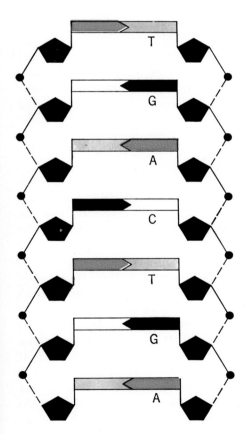
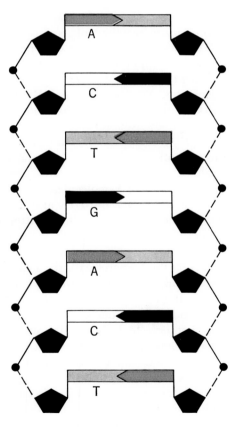

32-9 The replication process of Figure 32-8 has now been completed. The new nucleotide sequences are labeled here and in Figure 32-8 with the letters of their purine (*A* and *G*) and pyrimidine (*C* and *T*) components. How do the two new fragments of DNA molecules compare with the original in Figure 32-6?

Now we come to the test of the model and the hypothesis. We have formed *two* double strands where we had but *one* before. Look very carefully at both of these new molecules (Figure 32-9) to see if they are *exactly* like the original molecule (Figure 32-6). If we compare the new products with the original, we see that indeed we have been able to manufacture two *exact copies* of the original, by using the model. Each new DNA molecule is a *replica* of the original; the process of making an exact copy is called **replication.** The model has met its first test: it is able to provide an explanation of how a huge, complicated molecule can be copied exactly. If this is indeed the mechanism a cell uses, every descendant cell gets an *exact* copy of the hereditary instructions of its parent cell.

The best evidence that this really happens was supplied by a very ingenious experiment reported in 1958 by two young Americans, M. Meselson and F. W. Stahl, working at the California Institute of Technology. They used a *heavy* isotope of nitrogen (N^{15}) to repeatedly label the nucleotides synthesized by a bacteria culture while it was reproducing and, therefore, making new DNA molecules. You will recall that there are nitrogen atoms in both the purines and pyrimidines. After many generations, the bacterial DNA was heavier than normal, and this was possible to measure. Next the bacteria with the heavy DNA were supplied with ordinary nitrogen (N^{14}), from which they synthesized their nucleotides. After one cell division, all the new bacteria had DNA that was exactly intermediate in weight between the heavy DNA and ordinary DNA! Each new strand of DNA that was made in the replication process therefore must have been "light"; and each new molecule of DNA must have consisted of a double helix made up of one light strand and one heavy strand. In the next cell division half the bacteria had one heavy and one light strand; and half had

two light strands. This is exactly what the model of the DNA molecule and its replication predicted.

In Figures 32-6, 32-8, and 32-9, let us assume that the original strands have purines and pyrimidines with heavy nitrogen in them. The new strands that are made are labeled A, G, C, T, etc., in Figures 32-8 and 32-9. Let us assume that these new strands have light nitrogen in them. See if you can make a diagram to represent the results found by Meselson and Stahl in the next cell division. Start with one half of the diagram of Figure 32-9, and remember to use light-weight (labeled) nucleotides as raw material for the replication.

HOW GENES ACT

It would do little good to have an exact copy of the DNA of the parent cell, however, if the DNA did not possess some means of transmitting instructions that guide and control the development of the offspring cells. How does the gene act? What does the gene *do* in the cell that its effects are so far-reaching?

Let us raise a typical problem about gene action. If a person inherits from his parents a pair of genes for brown eyes, how do these genes *act* to make eyes brown? The pigment is certainly very complex from a biochemical standpoint. Somehow the genes in the iris cells of the eye are able to organize the chemicals that form dark pigment, which in turn is deposited in a particular concentration; the result is brown iris color. It is reasonable to assume that different pairs of eye-color genes might start with the same store of materials, and yet the person might end up with lighter brown or darker brown eyes, or even green eyes splotched with brown, depending upon the concentration and distribution of pigment. Blue eyes do not contain a blue pigment; the iris appears blue because longer wavelengths of light are absorbed and shorter wavelengths are reflected back from the framework of the iris.

We are faced with an additional problem. The genes for brown eyes are transmitted through the sperm and egg cells. The zygote develops into a complex organism by growth and differentiation. But the eyes do not attain their final form until rather late in development. The genes that determine eye color are faithfully transmitted, through each mitosis, until they perform their specific function in the cells of the eye. They are also transmitted to all the other cells of the body, including those that give rise to the reproductive cells for the next generation. Yet they make brown pigment only in the iris of the eye.

How many chemical steps are there in the production of a complex pigment molecule? No one is certain. There may be many steps involved, or only a few. If we can succeed in finding out the primary effect of each gene, we will have learned a great deal about how genes act.

The Two Roles of a Gene

Clearly, every gene has *two* roles to play. First, genes pass on replicas of themselves, like carbon copies, to all cells that descend from the original fertilized egg. This is the process of *replication* of DNA and is certainly one essential activity of genes.

Second, the genes control, by their *actions*, each and every step of an organism's development, from the first effects in the zygote, through the development of the embryo or seedling, to the full functioning of the adult. If this were not so, offspring would not resemble their parents as closely as they do in structure, function, and behavior. The control of cell activity is the second essential role of genes.

We have already discussed the process of gene replication. Now we want to look more closely at the problem of gene action. There are at least two ways of trying to discover how genes act:

1. We could study the embryonic development of individuals that have different genotypes. By studying earlier and earlier stages we could locate the point at which their development begins to diverge. This tells us what the first *visible* beginning of their difference is. For example, an animal with the hypothetical genotype PP might develop an extra finger or toe when the digits begin to differentiate, while one with genotype pp would not. This kind of study tells us *when* a certain difference first becomes visible. But a visible change is almost certainly preceded by nonvisible chemical differences.

2. Another possible approach is to investigate the way genes act in individual cells, either in very early stages of development or in organisms with very simple structures. We might try to discover if there are *biochemical* differences when a certain allele is present or absent in the gene complex of the nucleus. Thus we may have a chance to detect more *directly* the effects of the gene being studied.

Both of these approaches, taken together, are necessary to give us the full story of gene action.

Gene Action in *Neurospora*

Perhaps you can see how difficult it is to trace the actions of a gene that functions in a large and complex organism. In microorganisms it is easier to obtain information about gene action at the cellular level. The salmon-pink bread mold *Neurospora* (nyoo·ROS·po·ra) has been widely used for such studies (Figure 12-10, page 241). This mold grows luxuriantly in a test tube containing only a dilute mixture of salts, some table sugar, and one vitamin (biotin).

If we analyze this mold chemically, we find that the mature organism consists of a

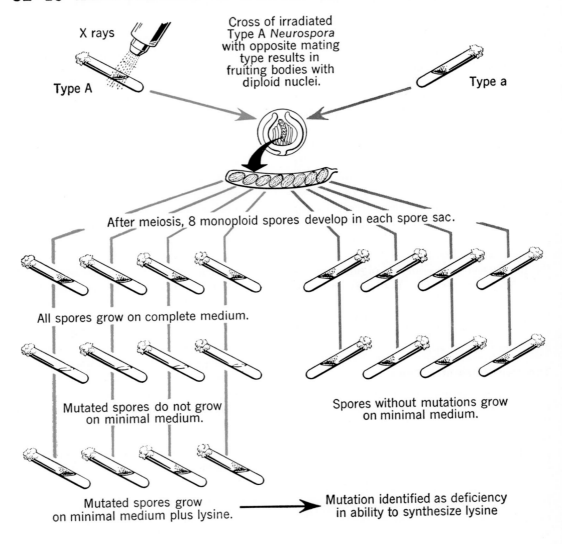

X rays

Type A

Cross of irradiated Type A *Neurospora* with opposite mating type results in fruiting bodies with diploid nuclei.

Type a

After meiosis, 8 monoploid spores develop in each spore sac.

All spores grow on complete medium.

Mutated spores do not grow on minimal medium.

Spores without mutations grow on minimal medium.

Mutated spores grow on minimal medium plus lysine.

Mutation identified as deficiency in ability to synthesize lysine

whole range of complex proteins (with their constituent amino acids), carbohydrates, and fats, a large number of vitamins, nucleic acid components, pigment, and so on. The mold evidently synthesizes for itself, from the simple raw materials in the test tube, a large number of very complex chemical compounds. Furthermore, these compounds are put together in a particular way, for each individual mold organism closely resembles in its chemical abilities the parent mold that originally supplied the spores.

The important thing is that while microorganisms such as *Neurospora* do not appear to be very complicated structurally, they are obviously very complex (and very competent) biochemically. The situation is very different in man. Man has a very complicated structure, but his nutritional requirements are also very extensive: a whole battery of necessary carbohydrates, amino acids, fats, vitamins, and salts must be taken in continuously. It appears that over a very long period, the organisms that have led to the evolution of man have lost the ability to synthesize a great many essential substances—an ability that microorganisms still possess.

In the 1940's we learned that microorganisms may also lose some of their synthesizing abilities—by mutation. G. W. Beadle and E. L. Tatum at Stanford University, California, treated spores of *Neurospora* with X rays or ultraviolet rays and tested the treated spores to determine if they had been changed in any way. Beadle and Tatum were particularly interested to see if any of the abilities of the mold to synthesize complex organic substances had been impaired.

They found that some spores cannot grow at all on the usual medium. These spores can survive, however, if nutritional supplements, such as amino acids and vitamins, are added to the medium. Beadle and Tatum worked out a technique in which a "minimal" medium (consisting only of salts, sugar, and biotin) was supplemented by a whole collection of vitamins and amino acids to make a "complete" medium. Of course, spores with genes that have not been affected by radiation can germinate and develop on a minimal medium. But spores with genes that have been changed by the radiation cannot—they have to be supplied with additional nutrients that they no longer make for themselves.

Over a period of time, Beadle and Tatum found that virtually every substance normally synthesized by the mold is subject to genetic control. The gene or genes responsible for any particular biochemical synthesis of a substance can be damaged (made nonfunctional) by radiation. Figure 32-10 diagrams a typical experiment with *Neurospora.*

Beadle and Tatum found some mutations that seemed to affect closely related steps in a "chain" of chemical syntheses. We might designate the compounds synthesized in one such series of steps as O, C, and A, for the time being. (As the story unfolds you will learn that these letters refer to specific substances.) Careful experiments revealed that:

Mutant #1 would grow if either O, C, or A was added to the minimal medium

Mutant #2 would grow if either C or A was added to the minimal medium

Mutant #3 would grow *only* if A was added to the minimal medium

(Note that compound A is needed for growth.)

Various explanations for these observations are possible. Certainly the compounds must have some relationship to one another. One hypothesis might be that mutant 1 actually has not one but three mutated genes—one that controls the synthesis of O, another C, and the third A. A second hypothesis might be that a single gene is responsible for the synthesis of three substances at once. The hypothesis suggested by Beadle and Tatum (on the basis of Beadle's earlier studies with the fruit fly) was that each mutation is of a single gene that controls *one step* in the synthesis of a particular kind of molecule.

We might diagram such a chain of reactions as follows:

Some prior substance → (Gene 1) → O → (Gene 2) → C → (Gene 3) → A

This diagram suggests that gene 1 functions by converting some prior substance into O; gene 2 by converting O into C; and gene 3, in turn, acts by converting C into A.

If gene 1 were damaged by X rays, then the mold could no longer grow, unless its normal function of making O were compensated for. This could be done by adding the product that gene 1 usually provides. In other words, normal growth would occur if we were to add some O to the minimal medium. But note that we could also take care of this deficiency by adding either C or A—we would just be supplying the compound in a somewhat more advanced stage of synthesis, and thus would bypass the normal functions of genes 2 and 3.

If gene 3 mutates, however, we cannot fill this deficiency by adding the prior substances O or C. Gene 3 is responsible for converting C to A, and we have no alternative except to add A to the medium. By reasoning like this, we can arrange a series of chemical steps in the proper order. We simply have to know what supplementary substances added to the minimal medium will permit the mutated mold to grow.

Genes and Enzymes

From studies such as this we can learn about the *kinds* of biochemical reactions that genes normally control. It turns out that these are very often the reactions that, in living cells, take place only because specific *enzymes* are present to catalyze the reaction. Enough evidence has now accumulated to suggest strongly that genes often—perhaps always—do their work through their effects on enzymes. Both genes and enzymes show unusual specialization of activity (specificity). Perhaps each gene is responsible for the specificity of a particular enzyme.

This relationship between genes and enzymes has been called the "one gene—one enzyme" hypothesis. It has been a very productive idea for suggesting additional experiments to learn more about gene action. George Beadle, now Chancellor of the University of Chicago, shared a part of the 1958 Nobel prize in medicine and physi-

ology with E. L. Tatum for these experiments using *Neurospora* to attack this most important problem of genetics.

In the light of this hypothesis we can refine our earlier diagram a bit to include the role of the enzymes controlled by the genes:

Gene 1	Gene 2	Gene 3
↓	↓	↓
Enzyme 1	Enzyme 2	Enzyme 3

Some prior substance ——↓——→ O ——↓——→ C ——↓——→ A

Is this relationship between genes and enzymes purely hypothetical? You can be quite sure that geneticists and biochemists were soon looking at mutant types of *Neurospora,* and bacteria, and even humans, to see whether a particular enzyme is absent or reduced in activity once the specific biochemical step blocked by a mutation had been identified. Many cases were found.

For example, in humans there is a special type of low grade mentality (a form of idiocy) caused by the failure to convert the amino acid phenylalanine (fen·il·AL·ih·neen) into the similar amino acid tyrosine (TY·ro·seen). Only a single biochemical step seems necessary for this conversion. The mental defect is known to be inherited as a simple recessive trait, so there is a difference of only one allele between these idiots and persons whose development is normal. The enzyme responsible for the conversion of phenylalanine to tyrosine was identified in the liver. The final proof of the gene-enzyme relationship was the discovery that this enzyme is absent in the liver tissue of persons so affected by idiocy.

We can get an even clearer idea of what genes do by looking in detail at the compounds O, C, and A, which we used in our theoretical discussion (page 561). Actually, these letters stand for three amino acids that are very similar to one another—ornithine, citrulline, and arginine (see page 425). Let us now substitute the actual chemical structures of these three molecules for their abbreviations (Figure 32-11). It is easy to see that the three molecules all have the same basic structure, except for the group of atoms outlined in the dotted boxes. Unless we know precisely what molecule has preceded ornithine in the synthesis, we cannot be sure just what enzyme 1 has done. Enzyme 2, however, quite clearly catalyzes the addition of four atoms to the molecule of ornithine: one each of carbon, oxygen, nitrogen, and hydrogen, in a particular arrangement. Or, to put it in another, more informative way, it has substituted a urea group—$CO(NH_2)_2$ *less* one hydrogen atom—for an amino group, NH_2. Enzyme 3, in turn, acts to replace the atom of oxygen with a nitrogen and a hydrogen atom.

From this example, we see that one way in which genes act is to control enzymes, which make possible the addition or removal of *specific groups of atoms* from molecules that participate in the essential life activities of plants and animals. The series of compounds—ornithine, citrulline, and arginine—whose story has been worked out in *Neurospora*, also occurs in many other species, including man. The compounds are now known to be synthesized by the same steps, too. We have thus actually gained a greater understanding of man's biochemistry by studying that of a mold!

Gene Action in Man

Another valuable clue to how genes actually function on the cellular level comes from the work of Vernon Ingram and his associates, working at Cambridge University in England. There is a defect in man, sickle-cell anemia, that is inherited as a simple recessive trait. In affected persons the red blood cells become distorted (shaped like sickles) when the oxygen concentration is low. The red color of red blood cells is due to the oxygen-carrying pigment hemoglobin, which is a protein.

When we study the chemical structure of hemoglobin in normal individuals and in those with the sickle-cell trait, we find that there is a slight chemical difference between the two kinds of hemoglobin. Now if we could identify this chemical difference, we would know exactly what role the mutant gene must play in the manufacture of the hemoglobin molecule.

The hemoglobin molecule is made up of two halves, each of which contains about 4,000 atoms, arranged in some 300 amino acids of 19 different kinds. Ingram's goal was to break this molecule down, bit by bit, until he could detect the difference in amino acid units between normal hemoglobin and sickle-cell hemoglobin.

This careful work showed that the half-molecule of sickle-cell hemoglobin differs in only *one amino acid* from normal hemoglobin. At one place in the chain of amino acids, glutamic acid is replaced by **valine** (VAY·leen), an amino acid essential to many proteins, including hemoglobin, but disadvantageous at this particular spot.

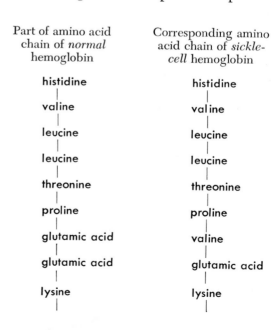

Part of amino acid chain of *normal* hemoglobin	Corresponding amino acid chain of *sickle-cell* hemoglobin
histidine	histidine
valine	valine
leucine	leucine
leucine	leucine
threonine	threonine
proline	proline
glutamic acid	valine
glutamic acid	glutamic acid
lysine	lysine

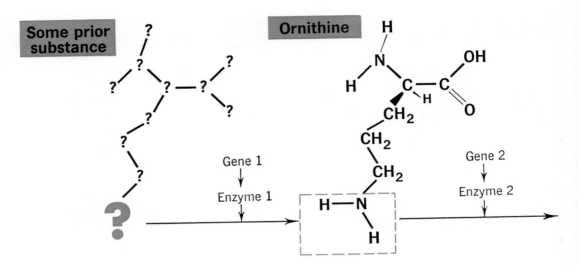

32-11 A diagram of the gene-enzyme relationship for the series of steps by which ornithine, citrulline, and arginine are formed, in succession, in the pink bread mold *Neurospora*. The same steps occur in the liver of man, as part of the ornithine cycle leading to the formation and excretion of urea (Figure 24-4, page 425).

The evidence is clear that the mutant, or changed, allele responsible for the sickling of the red blood cells causes a valine unit to be substituted for a glutamic acid unit at one point in the molecule. Only one amino acid unit among three hundred is affected by the altered gene. This discovery suggests that a gene mutation is able to change a single unit of a very large molecule without altering the rest of the molecule at all. We also know something else, perhaps just as important: the substitution of a single amino acid unit in the normal hemoglobin molecule can have a profound effect on the blood cells of an individual with this hereditary trait.

We have come very close to learning what a single gene may do. Again, a gene seems to determine the *unique structure* of a molecule, or of one part of a molecule. Have protein differences between individuals and species arisen by mutations of single genes that have gradually resulted in modifications of distinctive protein molecules, amino acid by amino acid?

THE ROLE OF DNA AND RNA

By now we have a picture of the close relationship that must exist among genes, the enzymes they control, and the chemical molecules that are affected by enzyme action. More questions naturally arise in our minds. How does the gene exert its control over the enzyme? How does a change (mutation) in a bit of DNA in the nucleus bring about the insertion of a different amino acid at one particular place in a protein molecule?

Recent experiments have thrown considerable light on the problem. We believe that the genes themselves do not act directly in the multitude of chemical reactions that take place in the cell. There is a fairly simple reason for thinking this: the genes are located within the nucleus of the cell, while many of the cell activities occur in the cytoplasm. The gene must therefore act indirectly in most instances.

What is the link between the "boss" genes in the nucleus and the "worker" enzymes in

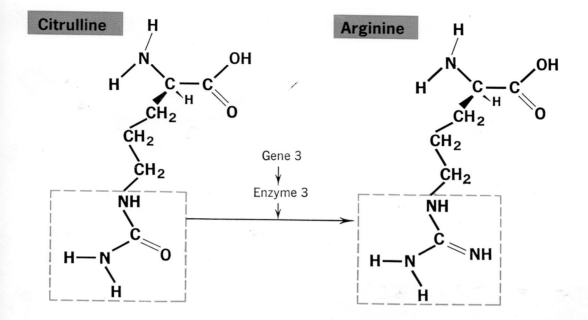

Citrulline | Arginine

Gene 3
↓
Enzyme 3

the cytoplasm? Recent studies provide very strong evidence that the "messenger" that carries the instructions of the genes to the synthesis of proteins (and, therefore, of enzymes) in the cytoplasm is none other than RNA. While the relative distribution of DNA and RNA differs from cell to cell and from organ to organ, we generally find large amounts of RNA in the cytoplasm as well as some in the nucleus. As a rule, about 90 percent of a cell's RNA is found in the cytoplasm.

You will remember that RNA has much in common with DNA: both are made up of nucleotides. The primary differences are that the sugar of RNA is *ribose* instead of *deoxyribose*, and thymine is not present in RNA. Instead of thymine, we find *uracil* (yoo·ra·sil), a pyrimidine very similar to thymine. The two purines and two pyrimidines present in RNA, therefore, are adenine, guanine, cytosine, and uracil. We do not know the details of the structure of RNA, but from what we know of its chemical composition we suspect that it is probably much like DNA.

What do we know about RNA? Besides the fact that we find RNA in all cells, we know that there is more in some cells than in others. Cells with the most RNA actively engage in protein synthesis. Pancreas and liver cells, for example, synthesize large quantities of proteins; and in these cells we find large amounts of RNA. In the silk gland cells of the silkworm we also find large amounts of RNA, in agreement with the function of those glands, which is to produce a protein, silk! Yet nerve cells contain very large amounts of RNA and perhaps synthesize little protein. Maybe RNA does something else, too.

Where in the cell does protein synthesis actually occur? By using techniques that break down cells into their components, biologists have learned that the small granules of the cytoplasm called *ribosomes* (page 128) contain most of the cellular RNA. These small particles are made up of about half RNA and half protein.

All of our evidence now points to the conclusion that RNA plays an essential role in protein synthesis. Just what kind of inter-

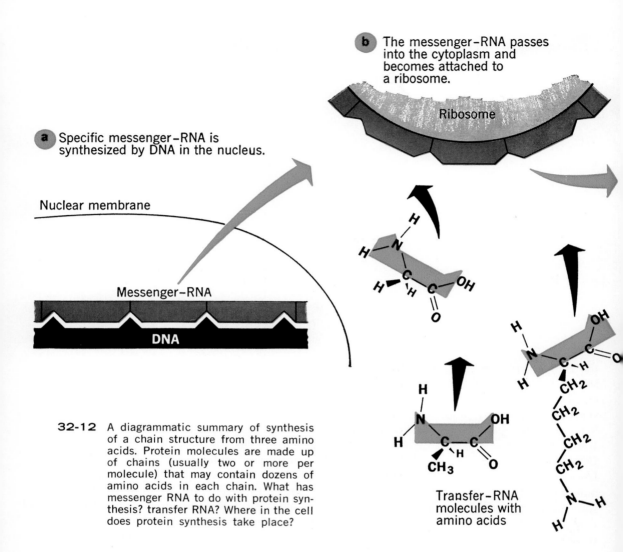

a Specific messenger-RNA is synthesized by DNA in the nucleus.

b The messenger-RNA passes into the cytoplasm and becomes attached to a ribosome.

Ribosome

Nuclear membrane

Messenger-RNA

DNA

Transfer-RNA molecules with amino acids

32-12 A diagrammatic summary of synthesis of a chain structure from three amino acids. Protein molecules are made up of chains (usually two or more per molecule) that may contain dozens of amino acids in each chain. What has messenger RNA to do with protein synthesis? transfer RNA? Where in the cell does protein synthesis take place?

play does seem to take place among genes (DNA), RNA, and protein?

Using a number of different techniques, especially those in which radioactive atoms are incorporated into molecules, it is possible to trace the main steps of protein synthesis (Figure 32-12):

1. The gene in the nucleus, probably a portion of a DNA molecule, controls the synthesis of specific RNA that is *complementary* to the DNA. In other words, DNA serves somewhat as a template, or mold, for the formation of

RNA; this RNA is thus a reverse copy of its DNA template.

2. This RNA, which is known as **messenger RNA,** passes into the cytoplasm and becomes associated with the ribosomes. A particular pattern, or configuration, is produced on the ribosomal surface; in effect the RNA itself now becomes a template for protein synthesis.

3. Other sorts of RNA, already free in the cytoplasm, pick up individual amino acids and carry them to the ribosomes.

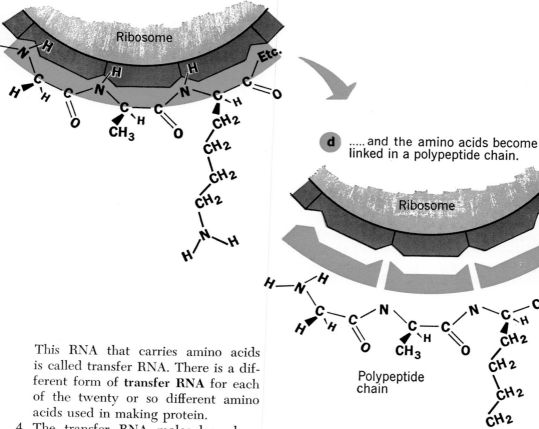

c Specific transfer–RNA molecules with amino acids assume positions on the RNA......

Ribosome

Etc.

CH₃

CH₂

CH₂

CH₂

CH₂

d .....and the amino acids become linked in a polypeptide chain.

Ribosome

Polypeptide chain

CH₃

CH₂

CH₂

CH₂

CH₂

This RNA that carries amino acids is called transfer RNA. There is a different form of **transfer RNA** for each of the twenty or so different amino acids used in making protein.

4. The transfer RNA molecules, along with their amino acids, assume positions on the RNA of the ribosomes in a specific order. This order is determined by the surface pattern (again a sort of template) of the RNA of the ribosomes.

5. The amino acids become linked to one another in a specific order, according to the order of their RNA carriers; thus a new **polypeptide** (pol·ih·PEP·tide) chain, a part of a protein molecule, is synthesized.

6. The transfer RNA molecules are freed, and each one again becomes available for picking up another amino acid of a particular kind.

This series of steps, as summarized in Figure 32-12, leads us to another question: How is the "information" of heredity contained in the DNA molecule? What is the nature of the instructions passed along by the DNA to the messenger RNA?

The Code of Heredity

What are the "letters" in the DNA "alphabet"? The sugar and the phosphate groups are the same in all nucleotides. However, the purines and pyrimidines are different.

They, then, must represent the letters. If so, we have only four letters in our DNA alphabet—the nucleotides of adenine, thymine, cytosine, and guanine. By being able to use these over and over and in a great variety of combinations, the number of arrangements ("words") that could be made is virtually without limit.

As you have already learned, the kinds of substances that are unique for each type of organism are nucleic acids and proteins, especially the enzymes. If the DNA is to determine the *exact nature* of the proteins that are manufactured by a given cell, then the DNA code must be able to determine the *exact order* of the amino acids in cell proteins. This deduction is necessary, since the same twenty or so amino acids are used in synthesizing the proteins of all organisms. Just as the *sequence* of the purines and pyrimidines spells out the individuality of the DNA, so the *exact order* of amino acids in a protein molecule is what makes it individual.

If the information of heredity resides in the *order* of the purines and pyrimidines along the DNA chain, then a particular group of these purines and pyrimidines, perhaps a *triplet*, might specify the insertion of a particular amino acid in a certain place in a protein being synthesized. For example:

This code along one strand of chromosomal DNA . . .	. . . signifies this amino acid in the synthesis of protein
—adenine—adenine—adenine	phenylalanine
—adenine—cytosine—cytosine	glycine
—adenine—cytosine—adenine	valine
—adenine—thymine—adenine	tyrosine

If a given protein in the cell consists of 1,000 amino acids arranged in a particular order, then the code, in which 3 nucleotide units are required for each amino acid specified, would consist of some 3,000 nucleotide units.

You might suppose that this code is purely hypothetical. To "crack the code," and discover the basic secret of heredity, might seem a feat that would take a century or more from the time DNA was first identified as the hereditary material. But science has a way of gathering momentum with each new discovery. More and more able investigators heed the challenge, and rivalry in the quest for the breakthrough becomes keener and keener. The pace of scientific advance is not arithmetic. It is geometric, increasing in each period by some multiple of the knowledge gained in the corresponding period before. Thus, if our knowledge of important biological principles doubled between 1900 and 1915, it doubled again between 1915 and 1930, and doubled again between 1930 and 1945, and doubled again between 1945 and 1960. This makes sixteen times as much significant biological knowledge today as in 1900! You might calculate how much it will very possibly have increased at this rate by the year 2000.

In 1961, less than 10 years after the structure of DNA was established, the hereditary code was cracked. Marshall W. Nirenberg and J. Heinrich Matthaei, working at the National Institutes of Health, made the first break, and almost immediately other teams met the challenge.

It was done in the following way. You will recall that DNA stays always in the chromosomes, while the enzymes and other proteins are synthesized at the ribosomes, out in the cytoplasm. Thus there is not only the problem of the code itself, but also of the transmission of the message from the nucleus to the cytoplasm. What is more natural than to suppose that RNA may act as a messenger, since it is present in the chromosomes and also in the ribosomes in large amounts. Could it be that the DNA code, as purine and pyrimidine sequence, is transferred, in *complementary form*, to new-made RNA molecules—in a manner similar to that by which a DNA molecule replicates itself (pages 555–58)?

Recall that in the double helix of DNA, adenine always couples with thymine, and guanine with cytosine. When DNA replicates, each strand acts as a template for the synthesis of a new partner, or complementary strand. Similarly, it may be that a DNA strand acts as template for the synthesis of a (messenger) RNA strand. In this case, however, instead of adenine coupling with a thymine unit—as in DNA replication—adenine couples with a *uracil* unit. (Remember that RNA contains the pyrimidine uracil instead of thymine.) Suppose that the sequence of purines and pyrimidines in a segment of a DNA strand runs as follows: . . . cytosine, guanine, adenine, thymine, adenine. . . . Then, if our hypothesis is correct, the sequence in a complementary strand of new-made messenger RNA would be: . . . guanine, cytosine, uracil, adenine, uracil. . . . Thus the code (as nucleotide sequence) is transferred, in complementary form, from DNA to messenger RNA.

Nirenberg and Matthaei tried a method first developed by Severo Ochoa of New York University. They made an artificial RNA consisting of nothing but endless repetitions of the *uracil* nucleotide. Then they put this artificial RNA into a medium containing ribosomes from bacteria and a mixture of all the usual amino acids. Surprisingly enough, a polypeptide chain is made from a mixture of this sort, which is entirely without living cells. They examined the polypeptide chain to see what amino acid or acids had been incorporated into it. Only phenylalanine had been used. So the code (using a triplet) for phenylalanine must be . . . U–U–U . . . (meaning Uracil-Uracil-Uracil) in the RNA. If the hypothesis is correct, the U–U–U sequence of RNA would be made by DNA with an adenine sequence of A–A–A. Thus the code word for phenylala-

nine is . . . A–A–A . . . in the DNA. As Ochoa and others joined in the cracking of the code, it seemed more and more likely that the code *is in fact a triplet* of nucleotides, and not some other number of them.

We might compare the DNA molecule with the alphabet of a language. The English language is made up of thousands of words, and yet it has an alphabet of only 26 letters. Such an immense variety of words is possible because of the *number* of letters used in a word, and the *arrangement* of these letters within the word. With no more than the four letters N, O, E, and T—our analogy is to the *four* nucleotides in DNA that may be used in triplets—we can make such words as *net, one, ten, toe, too, ton,* and *not,* as well as many additional "words" that have no meaning in our own language. Four letters can in fact be put together in 64 different triplets, far more than sufficient to code the 20 different amino acids. Already the experiments reveal that several different triplets of the DNA may be used to code the same amino acid.

It is possible to put such words together to form a meaningful message that is communicated from person to person. In an analogous way, it seems that the four nucleotides of chromosomal DNA (or messenger RNA), in various sequences of three's (triplets), "communicate" directions for the synthesis of proteins, especially enzymes. Such a control over protein synthesis thus becomes an indirect control over all the chemical reactions of the cell.

GENES IN DEVELOPMENT

Another question about gene action was raised indirectly in Chapter 29 when we were investigating some of the complicated events of development. The problem is this. As far as we know, every gene is present in every cell of a developing embryo. The orderly replication of DNA in mitosis guarantees that every daughter cell of the original zygote will have a full set of chromosomes with their accompanying genes. How, then, can we account for the fact that different cells become specialized in development to do different things?

This is a question to which we have no clear answer at the moment. The difficulty can be understood from an example. One enzyme, produced by the cells of the stomach lining, is very useful in digesting steak. Another enzyme, produced in the cells of the fingers and toes, helps form the protein keratin (KEHR·a·tin) of the fingernails and toenails. We are quite sure that the genes governing the production of both these enzymes are present in the cells of the stomach lining and in those of the fingers and toes. But we do not understand why it is that one kind of cell forms one sort of enzyme while the other kind of cell forms a different enzyme. If the nuclei are identical, as presumably they are, then perhaps we might look to the cytoplasm of the cells for clues. Perhaps their cytoplasms are *not* identical. Perhaps a gene can act in one sort of cytoplasm but be inactive in another.

The Nucleus-Cytoplasm Team

Possibly the study of simple forms of life, or early developmental stages of higher forms, might throw light on some of the relationships between nucleus and cytoplasm.

An organism that has been very useful in such studies is a large, one-celled alga, *Acetabularia* (as·e·tab·yoo·LAY·rih·a—Figure 32-13). This interesting form grows to a length of 6–9 cm (2–3 inches), a size easy to work with. Let us consider two distinctive species, *A. mediterranea* (med·ih·teh·RAY·ne·a) and *A. crenulata* (kren·yoo·LAY·ta), that inhabit European marine waters. *A. mediterranea* has a cap shaped like an umbrella, atop a long stalk of cytoplasm. The nucleus of the alga is imbedded in the base of the cell. *A. crenulata* looks a good deal like *A. mediterranea*, except that its cap is very irregular in appearance.

Now we can carry out a very simple experiment. The cap is removed from one species and thrown away. Next, the cytoplasmic "stem" is cut off and grafted to the base of an alga of the *other* species (after the second alga has had its own "stem" and cap cut off, and the cap thrown away). In such an experiment a whole new alga forms from the joined pieces. The new organism becomes complete—with cap, "stem," and base. The crucial question is this: Will the newly developed cap resemble the species from which we took the "stem" (cytoplasm), or the one from which we took the base (nucleus)? As it turns out, no matter which species of alga we may use as base or as "stem" of the graft, the cap that eventually regenerates is always characteristic of the species supplying the nucleus. Therefore the nucleus of each grafted cell must have exerted its influence through "alien" cytoplasm in determining the form of the cap. We can conclude, then, that this is evidence for the *nuclear control* of the developmental processes forming a new cap. Here the effect of the nucleus must be transmitted to (and through) the cytoplasm. We have already considered how this might come about—the DNA of the nucleus transmits its instructions by way of RNA molecules, which in turn direct the synthesis of the essential substances necessary for the development of a new cap.

In the *Acetabularia* experiment, which we diagramed in Figure 32-13, the nucleus exerts a strong influence on the development of a cap characteristic of the species supplying the nucleus. Sometimes, however, the cytoplasm places a severe restriction on what the nucleus can bring about. A good example of this is seen in experiments on a certain species of sea urchin, an invertebrate animal whose embryos have been a favorite of experimental embryologists for many years. Sea urchin eggs are easily obtained, and can be fertilized with sperms in pans of seawater in the laboratory. Sea urchins normally produce eggs and sperms during the summer months, when college and university biologists who carry out nearly all such experimental investigations can get away to work in the seashore laboratories.

When a fertilized sea urchin egg has divided into two or four cells, the cells can be separated from one another by shaking them in seawater that lacks calcium ions. Each of the cells continues to develop and becomes, in time, a small but complete sea urchin larva. From this result we conclude that each quarter of the original cytoplasm supplies all the substances and conditions necessary for the development of a complete embryo. Although the nucleus of the zygote undergoes two mitoses before the four cells are separated, each nucleus that results still controls the entire development of the embryo. In this case, the nucleus and cytoplasm of each cell function together as an effective team.

Now contrast this with another experiment on sea urchin eggs (Figure 29-3, page 497). In the first experiment we let the embryos separate along the natural planes of cell division. These run from the top to the bottom of the egg, much like the planes between the sections of an orange. In our second experiment, instead of dividing a sea urchin egg in this way, we cut *across* the axis of an *unfertilized* egg—much as when you cut an orange in two before squeezing it for juice. Now we have two halves of an egg; sometimes the nucleus is located in the upper half and sometimes in the lower half.

Both halves heal, each forming an apparently normal cell. Then we add sea urchin sperms. A sperm will enter each half of the egg cell. If the half has a nucleus, the half will be diploid. If the half is without a nucleus, then it will have only the monoploid number of chromosomes contributed by the sperm. Both halves proceed to develop, but development does not continue normally (control experiments show that the abnormalities are not due to chromosome num-

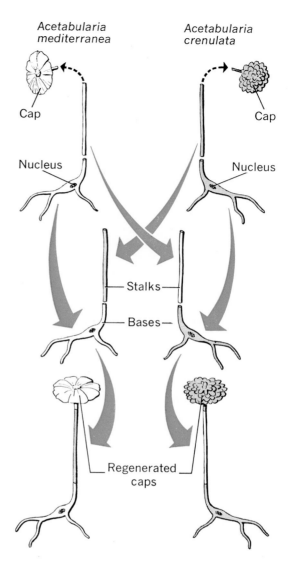

32-13 Evidence of nuclear control of the "cap" structure in two species of *Acetabularia*. Can you suggest variations upon this experiment, to confirm or to further investigate the findings?

ber). Typically, the *upper* half develops into a hollow ball of cells with many cilia, but it forms no internal tissues. It swims around for several days and then dies. The *lower* half too is very abnormal and incomplete, and dies before long. Neither of the half "embryos," then, is able to develop into a normal embryo, or even to survive for long with its abnormalities.

What conclusions can we draw by comparing the two experiments? Apparently the cytoplasm of the sea urchin egg, even before fertilization, is organized along an axis running from the top to the bottom of the egg. On the basis of this hypothesis, each of the first four cells of the embryo must receive similar cytoplasm; hence each cell must have the materials and organization necessary for normal development. In the second experiment, when an unfertilized egg is cut apart, the upper half of the egg must receive some of the materials needed, but not others. Similarly, the lower half of the egg must receive certain materials that are absent from the upper half, and must lack others that are present in the upper half. This means that different materials must be contributed to the two halves of the egg and thus to the cells of the developing "embryo" derived from these halves. Finally, we can conclude from many similar experiments that such materials of the cytoplasm indeed affect and limit what the genes in the nucleus are able to do in controlling the path of development.

We begin to get some idea of a team—the nucleus and the cytoplasm. We might imagine the DNA of the nucleus as the coach who has a good chance of winning the football game (producing normal development) if he is given a fair supply of husky, energetic guards, tackles, ends, centers, and backs (enzymes, RNA, amino acids, plenty of ATP, and so on). But even if he is the very best coach, he cannot win a game with all guards and no ends, or all backs and no linemen! In the same manner, the nucleus cannot function if it is provided only with a part of the conditions and materials needed for development. You must always remember that, ultimately, the nucleus can work only on, in, and with the cytoplasm.

GUIDE QUESTIONS AND PROBLEMS

1. What are two distinctly different roles of the gene?
2. How may the problem of gene action be studied?
3. What is the life history of the pink bread mold *Neurospora*?
4. What advantages does *Neurospora* offer the geneticist studying its biochemical behavior and its heredity?
5. One worker in *Neurospora* genetics has characterized inheritance in *Neurospora* as a one gene-one enzyme relation. How has this been verified experimentally?
6. What genetic situation in man corresponds to this pattern in *Neurospora*? How?
7. How is DNA related to protein synthesis? What is the evidence upon which this is based?
8. What are some of the unsolved problems of gene action?
9. How do the experiments with *Acetabularia* and sea urchin eggs increase our understanding of the interaction of nucleus and cytoplasm in heredity?
10. What do you suppose would be the result of combining a nucleus from *Acetabularia mediterranea* and a nucleus from *A. crenulata* in a single plant?
11. What is the experimental evidence that links DNA with heredity? How conclusive is the evidence?
12. The mold *Penicillium* does not require biotin in its culture medium, as *Neurospora* does. Does this fact suggest that biotin plays no role in the metabolism of *Penicillium*? Explain.
13. What are some of the major problems in studying human heredity?
14. Is it valid to utilize the results of experiments with bacteria and viruses in interpreting the role of DNA in higher living forms? Explain.

SUGGESTIONS FOR ADDITIONAL READINGS

See the references at the end of Chapter 30, especially the book, *Heredity*, by Bonner, and the article, "Messenger RNA," by Hurwitz.

33

GENES IN

POPULATIONS

In earlier chapters we have learned how genes may act in individual plants and animals. The regular actions of genes result in a variety of genetic traits that in many cases are easy to recognize. We can distinguish blue eyes from brown eyes, round peas from wrinkled peas, black coat color from white coat color, type A blood from type B blood.

Early geneticists put a great deal of effort into studying the occurrence of just such traits in single family lines. They recorded the appearance of the parents and the distribution of the trait in the first, and sometimes the second, generation of offspring. From this kind of information, they were able to recognize the patterns of heredity that we studied in Chapter 30, and by using the basic principles worked out by Mendel, they were able to understand the manner of inheritance. The use of symbols for gene pairs greatly helped in these studies. But there are other questions that geneticists ask, and a number of these are becoming very important. They are questions that the usual kind of study of family he-

redity cannot answer, so we must devise new techniques. Most of these problems deal with *populations* of individuals, without regard to the precise identity of the parents. They are questions such as these:

1. In the United States *what proportion of the population* has type AB blood? What proportion has Rh-negative blood—another important blood group? What proportion of the population has blood that is both type AB and Rh negative? The answers to these questions are essential for hospital blood banks. They are questions that a subdivision of the field of genetics—population genetics—can answer.
2. How many "harmful" genes are there in the population? To what extent will high-energy radiations from X rays, or from radioactive fallout, or from nuclear reactors, tend to increase the general level of harmful genes in the population?

In other words, we would like to know how *frequently* certain genes occur in a population. The study of *gene frequencies* is the basis of population genetics.

POPULATIONS

Questions affecting entire populations are difficult ones, and it might seem impossible to get any answers at all. Certainly a human population is a complicated assemblage of individuals—persons of all ages, some married, some unmarried, some with many children, some with none.

Let us list some of the complications a geneticist must consider:

1. Some members of the population are too young, and others too old, to contribute children to the next generation.
2. Some members of the population, even if they are of the right age, will not have children.

3. Of those who have children, there may be distinct preferences for mates. Perhaps blondes will prefer blondes, or tall persons will prefer tall persons.
4. Some parents will have more children than others.

It is impossible for the geneticist to know everything he *should* know about populations to arrive at accurate conclusions. He therefore uses a simple *model* of the population he wants to study. The model we will use is an oversimplification, but it is supported by much data from human populations. As we learn more about populations, we can refine our model. Although we refer to human populations in most cases, the principles can be applied in general to sexually breeding populations.

Let us list our assumptions about a population. These assumptions are the basis of our model.

1. We assume that all members of the population will mate and produce offspring.
2. We assume that all matings, regardless of the genotypes of the parents, will produce the same number of offspring.
3. We assume that mating is at random. This means that the population is large, and that the choice of a mate does not depend upon the trait we are working with. For example, the frequency of matings between blondes and brunettes will depend strictly upon the proportions of blondes and brunettes in the population, and upon no other factors.

Now we can look at an example of how these assumptions make it possible to study the frequency of a gene in a population.

Sampling a Population

The population geneticist who is interested in knowing what kinds of genes are in a population and what their frequencies are must first of all define the population he plans to study. He could work with the entire population of the United States, for instance. That would be quite different from working with the entire population of the smallest state, Rhode Island. Or he may be interested in analyzing the population of a single city, such as San Francisco, or perhaps just a part of a city, such as the Chinese population of San Francisco.

This done, two main problems face the population geneticist. One difficulty is that he can hardly hope to examine everyone in a population—even in a small population—to see if each individual possesses the genetic trait in question. The second difficulty is that many traits, especially recessive ones, cannot be detected in heterozygous individuals. A person heterozygous for a recessive gene will appear to be like a person who does not carry the gene; there is no easy way of knowing whether a brown-eyed person carries the allele for blue eyes, for example.

The geneticist solves the first problem by taking only a *sample* of the population. He meets the second difficulty by using an easy mathematical relationship that is based upon our simple model of the population.

Let us use a hypothetical example to show how a geneticist goes about taking a sample of a population in order to study some hereditary trait. First, he makes the sample as large and as random as possible. He takes special precautions that the sample is representative of the entire population, since he wants to draw conclusions that are applicable to the entire population. So, he avoids oversampling any special group within the population, for that would distort his conclusions (Figure 33-1). Persons who make "opinion" polls have the same problem; if one wanted to take a poll of opinion on income taxes, he would not ask only millionaires!

In one famous opinion poll taken just before the presidential election of 1936, peo-

Jim Theologos

33-1 Sampling a population in a representative way poses many problems for the population geneticist. What would be wrong with sampling a city's population by selecting only people like these, who work each weekday in the midtown area of the city? What would be wrong with sampling only those who stayed at home during the week?

ple were interviewed by telephone. The poll clearly indicated that Alfred M. Landon would win the election. In the actual election, Franklin D. Roosevelt won by a landslide. People who did not have telephones were not included in the poll, of course. The poll was not a good random sample, and it failed to predict the behavior of the entire voting population. People with telephones tended to vote for Landon; those without telephones tended to vote for Roosevelt— but not directly because of the telephones, of course. It was a time of widespread business depression, and people who could not afford telephones liked the Roosevelt promise of a "New Deal."

Returning to our population sample, the scientist counts the individuals in his sample who possess the trait. He can assume, if his sample is a good one, that the trait occurs in the same proportion of individuals in the whole population. Let us say that the geneticist is interested in knowing how many persons in Baltimore can taste **phenylthiocarbimide** (fen·il·thy·oh·KAR·bih·myd —PTC), a substance that is very bitter to some persons (called tasters) but that by

others (called nontasters) cannot be tasted at all. (In Laboratory Exercise 33-1 you will make a similar analysis of another human hereditary trait—the ability or inability to roll the tongue into a **U** shape.)

Persons who can taste PTC carry a dominant allele T, while those who cannot are homozygous recessive (tt). Since a taster may be either homozygous for the allele T, or heterozygous, let us indicate the trait, when present, by putting the gene symbol in a box. Those who can taste PTC, then, will be indicated by $\boxed{T}$ and those who cannot, by $\boxed{t}$. These are symbols for the phenotypes, not the genotypes.

The investigation begins. The geneticist and his co-workers spread throughout the city of Baltimore, asking the persons in their sample population, who have been selected from all walks of life, to test their taste for PTC. After several weeks, the workers find they have examined 5,000 persons for this trait. This seems like a lot of people, and it is, but compared to Baltimore's total population of about 1 million, it represents a sample of only 1 person in 200.

After the counts of all the workers are totaled, suppose it is found that 3,200 people can taste PTC, while 1,800 people cannot. The geneticist then calculates the *percentage* of people who are tasters, and finds (dividing 3,200 by 5,000) it to be 0.64, or 64 percent. We would represent this as $\boxed{T} = 0.64$, or 64 percent. By a similar calculation (1,800/5,000) we find that $\boxed{t} = 0.36$, or 36 percent.

Now we still have the problem of finding what percentage of the tasters are homozygous, and what percentage heterozygous, for the *T* allele, and what happens to these percentages generation after generation.

The Gene Pool

The geneticist who works with problems like the one described thinks of *all* the genes that the members of a population may contribute to the next generation as the **gene pool**. In a sense, any offspring represents a random sample from this gene pool.

If there are two alleles of a gene (such as *T* and *t* of the PTC-tasting example), then a certain proportion of the alleles in a population are *T*'s and the rest are *t*'s. The ratio might be 10 percent and 90 percent, or 50 percent and 50 percent. Since many different values are possible, let us designate the percentage (proportion) of *T* alleles as "p," and the proportion of *t* alleles as "q." If there are only these two alleles, they naturally must total 100 percent, or 1, which in this case means "all" or the "whole"—just as $\frac{1}{2} + \frac{1}{2} = 1$, or $\frac{1}{2} + \frac{1}{4} + \frac{1}{4} = 1$. In this case, $p + q = 1$. It is easy to see, by simple algebra, that $p = (1 - q)$, if we transpose q. Likewise, $q = (1 - p)$.

For the time being, then, let us consider p and q to be frequencies of two alleles, *T* and *t*, of the same gene. In other words, of all the sperm cells produced by the male members of the population, p of them will carry the *T* allele, and q of them will carry the *t* allele. Likewise, of all the egg cells of all female members of the population, p of them will carry the *T* allele, and q of them will carry the *t* allele. For instance, if p is 0.2, then q must be 0.8; this simply means that 0.2, or 2 out of every 10, gametes carry *T*, while 0.8, or 8 out of every 10, gametes carry *t*.

Let us summarize thus far:

	Frequency of T	Frequency of t
In sperm cells	p	q
In egg cells	p	q

Another way of thinking about these values is to imagine that they are probabilities (recall Laboratory Exercise 30-2). If one were to "select" a gamete at random from the gene pool, then the probability that it carries the *T* allele is p. (In the example above, if p is 0.2, then the probability that a given gamete carries the *T* allele is also 0.2, or 2 out of 10.)

Now we are ready for the important question. What proportion of the next generation will be *TT*, or *Tt*, or *tt*? To determine this, we need merely refer to a rule of probability: the chance of two independent events occurring together is the product of their chances of occurring separately.

Under the conditions that have been stated, the particular kind of sperm that fertilizes a particular egg depends on only one thing: the frequency of that kind of sperm and the frequency of that kind of egg in the population's gene pool. Whether or not the sperm carries a particular allele is quite independent of the allele the egg carries.

QUESTION: What proportion of the next generation will be *TT*?

ANSWER: *TT* individuals can result *only* when *T* eggs (probability = p) are fertilized by *T* sperms (probability = p). The product of these two probabilities is $p \times p$, or p^2. [Again, if $p = 0.2$, then $p^2 = (0.2)^2$, or 0.04. Four individuals out of 100, or 4 percent, will have the genotype *TT*.]

QUESTION: What proportion of the next generation will be *tt?*

ANSWER: *tt* individuals can result *only* when *t* sperms (probability = q) fertilize *t* eggs (probability = q). The product of these two probabilities is q × q, or q². [If q = 0.8, then q² = (0.8)² = 0.64. Therefore, 64 out of 100, or 64 percent, of the offspring will have the genotype *tt*.]

QUESTION: What proportion of the next generation will be *Tt?*

ANSWER: Here we must be careful. *Tt* individuals can result from *two* kinds of events—*T* sperms can fertilize *t* eggs, or *t* sperms can fertilize *T* eggs. Each of these events has a probability of p × q, or pq. Since there are two ways it can happen, we double the probability: 2 pq. Therefore, the next generation will have 2 pq individuals with the genotype *Tt*. [Substituting from our earlier example, 2pq = 2(0.2) (0.8) = 0.32. Therefore, 32 percent of the next generation will be heterozygous *Tt*.]

Summarizing the next generation:

p² offspring will be *TT*
2pq offspring will be *Tt*
q² offspring will be *tt*

This mathematical relationship that we have derived was first recognized in 1908 by an English mathematician, G. H. Hardy, and a German physician, W. Weinberg. They realized that if random mating occurs, the frequencies of the different kinds of zygotes remain the same, generation after generation. Of course, this holds true only if there are no "upsetting" influences, such as mutation or selection.

Geneticists call this mathematical relationship the **Hardy-Weinberg Principle.**

Let us state it again. If, in a large, randomly breeding population, p represents the frequency of allele *T* and q represents the frequency of allele *t* of a given gene, and if there are no upsetting influences, such as mutation or selection, then the zygote genotypes will occur in the following frequencies in every generation:

Genotype	Frequency
TT	p²
Tt	2pq
tt	q²

Another way of stating that the frequencies of the different genotypes remain the same from generation to generation is to say that the population is *in equilibrium.*

How do we know that the zygote frequencies remain the same? A bit of simple algebra proves that this is so. From the Hardy-Weinberg Principle we know that all possible kinds of individuals are accounted for, so that

$$p^2 + 2pq + q^2 = 1$$

where, again, 1 represents unity, or all the individuals in the population. This expression is no doubt familiar to you, since it is the expansion of the binomial $(p + q)^2$. In this case, where only two alleles of a gene are involved, the relative frequencies of the alleles contributed by the males to the next generation are expressed by $(p + q)$; similarly, those contributed by the females are summed by $(p + q)$. The frequencies of the kinds of zygotes that result from the random union of these gametes are obtained by taking the product of these expressions or, in this case, squaring the expression:

$$(p + q)^2 = p^2 + 2pq + q^2$$

Let us now calculate the frequencies of the *genes* in the gene pool of the *next* generation. *T* alleles come from *TT* individuals and *Tt* individuals. All the gametes of *TT* individuals will contribute *T* alleles, and *half* the gametes from *Tt* individuals will contribute T alleles. By reasoning similarly about the t allele, we can summarize the genes in the following chart:

Genotype of zygote	TT	Tt	tt
Frequency of zygote	p^2	$2pq$	q^2
Frequency of T alleles	p^2	pq	—
Frequency of t alleles	—	pq	q^2

All alleles are accounted for. We see that the frequency of T alleles in the next generation will be $(p^2 + pq)$. Now, if we use the relationship $q = (1 - p)$, we can see that $p^2 + pq = p^2 + p(1 - p) = p^2 + p - p^2 = p$. That is, the frequency of T alleles in the new generation is p, just as it is in the preceding generation. As often as we want to do this, the frequency of the T allele will be p—the population is *in equilibrium* for this allele.

The same kind of calculation proves that the frequency of t alleles remains the same generation after generation. You should do the calculation for the t allele and show that its frequency is always q.

Applying the Hardy-Weinberg Principle

This very important principle allows us to determine the frequency of a particular recessive allele in a population if we know the frequency of the homozygous recessive zygotes carrying the allele. Let us return to our study of the PTC-tasting trait in the population of Baltimore. You will recall that 64 percent of the people taste PTC, while 36 percent do not. If allele T permits tasting, then allele t in the homozygous condition does not.

This is all the information we need to know. The frequency of tt in the population is q^2. We know the value of q^2, so we can determine the frequency of t in the population. In this case, q^2 is 0.36. We find q by simply taking the square root of 0.36; the answer is 0.6. (Check: square 0.6 to see that this is so. Watch your decimal point!) In other words, 6/10, or 60 percent, of the *alleles* in the population of Baltimore for the PTC-tasting trait are recessive. Since $p + q = 1$, naturally 4/10, or 40 percent, of the alleles in the gene pool are dominant for this trait: $p = 0.4$.

QUESTION: How many persons are homozygous dominant (TT) for PTC tasting?

ANSWER: p^2, or $(0.4)^2 = 0.16 = 16$ percent.

QUESTION: How many individuals are heterozygous (Tt) for the trait?

ANSWER: $2pq$, or $2(0.4)(0.6) = 0.48 = 48$ percent.

Now we see that all individuals (and all alleles in the gene pool of the population for this particular trait) are accounted for: 16 percent TT + 48 percent Tt + 36 percent tt = 100 percent. Figure 33-2 summarizes our calculation of the genotypes.

The Hardy-Weinberg Principle can be used to make genetic predictions in other ways. For example, suppose that in this population a person who is not a PTC taster marries a PTC taster. What are their chances of having nontaster children? These parents can have nontaster children only if the taster parent is heterozygous (Tt) for the trait. Now, the probability of a taster individual's being heterozygous equals the frequency of the heterozygotes in the population divided by the frequency of *all* tasters in the population (heterozygotes plus homozygous dominants). The calculation in this instance is:

$$\frac{0.48}{(0.48 + 0.16)} = \frac{0.48}{0.64} = \frac{3}{4} = 75 \text{ percent}$$

We estimate, therefore, that three out of every four PTC tasters in this population are heterozygous for the trait (Tt). If the mate *is* heterozygous, then the probability of having nontaster (tt) children is 0.5, or 50 percent; for $Tt \times tt$ yields ½ Tt + ½ tt offspring. The *over-all* probability of nontaster children from this kind of marriage is

33-2　A STUDY OF A POPULATION IN EQUILIBRIUM FOR A GIVEN PAIR OF TRAITS

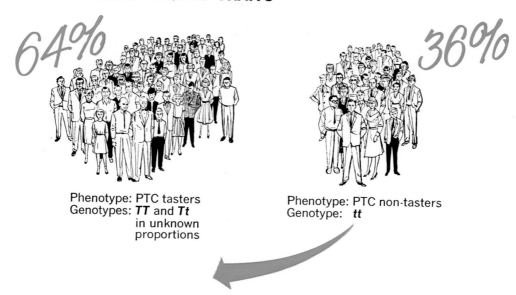

Phenotype: PTC tasters
Genotypes: *TT* and *Tt*
　　　　in unknown
　　　　proportions

Phenotype: PTC non-tasters
Genotype:　*tt*

For a pair of contrasting traits, **T** and **t**, controlled by a single pair of genes, if 36 percent (or 0.36) of the population is **tt**, then the frequency of gene **t** in the gene pool is $\sqrt{.36}$ or 0.6. Sixty percent of the total number of **T** and **t** genes must therefore be **t**, and the remaining forty percent **T**.

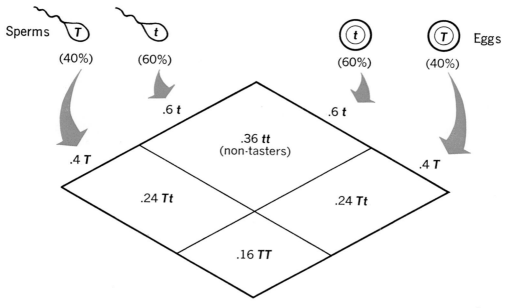

Sperms　(T)　　(t)　　　　　　(t)　　(T)　Eggs

(40%)　　(60%)　　　　　(60%)　　(40%)

.6 t　　　　.6 t

.36 **tt**
(non-tasters)

.4 T　　　　　　　　　　　.4 T

.24 **Tt**　　　　　　.24 **Tt**

.16 **TT**

Genotype proportion: 16% **TT**, 48% **Tt**, 36% **tt**

the product of the probability that the taster parent is heterozygous (75 percent) and the probability that the children are nontasters (50 percent). Using our probability rule, $0.75 \times 0.50 = 0.375$, or 37.5 percent, the probability of having nontaster children.

For a population in equilibrium, then, the geneticist can determine the frequency of a given allele in that population if he knows accurately the relative size of *one* of the classes of individuals. In the above case, the only group known accurately is that of individuals who *cannot* taste PTC. From this knowledge we are able to determine all other information desired (Figure 33-2).

When a trait is sex-linked, as is red-green color blindness in man, the Hardy-Weinberg Principle must be modified. In Laboratory Exercise 33-2 you will learn how to deal with this situation.

Our knowledge of the genetics of populations thus becomes a valuable tool in the hands of the geneticist. The more we know about the distribution of alleles that affect health, intelligence, and other abilities in human populations, the more success we are likely to have in coping with problems in which the welfare of the entire population is involved. If, for example, we are to assess the genetic effects of radiation in this atomic era, we must have accurate means for determining the frequency of harmful genes in the population. Such determinations, made from time to time, will tell us to what extent our store of harmful mutations in the gene pool is being increased.

POPULATIONS IN TRANSITION

We have concluded that the frequencies of various kinds of genes in a population's gene pool do not change of themselves; but over a long period of time we can expect changes to occur.

Let us list the primary factors that cause gene frequencies to change:

1. *Mutation.* Mutations of the alleles of a particular gene occur very rarely under natural conditions. Little by little the frequencies of the alleles change in favor of the one that is most stable, that is, has the lowest mutation rate. A more mutable allele tends to become relatively rarer.

2. *Natural selection.* Suppose that the allele A gives its possessors a slight advantage in surviving to reproductive age or in greater fertility over individuals who have the allele a. Those individuals with A therefore produce a slightly higher proportion of offspring than individuals with a. Thus the frequency of A in the gene pool tends to increase and the frequency of a to decrease.

3. *Isolation.* It is possible for a large natural population to be broken up into smaller populations. Perhaps a river becomes too wide to be crossed, thus separating the population into two parts. It is quite possible that these parts are not random samples of the original population. Random breeding within each smaller population brings each to an equilibrium again, but the two new equilibria may be quite different from the original one.

4. *Emigration and immigration.* Very few populations are completely isolated. Terrestrial species that live on islands, far from the mainland, and that are not able to cross the open sea, are perhaps the most completely isolated. Even so, a few individuals of various species occasionally may be blown or rafted to or from such remote islands. In most populations, individuals leave or join the population more frequently. From a genetic standpoint, these emigrations (away from) or immigrations (to) may result in a subsequent change in the gene pool of the population. In par-

ticular, individuals that come from another population with different frequencies of alleles change the nature of the gene pool of the population they join.

A population whose gene pool is in transition is an evolving population. When the gene pools of two populations become different enough, the populations may not be able to interbreed any longer. This final degree of *genetic isolation* usually takes a long time to come about. Many mechanisms are involved, and geographical separation is nearly always necessary. Eventually two new species arise. We will learn more about problems of speciation in Chapter 35.

IMPROVING GENETIC LINES

Long before he had an insight into the principles of genetics, man sought to improve the quality of his domesticated plants and animals, since they provide him with food, clothing, transportation, and protection. He wanted fruit and vegetable plants that would produce more food on less land and with less of his labor, cows that produce more milk, chickens that lay more eggs, cattle and hogs that have more flesh usable for meat, and grain plants that give large crops and are resistant to disease.

The processes man used to bring about these desirable ends are essentially the same as the natural processes that change the gene pools of populations. Man did not know how to introduce more mutations into his stocks, and hence more variation; but he certainly took notice of the variation already there and selected as parents of the next generation those organisms with the traits he desired. This process is called **artificial selection,** to distinguish it from **natural selection.** Natural selection promotes the increase of certain genotypes adapted to a particular set of environmental conditions. Artificial selection promotes the in-

crease of those forms that man wants for his own purposes (Figure 33-3).

Man also recognized the role of isolation, for he kept separate the gene pools of the domestic plants and animals he desired— by preventing their breeding with less desirable types. In other words, he restricted the flow of unwanted genes into his special breeds. Even today the owners of pedigreed stock take special care that their animals mate only with animals that have similar pedigrees; thus, the gene pools are not diluted or modified, except by mutation (which cannot be prevented).

In recent years, armed with genetic knowledge and techniques, man has applied new tools to old problems. The effectiveness of these techniques in increasing the quality and quantity of his farm animals, his food plants, and even his ornamental plants has been truly phenomenal. One of the most dramatic examples of the application of known genetic principles is the development of hybrid corn, which was discussed in Chapter 30.

It is important to remember that when we speak of improving genetic lines, we usually mean that the improvement should be in the direction of increased use or value to man. We must ask the purpose of the proposed improvement, and know something about the environment in which the improved strain is to live. A trait considered an improvement in one environment may prove to be a severe handicap in another. In the case of a dog, for instance, a heavy coat of hair in the arctic area is a great improvement over scanty hair, but at the equator the heavy coat may be a handicap.

One example of how special traits are developed in domestic animals is provided by American cattle breeders. Some diseases of Shorthorn cattle are transmitted by insects that pierce the thin skin of the animals. Shorthorn cattle are good meat producers. Brahman cattle, another breed, have thick, almost "insect-proof" skins. However, they

33-3 VARIETY THROUGH ARTIFICIAL SELECTION

Light Sussex

Barred Plymouth Rock

Blue Orpington

English Redcap

White Leghorn

Cockerel-Australorp

Silver Campine

Game Cock (Old English Red-breasted)

Golden Penciled Hamburg

All photos, Grant Heilman

are not such good meat producers. The raw material available to the cattle breeder, therefore, was an insect-susceptible, good meat producer strain and an insect-resistant, poor meat producer strain. Clearly a little genetic recombination was desirable!

Breeders began to cross American Shorthorn cattle with Brahman cattle. From among the offspring, animals with the desired characteristics—good meat production and thick skin—were selected for future crosses. After repeated selection, a true-breeding strain was developed. The result was a beautiful breed of cattle known as the Santa Gertrudis, which has a thick, almost insect-proof skin stretched over the fine beef of American Shorthorn cattle. These cattle can graze unharmed in areas that would be deadly to thin-skinned cattle.

The utilization of hybrid vigor in developing strains of maize is but one of the triumphs of genetics in plant breeding. A few other examples may be mentioned. In the cultivated tomato, wilting caused by a fungus known as *Fusarium* (fyoo·SAY·rih·um) is one of the worst problems. It was discovered that a wild tomato species from Peru possesses a gene for resistance to *Fusarium* wilt. This wild species, however, produces poor fruit. By crossing the cultivated tomato and the wild one, a hybrid with resistance was obtained. This did not solve the problem, however, because most of the desirable qualities of cultivated tomatoes were diminished in the hybrid. But by repeatedly crossing the hybrid plants back to the cultivated tomato, and by selecting for further crosses the plants resistant to wilt and high in other qualities, a desirable plant was eventually obtained. This amounted to nothing less than introducing the gene for resistance to wilt into the best cultivated varieties.

In wheat, the fungus that produces stem rust causes enormous losses. By a cross between the high-yielding Marquis wheat developed in America and a Russian variety found to be resistant to the stem rust, a fine new variety named Ceres was produced. Released in 1926, it had become by 1934 almost the exclusive variety grown in the Dakotas and neighboring regions. Unfortunately, mutations and hybridizations occur not only in wheat and other crop plants, but in wheat stem rust and other disease organisms. In 1935 a disaster of enormous proportions occurred. Either a mutation in the stem rust enabled it to overcome the resistance of the Ceres wheat and to spread like wildfire through the great wheatfields, or a natural hybrid arose through sexual crossing and recombination of different strains of stem rust during its sexual stages (spent on the barberry plant, its host) and produced the same effect. The wheat crop was almost wiped out wherever Ceres had been planted!

The wheat breeders had to begin again, trying to produce by hybridization and selection a new variety that would be resist-

ant to the new strain of stem rust. In time they were successful; but this process is often slow and difficult. Since the new varieties are always threatened by the possibility of mutation and selection in the plant parasite, we are naturally led to ask: is there a quicker way? Maybe not. Yet the ability to induce mutations by artificial means, such as X rays, offers one avenue of hope. Growers of barley have found that it is possible to produce by X rays mutations of significant commercial value. It may even be possible to produce by X rays mutations of significant resistance to wheat stem rust upon the existing varieties of wheat. But whether we find single mutants, or breed new resistant varieties by hybridization and selection, it is obvious that in the future we had better be prepared for evolutionary changes in the stem rust, too. Instead of releasing for general cultivation all the resistant varieties which can be developed, we might well reserve some of them for the evil day when our widely grown varieties succumb to fresh onslaughts of some new strain of stem rust. And of course we can help reduce the danger by eradicating the native barberry in wheat-growing regions of the country.

In the growing of cotton and tobacco, fruits and vegetables, flowers, and even trees for timber, the work of the plant breeder has utilized the growing knowledge of genetics. By producing hybrids, by inducing mutations, by doubling chromosome number to make vigorous plants, he has the basis for developing desirable strains. These first steps are followed by selection and the breeding of pure lines. By these biological techniques, the supply of useful plant products and the food of the world have been multiplied many times. Nowhere is this more evident than in the United States, where the natural fertility of our recently virgin soils and the ingenuity of the plant breeder have combined to give us about the highest standards of nutrition in the world.

An important technique used by animal breeders today is **artificial insemination** (ar-tih-FISH-al in-sem-ih-NAY-shun). Sperms from animals of high quality are collected, stored in frozen condition, and used for inseminating females. With improved storage techniques, it is possible to preserve sperms long after the death of the donor male. This technique is used most widely today by cattle breeders.

HUMAN HEREDITY

Artificial insemination is applicable also to man. Under what circumstances do you think it should be used? Or does it raise so many questions that you think it should be prohibited?

From time to time we hear of proposals to "improve the human race." Such schemes may depend on "eliminating undesirable genes" or "encouraging geniuses to have more children." There are two main problems we must recognize when we try to judge such schemes. One of these is our relative lack of accurate knowledge about most of human heredity; the second is that it is never quite clear in just what direction we want to guide the path of human improvement. Certainly the elimination of large gene pools from the face of the earth, as Hitler tried during World War II, is neither morally nor scientifically defensible.

A third problem lies in not knowing whether a difference in human traits is inherited or not. We have already mentioned that identical twins raised in different environments present unusual opportunities to study the interrelationships of heredity and environment; but, unfortunately, the number of such twin pairs available for study is relatively small.

Much of what we know about human heredity comes from the study of relatively rare traits—those controlled by genes that have a low frequency in the gene pool. From a few of these studies we have learned how the traits are inherited and what the effect of environment is on their expression. In some of these studies, too, we have obtained data on the frequency of mutation. For the more common traits possessed by all of us—such as blood type, intelligence, and so on—in some cases we know a great deal, in others our knowledge is scanty indeed.

We will list a few human traits and briefly indicate what we know of their heredity.

Blood types. The inheritance of blood types is, in most cases, more complicated than at first thought. The A, B, AB, and O blood types are controlled by three main alleles occurring at one locus (Chapter 30).

A particular Rh antigen (Rh stands for rhesus, the kind of monkey in which the antigen was first identified) is present in about 85 percent of the white population. We say that these individuals are Rh-positive. They are *RR* or *Rr*. The remaining 15 percent of the population is *rr*, known as Rh-negative. You can see that these are population data, not data of individual families. The percentages among Negro populations are somewhat different. Among Mongoloid populations the Rh-negative allele is almost wholly absent.

The Rh factor is sometimes very important to the health of newborn babies. If the mother is *rr* and the father is either *RR* or *Rr*, the offspring is, or may be, *Rr*. In some instances, the red blood cells (carrying Rh antigen) of the fetus pass through the placenta into the circulation of the mother and cause in her the production of antibodies against the Rh antigen. These antibodies pass back into the circulation of the fetus and begin literally to destroy its red blood cells. If the damage is widespread, the fetus is killed and a miscarriage results. If there is less damage, the baby may be born alive but suffering from severe anemia and jaundice (a greenish-yellow color due to pigments from the destroyed red blood cells). A complete substitution of the baby's blood by blood from a donor who does not possess anti-Rh antibodies may save the infant's life and allow it to begin making a fresh supply of red blood cells.

A transfusion of Rh-positive blood will also induce in an Rh-negative mother the production of anti-Rh antibodies; this greatly increases the chances of damage to any Rh-positive child she may bear. Clearly, it is of the greatest importance to know your Rh blood type. This is especially true if you are female, in order to assure blood transfusions of the correct type and thus prevent possible damage to unborn children. About 10 percent of all babies in the white population are Rh-positive babies born to Rh-negative mothers. (A problem is given on page 587 to show you how this may be determined from application of the Hardy-Weinberg Principle.) Not all the mothers of these babies develop antibodies, at least in their earlier pregnancies; therefore, there are not as many damaged babies as the percentage just given would suggest. Still, about 1 in 150 of all babies in the white population are so affected. This is about 27,000 in the United States every year. The frequency of affected newborn is much less in the Negro portion of the population.

The ABO blood groups have been known since 1900. Yet a similar incompatibility of maternal and fetal blood in the case of these blood groups was discovered only after the Rh disorder had been explained in 1942. Why was this?

The ABO blood incompatibility is much more severe than the Rh type, and it kills the fetus during an early stage of its development, causing an abortion. It most often occurs when the mother is of blood type O and the fetus is of blood type A, B, or AB. (Remember that persons of type O already carry anti-A and anti-B antibodies. Type-O persons do not have to be stimulated to make these antibodies as is the case with Rh-negative persons and Rh antigen.) Is this likely to be of common occurrence? Apply the Hardy-Weinberg Principle and see.

The frequencies of the alleles I^A, I^B, and i, respectively, are about 0.25, 0.08, and 0.67 in the white population of the United States. The frequencies of persons of type A, B, AB, and O are, for the same population, about 0.40, 0.11, 0.04, and 0.45, respectively.

It is also possible for incompatibility to occur when the mother is of type B and the fetus of type A, or when the mother is of type A and the fetus is of type B. It is now thought that ABO incompatibility is responsible for a great number of the deaths among the unborn. Much apparent sterility in marriage is really due to this cause, too. Why do you suppose the blood groups exist, then? Wouldn't it be better if the mothers and fathers always had the same blood group? No losses of embryonic and fetal life would occur because of blood-type incompatibility. The situation would be as it is among the Chinese and Japanese with respect to the Rh blood disorder. Since scarcely any Chinese or Japanese are Rh-negative, the disorder of the newborn is almost unknown in those people.

The answer, of course, lies in the character of natural selection. We can only suppose that blood groups A and B and Rh-positive must confer some advantages that compensate for the damage they do. Natural selection, as we will see further in Chapter 35, always balances the advantages and disadvantages of possessing a particular genotype.

Hemophilia. A famous sex-linked recessive condition, hemophilia usually appears in males, causing their blood to clot very slowly. The responsible gene can almost be classified as a lethal. (See Chapter 31.)

Color blindness. Inability to distinguish red from green is sex-linked (Chapter 31). It occurs in about 8 percent of males, but rarely in females, who are not affected unless they receive *two* recessive genes.

Baldness. Hereditary baldness is dominant in males, recessive in females. The respective sex hormones promote or overcome its dominance!

Diabetes mellitus. In this hereditary disease, lack of the hormone insulin causes inability of the body to utilize sugar properly. Many cases appear to be due to a single recessive gene. The disease may be mild or severe (are multiple alleles perhaps involved?), or it may not appear at all, depending on environmental factors. (Laboratory Exercise 33-3 illustrates the great importance of the environment in determining the phenotype resulting from a particular genotype.)

Eye color. Eye color is a complex trait not at present completely understood. It seems that a true, pure blue eye is due to a single gene that is recessive to a gene for pigmented eye. We must lump together under "pigmented" any eye with even the least spot of brown pigment (including hazel eyes), and also green and gray eyes. There are probably other genes that affect eye color when the pigment gene is also present.

Skin color. The amount of dark pigment seems to be controlled by four to eight pairs of independently assorting genes with non-dominance at each locus; many grades exist between blond and black. (Exposure to sunlight also modifies the amount of color in the skin.)

The reddish and yellow pigments of certain races are different from the shading from blond to black.

Height and weight. There is a definite genic influence here, but environmental differences such as diet play an important role, too. Extreme variations in height, such as dwarfism and giantism, are usually due to activity of pituitary hormones, and these hormones, too, are under genetic control.

Resistance to tuberculosis. Probably many genes as well as environmental conditions play a part in resistance to this disease. The evidence from studies of identical twins shows that the amount of resistance is strongly influenced by heredity.

Schizophrenia. The evidence from twins shows that this commonest type of mental disease is strongly influenced by heredity. One authority suggests that a single recessive gene is involved. Environmental factors are also highly important.

Feeble-mindedness. There may be many causes for what is generally considered feeble-mindedness. While normal intelligence depends on the proper functioning of many genes, a defect in the function of any one of these may result in an impairment of mental activity. Some conditions of feeble-mindedness have a strong hereditary determinant; others may be due to injuries before or at birth. One special type of feeble-mindedness, Mongoloid idiocy, is the product of a single extra chromosome (Chapter 31). Another well-known type, **phenylpyruvic** (fen-'l·py·ʀoo·vik) **idiocy,** is a simple recessive trait caused by the failure to produce a certain enzyme (Chapter 32).

Intelligence. Intelligence is not easy to define and is even more difficult to measure. We are not sure whether it is a single trait or many competencies combined—most likely it is the latter. The most common type of intelligence test is one that gives an intelligence quotient (IQ), measured by a particular level of response in visualizing objects in space, memorizing, and reasoning. Verbalization and vocabulary are important. Judging from IQ tests of identical twins, there is a very strong hereditary factor in intelligence. But environment also plays an important role, and it is the interaction of heredity and environment that finally determines the "intelligence" of an individual.

In all probability, many genes contribute to the determination of the hereditary component of intelligence. If genes also are largely responsible for certain types of *motivation* toward learning, then the situation is still more complicated.

The information that has been reviewed here on human heredity is extremely limited, and there are good reasons why our knowledge of human heredity is not as far advanced as our knowledge of the heredity of some other organisms. The long span of years of a human generation, the difficulty of accurately measuring many human characteristics, the impossibility of using planned matings, and the relatively small number of offspring per family all represent handicaps to the geneticist. But in spite of these difficulties, the advances in our understanding of human heredity are taking place rapidly.

GUIDE QUESTIONS AND PROBLEMS

1. What complications does a geneticist face in studying populations?
2. How does a simple model of a population enable a geneticist to deal with a problem in inheritance?
3. What assumptions about his population model does the geneticist make?
4. How does the population geneticist go about the job of sampling a population?
5. What does the term *gene pool* mean?
6. How does the Hardy-Weinberg Principle help clarify the nature of a gene pool from generation to generation?
7. Why is it significant to know the distribution of alleles in human populations?
8. What factors can cause gene frequencies in a population to change?
9. What is meant by artificial selection? How has man used artificial selection in both plant and animal breeding?
10. What are some of the major difficulties in any plan designed "to improve human heredity"?
11. A group of students were tested and were found to be 70 percent tasters, and 30 percent nontasters, of PTC (page 575). Use this information to compute the probable distribution of genotypes in the sample.
12. Assume that the frequency of the Rh-negative blood type in a population is 16 percent (0.16). Assume also that there is no difference caused by sex; that is, 16 percent of the males and 16 percent of the females

are Rh-negative. What is the frequency of the *r* allele? From this, determine the frequency of the *R* allele. Now you have the basis for calculating the Hardy-Weinberg expectations. How many *RR*, *Rr*, and *rr* persons are there in the population?

Next calculate the frequency of matings in which the husband is *RR* and the wife *rr*. Here you can use the product rule of probability, since the Rh blood types do not generally have anything to do with choices of mates. All these matings will produce only *Rr* offspring.

Next calculate the frequency of matings in which the husband is *Rr* and the wife is *rr*, by multiplying the probabilities (a) that a man is *Rr*, and (b) that a woman is *rr*. These matings are expected to produce ½ *Rr* and ½ *rr* offspring. The latter, of course, are not expected to run a risk of the blood disorder, since they are exactly like their mothers in being *rr*.

Now add the two figures for the frequency of babies that will be *Rr* in *rr* mothers. Does your total agree with the figure given in the text (page 585)?

SUGGESTIONS FOR ADDITIONAL READING

Books

Srb, A. M., and B. Wallace, *Adaptation*. Englewood Cliffs (N. J.), Prentice-Hall, 1961.
  Contains a concise review of genetics as related to the problems of adaptation.
Stern, C., *Principles of Human Genetics*, 2nd ed. San Francisco, Freeman, 1960.
  Excellent text; good discussion of the Hardy-Weinberg Principle.

Magazines

Allison, A., "Sickle Cells and Evolution." *Scientific American*, Vol. 195 (August 1956), pp. 87–88.
Boyd, W. C., "Rh and the Races of Man." *Scientific American*, Vol. 185 (November 1951), pp. 22–25.
Glass, B., "The Genetics of the Dunkers." *Scientific American*, Vol. 189 (August 1953), pp. 76–81.

CONTINUITY

34

DARWINIAN

EVOLUTION

Of all the theories you may study in biology, evolution occupies a unique place. It is the most inclusive of the great unifying principles of biology. It is so much a part of the foundation of biology that the science can hardly be understood without it. It has been referred to in this way: "The theory of evolution is to biology as the atomic theory is to chemistry and physics."

What does evolution mean to the biologist? It means, at its simplest, that living things change; that a whole species may alter; that some species may die out and others arise. It means, therefore, that the plants and animals that now inhabit the earth were not the first plants and animals. It also means that many plants and animals that once flourished are no longer alive. We know of these extinct organisms only by such fossil remains as we discover.

Evolution also means the field of inquiry in which scientists try to discover how this process of change occurs and what effects it has had over the ages. It is the field that asks such questions as these: What is the

origin of the individual changes that are the raw materials of evolution? What forces and factors control the direction in which a species may evolve? How rapidly does evolutionary change take place, and what factors control its rate? What is the past history of plants and animals living today? What plants and animals lived in the past but are no longer alive?

Evolution is a scientific theory. It has been developed to account for an existing body of data. It has been tested for nearly a century against a greater and greater accumulation of evidence. Like all scientific theories, it has grown and been revised as research reveals more and more facts about living things. Hence, the modern theory differs from the views developed by Charles Darwin (1809–1882; Darwin was born on the same day, in the same year, as Abraham Lincoln). The test of time and of accumulated data has led not to the downfall of the theory, but to its extension to explain more and more biological phenomena.

DARWIN'S CONCEPTION OF NATURAL SELECTION

Let us begin with an outline view of Charles Darwin's contribution to the theory of evolution, a contribution that is summed up in the phrase **natural selection.** His views were published in detail in a book, *The Origin of Species.* The first edition appeared on November 24, 1859, more than a century ago. Darwin was not the first to think about evolution. Many theories of evolution are older than his. Nevertheless, his theory is so close to the modern view that it serves as a convenient introduction to the subject. In very brief summary, here is Darwin's report.

First, in every species of living things there are many differences among the individuals. In many species it is safe to say that no two individuals are precisely alike.

Furthermore, as Darwin knew from the breeding of domesticated animals, many of these individual differences are inherited.

Second, it is clear that the process of reproduction operates in most cases so that each generation is larger than the one before. One amoeba, for example, divides to produce two. These two divide, and the next generation will number four. Then there will be eight, sixteen, thirty-two, and so on. Sexually reproducing organisms can multiply even more per generation, since two parent individuals can usually produce more than four offspring, and often very many more. A doubling (or any increase by a factor greater than one) per generation is known as a geometric rate of increase, or a **geometric progression** (Figure 34-1).

Third, it is clear that if this increase were to go unchecked, the number of individuals of any species would soon be greater than the available food could possibly support— or than available space on the earth could accommodate.

Fourth, it is clear that in nature this increase is checked. The actual number of organisms in a species does not continue to increase vastly over long periods of time. In fact, the sizes of most populations seem to remain nearly the same. Clearly, either the existing parent organism must fail to reproduce at a geometric rate of increase, or else many members of each generation must die before reaching the age of reproduction. It is evident that many do die young. Why do some die but not others? Darwin thought there must be a **struggle for survival,** a competition among members of a species for the available food, light, water, places to live, and whatever else was important for survival.

In this competition, individuals with certain characteristics will more often survive to have offspring than the individuals that do not have these valuable characteristics. Hence, in each generation we should expect a slight increase in the number of

individuals that do possess valuable characteristics, and a decrease in the number of individuals that possess alternative characteristics.

Here, then, is a process involving: (1) the presence of individual, hereditary variation; (2) the tendency to increase in numbers; (3) the struggle for survival (or competition

34-1 A COMPARISON OF INCREASE IN NUMBERS IN A GEOMETRIC AND AN ARITHMETIC PROGRESSION

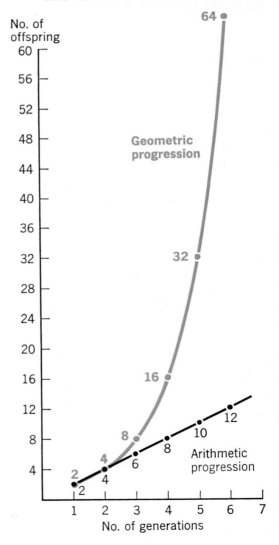

for the needs of life); and (4) a difference in the contribution that different types of individuals make to succeeding generations. This whole process, and especially the struggle for survival and the difference in rate of reproduction between the "winners" and the "losers" of the struggle, Darwin called *natural selection*.

By natural selection, a species of organisms becomes *adapted* to its environment. In the particular habitat in which it lives, it acquires, through the process of natural selection, characteristics that improve its chances of survival and reproduction.

Development of the Theory of Evolution

The theory of evolution was not composed by Darwin out of thin air. The clues that led him to it were gleaned from the discoveries of other men of science as well as from his own studies and experiences.

It was the science of geology—the study of the earth—that laid one foundation for Charles Darwin's work. In the early 1830's, Charles Lyell, an English geologist (Figure 34-2), published a masterwork in geology. In it he pointed out that the earth need no longer be treated as a mystery. The mountains, valleys, deserts, rivers, lakes, and coastlines could have come about through the action of existing forces and natural conditions. A river flowing across a plain slowly carves a valley. Mountains are worn down to hills and finally to plains.

Lyell described the evidence for concluding that such changes had occurred throughout the ages. He greatly extended man's conception of the age of the earth and, hence, the time during which such changes had been occurring. This work fired the imagination of the young naturalist Charles Darwin, for it raised very vividly in his mind such questions as these: If the earth of today has had a long history of change, what was it like thousands of years ago? Did it have the kinds of life we now have? What other life may have existed?

American Museum of Natural History

34-2 Charles Lyell, the English geologist whose work was partly responsible for Charles Darwin's initial, then enduring, interest in the life of the earth's past.

In 1831, when he was twenty-two years old, Darwin set out to study some of the earth's living things. He sailed as ship's naturalist on H.M.S. *Beagle* (Figure 34-3) on a voyage to chart the remote coasts of South America and islands of the Pacific.

Along the coast of South America, Darwin spent long hours ashore collecting and observing. Strange animals greeted his eyes. He was impressed by the tremendous numbers of living things and the small chance for survival that any new individual would have. Later the *Beagle* sailed to the Galápagos (ga·LAH·pa·gus) Islands, some 600 miles off the west coast of South America. Here Darwin accidentally found a living laboratory of evolution. He became aware of the great variations among the organisms that lived upon these islands. There were huge tortoises, which were recognizably different on each island. The common birds were a group of finches which differed from the finches of the mainland. Closely related species had beaks of very different sizes and shapes (Figure 34-4), adapted to feeding on completely different kinds of food. How

American Museum of Natural History

34-3
Charles Darwin and H.M.S. *Beagle*, on which, in 1831, he sailed as ship's naturalist. His records of observations made on this voyage—among them his recognition of evolution on a small scale in the Galápagos Islands—were later to become famous as evidence in support of his theory of evolution.

was one to explain all this diversity on a few small islands in the remote Pacific?

Darwin returned to England in 1837. The following year he read a work written by the English political economist Thomas R. Malthus (1766–1834), *An Essay on the Principle of Population.* In it he read that the rate of reproduction was such that the human population increased many times more rapidly than the available food supply. Malthus believed that the food supply increased arithmetically, but that the human population increased geometrically (Figure 34-1). Such a relation could result only in a struggle for food and, hence, for existence itself. Some men starved in Malthus' time, and some men starve today.

Darwin also studied, among other things, variations in the breeds of domestic pigeons. By careful selection over some centuries, pigeon fanciers had developed numerous strange types. All of these originated from the common pigeon, like the kind now living in many cities. These observations, as well as others showing the origin of new

varieties among cultivated plants, served as still another clue in Darwin's discovery of the role of natural selection in evolution.

With these observations, Darwin had the information needed to formulate a theory of evolution. He worked slowly and carefully. In 1842 he wrote, for himself, a brief 35-page sketch of his theory. Two years later he enlarged this into an essay of 230 pages, which he showed his friends Charles Lyell and the botanist Joseph Hooker, but he did not publish it. He also corresponded with the American botanist Asa Gray about his work. For the next fifteen years, Darwin continued to collect facts to support his ideas in an effort to produce a thoroughly convincing scientific theory.

In 1858 Darwin received a letter from a fellow naturalist, Alfred R. Wallace (1823–1913), who was traveling at the time in Malaya. Wallace enclosed an essay that he had written, and he asked Darwin to read it and then forward it to Lyell. In the essay, Darwin found, almost in his own terms, the theory of *the origin of species by means of nat-*

Reprinted with permission; © 1953 by *Scientific American*, Inc. All rights reserved.

34-4 Finches of the Galápagos Islands. The variations in the beaks and in the manner of feeding fired Darwin's imagination. How was this diversity to be explained?

ural selection. Darwin almost yielded to Wallace the honor of being the first man to announce the theory. However, his friend Joseph Hooker arranged to present the two papers under joint authorship using a single title, *On the Tendency of Species to Form Varieties; and on the Perpetuation of Varieties and Species by Natural Means of Selection.* The papers were presented to the Linnean Society in London on July 1, 1858.

Darwin then hastened to complete his book, *On the Origin of Species by Means of Natural Selection.* It appeared in November of 1859. It contained convincing evidence that animal and plant species had undergone a long process of change.

Darwin's ideas were well received by many scientists, and by a large segment of the public. There were debates, however. The defense and support of the theory was taken up by Joseph Hooker and Thomas Henry Huxley (1825–1895). Darwin himself scarcely entered the debate publicly.

Only a passing reference to man's place in evolution was mentioned in *The Origin of Species.* Twelve years later, Darwin's *Descent of Man* was published. This was the study of the evolution of man.

Darwinian Evolution and Its Relationship to Genetics

In the period immediately following Darwin's contributions, August Weismann (1834–1914) was able to focus the attention of biologists upon the **germ cells** as the basis of evolutionary changes. He pointed out that body cells usually have no direct influence on the production of the next generation. The reproductive cells alone would be involved directly. And the reproductive cells, he thought, were isolated from changes brought about by the environment in the rest of the organism.

In a test of whether environmental changes in parents influenced the nature of offspring, Weismann cut off the tails of *twenty* generations of mice, to find that the twenty-first generation still had tails just as long as those of the first generation. This made quite an impression on his fellow scientists, for it showed that cutting off body cells, or scars and mutilations, did not change the heredity of the organism. From this time in the 1890's until today, the study of evolution has been closely intertwined with that of genetics. Genetics is concerned with characteristics that are inherited. It is these characteristics that are important in evolution, as Darwin recognized. We might say that evolution is chiefly the natural selection of genetic differences.

EVOLUTION, GENETICS, AND THE ENVIRONMENT

There have been other theories to explain how evolution occurs, but none has been established as "true." One of the most interesting and important was proposed by the French naturalist Jean B. Lamarck (1744–1829). In an example often quoted, he tried to explain how the giraffe had come to live in an area in which there was not enough vegetation growing on the ground for all individuals to eat. Figure 34-5a shows how Lamarck proceeded from thinking about an animal's *needs* to what might be called its "desires." Needs (food, for example) would create desires to satisfy the needs in a certain way (eating the leaves of trees rather than competing for the available grasses). Satisfying the desires would lead to the use or disuse of certain parts of the body. These parts would either be strengthened and enlarged, or would diminish in size and become weak and functionless, depending upon whether they were used or not used. In time the changes would become inherited, or so Lamarck believed, and thus the environment would have directly stimulated the altered nature of the species.

This conception of evolution is different from Darwin's view. Darwin began by as-

34-5 A COMPARISON OF LAMARCKIAN AND DARWINIAN THEORIES—THE EVOLUTION OF LONG-NECKED GIRAFFES

a Lamarck's theory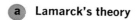

b Darwin's theory

Ancestral giraffes probably had short necks that were subjected to frequent stretching to enable the giraffes to reach the foliage of trees.

Ancestral giraffes probably had necks that varied in length. The variations were hereditary. (Darwin could not explain the origin of variations.)

The offspring had longer necks that also were stretched frequently in the quest for food.

Competition and natural selection led to survival of longer-necked offspring at the expense of shorter-necked ones.

Eventually the continued stretching of the neck gave rise to modern giraffes.

Eventually only long-necked giraffes survived the competition.

Existing data do not support this theory.

Existing data support this theory.

suming that the species is full of hereditary differences (Figure 34-5b). He was not at all clear in respect to where these differences came from. We now know that they arise from mutations of the genes and from alterations of chromosomes (see Chapter 31). But Darwin thought that such mutations as he was aware of were too sweeping in their effects on the organisms, and in consequence too detrimental, ever to be of much significance in evolution. So perhaps, even he thought, the effects of the environment and of use and disuse might be expressed by heredity. At first glance this may seem to be the same as Lamarck's point of view, but it was not.

The real difference between Lamarck's and Darwin's ideas is that according to Darwin, those hereditary variations that in the end survive and become established do so because of natural selection. Whereas Lamarck's idea would lead one to suppose that *all* characteristics are adaptive and spring directly from the organism's response to its environment, Darwin's theory proposes that adaptive characteristics are only the few among *many* hereditary variations that most successfully promote the survival and reproduction of their bearers.

The Lamarckian account of the development of change is simple, clear, and attractive, but unfortunately wrong. Lamarck and many others have repeatedly sought confirmation of the theory, but today no evidence exists to support it. Our knowledge of inheritance tells us that stretching the legs or neck does not affect the DNA of the gametes and cannot, therefore, change later generations.

The Expression of Genes in Different Environments

What is inherited by successive generations of plants or animals is a set of genes that determine specific functions. Of course, environment may modify the way the genes work to produce various traits (Chapter 30, pages 508–10).

34-6 FOOD AS AN ENVIRONMENTAL INFLUENCE UPON GENES IN RABBITS

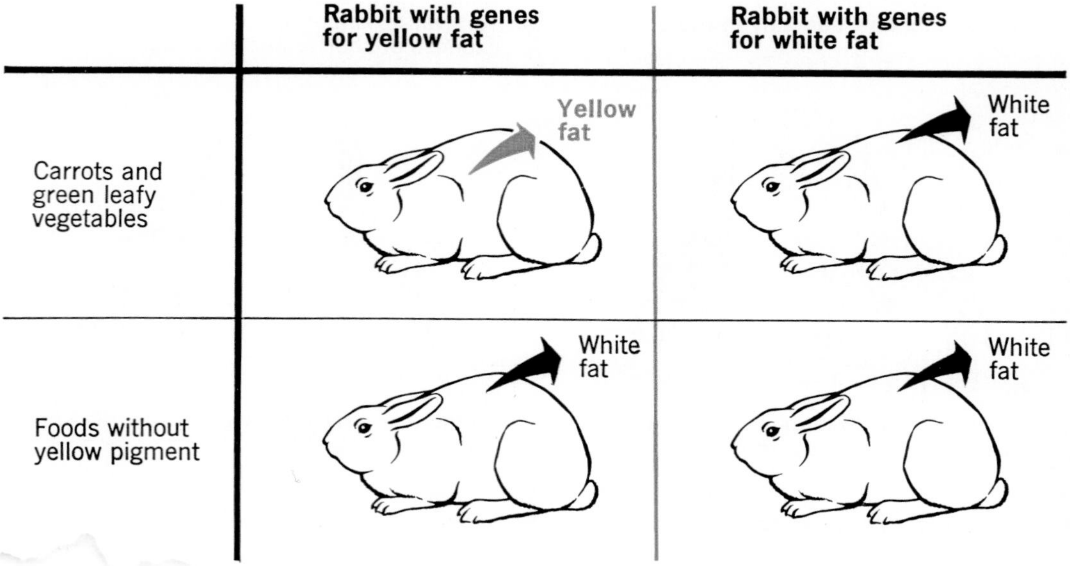

	Rabbit with genes for yellow fat	Rabbit with genes for white fat
Carrots and green leafy vegetables	Yellow fat	White fat
Foods without yellow pigment	White fat	White fat

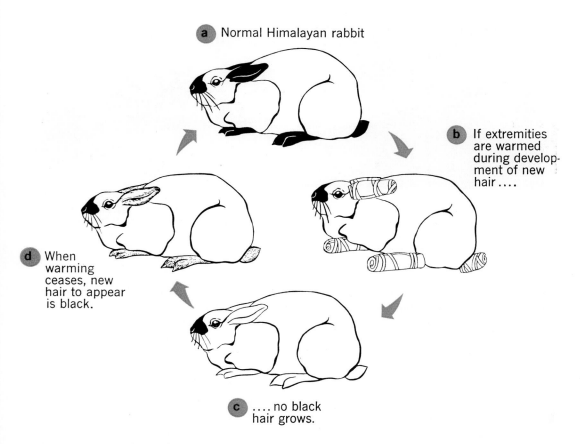

a Normal Himalayan rabbit

b If extremities are warmed during development of new hair....

d When warming ceases, new hair to appear is black.

c ....no black hair grows.

34-7 Temperature as an environmental influence upon genes in a rabbit. If the rabbit should reproduce while in state **c**, what would be the coloration of the offspring?

For example, in rabbits, yellow fat and white fat are genetically determined characters (Figure 34-6). However, yellow fat can be formed only in rabbits whose diet consists of carrots and leafy vegetables rich in yellow pigments. If we place rabbits that are homozygous for a gene for yellow fat on a diet lacking carrots and leafy vegetables, they develop white fat. The rabbits with white fat genes have an enzyme that breaks down the yellow pigment. Hence, their fat is always white, on any diet.

The enzyme that breaks down yellow pigment is absent in the yellow-fatted rabbits, but a change in diet alters the appearance of the rabbits. Is there in consequence any

change in their genetic constitution? Breeding tests show that the genes are not changed. Furthermore, when these rabbits are given a diet of carrots and leafy vegetables again, their fat turns yellow.

Another example of the effect of the environment upon the expression of genetic variability is the Himalayan rabbit, which normally has a black nose, black feet, and black tips of ears (Figure 34-7). By altering the environment we can change the appearance of the Himalayan rabbit to resemble that of a white rabbit.

Thus, as in Chapter 30, we can see that the environment can alter the phenotypic expression of genotype. However, the en-

National Park Service

34-8 Protective coloration. In the photograph at the left, a kangaroo rat and a white mouse are seen against a dark background. The rat is difficult to see. At the right, the same two animals are shown against white sand. In each situation, which animal would be more likely to be seen and captured by a predator?

vironment does not directly cause the appearance of new adaptive hereditary characteristics. As pointed out previously, the role that environment plays in the process of evolution is that of eliminating, through natural selection, those hereditary traits that are nonadaptive, harmful, or relatively undesirable. This increases the frequency of alternative traits that are adaptive, beneficial, and relatively desirable.

Adaptation and Selection

You have learned that evolution consists of changes, through time, in populations of organisms, and that these changes are usually, if not always, adaptive. Organisms have become adapted to their environments because, in the past, those individuals with the best genetically determined adaptations have left more offspring than the individuals with poorer adaptations.

This is Darwin's concept of natural selection, now supported by a large number of experiments performed with all the care and precision that modern biology requires.

The modern evolutionist tries to duplicate in the laboratory some particular phases of nature in order to gain insight into some of the aspects of natural selection. One example is an experiment with deer mice

(*Peromyscus maniculatus* — pee·ro·MIS·kus ma·nik·yoo·LAH·tus). There are two color varieties in this species, buff and gray. Under carefully controlled conditions in a University of Michigan laboratory, these mice were exposed to the attacks of a barn owl. A "jungle" of interlacing sticks gave some cover to the mice. The room was kept almost dark, so that the owl could barely distinguish its prey. On alternate days the floor was covered first with pale-colored soil, which matches the buff-colored mice, and then with darker soil matching the gray mice. Each day, four buff-colored mice and four gray mice were released and exposed to the owl for fifteen minutes. According to the kind of soil used on a particular morning, one set of mice was conspicuous and one set was protectively colored. In 44 trials on each soil type, almost twice as many of the conspicuous mice were taken as of the better-concealed type (107 compared to 62).

Let us go to White Sands National Monument in New Mexico for an example from nature that is similar to the experiment we have described. Here we find dunes composed of white gypsum crystals. On these dunes there are white lizards, white grasshoppers, white beetles, and white mice.

Outside the area, where the soil is reddish and darker, the animals of the same species are red-brown in color, much like the background (Figure 34-8).

The light-colored animals that now live on the white sand dunes are the product of mutation and natural selection that have been going on for thousands of years. Any mutation that would give a paler coloration would be selected. Any mutation that would darken the animal would be eliminated. The white sand has no effect on the origin of the mutations. Mutations to dark or light occur by chance. But once they do occur, natural selection will determine what happens to them.

Most species of animals are relatively inconspicuous in their native environment. Throughout the ages the conspicuous individuals have been captured more frequently than the inconspicuous individuals. This often leads to remarkable resemblances between the animals and their surroundings. The ptarmigan on the left in Figure 34-9 is an example. The color and pattern of its plumage blend almost exactly with the plants, rocks, and soil of its habitat. The in-

dividual on the right is in winter plumage —white feathers against the white snow.

In Laboratory Exercise 34-1 you will work with another situation in which natural selection is effective because of the different degrees of protection afforded by hereditary differences of color—in this instance, in moths.

In recent years there have been many examples of selection in response to insecticides and drugs. You have probably heard that when DDT was first used, it successfully killed houseflies. Now, a number of years later, we find that the houseflies have developed a resistance to DDT. How do we explain this resistance?

During the first year of DDT use, nearly all the flies were killed by the insecticide. However, there were a few flies that, because of their genetic makeup, were not killed by DDT. Since this type survived and reproduced, there were more of the resistant type later on in the locality where DDT had been used. Hence, the next year this insecticide was less effective. Eventually, wherever DDT was used for many years, only DDT-resistant flies were left. *The DDT*

Left, John A. Moore; *right*, George Andrews from Colorado Game and Fish Dept.

34-9 Protective coloration in ptarmigans. Are these two individuals members of two different species? Surprisingly, no. The two ptarmigans were merely photographed at two different times of the year. What environmental factor do you suppose is chiefly responsible for the seasonal change in the birds' plumage?

does the selecting. It does not cause the genes of the flies to mutate to alleles that give resistance.

When resistant flies are crossed with susceptible ones, the F_1 progeny is found to have an intermediate degree of resistance. In the F_2 generation a complex segregation of resistant, susceptible, and intermediate types is found. That type of segregation (see Chapter 33) indicates that the difference between full resistance and susceptibility is based upon a number of pairs of genes located at different points on the chromosomes.

Here a miniature of evolution unfolds before our eyes. Those flies that had the genes for resistance, though few in number at first, have come to comprise almost the total population of houseflies in certain areas. The use of DDT was a selective factor that discriminated against the ordinary housefly and permitted the resistant variety to become the usual form.

Other examples similar to this are known. You have read earlier that certain bacteria have developed a resistance to penicillin (Chapter 11). An example occurs in bacteria of the species *Staphylococcus aureus*. In one experiment a culture of about 100 million bacterial cells was exposed to a relatively weak dose of penicillin. Fewer than ten cells survived. These ten cells became the parents of the succeeding generation. Although the progeny of these cells survived well on the same weak dose, nearly all were killed when the concentration of penicillin was doubled. Again, however, a few survived. The survivors could then be isolated, cultured, and exposed to an even stronger dose of penicillin. This process was repeated five times. Finally, a strain of bacteria was obtained which could withstand a dose 2,500 times as strong as the dose that killed most of the cells of the original culture of bacteria.

The differences between this experiment and the one with flies and DDT are that

(1) the population of bacteria had many more individuals and reproduced much faster than the population of flies, and (2) most if not all of the cells of the bacteria were produced by asexual reproduction, so that there was no apparent genetic recombination. Resistance in the bacteria must have been based on a rapid increase of cells already having a particular genotype. However, resistance increased in a number of separate steps, each time involving the survival of only a few of a very large number of cells. It must have been that a number of mutations, occurring one after the other, produced the apparently gradual increase in resistance. As will be emphasized in the next section, mutations of a particular gene are very rare events. Hence, rapid successions of particular mutations, such as the ones that occurred in *Staphylococcus,* could take place and produce resistance only in populations of organisms that, like these bacteria, can produce millions of offspring in a few hours or days.

Many reports have been published of patients with bacterial infections that are resistant to antibiotics. These are recognized as resulting from the same kind of action as that just described for *Staphylococcus aureus*. Again we see the work of natural selection. As the environment changes—that is, as more penicillin is added—one type of bacterium gains an advantage over the other.

The same process of natural selection by the environment applies to all other organisms as well as to flies and bacteria. Look now at Laboratory Exercise 34-2. It describes and lets you analyze a situation of special interest in human heredity and evolution. It shows how a gene that we normally regard as very harmful (the one that produces sickle-cell hemoglobin in red blood cells) can in certain environments become the salvation of the population. Once again, this is natural selection at work.

A Summary of Natural Selection

Evolution is an idea that developed gradually over centuries. Charles Darwin, in his book *On the Origin of Species by Means of Natural Selection*, proposed the first well-established mechanism for evolution, natural selection. This involves the selection by the environment of the best adapted of existing hereditary variations and of whatever new variations may arise.

In our examples we have demonstrated how adaptation results from natural selection. An adaptation is not an individual adjustment to a particular set of circumstances. It is based on the genes that the individual has inherited. He has received these genes from his ancestors, and he passes them on to his descendants. Under changing circumstances some traits will prove advantageous. The individuals having the genes for these traits will survive and have more offspring than will individuals that lack these genes.

Selection may be thought of as giving direction to evolution, since it results in adaptation of organisms to their environment. Evolution may be thought of as a series of adaptations, each added to or discarded from a particular species, over long periods of time.

THE EVIDENCES OF EVOLUTION

In *The Origin of Species* Charles Darwin did more than propose the theory of natural selection. He also summarized in a critical and masterly way the evidences for the existence of evolution.

Now that we have examined the theory of natural selection and have seen on what a strong basis it rests today, let us see how Darwin recapitulated the evidences of evolution and how they have been enlarged since his time.

Darwin summarized his evidences of evolution under five principal categories:

1. Evidence from inheritance and breeding, especially evidence of variation under domestication
2. Evidence from geographical distribution
3. Evidence from the geological record, that is, from fossils
4. Evidence from "mutual affinities of organic beings," especially homologies— that is, our biological theme of the unity of plan and diversity of pattern
5. Evidence from embryology and rudimentary organs

We will not limit our discussion to the evidence known to Darwin, but will draw also on the vast fund of knowledge accumulated since his time.

The Evidences from Inheritance

Darwin was not able to draw many conclusions directly from his knowledge of heredity, for Mendel's work was unknown to him, and he had a very crude idea of heredity in general. He was able to state clearly that only hereditary variations would have any meaning for the evolutionary process. He thought most of these were very slight differences, since all the large differences, or "mutations," that were known in his time were so harmful to their possessors that it did not seem at all probable that they would increase an individual's chance of survival. Today, of course, we know that mutations may produce very small effects as well as large ones, and occasionally beneficial effects as well as predominantly harmful ones.

Perhaps the best argument for the unavoidability of evolution is the following: The hereditary traits of all living organisms are a product of their genes and chromosomes. Now, genes and chromosomes are demonstrably subject to mutation, that is, to change. How can the characteristics of a species remain the same if its genes and chromosomes are subject to change? That would be possible only if every fresh change introduced by mutation were to be eliminated. But we know that this is not so. Some chromosome changes and gene mutations persist in populations for many generations, and probably indefinitely. It must follow that the hereditary makeup of a species is not, now and forever, immutable. On the contrary, as time passes, the hereditary makeup is subject to change. And that, basically, is evolution.

Apart from the evidence derived from naturally occurring mutations, there is today a great weight of evidence from the study of induced mutations. Man can now subject the genes and chromosomes of plants or animals or microorganisms to X rays or other radiation, to **colchicine** (KOL-chih-seen—a compound obtained from a certain type of herb), or to certain chemicals resembling the purines or pyrimidines of DNA, and can produce mutations in large numbers. He can study the effects of the mutations upon viability and fertility. He can introduce mutations into laboratory populations or even into wild populations, and see what happens. All of these experiments convince us not only that evolution occurs, but that we now have the power to speed it up or to alter its course.

Darwin himself was much impressed, in his day, by man's successes along these lines. Although all the plant and animal breeders of the past could utilize artificial selection only on whatever variations they were able to notice, they had been phenomenally successful in breeding special types of domesticated animals and cultivated plants. An example with which Darwin was especially struck, you may recall from page 592, was the number of varieties of pigeons produced by artificial selection.

Evidence from Geographical Distribution

During his voyage on the *Beagle*, Darwin very early visited the Cape Verde Islands, which lie near the equator off the coast of Africa. These islands are volcanic in origin. Their plants and insects, birds, and other animals resemble closely those to be found on the nearby shores of Africa. Several years later, when Darwin reached the Galápagos Islands, he was struck by the very great similarity of the climate and terrain to that of the Cape Verde Islands. But the plants and animals were totally different, being this time clearly more like the species on the west coast of South America, about 1,000 km (600 miles) to the east. The resemblance in each case to the flora and fauna of the nearby mainland made it reasonable to think that the organisms had come from there. Such an origin, followed by **isolation** and **adaptation** in their new homes, would best explain what had happened to these species.

Many other kinds of geographic evidence pointed to dispersal and colonization, followed by isolation and evolution in the new homes, but nothing was quite as dramatic as the evidence from the oceanic islands. The barriers of the land—mountains, rivers, deserts—provided additional evidence. The barriers to marine dwellers, such as the isthmus between North and South America, which prevents fish only a few miles apart from ever mingling, seemed responsible for great differences between those species of fish. Here the effects of isolation were again plain.

The absence of frogs and other amphibians, which are strictly freshwater vertebrates, from nearly all isolated oceanic islands, and the renewal of life on Krakatoa after it was devastated by volcanic action (see page 172), showed clearly how living things spread to every vacant habitat within the limits of their capacity, and as chance permits.

The startling divergence of such groups as the finches of the Galápagos (Figure 34-4) reveals how wide a modification a few forms can assume in time, if they have a good habitat with no competitors.

Fossil Evidences for Evolution

The record of evolution is given to us by the thousands of *fossil* animals and plants that scientists have dug from the rocks. These organisms lived thousands or millions of years ago, often under conditions very different from those now existing. For instance, one can go to the desert of southern Wyoming, more than a mile above sea level, and find hundreds of fossils of fish that once lived in the sea. Farther south, in the desert of Arizona, is the Petrified Forest. Trees of this forest, when they were alive many millions of years ago, must have lived in a mild, moist climate—a climate not even remotely similar to the harsh desert where their remains are now.

Fossils have been formed and preserved by a succession of lucky accidents. Unless one of these accidents happens, dead organisms sooner or later disappear. If an animal dies on an open hill slope or in a dense forest, the flesh is at once attacked by all sorts of other organisms, from vultures and jackals to maggots and bacteria. All except the bones are quickly gone. Even the bones decay unless they are preserved in some special way. The wood, leaves, and fruits of plants suffer a similar fate.

But sometimes an animal is sucked to its death in the quicksand beside a stream, or dies in a stream bed and soon becomes buried underground, surrounded by sediment and water. Larger animals cannot reach him, the water prevents attacks by other organisms, and the bones are replaced by mineral matter (Figure 34-10a–c). In other instances the eruption of a volcano buries all of the surrounding animals and plants in several feet of ash and cinders. These organisms, too, are preserved as fossils. Still other fossils, like the remarkable series dug up in Rancho La Brea, in the city of Los Angeles, have been preserved in tar pits.

Animals that live in water have a much greater chance of becoming fossils than those living on land. Hence most of the fossil animal life known to us consists of remains of organisms that lived in the oceans or in lakes and rivers. Most of the plant fossils, on the other hand, were trees and smaller plants that grew where, when they fell, they could be converted to coal.

As the years go by, the sedimentary layers or tar in which the fossils are entombed become covered by other deposits, which also are gradually mineralized into rock by the infiltration of silica, carbonates, and other materials carried by underground water. The fossils are gradually buried in the earth under several to many feet of rock.

They may become exposed again years later by changes in the earth's surface. Portions of the earth's crust may become lifted up during mountain-building movements. When this happens, streams will cut gorges or canyons through the fossil beds, exposing some of the fossils.

In other phases of mountain building, the rocks can crack, and part of a fossil bed can be moved upward many feet. This is known as faulting, and it usually happens during violent earthquakes. In the Chilean earthquake of 1960, some layers of rock were moved 300 meters (1,000 feet). Erosion then may expose parts of the uplifted fossil bed (Figure 34-10d–f).

Still other types of mountain-building movements tilt strata upward, or bend them. Then their broken edges are exposed on the surface of the ground, and one can see successively older beds simply by traveling over part of the earth in a straight line. In eastern Pennsylvania, for instance, one can find fossils of the coal forest trees which existed 250 million years ago. Then, traveling northward through New York State, one finds successively older fossil beds, until one reaches the strata lying at the foot of the Adirondack Mountains, which contain fossils laid down more than 500 million years ago.

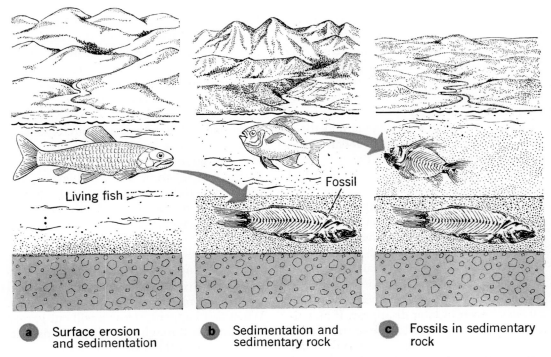

| a | Surface erosion and sedimentation | b | Sedimentation and sedimentary rock | c | Fossils in sedimentary rock |

34-10 A hypothetical sequence showing the physical changes (erosion, sedimentation, and formation of sedimentary rock) associated with fossilization in a stream bed. Silica, carbonates, and other materials from circulating underground water infil-

Determination of the Age of Fossils

Fossils are studied to discover trends in evolution, and to find out, if possible, which fossil animals were ancestors of what others. This kind of undertaking requires some method for dating fossils.

Relative age can usually be determined by the position of the fossil in the sedimentary rock. The lower the layer, the older the rock (and the fossils it includes).

This method, however, tells us only relative age, and occasionally it leads us into error, since faulting and subsequent overthrusting can cover younger rocks with older rocks, as in the base formation of the Sierra Nevada Mountains (which have been formed primarily by the shifting of part of the earth's crust upward and over another part of the crust).

Recently it has become possible to determine the age of some rocks in actual years—though only approximately. Two of the methods that give us this more accurate dating are those using uranium-lead ratios (Chapter 13) and carbon-14. The carbon-14 technique is based on the fact that all living things originally contain a constant amount of a heavy isotope of carbon, carbon-14. This radioactive carbon decays by one half every 5,560 years. By measuring the amount still present in fossils, we can determine the age of the fossil with an error of only a few percent, up to the age of 25,000 years. With less accuracy the method can be used on materials that are somewhat older, but less than 40,000 years old.

Other radioactive or chemical methods of dating, based on isotopes of fluorine and ar-

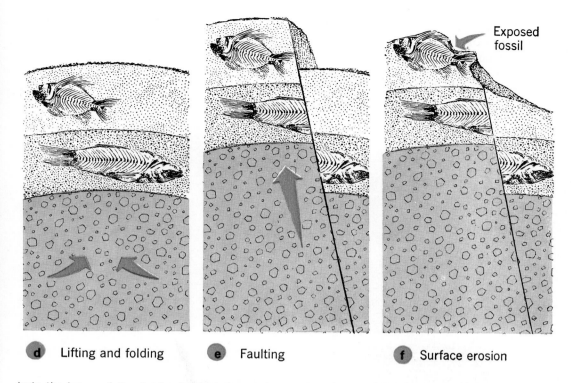

Exposed fossil

d Lifting and folding **e** Faulting **f** Surface erosion

trate the bones of the dead animals and very slowly mineralize the bones to rock. Disturbances of the earth's crust may later cause the fossils to become elevated, and erosion may expose them. How do scientists determine the age of a fossil?

gon, have been introduced recently to help fill the gap between the uranium-lead method, which is useful only for very ancient materials, millions of years old, and the carbon-14 method, useful only for materials less than 40,000 years old.

With the use of such techniques, there have been many spectacular discoveries. For example, a small four-toed animal about the size of a large cat was found fossilized in strata some 60 million years old. From this animal can be traced a gradual line of descent, with continuing slight changes, to the modern horse (Figure 34-11). Similar evolutionary sequences have been established accurately for the elephant, the giraffe, and the camel.

This fossil evidence dramatically shows that life has been gradually changing over millions of years from one form to another. There is no longer any reasonable doubt that evolution occurs, and that it has occurred all through the ages of the past.

Evidences of Evolution from Homology

Students of comparative anatomy have long known that the species that make up any larger group—such as phylum, class, or order—have numerous resemblances in structure (Chapter 20). For example, all the species of Phylum Chordata have at one time or another in their lives a notochord, gill slits in the pharynx, and a dorsal nerve tube. The species of a class would have more in common, and the species of an order still more. The species of a genus might be so much alike that only a specialist could tell them apart.

These resemblances are interpreted as a consequence of evolution from a common ancestor. The species of Phylum Chordata are alike because, at one time in the remote past, they had the same ancestor. The resemblances of the members of a class would be still closer, since they would have had their common ancestor more recently than the common ancestor of all the species of a phylum.

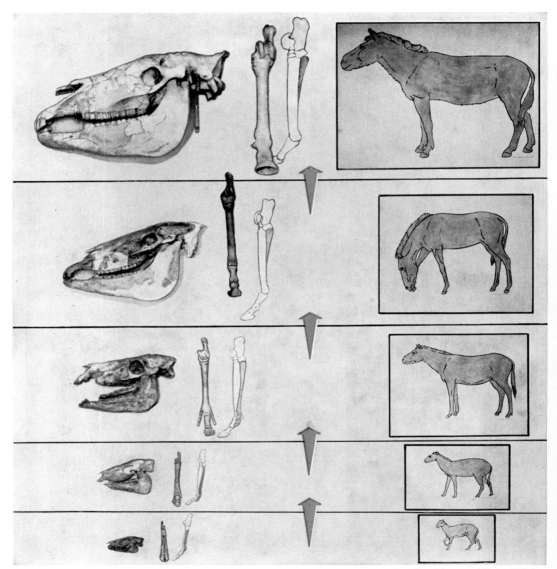

American Museum of Natural History

34-11 Five stages in the evolution of horses, as reconstructed from fossil evidence. The drawings at the right show comparative sizes, beginning with the ancestor of 60 million years ago. At the top is an extinct member of the modern genus *Equus.* In the skulls at the left, note the relative sizes and the changing proportions. For example, follow the increasing size of the gap between the front teeth and the back teeth. The drawings of the front foot (front and side views) show the progressive loss of the side toes and the strengthening of the middle toe.

During the course of evolution, the structures of the various descendants of the common ancestor became increasingly different. In many cases, however, some evidence of similarity still remains. Thus the wing of a bat, the arm of a man, and the flipper of a whale all have the same basis of structure in spite of their superficial dissimilarity (Figure 20-1, page 363). The basis of this similarity is the origin of all three modifications of the limb from the same appendages of the primitive reptiles. This type of relationship of structure is homology (Chapter 20), the principal basis for classifying plants and animals according to their relationships.

Evolution tends to be a conservative process. Rather than develop structures anew, it tends to remodel existing ones. For example, the fishes developed an exceptionally complex group of structures that support the gills. In land vertebrates, these structures have become modified into other organs, such as the upper and lower jaws and the bones of the middle ear. The muscles of the human face are very largely derived from the muscles of the gill arches of ancient fish.

Sometimes an organ is not remodeled into something new during the process of evolution, but instead becomes reduced—and may even lose its function. Such organs are spoken of as **vestigial** (ves·TIJ·ih·al) **organs.** Good examples are the tailbone, ear muscles, and appendix of man.

The appendix (Figure 21-7) is a pouch that leads off from the large intestine and has no important function in man. It has been removed from thousands of persons without ill effects. In other animals, such as the rabbit, the appendix is well developed and serves a useful function in digestion.

The muscles around the ear also are of little use to man, but they move the large outer ears of some animals, such as the donkey or the horse, and allow the ears to be directed toward sounds.

Vestigial organs are not confined to man. The whale has skeletal vestiges of hind limbs buried in the flesh where its tail begins. The python (a snake) has tiny bony structures beneath the skin which are all that remain of its hind legs (Figure 34-12a). The vestigial wings of such flightless birds as the kiwi (Figure 34-12b) are also an example of organs that became useless, but neither lost nor modified into different structures.

The unity of body plan that is so easily seen when comparative anatomy is studied is revealed in microscopic structures as well as gross anatomy. The fact that we can, as in Laboratory Exercise 3-8, examine the common features of all cells and arrive at a concept of the "generalized cell" is one evidence of this. The remarkable uniformity of the mechanism of mitosis in all cellular organisms, and the essential likeness of meiosis and fertilization and the gametes in all sexually reproducing organisms, are homologies. Then there are similarities of physiological mechanisms and of biochemical aspects that likewise reveal the unity of plan among living things. Is it not remarkable that all living things should use nucleic acids, and most of them a particular nucleic acid, DNA, for the vehicle of heredity? Is it not equally a sign of relationship that all organisms use ATP for energy transfers, or that almost all plants use chlorophyll for photosynthesis?

Whence comes this wonderful unity and similarity that is evident throughout the great diversity of more than a million species of animals and nearly half a million species of plants? It need not, of course, come about because all of them have descended from a common ancestor, one who had, by a long process of evolution, acquired these superior devices. But since in our experience all organisms *do* inherit their characteristics from their ancestors, evolution is one way of explaining unity of basic plan combined with diversity in detail.

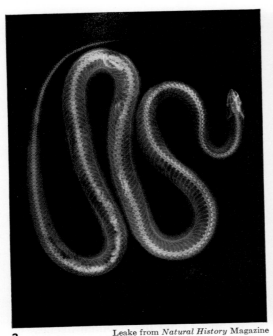

a   Leake from *Natural History* Magazine   b   American Museum of Natural History

34-12   Vestigial organs. Photograph **a** is an X ray of a python. Can you find the vestigial hip bones? Photograph **b** shows the skeleton of a kiwi. The arrow points to the small bones of a vestigial wing. (The wing bones appear somewhat like a "V" lying on its side; the small bones have been highlighted in white, so that they can be distinguished more easily.) Do you suppose the tail is also vestigial?

Evidence of Evolution from Embryology

Not only does the field of comparative anatomy provide evidences for evolutionary patterns, but embryology, as well, gives us data on paths of evolution. The similarities of embryological development among multicellular animals were intensively studied during the latter half of the nineteenth century. These studies led to the conclusion that the embryonic development of the individual repeated the evolutionary history of the race. Thus, it was thought to be possible to trace the evolutionary history of a species by a study of its embryonic development. This idea was so attractive as to gain the status of a biological principle. It was summarized in three words, "ontogeny recapitulates phylogeny," which means that the development of the individual repeats the evolution of the race. So great was the

desire on the part of some to strengthen this idea, that a classic series of drawings showing embryonic similarities was produced in which the resemblances of the embryos of fish and man were remarkable. They were so remarkable, in fact, that further investigation showed that overzealous artistry had indicated a few resemblances that did not quite exist!

Today the idea of embryonic resemblances is viewed with caution. We can see and demonstrate similarities between embryos of related groups, as shown in Figure 34-13. However, while a certain amount of recapitulation is unquestioned, the old idea that a human passes through fish, amphibian, and reptile stages during early development is not correct.

We have now completed our discussion of factors that are responsible for evolution.

34-13 EMBRYONIC COMPARISONS IN FOUR ANIMALS

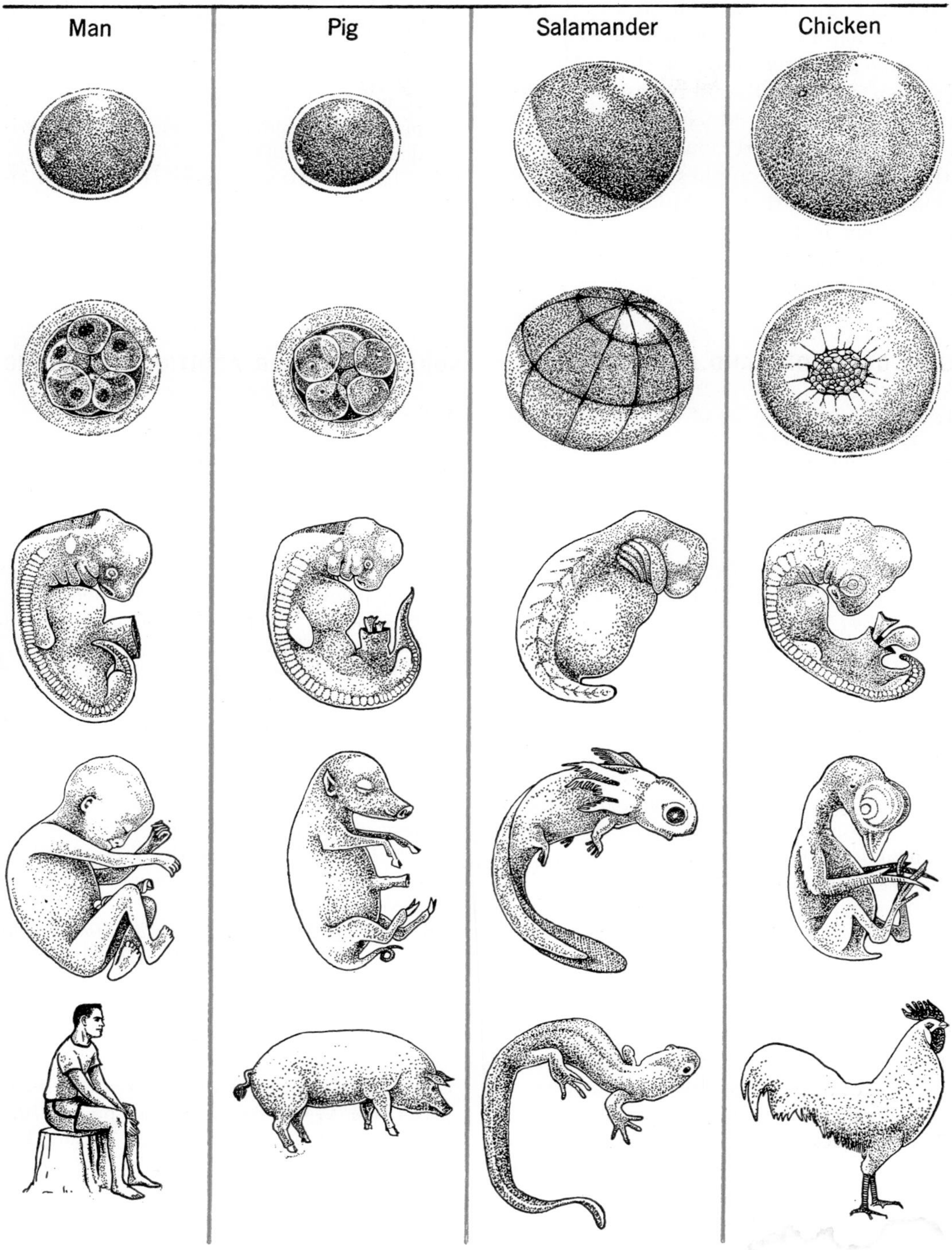

Man	Pig	Salamander	Chicken

In the most general terms they are *inherited variations* and *natural selection,* followed by *isolation,* and in turn followed by variations and natural selection again. Next we shall make a closer study of the inherited variations and how they serve as the mechanisms of evolution. Much that follows is in the nature of reasonable hypothesis rather than fact as it applies to the past. We can only assume that evolution as it takes place today is the same process that has been occurring on earth for hundreds of millions of years.

GUIDE QUESTIONS AND PROBLEMS

1. How does the theory of evolution serve as the great unifying principle in biology?
2. What did Darwin emphasize as the major factors in causing evolutionary changes?
3. What did Darwin mean by natural selection?
4. How did Lyell's work influence Darwin?
5. What was the role of Darwin's voyage on the *Beagle* in defining the problem to which he devoted most of his life?
6. What are the differences between artificial selection (Chapter 33) and natural selection? In what ways are they similar?
7. What was Lamarck's explanation of the factors responsible for evolution?
8. What specific evidence can you suggest which supports the idea that environmental modifications are not inherited?
9. How does natural selection help to explain the variations in color in deer mice, birds, or other animals in two different environmental situations?
10. What are the advantages of using microorganisms such as *Staphylococcus* in studies of natural selection?
11. How would the extinction, or disappearance, of a species of animal or plant be explained according to natural selection?
12. How does natural selection serve as a creative force in evolution?
13. If some adaptations are lost by a species over a long period of time, what might the effect on the organism be?
14. What is the evidence that genera and larger categories of animals and plants evolve as a result of the same processes that produce new species?
15. How do fossil remains provide additional evidence for evolution?
16. How do the anatomical structures of present-day animals provide additional evidence for evolution?
17. What is a vestigial organ? How can we interpret vestigial organs?
18. What additional evidence of evolution is provided by a study of the embryological development of animals?

SUGGESTIONS FOR ADDITIONAL READING

Books

Darwin, C., *The Origin of Species.* [1859] New York, New American Library, 1958.
   The classic work in evolution.
—— *The Voyage of the Beagle.* [1840] New York, Bantam Books, 1960.
   The story of Darwin's journey and his theory of evolution by natural selection.
Dobzhansky, T., *Evolution, Genetics, and Man.* New York, Wiley, 1955.
   One of the leading recent discussions of evolutionary processes.
Huxley, J. (ed.), *The Living Thoughts of Darwin.* New York, Fawcett Publications, 1958.
   Excellent development of Darwin's theory of evolution by natural selection.
Simpson, G. G., *The Meaning of Evolution.* New Haven, Yale University Press, 1949.
   Another of the leading recent accounts of evolutionary processes.
Srb, A. M., and B. Wallace, *Adaptation.* Englewood Cliffs (N. J.), Prentice-Hall, 1960.
   Brief but interesting discussion of natural selection.

Magazines

Eiseley, L., "Charles Darwin." *Scientific American,* Vol. 194 (February 1956), pp. 62–70.
Kettlewell, H. B. D., "Darwin's Missing Evidence." *Scientific American,* Vol. 200 (March 1959), pp. 48–53.
Lack, D., "Darwin's Finches." *Scientific American,* Vol. 188 (April 1953), pp. 66–68.

35

THE MECHANISMS

OF EVOLUTION

Darwin believed that two sets of conditions were necessary for evolution to occur. First, there must be a variety of heritable characteristics among the individuals of a species. Second, natural selection must operate. Thus, over the course of time some of the heritable characteristics would be selected because they allowed the individuals possessing them a greater chance for survival and reproduction.

The heritable characteristics, then, are the raw materials of evolution. Natural selection chooses among these raw materials and selects those that increase the chances for survival of individuals. Heritable characteristics that are "good" in terms of increasing the probability of survival and reproduction will slowly increase in frequency over the course of time. Those that are less useful in allowing individuals to survive and reproduce will gradually decrease in frequency.

Darwin knew little about the cause or nature of heritable variation. Biologists had to wait until the beginning of the twentieth century, and the rise of modern genetics, before they were to understand the basis of variability. In Chapters 30–32 we learned that genetic variability originates in two main ways. First is the mutation of a gene, some alteration in its chemistry that changes the effect it has on the developing organism. Second is the constant recombining of different alleles, which have arisen in the past, to produce *different combinations* of inherited characteristics. We learned a little about these processes in the chapters on genetics. We learned that a mutation can be understood as a change in the genetic "code" of a gene. We learned how the crossing over of homologous chromosome strands and the independent assortment of nonhomologous chromosomes during meiosis leads to new combinations, much as the repeated shuffling and dealing of a deck of cards into "hands" can produce an enormous number of different combinations of cards. Now we shall learn how these processes contribute to evolution. We begin with mutation, for without mutation there would be no alternative alleles that could be recombined.

MUTATION

One of the most curious aspects of mutation, as a source of raw material for evolution, is that two characteristics of the process *seem* at first sight to make it improbable as a source of the heritable variety that we know exists in species. These two characteristics are: (1) the extreme rareness of mutations, and (2) the harmful nature (to the organism) of most mutations.

The Rates of Gene Mutation

Some genes, like some people, are abnormally changeable. One of the genes needed to produce colored grains in an ear of corn, for example, may mutate as often as once in 2,000 germ cells. Other genes are so stable that they fail to mutate during

Life photo, © Time, Inc.

35-1 Hermann J. Muller in his laboratory. For his discovery and analysis of X-ray induced mutations in *Drosophila,* he was awarded a Nobel prize in 1946.

genes, many individuals, and much time all add up to mean that mutation provides ample variability (Table 35-1). Thus, in man there are probably more than 20,000 genes per gamete, and each person comes from a union of two gametes. Hence the probability that you have *some* freshly mutated gene is about two in five.

The Effects of Gene Mutation

We can study the proportion of harmful to beneficial gene mutations by speeding up the mutation process. This can be done by means of X rays, as H. J. Muller discovered in 1927 (Figure 35-1). It can also be done by means of gamma radiation from radioactive isotopes (Figure 35-2).

When Muller used the X-ray method with *Drosophila,* he found by far the greater number of mutations to be harmful. They were so harmful, in fact, that often a fly made homozygous for the mutation died. Apparently, most genes are so completely fitted into the chemical life of the cell that they are indispensable. Any change in one of them, and the cell may not survive—*cannot* survive, when the cell is homozygous for the mutant gene. Such mutations—and there are many—are called **lethals.**

Other mutations, though not lethal, produce individuals that are less effective (less viable or less fertile) in the normal environment. For example, we can put 20 normal *Drosophila* with 20 *Drosophila* that have the mutant gene for white eyes and let these flies interbreed. After a few generations the entire population of flies in the bottle will have red eyes. Natural selection will have eliminated the flies with white eyes. The white-eyed mutant fly cannot survive and develop to adulthood as well as flies that are wild-type. Most other mutant traits show a similarly reduced viability or fertility.

So, once again, we must ask how mutation can possibly produce individual variation that can serve as raw material for *adaptive* evolution.

millions of cell divisions. The mutation rates of most genes fall between these two figures. A mutant form of any particular gene will be found about once in 100,000 germ cells, as an average figure.

How, then, if mutation of a particular kind of gene happens so rarely, can mutation supply the necessary raw material for evolution? The answer is that there are a great many opportunities for mutation. There are probably thousands of genes in each individual germ cell; and for each species there may be thousands or millions of individuals producing germ cells in each generation. Again, there are many generations of individuals over the span of evolutionary time. Hence, though any particular kind of gene mutates rarely, the many

One answer has already been given. Mutation itself is a rare event, and beneficial mutations even rarer. However, the number of opportunities for beneficial mutations is still very large. Table 35-1 is a set of calculations to show what can be produced.

TABLE 35-1

Calculation of the Probable Number of Beneficial Mutations That Can Occur During the Evolutionary Lifetime of a Species

(Based upon conservative estimates of gene number, population size, and number of generations during which the species exists)

Average Data

1. Mutation rate per gene.....1/100,000
2. Number of genes in the organism capable of mutating....1,000
3. Proportion of mutations that are beneficial...........1/1,000
4. Population size of the species............100,000,000
5. Number of generations in the evolutionary life of the species................10,000

Calculations

6. Number of beneficial mutations per individual per generation equals **(1.)** × **(2.)** × **(3.)**, or 1/100,000 × 1,000 × 1/1,000 = 1/100,000.
7. Number of beneficial mutations in the species population per generation equals **(6.)** × **(4.)**, or 1/100,000 × 100,000,000 = 1,000.
8. Number of beneficial mutations during the evolutionary life of the species equals **(7.)** × **(5.)**, or 1,000 × 10,000 = 10,000,000.

There is a second way in which the predominantly "harmful" nature of most mutations can contribute to adaptive evolution.

This way is best seen in an illustration. Suppose that we are dealing with a species that lives in a climate with a temperature varying from 35° to 40° C. Suppose that the normal member of this species can survive a temperature range of 10° C—from 32° to 42° C. Now suppose that in some members of the species a mutation occurs that shifts the range of tolerable temperature to 28°–38° C. Clearly, the mutant organisms will not survive the hottest times of the year. But finally, let us now suppose that the climate changes so that the temperature ranges from 30°–35° C. Which organism is best adapted to survive? Clearly, the one with the new mutant gene.

Let us take another and somewhat different example. Suppose that a mutation has occurred that increases the wing size of a bird. Assume further that this larger wing is too big for the bird's muscles. We then have a mutant bird that cannot fly and that may, therefore, soon be killed by a predator. Surely we would call the mutant gene that produced this condition harmful.

Or suppose that another mutation has given another bird muscles that are stronger than normal—so strong, in fact, that at the first attempt at flight, the strong muscles break the bird's wings. Here again we have a harmful mutant gene.

But suppose that *both* these mutant genes occur together or are brought together (recombined) in sexual reproduction between parents with mutant gametes. Then we *may* (but the chances are still slim) have a bird with a greater capacity for flight. If so, this enhanced flying ability could be highly beneficial.

We can sum up what is shown by these two examples by saying that the effect of a gene is neither wholly harmful nor wholly beneficial, but only relatively so. In our example of a changing climate, the mutant gene was harmful in the first environment, but beneficial in the later, cooler environment.

In our second example, that of mutations for wing size and muscle strength, each mutation was harmful by itself. The two mutations may (or may not) have been beneficial when both were present. If they were beneficial, then the value of each was relative to the other genes that were present (almost any one of which could have introduced its own problem of survival)—and also relative to the environment.

This relativity of the "goodness" and "badness" of mutations would go a long way toward explaining how mutations can supply the raw material for adaptive evolution, except for one further matter—the simple fact that in the original environment in our first case, the gene was extremely harmful. How, then, could the mutation persist in the population until a climatic change occurred?

The same problem faces us in the second example. The wing mutation and muscle mutation were each extreme handicaps to the birds that possessed one or the other. How, then, could the mutations endure in the population until they were brought together to produce a possibly beneficial combination?

A solution to this remaining problem is found in another characteristic of mutations. *Most mutations are recessive.* We can see immediately how this fact permits the gene to remain in the population for a long time. As long as it is present in an animal along with its normal allele (*Aa*), it will have little effect, either harmful or beneficial. Only when it is present in the homozygous condition (*aa*) will it produce effects that lead to its being "selected against" by the environ-

Brookhaven National Laboratory

35-2 An aerial view of the "Gamma Garden" at Brookhaven National Laboratory, located on Long Island near New York City. In the center of the circular plot is a radioactive cobalt source. Different kinds of plants are grown in rows or sectors, at varying distances from the center. Usually each kind of plant appears in several rows, and is thereby exposed at several different distances from the radioactive source. In what respects is this plan better than one in which all plants of a single kind would be grown at the same distance from the radioactive source?

ment. And the Hardy-Weinberg Principle (Chapter 33) suggests that it will occur in a homozygous condition only a small proportion of the time.

Assume, for example, that 1 percent of some gene A has mutated to a. Then, 0.99 of the genes are A, and 0.01 are a. As these genes pool to produce another generation, only 0.0001 of the resulting organisms will have the gene in the homozygous condition. Meanwhile, almost 0.02 of the organisms will be carrying the recessive mutant in a harmless, heterozygous condition.

In this way, even if the mutant is completely lethal in the homozygous condition, it will be selected against very, very slowly. There will be many individuals in the population that will carry the mutant gene over many generations, giving time for environmental change or new combinations to occur.

Thus, we can see that any species of considerable size and age will carry a load of mutations for natural selection to work upon. We can also understand that this would not be true when the genes and chromosomes are in the monoploid condition, for in that case the harm done by the mutant gene would not be suppressed by the presence of a normal, or better, allele. Perhaps this is why the gametophyte generation has dwindled away in the course of plant evolution (see Figure 14-20, page 284). Certainly—and it is a very remarkable fact—*genes do not express themselves in the gametes*, so that even lethal genes are transmitted through the sperm and the egg.

RECOMBINATION

Let us look at a real example of the combination of individually "bad" genes to yield "better" organisms (Figure 35-3). In the moist canyons of the Pacific coast, from sea level to timberline, there lives a species of columbine with red flowers, much like the Eastern columbine. Its flowers are in a nodding position and have relatively long, straight spurs. In Europe there lives another species of columbine that has curved purple flowers and short spurs.

The differences between these two species represent adaptations to different animals that pollinate the flowers. The red columbine is pollinated by hummingbirds. To a bird, colors are brightest in the red part of the spectrum; hence the flowers of the red columbine are bright and conspicuous to the hummingbird. The nodding position of the flowers is an adaptation to the way in which hummingbirds usually visit flowers, by hovering near them and putting their beaks in from below. Finally, the length of the spur of the red columbine is just right for the hummingbird's beak. When the bird is sucking up the nectar at the bottom of the spur with its beak, its head feathers deliver pollen to the stigmas and receive pollen from the anthers of the flower.

The European purple columbine is adapted to being pollinated by bumblebees, whose eyes are sensitive to violet and ultraviolet colors. They suck nectar from flowers by means of a short, curved proboscis. The curve of the spurs of the purple European columbine just fits the proboscis of the bumblebee, so that when the bee is getting nectar it pollinates the columbine.

These two species are easily crossed, and the hybrid is fertile. By artificial selection in the garden, we could easily get a flower with the red color and nodding position of the red columbine, but the curved spur of the purple columbine—or any other combination of characteristics that we might desire. But in nature we find *only the two combinations* of characteristics that have been described. This is because flowers with those particular combinations are most often pollinated and produce more seeds than do flowers with other combinations of characters. We can say, in fact, that

35-3 Interdependence in evolution. It is no accident that in **a** the European columbine and the bumblebee are so well suited to one another. The short, curved spurs of the flower yield their nectar to the short, curved proboscis of the bumblebee. (The proboscis is folded and not visible; after the bee has entered the flower, the proboscis is extended.) As the bumblebee feeds, it pollinates the flower with pollen from another flower, and at the same time acquires pollen that it will carry to other columbines. Can you now explain the nature of the relationship seen in **b**, between the hummingbird and the western (American) columbine?

mutations for long spurs in the columbine are beneficial *in combination with* genes for red flowers, but harmful in combination with genes for purple flowers.

A particular successful combination of characters, like either of the two types of flowers just mentioned, is an *adaptive peak* —a kind of peak of evolutionary perfection. Any mutation that changes these characters carries the species away from the "peak" into an adaptive "valley," and so is harmful under these conditions. In order to reach another adaptive "peak," the population must acquire, at the same time, particular genetic differences in several characters. An individual mutation is harmful or beneficial depending upon the other genes with which it is associated.

Sexual Reproduction and Recombination

From cases like the columbine, we realize that in higher animals and plants *genetic recombination* is as necessary as mutation, to provide the variability required for evolution. Since the only way in which genes can become recombined in higher organisms is by means of the sexual process, sexuality can be regarded as essential to evolutionary change in these organisms.

The importance of sexuality and genetic recombination for generating variability is shown in Figure 35-4. Let us assume that in an original population, all of the individuals are *AABB*. Let us also assume that this is the most adaptive genotype in the original habitat of the population. But now the environment changes and becomes

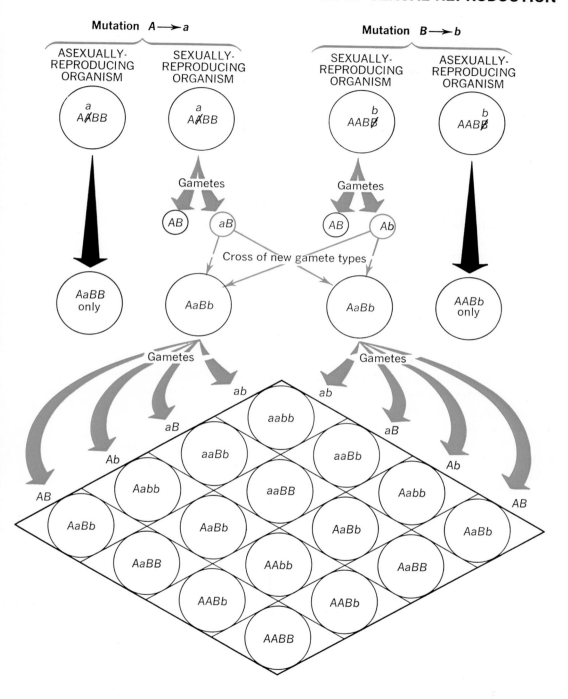

more variable. We might imagine that *A* and *B* are genes that make the animal large. *If food is abundant,* the animal can produce many offspring. But the environment could change from one with plenty of food to one in which food was scarcer. Under such conditions, an animal that was smaller and used less food might be more successful. Gene *A* might mutate to its recessive allele *a,* which represents a gene for smaller size of legs, and gene *B* might likewise mutate to allele *b,* a gene for smaller size of body. Under some conditions, the most adaptive course of evolution would be to change the population from all individuals having *AABB* to all having *aabb.*

Would sexual reproduction and genetic recombination enable this change to take place more rapidly than mutation and selection alone, without recombination? An answer to this question is given by Figure 35-4. If we use the most common mutation rates given earlier in the chapter, we can say that each individual mutation, from *A* to *a,* or from *B* to *b,* will take place in 1 out of each 100,000 sex cells, and so may be expected in 1/100,000 of the surviving progeny, as either *AaBB* or *AABb.* Using the method of multiplying probabilities, which you learned in Chapter 33, you can calculate that the chance of both mutations occurring in the same individual is 1 in 10 billion $(1/100,000)^2$. This chance is so small that the two mutations are never likely to occur together.

If only asexual reproduction were to occur (represented in Figure 35-4 by the black arrows for the individuals on the extreme left and extreme right), then the individual resulting from the first mutation, *AaBB* or *AABb,* would have to produce (on the average) 100,000 offspring before another desirable gene could be added to the combination by a second mutation. Even then, we would be two mutations short of an individual homozygous for both traits.

In a sexually reproducing population, the situation would be similar only up to the point at which the two mutations had occurred independently. Even here the similarity is limited, because the mutations could take place in different individuals and be combined through eventual reproduction among the offspring. If an *AaBB* individual mated with an *AABb* individual (represented in Figure 35-4 by the yellow arrows for the individuals near the top center of the diagram), one fourth of the offspring would contain both of the mutated genes and have the genotype *AaBb.* If such double heterozygotes should mate with each other they could produce, in the next generation, nine different genotypes, seven of which would contain one or both of the mutant genes.

This example is a much simplified model of the actual consequences of mutation. For example, consider the fact that in any crossbreeding population hundreds or even thousands of different gene combinations already exist. If each mutation can triple the number of existing gene combinations, it can eventually make thousands of new genotypes by recombination with other genes.

Two Experiments Illustrating the Importance of Recombination

The great importance of genetic recombination in providing the immediate source of variability upon which selection may act is shown by the contrast in the results of two experiments. About 1905, the Danish geneticist W. L. Johannsen performed an important experiment with garden beans. From a bag of seeds of a well-known commercial variety, he selected the largest and the smallest beans. He then grew a crop from the largest beans and one from the smallest beans in separate plots of ground. As expected, the average size of the beans descended from the large seeds was larger (Figure 35-5) than that of the crop derived

35-5 JOHANNSEN'S EXPERIMENT—
SELECTION FOR SIZE IN BEANS

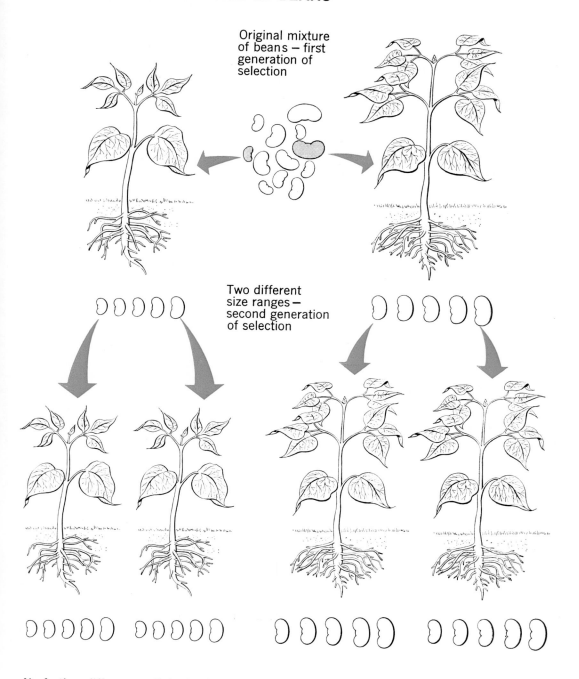

Original mixture of beans – first generation of selection

Two different size ranges – second generation of selection

No further difference (Only the first generation of selection produced measurable results.)

from the small seeds. In each of the two fields, he then selected again the largest and the smallest beans, keeping them separated into four groups this time (Figure 35-5). The next year he found that this second generation of selection had produced no further effect. The effects of the original selection were preserved. But the smallest beans from each of the two fields of the second generation of selection gave rise to a third generation with beans just as large as those derived from the largest beans in the *same* field (Figure 35-5). Johannsen continued this selection for three more generations. He showed that after the first generation, selection had no effect in either increasing or decreasing bean size.

He explained this result by assuming, correctly, that all of the size differences between the beans in the same field grown in the second and later generations were due to environmental modification. In the first generation of selection, he had managed to sort out two pure lines. Each consisted of homozygous, true-breeding beans.

Johannsen thought that the homozygous pure line was the typical genetical constitution of organisms in nature. He therefore concluded that natural selection could not be important in evolution. Most geneticists of his day agreed with this conclusion. For this reason, Darwin's theory of natural selection was regarded by many scientists during the period 1905–30 as either disproved or of relatively little importance.

While Johannsen's experiments were being performed, another experiment on artificial selection had begun. In 1895 the **agronomists** (a·GRON·o·mists) at the University of Illinois decided to find out for how many generations they could produce changes by continuous selection. They used field corn, which is normally cross-pollinated. They started with a hybrid produced by a cross between two of the varieties grown by farmers at that time. They selected for four

different characteristics: high protein content of the kernels, low protein, high oil content of kernels, and low oil. This experiment was continued for fifty generations; the most recent published results were obtained in 1949 (the experiment was briefly interrupted during World War II). In all four lines the population responded to selection for at least thirty-five generations. In the cases of high oil and low protein, a significant change took place in the populations even between the forty-fifth and fiftieth generations. During the experiment, the protein content was more than doubled in the high protein line, and reduced to less than half of the original concentration in the low protein line. Even greater results were obtained by selecting for high and low oil content (Figure 35-6). The kernels of the original population contained 4.7 percent oil. Fifty generations later, the average oil content in the high line was 15.4 percent; in the low line, 1.0 percent.

The results of this experiment with corn are completely different from those of Johannsen with beans. In corn, selection did have a strong effect and was still producing some changes in the population even after forty-five to fifty generations of selection for the same character. How can we explain this difference?

One might, at first, suppose that the corn population responded to selection because mutations were constantly taking place in the desired direction, and that this was not happening in the bean population. But the facts that we know about mutation rates in plants, combined with the figures on the number of plants used by the Illinois agronomists in their experiment, both speak against this hypothesis. In each line of corn being selected, the number of plants raised per generation was between 200 and 300. If we multiply these figures by 50, the total number of generations raised in each line, then we calculate that the total number of plants raised in each of the four selected

35-6 RESULTS OF SELECTION FOR HIGH AND LOW OIL CONTENT IN KERNELS OF CORN

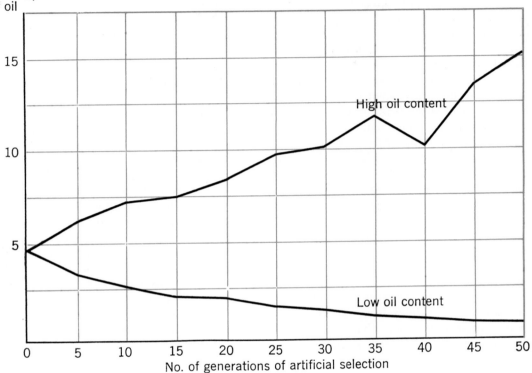

lines was between 10,000 and 15,000. We do not know the actual rate of mutation for changes in oil or protein content. But the rate of mutation for many other characteristics in corn has been measured, and for most characteristics it is as low as one mutation in 50,000 plants—or lower. Hence the occurrence of even one mutation in the desired direction during the fifty generations of the experiment is unlikely.

The slow, steady way in which the populations responded to selection shows that many genetic differences were being sorted out. Unless mutation rates were much faster than normal, and we have no reason for believing that this was so, *the different*

genes for changed protein and oil content that were being selected must all or nearly all have existed in the population before selection began.

We must conclude, therefore, that the difference between Johannsen's results with beans and those of the Illinois agronomists with corn was due not to differences in mutations but to differences in the amount of genetic variability present in the populations *before selection began.* This can be explained by the difference in the way the two species breed. The garden bean is usually self-fertilized. Pollen from the anthers is deposited on the stigmas of the same flower. As a result of self-fertilization, the beans have become genetically homozygous at all or most of their gene loci (pl. of *locus*). Hence, the different plants of any pure line are practically identical in gene content. After the first generation, when Johannsen selected pure lines from a mixed population, the differences between larger and smaller beans in either pure line were due to the effect of the environment rather than to differences in genes. This explains why the progeny from the smaller beans of either pure line turned out to be as big as the progeny of larger beans of the same line.

Corn, on the other hand, is normally cross-fertilized. Pollen from the tassels of one plant is carried by the wind to the ears of another plant. If corn is artificially self-pollinated, the progeny is always poorer than progeny from cross-pollination, because self-pollination makes the progeny homozygous for the harmful recessive genes that are present in every population. Because of cross-fertilization, plants of corn are heterozygous for many pairs of allelic genes. The different individuals of the same variety differ from each other in gene content much more than do beans of the same variety. (In this respect people are like corn, not like beans.)

In such cross-fertilizing populations there is a great store of genetic differences, sometimes called a **gene pool.** Selection, whether artificial or natural, sorts out particular gene combinations from this pool, and so can bring about genetic differences between different lines derived from the same gene pool. Each selected line has a smaller gene pool and hence less variability than the unselected population from which it was derived. If selection does not occur too rapidly, mutations can gradually replenish the gene pool and make still further selection possible.

It follows that in a cross-fertilizing population, the variability upon which natural selection acts has been acquired by mutations that have taken place in past genera-

tions and that have been stored up in the "gene pool." Since most populations of higher animals and plants are cross-fertilizing, this relationship between mutation and selection is the usual one. The results obtained by the Illinois agronomists are like those which we would expect if natural selection were acting on the usual type of population found in nature.

NONADAPTIVE EVOLUTION

We have often discussed adaptation in the foregoing chapters of this book. Adaptation—the process by which an organism becomes fitted to survive in its environment —really has two aspects. The individual adapts to its environment. For example, if you move from sea level at Houston, Texas, to an altitude of one mile above sea level at Denver, Colorado, the number of red corpuscles in your blood will gradually increase; this compensates for the lower concentration of oxygen in the air at a high altitude. This adaptation, of course, does not affect your genes, your descendants, or the future characteristics of the human species. But the species as well as the individual may adapt to its environment. This is the kind of adaptation that we have been discussing throughout the present chapter. It is a consequence of natural selection, fitting the species to its environment.

Nearly all evolution seems to be of this sort. Nearly all—but not quite all. By applying mathematical ideas to genetics, Sewall Wright, an American geneticist, has shown that variation can sometimes occur in a definite *direction* (which means evolution) even without the guidance of natural selection. This process is called **random genetic drift.**

Our study of the Hardy-Weinberg Principle has shown us that we should expect existing frequencies of genes in a population to be maintained, unless modified by some directing factor. Mutation and selection will modify the frequencies of the alleles that are present. Migration of a population to a new environment (followed by selection of genes with respect to the new environment) will do the same. Or, migration of one population into an area already occupied by another population of the same species will result in modification of the frequencies of alleles in both.

Mutation, recombination, selection, migration—these are the important forces that modify the stability of populations as expressed in the Hardy-Weinberg Principle. Is there anything besides? Yes, there is the effect of chance itself, and this is what Sewall Wright has demonstrated.

Suppose we had a human population with its blood group alleles distributed in the frequencies 25 percent I^A, 10 percent I^B, and 65 percent i. The Hardy-Weinberg Principle tells us to go on expecting these frequencies as long as mutation, selection, and migration do not disturb them. Now if the population is a very large one, chance deviations should cancel out, and that is indeed what we will find. But suppose that instead of being very large, this population is very small. Suppose that it comprises only 50 persons per generation. We would expect to find among the 50 children (assuming that the population is constant in size) 25 I^A, 10 I^B, and 65 i alleles.

Yet we know from experience in penny-flipping, card-shuffling and dealing, and genetic experiments, that we do not always get *exactly* what is to be expected on the basis of chance. In penny-flipping, we expect always an equal number of heads and tails; but if you flip a penny only ten times, you might experience a "run of luck" and obtain 9 heads and 1 tail, or even all heads or all tails. In dealing a shuffled deck of cards, you expect half the cards dealt to be black in color, half red; but the first five you deal may all be red, or all black, or any combination of the two. In other words, we know that small samples do not give us a proper representation of the real chances of getting heads or tails, red or black.

Similarly, in our small hypothetical population, instead of the expected proportions, we might find that purely by chance there were 26 I^A, 8 I^B, and 66 i, or some other different combination of frequencies. If this actually occurred, what should you expect in the next generation? Not 25 percent I^A, 10 percent I^B, and 65 percent i but, according to the Hardy-Weinberg Principle, a repetition of the existing frequencies, namely, 26 I^A, 8 I^B, and 66 i. To be sure, one might actually find that the third generation would revert to the original frequencies. On the other hand there might be a further reduction in the number of I^B alleles in the little population. This reduction might even happen a number of times, until the I^B allele had completely disappeared from the population, in which case it could never return unless reintroduced by mutation or by migration of some other population in which the allele is present.

Now this occasional run of luck affecting the frequencies of the alleles present at one genetic locus would be equally probable for every other gene. So if one examined a large number of genetic characteristics, under the control of a large number of independent genes, one would inevitably, by chance itself, find some whose frequencies had shifted far away from the original frequencies. This is exactly what Bentley Glass and his colleagues found had happened in a small population of Dunkers, a religious sect, in southern Pennsylvania. These people for many generations have seldom married outside their own group. They are thus genetically isolated. Among these people, one finds frequencies of the blood groups and other inherited characteristics that are far from what you might expect from their German ancestry and also far from the composition of the American population living around them. Other geneticists have more recently found this to be true of other small, isolated groups.

Another kind of small sampling may be of considerable importance in evolution. When a *few* individuals leave their parent population and start a new and isolated population somewhere else, they are very unlikely to represent exactly the frequencies of the genes in the parent population. If this atypical sample arrives in some place where it can live well and reproduce effectively, it may in time become a large population. The population would not reflect the frequencies of the genes in the old population, but only those of the unrepresentative founders of the new population, as further modified by selection and random genetic drift while the population was small.

Do very small, isolated populations of this sort, in which nonadaptive evolutionary changes may occur, really play a significant role in evolution? In the long run, perhaps not—it is the adaptive changes that seem to prevail. Still, no species is as perfectly adapted as it conceivably might be. A part of the reason may be that in many species, including our own, there is really no one continuous population, but instead a multitude of isolated ones. Some of these turn out more successful than others in their genetic constitution. Chance, nonadaptive traits established in small successful colonies may persist in the species as a whole in any larger populations that later come into being. That seems to be the story of human evolution: we are a species that for hundreds of thousands of years lived divided into little hunting groups, not much bigger than families. Then, one day, some few of these tribes started to cultivate plants, assured themselves of a steadier food supply, and settled down in villages and towns. Civilization has been accompanied by the growth of human populations to very large size; but perhaps our races still manifest some nonadaptive traits established by random genetic drift.

In this section we have discussed the influence of a fifth principal factor in the evolutionary system: *size of population* (the other four being mutation, recombination, selection, and migration). In large populations evolutionary change is principally guided by natural selection; in very small populations chance plays a role and may lead to some nonadaptive characteristics.

A sixth, indispensable factor is needed to render the changes permanent—in other words, to produce species and not simply different populations and races. The remainder of the chapter will deal with this factor, **isolation.**

THE ORIGIN OF SPECIES

Thus far, the process we have been describing has produced no new species. Mutation, recombination, selection, migration, and possibly random genetic drift, have merely brought about changes within species. To Darwin and other biologists of his day, however, the big question was, "Do new species evolve from previously existing species?" If so, how does this come about? This question loomed so large in Darwin's mind that he called his great book *On the Origin of Species* . . . , even though much of its content dealt with other phases of evolution. In this section we shall study the way in which modern biologists are attacking this same question of origin.

When biologists first named species, they were thinking about the kinds of organisms that are the most nearly related to each other. Thus the horse, donkey, and zebra are kinds, or species, of horselike animals. They are placed in the genus *Equus*, which is the Latin word for "horse." Similarly, dog, wolf, and coyote are species of doglike animals. Cat, lynx, mountain lion, and African lion are species of catlike animals. We also recognize many kinds, or species, of such plants as oak trees, wild roses, and lilies (refer to Chapter 14).

35-7 An example of variation in a species. Most of these dogs appear different from one another in a number of ways. Why are they not considered separate species?

Not all animals and plants that look different from each other belong to different species. A great Dane, Airedale, greyhound, bulldog, and Pekingese are very different from one another, yet we consider them as belonging to the same species, the domestic dog (Figure 35-7). Among wild species, the wood mouse of North America includes thirty-seven races which in their typical forms are recognizably different in size, color, length of ears and tail, and reproductive habits. All thirty-seven races are considered to belong to a single species.

A notable example of variation in a wild species is the change that has taken place in the moth *Biston betularia* (BIS·ton bet-yoo·LAY·rih·a) in the industrial regions of England during the past century. A century ago all the individuals were white, lightly speckled with black. Today, around Manchester, the population is composed mostly of dark, almost black, individuals, although there are a few light-colored individuals with which they may interbreed. As we move away from Manchester, the propor-tion of light individuals gradually increases. An explanation of this evolutionary change is studied in Laboratory Exercise 34-1.

Why do we not consider these different forms as separate species? The reason is that they are linked by a large number of intermediate individuals. And this is the case because the different races or breeds can usually mate with each other to produce vigorous, fertile offspring. Even if the most extremely different varieties within a species cannot breed with each other, as would be true of a great Dane and a Pe-kingese, they can contribute to the gene pool of the domestic dog species by cross-ing with intermediate breeds or mongrels. So we do not have a new species. A new species must be isolated. It must not inter-breed with any other species to a significant extent, or its distinctness may disappear.

There are three main ways in which the isolation that keeps species distinct is built up and maintained. One of these is *separa-tion in time*. A species that disappeared one million years ago obviously cannot interbreed with a species living today. A second means of isolation is *geographic separation.* Related species may not overlap in their territories, and so never meet. A third, and most important, kind of isolation is *genetic isolation.* Related species may meet but do not interbreed to any significant extent. Let us consider each of these.

Isolation by Time—
One New Species from One Old

Perhaps no evolutionary line is more completely known from fossils than the evolution of the horse family since **Eocene** (EE-o·seen) time, some 60 million years ago. The earliest known horse was scarcely larger than a fox terrier. It had a short muzzle, low-crowned teeth, and was a browsing animal, not a grazer. It had four toes on each front foot and three on each hind foot—with tiny hooves—and it was clearly a creature of the forests rather than the plains. Its brain was poorly developed, too, in comparison with a modern horse, even when allowance is made for size. It was probably no closer to a modern horse in intelligence than was a primitive monkey to one of the great apes, or even man. The modern horse is a relic of a great tribe that evolved mostly in the forests and on the plains of North America—a rather strange situation when one remembers that all present members of the family have been derived from the Old World and that the American Indians were paralyzed with fright when they first saw Spaniards riding these strange beasts! The modern horse has a long muzzle, with a great gap between the front and back teeth. Its teeth are high-crowned and well covered with cement, a fine adaptation for eating the coarse dry grasses of the prairie. It has only one toe on each foot, the others having disappeared completely or been reduced to small splint bones. The hoof is relatively much larger.

All of these differences are connected in the fossil series by very gradual changes.

The **paleontologist** (pay·le·on·TOL·o·jist) G. G. Simpson has estimated that the populations of horses were so great at every intervening time that one might expect 150,000 favorable mutations of every gene involved in the evolutionary trend of each characteristic. The change produced by each favorable mutation that became established through natural selection must then have been almost unobservable.

Now how can we divide this sequence of horses into species? One has to be arbitrary in such a situation. The fossil records of horses must have involved, with the passage of time, a succession of a great many species, even though many were on side branches not leading to the three horse species (horse, donkey, and zebra) of the present day. The populations at one time were always the descendants of those living earlier, and gave rise to new generations after them without a break. One species was simply transformed gradually into a new species through the accumulation of genetic differences. After many changes, if the changes are great enough, most biologists would probably agree to call the populations at two very different times different species.

Geographic Isolation—
Two or More Species from One

In a large continuous population of a species that spreads over a considerable geographic range, we often find **clines,** that is, regular increases or decreases in the frequency of an inherited characteristic as we pass from north to south or east to west. For example, in North America the red fox is subject to a mutation, incompletely dominant, that produces the beautiful silver fox when it is homozygous. Heterozygous individuals are known by fur trappers as the cross fox, with mingled red and silver hairs. In the North American populations of the fox, the silver type is by far the commonest in the north, the red type in the more southern regions. The cross fox is found most abundantly in between. This cline is plainly related to natural selection, since the silver fox is less conspicuous when hunting its prey across the snow and the red fox is less conspicuous when hunting in the woods and meadows in areas where there is less snow.

One can often find clines that are the results of migrations and the intermingling of two populations that were once more isolated by distance and more distinct. In man, blood group B is commoner in the peoples of eastern Asia than anywhere else in the world. As one moves from Mongolia westward into Europe, there is less and less of blood group B in each population. The frequency of the allele drops from nearly 0.30 in Mongolia to about 0.10 in western Europe. Nearly all of the change along the cline can be attributed to the Mongol invasions in historic times (A.D. 500–1500), for there seems to have been very little blood group B in the earliest people of Europe. We can often divide a large, widespread species into geographic **subspecies** or **races** on the basis of distinctions of this kind; but in reality these nearly always merge gradually into each other, with gradual clines rather than all-or-none distinctions.

It is not uncommon in the history of biological exploration to find examples of populations that at first have been thought to be two distinct species on the basis of their appearance, but later have been discovered to be connected by intermediate populations. We cannot always be sure whether the situation represents two subspecies that are on their way to becoming separate species, or whether the two populations, having been formerly separated, are in fact merging into one.

A clearer picture is presented by what is called a **ring of races.** For example, in the coastal area of southern California there lives a salamander that is light and rather even in color (see Figure 35-8). Farther north it gives place to a darker race, and this in turn is replaced in northern California by a still darker, uniformly colored type that ranges beyond the coastal regions into the interior. In the interior the dark type is replaced, toward the south, by a mottled form. Farther south, in the Sierra Nevada region across the hot dry valley from the coastal habitat, this mottled form is replaced by a differently mottled form. Finally the ring is completed by another type of boldly mottled salamander, which intrudes on the coastal territory of the original form. Suppose we call these "races" or subspecies simply A, B, C, D, E, and F, in the order of the geographic ring described above. Now where they meet, A and B interbreed. Similarly, B and C interbreed; and C interbreeds with D, D with E, and E with F. But to our astonishment we find that in evolution, things that are equal to the same thing are *not* equal to each other! *For A and F, where they overlap in territory, do not interbreed at all.* If the chain of connecting races were to be broken, the now continuous species with its distinct, noninterbreeding ends would have to be regarded as two species, instead of one. A few rings of races of this kind are known in the world, especially among the birds of the Old World. Also known are rings of species in which each species is replaced in an adjacent area by a different but quite similar related species. We can easily imagine the rings of races becoming rings of species in the course of evolution.

On groups of neighboring islands, there are often similar but different species or subspecies of birds or other vertebrates. This, of course, was the situation Darwin found in the Galápagos Islands (Chapter 34). Very likely all the species of finches now found there are descended from one or a very few original males and females that reached the islands from the mainland at some time after the islands' relatively re-

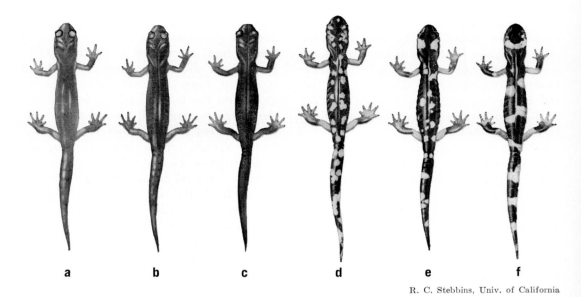

a　　　　b　　　　c　　　　d　　　　e　　　　f

R. C. Stebbins, Univ. of California

35-8　A ring of races. These six salamanders are inhabitants of California and nearby areas. Complex interrelationships have led to their being considered subspecies of one species. Salamanders **a** and **b** will interbreed, as will **b** and **c**, **c** and **d**, **d** and **e**, and **e** and **f**. But **a** and **f**, although they come in contact, will not interbreed.

cent volcanic origin. Since then, the geographic isolation from the mainland has permitted these island species to evolve independently. The distances over water between the several islands are great enough to prevent much interbreeding of the isolated populations. One would, then, expect to find at least one species of finch on each populated island. But how can we explain the presence of several very distinct species on a single island? The problem is more complex than we perhaps thought. Another kind of isolation is involved.

Genetic Isolation— Barriers to Crossbreeding

Even if two populations look much alike, we assign them to different species if they do not cross successfully with each other and produce vigorous, fertile offspring. For instance, the wild coyote looks much like a mongrel dog. Hybrids between coyotes and dogs are rare. Mating between the two

species takes place less readily than between individuals of the same species. The male F_1 hybrids are sterile. Thus, dogs and coyotes can exist side by side and remain distinct from each other.

Reproductive separateness, or isolation, of species takes various forms:

1. Sometimes hybrids cannot be formed at all, or die when young. For example, the eggs of a bullfrog fertilized with sperms of the common leopard frog start to divide, but the embryos soon die.
2. The hybrids may be vigorous but completely or partly sterile. A cross between a horse and a donkey gives us a mule. But a mule is sterile. The same is true of crosses between chickens and turkeys or pheasants.
3. Individuals of two different species may not cross in nature, but they may form vigorous fertile hybrids if crossed

artificially. The mallard and pintail ducks are an example. They are found in the same habitats throughout North America, and individuals intermediate between them are relatively rare. Yet when they are put together in the same pen, they will mate with each other, and the hybrids are fertile. The reason they do not cross in nature is that their mating instincts and nesting habits are very different. Hence the situation rarely arises when a mallard duck, ready to raise a family, encounters a pintail drake in a condition to do the same, or vice versa.

Different courtship patterns may also isolate species. The male of the grouse or woodcock performs an elaborate dance in front of the female before mating takes place. This dance apparently stimulates the sex hormones in the female who watches it and causes her to release her egg cells. Since females are most strongly stimulated by the dance of males of their own species, there is little mating with males of other species.

Many flowers such as orchids, milkweeds, and snapdragons have evolved complex shapes and colors, which insure that flower-pollinating bees will visit only one kind of flower at a time. One experimenter planted alternate rows of a garden with two species of snapdragons having different flowers. When he watched the bees pollinating these flowers, he found that a bee would usually visit flowers of only one species during a particular flight. It would regularly fly over the row containing the second species. Other bees from the same hive would visit and pollinate the second species. Tests of the seeds from this field showed that only 2 to 3 percent of the seeds formed by bee pollination were hybrid. Artificial cross-pollination, carried out as a control, yielded large numbers of vigorous hybrids.

This reproductive isolation is, on the one hand, a basis of our definition of species and, on the other hand, a major factor in creating one species from another. Therefore, the problem of the origin of species is basically one of discovering how this reproductive isolation takes place.

We find that it almost always begins by physical separation of one part of a population from the remainder, as, for example, when part of a population crosses a stream bed during a drought and cannot return after normal rains. Hurricanes blow birds from mainland to islands, and so on.

Once separation occurs, natural selection may act differently on the two populations and lead to reproductive isolation.

Many examples have already been given in which partial or complete reproductive barriers are developed. The ring of races in salamanders (Figure 35-8) is one of these.

Polyploid Species

In most groups of animals and in many plants, the origin of species is a process requiring hundreds of thousands of years. But there is one way in which species can originate almost instantaneously. This is through a cross between two existing species, *followed by doubling of the chromosome number of the hybrid.* For instance, in 1928 a Russian geneticist, Karpechenko, crossed a radish with a cabbage (Figure 35-9). The resulting plant was very large and vigorous, but when it blossomed it turned out to be completely sterile. Karpechenko studied this plant and found that the chromosomes did not pair in meiosis. The cause? The 9 chromosomes derived from a radish do not "match" the 9 derived from cabbage—i.e., they are not homologous. Because they are single, the chromosomes in the hybrid do not go to the equator of the spindle, and many of them are not included in the spores that result from meiosis. Hence the pollen grains formed by these spores are sterile and empty.

Occasionally meiosis fails altogether and there is no reduction in the number of chromosomes. Thus, quite rarely, pollen grains and egg cells are produced that have all of the 18 chromosomes (9 of the radish parent and 9 of the cabbage parent). Karpechenko learned that he could increase the frequency of these unusual gametes by subjecting the buds of the hybrid plant to various shocks and severe treatments. When gametes of this type unite, they produce a plant with twice the normal number of chromosomes —36 instead of 18. Since this plant has half its chromosomes derived from the radish and half from the cabbage, it is still intermediate, like the sterile hybrid. But when meiosis takes place in this 36-chromosome plant, the 18 chromosomes derived from the radish pair with each other, and those from the cabbage do the same. Consequently, meiosis is normal, and the gametes receive 18 chromosomes, 9 of the cabbage type and 9 of the radish type. Offspring from these gametes are fertile and breed true for an intermediate phenotype like that of the F_1 hybrid. Since the hybrid has more chromosomes than normal, actually two diploid sets, it is said to be **polyploid** (POL·ih·ploid).

When the polyploid hybrid is crossed with either of its original diploid parental species, the offspring are sterile. Consequently, a polyploid hybrid has all of the essential requirements of a distinct species. It looks different from any other species, including its original parents; it is fertile and breeds true; and it forms sterile hybrids when crossed with any other species, including its own original parents. Thus a new polyploid species has been created.

Karpechenko's polyploid species was the first species in all history to be made artificially by a man. Since his work, many doubled hybrids have been made in various groups of higher plants, and many well-known species have been shown to be doubled hybrids. Examples are cultivated wheat, cotton, and tobacco; garden flowers such as the cultivated marigold and larkspur; and wild species such as the blue flag iris and the "Jerusalem artichoke."

Colchicine, a drug obtained from the crocus and used for treating gout, has been found to be very effective in doubling the chromosome number of cells exposed to it. It does this by destroying the spindle on which separation of the chromosomes into two groups normally takes place. Through the use of colchicine, the artificial production of polyploid species has become a major achievement in man's control of the evolutionary process in plants.

THE ORIGIN OF GENERA AND LARGER GROUPS

The final question which we must ask about the forces of evolution is: Can mutation, recombination, selection, genetic drift, and barriers to crossbreeding explain the major trends of evolution, such as the divergence of catlike from doglike animals and the evolution of the horse from its small primitive ancestors?

The mechanisms that govern these major trends of evolution cannot be studied directly, since they took place many thousands or millions of years ago. Nevertheless, the kinds of variation that we see in existing populations, plus the types of evolutionary trends deduced from the most complete series of fossils, provide strong evidence for the belief that the same evolutionary forces we see in operation today have guided evolution in the past.

In the first place, some of the characteristics that we see varying in existing populations are like those whose change over long periods of time has made the major trends of evolution. For instance, mutations for a greater or lesser amount of webbing of the toes are common in human populations. In our species they are obviously of no selective value. But the same type of mutation occurring in an animal like the otter, which spends much of its time swimming, might help it to swim better.

Along the coast of California there lives an animal known as the sea otter. It is obviously related to the common otter, though zoologists place it in a different genus. It has webbed toes and spends all of its time in the water. Its ancestors probably evolved along a different line from that leading to the common otter partly because of the appearance and establishment of mutations for webbed toes. Similar mutations probably played an important role in the evolution of seals from land-inhabiting ancestors.

There is another type of evidence showing that the origin of genera and families of organisms is governed by the same forces as those responsible for the origin of species. In many instances, even experienced students of a group of organisms cannot agree as to whether two species should be placed in the same or in different genera. Furthermore, genetic evidence has sometimes shown that species of animals or plants that all biologists had previously placed in separate genera are actually as closely related as species belonging to the same genus.

For instance, the yak, a long-haired species of the cattle family living in Tibet and other high mountain regions of Asia, has been placed by most zoologists in a separate genus from domestic cattle. But hybrids between yaks and cattle are often bred, and progenies from such hybrids are among the breeds of cattle normally raised in parts of mountainous Central Asia.

The evolution of a new genus is apparently the result of the appearance in a species of a particularly successful combination of characteristics. As this species and its descendants spread over a large area, they become broken up into different species. Each of these derived species may retain the successful combination of characteristics and gain new characteristics by recombining genes from the gene pool present in the originally successful species of the evo-

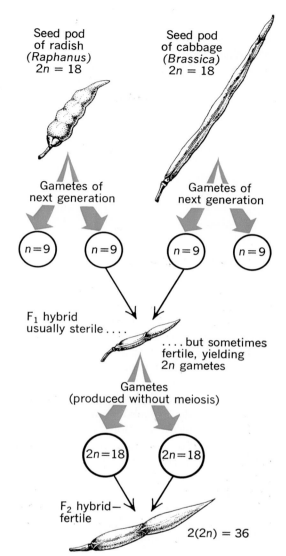

35-9 A diagram of Karpechenko's cross of a radish with a cabbage. (Only the seed pods of the parent plants and of the hybrids are shown.) The F_1 hybrid was sterile. Its nonhomologous chromosomes caused the meiotic process to be interrupted—or to produce sterile gametes. Occasionally meiosis failed altogether, and fertile gametes with 18 chromosomes were produced. (In what respect are these gametes with 18 chromosomes appropriately described as $2n$? In what respect are they *not* truly $2n$? Are the two sets of chromosomes in each gamete homologous?)

lutionary line. With the passage of long ages, new mutations and recombinations take place, and the closer relatives of the originally successful species may die out. From these considerations we see that in the origin of genera and higher categories, we need to consider only two factors that were not considered in the origin of species. These are the multiplication of populations having a particular combination of genetic characteristics, and the extinction of intermediate populations. Such events are almost certain to take place during the long ages of evolutionary time.

CONCLUDING REMARKS

We have learned that mutation, recombination, selection, and isolation (or barriers to crossbreeding) are the principal mechanisms of evolution. Migrations also modify the frequencies of genes. Random genetic drift may be important in small populations; and doubling the chromosome number in a sterile hybrid may create new species abruptly, especially among plants.

Mutation, recombination, selection, and isolation, acting over long periods of time, produce new varieties and species. The origin of higher categories depends not only upon these four processes but upon two others: (1) multiplication of populations with particular genetic characteristics, and (2) extinction of intermediate populations.

GUIDE QUESTIONS AND PROBLEMS

1. What are the principal mechanisms of evolution?
2. What considerations seem to suggest that gene mutations might not provide the raw material for evolution?
3. How did H. J. Muller contribute to the study of mutation?
4. What factors make possible the occurrence of enough beneficial gene mutations to provide raw materials for adaptive evolution?

5. What characteristic of most gene mutations permits them to survive in the population for a long period of time?
6. How may one and the same gene mutation be either harmful or beneficial?
7. How do the European and American columbines illustrate your answer to question 6?
8. How does sexual reproduction bring about the recombination of mutant genes?
9. How did Johannsen's experiment lead him to the conclusion that natural selection was not a significant factor in evolution?
10. What basic factor probably accounts for the difference between Johannsen's results and the experiments in Illinois with corn?
11. What does the term *species* mean to a modern biologist?
12. What types of barriers to crossbreeding exist in nature?
13. How does reproductive isolation help us to define a species?
14. What is a polyploid species?
15. What is the evidence that genera and larger categories of animals and plants evolve as a result of the same forces that produce new species?

SUGGESTIONS FOR ADDITIONAL READING

Books

Dobzhansky, T., *Evolution, Genetics, and Man.* New York, Wiley, 1955.
    An introduction to evolution and genetics.
Dowdeswell, W. H., *The Mechanism of Evolution.* New York, Harper & Row, 1960.
    A modern report on natural selection.
Huxley, J., *Evolution in Action.* New York, Harper & Row, 1953.
    A modern view of the evolutionary process.

Magazines and Journals

Dobzhansky, T., "The Genetic Basis of Evolution." *Scientific American,* Vol. 182 (January 1950), p. 32.
Glass, B., "The Genetics of the Dunkers." *Scientific American,* Vol. 189 (August 1953), p. 76.
Hollander, W. F., "Lethal Heredity." *Scientific American,* Vol. 187 (July 1952), p. 58.
Ryan, F. J., "Evolution Observed." *Scientific American,* Vol. 189 (October 1953), p. 78.

36

THE ORIGIN

AND THE HISTORY

OF LIFE

In the previous two chapters, we examined the natural forces that, working together throughout the long history of living things, have changed the plants and animals of the past into those living today. We have read about the weaknesses in the use-and-disuse theory of evolutionary changes as stated by Jean Baptiste Lamarck and others. We have surveyed the ideas of Charles Darwin and Alfred Russel Wallace, who independently arrived at a theory of evolution by means of natural selection. And we have noted carefully the ways in which modern scientists have strengthened this theory with observation, experiment, and reasoning.

In particular, we have studied modern views about gene mutation and the recombination of genes. We have thought about how these mechanisms provide a natural pool of variability within species of plants and animals. We have also studied how these variations are selected by various environmental conditions. And we have examined the significance of geographic and genetic isolation, as well as of time, in the origin of new species. All of these phenomena play their part in evolution.

Scientists have yet to find any facts in nature or in the laboratory that cannot be explained on the basis of the theory of evolution, and there are many facts that are inexplicable without it. Nevertheless, we need more information on all problems of evolution: How did life originate? What is the evolutionary history of the major groups of plants and animals? How do genetic variability and selection form races, species, and genera? We have considerable information on all of these topics. We need more—the desire for knowledge is insatiable.

THE ORIGIN OF LIFE

One of the most interesting questions about evolution is how life started. What did the first organisms look like? Where did they live? When did they live? Where did they come from?

We do not have many facts to help us answer these questions. The one thing we can be relatively sure about is that new life is not starting now. In Chapter 2 we learned about the hypothesis of spontaneous generation. Using Pasteur's and others' experiments as evidence, there is no reason to believe that spontaneous generation can occur today.

If life does not arise spontaneously, where did all the animals and plants living today come from? The answer is, of course, from their parents! But that answer does not satisfy us. We certainly want to know where the parents came from, where the parents' parents came from, and so on. We cannot escape the question.

There are three scientific possibilities. First, living things could always have existed on the earth. In this case there would have been no beginning. Second, the ancestors of the earth's plants and animals could have come from some other world, that is, from outer space. Third, life could have originated on earth at some remote time in the past.

The first possibility, that life was always present on the earth, can be excluded. Astronomers and geologists are convinced that the earth had a beginning about 5 billion years ago, though just how is not so clear. Neither the earth nor its inhabitants, therefore, could have existed for all time. There must have been a beginning of life on the earth.

That leaves us with the second and third possibilities—either life came to the earth or it started on the earth.

Life from Other Worlds

A favorite way of explaining the origin of life on earth has been to suggest that life was introduced by way of dust particles or meteorites from distant parts of the universe.

There are two objections to this hypothesis. First, it explains only the appearance of life on earth. We are still left with the problem of explaining how life arose on some distant planet.

The second objection comes from our knowledge of outer space. The tremendous extremes of heat and cold, the excessive radiations, and the lack of an atmosphere in outer space cannot be tolerated by any known forms of life. Furthermore, meteors would make poor vehicles to carry life. The meteors, or shooting stars, often seen at night are particles of stone or metal that burst into flame as they plunge into the "sea of air" surrounding the earth. Surely, bacteria hitching a ride on one of these shooting stars would come to a blazing finish in the upper atmosphere, provided, of course, that they had not been destroyed already by deadly radiation or by the violent extremes of temperature in outer space. Neverthe-

less, scientists have not given up looking for evidences of life in the inside of meteorites.

With the possibility of being able to travel in space, scientists are busily making plans to look for evidence of life in space, as well as on the moon and any planets that can be investigated. It will be difficult to study the origin of life on other worlds. It may be more profitable to ask if life could have arisen on the earth.

The Origin of Life on Earth

There are many reasons, none entirely convincing, that make us suspect that life did originate on the earth by spontaneous generation. That is, it appeared when there was no life before. This may sound very strange, if you remember the arguments given in Chapter 2 to show that spontaneous generation is impossible. The arguments of Chapter 2 are still valid, but they are valid only for the conditions of today. The earth of 5 billion years ago was a very different place from what it is today. One most profound difference, of course, was the absence of hordes of hungry living things, seeking every bit of available nourishment.

Many astronomers, geologists, and chemists are reasonably sure that at some early stage in the earth's history, it was a molten mass. At such high temperatures atoms combine, separate, and recombine in a variety of ways. The earth's crust was a seething test tube.

Slowly the earth cooled. As it cooled, new chemical compounds were formed. Enough is known about the behavior of chemical substances at high temperatures for us to be sure that the atmosphere then was very different from that of today.

Today our atmosphere is composed of nitrogen, oxygen, carbon dioxide, water vapor, and traces of other gases. When the temperature of the earth was very high, however, these gases could not have existed in the atmosphere. The oxygen would have combined with hydrogen (to form water) and with elements of the earth's crust—such as silicon, aluminum, and iron. Similarly, nitrogen would have combined with hydrogen, forming ammonia (NH_3), and with elements of the earth's crust. The oxygen and nitrogen, therefore, would be present in the atmosphere only in the form of reduced compounds, not as free gases (O_2 and N_2). Even today, oxygen exists in the atmosphere largely because it is released by the photosynthesis of green plants.

The primitive earth probably had an atmosphere of methane (CH_4), ammonia (NH_3), water vapor (H_2O), and hydrogen (H_2). It is believed that these relatively simple substances gradually combined into increasingly complex molecules. Finally these complex molecules associated to form systems that had a unique feature: they were self-producing. That is, they could make from the chemical substances around them other systems like themselves. Life had started.

How could all this have come about? No chemist can combine methane, ammonia, water vapor, and hydrogen and produce a living creature. Yet we are beginning to believe that some of the steps that must have occurred in the origin of living things can be repeated in the laboratory.

Harold Urey (Figure 36-1), a Nobel prizewinner then at the University of Chicago, had become interested in the evolution of chemical compounds under primitive earth conditions, and he discussed this with one of his students, Stanley Miller (Figure 36-2). In May 1953, Miller published in *Science*, a famous scientific journal, an article entitled "A Production of Amino Acids Under Possible Primitive Earth Conditions." The article begins as follows:

The idea that the organic compounds that serve as the basis of life were formed when the earth had an atmosphere of methane, ammonia, water, and hydrogen

United Press Int.

36-1 Harold Urey, whose interest in events on the primitive earth encouraged Stanley Miller (Figure 36-2) to provide a dramatic bit of evidence in support of the spontaneous origin of life.

instead of carbon dioxide, nitrogen, oxygen, and water was suggested by Oparin [a Russian scientist].

In order to test this hypothesis, an apparatus was built to circulate CH_4, NH_3, H_2O, and H_2 past an electric discharge.

Figure 36-2 shows the basic design of the apparatus used by Miller in his experiments. The apparatus contained water in a flask, and the application of heat caused the water to boil continuously. The rest of the apparatus was filled with methane, ammonia, hydrogen, and water vapor.

The electrical discharges were intended to duplicate conditions that we assume were present on the primitive earth—violent electrical storms, much more severe than any occurring today. Actually, ultraviolet radiation should have been used too, since it

36-2 Stanley Miller, shown with apparatus designed for the now famous experiment that demonstrated amino acid synthesis in a simulated primitive atmosphere.

was a prevalent form of energy on the primitive earth. But in this particular experiment, the principal requirement was to provide intense bursts of energy.

Miller allowed the experiment to run for a week. At the end of that time his originally colorless solution had turned red. He analyzed the solution and found that a great variety of organic molecules were present. Some he could not identify with certainty. However, some of the molecules present were *amino acids*. All of these acids contain carbon, hydrogen, oxygen, and nitrogen. Amino acids are the structural units of proteins (page 106).

And so it may have started. The gases of the primitive atmosphere, exposed to light-ning and ultraviolet light, could have combined to form simple organic compounds. As the earth continued to cool, the water vapor would have condensed to form pools, lakes, and oceans. Simple organic substances would begin to accumulate in these waters. Millions of years passed, and the waters became a "hot thin soup."

The compounds of the soup could be expected to react with one another, producing a variety of chemical substances. For example, the way amino acids might have been tied together to form the first protein molecules was suggested by Sidney W. Fox of Florida State University. Fox took a mixture of 18 to 20 amino acids and heated it to the melting point. When the mass was allowed to cool, he discovered that many of the amino acids had bonded together to form chains not unlike those characteristic of protein structure. In a paper given in 1957 during a conference on the origin of life, Fox stated:

The prebiochemical distance from such organic compounds as amino acids to the origin of life, however, must be quite large. . . . The work to be described in this paper, however, began with an attempt to understand only the prebiochemical origin of protein. The experiments yielded a succession of unexpected results and stimuli for new experiments such that a unified theory of biochemical origins is emerging.

Another example comes from the work of Melvin Calvin of the University of California. He was able to show that gamma radiation, acting on a mixture of methane, ammonia, hydrogen, and water, produces molecules of amino acids and sugars. Also produced are some biologically important compounds tentatively identified as purines and pyrimidines. Purines and pyrimidines (see Chapter 32) are very important in the function and heredity of living organisms. Vital substances such as ATP, DPN, and the nucleic acids are made from purines and pyrimidines.

We do not have experimental evidence for the next steps in the origin of life. We must guess. Some chance association of proteins, purines, pyrimidines, and other organic compounds might have given rise to a system that could reproduce. Such a system would have to have a boundary separating it from the rest of the "hot thin soup," its environment. It would need to be able to obtain chemical energy from other substances in its environment. Furthermore, it would have to be able to draw in chemical substances from the environment, and, from these substances, make more of itself. That is, it would grow.

Once a system can reproduce itself from raw materials of the environment, we can say that it is alive. The primitive systems of living matter probably formed and disintegrated on many occasions. But some systems survived, and from these, life on the earth originated.

No doubt changes were slow over thousands of years. A living mass would come to contain many proteins, enzymes, and nucleic acids. Possibly it would be broken into smaller parts from time to time. Each subglob could then start a new living mass. It is reasonable to suppose that natural selection began to operate this early. The systems that were best organized and most stable, that grew the fastest, that divided most frequently, and that transmitted their own qualities most effectively to their descendants would survive and displace the others.

Life at this time would be carrying on a heterotrophic existence (page 199). Later, as the conditions of the earth changed, and as a new kind of atmosphere arose, organic compounds would cease to be produced. The heterotrophic life would have gradually become difficult. It would have finally become impossible if the supply of organic materials in the primitive oceans had been exhausted.

This dilemma must have been avoided by the evolution of a photosynthetic process. Once we can assume that this step was taken, we can make reasonable guesses about the major steps leading to the evolution of the primitive organisms.

While we cannot consider that the hypothesis just outlined has been fully established, it has offered us an opportunity to demonstrate the kind of speculative thinking that precedes the creation of sound hypotheses. More than that, it has given us a chance to see how scientists try to accept only those hypotheses that can be tested by experiment and that will account for all of the known and relevant facts.

PRIMITIVE ORGANISMS

Certainly we have no direct or indirect fossil evidence that the earliest living things were associations of organic molecules living in a hot thin soup. The earliest known organisms to be preserved as fossils were almost certainly cellular. They were probably similar to modern microorganisms, particularly blue-green algae and bacteria.

Fossil remains of blue-green algae have been found in rocks that are about 1.6 billion years old (and indirect evidence suggests that some rocks 2.3 billion years old may represent the remains of blue-green algae—see Chapter 13).

Bacteria, although nearly impossible to recognize in a fossil state, may be very ancient. Iron pyrite is a common product of the chemical action of bacteria. Many geologists believe that the vast deposits of iron ore found in northern Minnesota were made by bacteria that lived about a billion years ago.

Although the evidence is still inconclusive, it suggests that for more than a billion years, the dominant and perhaps the only forms of life on earth were microscopic organisms such as algae, bacteria, and molds.

We know that cells of blue-green algae and bacteria differ from even the simplest of protozoans and molds in lacking a well-defined nucleus. The genes of bacteria and blue-green algae are arranged on a linear thread as in higher organisms. Most often there is only one thread per cell. Even the most powerful of microscopes has not revealed in these organisms well-defined nuclear membranes or mitotic spindles. One might say that at this level of organization, the division of labor between nucleus and cytoplasm, so characteristic of higher organisms, is poorly developed.

Blue-green algae carry out photosynthesis. However, their chlorophyll is scattered through the cytoplasm in the form of small granules, rather than in elaborately constructed chloroplasts like those found in other algae and in all green land plants.

These facts lead us to believe that the first great advances made by organisms after the appearance of living cells were the evolution of a well-organized nucleus, a division of labor between nucleus and cytoplasm, and the development of the mitotic spindle, asters, and other structures associated with mitosis. These evolutionary advances may have been completed more than 2 billion years ago.

The next type of evolutionary advance, toward greater size and complexity of structure, was made several times and in several ways. This consisted of the development of a multicellular and differentiated plant body, consisting of cells having different functions. This took place in at least three separate lines of chlorophyll-bearing, photosynthesizing organisms. One such line led to the red algae. From another the brown algae evolved. The third line gave rise to the green algae and later to the land plants.

Increasing size in all of these plants was accompanied by increasing complexity and differentiation of their tissues. All of them have specialized cells that aid in attachment to the ground or some other substrate, as well as structures that expose the maximum amount of photosynthesizing tissue to the light. Special supporting and conducting tissue is not present in most algae. They are supported by the water in which they live. Mineral elements can readily diffuse from the water to all parts of the plant. However, in the larger kelps, some of which reach a length of 500 to 600 feet, supporting and conducting tissues have been developed.

Sexual reproduction also evolved, as we have seen in Chapter 13, and plants acquired an alternation of generations.

The Fossil Record

In all probability, the events so far described occurred more than a billion years ago. Yet any certain knowledge of these an-

Both, M. F. Glaessner, Univ. of Adelaide, Australia

36-3   Two of the oldest known animal fossils. These fossils were found in Pre-Cambrian rocks in South Australia. The one at the left has been tentatively identified as a type of marine worm; the one at the right as a jellyfish. For a soft-bodied animal such as a jellyfish to leave a "puddle" that has fossilized and persisted through changes in the earth's crust for more than 600,000,000 years is indeed amazing.

cient events is scanty. This is because fossils of early organisms are exceedingly rare. The cause of this is twofold. First, most of the early animals and plants were small and had soft bodies. They decayed and left no traces. Second, the sedimentary rocks that formed during these early times have generally been altered so much by heat and pressure that fossils in them would have been destroyed.

Fossils first become abundant in the sedimentary rocks deposited about 600 million years ago. During the period from 600 million years ago to the present, other sedimentary rocks have been forming. These rocks contain the fossils that tell the story of evolution. Each layer of rock contains the information about the time it was formed. Not only can we tell what sorts of animals and plants were alive at the time, but often we can tell something of the character of the environment as well. Thus, if the rock contains marine organisms, we

know that it was deposited at the bottom of the sea. If it contains tropical organisms, we know that it was formed when the climate was warm.

The geologists have named the major layers of rock and have estimated their ages (Table 36-1, next page). (Some of the methods for dating rocks were described in Chapters 13 and 34.) The Cambrian rocks were formed between 500 million and 600 million years ago. In them we find a variety of animals and plants. In the older Pre-Cambrian rocks, fossils are rare, although new discoveries are being made (see Figure 36-3). It is only from the past 600 million years that we have a good fossil record. Tremendous events had occurred before the Cambrian period, however. This we know because already in the Cambrian we find a rich variety of complex animals and plants.

Let us now reconstruct briefly the history of animals and plants during the past 600 million years.

TABLE 36-1 A GEOLOGIC TIME SCALE, WITH NOTES OF EVENTS IN THE EVOLUTION OF LIFE AND ENVIRONMENTS

ERA	PERIOD (and Epoch for Cenozoic Era) Also approximate time since beginning		PLANTS	ANIMALS	CLIMATES
CENOZOIC	Quaternary	Recent	Dominance of herbs / Increase of herbs / Decrease of trees	Human cultures / Extinction of many large mammals / Early man	Climatic zones and changes of season / Periodic continenta glaciers in north
		Pleistocene			
		— 1,000,000 years ago			
		Pliocene	Rise of herbs / Spread of grasslands	Abundant mammals	Cool and temperat climates away from equator
		— 13,000,000 years ago			
		Miocene	Development of grasses / Reduction of forests	Increase of mammals	Cooling of climates
		— 25,000,000 years ago			
	Tertiary	Oligocene	Worldwide tropical forests	Appearance of modern mammals	Warm climates stil widely spread
		— 36,000,000 years ago			
		Eocene	Extension of angio-sperms	Archaic mammals	Zoned climatic belt well established
		— 58,000,000 years ago			
		Paleocene	Modernization of angiosperms	Evolutionary "explosion" of mammals	Development of cli belts
		— 63,000,000 years ago			
MESOZOIC	Cretaceous		Rise of flowering plants / Decrease of conifers	Decrease of reptiles / Climax of dinosaurs / Beginning of teleost fishes	Birth of modern mountains / Development of cli diversity
	— 135,000,000 years ago				
	Jurassic		Conifers and cycads dominant / First known flowering plants	Dominance of dinosaurs / First birds / Spread of reptiles	Culmination of wor wide warm climate
	— 180,000,000 years ago				
	Triassic		Increase of conifers / First known cycads	Transition, reptiles to mammals / Rise of progressive reptiles	Worldwide tropical and subtropical climates
	— 230,000,000 years ago				
PALEOZOIC	Permian		Dwindling of ancient plants / Seed ferns extinct	First dominance of reptiles	Climates become / Glaciation in south hemisphere
	— 280,000,000 years ago				
	Carboniferous (Pennsylvanian)		Great tropical coal forests	Amphibians dominant on land	Uniform climates throughout world
	— 310,000,000 years ago				
	Carboniferous (Mississippian)		First known mosses, seed ferns, and conifers / Early coal forests	Rise of insects	Uniform climates / Spread of tropical
	— 345,000,000 years ago				
	Devonian		First forests / First known liverworts, horsetails, and ferns	First amphibians / Wide radiation of early fishes	Broad distribution of uniform climate / Increased tempera
	— 405,000,000 years ago				
	Silurian		First known land plants — club mosses	Wide expansion of the invertebrates	Slight climatic coo
	— 425,000,000 years ago				
	Ordovician		Marine algae domi-nant	First indication of fishes	Warm climates
	— 500,000,000 years ago				
	Cambrian		Algae, fungi, and bacteria / First plant spores	Invertebrates numerous and varied	Climates become progressively warmer
	— 600,000,000 years ago				
PRE-CAMBRIAN			Bacteria, fungi, and algae	Primitive invertebrates	Cool climates at e of Pre-Cambrian / Glaciation
	— 5,000,000,000 years ago				

LIFE IN THE PALEOZOIC

Though making a very sudden appearance in the Cambrian rocks, the fossils found there represent nearly every major phylum of animals living today. We find protozoans, sponges, coelenterates, mollusks, arthropods, and echinoderms (review Chapter 20). In fact, we find fossils of all the major phyla except our own, the Chordata. Figure 36-4 shows the fossil situation for eleven phyla, including the problematical matter of several worm phyla (for which the fossil record is very sketchy indeed. Why do you suppose this is so?).

This apparent explosion of animal life at the beginning of the Cambrian is in a sense discouraging. It means that we find it difficult to learn much about the evolution that took place before the beginning of the Cambrian. If the major phyla of invertebrates were already present in the Cambrian, they must have evolved during earlier periods. Perhaps some day we will find an abundance of Pre-Cambrian fossils. The recent finds, since 1947, in South Australia make us more hopeful (Figure 36-3). New parts of the world must be explored for the fossils of earliest animal life.

The invertebrates that were fossilized during the Cambrian were those with skeletons. Possibly it was not until this time that most of the invertebrates had evolved skeletons. The fossil protozoans, for example, are not like *Amoeba, Paramecium,* or *Euglena;* rather, they are species with shells or internal skeletons. You probably think of sponges as soft and perishable animals. Yet many sponges have an internal skeleton of hard spicules. Some of these are preserved in the Cambrian rocks.

There are fossil algae from the Cambrian. This is the only direct evidence we have of the plant life of that time. There must have been many bacteria, fungi, and possibly other primitive plants that died without leaving a trace.

As far as we know, all of the Cambrian animals and plants lived in the seas. The land masses must have presented a desolate appearance. No plants or animals—just the inorganic substance of the earth's crust.

But the seas were full of life (Figure 36-5). On the ocean floor were sponges, coelenterates, and **brachiopods** (BRAY·kih·o·podz—shelled animals with a superficial resemblance to mollusks but belonging to a separate phylum). But there were more active animals as well. Dominating the scene were large arthropods, the **trilobites** (TRY·lo·byts—Figures 36-5 and 36-6). Some were 30 cm (1 foot) in length. They swam and crawled with their many legs along the ocean floor.

Trilobites were exceedingly abundant in the Cambrian but became extinct by the end of the **Paleozoic** (pay·le·o·ZOH·ik). Trilobites were, like all groups of animals and plants, an experiment in evolution. This experiment, a great success for over 300 million years, came to an end. Why? We can only guess.

As millions of years rolled by, new kinds of animals and plants evolved. In the seas of the **Ordovician** (or·doh·VISH·an) and **Silurian** (sih·LYOO·rih·an) periods, great reefs were built by corals and algae. Along these reefs lived brachiopods, trilobites, mollusks, and other animals. The **nautiloids** (NAW·tih·loidz) were especially common; these mollusks were the ancestors of today's squids and octopuses.

The eurypterids (yoo·RIP·ter·idz—Figure 36-7) were among the more spectacular animals of the Ordovician and Silurian periods. They were gigantic predatory arthropods, some of them 3 meters (10 feet) in length.

Plants Invade the Land

An event of major importance occurred fairly early in the Paleozoic—near the end of the Cambrian period (see Chapter 14). Green plants invaded land. An entirely new environment, with great possibilities for

36-4 ANIMAL LIFE ON EARTH—A TIME SCALE
(FOR PLANT LIFE, SEE FIGURE 13-1, PAGE 246)

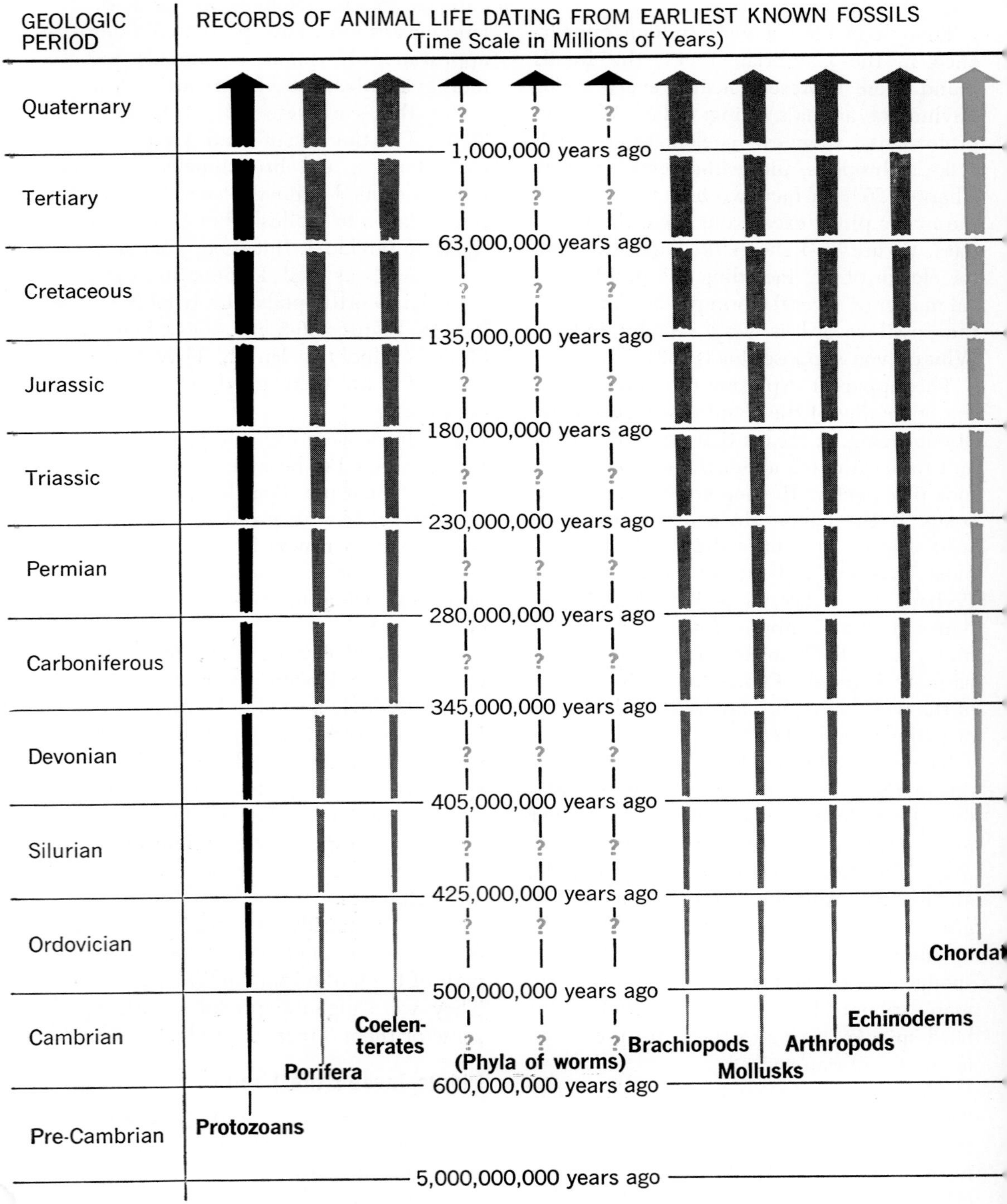

GEOLOGIC PERIOD	RECORDS OF ANIMAL LIFE DATING FROM EARLIEST KNOWN FOSSILS (Time Scale in Millions of Years)
Quaternary	
	1,000,000 years ago
Tertiary	
	63,000,000 years ago
Cretaceous	
	135,000,000 years ago
Jurassic	
	180,000,000 years ago
Triassic	
	230,000,000 years ago
Permian	
	280,000,000 years ago
Carboniferous	
	345,000,000 years ago
Devonian	
	405,000,000 years ago
Silurian	
	425,000,000 years ago
Ordovician	Chordat
	500,000,000 years ago
Cambrian	Echinoderms / Arthropods / Brachiopods / Coelenterates / Mollusks / (Phyla of worms) / Porifera
	600,000,000 years ago
Pre-Cambrian	Protozoans
	5,000,000,000 years ago

American Museum of Natural History

36-5 A model of life in a Cambrian sea. At the left, a jellyfish floats in front of an alga. Directly beneath the jellyfish, at the extreme bottom of the photograph, are two brachiopods. Standing at the right of the brachiopods is a sea cucumber, alongside which is an annelid worm the size of the sea cucumber. The next large organism to the right is an arthropod, a trilobite, and above it is *Sidneyia,* another arthropod. Other organisms include sponges and more algae, worms, and shelled forms.

evolution, was opened up. Green plants seem not to have evolved above the algal stage of complexity as long as they remained in the sea. Once they invaded land, however, they evolved into the tremendous diversity of types that characterizes our landscape.

Green land plants evolved in two principal directions. One group remained small and developed the ability to colonize on almost bare rock. In this situation, moisture is abundant at some seasons, but soil and available mineral matter are scanty. This first group gave rise to the mosses and liverworts. The second group evolved an ever-increasing amount of conducting and supporting tissue, and real leaves. These became the ferns and all other higher plants—the trees, shrubs, and herbaceous flowering plants.

The invasion of land by green plants was an event of enormous importance for animals. Being heterotrophic, animals require complex organic compounds as food. The animals of the Cambrian seas depended directly or indirectly on the algae for their food. Since there were no green plants on land at this time, there was no source of food for animals. The invasion of land by green plants was, therefore, an evolution-

American Museum of Natural History

36-6 Fossil trilobites. Several of these once-abundant animals appear in the model of Cambrian life in Figure 36-5.

N.Y. State Museum and Science Service

36-7 A model of life in a Silurian sea. Two large eurypterids dominate the scene. A third is almost hidden from view beneath an outcropping of the sea bottom (lower right). Numerous snails and clusters of Silurian plants also can be seen.

ary step that had to be taken before animals could also invade the land and live there permanently.

The Beginnings of the Chordates

There are a few fossils from Ordovician rocks that, from our point of view, are extremely interesting. They do not look like much—just fragments of bones and scales. Why are they so exciting? They are the earliest fossil chordates—the first known examples of our own phylum. During the Silurian and **Devonian** (de·VOH·nih·an) periods they became abundant.

These early chordates are primitive fish, called ostracoderms (Figure 36-8). In some, the body was covered by bony plates and scales. The ostracoderms had a primitive vertebral column, so they were vertebrates as well as chordates. Some of the ostraco-

derms were bottom feeders. They sucked mud containing food material into their mouths. There are no ostracoderms living today, but the lamprey and hagfish are fairly closely related to them.

Perhaps the most interesting thing about the ostracoderms is their lack of jaws and paired fins. Jaws are present in all higher chordates, where they are important in capturing and grinding food. The ostracoderms sucked in their food. Paired fins are important in the higher fish as an aid to swimming. In the course of evolution, paired fins of certain fish evolved into the legs of chordates that live on land (amphibians, reptiles, birds, and mammals). The paired fins of fish, then, are homologous to the arms and legs of the higher chordates.

Even without being told what they are, you might have classified the ostracoderms seen in Figure 36-8 as fish. In other words, you would have put them in our own phylum and not in any other. But what did they evolve from? Ostracoderms did not "just happen." They must have evolved from more primitive ancestors. Part of the answer must lie buried somewhere in the Cambrian rocks.

In the Devonian period there were also more advanced fish with jaws (Figure 36-8). Some of these had paired fins. They were the ancestors of still more advanced fish and of the higher vertebrates.

The Amphibians

Fossil evidence from the later part of the Devonian period indicates that large populations of fish belonging to a group known as the "lobe-fins" were already living in shallow, fresh water; and there is every reason to suppose that some of these animals first crawled from pool to pool and then,

spending more time on the land, gave rise to the terrestrial populations that we recognize as Amphibia (Figure 36-9).

The amphibians were the first chordates to come out on land. Many structural and physiological changes were necessary for life on land. The paired fins evolved into legs. Gills could no longer be used in respiration. Lungs, which were already present in the lobe-finned fish, became the chief structures where oxygen could pass from the environment into the blood.

The earliest amphibians known from the Devonian still looked like, and presumably behaved much like, fish (Figure 36-9). Animals of this sort probably wandered upon the land for tens of millions of years before the definitely terrestrial types of the later Paleozoic evolved. All presently existing amphibians are much modified from their Devonian ancestors. Yet they retain many features that show how the transition

Both, American Museum of Natural History

36-8

(Above) A model of early fish in a Devonian sea. At the bottom center, and in the second photograph (right), are models of ostracoderms, early jawless fish. Also shown are several species of more advanced fish, with jaws and with some of their fins in pairs. What was the significance of the paired fins in the evolution of land-inhabiting vertebrates?

36-9 A lobe-finned fish and a primitive amphibian. In the late Devonian, some of the lobe-finned fish may have crawled out on land and moved from pool to pool in an amphibious manner. Probably they were ancestral to the amphibians.

from water to land was made. The modern forms are by no means a precariously existing remnant, but are quite numerous and successful. However, they do not succeed in maintaining themselves in any great variety of habitats. Broadly speaking, they are unable to survive for very long unless they are close to water.

Other Invaders of the Land

The amphibians were not the first animals to invade the land. In the previous period, the Silurian, some scorpions left the water. Neither scorpions nor amphibians, nor any other animals for that matter, could live on land for long unless green plants were there. As we have already seen, green plants had invaded dry land by the time of the Silurian period and to some extent even earlier.

Land plants were not very common in the Silurian, or even early in the Devonian. By the end of the Devonian, however, there were forests. The plants in these forests were not like those in our forests today. The Devonian trees were actually giant club mosses and horsetails (Figure 14-10a and b), and tree ferns (Figure 36-10).

There was even a more spectacular development of land plants in the **Carboniferous** (kar·bon·IF·er·us) period, 345 to 280 million years ago—commonly subdivided into the Mississippian (early) and Pennsylvanian (late) periods. This is the time in geological history when the great coal deposits were formed, as the name "Carboniferous" implies. Coal, which is so important

economically, is found in many parts of the world. Coal beds are the fossilized remnants of plants that grew in swamps. (Laboratory Exercise 36-2 provides a study of some plant fossils from "coal balls" formed in these beds.) The world in those days was largely tropical and subtropical, even in areas where it is now very cold, such as Greenland and Antarctica. The forests were jungles of lush vegetation (Figure 36-11). Sometimes the trees were more than 30 meters (100 feet) in height, though they were not the trees we know. Most of them were related to the club mosses.

These spectacular examples of evolution among the plants were rivaled by those of animals. Dragonflies (Figure 36-11) with wing spans of 50 cm (20 inches), giant cockroaches, and other primitive insects lived in the Carboniferous forests. Many species of amphibians lived in the swamps.

The Rise of the Reptiles

During the Carboniferous period, one group of amphibians evolved into reptiles. This was a momentous change.

The amphibians never really conquered *dry* land. The adults often were forced to stay near water. This is true of modern amphibians as well. In addition, the embryonic stages are nearly always found in water. If not, they occur in wet earth or wet vegetation. Reptiles, on the other hand, have an outer skin that is much less permeable to water. They can live in very dry places; as you may know, reptiles are often abundant in desert regions. In addition, reptiles characteristically lay eggs that develop on land. With a protective outer skin and an egg that could develop on land (see page 468), the reptiles were set to rule the living world for some 200 million years.

The warm seas of the late Paleozoic had a rich variety of invertebrates as well as vertebrates. Corals, brachiopods, mollusks, and echinoderms were abundant.

But as the Paleozoic era drew to a close, the environment began to change. Some parts of the world that had been warm now became increasingly cold. Shallow seas were restricted by the emergence of land masses. Great mountain chains were pushed upward. Our own Appalachian Mountains are the remains of a mighty upheaval that occurred at this time.

This was a period of crisis for marine invertebrates. Many forms became extinct —though we can only guess the reason. Their rates of mutation and recombination were presumably not sufficient for the evolution of populations capable of living under the new conditions.

On land, however, the story was different. The uplifted lands of the **Permian** (PER-mih·an) period held an increased variety of environments. No longer were the continents low and covered with monotonous jungles. There were hills and lowlands, swamps and deserts, and varied climates. This variety of habitats offered many new opportunities to animals that could take advantage of them. Such animals were the reptiles, until then of small size and hardly more than competitors on an equal footing

Chicago Natural History Museum

36-10 Tree ferns of today, similar to those of the Carboniferous period. Tree ferns occur in a few places in the tropics, and in Australia, New Zealand, and Hawaii.

36-11 A reconstruction of a forest of the Carboniferous period. The trees were relatives of today's club mosses, ferns, and gymnosperms. Note the giant dragonfly (right center). Can you find two other insects that are shown?

Chicago Natural History Museum

with the numerous amphibians that had dominated the Carboniferous swamps (Figure 36-12). In this period of rising land and increasing dryness, however, the reptiles had a great advantage because of their land-laid eggs, in which embryos could develop far away from swamps and streams. Consequently, there was an expansion of reptiles during the Permian period. As Permian history ran its course, the reptiles became increasingly dominant, the amphibians increasingly reduced. The Age of Reptiles had begun.

LIFE IN THE MESOZOIC

With the dawn of the **Mesozoic** (mes·o-ZOH·ik) era, there was a new outburst of reptilian evolution. This can be correlated with the increase of land areas and consequent increase in ecological opportunity for land animals. Many new kinds of reptiles evolved. These varied from small species to the giants among the dinosaurs (Figure 36-13). Some became flying reptiles (*Pteranodon* [te·RAN·o·don] in Figure 36-13). Others evolved into aquatic forms (*Ophthalmosaurus* [ahf·thal·mo·SAW·rus] and *Elasmosaurus* [e·las·mo·SAW·rus] shown in the same figure). Some were carnivorous; others were herbivorous. Some lived on dry land; others lived primarily in swamps (Figure 36-14).

The plant world was also changing. The earlier forests of club mosses, horsetails, and ferns were now overshadowed by forests of cycads, ginkgos, and conifers. Representatives of these three groups are still living (Figure 36-15).

Reptilian Experiments: The Birds and Mammals

During the middle period of the Mesozoic, known as the **Jurassic** (ju·RAS·ik), one group of reptiles gave rise to the birds. The first birds had feathers, for the most part, instead of scales (Figures 36-14 and 36-16), but in many ways they were still basically reptilian. They had teeth, a long bony tail, and claws on several digits of each wing. No modern bird has teeth. All have a very short bony tail, with tail feathers set in like a fan. And only one living species of bird has retained the characteristic of claws on its wings.

In the early days of the Mesozoic, the reptiles also gave rise to another class of chordates, the mammals. For nearly 100 million years, the mammals were small, scarce, and apparently not important in the Mesozoic way of life. Their day came later.

The Decline and Fall of the Mighty Reptiles

In late **Cretaceous** (kre·TAY·shus) times, barely 100 million years ago, the dinosaurs reached their evolutionary peak. Many new groups, each adapted to a different way of life, developed, giving the reptiles a variety never previously attained. Then, while seemingly at the height of their develop-

ment, these mighty reptiles became extinct. The reason is one of the puzzles of paleontology. Numerous theories have been advanced; not one is a satisfactory explanation.

But the extinction of the characteristic reptiles of the Mesozoic points up an important principle: extinction of species can be important in evolution. Extinction weeds out the old, and so makes way for the new. Most of the land habitats of the Mesozoic seem to have been occupied by the reptiles. When these reptiles became extinct, the inconspicuous group mentioned before—the mammals—could then exploit the land.

THE CENOZOIC—AGE OF MAMMALS

The last part of the Mesozoic and the first part of the **Cenozoic** (see·no·ZOH·ik) was a period of mountain-making. All of the

36-12 A scene in Texas during the Permian period. In the foreground and the right background are two large amphibians (*Eryops*). One is feeding on a smaller amphibian. In the center background are two primitive reptiles (*Dimetrodon*).

X 1/88 *Pteranodon*

X 1/100 *Allosaurus*

X 1/105 *Elasmosaurus*

X 1/48 *Ophthalmosaurus*

X 1/115 *Triceratops*

X 1/45 *Rutiodon*

X 1/210 *Brontosaurus*

X 1/100 *Corythosaurus*

36-13 Some Mesozoic reptiles. In this figure and in Figures 36-9 and 36-19, the actual sizes of the animals are indicated by the fractional equivalents listed alongside each specimen. The largest of all these animals was *Brontosaurus.*

great mountain systems of the present—the Rockies, the Andes, and the Himalayas—were born. The uplift of these huge mountain chains greatly affected the environment and, therefore, the evolution of Cenozoic animals and plants. High mountains modify the wind patterns and, hence, the amount of rainfall reaching different re-

gions of the earth. The mountains can influence the formation of forests or of deserts.

The mammals took over where once the reptiles had ruled. The first part of the Cenozoic witnessed an explosive evolution of the mammals. All of the major groups that we know today were present. There were also many mammals that evolved and then became extinct (Figure 36-17).

Laboratory Exercise 36-1 deals with characteristics that enabled the mammals to radiate adaptively into the habitats vacated by dinosaurs and other "ruling reptiles" of the Mesozoic. Natural selection resulted in **convergent evolution,** whereby some mammals came to resemble more and more those animals whose places they took. The porpoise, for example, resembles the extinct ichthyosaur in body shape and fish-eating habits.

Mammals arose from a different reptilian stock than the one from which birds were derived. Both birds and the mammals, which escaped the destructive forces that caused the extinction of the Mesozoic reptiles, have two things in common. First, they have a far more effective protection against changes of environmental temperature than is found in any reptile; and second, they usually care for their eggs and their young.

Mammals maintain a constant body temperature, independently of the environment, partly by means of the insulation offered by *hair*. Most female mammals *retain their eggs in the body,* where embryonic development takes place; thus they usually bring forth living young. They care for the young after birth and feed them with milk secreted by the *mammary glands* (Chapter 27). The teeth of the different mammals are highly specialized for specific diets (Figure 36-18).

The mammals of today are divided into three main groups: the egg-laying mammals, the pouched mammals, and the placental mammals.

Two mammals that suckle their young but also lay eggs (Chapter 27) have survived to

36-14 A Jurassic scene in Europe. In the tree at the right is the ancestral bird *Archaeopteryx.* In the lake are two giant herbivorous dinosaurs. The trees are cycads, as are the smaller plants in the left- and right-hand lower corners.

H. Schroder from Nat. Audubon Society

36-15 A living cycad. Compare this specimen with one of its ancient relatives—the Jurassic cycad occupying the lower left corner of Figure 36-14.

this day. These are the duckbill **platypus** (PLAT·ih·pus—Figure 27-5) and the **echidna** (e·KID·na), which live in Australia and on some of the nearby islands. They are the survivors of what was probably a much larger number and variety of small egg-laying mammals.

Pouched mammals are very widely diversified in the Australian region. They also occur in the New World. Examples are the kangaroos of Australia and the opossums of the New World. In these forms, the young are born very early in their development and find their way into a pouch on the female's belly. Here they are nourished with milk and complete their development (Figure 27-5).

The placental mammals, the third group, are characterized by the presence of a placenta (Chapter 27), an organ for nourishing the young within the body of the female parent. Nearly all familiar mammals (except those native to the Australian region) are placental mammals.

Ten million years ago the mammals were not strikingly different from many alive today. Figure 36-19 shows some that lived in North America during the **Pliocene** (PLY·o·seen). The forerunners of man were present during the Cenozoic; we shall devote the next chapter to them.

The Rise of the Angiosperms

The changes during the late Mesozoic and early Cenozoic, which were so important for the evolution of animals, were equally important for the evolution of plants (Chapter 14). The earliest angiosperms (flowering plants) appeared late in the Mesozoic. They probably lived in mountainous regions, while the conifers and cycadlike plants dominated the plains. The angiosperms did not become the dominant terrestrial plants until the Cenozoic.

The environmental change that gave the flowering plants their first advantage over gymnosperms (the pines and their relatives) was probably associated with the rise of new kinds of animals. Flowering plants are superior to gymnosperms chiefly in their better solutions to the problems of cross-fertilization, seed dispersal, and estab-

Carnegie Museum, Pittsburgh

36-16 A fossil *Archaeopteryx*, the oldest known bird, of Jurassic age. A drawing of the bird, perched in a tree, is included in Figure 36-14.

lishment of seedlings. Insects and birds are much more efficient agents for transporting pollen than are wind and water. Birds and small mammals are the only means by which large seeds such as acorns and nuts, which contain a generous food supply for the young seedling, are transported for long distances. The extensive spread of angiosperm trees was probably brought about largely by these animals and by the retreat of inland seas.

The fossil record of insects at this time is very imperfect, but there is some evidence that the bee family was actively evolving. Butterflies also appeared on the scene. These insects were taking over the role of pollinating flowers from the more primitive beetles, which are the pollinators of the most primitive flowering plants even today. Beetles, bees, butterflies, birds, and early mammals must have had a strong selective influence in the evolution of the families and genera of flowering plants. At the end of the age of dinosaurs, about 70 million years ago, the plants of the earth were essentially like those of modern times.

CONCLUDING REMARKS

We know from the fossil record that life extends back through long geologic ages, but we do not know how it originated. There have been numerous theories as to the origin of life, one of recent interest being the "heterotroph hypothesis" presented early in this chapter. Random formation of organic compounds by natural forces was followed in the primeval "soup" by the action of natural selection on the first near-living and living systems.

For many millions of years, organisms were soft-bodied and thus were not often

36-17 An Eocene (early Cenozoic) group of mammals. The large mammal is *Uintatherium*. At the left are two early horses, *Hyracotherium*, that have been frightened by a primitive carnivore, *Mesonyx*, shown crouching in the immediate foreground.

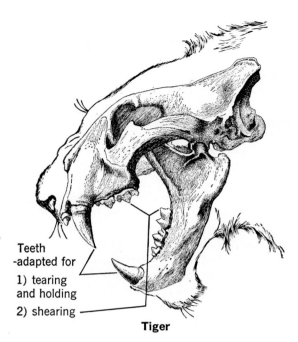

Teeth
-adapted for
1) tearing
and holding
2) shearing

Tiger

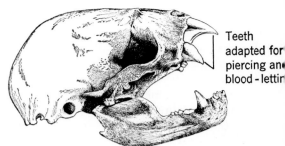

Teeth
adapted for
piercing and
blood-letting

Vampire bat

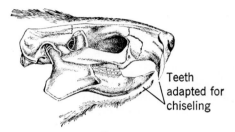

Teeth
adapted for
chiseling

Rat

36-18 Some examples of specialization in mammalian teeth. There are many other patterns than the four that are shown; for example, can you think of an animal that is not classified as a herbivore but that has at least some of its numerous teeth adapted for grinding?

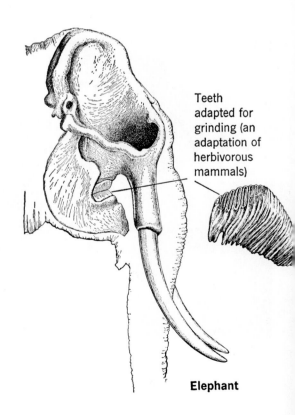

Teeth
adapted for
grinding (an
adaptation of
herbivorous
mammals)

Elephant

preserved as fossils. The main fossil record begins in rocks about 600 million years old. From that time until today, there is a continuous record of the evolution of life.

At the beginning of the Paleozoic era, the first great time division of the fossil record, life was confined to the sea. Plants were simple, but there were many kinds of invertebrates. Early in the Paleozoic, plants and invertebrates emigrated to the land. At about this same time the first fishlike vertebrates arose. By the middle of the Paleozoic, the fish had evolved along several divergent lines, leading to the major groups of modern fish. At this time one group of fish ventured onto land, and in so doing evolved the amphibian way of life. The amphibians in turn rapidly evolved, becoming the dominant

X 1/55

X 1/110

Ground sloth

Straight-horned bison

X 1/32

Woolly rhinoceros

X 1/64

Saber-toothed cat

X 1/38

Giant short-faced bear

X 1/72

Woolly mammoth

36-19 Some Pliocene (late Cenozoic) mammals. How many remind you of closely related mammals that live on the earth today? Several of these examples became extinct only within the past 10,000 years or so; some were hunted by early man.

land animals during the age when great coal forests blanketed the land. At the end of the Paleozoic, the continents were further uplifted and environments became varied. The reptiles, which had evolved from amphibian ancestors, became the dominant land animals.

With the beginning of the Mesozoic era the reptiles became quite numerous and varied on the land and in the sea. The dinosaurs arose and became the rulers of the land for more than 100 million years. Some reptiles flew through the air, which they shared with primitive birds. Toward the end of the Mesozoic, the dinosaurs and many other reptiles became extinct. The great extinction of reptiles occurred when the modern mountain systems were being born.

The Cenozoic era, the last great division in the history of life, was marked by the continued uplift of mountains and the cooling of climates. At the beginning of the Cenozoic, there was a great multiplication of mammals, which had first appeared during the time of the dinosaurs. About the middle of the Cenozoic, the modern groups of mammals evolved.

GUIDE QUESTIONS AND PROBLEMS

1. What facts might be presented against the hypothesis that life arrived on earth from some other world?
2. In what kind of surroundings did life probably originate on earth? How were these environmental conditions different from those on the earth today?
3. How do the experiments of Urey and Miller provide some support for the hypothesis of the chemical origin of life?
4. What additional evidence is provided by the experiments of Fox and of Calvin?
5. How can we explain the absence of fossil remains of the earliest forms of life?
6. Why is it believed that life originated in the water?
7. What were probably the first types of organisms on the earth?
8. What effects did the changes in continental areas at the close of the Paleozoic have upon animal and plant life?
9. What were the major features of the Mesozoic?
10. Why is extinction of species important to the evolution of life?
11. What changes in the earth's surface were taking place during the early part of the Age of Mammals?

12. What are major features of the evolving plant and animal life during the Cenozoic?
13. How can we interpret the presence of vast coal deposits in Greenland?
14. What factors of climate and environment led to the success of the dinosaurs?
15. How might we explain the extinction of the dinosaurs?

SUGGESTIONS FOR ADDITIONAL READING

Books

Beerbower, J. R., *Search for the Past: An Introduction to Paleontology.* Englewood Cliffs (N. J.), Prentice-Hall, 1960.
> A well-illustrated story of fossils.

Colbert, E. H., *Evolution of the Vertebrates.* New York, Wiley, 1955.
> Authoritative account of the fossil story of the vertebrates.

—— *Dinosaurs, Their Discovery and Their World.* New York, Dutton, 1961.
> A study of a fascinating group of animals.

Moore, R. C., *Introduction to Historical Geology,* 2nd ed. New York, McGraw-Hill, 1958.
> An excellent text on earth and life history.

Simpson, G. G., *Life of the Past: An Introduction to Paleontology.* New Haven, Yale University Press, 1953.
> An authoritative, yet popular account of fossils and their study.

Magazines and Journals

Abelson, P. H., "Paleobiochemistry." *Scientific American,* Vol. 195 (July 1956), pp. 83–84.

Colbert, E. H., "The Ancestors of Mammals." *Scientific American,* Vol. 180 (March 1949), p. 40.

Deevey, E. S., Jr., "Radiocarbon Dating." *Scientific American,* Vol. 186 (February 1952), pp. 24–28. (A correction to this article appears in the April 1952 issue, p. 2.)

Glaessner, M. F., "Pre-Cambrian Animals." *Scientific American,* Vol. 204 (March 1961), pp. 72–78.

Southern, H. N., "A Study in the Evolution of Birds." *Scientific American,* Vol. 196 (May 1957), pp. 124–28.

37

THE EVOLUTION

OF MAN

We wonder about the origin of man—man the upright biped (BY·ped), the creature of three-dimensional vision, the omnivore, the thinker, the inventor of tools, and the gossip. From whom did he inherit his vertical skeleton, his precariously balanced head, his broad pelvis, his long legs, and his narrow flat feet? From whom and by what devious path of evolution did he acquire his forward-looking eyes mounted in a movable head and controlled by wonderfully coordinated sets of muscles; his unspecialized teeth; his independently mobile arms ending in grasping fingers and opposable thumbs; his complex brain; and his voice box linked to a speaking mouth?

The answers to these questions are incomplete. Yet many facts are available from which we can construct the past changes leading to modern man.

FOSSIL FINDS AND EMERGING MAN

After Charles Darwin published his *Descent of Man* in 1871, many professional and amateur scientists entered into long discussions about man's near relatives. Darwin himself carefully described man and apes as having evolved separately from some common "ancient . . . anthropomorphic subgroup. . . ." (*Anthropomorphic*, pronounced an·thro·po·MOR·fik, means "man-like" or "with characteristics of man.") At that time, however, the fossil record of both apes and man was almost completely unknown.

A Dutch anatomist, Eugene Dubois, became convinced that the fossil-bearing strata near Trinil, Java (an island of Indonesia), would be a likely place to look for evidences of prehistoric man. In 1889, he resigned his position and took a government job in Java to be close to the site. The strata he wanted to examine had been laid down by volcanoes about 500,000 years ago. In two seasons of digging along the banks of the Solo River, Dubois unearthed a small piece of human jawbone, several teeth similar to those of apes, and a partial skull suggesting a brain too big for an ape and too small for any known man (Figure 37-1). The next year he located a fossil thighbone, the straightness of which suggested that it came from an erect primate (man is the only primate truly erect in posture).

Dubois' description of "Java man," which he named *Pithecanthropus erectus* (pith·e·KAN·thro·pus e·REK·tus), rekindled the scientific controversy over the "missing link." Under the tremendous pressure of arguments from both sides, Dubois finally disclaimed his interpretations and hid the actual specimens in the dirt beneath his dining room floor. There they remained until the 1920's, when he was finally persuaded to exhibit them publicly. Later finds of *Pithecanthropus* in Java include parts of a number of individuals, including one child. A giant-sized type also has turned up.

Fossils similar to the Java men have been discovered in other parts of the world. In 1924, W. C. Pei discovered "Peking man" (Figure 37-1). During the next twelve years,

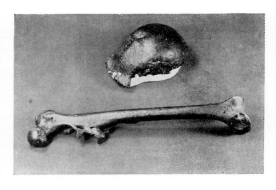

37-1 (Above and above left) A fossil cranium and thighbone and a cast of the probable appearance of an adult male *Pithecanthropus erectus*. (Below and below left) A fossil skull and a cast of the probable appearance of an adult female of the popularly called "Peking man" (*Pithecanthropus pekinensis*).

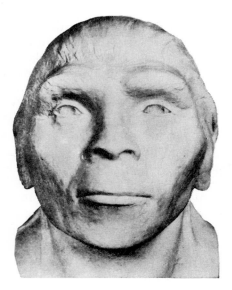

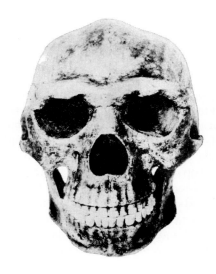

All photos, American Museum of Natural History

parts of more than forty individuals were dug up from a cave floor at Choukoutien, near Peking, China. Whereas only a few crude flint tools had been found near the fossils of Java men, a whole array of "chopping" tools (rough stones chipped to an edge on one end, somewhat like a modern chisel) were found among the split bones

and punctured skulls of Peking man and the animals he ate.

Recently, a skull and three jaws closely resembling those of Java man were uncovered in Algeria and were given the distinctive title of "Atlantic man." Supplementing the fossils of Java man and similar finds are widespread deposits of chipped pebbles and a few hand axes from the same period, suggesting that tool-using men similar to Java man lived over many areas in Asia, Africa, and Europe between 600,000 and 350,000 years ago. Whether these rather large-skulled creatures with protruding bony ridges over the eyes and with protruding jaws were true men or not depends, of course, on how *man* is defined. The fossil evidence clearly shows that this "pre-man" was becoming modern man, a creature set apart from the rest of the animal world by his ability to invent and to use tools, as well as by details of his anatomy and by the size and proportions of his brain.

"The Southern Apes"

On a June day in 1938, Gert Terblanche played on his school desk with "four of the most beautiful fossil teeth ever found" while waiting for the teacher to call a recess of his one-room school near Kromdraai, South Africa. He had knocked the four teeth out of a lumpy rock on his father's farm with a hammer and had given a fifth tooth to Mr. Barlow, the foreman at the local quarry at Sterkfontein. It was not until his teacher interrupted the recess ball game and introduced him to the great paleontologist Robert Broom that Gert realized the teeth had any scientific importance.

Dr. Broom, who had been alerted by Mr. Barlow, spent the afternoon telling Gert and his classmates many fascinating tales about fossil men. When school was finally over, Gert somewhat reluctantly led the paleontologist up the hill to look for more fossils. Together they exhumed many teeth, a right lower jaw, and most of the left side of a fossil skull. These well-preserved fossils added greatly to the incomplete knowledge of the "southern apes," as newspapers had been calling the fossils previously collected in South Africa.

Additional specimens, belonging to something like one hundred individuals, have been collected since then by Robert Broom

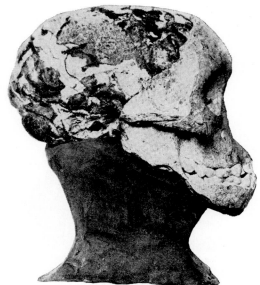

American Museum of Natural History

37-2 The fossil skull of an australopithecine. Many fragments are missing, but the basic characteristics of the skull are clear. What is not too clear is how this "southern ape-man" fits into the immediate family tree of either man or the apes.

and Raymond Dart. Interestingly, some of the specimens of the "southern apes" antedated Java man, while others survived to be his contemporaries.

Except for features of the lower jaw and teeth, the skulls (Figure 37-2) of the **australopithecines** (aus·tray·loh·PITH·e·seenz— "southern apes") resemble those of modern apes. Their jaws, however, do not protrude as much, and the back of the skull does not have as large ridges for the attachment of muscles. The opening in the australopithecine skull, through which the brain and spinal cord connect, is farther forward than it is in apes. Also, the teeth and jaws resemble those of man more than those of apes. Moreover, the five pelvic girdles so far unearthed are more broadly bucket-shaped than those of apes. This evidence is interpreted to mean that the "southern ape-men" walked erect.

Painting by Peter Bianchi, courtesy *National Geographic Mag.;* © National Geographic Society

37-3 A drawing of the probable appearance of an adult male *Zinjanthropus*. The recently discovered skull, not quite as large as that of modern man, consisted of more than 400 fragments. Missing was the lower jaw. *Zinjanthropus* is the oldest known toolmaker.

The authorities do not agree as to whether the australopithecines should be placed with man in the family Hominidae (see Table 20-1, pages 362–63), or with the great apes in the family **Pongidae** (PON·jih·dee). While they argue the fine point, it is sufficient for us to see that the australopithecines stand at an *earlier* place than modern man in time and at an *intermediate* post between the great apes and modern man in their structural features.

In July, 1959, a most amazing find was made by Dr. and Mrs. L. S. B. Leakey in Olduvai Gorge in Tanganyika. In strata corresponding to the estimated time of the early australopithecines, and subsequently determined by potassium-argon dating to be approximately 1,750,000 years old, they discovered a remarkably well preserved skull of a "southern ape-man" and named him *Zinjanthropus* (zin·JAN·thro·pus—Figure 37-3). With these remains, the Leakeys

found a primitive hand ax. Apparently *Zinjanthropus* made and used tools. Perhaps he passed on this skill to his descendants.

The fossilized remains of a *Zinjanthropus* child have subsequently been found, and while scientists at first were not in accord about the age of *Zinjanthropus*, further tests have confirmed the one and three-quarter million year old date. Apparently, then, the early australopithecines of South Africa may be this old, too.

Did early man communicate his knowledge by illustration and imitation? Did he develop hand signs to indicate certain objects or specific notions? Or did he devise a series of sounds for the same purpose? We may never know the answer. But the presence of his tools makes us suspect that he had already developed some simple method of communication. We cannot imagine how a young man could learn from his elders how to make even a simple tool, unless the parents could in some way show him how. Types like the "southern ape-man" may have been ancestral to Java and Peking man. Both used their brains to invent things and to communicate.

Early Pre-Man

Although many fossil remains of man are known from the various parts of the **Pleistocene** (PLISE·toh·seen) period (the last million years, as shown in Table 36-1), there is a great gap in the record which reaches back for 15 or 20 million years. From the far edge of this gap, in the **Miocene** (MY·o·seen), we have fossils of *Proconsul* (proh·KON·sul—a very early but unspecialized African anthropoid) and some apelike fossils.

Most anthropologists maintain that the fossils of *Proconsul* do not show enough distinctly human features to classify it as an early hominid, that is, a member of the family Hominidae, which includes only *Homo*, *Pithecanthropus*, and, according to some authorities, the australopithecines and

Zinjanthropus; they regard it as ancestral to the apes. Others insist that it is primitive enough to have come before the division between the hominid and ape lines of descent. The exact position of *Proconsul* in the family tree, therefore, remains uncertain. Until we have more fossils of this and other Miocene anthropoids, the point of divergence of the hominid and ape lines will remain uncertain.

Primate remains of any kind from the 15 to 20 million years preceding the Pleistocene are scarce. One group of them from lignite coal mines in Italy, consisting of fossil teeth of early Pliocene and late Miocene age, has been known for many years. For almost a century they were classified as *Oreopithecus* (or·e·o·PITH·eh·cus) and regarded as one of the line evolving toward the present-day Old World monkeys. After World War II, Dr. Johannes Hürzeler of the Natural History Museum in Basel, Switzerland, became curious about these teeth. He re-examined the original fossils and began to suspect that their identification was incorrect. To obtain further specimens, he began frequenting lignite coal mines near Bacinello, Italy, and succeeded in adding to the tooth collection. Then, on August 2, 1958, cooperative miners finally laid bare a slab of coal on which lay an almost completely fossilized skeleton of *Oreopithecus.* The press immediately announced the discovery of an ancient pre-man who had lived at least 10 million years ago.

Scientists who examined the skeleton were more cautious, however, announcing only that the skull and its teeth were more like those of an "unspecialized" man, and not like those of any ancestral monkey or ape. Subsequent careful studies, which require a great deal of time, have now confirmed that *Oreopithecus* has so many humanlike, rather than apelike, features that most authorities incline to place it as the earliest known representative of the family of man—the Hominidae.

Fossils and Dates

Fossils from more than 30 million years ago can now be dated fairly definitely by use of the uranium-lead method (Chapter 13). Organic material preserved up to 40,000 years ago reveals its correct sequence and time when tested by the carbon-14 dating method. Man, however, emerged more recently than 30 million years ago, and earlier than 40,000 years back. Neither the uranium nor the carbon-14 methods will serve to cover the intervening time span. Fortunately, new methods that fill in the gap have recently been developed, including potassium-argon dating (used recently for *Zinjanthropus*) and another method involving an isotope of fluorine.

An additional guide to dates is available for the last 600,000 years. Four times during this period, great glaciers have extended southward into the mid-latitudes of the Northern Hemisphere. Four times they have retreated, as the earth warmed up.

We know about these changes through a careful study of the fossils preserved in the strata deposited during each glacial and interglacial period. In some places, unfortunately, the glaciers cut deeply into strata deposited earlier, and, upon melting, dropped their scrambled remains into huge jumbled piles. In other places, caves and undisturbed sites have yielded datable fossils and other evidences of the manlike, rather than apelike, creatures who lived during the Ice Ages. Some of these evidences of human activity (artifacts) consist of charcoal from campfires, broken tools, and bones of nonhuman animals eaten during primitive feasts.

MAN'S PAST RECONSTRUCTED

During the past ninety years, paleontologists have reconstructed the story of man's origin. In ever greater detail they have picked and brushed the earth away from the fossil remains of primates and similar

Early Mammals and the First Primates

Long before the dinosaurs disappeared from the surface of the earth, ancestors of mammals were becoming distinct from the other reptiles through natural selection. Very early, a line of insectivorous (in·sec-TIV·o·rus) shrews, which we know today only from fossils, took to the trees. From them evolved the first primates. These creatures were enough like the shrews of the present that we can assume that they had sensitive noses, ears that distinguished clearly between sounds of different pitch, and a rather fine sense of balance. Life in the trees must have encouraged them to rely upon the senses of sight and hearing, rather than upon the sense of smell. Ground animals, by contrast, seem to profit more from their sense of smell than from good vision—especially if they live in the thickets or woods.

The ancient tree shrews gave rise to one group of descendants, the lemuroids (LEM-yoo·roids), most of which retained less specialized grasping feet and hands. We suspect that they had bushy tails useful for balancing when leaping from branch to branch, much as a squirrel's tail helps him. We know these facts from the close correspondence between skeletons of fossil lemurs and those of lemurs living today (Figure 37-4) in the Malagasy Republic (formerly Madagascar).

Fossils of different descendants of the ancient tree shrews have flatter snouts and enlarged eyes. They demonstrate progress toward greater emphasis on vision and less on smell. This line of descent is seen in two species of lemurs native to India, and it led to the tarsiers. The shift in eye position from the sides of the head to the front was of very great importance. It meant that objects could be seen by both eyes at once. This in turn made stereoscopic vision possible. In stereoscopic vision, the images from each of the two eyes are so blended that the brain is able to make accurate judgments of the

New York Zoological Society

37-4 A ring-tailed lemur. For its evolutionary relationship to other groups of living primates, see Figure 37-8.

animals over an expanding area of the earth's surface. The story started, of course, with the dawn of life.

Man appeared only after hundreds of millions of years during which the invertebrate and other vertebrate animals evolved (see Chapter 36). You have already learned about the evolutionary changes that antedated the appearance of man and his living relatives. You have also considered the forces shaping the course of evolution. There is every reason to believe that the evolution of man is a result of the continuing action of these same forces, principally mutation, recombination, natural selection, and isolation.

relative nearness and distance of objects. Evolution toward stereoscopic vision gave the tarsiers a considerable advantage by helping them in judging distances as they leaped from tree to tree. Despite these gains, most of the tarsiers died out, leaving only a single modern species in the East Indies (Figure 37-5) in comparison with hundreds of Eocene fossils.

Further descendants of the tree shrews became specialized in other directions as the Eocene age ended, about 36 million years ago, and the **Oligocene** (OL·ih·go·seen) began. They show the same reduced snout and reliance upon binocular vision, and have nails on all fingers and toes. Some of them became ancestral to today's marmosets and to New World monkeys with prehensile tails — tails adapted for grasping (Figure 37-6a). Others evolved toward mankind and toward Old World monkeys with stubby tails (Figure 37-6b). Each group became more and more distinct, developing into the close relatives of the capuchin (organ-grinder) monkey on the one hand and the rhesus monkey of India on the other. Both of these latter groups de-

New York Zoological Society

37-5 A tarsier. Only one of once numerous species survives today, notwithstanding the characteristics that have helped make other primates so successful.

veloped grasping paws, three-dimensional vision, and strongly muscled forelimbs valuable in reaching for tree branches. They

a

b

Both, New York Zoological Society

37-6 New and Old World monkeys. **a** A long, grasping tail, covered with hair to the tip, characterizes most New World monkeys, native to South America. **b** Shorter or slender tails characterize Old World monkeys. This mandrill is native to Africa.

37-7 The four living great apes. **a** An orang-utan, native to the East Indies. **b** A gorilla, native to Africa. **c** A chimpanzee, also African. **d** Two gibbons, native to Southeast Asia and the East Indies. In all four of these primates, note the length of the arms as compared with the legs.

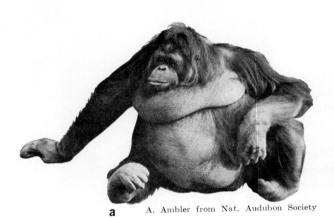

a   A. Ambler from Nat. Audubon Society   **b**   Bucky Reeves from Nat. Audubon Society

scrambled through the forest, usually on all fours. Both types of modern monkeys show decrease in emphasis on the sense of smell. Both have a much enlarged cerebrum.

The Parting of the Way for Man and the Apes

More than 25 million years ago, probably in the late Oligocene or in the early Miocene, the ancestors of the apes and of man began evolving along separate lines. Both apparently evolved from upright terrestrial primates, probably from close relatives of *Proconsul*. The ancestors of today's great apes apparently returned to the trees—if they had ever really left. Swinging through the trees on arms that grasped the branches became a selective factor of increasing importance. Apes' arms became even stronger, well muscled, and longer—longer than their legs (Figure 37-7).

While the apes ranged among the trees and developed sharply crested teeth and long arms, the human family evolved as upright ground animals. Human types pro-

gressively developed longer and straighter legs, with feet fitted for striding instead of shuffling. Prehensile use of the big toe tended to disappear. They retained, however, their relatively acute mammalian hearing and excellent three-dimensional vision. Their grasping hands, freed for new uses, were served by an enlarging cerebrum. Presumably their upright position was served by the evolution of a broad, basin-shaped pelvic girdle upon which the trunk of the body balanced easily.

An additional evolutionary change that occurred in pre-man's skull allowed him to assume a truly erect posture. The hole through which the brain connects with the spinal cord gradually shifted underneath the cranial cavity, toward the jaw. This allowed him to look forward, while his back was straight and vertical. Great apes look forward too, but only by leaning forward and slightly hunching the back.

These changes, completed within 15 million years of the present time, produced an upright primate able to move quickly along

c

d

Both, Ylla from Rapho Guillumette

the ground. He could undoubtedly focus his eyes on objects he held and manipulated in his pliant hands. Pre-man, if not man the thinker, had arrived.

A synopsis of our discussion of primate evolution is shown in Figure 37-8.

A million years before the first great glacier crept southward to cover large areas of North America and Eurasia, *Zinjanthropus* was living and making tools at his Olduvai site in Africa, and at the same time or soon thereafter, a part of southern Africa was inhabited by the australopithecines. (The genus name is *Australopithecus*, but not all the known specimens have been assigned to this genus.) In many respects, such as the size of the brain and the shape of the face, the australopithecines were not unlike modern chimpanzees. But unlike chimpanzees, they walked in an upright posture and very probably lived on the ground rather than in trees. They had teeth much like the teeth of modern man, and it is possible that they ate a varied diet, including game that they killed.

Pithecanthropine Man

The first animals to which the name *man* is now definitely assigned were the **pithecanthropines** (pith·e·KAN·thro·peenz). (The name is derived from the genus *Pithecanthropus*, to which the first fossil found in Java was assigned.) Pithecanthropines have been discovered not only in Java but also in China (near Peking), and in Africa—so these early men were widely distributed during early and middle Pleistocene time. They stood upright, to a height of five feet or more. The brain was about midway in size between the brain of the australopithecines and the brain of modern man (Table 37-1). The forehead was low, with pronounced brow ridges above the eyes, and the jaws protruded. The pithecanthropines used fire and made crude stone tools. They had a crude culture.

Neanderthal Man

In late Pleistocene time, just before the beginning of the last glacial advance, **Neanderthal** (nee·AN·der·thal—Figure 37-9) **man**

37-8 A SUMMARY OF THE EVOLUTION OF PRIMATES

EPOCH	PROSIMIANS			MONKEYS		HOMINIDS	
	Tree shrew	Lemur	Tarsier	New world monkeys	Old world monkeys	Apes	Man
Recent							
11 thousand years ago							
Pleistocene							
1 million years ago							
Pliocene							
13 million years ago							
Miocene							
25 million years ago							
Oligocene							
36 million years ago							
Eocene							
58 million years ago							
Paleocene							
63 million years ago							

appeared in Eurasia and northern Africa. This man was rather short, heavily built, and exceedingly strong. Like *Pithecanthropus*, he had heavy brow ridges above the eyes, with protruding jaws, little chin, and a sloping forehead. He gives the impression of having been rather brutish. Yet Neanderthal man had a large brain, made excellent flint tools, and buried his dead with considerable ceremony. He was a man of intelligence and capability. He could hold his own and prosper in a cold and hostile world inhabited by numerous large, aggressive mammals.

During the last glaciation, perhaps 50,000 years ago, Neanderthal man disappeared. Various theories have been advanced to account for his extinction. It seems likely that he was overwhelmed and replaced by men very similar to ourselves—men who came out of the east. Perhaps the Neanderthals may have intermated with the newcomers; or perhaps they perished or were exterminated because of their inability to compete with a culturally more advanced type of man, with better tools and weapons.

Cro-Magnon Man

The successors to Neanderthal man were the people known as *Cro-Magnon* (kroh-MAG·non—Figure 37-10). Theirs was the peak of Stone Age culture. They lived in a world inhabited by woolly mammoths, woolly rhinoceroses, cave bears, wolves, bison, reindeer, wild horses, and other large mammals. They drew superb pictures of these animals deep within the caves of southern France and northern Spain (Figure 37-11, page 670). They carved tools and ornaments from ivory, and manufactured finely chipped stone arrow and spear points. They were vigorous, intelligent people of large stature.

During most of Pleistocene time, man shared the earth with many large mammals. To a Stone Age hunter, life was indeed uncertain, for he had to struggle with these

TABLE 37-1   AVERAGE CRANIAL CAPACITIES OF APES AND MEN

Name of living or fossil primate	Cranial capacity [1] (in cubic centimeters)
Modern apes	
Gibbon	100 cc
Orangutan	395 cc
Chimpanzee	400 cc
Gorilla	510 cc
Australopithecines	600 cc
Early men	
Java man	870 cc
Peking man	1050 cc
Neanderthal man	1450 cc
Modern men	
Cro-Magnon man	1660 cc
Australian bushman	1300 cc
Other modern men	1450 cc

[1] Average for males. The average for females is somewhat less.

large animals for his place on the earth. About 8,000 or 10,000 years ago there was a worldwide extinction of many of the large mammals that so characterized the Pleistocene epoch. The reasons for this extinction are obscure, but whatever may have been the causes of the late Pleistocene disappearance of large mammals, the event must have had considerable effect upon the cultural evolution of man. In a large sense, this was the beginning of modern times.

After nearly a century, it has become easier to look back to 1871, when Charles Darwin suggested the evolution of man from an anthropoid ancestry. Darwin had no fossil evidence to support his beliefs. His hypothesis was based on a study of living primates plus the evidence of evolution in other species. Since 1869, the fossil evidence has accumulated. Biologists today find that it fulfills Darwin's predictions and

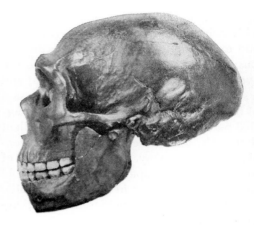

37-9 A fossil skull and a cast of the probable appearance of a Neanderthal man. Neanderthal remains and tools have been found in central and southern Europe, North Africa, Gibraltar, and in the Near East. Enough specimens have been discovered to establish considerable diversity within the type. The skull shown here is an unusually large one (1600 cc cranial capacity).

All photos, American Museum of Natural History

37-10 A skull and a cast of the appearance of a Cro-Magnon man. In every way his appearance was modern. The only striking difference between him and man today was that he had a considerably larger skull, and was often larger in overall size, than most people living now.

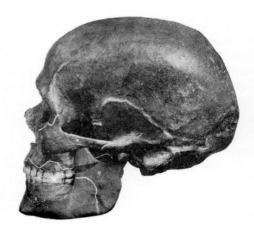

provides a satisfying, if somewhat incomplete, series of stages from the distant past to the present.

We know that the attainment of an upright posture predated the use of tools. We still cannot state with confidence which came first: man's enlarged brain, or his development of tools and culture. Perhaps each reinforced the other. When tools were first developed, those men with the more efficient brains were able to use their tools more effectively than others, in hunting and in protecting themselves. They prevailed over men of lesser capabilities—and developed still better tools. This, too, is natural selection. Man's way of life improved, and his level of culture gradually rose. As the process repeated itself, the progressive increase in human brain size came as a product of evolution through natural selection. It contributed toward greater mental efficiency, invention of superior tools, a higher level of culture, and selection of people with still more advanced brains.

TOOLS AND CULTURE

For evidence of the earliest cultural developments of mankind, we must rely upon fossils and discarded tools. It seems clear that early man was a hunter and a meat eater. Crushed baboon skulls are associated with fossils of some australopithecines. In the cave where Peking man lived are deposits containing the split bones and skulls of many wild animals and of man as well. They are associated with the remains of fire pits. Charred bones suggest that man had already learned to cook meat, perhaps to make it easier to chew.

The early tools were relatively simple. Gradually man, in his evolution, improved on the crudely flaked pebbles of the australopithecines and the chipped flints and stone tools of early men in Africa and Europe (and later, in America, which has been inhabited by man for at least 25,000 years and perhaps longer, as indicated by carbon-dating of two very old hearths, or fire pits, discovered recently in Texas). As man's tools improved, he no doubt hunted more efficiently (Figure 37-12).

Rapid improvement in tools during the last advance of the continental glaciers shows that modern men were highly inventive. Among these tools is a large variety of long flint blades of triangular cross section. They were made by splitting off one edge from a squared block of flint, then working the fragment to chip and pressure-flake a precise and often beautiful tool. Blades of other shapes presumably served as knives, scrapers, borers, and spear points. Since huge piles of bones from mammoths and horses of this time have been found, men are assumed to have hunted in groups, perhaps making seasonal drives for meat. While men gained knowledge of and some control over nature, human social organization became both more complex and more efficient. Presumably language grew more useful, too.

Between 10,000 and 6,000 years ago, *Homo sapiens* devised clothes and learned new skills in food gathering. In strata from this period, prehistorians have found such various bone tools as pins, needles with eyes, spool-shaped buttons, spear throwers, fishhooks, and bone arrow-straighteners similar to those used by Eskimos today. With improved techniques in hunting and fishing, the numbers of men increased, until they were limited again by the availability of game, edible plants, and fish.

Primitive man may have begun to support specialists in tool making and cave painting (Figure 37-11). Engravings and paintings from this period cover the walls of more than sixty caves in Spain alone. Tools and sacred objects interred with burials, both in the Old and New Worlds, suggest that man already looked toward going, after death, to a better world than the one in which he lived.

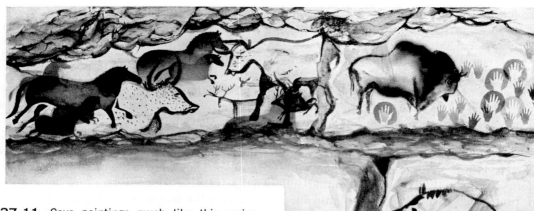

37-11 Cave paintings much like this series confirm the inhabitation of many caves of Southern France and Northern Spain by modern man, 25,000 or more years ago. Judging from this illustration, would you say that the people who lived in the caves were fishermen, or hunters, or planters of crops?

CONCLUDING REMARKS—
THE NATURE OF MAN TODAY

Scientists who specialize in studying man of recent times are known as **anthropologists** (an·thro·POL·o·jists). They believe that a long history of comparative isolation, extending back perhaps 25,000 years, is responsible for the measurable differences between native peoples in different geographic localities. All men can be classified, in a rough way, into such groups as the Negro, Mongoloid, and Caucasoid races. But anthropologists recognize that each of the features by which people might be so classified show tremendous variation within any given population.

It is true that in Africa, the East Indies, and Australia, the native population today has a high proportion of dark-skinned people. In Europe, the majority have light skin color. In eastern Asia, the greatest numbers have a skin shade between fair and dark. But many south European "whites" have darker skins than some equatorial African "blacks." Often there is considerable diver-

Caru Studios and Don Meyer

37-12 An assortment of stone tools. The two handles are reconstructions. These examples were discovered in the United States and range in age from very recent to 7,000 or more years old. The tools at the right, including the double-pointed hoe at the bottom, probably were used by women; they include a large hoe or adze blade (notched on each side for hafting to a wooden handle), a celt or hand axe, and four scrapers (for scraping hides). The tools at the left, including the black axe with reconstructed handle, were characteristically used by men; they include two flint blades or knives, a grooved axe-head, and six projectile points.

sity of skin color among the children of one pair of parents.

Similarly, many Oriental people have "slanted" eyes because of a slight difference in the distribution of fat above the lids. When the eyes are open, the upper lids disappear under overhanging folds (Figure 37-13). Some Western people have similar folds. And some Orientals do not.

The effects of prolonged geographical isolation and inbreeding can still be seen in some parts of the world. All South Ameri-

can Indians, for example, have blood type O; Australian aborigines have about 49 percent O, 48 percent B, 2 percent A, and 1 percent AB. Similar differences are evident in the incidence of the sickle-cell trait (Chapter 32), or the relative numbers in isolated groups afflicted with buck teeth.

Despite the fact that we can divide *Homo sapiens* into races on the basis of percentage differences of many inheritable traits, the different members of the human species are still much more alike than they are dif-

Courtesy of *Scientific American*

37-13 A comparison of Mongoloid (left) and Caucasoid (right) eyes. The difference in appearance is not a matter of eye structure, but of fat distribution above the eyes.

ferent. We rely so strongly on skull characteristics that even an expert would have difficulty distinguishing a headless skeleton of a light-skinned person from that of a dark-skinned individual. Without the skulls, a conclusive identification of Java man as distinct from Neanderthal man or modern man would be difficult.

All groups of men possess strictly comparable organs, and remarkable uniformity in a host of other physical and chemical characteristics. All racial types are known to be completely interfertile, and persons of mixed racial ancestry are in their turn fully fertile. They reveal no evidence of any biological lack of harmony among their traits. By biological criteria, all men are of one species.

The distribution of intelligence, moreover, seems to be an individual, not a racial, matter. Anthropologists who study cultures of men who have very different backgrounds from ourselves—different Indian tribes, native tribes of Australia, New Guinea, and other remote regions—all agree that people who have been brought up in completely different surroundings, with cultural traditions very different from ours, can think and behave so differently from

ourselves that many of us would consider them to have basically different human natures. Nevertheless, if a small baby is moved from his place of birth to a very different environment, he develops ways of thought and an outlook on the world that comes from the society in which he is brought up, rather than the culture of his parents. These facts have led many scientists to believe that human nature, while affected by both physical environment and heredity, is nevertheless most strongly influenced by culture and tradition. In short, we are all men, as our ancestors apparently have been for hundreds of thousands of years.

GUIDE QUESTIONS AND PROBLEMS

1. What physical traits seem to be specially characteristic of the human species?
2. What traits does man share with his primate relatives?
3. How is the presence of primitive tools in association with fossil remains of man interpreted?
4. What information about human evolution has been provided by studies of australopithecine fossils?

5. Why is there uncertainty about the time when the "manlike" and the "apelike" types diverged?

6. What new information about the antiquity of tool making was gained from studies of *Zinjanthropus* at Olduvai Gorge?

7. How long has man been on the earth? What is the evidence for this estimate?

8. Why are the fossil remains of *Proconsul* and *Oreopithecus* so noteworthy?

9. What are the major modern races of man? What characteristics distinguish each?

10. How can we use the evidences of man's early cultures as "tools" to interpret his development?

11. What is the justification for reconstructing a whole animal from the fossil bones of a few parts of the skeleton?

12. How could you support the idea that modern man is no more advanced in intelligence than man of 50,000 years ago?

SUGGESTIONS FOR ADDITIONAL READING

Books

Coon, C. S., *The Story of Man*, 2nd ed. rev. New York, Knopf, 1962.
> A description of human evolution and the history of a number of cultures.

Dart, R., and D. Craig, *Adventures with the Missing Link*. New York, Harper & Row, 1959.
> The story of the discovery of a fossil of a primitive hominid type.

Harrison, R. J., *Man the Peculiar Animal*. Baltimore, Penguin Books, 1958.
> Contrasts man with other mammals with respect to structure and function.

Howells, W. W., *Mankind in the Making*. New York, Doubleday, 1959.
> A very readable summary of human evolution and the origin of races.

Leakey, L. S. B., *Adam's Ancestors*. New York, Harper & Row, 1960.
> An excellent, up-to-date discussion of human evolution and the evolution of early human cultures.

Montagu, Ashley, *Man: His First Million Years*. New York, New American Library, 1958.
> The interesting story of man's cultural and physical development.

Magazines and Journals

Broom, R., "The Ape-Man." *Scientific American*, Vol. 181 (November 1949), pp. 20–24.

Daniel, G. E., "The Idea of Man's Antiquity." *Scientific American*, Vol. 201 (November 1959), pp. 167–68.

Deevey, E. S., Jr., "Radiocarbon Dating." *Scientific American*, Vol. 186 (February 1952), pp. 24–28.
> (A correction to this article is published in *Scientific American*, April 1952, p. 2.)

Eiseley, L. C., "Antiquity of Modern Man." *Scientific American*, Vol. 179 (July 1948), pp. 16–19.

—— "Man the Fire-Maker." *Scientific American*, Vol. 191 (September 1954), pp. 52–57.

Howells, W. W., "The Distribution of Man." *Scientific American*, Vol. 203 (September 1960), pp. 112–20.

Krogman, W. M., "The Man-Apes of South Africa." *Scientific American*, Vol. 178 (May 1948), p. 16.

—— "The Scars of Human Evolution." *Scientific American*, Vol. 185 (December 1951), pp. 54–57.

Sahlins, M. D., "The Origin of Society." *Scientific American*, Vol. 203 (September 1960), pp. 76–87.

Washburn, S. L., "Tools and Human Evolution." *Scientific American*, Vol. 203 (September 1960), pp. 62–76.

38

THE CULTURAL

EVOLUTION OF MAN

Sometime between 50,000 and 75,000 years ago, the gradually evolving populations of mankind reached the stage at which they were biologically like ourselves. If we could dress some of our ancestors of that time in modern clothes and parade them down the streets of our cities, people would probably not recognize them as different. In their mental ability, also, these men were probably our equals.

By 25,000 years ago, all men on the earth resembled one or another of the modern races of man. The thin, delicate, beautifully sculptured arrow and spear points that these men made out of hard flint required the greatest of skill and craftsmanship. Few, if any, of us today could duplicate the workmanship on these tools. Few, if any, of us would have the ability to live in the savage environment these men faced each day with their scanty complement of handmade tools and weapons.

Some of these early men entered the caves of southern Europe, and by the light of smoky torches, often sitting in most un-

comfortable positions, painted pictures of horses, mammoths, and oxen that show as high a degree of artistry as do many modern murals (Figure 37-11). Engravings and paintings from this period cover the walls of more than sixty caves in Spain alone. Furthermore, these men buried their dead in carefully constructed graves, and surrounded the corpses with spears, bows and arrows, ornaments, and other implements that they presumably thought would be useful to the dead in an afterlife.

We can be sure, therefore, that by at least 25,000 years ago, and probably much earlier, men had acquired some of the abilities that make modern life possible. These are the abilities to use tools; to talk and teach, so that the young generation can profit from the experiences of the elders; to work together and respect wise, intelligent leadership; and to look into the future toward a better life. The fruits of these abilities have become the story of mankind.

THE GREAT TRANSITION

In a great many ways, the men of 25,000 years ago were still at the mercy of their environment. They got their food by hunting game and gathering wild fruits, seeds, nuts, and roots. If game was scarce, or if a drought cut down the supply of wild food plants, they starved. They had to protect themselves constantly from lions, tigers, and other carnivores, and from the large herbivorous mammals such as mastodons and mammoths.

Since these primitive people could talk to each other, they may have had elaborate religious ceremonies, in which stories of their ancestors were told. Even today the Australian aborigines and the African Bushmen, who live as food gatherers, practice complex magical rituals. The culture of each group includes music and a rich vocabulary of spoken literature, as well as a belief in a supernatural power.

Remnants of the Past: Hunting and Food-gathering Peoples

We know that the knowledge of nature possessed by the Australian aborigines and African Bushmen is very extensive. Both these groups of people have detailed knowledge of the plants and animals they eat. They know about seasonal fluctuations in winds, in temperature, and in humidity; about tidal changes when they live by the sea; and about the movement of planets in the sky, as well as the phases of the moon. This knowledge is intricately woven into living habits and is needed for survival.

In their use of the parts of kangaroos, the Australian aborigines demonstrate how fully they exploit their environment. They bind their spears with its sinews, eat its flesh, and make tools and pins from its bones. Its fat is mixed with red ochre to make cosmetics. Paint is made by blending its blood with charcoal. Its teeth and claws are strung as beads.

The Bushmen of the great Kalahari Desert (Figure 38-1) have devised a comparable number of uses for the tsama melon. The pulp of the melon is used for food. It yields water for quenching thirst and for boiling meat. Splinters from shoulder blades of the gemsbok antelope are thrust into the green tsama melons. This softens the bone splinters so that they can be carved into arrow points. The melon seeds are roasted and eaten, or ground into flour for cakes. Children bait mousetraps with the seeds. The dried rinds are used as mixing bowls, cooking pots, and dishes from which to eat. The rinds are filled with urine into which hides are put to be cured. Children use the dried rinds as toys, drums, and targets. Adults use them as resonators by holding them against musical instruments.

Undoubtedly the hunters and food gatherers 10,000 to 25,000 years ago had a similar knowledge of their environment and made a comparable use of materials in it.

They probably cooked their food in open fires or in huge pits, as do many tribes of modern times. And they may have used forest or grass fires to drive game animals into places where they could be captured. Because game and edible plants became scarce from time to time, these ancient men could not always live a settled life in villages, but often had to be moving in search of food.

The Dawn of Agriculture

The conditions that made a settled life possible, and laid the groundwork for the rise of civilization, were the cultivation of plants and the domestication of animals. We believe that this happened some time between 10,000 and 7,000 years ago. The remains of men who, according to the radiocarbon method of dating, are more than 10,000 years old are accompanied only by hunting tools, remains of wild plants, and implements for preparing such plants for food. More recent remains begin to include hulls of grains related to modern wheat and barley, as well as such tools as sickles, which would be useful only in harvesting cultivated grains.

We who take agriculture for granted can hardly imagine how many skills had to be learned before men could raise sufficient crops to support themselves. For seed crops, men had first to learn which seeds could be saved and which would grow quickly into mature plants. Then they had to learn how to clear the ground, and how to dig it up or plow it so as to have a loose, well-aerated soil. Next they had to learn *when* to plant, so as to avoid freezes and drought, which would kill the young seedlings. But they could not plant too late if they hoped to get a ripened crop before the killing droughts or frost of a later season.

During the long months when the crop was growing and ripening, they had to learn how to keep out destructive animals such as wild cattle, birds, and insect pests.

38-1 A family group of African Bushmen of the Kalahari Desert. Like the hunting and food-gathering peoples of 10,000 to 25,000 years ago, they are nomadic. They live in small bands, and gather roots and vegetables and hunt animals for their subsistence.

Peabody Museum

They also had, doubtless, to defend their crops at all times from other tribes, who had not yet started to learn about agriculture but were willing and ready to raid the fields of those who had. Finally, they had to learn how to harvest the crop quickly and store it in an edible condition, since it would be needed long after harvest, during the winter months.

The Origins of Cultivated Plants and Domestic Animals

While men were learning these arts of agriculture, they were also improving the wild plants that they cultivated. This involved conscious, artificial selection for characteristics that are very different from the traits that fit plants to survive in the wild. If the seeds were to be eaten, plants were selected with as large and as many seeds as could be found. Such seeds contain more stored food than the seedlings actually need, and are so heavy that they cannot easily be dispersed by natural means. *Natural selection* does not favor them, but *artificial selection* does.

The early cultivators had to rid their plants of a characteristic that is found in all wild, seed-bearing annual plants. This is the tendency for the seeds to break away from the plant as soon as they are ripe. In all of the wild grasses related to wheat, barley, rice, and other grains, the seed head shatters or breaks up into pieces containing one or two seeds just as soon as the seeds are ripe. This trait is of great advantage to the plant in seed dispersal, but disadvantageous to man. Fields of such grains can be harvested only by hand. In today's strains of cultivated grains, on the other hand, the seed heads are stiff and hold their seeds until they can be harvested with scythes, sickles, or combines.

Studies in genetics have shown that the differences between shattering and stiff, nonshattering seed heads are usually determined by one or two pairs of genes. Hence the most important step in the evolution of cultivated cereals from the wild ancestral grasses was taken when the early cultivators found and selected plants having mutations for stiff seed heads.

Another difference between cultivated grains and their wild relatives is that in the wild plants the hulls stick closely to the grains. This protects the seeds until they are ready to germinate. Man, on the other hand, wants his grain free of hulls. Hence mutations that cause the grains to fall out of the hulls easily during the threshing process are desirable. Plants carrying these mutations were long ago selected by man from among the many cereal species.

As a result of many generations of artificial selection for the kinds of characteristics mentioned above, our cultivated food plants have come to differ from their wild relatives in a large number of genes. They are beautifully adapted to serve our needs, but they cannot grow by themselves without man's help.

The domestication of wild animals required corresponding time and patience. The wild relatives of many domestic animals, which in some instances belong to the same species, are noted for their intractability, savageness, and ferocity. This is particularly true of the Eurasian wildcat, wild cattle (now extinct), and wild boars, which are the ancestors of our domestic cats, cattle, and pigs. Genetic studies of wild and tame rats have shown that tameness is largely under the control of genes. Other domestic animals probably differ similarly from their wild relatives.

The domestication of animals, therefore, must have involved much more than simply capturing animals and keeping them penned up. It is very unlikely that early men could have caught and handled the adults of these wild beasts. They probably killed the females for food, then raised the orphaned young. Many people today, both savage and civilized, like to raise the young of wild animals and keep them as pets. Often these wildlings, as they grow up, become too unruly to handle, but some of them are tame enough to keep and even breed in captivity. The first domestication of animals must have been brought about in some such fashion.

At first glance, we seem to have introduced a dilemma—a question of how tribes of nomadic hunters could have spent enough time in one place to learn about agriculture and the domestication of a wide number of different animals. The hunters had to move from place to place in order to find enough game to keep themselves alive. But they could not find the time to learn cultivation of plants and domestication of animals until they were able to stay in one place. How, then, could they have learned these arts?

Recent observations of modern tribes, and of the remains of ancient settlements, have suggested a possible solution. Many of the Indians of California and elsewhere were very poor hunters and did not cultivate plants. They lived on the seashore or along lakes and rivers, and got most of their food by fishing or gathering shellfish. Fishhooks are among the tools found in the remains of settlements that existed before the dawn of agriculture.

This suggests that the first people who settled down and lived in villages were fishermen. Those living on lakes had to stay on the same lake most of the time, because boats were difficult to build and could not easily be carried over land. Also, the supply of fish in those days was probably almost inexhaustible, so that once a tribe had discovered a good place for fishing they could stay there indefinitely. This was particularly true in the tropics, where the supply of both seafood and edible plants was unusually large.

While the men were fishing, the women were probably hunting for edible seeds and roots. They brought the best kinds in large baskets and roasted the biggest roots with the fish, as do many of the South Sea Islanders today. After the meals, the fish bones and other refuse were discarded near the settlement, eventually forming large mounds. As the rains mixed these mounds of refuse with dirt, they made piles of loose, well-fertilized soil. The women probably threw some of the smaller, tougher roots onto these dumps, where they must have grown very well since they found an ideal soil texture, good fertilization, and little competition from other plants. From such accidents, people probably got the idea of purposely bringing in extra roots and planting them around the refuse heaps. The roots that grew to the largest size and had the best flavor could then have been broken into pieces, some for eating and some for planting. Agriculture may have begun in this way, possibly with the cultivation of tropical roots such as yams, taro, and sweet potatoes.

In regions like the Middle East, parts of Africa, and the highlands of Mexico, the climate was too dry and cool for cultivating these tropical roots. But the seedlings of wild grasses related to wheat, barley, and other grains must have grown very well on refuse heaps. We can imagine, then, that the cultivation of these grains, which is much more difficult than raising root crops in a tropical climate, may first have been tried by people who migrated out of the tropics. Perhaps they settled in such areas as western India, the Middle East, parts of China, and the highlands of Mexico, Central America, and the Andes. They may already have been in the habit of cultivating root crops. Now they turned to seed crops, because the roots would not grow in the new environment.

Or perhaps certain tribes discovered agriculture independently of the early tropical peoples, by learning how to domesticate wild grasses. For example, the American Indians who domesticated maize (corn) and the "Irish" potato are not likely to have learned about agriculture from the Old World. They were descended from primitive hunters who made their way into North America long before the dawn of agriculture anywhere.

The oldest known villagelike settlements, which include evidence that plants were cultivated and animals were domesticated, have been found in the Middle East, particularly in Palestine and northern Iraq. They occur in the hills surrounding the great fertile valley of the Tigris and Euphrates, which considerably later was the scene of the oldest known civilizations. We cannot be sure, however, that these were actually the oldest communities that practiced agriculture. Since they existed in a very dry climate, the remains of these communities were not easily decayed, and could not be overgrown by trees and undergrowth.

We are unlikely to find any remains of primitive communities that may have existed in such regions as eastern India, Burma, and Malaya. All organic material would long ago have decayed; the great rivers and torrential rains would have covered the stone tools with many feet of dirt and silt. Later people cultivating the same areas would long ago have destroyed any chance remnants, which might otherwise have survived.

Indirect evidence that agriculture appeared in other regions before it appeared in the Middle East is suggested by the probable origins of some of our cultivated plants and domestic animals. Evidence, chiefly from the distribution of wild relatives of these plants and animals, suggests that they arose in restricted parts of the earth and spread from these centers, either through being carried by migrating people or by trade between tribes.

Although many of these centers have been recognized, as few as four of them have probably contributed the great majority of man's most useful plants and animals. These are: (1) tropical, southeastern Asia, (2) temperate, southwestern Asia, (3) subtropical or temperate Mexico and Central America, and (4) the central Andes of South America (Figures 38-2 and 38-3).

We do not know whether agriculture originated independently in each of these four centers, or whether the ideas of cultivating plants and of domesticating animals arose in one or two of them and was carried to the others. A final answer to this particular question will probably never be given.

Southeastern tropical Asia extends from eastern India to Burma. The cultivated plants that arose in this center of agriculture were rice, bananas, sugarcane, bamboo, and tropical root crops, particularly yams and taro. Here the first animals may have been domesticated. These were household animals: the dog, pig, and chicken. The pariah dogs of India and the wild dingo of Australia are more like mongrel domestic dogs than are any other doglike animals. They are probably descended from a jackal-like animal, which at some very early time learned that the refuse heaps of fisher folk were filled with food. After they had come to be familiar sights about encampments, they were domesticated—perhaps because the puppies were taken for pets.

Wild pigs related to domestic ones are still to be found all the way from Europe through Asia to the islands of the Pacific. Both the living breeds of pigs and fossil bones of pigs found in association with early cultivators are more like the wild pigs of southeastern Asia than any other wild types.

The modern wild pigs still like to root in the village plantings of that region.

Chickens are clearly derived from the jungle fowl of southeastern Asia.

The southwestern Asiatic center of cultivation extends from the hills of Palestine northward to the mountains of eastern Turkey, Armenia, northern Iraq and northwestern Iran, and eastward to Afghanistan and Soviet Central Asia. This is the ancestral home of most of our familiar crops and farm animals. The wild ancestors of wheat, barley, rye, and oats are found here, as well as those of the forage plant alfalfa. Peas and flax also originated here, and probably muskmelons, canteloupes, and their relatives. Apples, peaches, apricots, plums, grapes, almonds, and walnuts were cultivated first either here or in the mountains of Asia farther to the east.

This center is also the place where our larger meat, milk, and draft animals were probably domesticated. Most likely the first of these were sheep and goats, since they could be more easily captured and tamed than could cattle and horses. At a time when game was abundant, the few animals that could have been raised probably contributed little to the people's supply of meat. Perhaps these animals were originally used for milk and wool, rather than meat.

Wild cattle, which were much larger and fiercer animals, were probably domesticated later, although their remains are found in the ruins of the earliest agricultural villages of the Middle East. Oxen, which are bulls castrated to render them docile, were the first draft animals. Some of the earliest records that we have show them pulling ceremonial carts. In this region the moon goddess was regularly worshiped. The resemblance of the cow's horns to the "horns" of a crescent moon is believed to have been one reason why cattle were regarded as sacred animals by many primitive peoples. It is entirely possible that at first the domestic cow was a "holy cow."

38-2 THE GEOGRAPHIC ORIGINS OF SOME IMPORTANT DOMESTICATED PLANTS

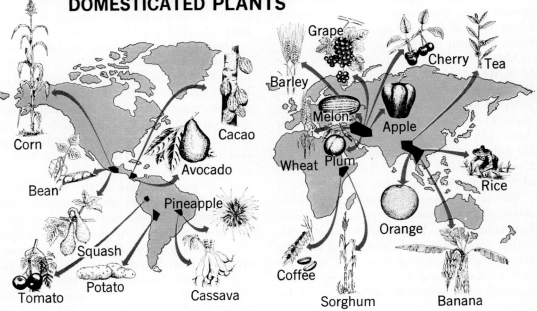

Corn

Cacao

Avocado

Bean

Pineapple

Squash

Tomato

Potato

Cassava

Grape

Barley

Cherry

Tea

Melon

Apple

Wheat Plum

Rice

Orange

Coffee

Sorghum

Banana

Another animal domesticated for doing work, the donkey, originated in northeastern Africa. It quickly was "adopted" in the Middle East. Camels probably were domesticated in Arabia. This is uncertain, however, since the camel is the only domestic animal that at present has no truly wild relatives. Horses were first domesticated in the Middle East or central Asia. They were the latest of all farm animals to be domesticated. The first tame horses known to us pulled war chariots in the early days of civilization. There is no evidence that horses were used as draft animals, for peaceful occupations, until later on in historic times.

The only center of cultivation in North America that has contributed many of our crop plants is the area of the highlands of Mexico and Central America. This is the original home of maize, beans, pumpkins, squashes, tobacco, and probably upland cotton. These crops were cultivated in the southwestern United States, in Central America, and in many parts of South America for thousands of years before Columbus.

The only domestic animal of the New World that is of any general importance, the turkey, was first domesticated in Mexico. Two other American centers may be as old as, or older than, the Mexican one. One is the northwest coast of South America, which contributed the sweet potato, the cocoa tree, and perhaps the pineapple. The other is the central Andes, from which came the potato and tomato.

Next to food, probably nothing was more important to primitive man than clothing, except in the tropics. The early men of Europe undoubtedly made their clothing of the skins of the animals they killed. One may guess that these early men, like apes, were quite hairy, for until man learned to make clothes for himself hairiness would have had great importance in natural selection. By the time of Cro-Magnon man, within the past 50,000 years, the hides were cut and sewn together with thongs of raw-

38-3 THE GEOGRAPHIC ORIGINS OF SOME IMPORTANT DOMESTICATED ANIMALS

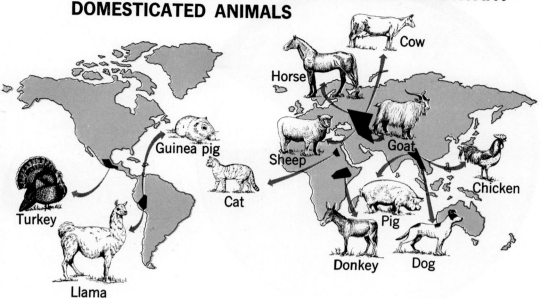

Horse

Cow

Guinea pig

Sheep

Goat

Cat

Chicken

Turkey

Pig

Donkey

Dog

Llama

hide, just as Eskimos make their clothes today. We know this because of the bone needles that the Cro-Magnons made.

Clothing took an entirely new turn with the invention of weaving. The weaving of cloth is almost as old as agriculture, having started in Egypt and Mesopotamia with linen woven from the stiff, strong fibers of the stalks of flax plants. Wool and cotton fabrics were later inventions, since they both involved the rather difficult problem of spinning short fibers into longer threads. The cotton that was first utilized was Old World cotton. It was derived from the hairy seeds of diploid species of cottons found in India and Africa. There are wild diploid cottons in North and South America, too, and somehow—it is hard even to guess how —the chromosome number of a hybrid between an Old World and a New World cotton species was doubled (see also Chapter 35, pages 629–30), and the new polyploid species provided the basis of the cotton fabrics woven by the Indians of Mexico, as well as the basis of our modern cotton culture.

One wonders: Was weaving invented quite independently in the Old and New Worlds? How did cotton come to be recognized on both continents as an ideal natural fiber? Wool, woven from the hair of domesticated llamas and alpacas, was made into cloth by the Indians of Peru. How and when did they learn to do this? History is blank regarding all these matters, and it seems likely that we will never know the answers to many of our questions. Yet one thing is sure: the inventiveness and ingenuity of the human species are not recent developments.

Agriculture and the Rise of Civilization

Civilized communities, with houses, public buildings, governments, laws, and written records, could not arise until people had solved the problem of staying in one place. This, in turn, meant having an assured supply of food. Thus, agriculture was, and is, necessary for civilization. A second requirement for civilization is organization and division of labor. According to all of our records, the first organizations of this

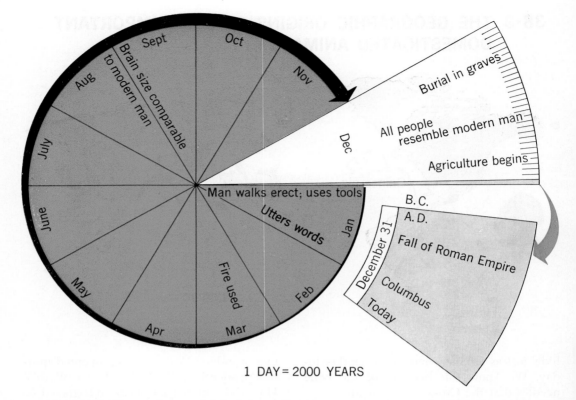

1 DAY = 2000 YEARS

38-4 The last 730,000 years of human evolution on a one-year time scale. January 1 corresponds to 1,000,000 years after *Zinjanthropus* or approximately 100,000 to 200,000 years before Java or Peking man. The date is, of course, arbitrary.

type began under the direction of a powerful leader. One way of gaining power over other men was by owning land. Hence, when land became the source of food through agriculture, the head of a landowning family could marry his sons and daughters into other landowning families, so that his eldest or most aggressive son could control more property, and so on. Fathers or leaders of large families thus became local "kings." About these rulers were grouped soldiers, priests, tradesmen, artisans, and others. By conquering neighboring people, they acquired large numbers of slaves who built cities, palaces, temples, and pyramids. In this way were born the first great civilizations, in Egypt, Mesopotamia, and the Indus valley of western India.

CULTURAL EVOLUTION AND ITS FUTURE

You can see from this brief account of man's rise that the change from the savage, Stone Age type of existence to modern civilization took only a tiny fraction of the amount of time needed for man to evolve from his apelike ancestors. Furthermore, if we list in order the various discoveries that gave man his increasing control over nature, we see they have been made at a pace that has been increasing with terrifying rapidity.

If we bring the succession of changes down to a scale that we can more easily understand than the thousands of years actually involved, we can get a hint of the speed with which man's evolutionary line is racing toward unknown accomplishments. Suppose that we reduce to one "year" the last 730,000 years of time on the earth (Figure 38-4). In this case, each hypothetical "day" represents 2,000 actual years.

January 1 would find man's ancestors able to walk erect and use primitive tools, to hunt in bands and call to each other, but probably unable to talk in recognizable words. Speech evolved slowly, during January and February. Fire probably began to be used during March or April—for protection, for driving game to places where it could be killed, and finally for cooking. During the whole summer man's ability to talk, make tools, and use fire was gradually improving. The size of his brain was increasing. The first men with a brain size comparable to ours, the Neanderthals, appeared about September 1. Burial in graves, indicating belief in an afterlife, appeared among the Neanderthals about December 6 of this hypothetical year.

By December 18, all people on earth, the Cro-Magnons and their contemporaries, resembled modern men in appearance. The beginnings of agriculture (Figure 38-5a) came about December 26, while the entire span of known civilization would occupy only the last three days, December 29 through 31. The birth of Christ would have been at about 12:30 A.M. on the morning of December 31. American Independence would date from 9:59 P.M. of New Year's Eve, with the invention of the steam engine and the discovery of electricity occurring at about the same time. Railroads, steamships, factories, and the telegraph would appear between 10:00 and 11:00 P.M. of that last evening; telephones, automobiles, and electric power between 11:00 and 11:30; and the last half hour would see man conquering the air, talking to anyone anywhere by radio, and learning how to destroy every living thing, including himself, if he wills.

We can measure evolution in terms of a change in the relationship of a species to its surroundings, as well as in terms of changes in the organism's body. If we do, we find that human evolution, which went on for several hundreds of thousands of years at a fairly rapid pace compared to the evolution of other organisms, has in the last 25,000 years speeded up tremendously. No slackening of the pace is in sight for the future. The remarkable fact is that man has carried out this phenomenal transformation of his way of life without changing noticeably his outward appearance. Man has discovered a new kind of evolution, *cultural evolution*, which is independent of physical changes in his body. In order to have any idea of what the future has in store for mankind, we must understand fully the differences between cultural evolution and organic evolution.

The first new feature of cultural evolution is that, in determining human behavior, it has substituted *cultural inheritance* for physical heredity via the genes. We can think of heredity in the broadest sense as the transmission of traits from one generation to the next. In animals that cannot learn, this has to be done only by physical determiners, or genes. The genes make an animal like its parents, quite independently of anything the parents may do. But once animals are able to learn, certain traits of behavior can be handed down from parents to offspring by the learning process itself. We see the beginnings of this new kind of "heredity" in such animals as birds. The young of some birds learn how to fly by imitating their mothers. Careful studies of bird songs have shown that the birds of a species in one particular region have songs slightly different from the same species in a different region. This is because the young birds imitate the songs of their parents. But in birds and all other animals, heredity by learning is much less important than heredity via the genes. Man is the only organism whose every act, from eating and sleeping to traveling over the earth and reproducing his kind, is greatly influenced by traits which he has learned. But we must not forget that his ability to learn is also a product of his genetic inheritance and his evolution.

A second feature of cultural evolution becomes clear when we think of man's relationship to his environment. About a century ago Alfred Russel Wallace, the evolutionist who with Darwin proposed the Theory of Natural Selection (Chapter 34), remarked that while animals become adapted by changing themselves to fit the environment, man alters the environment to fit his needs. Animals become adapted to cold weather through natural selection of genes that cause their bodies to become encased in fat or fur, or through selection of genes that cause them to go to sleep in a warm shelter during the winter months. Man has become adapted to cold by learning how to make and wear warm clothes, and to build and heat houses. He provides a new environment for himself, like that of the tropics, in which he can function normally throughout the winter.

Birds and bats are able to fly because they have evolved great changes in their front limbs, backbones, and other structures. Man has succeeded in flying by building machines, which he can run with his unaltered body, and which carry him through the air much faster and farther than any bird.

A third feature of cultural evolution is that it has enabled man to modify his environment by means of learned cooperation. Cooperation is highly developed in many societies of animals. The life in ant-hills and beehives provides familiar examples. But the individuals of these societies have instincts for cooperation given them by the action of their genes. They do not have to learn how to work together. Man must be *taught* to cooperate with his fellowmen, for he has many remnants of antisocial behavior. All of our laws, morals, and codes of ethics are based upon this in-

escapable duality of man's nature: the inner warfare between his social yearnings and his selfish egoism. The manufacture and operation of complex machines, such as airplanes, radios, and electronic computers, require cooperation between more people of different abilities and skills than existed in a whole tribe of primitive men. As society and its material goods become more complex, the emphasis on cooperation will have to become greater.

Fourth and finally, man's cultural evolution has been determined in large part by the ability of some men and women to look ahead and foresee a better world than the one in which they have lived. This quality of foresight is uniquely human; no other animal has it. We must admit, sadly, that far too few men possess this quality. Furthermore, many of the ways that have been used to develop cooperation, particularly slavery and the rigid decrees of dictators, tend to stifle the capacity for foresight that many people might otherwise have. Here we are faced with the great dilemma of modern times. How can we maintain the cooperation among men of all sorts, which is needed to keep our complex society running, without stifling the individuality and iniative that we need for further progress? We in the United States believe that we have found the answer to this problem in democracy. Our own progress over the last two centuries supports this belief better than any words could do. But we must remember that democracy is one of the cultural traits that, more than any other, must be passed down from one generation to another by teaching, learning, and setting examples. If we should ever take for granted this democratic heritage, we shall surely begin to lose it.

In the last four centuries man's cultural evolution has entered a culminating phase. This is the period of the Scientific-Industrial Revolution, which began modestly and inconspicuously with the introduction by

a

38-5

An indication of man's rapid cultural evolution.
a The first step toward settled, stable communities was the beginning of agriculture. **b** The technological (or industrial) revolution introduced a rapidly changing culture that has led to **c** in less than 1/20 of the time required to go from **a** to **b.** How will our culture continue to change in the next fifty years?

Upper, American Museum of Natural History;
center, Yale Univ. Art Gallery; *lower*, U. S. Air Force

b

c

Galileo and Vesalius of critical observations and experiments in physics and biology. Who would have foreseen the tremendous technological developments that would so swiftly follow the discoveries in pure science? The circumstances of human life change faster and faster (Figures 38-5b and c). The pace can best be assessed only in terms of a logarithmic increase. Three times in human history the sizes of human populations have increased at a logarithmic rate: once when toolmaking was achieved; a second time when agriculture was introduced; and now a third time, marked by the application of science to all the problems of human existence. In each of the former cases, the progress in technology later diminished and came to a relative standstill; and the population likewise leveled off at a plateau where the means of subsistence for the population was in balance with its numbers. Will this happen again? The outcome would seem to depend on whether or not the scientific advance, upon which our present technological civilization is based, will continue indefinitely, or will come to a halt. What do you think? Will we soon know everything about nature? Will the era of exploration and discovery in science come to an end, like the era of geographical exploration and discovery that waned when all the world had been penetrated and mapped? At least we can say that at this moment no one can see any end to the scientific enterprise, no day when history will come to an end because everything is known and everything is managed for the best possible welfare of humanity.

Cultural evolution depends upon the transmission from each generation to its successors of all that has been learned, invented, and created. As modern industrial society comes to depend more and more completely upon technological advances that, in turn, grow from scientific discoveries, what should most properly be emphasized? At least it seems clear that education must fit each new generation to live in a new environment, for man is continually destroying his environment and creating another anew. Education in science would appear to be an essential, central matter. It seems obvious that it is not safe for apes to play with atoms. Neither can men who have relinquished their birthright of scientific knowledge expect to rule themselves.

Not even the wonderful capacity of the human brain can learn and remember everything. What is it about science that is of paramount importance in our cultural evolution? In the course of studying this book and doing the laboratory exercises that form an integral part of your study of biology, has it become clear to you that a mere knowledge of facts is not enough? Neither is a broad understanding of biological concepts and principles sufficient, although that is far better and indeed quite essential. You must also see the science of biology as a part of man's cultural evolution, the sweep of which is daily changing our ways of life. You must appreciate the nature of this human conquest which, more than toolmaking and more than agriculture, makes man like the ancient gods in his power to control nature and to work "miracles." What is it, behind this conquest, but the method you have so often tried and found fruitful, the method of science that involves careful, often quantitative observations, accurate reports, experiments with controls, hypotheses that you can test, and sound logic?

GUIDE QUESTIONS

1. What is the evidence that prehistoric man had many abilities equal to those of modern man? What is the most major accomplishment he did *not* share with modern man?
2. What were the characteristics of the food-gathering way of life? Why does it seem reasonable that this nomadic existence gave way to communities under one-man rule, rather than to prehistoric democracy?

3. What were some of the major problems that had to be solved before a settled, agricultural life was possible?

4. What is the evidence that prehistoric man had a practical, working knowledge of plant breeding?

5. How is the development of agriculture related to the rise of civilization? What immediate changes in human relations probably took place in the first agricultural settlements of prehistoric times?

6. What insights into the political, social, and technological problems presently facing man does the study of cultural evolution provide?

7. What justification is there for the statement that most of the major discoveries responsible for modern civilization were made in prehistoric times?

8. How has the use of C^{14} (radiocarbon) dating helped to make more accurate our knowledge of cultural evolution during the past 15,000 years?

SUGGESTIONS FOR ADDITIONAL READING

Books

Bates, Marston, *Man in Nature.* Englewood Cliffs (N. J.), Prentice-Hall, 1961.
> A discussion of many of the topics treated in this chapter.

Childe, V. G., *What Happened in History.* Baltimore, Penguin Books, 1949.
> Particularly good on man in prehistory.

—— *Man Makes Himself.* New York, New American Library, 1952.
> Interesting and exciting story of the development of civilization.

Clark, John G. D., *World Prehistory—An Outline.* New York, Cambridge University Press, 1961.
> An up-to-date account of prehistoric man; covers all continents.

Coon, C. S., *The Story of Man,* 2nd ed. rev. New York, Knopf, 1962.
> Exciting story of the history of man.

Schery, R. W., *Plants for Man.* Englewood Cliffs (N. J.), Prentice-Hall, 1952.
> An interestingly written and well-illustrated account of plants useful to man.

Magazines and Journals

Braidwood, R. J., "The Agricultural Revolution." *Scientific American,* Vol. 203 (September 1960), pp. 130–34.

Butterfield, H., "The Scientific Revolution." *Scientific American,* Vol. 203 (September 1960), pp. 173–74.

Deevey, E. S., Jr., "The Human Population." *Scientific American,* Vol. 203 (September 1960), pp. 194–98.

Dobzhansky, T., "The Present Evolution of Man." *Scientific American,* Vol. 203 (September 1960), pp. 206–08.

Mangelsdorf, P. C., "Hybrid Corn." *Scientific American,* Vol. 185 (August 1951), pp. 39–47.

—— "The Mystery of Corn." *Scientific American,* Vol. 183 (July 1950), pp. 20–24.

—— "Wheat." *Scientific American,* Vol. 189 (July 1953), pp. 50–59.

Sahlins, M. D., "The Origin of Society." *Scientific American,* Vol. 203 (September 1960), pp. 76–87.

Washburn, S. L., "Tools and Human Evolution." *Scientific American,* Vol. 203 (September 1960), pp. 62–75.

CONTINUITY

39

THE LIVING

WORLD

Biology, as we have studied it so far, has been largely a science of analysis. We have divided wholes into their component parts better to understand the wholes. We have studied cells in terms of what chromosomes, ribosomes, mitochondria, and other cell structures do. We have studied organs in terms of what cells do, and whole individuals in terms of what the organs do. Evolution was studied largely in terms of its component processes—mutation, genetic recombination, natural selection, and isolation. Heredity was studied in terms of DNA, mitosis, meiosis, fertilization, and biochemistry.

The biological world, when so analyzed, is not our familiar world. We normally see animals and plants as parts of a greater whole: a sea star in a tide pool, a stand of birch trees, a woodchuck in a meadow, numerous species of animals and plants in a drop of pond water, a group of cactus plants in a desert, or a flock of birds in a tree. We see organisms in relation to other organisms—as parts of nature.

Look at the two photographs in Figure 39-1. The right-hand one conveys no more than would a stuffed animal in a glass case in an old-fashioned museum. The left-hand photograph tells us much more. It shows not only the animals, but some of the plants that serve as their food, and the water hole from which they drink. You can make some shrewd guesses about the relative abundance of water, the amount of sunshine, and even the climate. Thus when you see the animals in their habitat, you understand some of their biological problems, that is, what it means to be alive as a giraffe.

What Is an Ecosystem?

Animals and plants, as they exist in nature, are part of an ecological system, or **ecosystem** (EK·o·sis·tem). Ecosystem is a dynamic concept. It includes all the ways individual organisms interact with one another and with their nonliving environment. The predators, the prey, the producers, the decomposers, the energy sources, and the matter from which living substances are derived are all involved in the ecosystem. One could say that the word *ecosystem* just means "living nature" were it not for the fact that "nature" has so many different meanings.

An ecosystem may be in a square meter of prairie, the edge of a pond, a tide pool, a few cubic meters of surface water of the ocean, or a balanced aquarium. None of these is a complete and independent ecosystem—not even the whole world is. Perhaps the balanced aquarium comes closest of any on the list; all it needs is light and a proper temperature. The tide pool, on the other hand, is influenced by what occurs in the nearby ocean and on the shore. There are no sharp boundaries to the ecosystem that exists in a tide pool—or to most other ecosystems.

What are some of the minimum requirements for an ecosystem? They should be familiar to you by now. There must be an

South Africa Tourist Corp.

39-1   Three animals in and out of their environment. The importance of the environment to our understanding of the organisms that inhabit it is suggested by the obvious differences between the two photographs. Both show the same group of giraffes. But the photograph at the right conveys nothing of the animal's way of life—where they live, what they feed upon, whether their habitat is warm or cold, or densely overgrown by plants, or partly open and sunny—or even, as indicated on the left above, a suggestion of how cumbersome it is for the animals merely to get a drink of water.

energy source that organisms can use directly or indirectly. There must be available a supply of all the elements required by the organisms forming part of the ecosystem. There must be organisms or processes that cycle (see Chapter 8) the elements between organism and nonliving environment. Finally there must be suitable temperatures, humidities, and so on. An ecosystem, then, involves organisms, energy, matter, cycles, and climates—all interacting to constitute living nature.

When one thinks of the tremendous complexity of a single living cell, adds the even greater complexity of a multicellular organism, and finally sets this seemingly delicate mechanism in the world of space and time, one wonders how there can be any life at all! Yet there is—and organisms are

so successful that they are present in nearly every nook and cranny of the earth's crust. We will now survey some of the main places where organisms are found, and explore the problems that are peculiar to living in these places. Our examples will be from the major habitats of the world.

LIFE IN THE OCEANS

We terrestrial animals tend to forget that the most extensive habitat for life consists of the world's oceans (Figure 39-2a). The oceans occupy about 70 percent of the earth's surface. Even this figure does not give a true estimate of the space available for marine life. On land, organisms occupy a flat and narrow zone. A few live to the extent of several meters below the surface.

Trees are usually less than 20 meters high. Nearly all terrestrial life is thus restricted to a zone about 30 meters thick. The average depth of the oceans, on the other hand, is roughly 4,000 meters. Since organisms are found throughout the depths of the oceans, the actual space available for marine life is some 300 times as great as the space available for terrestrial life.

Life in the earth's oceans—or in the sea, as we usually refer to ocean waters—depends as life does elsewhere on the presence of light. Where there is light in the sea, plants are able to carry on photosynthesis, and hence develop and reproduce. These plants, the primary producers, are eaten by animals. These animals are the primary consumers. They, in turn, are prey for the secondary consumers, and so on.

With light, the sea becomes a factory for life. The energy of light is stored in carbon compounds, which are used for the substance and energy of all organisms. The mass of living matter present in the sea is far greater than that on land. This life is not at all obvious. If you were to examine the surface waters of the North Atlantic, the chances are that you would see only water. Yet a liter of this water might contain 500,000 bacteria, 1,000,000 microscopic plants, and 150 microscopic animals.

Many of the animals move by means of cilia, flagella, or legs of some sort. A few of the plants move by means of flagella. For the most part, however, all of these organisms of the surface waters of the open sea are at the mercy of wind and waves. These more or less helpless drifters are known as **plankton.** They are insignificant to the unaided eye, but the role they play in the life of the sea is vital. Under the microscope they take on a truly wondrous variety of forms and colors.

The primary producers of the open-sea plankton are single-celled plants. The most abundant are diatoms (Figure 39-3). These are algae having an outer skeleton composed largely of silica, which is almost identical to glass. Diatoms contain a pigment similar to the chlorophyll of green plants. It enables them to transform the energy of light into the chemical energy of glucose and other carbon compounds that are characteristic of the plant, or producer's, way of life.

The primary producers next in order of abundance are the dinoflagellates (dy·no-FLAJ·e·layts). Each dinoflagellate has two flagella—a structural characteristic that we are accustomed to considering as animal-like. Some dinoflagellates possess chlorophyll and are photosynthetic; others lack chlorophyll and are heterotrophic in their nutrition. Obviously the usual distinction between green plants and animals breaks down in the dinoflagellate group. Botanists recognize their plantlike characteristics and classify them as algae, while zoologists classify them as protozoans.

Diatoms and dinoflagellates, plus a few other microscopic algae and some of the larger floating seaweeds, green, brown, and red, are the basis of all other life in the open sea. None of the higher plants, such as liverworts, ferns, mosses, or seed plants, has evolved species that can live in the open sea. (A few species of seed plants occur in shallow coastal waters.) Being photosynthetic, the marine algae can live only where there is light. It is not surprising, therefore, to find them restricted to the surface layers of the water—nearly always to the top 100 meters. Here they serve as food for a variety of small animals, which are the primary consumers. Among these are protozoans, various crustaceans, larval fishes, and representatives of nearly every other group of animals (Figure 39-4). The primary consumers serve as food for secondary consumers, which range in size up to the giant whales, whale sharks, and giant squids. And, of course, there are numerous decomposers, primarily bacteria, that render the bodies of dead organisms into inorganic and

a Oceans

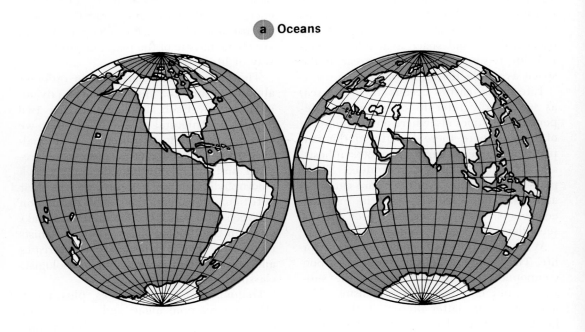

c Grasslands

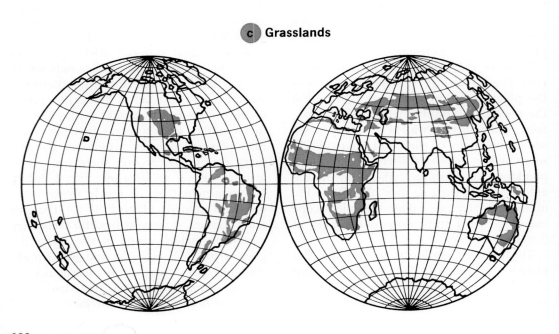

b Forests

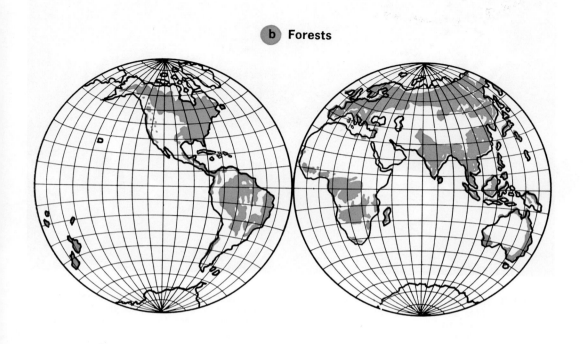

d Deserts

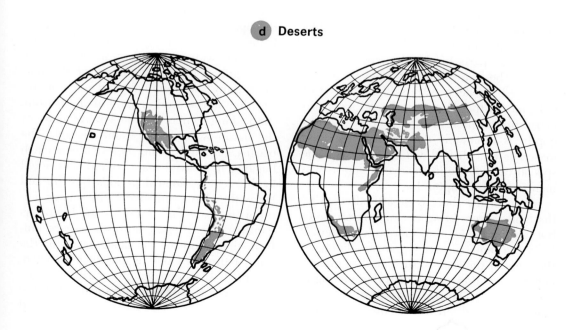

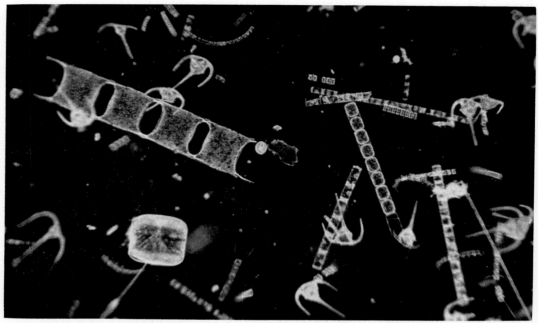

D. P. Wilson

39-3 Diatoms and dinoflagellates, the leaders in world food production. The dinoflagellates seen here resemble miniature miners' picks, with a bulge where the "handle" meets the "head." The other organisms are diatoms. These two microscopic types of food-producers account for perhaps 85 percent of the world's photosynthesis.

simple organic compounds. The food web near the surface of the open sea is not unlike that on land (Figure 39-5).

In other parts of the sea, conditions of life may be quite different from those just described. In deep waters, the absence of light means that there can be no local primary producers. All life in the lightless depths is ultimately dependent upon food materials that drift down from above. The special case of life in the ocean depths was mentioned in Chapter 18.

Life near the shore is greatly affected by the land. Rivers bring not only fresh water but also organic and inorganic materials from the land masses. Organisms living at the edge of the sea are subjected to greater environmental extremes than those living in the open sea. The rise and fall of the tides may cover and uncover shore organisms,

and water temperatures vary more than in the open sea. The salinity is also variable, being decreased by river water and the runoff of rain water. Many organisms along the shore attach to rocks, pilings, or the bottom. Many shore animals and microorganisms live in the mud or sand of the bottom.

Speaking generally, the environment of the ocean is the most stable of any. The oceans were in existence before life on earth began. They have expanded and contracted in different geological periods but, by and large, they have provided a continuous medium—in space and time—for the life of organisms. Their temperatures are more uniform than those of the land masses at the same latitude. There is plenty of oxygen, except in the deep waters of some of the seas, such as the Mediterranean, that are cut off from the main masses of water. And there is plenty of water, which is not always the case in a land environment.

The seas, then, provide one of the most reliable environments. It is here that life originated. It is also to this habitat that organisms were restricted for the first two billion years of their existence. Enormous evolutionary changes took place before organisms could live on land. Among animals and plants only the most advanced—seed plants, higher vertebrates, and arthropods—reached their highest development on land.

LIFE ON LAND

The seas are characterized by constancy; the lands by variability. The seas have always existed and been connected. Land masses, by contrast, have had their ups and downs. At one time or another nearly every bit of land has been covered by sea. Even areas where today we find great mountain ranges were once under water. It is probable that no more than 10 percent of the land today has been above water continuously since the Cambrian period began.

General Problems of Life on Land

A jellyfish in the ocean maintains its body form; on the shore it collapses into a shapeless mass. All marine organisms are supported by water. Terrestrial organisms lack such support. Land plants and land animals must have some other means for supporting their living substance, which is so largely water. Plants have evolved rigid cell walls; animals have evolved skeletons and other supporting devices (see Chapter 26).

D. P. Wilson

39-4 Some primary consumers in the ocean, as seen under the microscope. At the top center is a crab larva, and beneath it an arrow worm (extending diagonally up to the right). Five or more minute crustaceans called copepods can also be seen, two at the lower right and the remainder at the upper left. At bottom center is a medusa (jellyfishlike stage) of another marine animal.

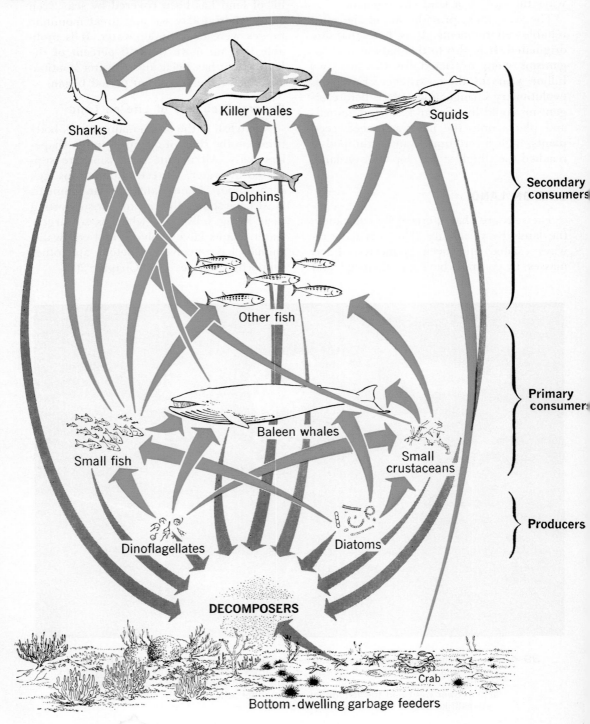

Sharks

Killer whales

Squids

Dolphins

Other fish

Baleen whales

Small fish

Small crustaceans

Dinoflagellates

Diatoms

Secondary consumers

Primary consumers

Producers

DECOMPOSERS

Crab

Bottom-dwelling garbage feeders

Most aquatic organisms die rapidly when exposed to air—the water evaporates so quickly from their bodies that cellular metabolism is disrupted and then destroyed. Since the most abundant compound in an organism is water, and since water passes freely through cell membranes, the conservation of water is a problem for organisms that live on land. Terrestrial plants and animals have special devices that conserve water. As a rule, the body has a waterproof covering—which keeps water *in*. Respiratory surfaces, which are always areas where water would be lost by evaporation, are internal. Recall the example of lungs in terrestrial chordates, tracheal tubes of insects, and air spaces behind the stomata in plants.

In contrast to the near consistency of chemical composition of sea water, composition of the land masses varies greatly. On land one encounters great variations in the amount of water—ranging from marshes at one extreme to waterless deserts at the other. Soils vary tremendously with respect to their relative amounts of particular mineral substances and of humus. Oxygen and carbon dioxide are the only required substances that are nearly constant in amount. They are constant for the same reason that the sea is constant—they are part of a continuous and ever-moving mass. The sea of water and the sea of air are uniform chemically; land is not.

The temperatures of the sea are nearly always between 0° and 30° C. Temperatures vary greatly on land, not only from place to place but also with the season. The surface temperatures in some deserts may fall far below 0° C in the winter and rise above 50° C in the summer. Penguins are found in Antarctica where the air temperature may be −55° C, and organisms live in Death Valley, California, where air temperatures reach 54° C in the summer.

No organism, in its active state, can withstand all of the tremendous environmental differences encountered on land. (Man is the most widely distributed species, but solely because he is able to provide for himself a tolerable environment wherever he goes.) Each species has evolved adaptations for life in a restricted environment. Nature books abound in pictures and descriptions of the fascinating variety of plant and animal adaptations in the parts of the world less familiar to us.

The particular biological community that exists in any locality is controlled largely by soil and climate. These environmental aspects determine what green plants can grow there. The green plants, in turn, give the community its distinctive features. This is not surprising, for plants, as primary producers, are prerequisite for the life of heterotrophs. If the climate and soil will support a forest, one type of community exists; if they can support only a desert, another type of community prevails. For the most part, the animals that can live in a forest are quite different from those that can live in a desert.

On the land masses of the earth, there are three major types of biological community: the forest community, the grassland community, and the desert community.

The Forest Community

Wherever sufficient moisture is available, wherever temperatures are not too low, and wherever man has not destroyed them, the earth is blanketed with forests (Figure 39-2b). Forest trees belong to many different species. Some are gymnosperms, with narrow needlelike leaves, not shed every year. Others are angiosperms, with broad leaves, which in the temperate zones are shed annually.

A mature tree is generally a very tall plant, in contrast to plants that are not so woody. Its height may be thought of as an adaptation enabling it to obtain one of the factors necessary for its life—light. In an old and well-established forest, the large trees support the light-capturing photo-

U. S. Forest Service

39-6 A coniferous forest in Alaska, as seen from the air. Across the northernmost parts of the United States, and throughout large parts of Canada, coniferous forests are prominent. Farther south they give way to deciduous forests, or in drier areas, grassland.

synthetic tissue far above the ground. The smaller plants that grow in the shade on the forest floor are of two kinds. Some are shade-tolerant species; that is, they can grow in dim light. (Man has used some of these plants in interesting ways. Many house plants are species that normally occur in shaded tropical forests. They are adapted to live where it is hot and where there is not much light—conditions often prevailing in houses and apartments.) The second group of plants found growing on the forest floor are young trees of the species that make up the forest. The young trees begin their growth, but most of them soon die; there is not enough light for them. In a mature forest, the young trees are generally doomed to early death unless one of the larger trees is blown down. If this happens, the small trees nearby begin to grow rapidly in the newly available space. Usually many more compete for the place to live than can be supported by it. The smaller or weaker individuals become overshadowed and perish. After years have passed, probably only

a single tree will stand in the place of the one blown down long before.

If you think about this problem in relation to survival, the very numbers of doomed individuals become staggering. How many thousands of acorns will an oak tree produce during its life? Yet, on the average, only a single one will ever become a full-grown tree of the forest. The acorn that does survive is not only the fit in the evolutionary sense but also the lucky! This is frequently the way in evolution. Many of the young oak trees that perish in the shade of some larger individual may possess superior genes—yet, unless some "lucky" accident occurs, they never have a chance to mature and reproduce.

The species of trees that form a forest vary according to locality, soil, and climate. Coniferous species (pines, spruces, firs, cedars, and so on) characterize the northernmost forests (Figure 39-6). These forests extend in a broad zone across North America, from Labrador to Alaska, and from eastern Siberia to the northwest coast of Europe. This evergreen forest extends into the northern United States in some places— New England, the North Central States, and the Pacific Northwest. With the forests now generally gone from the more temperate regions of Europe and the United States, these northern coniferous forests today supply most of the wood used in manufacturing, in construction, and for making paper pulp or rayon.

The northern coniferous forests generally do not reach the Arctic Ocean. The climates of the northern parts of North America, Europe, and Asia are too severe for trees to grow. The northern treeless areas are known as **tundra**. Here a relatively small number of plant species form a mat-like covering over the thin soil (Figure 39-7). The upper few inches of soil thaw out during the summer months, but the deeper levels are permanently frozen (hardly a suitable habitat for trees with their deep roots). This is the land of the midnight sun—where during parts of June and July the sun never sinks below the horizon. Tremendous numbers of ducks, geese, and other aquatic birds breed in the ponds of these treeless wastes during the summer months.

South of the zone of coniferous forests, and wherever water is sufficient, one finds a temperate-zone deciduous forest. The eastern United States, most of England and central Europe, parts of China, and Japan were originally covered by forests composed of these broad-leaved trees. There are also southern coniferous forests in some areas. Most of the virgin forest in these lands was cleared away long ago—a part even in prehistoric times—but, even now, where man does not keep the land in crops or pasture, trees eventually return.

A few scattered stands of virgin forest still remain, often protected in state or national parks for the enjoyment of all. Here one finds huge trees, with relatively few plants growing on the forest floor. The trees

U. S. Dept. of the Interior

39-7 Arctic tundra. At the northernmost reaches of tree growth, tundra begins. In the summer, it resembles grasslands of warmer latitudes, but only the top few inches of soil are not frozen.

capture most of the light, and only shade-tolerant species can grow beneath them. The primary producers here, then, are largely the trees. Their leaves, flowers, bark, fruits, and seeds are the food of birds, mammals, insects, and other primary consumers. Not only do the living trees serve as food, but their leaves, accumulating on the forest floor every autumn (another name for this time of the year, "fall," refers to the time that the leaves *fall*) provide food for an even greater variety of organisms. The leaf litter is the home of huge populations of decomposers—bacteria, fungi, nematodes, protozoans, arthropods, and many other animals. Other animals, chiefly arthropods and vertebrates, are secondary consumers.

Great forests also occur in many parts of central Africa, southern Asia, and the tropical parts of the New World. The trees are

39-8 AVERAGE MONTHLY VARIATION IN TEMPERATURE AT THREE SELECTED LOCATIONS (TUNDRA, TEMPERATE FOREST, AND TROPICAL RAIN FOREST)

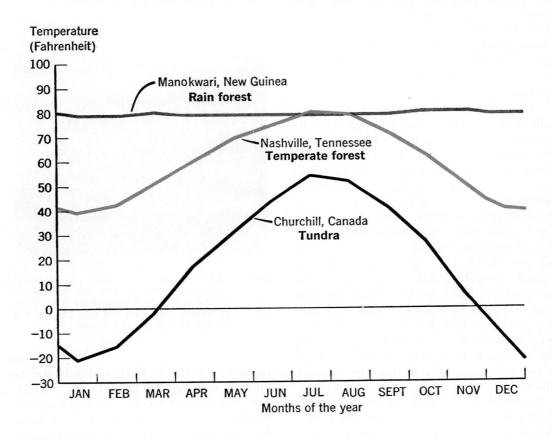

usually broad-leaved; the leaves, however, are shed irregularly, not seasonally as in a temperate-zone deciduous forest. The tropical forest is always green, never presenting the barren, winter appearance of a deciduous forest in the temperate zone. Many tropical forests are *rain forests* (a more popular term is "jungle"), referring to the fact that they occur only in regions of high rainfall. Here the temperature and humidity are always high. Frequently the trees have such a dense mass of leaves that little light reaches the forest floor. Once again, only the most shade-tolerant of species can survive at the lower levels of the forest.

The richness of life in a tropical rain forest staggers the imagination. All of the great naturalists of the eighteenth and nineteenth centuries lived in the temperate zones. When some of these men (Darwin and Wallace were among them) first visited tropical rain forests, they were overwhelmed by the variety and abundance of life they saw. The deciduous forests that they knew back home consisted largely of a few tree species. In a tropical rain forest, on the other hand, one might have to search a long time for two individual trees of the same species. Where there are a few dozens of species of insects in an English forest,

39-9 AVERAGE MONTHLY VARIATION IN RAINFALL AT THREE SELECTED LOCATIONS (TUNDRA, TEMPERATE FOREST, AND TROPICAL RAIN FOREST)

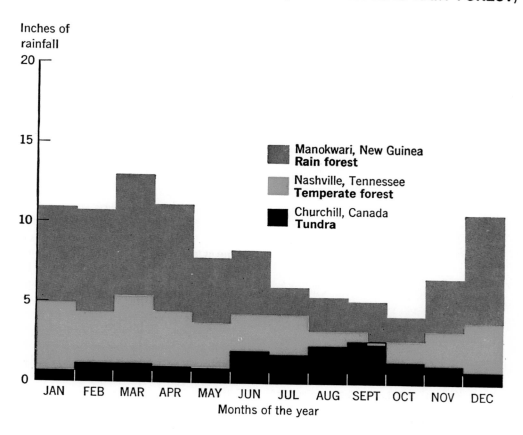

Inches of rainfall

Manokwari, New Guinea
Rain forest

Nashville, Tennessee
Temperate forest

Churchill, Canada
Tundra

Months of the year

there are hundreds or thousands in the Amazonian rain forest, for example.

The richness and diversity of life in the tropics is due to many factors. First of all, the environment has been stable for a very long time (reminding one of the stability of the marine environment mentioned earlier). In contrast, the great Pleistocene glaciers covered much of Canada, the northeastern United States, and Europe as recently as 10,000 years ago. As the ice melted back, there was a slow colonization by animals and plants of the formerly glaciated land. The tropics were almost unaffected by these recurring periods of stress for the species of plants and animals that inhabited the northern latitudes.

In addition to the uniformity of conditions over long periods of time, tropical forests are uniform in two important ways—water and temperature. Two chief problems for terrestrial organisms are those of securing water and finding tolerable temperatures. Generally, plenty of water is available in a rain forest, and temperatures are high and frequently nearly constant throughout the year. This relative constancy of the physical environment of a rain forest can be seen from the graphic data of Figures 39-8 and 39-9.

Kansas Industrial Development Comm.

39-10 A Kansas grassland. Vast regions of the central and southwestern United States are native grassland, most of which is used to raise crop plants.

In the warm, moist environment of a rain forest, plants grow in situations that would be impossible for them in the temperate zone. If dehydration is not a danger, many plants can cling to the trunks and branches of trees. Thus we find that many trees in the rain forest are covered with plants called **epiphytes** (EP·ih·fyts), which obtain their moisture chiefly from the air. There are many species of epiphytes, of which the pineapple family contributes a large number. All are reaching for the sun, so to speak, for in the lower levels of the forest there is too little light for most of them.

The Grassland Community

Water is always a necessity for plants, but the requirements vary from species to species. More water is required to support a forest than is available in large areas of the temperate zone and the tropics. Where there is less than enough water to support a forest, a grassland community develops (and with still less water, the result is a desert— to be discussed shortly). As a rough rule, grasslands occur where yearly rainfall averages 25 to 75 cm (10–30 inches). But more than the amount of rain is involved. For the growth of a forest, rains must be reliable; that is, they must come every year. Characteristically, grasslands are regions of frequent, and often severe, drought. These lands might receive enough water for tree growth during many years; but then will come a dry period during which the trees are killed. Thus, there can be no forests. The type of community that develops in a region depends not on the years with the most favorable conditions but on the years with the least favorable conditions.

The relation of water to the type of plant community supported is often vividly illustrated in a grassland (Figure 39-10). Most of the area supports grass, but along stream beds a narrow ribbon of trees clearly indicates that, given a little more water, trees could grow here.

The principal grassland communities of the world are the Great Plains of Canada and the United States, the pampas and other grasslands extending from southern Argentina into Brazil, the steppes extending from southern Russia to central Asia, the grasslands of much of central Australia (except the desert at the center), and the veldt and other grasslands of south and central Africa (Figure 39-2c).

Grasslands have been the home of grazing animals for millions of years. The Great Plains of North America was the home, until comparatively recently, of the bison (or American buffalo). The grasslands of

Africa, even today, are the home of many species of antelopes. Kangaroos are common grazing animals of Australian grassland. Man now uses many of these grasslands to pasture the cattle and sheep that provide his meat, hides, and wool.

Compared to forest communities, the grasslands are communities of stress. Forests provide a protective umbrella over the land. They provide shade and protection from the winds. They pass tremendous amounts of water into the atmosphere, by way of transpiration. In this way, humidity, always important for terrestrial animals and plants, is kept higher than it would be without the trees. The evaporation of water by forest transpiration also serves to moderate the temperature. Grasses and other relatively short plants of the grasslands, on the other hand, are not able to provide so effective an umbrella. Winds sweep across them; and grassland organisms are exposed to the sun, and to greater variations of temperature (temperature fluctuations from day to night are far greater in the open grassland than in the more protected forest).

A forest provides a greater variety of habitats than does a grassland. In general, animal life on land is restricted to the zone between the tops of the tallest plants and a few centimeters below the surface of the soil. In a forest the thickness of this zone may be as much as 30 to 45 meters. In a grassland community, on the other hand, this zone is generally less than 2 meters thick. The birds of a forest, for example, may nest on the ground, in holes in the trunks of trees, or at any level of the branches; in a grassland community birds usually nest on the ground or in burrows.

Grasslands are regions of greater stress than are the forests. They are subject to greater variations of temperature (Figure 39-8), moisture (Figure 39-9), winds, and intensity of sunlight; and there are fewer places for animals to retreat. Many grassland animals have evolved the burrowing habit; in burrows they withdraw from unfavorable conditions. Grasslands are also the homes of animals that are swift of foot —wild horse, antelope, gazelle, pronghorn, ostrich, and many others.

Since the grasslands are regions of stress, they are subject to easy destruction by man. We see this in our own country, where large areas of grassland have been converted to crop land. Sometimes the areas so exploited are those with enough rain in the "good years" for abundant crops, principally wheat—which, of course, is a grass. But grasslands are regions of frequent drought, and when the "bad years" come, crops fail. Since the land has lost its protective cover of permanent grass, it is subject to erosion. Large areas of our own country, for example, became a "dust bowl" during the 1930's, when land that should have remained covered in grass was broken by the plow. Even where grasslands are used only for grazing animals, they are often overgrazed. The grass mat is destroyed, and erosion then sets in. Thus, areas throughout the world that were grasslands in their natural state have been converted to near desert by improper use.

The Desert Community

Forest, grassland, desert: this is a sequence of increasing rigor of the environment. Grasslands cannot support trees, but conditions are favorable enough for the persistence of a continuous mat of vegetation. Deserts are the next step. Here, lack of water prevents the development of a rich mat of vegetation; one often finds only isolated plants with much bare ground between them (Figure 1-1, page 5).

In a true desert, insufficient rainfall (Figure 39-9) does not allow for the existence of permanently flowing streams. (Some deserts have rivers flowing through them; the Nile, for example, flows through the desert of Egypt, but its headwaters are in the well-watered areas of the interior.) There may

H. L. Parent from Nat. Audubon Society   **b**   H. W. Kitchen from Nat. Audubon Society

a

39-11 Plant growth on the desert. **a** Compare this close-up of part of the fluted stem of a saguaro cactus with the photograph of the entire plant in Figure 1-1, page 5. When rains come, the flutes expand as the stem stores water absorbed by the roots. The thick covering of the stem, and the modification of leaves into spines, protect the plant against loss of stored water. **b** The ocotillo, or cat's-claw, has another adaptation effective in conserving water: the leaves are very small, and during periods of drought, they are shed. When rains come, new leaves are grown.

be rivers in the desert—torrents after heavy rains, but otherwise dry washes. Deserts generally have less than 25 cm (10 inches) of rain during the year. Even the modest amount of rain they do receive may be most unreliable. Rain may be relatively frequent in one year, but then there may be almost none for the next several years. This unreliability of water is a condition for which many desert plants and animals are adapted.

Without a protective blanket of vegetation, the desert environment is highly variable. In nondesert regions, where plant growth is good, there is little runoff of rainwater. In a desert, with its widely spaced plants, runoff is rapid. Thus, what little rain does fall is not as available for plants as it would be in a grassland or forest. The few desert plants lose little water into the atmosphere, so the humidity is always low. Winds sweep unhindered

across the land. Temperature averages (Figure 39-8) do not reflect the fluctuations, which are generally extreme. Frequently, deserts are hot by day and cold at night; it is not unusual for the fluctuation to be as great as 30° C in twenty-four hours.

The great deserts of the world (Figure 39-2d) occur on all the continents except Europe and Antarctica. The Sonoran Desert is in the American southwest and north central Mexico. Deserts stretch across north Africa (the Sahara), through the Arabian Peninsula, and with interruptions, across central Asia and Mongolia almost to the Pacific coast. The central portion of Australia is also a desert. In South America much of the west coast, from northern Chile to Ecuador, is desert or near desert.

A permanent abundance of organisms in a desert is impossible. There is far less food than in the other major terrestrial habitats, since the primary producers are less numerous. Water is a chief limiting factor for plants as well as for animals. Both groups show numerous interesting ways for obtaining and conserving water.

Some desert plants have very shallow roots that may extend over a wide area. When rains do come, the plants rapidly take up water and store it in specialized tissues. Cacti and euphorbias store large amounts of water in their fleshy stems—water that tides the plants over long periods of drought. Other desert plants have deep root systems that take up water far below the surface. Many desert plants are well spaced, and their extensive root systems occupy a large cube of earth from which they extract water.

Plants lose water through their leaves (Chapter 15). When you remember this fact, you will not be surprised to learn that in deserts natural selection has promoted the development of plants with fewer and smaller leaves. There is nothing on a cactus plant that you will immediately recognize as a leaf (Figure 39-11a). Actually the spines are modified leaves; you can see that their exposed surface is very small. Most of the photosynthetic tissue of the cacti is in their enlarged stems. When leaves of a more typical sort are present on desert plants, they are usually small, thick, and either leathery or easily shed (Figure 39-11b). Not infrequently the stomata are sunk in little pits. All of these adaptations serve to prevent the loss of water.

The structure, physiology, and behavior of desert animals are evolved adjustments to their desert environment. Many of the species live in burrows, where, a few centimeters below the surface, the humidity is greater and the temperature fluctuations are less extreme than on the surface. Many desert animals are nocturnal, that is, are active only at night when the temperature is lower and humidity is greater than in the daytime. The water requirements of desert animals are often far less than those of their relatives living in the grasslands and forests. Many never drink at all; they rely solely on the water they get from their food and on what is produced during the oxidation of glucose and other organic molecules. One of the main requirements for water, at least in terrestrial vertebrates, is for the removal of nitrogen wastes. Some desert animals excrete uric acid, which requires very little water for its removal (Chapter 24); others excrete a very concentrated urine that contains urea.

A desert, seemingly an inhospitable environment, may become a luxuriant garden after heavy rains. Flowers grow rapidly from seeds that may have lain dormant for a decade. Animals, which were biding their time in an inactive state, begin to stir. The desert becomes a colorful living world—only to relapse into its usual condition when the rains pass and the water evaporates. Here, time is at a premium, and one finds that both animals and plants may grow with startling rapidity. Plants must grow, flower, and produce seeds while enough moisture remains for them to be active.

CONCLUDING REMARKS

Nearly every nook and corner of the earth's crust contains a host of organisms. Life is rich and varied wherever conditions are very favorable—in the surface waters of parts of the sea and in the tropical rain forest. Here the combination of light, warm temperatures, and plenty of water permits a luxuriant growth of the primary producers—green plants. With this bountiful base, there are numerous individuals at all levels of the pyramid of numbers (Figure 8-11). As one moves from favorable areas to areas of extreme stress—the deserts and the lightless depths of the oceans—the primary producers decrease, and so do all the animals and plants that depend on them. Yet no matter how severe the conditions, there is usually some life. There are algae that grow only in melting snow; many animals and plants spend their entire lives in lightless caves; some algae and bacteria live in hot springs where temperatures are always near the boiling point of water. That all these habitats are populated by organisms is a testimonial to the effectiveness of genetic variability and natural selection. The processes of evolution have perfected organisms for almost every conceivable way of life.

GUIDE QUESTIONS AND PROBLEMS

1. What are the conditions necessary for an ecosystem?
2. How is life in the sea dependent on light?
3. How would a cloudy, windy day affect the photosynthetic output of plant plankton?
4. How does the food web in the surface waters of the open sea resemble the food web on land?
5. How would life in a cave on land compare with life in the ocean depths?
6. What factors influence the maintenance of life in the ocean depths?
7. What factors affect life in the oceans near the shore?
8. In what ways are certain environmental conditions in the oceans more stable than the corresponding conditions on land? Which of the major land environments most nearly approaches the degree of stability of conditions in the oceans?
9. What problems faced by terrestrial plants and animals are not problems at all for most aquatic plants and animals?
10. What are some of the ways in which terrestrial plants and animals conserve water?
11. What are the characteristics of a forest community? a grassland community? a desert community?
12. How does a deciduous forest differ from a tropical rain forest?
13. What factors account for the richness and diversity of tropical life?

SUGGESTIONS FOR ADDITIONAL READING

Books

Barnett, L., and Editors of *Life* Magazine, *The World We Live In*. New York, Time, Inc., 1955.
> Excellent and beautifully illustrated descriptions of the world's biomes.

Bates, M., *The Forest and the Sea*. New York, New American Library, 1960.
> Includes several interesting chapters on oceanic biology.

Buchsbaum, R., and Mildred Buchsbaum, *Basic Ecology*. Pittsburgh, Boxwood Press, 1957.
> An excellent yet brief book on ecology.

Carson, R., *The Sea Around Us*. New York, New American Library, 1954.
> Beautifully written account of the oceans and their contained life.

—— *The Edge of the Sea*. New York, New American Library, 1959.
> An excellently written description of the life of the seashore.

Krutch, J. W., *The Desert Year*. New York, Viking Press, 1960.
> A naturalist views the patterns of life forms in the deserts of the American Southwest.

Morgan, A., *Field Book of Ponds and Streams*. New York, Putnam, 1930.
> Excellent guide to the life of freshwater habitats.

Storer, J. H., *The Web of Life*. New York, New American Library, 1956.
> A well-written introduction to ecology.

Magazines and Journals

Deevey, E. S., Jr., "Life in the Depths of a Pond." *Scientific American*, Vol. 185 (October 1951), pp. 68–72.

Hutner, S. H., and J. J. A. McLaughlin, "Poisonous Tides." *Scientific American*, Vol. 199 (August 1958), pp. 92–96.

Leopold, A. S., "Too Many Deer." *Scientific American*, Vol. 193 (November 1955), pp. 101–04.

Nicholas, G., "Life in Caves." *Scientific American*, Vol. 192 (May 1955), pp. 98–102.

Went, F. W., "The Ecology of Desert Plants." *Scientific American*, Vol. 192 (April 1955), pp. 68–75.

40

MAN AND

THE BALANCE

OF NATURE

No organism lives alone—and this includes man. He, too, is part of a community of living things, influencing and being influenced by other individuals of his own species, individuals of different species, and the nonliving environment. Let us consider some of these interrelations.

Most of man's activities tend to reduce the number of species of large animals and plants in his vicinity. With traps, guns, and poison he eliminates the predators: wolves, coyotes, foxes, cougars, lynx, bobcats, eagles, hawks, and owls. Almost at once he is faced with large numbers of other animals, for, with the predators gone, the primary consumers, such as deer, rabbits, mice, porcupines, and grasshoppers, multiply without their usual checks.

With fire, ax, and plow, man transforms the forest and the prairie. Where hundreds of plant species grew before, he raises crops of green plants in pure stands: wheat, corn, potatoes, and cotton. To safeguard these producers, he tries to eliminate all primary consumers, including caterpillars, scale insects, plant lice, and also disease agents of every kind. He simplifies the food web, removing the cross-connections that might give it stability. Man becomes a factor introducing stress into the environment. Many of the consequent fluctuations of numbers among the remaining species escape his control. Some of them can be disastrous to his plans.

Man for Himself

Man's role as a biological force is easy to see in all civilized areas today: deserts made to produce crops through irrigation, forest land transformed into fields, bare hill country planted in forest, clear rivers full of fish turned into polluted waters supporting almost none. He serves often as a geological force as well: leveling hills, filling swamps and bays, rerouting rivers, plowing fields, and otherwise exposing the soil to erosion, from rain and wind.

No other species has so triumphed over predators and infectious diseases. Modern public health measures are extraordinarily successful in the more advanced nations of the world in preventing the spread of contagious infections (Table 40-1). The expected improvements in this direction will be in extending the application of our knowledge to other peoples in ever larger areas of the earth.

Even where the best of medical care is combined with good nutrition, life is not prolonged indefinitely. Since the beginning of the century, more than twenty-two years have been added to the average age at death (Table 40-2); this is due largely to a reduced infant mortality. Little change is seen in the number of people reaching ninety or one hundred years of age, for in our country, people saved from death by improved controls over infectious diseases

TABLE 40-1 DEATH RATE AND CAUSE, PER HUNDRED THOUSAND OF THE POPULATION, IN THE UNITED STATES, 1900–1960

Cause	1900	1910	1920	1930	1940	1950	1960
Infectious diseases							
Influenza and pneumonias	202	156	207	103	70	31	37
Tuberculosis, all forms	194	154	113	71	46	23	6
Bronchitis	46	23	13	4	3	2	3
Diarrhea and intestinal diseases	133	117	54	26	10	5	4
Diphtheria	40	21	15	5	1	0.3	——[1]
Typhoid and paratyphoid fevers	36	26	8	5	1	——	
Syphilis and sequels	12	14	17	16	14	5	2
Measles	13	12	9	3	0.5	0.3	0.3
Whooping cough	12	12	13	5	2	0.7	0.1
Scarlet fever	10	12	5	2	0.5	——	——
Malaria	8	2	4	3	1	——	——
Erysipelas (a skin infection)	5	4	3	2	——	——	——
Smallpox	2	0.4	0.6	0.1	——	——	——
Degenerative diseases							
Heart diseases	137	159	160	214	293	357	366
Cerebral hemorrhage and thrombosis	72	76	82	81	91	100	110
Cancer, all forms	64	76	83	97	120	140	147
Cirrhosis of liver	13	13	7	7	9	9	11
Appendicitis	10	11	13	15	10	2	1
Diabetes mellitus	11	15	16	19	27	16	17
Kidney diseases	89	99	89	91	82	21	15
Senility	——	26	14	10	8	13	11
Congenital malformations	12	15	15	11	10	12	12
Other causes							
Suicide and homicide	11	20	17	25	21	17	15
Accidents	72	84	70	80	73	61	52
All other causes	515	321	271	237	183	149	137
ALL CAUSES	1719	1468	1299	1132	1076	964	946

[1] Dash lines indicate death rates that are significantly less than 0.1 per 100,000.

usually die of degenerative changes before reaching the age of ninety. In many other countries, people saved from fatal epidemics die of famine; they survive to demand food in excess of what their land can provide.

In the United States and other countries where medical care is most highly developed, a good many people with inherited disorders are now saved. They survive, reproduce, and pass along their genetic handicap. Natural selection no longer eliminates them as rapidly as in earlier times. In this and other ways, man has changed, and continues to change, the nature of the genetic balance in his own species. He has become a force affecting his own evolution.

AN ADEQUATE FOOD SUPPLY

Productivity of the soil is far from uniform over the world. So is the number of people the products of the soil must support. One of the biggest problems facing mankind today is to increase the amount of food available per person in the nonindustrialized countries. In far too many of them, living conditions are scarcely better today than they were a century or a thousand years ago.

Spectacular gains in food quality and in crop production are found almost exclusively in countries where the standard of living is already high. Where the standard of living is low, people cannot afford to buy better seed or fertilizer or to treat the soil scientifically.

Today, science has come a long way toward learning what man must eat in order to be healthy. Some of his needs are for simple compounds, such as pure water and trace amounts of iodine. His food should also supply a balanced assortment of proteins, fats, and carbohydrates.

To construct some of our important enzymes, we need special organic molecules produced by green plants. We get them in amounts of 0.01 gram per day or less—as vitamins. Man needs a daily supply of ascorbic acid (vitamin C), for he cannot store it. He also requires frequent replenishment of those vitamins he can store: caro-

tene (convertible into vitamin A), thiamine (B$_1$), riboflavin (B$_2$ or G), niacin (P–P), folic acid, cyanocobalamin (SY·a·no·co·BAWL·a·min—vitamin B$_{12}$), calciferol (kal·SIF·er·all—vitamin D), phylloquinone (fil·o·quih·NOHN—vitamin K$_1$), and possibly still others.

The Critical Proteins

Our proteins are made from about twenty different amino acids—all available in suitable foods. Actually, we can synthesize ten of the twenty we need. The remaining ten must be present in protein foods.

Some of the fatty acids, available through the digestion of fats, may also be essential in our diets. Carbohydrates, the prime source of energy, are less critical. For health, a person must have an adequate food supply, and in the ratio of approximately four pounds of carbohydrate for each pound of protein and each pound of fat. Our food must provide all the essential acids, vitamins, and other trace materials.

Animal proteins are the most efficient sources of the amino acids we cannot synthesize for ourselves. Plant proteins contain them too, but in proportions different from those we need. Hence, to get all we need of the ten critical amino acids from plant foods, we must eat much larger quantities of proteins. People whose diets are primarily of vegetable foods often get far

TABLE 40-2 THE CHANGING PATTERN OF BIRTHS, DEATHS, AND EXPECTATIONS OF LIFE IN THE UNITED STATES, 1900–1960

	1900	1910	1920	1930	1940	1950	1960
Live births per thousand of population	32.3	30.1	27.7	21.3	19.4	24.1	23.7
Deaths per thousand of population	17.1	14.7	13	11.3	10.8	9.6	9.5
Excess of births over deaths	15.2	15.4	14.7	10	8.6	14.5	14.2
Expectation of life at birth	47.3	50	54.1	59.7	62.9	68.2	69.7
Average increase in longevity since 1910	——	2.7	6.8	12.4	15.6	20.9	22.4

too little protein. Their diets fall much below the recommended ratio of 1 (of protein) to 4 (of carbohydrate) to 1 (of fat).

Protein deficiency shows up most conspicuously in children who have recently been weaned. The disease is called **kwashiorkor** (kwash·ih·OR·kor), indicated by inflammation of the skin, degenerative changes in the liver, and serious anemia. It was recognized first in Africa about thirty years ago. Today it is serious among the wheat eaters of Chile, the corn eaters of Africa, the rice eaters of Indonesia, and the millet eaters of India. Skim milk, which is a rich source of protein and is given in a dietary supplement, is the best remedy known. Unfortunately, there is not enough skim milk in the world to treat all sufferers from kwashiorkor.

Minimum Dietary Requirements

In 1950 the Food and Agricultural Organization of the United Nations attempted to find out the minimum dietary requirements for human health, and to compare this minimum with the average daily diet in the 70 countries participating in the survey. The food-energy requirement for an "average human body" at rest was found to be around 1,700 calories per day. Any exercise, even light physical activity, raises this average requirement to between 2,200 calories per day for women, and 3,000 for men. Members of small-statured peoples need fewer calories. People engaged in heavy work require more.

For an "average adult" the 2,800 calories recommended should include about 70 grams of protein per day. At least half of this protein should be of animal origin. Carbohydrates and fats in reasonable balance are needed to supply the other 2,400 calories. In addition, the daily intake should include 1.0 gram of absorbable calcium, 12 milligrams of iron in absorbable form, and at least the following amounts of vitamins: 4,700 International Units of vitamin A, 1.6 milligrams of B_1, 2.3 milligrams of B_2, 16 milligrams of niacin, and 70 milligrams of vitamin C.

Among the 70 countries participating in the United Nations survey, a high daily intake (about 2,750 calories per day) was found in all of Anglo-America, much of Europe, Australia, New Zealand, Argentina, and parts of the Soviet Union—about 30 percent of the world's human population. A low intake (less than 2,250 calories per day) was typical of about 50 percent of the world's population living over much of Asia, Egypt, Central America, and parts of South America. The remaining people were on a medium diet (2,250 to 2,750 calories per day).

In Java, where the total daily intake averaged only about 2,000 calories, the proteins eaten included only 4 grams of animal origin and 39 grams of plant origin. In the United States, by contrast, the average daily intake stood above 3,000 calories, with most of the 88 grams of proteins consumed coming from animal sources.

Medical men have sometimes argued that there is only one real disease of mankind: malnutrition. Certainly a large number of diseases, from **avitaminosis** (ay·vy·ta·min·OH·sis—lack of vitamins) to tuberculosis, are most prevalent among people on poor diets. Well-fed people who are not overweight are the healthiest.

The Unequal Distribution of Food

It is often difficult for us to understand why so many people in other parts of the world do not have sufficient food. In America north of the Rio Grande, good food is seldom a real problem. Even though the total number of farmers in America is smaller today than at any time since 1900, and the total area of all farms in operation also slightly less, food production annually exceeds that of any year prior to 1940.

This paradox of more from less has come through mechanization and the use of im-

	Calories	Proteins (grams)	Fats (grams)	Carbohydrates (grams)	Calcium (grams)	Phosphorus (grams)
Beef (hamburger)	1765	107	146.0	0	.044	.766
Milk (whole)	330	17	19.0	24	.057	.451
Corn (sweet)	412	13	3.0	98	.024	.252
Rice (white)	577	12	.5	127	.039	.218
Potatoes (boiled, peeled)	403	10	.5	93	.053	.272
Wheat (whole meal)	349	13	1.5	77	.044	.403

(Data from U. S. Dept. Agric., Agriculture Handbook No. 8, June 1950.)

proved genetic strains of crop plants (such as hybrid corn; see Chapter 30) and of domestic animals selected for high yield (see Chapter 33). In some areas, gain in production has come also through soil improvement and the use of proper fertilizers. In other areas, unfortunately, high productivity is attained through methods that exploit the soil, deplete its mineral nutrients, reduce its organic content, and lay the basis for destruction by erosion. At least in some parts of the world, destructive agricultural practices now are being replaced by methods utilizing knowledge of types of plant crops that help to reduce erosion, and that help to replenish the soil's supply of naturally produced inorganic and organic compounds. If this type of foresight could prevail, millions of acres of soil could be protected and maintained.

Over much of the world, however, the demand for food is so urgent that scientific agricultural methods cannot be followed. How can people sell part of the crop to buy fertilizers when every grain is needed to keep their children from starving? Where poverty and malnutrition are established, there is no money to pay for more efficient tools or better seed. Each plot of land must produce food continuously. There is never

an opportunity to improve the soil by letting it remain fallow for a year. Where the demand for food is so high, forest land was cleared and cultivated long ago; hence, there is no wood to use as fuel, so even the droppings of animals are dried and burned instead of being returned to the soil to aid in its fertility.

About 50 percent of the world's population is on a dietary allowance described by the United Nations as "low." Most of these people cannot afford the recommended animal proteins for the simple reason that an acre of land will yield 15 to 24 times as many dietary calories when planted with crops for human consumption as it will when used for crops to feed meat animals (which will later be food for man). Fifty pounds of beef per acre per year, with 1,765 calories per pound, is regarded as efficient production on a ranch. An acre of average farmland per year will give 3,715 pounds of wheat, or 4,158 pounds of potatoes, or 4,450 pounds of shelled corn, or 5,368 pounds of rice. As dairyland, the same acre will yield 3,000 pounds of milk.

From information on the food values per pound (Table 40-3), these figures on productivity of land can be converted into more meaningful numbers. An acre can furnish 2,400 calories per day per year for 3.54 people if planted in rice, 2.09 people if in corn, 1.91 people if in potatoes, 1.48 people if in wheat, 1.13 people if used for milk production, and only 0.10 person if used for raising beef.

The Statistical Office and the Population Division of the United Nations collected information and estimates for the year 1950 to get actual figures on food production and on world population. From their records, the combined food production of all land and water areas added up to some 5,760 billion calories per day. The world population was about 2,400 million. If the food produced had been divided equally among the 2,400 million people, each of them would have had 2,400 calories daily—the recommended minimum. The world had enough calories of food for everyone in 1950 but nowhere near enough usable proteins—especially animal proteins.

Growth of the World's Human Population

Now let us look at the rate at which the world population has grown. The total human population about the year 12,000 B.C has been estimated at 10 million. By A.D. 1650 the population had grown to 545 million. This became 728 million in 1750 and 1,171 million in 1850. In 1950 the total was 2,400 million.

Now, if we take the figure of 10 million people in 12,000 B.C. and the figure of 545 million in 1650, we can calculate the rate at which the population grew in those early years of human history. These calculations show that the population doubled less than six times in the entire period of 13,650 years. The average time required for each doubling was about 2,000 years.

After the mechanization of farming, which came with the Industrial Revolution, between 1650 and 1850, we find a different story. The 545 millions of people in 1650 grew to 1,171 million by 1850. This doubling required only 200 years. By 1950, the

1,171 million became 2,400 million. The greater availability of food and improved public sanitation and medical care had allowed another doubling in less than one century. Not only is the world population increasing, but so is the *rate* of increase.

In 1963 a committee of the National Academy of Sciences reported, "The present world population is likely to double in the next 35 years, producing a population of six billion by the year 2000." And further: "To appreciate the pace of population growth we should recall that world population doubled in about 1,700 years from the time of Christ until the middle of the 17th century; it doubled again in about 200 years, doubled again in less than 100, and if the current *rate* of population increase were to remain constant, would double every 35 years. Moreover, this rate is still increasing. . . . Had this rate existed from the time of Christ to now, the world population would have increased in this period by a factor of about 7×10^{16}; in other words, there would be about 20 million individuals in place of each person now alive, or 100 people to each square foot. If the present world population should continue to increase at its present rate of two percent per year, then, within two centuries, there will be more than 150 billion people. Calculations of this sort demonstrate without question not only that the current continued increase in the rate of population growth must cease but also that this rate must decline again. There can be no doubt concerning this long-term prognosis: *Either the birthrate of the world must come down or the death rate must go back up.*" [1]

Population growth has become one of the most serious problems for our species. Every reader of this book belongs to a generation that must help to solve this problem.

[1] *The Growth of World Population.* Report of the Committee on Science and Public Policy, National Academy of Sciences. Washington, D.C.: National Academy of Sciences—National Research Council. 1963.

The Competition for Land

Food producers and housing experts are wondering about the year 2000, less than 40 years away. Will the world then have 7 billion people needing to be fed and housed? As cities grow, land that could be used for food production is taken for other purposes. It is used for airports, industrial centers, housing developments, or is inundated behind tremendous dams built to yield hydroelectric power. At the same time, farms whose soil has been depleted are abandoned. Ranch lands become deserts. Fisheries everywhere seem doomed, often because the nursery shallows where fish might reproduce are filled in or polluted beyond use. Even with the help of an extensive conservation program, improvements in agriculture, animal husbandry, and fishing will have to be spectacular merely to keep production at a constant level. Can we increase the production of food sufficiently to support the expanding population, not to mention improving the standards of living?

The land surface of our planet totals about 57 million square miles. Of this, the 6 million square miles of Antarctica are uninhabited. So are another 14 million square miles elsewhere; they consist of ice sheets, tundras, deserts, and jagged mountains. Nor are the remaining 37 million square miles equally useful to man. Less than 5 million are in plant crops, yet essentially all suitable land is already being worked. Another 9.5 million square miles are used for pasture. They are too steep, too stony, or afford too little fertile soil for plant crops. Another 10 million square miles are in forests, from which man cuts his largest crop (trees). This leaves about 12.5 million for cities, roads, public parks, and other nonproductive land. Yet, if the world's human population continues to grow at an ever faster pace, as it now appears without doubt to be doing, more land may soon be needed for cultivation of crops.

AN ADEQUATE SUPPLY OF FRESH WATER

Although each human being continues to need approximately half a gallon of drinking water daily, our other uses for fresh water have changed markedly in the last century. Only a hundred years ago, nearly everyone in America depended upon water from wells or springs. Water was carried by hand into the house. Gutters collected rain water from the roof to be stored in cisterns for use in washing clothes and people. A few gallons of water sufficed for each person daily.

Today a half gallon of pure drinking water is needed by more than twice as many people as a century ago. Moreover, we have come to regard an abundance of fresh water as part of our high standard of living. We expect it to run freely from a faucet for washing dishes, clothes, the dusty car—or to carry away heat from air-conditioning equipment. Large reserves must be on hand for use in firefighting.

The second greatest use of water today is for transportation of wastes, particularly sewage and the discharge of industrial plants. Three gallons are required to flush a toilet and thirty gallons to take a shower. The number of gallons required per person for domestic use per day in the United States varies from twenty to eighty gallons. Every year the demand rises. Moreover, domestic use accounts for less than 10 percent of the water used. The remainder is about equally divided between irrigation and industrial use.

The United States and inhabited parts of Canada are fortunate in having an average annual rainfall of about 30 inches. Half of this fresh water evaporates unused. One sixth sinks into the ground and flows to the sea by way of subterranean streams. One sixth flows over the surface in the form of rivers. The remaining sixth is absorbed by vegetation; most of this is lost to the air.

Methods and Difficulties
in Providing More Fresh Water

If man is to maintain his food supply, he cannot steal water from the plants. To grow more food on arid lands, he needs extra water for irrigation. However, the amount available from rivers and artesian wells is already too small to provide enough water for everyone to have the standard of living he would like. In many countries the water situation is far worse than it is in the United States and Canada.

Every move to conserve fresh water is important. Yet only in remote mountain streams can unpolluted water be found to-day. Elsewhere, communities dump sewage and industrial wastes into streams and lakes from which other communities obtain their water supply. The money saved in dumping the raw sewage instead of rendering it harmless or disposing of it otherwise is largely lost in purifying this same water for later use.

Different schemes have been proposed or put into operation to increase the amount of fresh water available in specific areas. The most basic scheme is to trap more rain, to reduce evaporative losses and pollution from eroding soil, and to channel the moisture into springs, into rivers on the surface, and also into underground rivers where artesian wells can penetrate. Forests provide the most efficient trap for rain. They are valuable also in supplying wood, in sheltering wildlife, and in affording areas for recreation. Interwoven tree roots protect the soil from erosion; they help keep streams flowing all year with clear, unpolluted water.

The man who owns a forest often sees no personal gain in the river that flows away, or the wildlife, or the soil protection, or the recreational values. He sees only timber he could use for fuel, for paper making, for lumber, or for some other technological use. If he is a farmer or rancher, he is likely to regard a forest as occupying land on which cultivated crops or domesticated animals could be raised. Why not fell the forest?

Forests the world over are still being cut faster than they are being replaced. On the exposed forest soil, in many places, erosion is rapid. Spring rains produce disastrous floods with mud-laden water carrying the topsoil to the sea. Summer drought is common. The subterranean water supply sinks below the roots of crop plants. Rivers shrink, often to a series of stagnant pools. Yet, with more people needing more food it is hard to be foresighted and turn cropland back into forest. Over most of the world few men work in this direction.

Another possible source of water for industry and agriculture is water from the sea. Devices for extracting fresh water from the sea are already in operation on a limited scale. That scale must be increased many times over if the supply of fresh water is to keep pace with demands.

OUR LIVING RESOURCES

Our high standard of living in Anglo-America depends partly upon the fact that our population is still small enough that food, water, and space have only begun to limit us. It depends also upon a combination of accessible raw materials, industrial power, and skill. These advantages are not always to be found in many other parts of the world.

Uses and Abuses of Our Living Resources

Part of our technology is concerned with preparing chemical compounds such as solvents, detergents, fibers, drugs, fungicides, and insecticides. For many of these, man makes use of living organisms that carry on syntheses he cannot duplicate efficiently. Examples are endless: alcohols from bacterial fermentations; silk from silkworms fed on mulberry leaves; special fibers from cotton and flax; paper from a variety of dif-

40-1
Some extinct birds. At the upper left is the ivory-billed woodpecker; to its right, the Carolina parakeet. At the upper right is the passenger pigeon; at the lower left, the heath hen.

ferent wood pulps; antibiotic drugs from soil fungi; the insecticide rotenone, from a South American plant; rubber from the protective juices of many kinds of plants; pyrethrum, another insecticide, from a daisy of the Middle East.

No list that includes only the presently known uses of other living things is complete. At irregular intervals (often by accident), new and important uses are found for organisms that previously meant nothing to man. The whole concept of the use in medicine of antibiotic substances from molds and other organisms arose from Sir Alexander Fleming's discovery of bacterial inhibition by *Penicillium* in 1928.

Unfortunately, as he increases his need for food, water, and nonliving raw materials for technology, man for the most part overlooks the wealth of living things with which he still shares the earth. To overlook them is to press them progressively toward extinction (Figures 40-1, 40-2, 40-3, and 40-4).

40-2 Three animals saved from extinction. The European bison (top) and the white-tailed gnu (center) are known only in captivity. The American bison (bottom) lives today in protected herds.

Animals, particularly large ones, seem in greater danger of extermination than do plants. Island animals, such as the flightless dodo of Mauritius (exterminated in 1693), are especially vulnerable. Mainland ani-

mals are imperiled, too. In the last century and a half, America has lost the great auk (1844), the Labrador duck (1878), the Carolina parakeet (1920), the Eskimo curlew (1932), the passenger pigeon (1914), and the heath hen (1933). (See Figure 40-1.) Europe's bison (the wisent) and Africa's white-tailed gnu exist today only in zoos and sanctuaries provided for them (Figure 40-2). Our own American bison (Figure 40-2) almost disappeared before it was saved through special Congressional action. No longer does it need a place among the 600 different kinds of warm-blooded animals now most in danger of extinction (Figure 40-3).

Some of the more unusual and conspicuous plants have been saved from extermination. Lamas in Tibetan lamaseries are credited with rescuing the last wild ginkgo trees and propagating them. Eventually the world elsewhere became hospitable to having these trees introduced for shade. Today no wild ginkgo trees are known: they are entirely domesticated. The Save-the-Redwoods League in California was principally responsible for the setting aside of a few groves of these largest trees at a time when timber companies were ready to fell the last of them (Figure 40-4). The cypresses of California's Monterey Peninsula represent another kind of plant protected for the future after all others of their species had been destroyed.

Similar efforts on a smaller scale, to protect such plants as wood orchids, trailing arbutus, and other wild flowers, have been needed in many parts of the country to insure continuation of the native flora. The establishment of national parks and of wilderness areas, where the ecological balance is left as free of human influences as possible, are larger endeavors. They are aimed at preventing the extinction of living things that are interesting to some people now and may be highly useful to others in years to come.

40-3 Several animals threatened with extinction. At the upper left is the whooping crane; to its right, the trumpeter swan. Below at the left is the musk ox; below right, the key deer. All four are North American species. One, the musk ox, inhabits only the Far North, but efforts are being made to raise it in northern New England.

We have reached a stage where enormous numbers of species are dwindling toward disappearance because their habitats are being destroyed. Man simply leaves them too little room. In some instances this is deliberate, aimed at greater efficiency in food production. By spraying a thousand-acre rice field with one chemical compound from a low-flying airplane, all plants other than monocotyledons can be killed—thus eliminating almost all "weeds" among the rice. By similar methods, using a variety of poisons, every animal—mollusk, crustacean,

fish, amphibian, reptile, bird, and mammal —can be exterminated, but not always without the possibility of a dangerous contamination of the food product.

Few people would criticize man, or any other animal, for defending his food supply. Defense, however, implies invading competitors. Man has only a few real competitors. Most other species are either helpful to him or essentially neutral to his interests. Is it right to exterminate the neutral and helpful species by poisoning or crowding, even while claiming that we are

H. D. Wheeler from Nat. Audubon Society

40-4 The largest living things on earth—the California redwoods—escaped the lumberman's ax because of an alert citizenry. Clearly, man's role as an exploiter of other species must be tempered by one of concern for needless destruction.

lion years. Dinosaurs held a somewhat comparable position for 100 million years —then they became extinct. We would like to believe that man is here to stay. Yet permanence, even when measured in thousands rather than millions of years, depends upon an ecological balance that can provide overall stability.

The present explosive increase in human population, worldwide, represents a completely unstable situation, one with a highly questionable future. Already the presence of so many human beings has brought stress to the lives of most kinds of plants and animals from the arctic tundras to the equator and as far south as inhabitable land extends. Everywhere the number of species is shrinking, the food webs tearing and permitting wide fluctuations in populations of organisms that man regards as pests. In some areas, attempts are being made today to restore a balance and let man benefit from cross-connections in food webs.

Biological control of pests affecting man has become more highly regarded in the last decades. It consists in encouraging birds (Figure 40-5) and mammals that hunt crop-destroying pests, in aiding those insects that parasitize crop-destroying insects, in spreading disease-producing organisms that affect only destructive animals and plants. These procedures emphasize old and new relationships within the living communities. As pest numbers increase so do the populations of predators, parasites, and disease organisms. When pest numbers shrink, so do these dependent populations. Living control agents evolve as their victims do.

By contrast, chemical control has not proved as satisfactory. Since the 1940's when DDT and other synthetic insecticides came into wide use, many kinds of insects have evolved into insecticide-resistant strains. Houseflies, body lice, mosquitoes, and various insect pests of crops are not always destroyed by chemical agents that once seemed 100 percent effective. The few im-

defending our food supply? If "might makes right," there is no lasting limit to the application of the principle. In the process, moreover, it is probable that many useful species will be exterminated when we exterminate a few thought to be harmful.

Living Resources and the Stability of Man's World

The human species, as the sole survivor in the hominid line of the anthropoid primates, has developed and come to dominate the living world in less than one mil-

mune survivors gave rise to the physiologically different insects we meet today. In the field of medicine, a comparable change is seen in antibiotic-immune bacteria.

Where they are not destroyed by mass applications of insecticides, honeybees still pollinate flowers, dragonflies continue to destroy mosquitoes, and ladybird beetles devour sap-sucking aphids (plant lice). Chickadees hunt for aphid eggs on tree bark during winter. Continuation of these links in familiar food webs depends on us. Through poisoning campaigns we may gain higher yields from croplands for a few years —until the insects grow immune to the chemical agents. But do we gain enough to pay for ignoring and eliminating the agents of biological control, which work without charge at slightly less efficiency?

From our present vantage point we can look back into time and reconstruct the long, impressive pattern of evolving nature. We can claim a respectable place in it. We can also make one sure prediction: The species alive today are the ancestors of all the plants and animals the earth will ever have. Conditions are such that another origin of life (Chapter 36) seems impossible. As in the past and at present, and for as long into the future as man permits, plants and animals will interact with each other and with us. They serve us, far more completely than we know today, in maintaining a dynamic balance throughout the natural world. This balance is the sole stabilizing feature of the environment in which mankind continues to evolve.

GUIDE QUESTIONS AND PROBLEMS

1. How does man's activity tend to reduce the number of species of large animals in his vicinity?
2. In what ways has man become a force affecting his own evolution?
3. Why is a vegetable diet inadequate?

John Warham

40-5 Biological control. In the course of life within complex food webs, some species will control the populations of others. Here an owl flies away with a captured rodent, for example. How may biological control prove to be of more value than synthetic chemical controls?

4. What are the problems of food production as a result of the world's population growth?
5. What is the relation between the supply of usable fresh water and the cutting down of forests?
6. What are the consequences of the establishment of national parks and wildlife areas?

SUGGESTIONS FOR ADDITIONAL READING

Books

Carson, Rachel, *Silent Spring*. Boston, Houghton Mifflin, 1962.

A book that has stirred wide discussion because of the author's convictions about the ultimate harmfulness of man's chemical warfare against other species.

National Academy of Science, *The Growth of World Population*. Washington, National Academy of Sciences (National Research Council Publication 1091), 1963.

A factual report of the human birthrate and impending tragedy by overpopulation.

(See also references at the end of Chapter 39.)

41

A PERSPECTIVE

OF BIOLOGY

Each chromosome is replicated, and the cell divides, becoming two. A nerve impulse reaches the heart via the vagus, and the heart's rate of contraction slows. A mold secretes a substance into its surroundings, and colonies of bacteria nearby cease to grow. Three hundred million years of evolution convert the bones of the jaw region of primitive fish into the ear bones of the mammals. Urea, a waste product of the animal way of life, becomes an energy source for a microorganism. The islet cells of the pancreas secrete insulin, and the concentration of glucose in the bloodstream drops. The relative humidity decreases, and great trees slowly close their stomata. An advanced primate picks up a pointed stone, kills his enemy, and begins the rapid evolution to man. A strand of DNA with the sequence *adenine-guanine-adenine-thymine* serves as a template for the formation of a strand *thymine-cytosine-thymine-adenine*. Cells of the middle layer of a frog gastrula secrete a substance, and some of the cells of the outer layer are stimulated to form a brain and spinal cord.

These and many other facts are the data of biology: a tremendous body of knowledge obtained by observation and experiment. The accumulation of knowledge began centuries ago, but the rate of growth of man's understanding of biological problems was exceedingly slow until the last century. During the past 100 years the rate of progress has been tremendous—so much so that biology is essentially a product of the period since 1850.

No human mind can understand and remember all the facts of biology. A year from now it is probable that you will remember less than 15 percent of the facts you have learned from your course in biology. Regrettable as this may seem, it would be even more regrettable if you remembered *only* facts. It is far more important that you leave your biology course with a frame of reference that will last you throughout life. You should have the knowledge that will allow you to understand not only the biological problems that have been discussed within these pages, but also to interpret each new biological situation with which you are confronted. When a bird flies across your path and disappears into a shrub, it may give you satisfaction to recall what you know about birds. You may remember their origin: how one group of Mesozoic reptiles slowly evolved feathers and the ability to fly—and hence became birds. From your knowledge of food chains, you can probably guess the role of many species of birds in their habitat. Some are primary consumers, feeding directly on the fruits and seeds of plants. Others are secondary consumers, feeding on insects and small mammals, which in turn eat plant products. Possibly you will recall the avian egg and remember how it is of the same general type that allowed the vertebrates to colonize dry land. We placental mammals evolved a different scheme for our embryonic period, but we must be grateful to our earlier four-footed ancestors for perfecting an embryo that could live on land—an evolutionary advance that made us possible! You may wonder how a small bird can provide the energy required for flight. Let us hope that you will remember the source of all an animal's energy—molecules of ATP. The chances are that you have never studied a bird in detail, but you could probably give accurate answers to the questions: How does it digest its food? How does it obtain oxygen and eliminate carbon dioxide? How does it excrete its nitrogenous wastes? Do its wings and legs resemble our arms and legs? What controls its growth?

When you look at crops growing in a field, you may think of the many types of organisms that are there but not seen. These are the organisms that make the life of the crop plants possible—the many kinds of bacteria and fungi necessary for the carbon and nitrogen cycles to work. Perhaps you will notice the leaves of the plants—the silent, green leaves that have within them biochemical mechanisms far beyond the abilities of our own cells. Long ago in the history of life on this planet, they evolved some unique basic biochemical processes. They alone can capture the life-giving energy of the sun: energy for their own lives and for the lives of all animals.

Let us hope that the living world never looks the same to you again. Previously, you may have been struck by the beauty of a flower or the song of a bird, or you may have marveled that life could be present in an insect so small as to be scarcely visible. Now you have much knowledge—knowledge that will enable you to have deeper insights and deeper appreciation for life wherever it occurs.

Possibly you will be surprised that the data of biology can be united in a theory. That is, all the facts can be seen as part of a unified whole. One way of doing this is to stress the unique features of the *nature* of life and of the *process* of living—in other words, what life is and what it does.

Life is always associated with matter. This matter has the unique property of acquiring other matter and making it, too, alive. The properties of life are associated with a tremendous chemical complexity—a complexity maintained only by a continuous expenditure of energy.

Quite early in evolution, and probably from life's very beginning, the living structure was an organization primarily of compounds of carbon, hydrogen, oxygen, nitrogen, and phosphorus, plus traces of other elements. Probably these elements were built almost entirely into molecules of nucleic acids, proteins, fats, carbohydrates, and water. This is a reasonable assumption, since all life today is composed of the same elements and the same major classes of molecules.

Matter in the living state is in constant flux. A carbon atom, which yesterday was in a piece of bread, today may be part of you. Tomorrow it may be exhaled in a CO_2 molecule—shortly to re-enter the world of life in the photosynthetic reactions of a green plant. Life has been using that same carbon atom for at least a billion years. Some of your atoms were parts of the earliest living organisms, and later possibly of Aristotle or Caesar.

Also quite early in the evolution of life the photosynthetic mechanism must have evolved. The living state can only be maintained by a constant expenditure of energy. The only practical source of energy for life on the earth seems to be light—light from nuclear reactions occurring in the sun. The earth itself has sources of energy, but these sources are used not at all or only by a few of the simplest forms of life. Life, then, is the child of light.

Let us consider a primitive organism—possibly no more than a green blob—with a chemical complexity sufficient for it to utilize directly the energy of sunlight. For the moment let us concentrate upon the organism as a single individual. Is there a biological choice, so far as this individual is concerned, between immortality and eventual death? Will the green blob bask in the sun for all time, or will it be only a transitory stage in the continuum of life? A little reflection will quickly show that there could be no such choice. The green blob would always be exposed to the danger of being dashed to pieces by the waves of the primeval sea, or of being stranded on the shore and killed by the drying action of the air. Any primitive organism that may have tried the road of individual immortality is now extinct.

Life as we know it is always associated with reproduction. In view of the continuity of life *but the mortality of the individual,* it is not unreasonable to assume that reproduction is as old as life itself. That is, we should never call an association of nucleic acids, proteins, carbohydrates, fats, and water "alive" unless it can give rise to similar associations. Conceivably, and even probably, the ability to reproduce evolved long before the green blob stage (that is, the stage of a photosynthetic organism). A more primitive, colorless blob could have obtained its energy from the oxidation of organic compounds in its environment (see Chapter 36).

Reproduction, as we have learned repeatedly, involves a tremendous problem: how can the identity or near identity between offspring and parent be provided for? Not even the simplest of organisms can passively divide into living parts. Instead, there must be a mechanism ensuring that all of the biochemical "know how," which took so long to evolve, is passed on to the next generation.

The basis of the transfer of this information seems to be identical in all organisms today. From viruses to man, the sequence of bases in DNA (or, rarely, RNA) carries the hereditary information. Again, such universal association of nucleic acids with life suggests that their origin and that of life

itself must have occurred almost simultaneously, billions of years ago.

Possibly a strand of DNA, in a primordial sea containing many nucleotides and other organic compounds, was the first particle capable of reproduction. If so, here would be the first manifestation of life. The sea, in a sense, would be a vast cytoplasm—supplying the DNA with the materials (and an energy source) for making more of itself. But the sea of "cytoplasm" would be so dilute that reproduction would be incredibly slow. It might take centuries, in the absence of enzymes and ribosomes, for one DNA molecule of only a few pairs of bases to make another. The first step toward greater reproductive capabilities would come when DNA could be associated with RNA and some protein enzymes in a system in which the DNA could replicate more rapidly.

Once the ability to replicate or reproduce was present, a new force would enter: natural selection. Those molecules, such as DNA, which replicated, would increase—increase at the expense of those that did not replicate. The primordial sea would gradually consist of more and more of the replicating molecules. At all times the advantage would go to those chemical structures that could best utilize their environment—a principle true when life originated and true today.

As the environment became depleted of nonreproducing molecules, the reproducing ones could survive only by becoming associated in increasingly complex aggregates. For example, when the supply of adenine neared the exhaustion point, each kind of living, chemical aggregate would have to incorporate a system capable of synthesizing adenine from simpler substances—or extinction would be its fate.

Gradually, the seas must have changed from rich mixtures of organic compounds to solutions of almost purely inorganic salts. In other words, the seas gradually became of the nature that we observe today. All the evolutionary experiments in being alive would then have been forced to end for want of a continued supply of usable organic compounds. But the end did not come—some primitive form of life had evolved a photosynthetic mechanism. Possibly, the blue-green algae of today are reminiscent of this notable stage in life's evolution.

In the last few paragraphs still another phenomenon has been assumed but not actually stated: inherited variability. The replication of a complex structure, such as DNA, may usually be exact, but it cannot always be completely free of error. Thus, a daughter strand may differ from a parent strand. Perhaps the difference would be so great that the daughter strand could not replicate, and hence could no longer survive. On the other hand, the difference could be slight and be passed on in successive replications: it would be inherited.

Organisms by this time would have reached roughly the following degree of structural complexity: they would consist of an organized association of nucleic acids, proteins, fats, and carbohydrates that could replicate. The entire structure (should we call it a cell?) could be looked upon as specialized solely for reproduction. The nucleic acid would be the prime type of molecule—it would replicate. The remaining molecules would form systems that would make the replication not only possible but relatively efficient, by providing the necessary molecules and energy. To the ability to reproduce, we must add the phenomenon of inexact reproduction: that is, of mutation. Possibly this stage was reached several billion years ago. Once it had been reached, the rest of the story merely unfolds; no new forces are necessary—only the interaction of genetic variability and natural selection.

Our world has limited space and limited resources, while the powers of reproduction are almost unlimited. But there can be no unlimited production of life—the space and the resources are simply not sufficient. This means that there are increasing pressures to find a place to live and the resources for living. Inexorably the life that exists at any time will be the life that—of all the forms to evolve—is best able to utilize the environment.

This pressure to find a place to live—the competition for survival—has over the course of time led to the colonization of nearly every nook and cranny of our world. A tremendous variety of species has evolved—each an experiment in trying to live in a particular environment. A cubic meter of the forest floor may contain hundreds of species: protozoans, nematodes, annelids, arthropods, chordates, bacteria, fungi, mosses, liverworts, and flowering plants. All are successful in that they have survived until now. Each has an unbroken line of ancestors that stretches back to the origin of life on our earth. Biologically speaking, one cannot be "better" than another. A soil protozoan is a success in living as a soil protozoan—a tree or a mouse could not possibly be its equal in this respect. But, of course, a soil protozoan could not live as a tree or a mouse! Each has its own place in an integrated community of life.

Thus, when you look at the living world, remember that biologically speaking, the only criterion of success is being alive. The structure and functions of organisms have evolved solely because they aided survival. The variety of species that you observe is a consequence of this same force—each species has evolved in ways that perfect its life in a restricted environment.

Man, being alive, cannot escape the general problems that confront all life. Yet do not overlook the most important fact of all: in our own species alone is there a profound ability, through powers of the mind, to control our relation with the living world.

ACKNOWLEDGMENTS

Many individuals have been concerned with BIOLOGICAL SCIENCE: AN INQUIRY INTO LIFE since its inception as the BSCS Yellow Version in 1960. The following list includes those who have been more directly involved in its various editions, and the years of their participation.

Norman B. Abraham, Yuba City Union High School, Yuba City, California, 1961

Dean A. Anderson, Los Angeles State College, Los Angeles, California, 1960

John Behnke, Ronald Press, New York City, 1961

John Bodel, The Hotchkiss School, Lakeville, Connecticut, 1960

Charles R. Botticelli, Harvard University, Cambridge, Massachusetts, 1960, 1961

Donald H. Bucklin, University of Wisconsin, Madison, Wisconsin, 1960, 1961, 1962, 1963

C. Francis Byers, Elmira College, Elmira, New York, 1960

Archie Carr, University of Florida, Gainesville, Florida, 1961

Edwin H. Colbert, American Museum of Natural History and Columbia University, New York City, 1961

J. Maxwell Davis, Bosse High School, Evansville, Indiana, 1962

Judith Dobkin, University of Miami, Miami, Florida, 1961

Frank C. Erk, State University of New York, Long Island Center, Oyster Bay, 1960, 1961

Doris Falk, Fresno State College, Fresno, California, 1961

John G. Farrow, Scarsdale High School, Scarsdale, New York, 1960

Jack Fishleder, West Phoenix High School, Phoenix, Arizona, 1960

Jack Friedman, Syosset High School, Syosset, New York, 1960

O. Frota-Pessoa, UNESCO, Instituto Brasileiro de Educação, Ciencia e Cultura, São Paulo, Brasil, 1961

Eurgen Gennaro, Wisconsin High School, Madison, Wisconsin, 1960

Bentley Glass, The Johns Hopkins University, Baltimore, Maryland, 1960, 1961, 1962, 1963

Margaret Grant, BSCS, Boulder, Colorado, 1961

John Gundlach, Neenah High School, Neenah, Wisconsin, 1960

Wesley Hall, Fairview High School, Boulder, Colorado, 1960, 1961

Robert S. Hamilton, Boulder High School, Boulder, Colorado, 1960, 1961

Philip Handler, Duke University, Durham, North Carolina, 1960

Jewell Jordan, Commerce High School, Commerce, Georgia, 1960

Wilson Kispert, Cass Technical High School, Detroit, Michigan, 1961

Jane Larsen, BSCS, Boulder, Colorado, 1960, 1961

Victor Larsen, Jr., Adelphi College, Garden City, New York, 1960

William V. Mayer, Wayne State University, Detroit, Michigan, 1960, 1961, 1962, 1963

Lorus J. Milne, University of New Hampshire, Durham, New Hampshire, 1960

Margery Milne, Durham, New Hampshire, 1960

John A. Moore, Columbia University, New York City, 1960, 1961, 1962, 1963

Russell C. Oakes, Huntington High School, Huntington, New York, 1960, 1961

Glen E. Peterson, University of Houston, Houston, Texas, 1960, 1961

Gordon E. Peterson, San Marino High School, San Marino, California, 1960

James F. Ragin, Jack Yates Senior High School, Houston, Texas, 1961

Frederick A. Rasmussen, Finney High School, Detroit, Michigan, 1960, 1961

Clarence W. Rice, Cass Technical High School, Detroit, Michigan, 1961

Imogene Russell, Sandia High School, Albuquerque, New Mexico, 1960

Joseph J. Schwab, University of Chicago, Chicago, Illinois, 1960

George Schwartz, Forest Hills High School, New York City, 1961, 1962, 1963

G. Ledyard Stebbins, University of California, Davis, California, 1960

Wilson N. Stewart, University of Illinois, Urbana, Illinois, 1961, 1962, 1963

Zachariah Subarsky, Bronx High School of Science, New York City, 1960

Gerald D. Tague, Wichita High School East, Wichita, Kansas, 1960

Joyce B. Thompson, San Jacinto High School, Houston, Texas, 1960

Paul A. Vestal, Rollins College, Winter Park, Florida, 1960

Henry M. Wallbrunn, University of Florida, Gainesville, Florida, 1961

Claude Welch, Michigan State University, East Lansing, Michigan, 1960, 1961

Jonathan Westfall, University of Georgia, Athens, Georgia, 1960

Betty Wislinsky, West High School, Madison, Wisconsin, 1961

Robert L. Wistort, High Point High School, Hyattsville, Maryland, 1961

Louise A. Wolf, New York City, New York, 1962, 1963

Delaphine G. R. Wyckoff, Wellesley College, Wellesley, Massachusetts, 1960

Scientific societies that have reviewed experimental editions—and the members of the societies who undertook these reviews—include:

AMERICAN ACADEMY OF MICROBIOLOGY:
Dr. Perry Wilson (Chairman), University of Wisconsin; Dr. Raymond Doetsch, University of Maryland; Dr. Neal Groman, University of Washington; Dr. Michael J. Pelczar, University of Maryland; and Dr. Wayne W. Umbreit, Rutgers University

AMERICAN GENETIC ASSOCIATION:
Dr. Ralph Singleton (Chairman), University of Virginia; Dr. F. B. Hutt, Cornell University; Dr. D. T. Morgan, University of Maryland; and Dr. Marcus Rhoades, Indiana University

AMERICAN PHYSIOLOGICAL SOCIETY:
Dr. J. R. Brobeck (Chairman), University of Pennsylvania; Dr. Arthur W. Martin, University of Washington; and Dr. R. R. Ronkin, University of Delaware

AMERICAN PHYTOPATHOLOGICAL SOCIETY:
Dr. C. W. Boothroyd (Chairman), Cornell University; Dr. D. F. Crossan, University of Delaware; Dr. J. Dale, University of Arkansas; Dr. I. W. Deep, Oregon State College; Dr. C. W. Ellett, Ohio State University; Dr. W. H. English, University of California; Dr. D. W. French, University of Minnesota; Dr. Arthur Kelman, North Carolina State College; Dr. J. E. Mitchell, University of Wisconsin; Dr. J. H. Owen, University of Florida; Dr. G. K. Parris, Mississippi State College; Dr. D. W. Rosberg, Texas Agricultural and Mechanical College; Dr. L. F. Roth, Oregon State College; Dr. Thomas Sproston, University of Vermont; Dr. R. B. Stevens, George Washington University; and Dr. R. A. Zabel, Syracuse University

AMERICAN PSYCHOLOGICAL ASSOCIATION:
Dr. Donald Meyer (Chairman), Ohio State University; Dr. Carl Pfaffman, Brown University; and Dr. Stanley C. Ratner, Michigan State University

AMERICAN SOCIETY FOR HORTICULTURAL SCIENCES:
Dr. O. W. Davidson (Chairman), Rutgers University; Dr. Russell Eggert, State University of New Hampshire; and Professor A. F. DeWirth, Agricultural and Mechanical College of Texas

AMERICAN SOCIETY OF HUMAN GENETICS:
Dr. Arthur Steinberg (Chairman), Western Reserve University

AMERICAN SOCIETY FOR MICROBIOLOGY:
Dr. H. J. Blumenthal (Chairman), University of Michigan Medical School; Mr. Byron Bernard, La Porte High School, La Porte, Indiana; Dr. Arthur R. Colmer, Louisiana State University; Dr. Arnold L. Demain, Merck, Sharp and Dohme; Dr. S. G. Knight, University of Wisconsin; Dr. L. S. McClung, Indiana University; Dr. W. J. Walter, Montana State College; and Dr. E. D. Weinberg, Indiana University

AMERICAN SOCIETY OF PARASITOLOGISTS:
Dr. Norman Levine (Chairman), University of Illinois; Dr. David R. Lincicome, Howard University; Dr. O. Wilford Olsen, Colorado State University; and Dr. Marietta Voge, University of California

AMERICAN SOCIETY OF PLANT TAXONOMISTS:
Dr. C. Ritchie Bell (Chairman), University of North Carolina; Dr. L. Constance, Univer-

sity of California at Berkeley; Dr. Mildred Mathias, University of California at Los Angeles; Dr. J. Proskauer, University of California at Los Angeles; Dr. A. E. Radford, University of North Carolina; and Dr. Peter Raven, Rancho Santa Ana Botanic Garden

AMERICAN SOCIETY OF ZOOLOGISTS:
Dr. Carl Gans, University of Buffalo; Dr. Clarence Goodnight, Purdue University; Dr. Ronald R. Novales, Northwestern University; and Dr. J. Paul Scott, Jackson Memorial Laboratory

BIOPHYSICAL SOCIETY:
Dr. Richard S. Bear (Chairman), Boston University; and Dr. N. A. Coulter, Jr., Ohio State University

BOTANICAL SOCIETY OF AMERICA:
Dr. Adolph Hecht, Washington State University; Dr. S. N. Postlethwait, Purdue University; and Dr. John Thomson, University of Wisconsin

COUNCIL FOR EXCEPTIONAL CHILDREN:
Dr. Harry Passow (Chairman), Teachers College, Columbia University; Dr. Louis A. Fleigler, University of Denver; and Dr. Virgil S. Ward, University of Virginia

DEPARTMENT OF RURAL EDUCATION:
Mr. Fred Guffin, Fulton County Board of Education, Hapeville, Georgia

ECOLOGICAL SOCIETY OF AMERICA:
Dr. Frank Golley (Chairman), University of Georgia; and Dr. Paul Johnsgard, University of Nebraska

ENTOMOLOGICAL SOCIETY OF AMERICA:
Dr. Robert V. Travis (Chairman), Garden Pest Control; and Mr. George Senechal, Valentine City Schools, Valentine, Nebraska

GENETICS SOCIETY OF AMERICA:
Dr. David Nanney (Chairman), University of Illinois; Dr. Robert Edgar, California Institute of Technology; and Dr. E. S. Russell, Roscoe B. Jackson Memorial Laboratory

NATIONAL ASSOCIATION OF BIOLOGY TEACHERS:
Dr. Edward Frankel, Bureau of Educational Research, New York City Board of Education; Mr. William M. Smith, Thomas Carr Howe High School, Indianapolis; and Mr. Donald Winslow, Indiana University

NATIONAL ASSOCIATION FOR RESEARCH IN SCIENCE TEACHING:
Dr. W. C. VanDeventer (Chairman), West-

ern Michigan University; Dr. Ralph P. Frazier, Emporia State Teachers College; and Dr. Joseph Novak, Purdue University

NATIONAL CATHOLIC EDUCATION ASSOCIATION:
Rev. Mark H. Bauer, S.J. (Chairman), Georgetown University; Brother Bernardine, C.F.X., Archbishop Stephinac High School, White Plains, New York; Rev. Donald M. Chigar, Mount Carmel High School, Houston; Sister Mary Ivo, B.V.M., The Immaculata, Chicago; Sister Julia Marie, O.S.F., Holy Family College, Manitowoc, Wisconsin; and Rev. George A. Walsh, O.S.F.S., Cathedral Prep, Erie, Pennsylvania

NATIONAL SCIENCE TEACHERS ASSOCIATION:
Dr. Darwin Levine (Chairman), New York City Board of Education; Mrs. Leona Adler, New York University; Mr. Thomas Lawrence, Erasmus Hall High School, Brooklyn; Mr. Kenneth Meyer, Harrison, New York; Mr. Jesse Miller, Manhasset Public Schools, Long Island; and Mr. Robert Weinberger, Flushing High School, New York

POULTRY SCIENCE ASSOCIATION:
Dr. Walter C. Morgan (Chairman), South Dakota State College; Dr. D. W. MacLaury, University of Kentucky; Dr. George D. Quigley, University of Maryland; Dr. E. A. Shano, Cornell University; and Dr. D. W. Talmage, University of Connecticut

SOCIETY OF GENERAL PHYSIOLOGY:
Dr. R. R. Ronkin (Chairman), University of Delaware

SOCIETY FOR INDUSTRIAL MICROBIOLOGY:
Dr. John N. Porter (Chairman), Lederle Laboratories; Dr. Marlin A. Espenshade, Wyeth Laboratories, Inc.; and Dr. B. Malin, Eli Lilly and Company

SOCIETY FOR THE STUDY OF EVOLUTION:
Dr. John S. Mecham (Chairman), Auburn University; Dr. David J. Merrell, University of Minnesota; Dr. Robert Sokal, University of Kansas; and Dr. Robert K. Vickery, University of Utah

SOCIETY FOR THE STUDY OF GROWTH AND DEVELOPMENT:
Dr. Arthur Galston (Chairman), Yale University; and Dr. Robert L. DeHaan, Carnegie Institute of Washington

Individuals who reviewed experimental editions include:

Mr. Wilbur Pieter Bijhouwer, Chicago, Illinois
Dr. W. D. Billings, Duke University
Dr. Robert E. Bills, University of Alabama
Dr. H. J. Blumenthal, University of Michigan Medical School
Dr. Harold C. Bold, University of Texas
Mr. Ernest C. Borden, Phillips Exeter Academy
Dr. J. K. Brierley, British Ministry of Education
Dr. J. A. Campbell, Chemical Education Materials Study
Mr. L. C. Comber, British Embassy
Dr. Henry S. Conard, Grinnell College
Dr. Harriet Creighton, Wellesley College
Dr. R. F. Dawson, Columbia University
Dr. Fred D. Emerson, Elon College
Miss Janice B. Footlik, Peoria, Illinois
Mr. S. E. Frederick, Denver, Colorado
Dr. Shelby Gerking, Indiana University
Dr. Ira Gordon, University of Florida
Dr. Rollin D. Hotchkiss, The Rockefeller Institute for Research, New York
Dr. J. Gordon Kaplan, Dalhousie University, Halifax, Nova Scotia, Canada

Dr. Harlan Lewis, University of California
Professor James W. McFarland, Air Force Academy
Dr. Lindsay Olive, Columbia University
Dr. Leonard Ornstein, The Mount Sinai Hospital, New York
Dr. Dominick J. Paolillo, University of Illinois
Dr. Arnold Ravin, Rochester University
Dr. Isaac Schlectmeister, Southern Illinois University
Dr. Ray F. Smith, University of California
Dr. G. Ledyard Stebbins, University of California
Dr. Carl P. Swanson, The Johns Hopkins University
Dr. Kenneth V. Thimann, Harvard Biological Laboratories
Dr. Ruth B. Thomas, Eastern New Mexico University
Dr. R. A. R. Tricker, Staff Inspector for Science, Great Britain
Dr. Jacob Uhrich, Trinity University
Dr. Wayne W. Umbreit, Rutgers, The State University
Dr. Kenneth Wells, University of California
Mr. F. Wing, Carl Sandburg High School, Orland Park, Illinois
Dr. Orville Wyss, University of Texas

INDEX

(Page numbers printed in **boldface** refer to illustrations)

abiogenesis, 32, 34, 37, 41; *see also* spontaneous generation

absorption spectrum, of chlorophyll, **289**

Acetabularia, 570, **571**

acetaldehyde, **227**, 228

acetic acid, 83, 84, 102, 135, 164, 226, 228

acetyl group, 135

acetylcholine 443, 444

acidic solution, defined, 104

actin, 455, 456, **457**, 458

actinomycetes, 218

active immunity, 214–16

active transport, 421–22, 427, 428

adaptation to environment, 591, 598, 601, 602, 622, 684, **704**; *see also* environment, and evolution; natural selection; *names of environments*

adenine, 552, molecular structure of, **552**; 554, **554**, 555, 557, 565, 568, 569

adenine nucleotide, 552, molecular structure of, **552**; 568

adenosine diphosphate, *see* ADP

adenosine triphosphate, *see* ATP

ADP, 131, 132, 133, 135, **135**, **138**, 139, **227**, 296, 349, 350, 424, 431, 456, 457

adrenal glands, 444, **445**; cortex of, 444, 447; medulla of, 444

adrenaline, 443, 444, 447

aerobic respiration, 226, 227, 228; *see also* respiration

African sleeping sickness, 209, 364

afterbirth, 475

agar, 258, 331, 332, **332**

agriculture: beginnings of, 675–76, 678, 679, 683; and rise of civilization, 681–82, **682**

Agricus, **236**

air: analysis of, 93–94; as mixture of gases, 79, 94, 634; Priestley's experiments with, 76–79, **77**, **78**

air sacs: in grasshopper, **401**; in man, **415**

alanine, 107, 135; molecular structure of, **106, 108, 425**

alcohol, 82, 241, 290; produced by fermentation, 164, 226, 227, **227**, 229; as solvent of fats, 125

algae, 233, 254–56, 262, 269, 275, **282**, **283**, **284**, 364, **643**, 691; alternation of generations in, 252, 253, **254**, **255**; carbon dioxide absorbed by, 263; as early organisms, 245, 248, 638, 641; economic importance of, 258–59; as food, 257, 258; in hot springs, 174; nitrogen-fixing, 167, **169**; photosynthesis by, 254, 255, 263, 297, 638, 691; sexual reproduction in, 250–51, **251**, 252, 253, 263, **266**; and space travel, **256**, 257; spores of, 251

algin, 258

allantois, 468–69, **469**, 473, 474

alleles, 517, 519, 527; defined, 516; multiple, 521

alligator, **460**

Allosaurus, **650**

alternation of generations, 251–53, **254**, **255**, 265–66, **267**, 278–80, 281

Amanita verna, 236, **236**, **237**

amanitin, 236

Ambystoma opacum, 484, **484**

American Association for the Advancement of Science, 54

American Institute of Biological Science, 55

amino acids, **106**, 106–09, **108**, 114, 129, 130, 135, 166, 168, 339, 343, 392, 396, 397, 424, 709, 710; deamination of, 424, **425**; and DNA code, 568; experimentally produced, 635–36, **636**; and gamma radiation, 637; in hemoglobin molecule, 563; as products of protein digestion, 107–08, **394**; and protein synthesis, **566**, 566–67, 567

amino group, 107, 108, 135, 424

ammonia, 167, 350, 421, 422, 423, 424, 426, 635, 637, formula for, 167, 350, 635

ammonium ions, 167

amnion, 468, **469**, 473, 474

amoeba, **365**; asexual reproduction in, 462, **463**; sensitive to ATP, 455

Amoeba proteus, 451, **452**

amphibians: development of embryo of, 483–91, **485**, **486**, **487**, **488**, **489**, **490**, **491**, **492**, **492**;

evolution of backbone of, 459, **461**; fossil, 645–46, **646**; protection of embryo of, 468; reptiles evolved from, 646, 655

amylase: in digestion of starch, **393**; pH value for activity of, 122 (table)

anaerobic respiration, 226, 228; *see also* fermentation

anal pore, of *Paramecium,* **347**, 348, 350

analogy, in classification, 361–62

analysis, chemical, 83

anatomy, comparative, 607

Anatomy of Plants, **54**

anemia: pernicious, 224–25; sickle-cell, 563, 564, 671

angiosperms, *see* flowering plants

animal hemisphere, of fertilized egg, 485, **485**, 486, **486**, 490, 496

animals: body form of, 366, 367, **367**, **450**, 450–51; classification of, 358–64, 362–63 (table); coordination in multicellular, 431–48, **434**, **435**, **436**, **437**, **438**, **441**, **445**; defined, 342; development of, *see* development; digestion in multicellular, 344, 380–97, **383**, **385**, **386**, **387**, **388**, **389**, **393**, **394**; diversity among, 358–378, **368**, **369**, **370**, **372**, **373**, **376**, **377**; domestication of, 677, 678, 679, 680, 681; excretion in multicellular, 421–30, **422**, **423**, **424**, **425**, **426**, **427**, **429**; extinct, **639**, 641, **643**, 644, **644**, 645, **645**, 646, **646**, 647, 648, 649, **649**, **650**, 651, **651**, **652**, **653**, 655, **715**; in food webs, *see* consumers *and* food webs; nervous systems in, *see above,* coordination in multicellular; one-celled, 343–57, **347**, **348**, 351, 353, 354, 365, 451, **452**; and plants, similarities to and differences from, 341, 342, 343; reproduction in, 462–81, 463, 465, 469, 471, 472, 473, 474, 475, 476–77; respiration in multicellular, 412–20, **413**, **415**, **416**, **417**, **419**; summary of circulation, respiration, digestion, and excretion, **429**; support and locomotion in, 449–

carbon monoxide, 81, 82
carbonate, 162, 163, 164, 292; ions, 101, 163, 164
carbonic acid, 163, 293, 419
Carboniferous period, 246, 270, 274, 640 (table), **642**, 646, 648, **648**
carboxyl group, 107, 108
cardiac muscle, 453, 454
Carnivora, 360
carotene, 709
cats: classification of family of, 362 (table); *see also Felis*
catalyzed reactions, 119, 120
cat's-claw plant, **704**
cattle: Brahman, 581, 582; domestication of, 679, **681**; inheritance in shorthorn, 519, **520**, 581, 582; Santa Gertrudis, 582; tuberculosis in, 223
cave paintings, Cro-Magnon, 667, 669, **670**
Cebus monkey, and space travel, **256**, 257
cell(s), 59, 63, 84, **137**, 342, 380–81, **381**; animal, compared with plant cells, **56**, 59–60, **60**, 61, **62**, 63, **341**, 342; animal, metabolism of, **345**; bacterial, 195–98, **197**, **198**; blood, *see* blood cells; carbohydrates in, 109–13; chemical reactions in, 129–36, **134**, 139; compounds of, principal, 103–16; coordination of, in multicellular animals, 431, 447–48; cytoplasm of, *see* cytoplasm; differentiation of, during development of organism, *see* cellular differentiation; and digestion, **344**, 345, 380, 381, **381**; division (reproduction) of, 57, **57**, 60, 61, 140–53, **142–43**, **144**, 146, 147, 152, **200**, 200–01, 482; egg, *see* ova; elongation in shoots and roots, 328, 330, 332, 333, **333**; energy for, 129–36, 139; fats in, 113–14; fixation of, 58; Golgi bodies of, **58**, 59, 61, **137**, 138–39, 142, **384**; guard, 292, 293, 294, **294**, **295**, 299, 302, 334, 335; Hooke first to describe, 52, 53, 61, 63; of leaf, 287–88, 313; metabolism of animal, **345**; under microscope, **54**, **56**, **62**, 122, **123**, **124**, **126**, **127**; mitochondria of, **58**, 59, 60–61, **124**, **127**, 128, 129, **129**, 134, 135, 137–38, 142; nerve, *see* neurons; nucleic acids in, 114–15; nu-

cleus of, *see* nucleus of cell; physiology of, 118–39, **121**, **126**, **134**, **135**, **138**; plant, compared with animal cells, **54**, **60**, 60–61, **62**, 63, **341**, 342; proteins in, 104–09, 129; reproduction (division) of, 57, **57**, 60, 61, 140–53, **142–43**, **144**, 146, 147, 152, **200**, 200–01, 482; sizes of, 61; sperm, *see* sperm cell; stained, 58–59; water in, 103–04, 125; *see also* meiosis; mitosis
cell membrane, 60, 61, 63, 123–26, **126**, **137**; differentially permeable, 124; and diffusion across, 124–25; fatty materials in, 125; apparent pores of, 123, **124**
cell theory, 55–61, 63
cell wall, 53, 55, 61, 63; bacterial, 194, 195, 197, **197**; of diatom, **258**, 259; of woody plant, 123, **123**, 146
cellular differentiation, 326, 482, 483, 492; and embryonic induction, 499–501; problem of, 496, 498–99; *see also* development; embryology
cellulose, 112, **123**
Cenozoic era, 640 (table), 649–52, 656
central nervous system, 434, **434**
centrifugation, 128
centrioles, 60, **137**, 138, **150**; in mitosis, 142, 144, **144**, 148, 149
centromeres, 143–44, **529**, **530**
centrosomes, 60, **137**, 138; in mitosis, 142, 143, 144, **144**, 148, **149**
cereal grains, 315
cerebellum, **434**
cerebrum, **434**, 440; functional areas of, 441, **441**
Ceres wheat, 583
chaffinch, **450**
charged particles, 96, 97
Chase, Martha, 550
chemical bonds, 100, 102, 107, 108–15, 119, 120, **121**, 129–35, **131**; defined, 94, 98–99
chemical equation, 99
chemical reactions, 97–103; catalyzed, 119, 120; in living cells, 119–20, 129–36, **134**, 139
chemistry: early, 70–82; elements and compounds in, 79–80, **81**; in laboratory and in body, **85**; living, *see* biochemistry
chemotherapy, defined, 219
cherry, domestication of, **680**
chick embryo, 468, **469**, 609

chickens, sexual differences in, 467; variety through artificial selection, **582**; domestication of, **681**
childbed fever, 219
childbirth, 474–75, **476–77**
chimpanzee, 665, **665**; cranial capacity of, 667 (table)
chitin, 374, **374**, 458
Chlamydomonas, **248**, 249, 250, 251, **251**, 252, 262, 263
Chlorella pyrenoidosa, 257
chloride ions, 101
chlorine, 83, 101 (table); abundance of, 95 (table); bacteria killed by, 197, 219; as constituent of salt, 100; as element in organism, 101 (table); symbol for, 100, 101 (table)
chlorophyll, 61, 119, 136, 287, 290, 299, 314, 508–09; *a* and *b* types of, 249, 290; absorption spectrum of, **289**; bacterial, 200; formulas for, 290; and iron, 310; magnesium in, 291; nitrogen in, 291; and photosynthesis, **289**, **290**, 290–91
chloroplasts, 61, 119, 287, 290, 291, 292, **292**, **295**, 299, 300, 303
chloroquine, 20
Chordata, 360, 364, 376, **377**, 605, 606, 641, 644–45
chorion, 469, **469**, 473, 480
chromatids, 529, 530, 531, **531**, 542
chromosomes, 59, 60, **60**, 136, **137**, 138, 148, **148**, 152; bacterial, 195, **196**, 197; constancy of number of, 149–50, 151, 153; diploid number of, 151, **152**, 153, 528, 529, 531, **537**, and genetic continuity, 528–31; homologous, 529, 530, **530**, **531**, 542; human, 59, 147, 148, **148**, 149, 150, 151, 528, 536, 537, **538**, 546–47, **547**; independent assortment of, 529–30, **534**; in meiosis, 150–51, 153, 528–29, 530–31, **530–31**, **534**, 542, **543**; in mitosis, 143, 144, 146–48, **147**, 149, 529; monoploid number of, 151, 153, 528–29, 531, 535; nondisjunction of, 544, 545, **545**, 546–47; and polyploid species, 629–30; replication of, 146–48, **147**, 149, 153, 528; segregation of homologous, 529, 531, **531**, 534; sex, discovery of, 535–41, **537**, **538**; synapsis of, 529, 530, 542; and theory of heredity,

chromosomes (*continued*)
532–33, 535, 542, 544, 546; in
Ulva, 252–53, **255**; X, 536,
537, 538, 541, 542, 544, 545,
546; Y, 536, 537, 538, 542,
544; *see also* genes
chymotrypsin, **394**
cicada, 375
cilia, 248, **346**, 346–47, **347**, 367,
451, 452, 455, 691
cinchona, 11, 12, 19
circulatory system: closed, 401,
410; of earthworm, 399–402,
400, 401, **413**, 413–14; of
grasshopper, **401**, 401–02; of
man, 402 **403**, 405–07, **407**,
408, 409, 410, **410**, **429**, 430;
open, 401–02, 410; *see also*
transportation
citrulline, 562, 563; in formation of urea, 424, **425**; structure of, **565**
clam worm, **372**
class, as group of orders, 360
classification: analogy in, 361–
62; of Animal Kingdom, 358–
64, 362–63 (table); biochemistry as basis of, 362, 363, 364;
homology as basis of, 361,
362, **363**, 364, 607; physiology
in, 362, 363, 364; of Plant
Kingdom, 282–83; of species,
359–61
climax community, 174, **174**
clines, 626–27
Clonorchis, **369**
closed circulatory system, 401,
410
Clostridium, resistant to boiling,
42
Clostridium botulinum, 212, **212**
clothing, in cultural evolution,
680–81
clotting of blood, 105
club mosses, **271**, 273, **274**, **282**;
Devonian, 646, **647**
coagulase, 211
coal, 163, 244, 603, 646; combustion of, 164
coal-ball, 646
cobalt, 95
cocci, 194, **194**, **196**
cockroach, fossil, 646
Coelenterata, 366, 367, **367**, **368**,
464, 641
coenzymes, 122; riboflavin, 133;
134
Cohn, F. J., 194
colchicine, 602, 630
coleoptile, 330, 331, **331**, 332,
332, **333**
colonization, 172, 173, 602; of
land by plants, 260, 266–68

colony of cells, 248
color blindness, 539–40, 585
colostrum, 475
columbine, genetic recombination
in, 615–16, 616
combustion: of fuels, 164; and
respiration, 76, 82, **85**, 166;
see also burning
community: climax, 174, **174**;
desert, **5**, 160, 703–05, **704**;
forest, **5**, 174, **174**, 697–702;
grassland, 702–03, **702**; as level
of biological organization, 155,
161, 170
companion cells, in sieve tube,
304, **305**, **306**, 307
compound microscope, 60, 80,
141, 148–49, 194
compounds, 81, **81**, 82; covalent,
99, 101; defined, 79, 94; inorganic, 83, 93; ionic, 101; organic, 83, 93, 102; *see also*
biochemistry *and names of individual compounds*
cone-forming plants, **271**, 273,
274, 277, 282–83
coniferous forest, **698**, 698–99
consciousness, 441
conservation of energy, law of, 90
conservation of mass, law of, 79,
80, 90, 118, 343
consumers, as animals, 161, 170,
171, 172, **176**, 177, 691, **695**,
696, 699; primary, 161 (defined), 170, **171**, 172, 175, **176**,
691, **695**, **696**, 699; secondary,
161 (defined), 170, **171**, 172,
175, **176**, 691, **696**, 699
contractile vacuoles, of *Paramecium,* **347**, 351, **351**, 352
contractility, 455–58, **457**
control, experimental, 35–36, **36**,
442, 500, 501, **549**
convergent evolution, 651
cooperation, as feature of cultural evolution, 684
coordination, 431–48; breathing
as example of, 431–33; need
of, in multicellular animals,
431, 447–48; in *Paramecium,*
352, 433
copepods, **695**
cork, Hooke's description of, 49–
52, 53, 63; under microscope,
49, 49–52, 305
corn: civilizations based on, 315;
domestication of, **680**; experiments with, by Illinois agronomists, 620–21, **621**, 622;
hybrid, 524–25, **525**, 581; pollination of, 322
corn grain, parts of, 321, **322**
coronary thrombosis, **405**

corpus luteum, 476, 477, 478,
479, 480
Correns, Carl, 527
cortex: adrenal, 444, 447; of root,
309, **309**, 310, 316; of stem,
268, 269, **273**, 302, 303, **303**,
316, **328**
cortisone, 444, 447
Corythosaurus, **650**
cotton, in cultural evolution, **680**,
681
cotyledons, **320**, 321, **322**
courtship patterns, and genetic
isolation, 629
covalent bond, 101; defined, 99
cowpox, 214
crab: horseshoe, **373**; soft-shelled,
458; larva of, **695**
crane, whooping, 716, **717**
creatine phosphate, 457, 458
Cretaceous period, **246**, 276, 640
(table), **642**, 649
Crick, F. H. C., 553, 554, 555
Cro-Magnon man, 667, **668**, 680,
681, 683; cave paintings by,
667, 669, **670**; cranial capacity
of, 667 (table)
crop, of earthworm, 386, **386**
crossbreeding, and genetic isolation, 628–29
crossing-over, in genetics, 542,
543
cross-pollination, 277, 335, 513,
518, 622
Culex mosquito, 17, **18**
cultural evolution of man, 674–
86, **685**; features of, 683–84;
future of, 683–86, **685**
cultural inheritance, 683
culture, and tools, 669, **671**
curlew, Eskimo, 716
cutin, 262, 294, 302, **303**
cuttlefish, **372**
cyanocobalamin (vitamin B_{12}),
224, 225, 709
cycad, **651**, **652**
cycle(s), 161–68, **162**, **163**, **165**,
168, **169**, 177; carbon-hydrogen-oxygen, 161–66, **165**; nitrogen, 166–68, **168**, **169**;
ornithine, **425**, 426; phosphorus, **162**, **163**; reproductive,
477–79, **478**, 479, 480
Cyclops, **383**
cyclotron, 296
cypress tree, 717
cysts, of microorganisms, 356
cytochromes, 133, 134, **134**, 138
cytoplasm, 59, **124**, 126, 128, 133,
134, 136, 142, 146, 147, 195,
197, 568; and nucleus, 570–72;
protein synthesis in, 565, 566,
566–67

cytosine, molecular structure of, **551**, 554, **554**, 555, 557, 565, 568, 569

Dalton, John, Atomic Theory of, 80–82, 91, 93, 94

Dart, Raymond, 659

Darwin, Charles: and evolution, 158, 589–92, **592**, 594, **595**, 596, 601, 602, 611, 620, 624, 627, 633, 657, 667, 684; experiments of, on growth curvature of seedlings, 329–30; rain forest visited by, 700

dating, radioactive, 157, 244, 604–05, 661

DDT, 20, 719; houseflies resistant to, 599–600

death rate in United States, 708 (table)

deciduous forests, 174, 699, 700

decomposers, 161, **162**, **163**, 164, **165**, 165–66, 167, **169**, **171**, 175, 177, 222, 235, 691, 699

deer, **467**, **717**

deficiency diseases, 710

dehydration, foods preserved by, 224

deoxyribonucleic acid, see DNA

deoxyribonucleoprotein, 136

deoxyribose, 551, molecular structure of, **551**, 552, **554**, 555, 565

Descartes, René, **66**, 66–67, 91

Descent of Man, Darwin's, 594, 657

desert, as habitat, **5**, 693, 703–05, **704**

desert community, **5**, 160, 703–05, **704**

development, 4; abnormal, 502–03; in amphibians, 483–91, **485**, **486**, **487**, **488**, **489**, **490**, **491**, 492, **492**; analysis of, 494–503; controlled by genes, 559, 569–72; post-embryonic, 501–02; processes of, in animals, 482–83; see also cellular differentiation; embryology

Devonian period, **246**, 268, 269, 270, 640 (table), **642**, 644, 645, **645**, 646

de Vries, H, 527

diabetes mellitus, 108, 430, 444, 446–47, 586

diaphragm, **415**, 417, **417**, 418

diastase, 86, 87, 88, 119

diatomaceous earth, 259

diatoms, **23**, 691, **694**, **696**; cell wall of, 258, **258**, 259; under microscope, **33**, **694**; in plankton, 259, 691, **694**

2,4-dichlorophenoxyacetic acid, 334

dicots, **323**, 324, **324**, 328–29

Didinium, 356, **365**

differentiation, cellular, *see* cellular differentiation

diffusion, 398; across cell membrane, 124–25, 293; defined, 103; in paramecia, 350, 351, **351**

digestion: in earthworm, 385–86, **386**, 402; extracellular, **344**, 345, 382, **383**; of fats, 391, 392, 396; function of, 382; in grasshopper, **387**; in *Hydra*, 383, 383–85; intestinal bacteria important in, 225, 395; intracellular, **344**, 345, 347, **383**; of maltose, **121**; in man, 386–97, **388**, **389**, 391, **392**, **393**, **394**, 395, **429**; in *Paramecium*, 347–48, **348**, 382; in planarian, 385, **385**; problems of, for multicellular animals, 380, **381**, 382; of proteins, 389, 390, 392, **394**, 396, 397; Spallanzani's study of, 84, 86, **87**, 119; of starch, 86, **87**, 88, 387, 390, 391, **393**, 396

Dimetrodon, **649**

dinoflagellates, 691, **694**, **696**

Dinosaur National Monument, 157

dinosaurs: Age of, 460, 648–49, **650**, **651**, 656; decline and fall of, 649, 656, 718; in food web, 175, **176**; fossil bones of, **156**

dipeptidase, **394**

diphosphopyridine nucleotide, *see* DPN

diphtheria, 212, 213

Diplococcus pneumoniae, 211

diploid number, in chromosomes, 151, **152**, 153, 528, 529, 531

disease, 209–10; antibiotics for treatment of, **216**, 217–19, **218**; bacteria as cause of, 42–43, 181, 197, 200, 207–09, 210–13; chemotherapy for, 219, 222; control of, 213–22; deficiency, 710; degenerative, as cause of death, 708 (table); disinfectants for control of, 219; fungi as cause of, 209, 235, 237–39; Germ Theory of, 207, 226; infectious, as cause of death, 708 (table); immunization against, 214–16; nematodes as cause of, 369; protozoans as cause of, 209, 364; sulfa drugs for treatment of, 222; viruses as cause of, 181, 183, 184, **184**, 185, 186,

189, 213–14, 215; *see also* host; pathogens

disinfectants, 219

divergent evolution, 284

DNA, 115, 136, 138, 146, 147, 148, 152, 153, 382, 528, 548, 596; in bacteria, 195, **196**, **197**, **558**; code of, 567–69; as genes, 548, 550; mutations in, 158; of phage, 186–87, 189, **190**, 191, 550; replication of, 555–58, **556**, **557**, 559, 569; and RNA, 564–67, **566**, 569, 570; molecular structure of, 551, 552, 553, **553**, **554**, **555**; Watson-Crick model of, 553, 554–55, **555**, **556**, 574; X-ray study of, 553, 554; *see also* genes

dodo, 716

dogs, 624, 625, **625**, **681**

dolphin, **696**

domestication of animals, 677, 678, 679, 680, **681**

domestication of plants, 676, 677, 678, 679, **680**

donkey, domestication of, 680, **681**

dorsal lip, of blastopore, **486**, 487, 490, **490**

dorsal nerve tube, in chordates, 376, 605

dorsal vessel, in earthworm, **400**, 401

double cross, in genetics, 524, 525, **525**

double fertilization, 321

DPN, 133, 134, **134**, 138, 297, 637

dragonfly, in Carboniferous period, 646, **648**

Driesch, Hans, 495, 496

Drosophila melanogaster, 535, 536, 540, 541, 542, 546; chromosomes in, 528, **537**, 538, **546**; effect of temperature on curly-wings trait in, 508, **509**; mutations in, induced by X rays, 612; nondisjunction of chromosomes in, 544, 545, **545**; sex determination in, **537**, 538, 544; sex-linked inheritance in, 538–39, **539**; X and Y chromosomes of, 536, **537**, 538, **539**, 541, 542, 544, **544**, 545, **545**, **546**

Dryopteris, **279**

Dubois, Eugene, 657

duck, Labrador, 716

duckbill platypus, 470, **471**, 652

Dutch elm disease, 239

Dutrochet, R. J. H., 55

dwarfism, 502, 586

dysentery, amoebic, 209, 364

flowers (*continued*)
512, **512**; variety among, 322, **323**, 324, **324**
fluorine, 95; isotopes of, 604
fly, *see* housefly
fly, fruit, *see* Drosophila melanogaster
folic acid, 709
follicles, ovarian, 472, **474**, 476, 478, 479
follicle-stimulating hormone, 479, 480
food: adequate supply of, 709–13; algae used as, 257, 258; calcium in, 710; calories in, 710, 711, 712; canned, 222; carbohydrates in, 709, 710; dried, 224; energy from, 118, 119, 135; as environmental influence on genes in rabbits, **596**, 597; fats in, 709, 710; for growth, 118, 119; iron in, 710; oxidation of, 88; for *Paramecium*, 347, 356; preservatives for, 224; proteins in, 709, 710; refrigeration of, 223–24; unequal distribution of, 711–12; values per pound, after cooking, 711 (table); vitamins in, 709, 710–11
food-gathering and hunting peoples, 675
food vacuoles, of *Paramecium*, 347, **347**, 348, **348**, 349
food webs, 170–72, **171**, 177, 255–56; in forest community, 699; fossil, 175, **176**; under natural stress, 174–75; in ocean, 691, 694, **696**
foot, of sporophyte, 265, **265**
foot-and-mouth disease, 185
foresight, in cultural evolution, 684
forest: climax, **174**; coniferous, **698**, 698–99; deciduous, **174**; food web in, 699; as habitat, **693**, 697–702; monthly temperature variation in, **700**; rainfall variation in, **701**; tropical (tropical rain), **5**, 700–02
formaldehyde, 215, 219
Forsythia, 318
fossils, 7, **156**, 603, 638–39, 654; Cambrian, 260, 639, 640 (table), 641, 643, **643**; Carboniferous, 270, 274, 640 (table), 646; Cenozoic, 651; Cretaceous, 276, 640 (table), 649; dated by radioactive clock method, 157, 244, 604–05, 661; Devonian, 269, 270, 640 (table), 644, 645, 646; earliest-known animal, **639**, **642**; and

emerging man, 657–61, **658**, **659**, **660**, **668**; earliest-known plant, 246; Eocene, 663; as evidence for evolution, 603–05, **604**, **605**; Jurassic, 648, **652**; Mesozoic, 640 (table), 648–49, 655–56; Miocene, 660, 661; Ordovician, 640 (table), 644; Paleozoic, 640 (table), 641, 643–48, 654–55; Permian, 640 (table), 647–48; Pleistocene, 660, 661, 667; Pliocene, 661; Pre-Cambrian, 245, **247**, 639, **639**, 640 (table), 641; Silurian, 640 (table), 644, 646; *see also* evolution
fox, mutations in, 626–27
Fox, Sidney W., 636, 637
Franklin, Benjamin, 75
freezer, food, 223, 224
French Academy of Science, 38, 39, 41
frog: blood cells of, **62**; eggs of, 483, 494, 495, 496; heart of, **442**, 442–43; number of chromosomes in, 59; protection of embryo of, 468; respiration in, 412; tropical, 377
fructose, 110, 111; formula for, 110; molecular structure of, **111**
fruit fly, *see* Drosophila melanogaster
fruits, 277–78, **278**, 322
FSH, 479, 480
fungi, **282**, 337; bracket, **235**, 237; as decomposers, **162**, **165**, 166, 235; diseases caused by, 209, 235, 237–39; evolution of, 233, 234, 242, **246**; importance of, 234–39; spoilage caused by, 235, 237; wood-rotting, 237; *see also* molds
Fusarium, 583
fusion nucleus, of flowering plant, **320**, 321

galactose, 110; formula for, 110; molecular structure of, **111**
Galápagos Islands, 591, 602, 627
Galen, 409
Galileo, 47, 67, 686
gall bladder, **388**
gall insects, 30, 31, **32**
gametes, 317, 464, 465, 466, 512, 515; in algae, 250, 252, 253, **254**, **255**; defined, 201; formation of, 530–31; in molds, 233; in polyploid hybrids, 630, **631**; and probability in genetics, 516
gametophytes: defined, 252; in moss plant, 265, **267**, **278**;

trend in evolution of, **284**; in *Ulva*, 253, **254**, **255**, 265; in vascular plants, 279, 280, **280**, **281**, 284, **284**
"Gamma Garden," 614
gamma radiation: and production of amino acids, 637; and production of mutations, 612, 613
gangrene, gas, 211, 212
Garibaldi, **377**
gastric juice, 84, 119, 122, 389, 390, 391, 396
gastrin, 390, 444
gastrulation, 486, **486**, 490, 500
Geiger-Müller counter, 296
gene pool, 576–78, 581, 622
generation (in experiments in genetics): F$_1$, 513, 514 (table), 515, 517, **518**, 519, **520**, 524; F$_2$, 513, 514 (table), 515, **518**, 519, **520**, 524; P$_1$, 513, 514 (table), **518**, **520**; *see also* genetics
genes, 466, 496, 514, 527, 532, 548, 596, 683, 684; action of, 558–64; bacterial, 195, **196**, **197**, 558; for blood-type, 521; chemical nature of, 548–58; crossing over, 541–42, **543**; development controlled by, 559, 569–72; as DNA, 548, 550; dominant, 514; and enzymes, 562–63, 564, **564**, 570; for eye color, 519, 535, 538, 542, 558–59, 586; food as environmental influence on, **596**, 597; for hair color, 519, 522; for hemophilia, 540, **540**, 541, 585; linkage groups of, 533, 535, 541; in man, 563–64, 585–86; mutant, *see* mutations; in *Neurospora*, 559–62, **560**, 561; in populations, *see* populations; recessive, 514, 515; sex-linked, 536, 538, 539, **539**, 541, **544**; for skin color, 586; temperature as environmental influence on, 597, **597**; of viruses, 190, 191, 550; *see also* chromosomes; DNA; genetics; heredity; traits
genetic continuity, 140–41, 146, 148; and chromosomes, 528–31
genetic drift, random, 622, 624
genetic isolation, 581, 628–29
genetic recombination, 205, 541–42; in bacteria, 204–05, **205**; defined, 190; and evolution, 615–18, **616**, **617**; experiments illustrating the importance of, 618–22, **619**, **621**; and sexual reproduction, 616, **617**, 618

genetics, 151, 611, 677; Bridges' work in, 542, 544, 545, 546; and crossing-over, 542, **543**; defined, 7, 507–08; double cross in, 524, 525; evolution related to, 594 (*see also* mechanisms of evolution); Hardy-Weinberg Principle in, 577, 578, 585, 615, 622, 623; independent assortment in, 524, 529–30, **534**, 541; Mendel's work in, 510–17, **518**, 519, 522, 523, 524, 527, 533, 541, 548; Morgan's work in, 535, 536, **536**, 541, 542; probability in, 516; segregation in, 515, 517, 529, 531, **531**, **534**; Sutton's work in, 532–33, 535, 538, 539, 541, 548; test cross in, 519; *see also* breeding; chromosomes; DNA; genes; heredity; sex determination; traits

genotype, defined, 515, 516

genus (genera): defined, 359, 360; origin of, 630–32

geologic time scale, **246**, 640 (table), **642**, 666 (table)

geology, and Darwin, 591

geometric progression, **590**, 592

geotropisms, 329, **330**, 332, 333

germ cells, defined, 594

Germ Theory of Disease, 207, 226

giantism, 502, 586

gibberellins, 334

gibbon, 665; cranial capacity of, 667 (table)

ginkgo tree, 716; leaf of, **270**

giraffes, **585**, 689, **690**

girdling of trees, 307, **307**

gizzard, of earthworm, 386, **386**

glands (or gland cells): digestive, 387–390, 391, 392; of grasshopper, **387**; in *Hydra*, **383**; of man, 386–397, **388**, 392; endocrine, 444–45, **445**, 479, 480; mammary, 470, 475, 479–80, 651

Glass, Bentley, 587, 623, 632

Gloeocapsa, 248, **248**

glucose, 109, 111, 166, 177, 339, 342, 412; cellulose made of, 112; energy from, 131–33, 135, **135**, 139; and fermentation, 164, 227, **227**, 228; formula for, 109, 132; in human blood, concentration of, 430, 446, 447; maltose converted into, during digestion, 392, **393**, 396; molecular structure of, 111, **111**, **112**, 120, 131, 132, **393**; in muscle fiber, 457, 458;

and nephrons 427; oxidation of, 119, 129, 130, 132, 133, 420, 431, 458; synthesized in plants, 119, 136, 299

glutamic acid, 563

glycerol, 113, 114, 135, 391, 392, 396; molecular structure of, **112**, 113, **114**

glycine, 107, 568; molecular structure of, **106**, **108**

glycogen: molecule of, 111, 112; stored in muscle, 457–48

glycyl-alanine, molecular structure of, 107, **108–09**

gnu, white-tailed, 716, **716**

goat, domestication of, **681**

Golgi bodies, **58**, 59, 61, **137**, 138–39, 142, **384**

gonads, defined, 465

gonorrhea, 210

gorilla, **664**; cranial capacity of, 667 (table)

grana, of chloroplasts, 291, **291**, **292**

grasshopper, **373**, **374**, 374–75; chromosomes of, 538; digestive system of, **387**; excretion in, 423–24, **424**; locomotion of, 453, **454**; respiratory system of, **401**, 414; transportation in, **401**, 401–02, 411

grassland, as habitat, **692**, 701–03

grassland community, 701–03, **702**

Gray, Asa, 592

green land plants, 243, 256, 337; alternation of generations in, *see* alternation of generations; ascent of water in, experiment to show, 312–13, **314**; asexual reproduction in, 317–19, **318**; classification of, **282–83**; chlorophyll in, *see* chlorophyll; colonization of land by, 260, 266–68; development of, 324–34, **325**, **326**, **327**, **328**, **330**, **331**, **332**; evolution of, 243, 245, **246**, 249, 260, 266–68, 269–75, 280, **284**, 284–85, 641, 643–44, 652–53; flowering, *see* flowering plants; fruits of, 277–78, **278**; gametophytes of, *see* gametophytes; growth of, **325**, 325–26, **326**, 327, **327**, 328, **328**, 329, 330–31, **331**, **332**, 332–33, 334; heredity in, *see* genetics; leaves of, *see* leaf; movement of materials in, 311, 313; nitrogen sources for, 167; nonvascular, 260, **261**, 261–66, **262**, **264**, **265**, 268 (*see also* liverworts; mosses); as obligate aerobes,

228; photosynthesis in, *see* photosynthesis; pollination of, 276–77, **320**, 321, 322, 324, 335, 512, **512**, 615, 629, 653; root of, *see* root; seeds of, 274–75, **275**, 277–78, 324, 653, 676; sexual reproduction in flowering, 319–24, **320**, **322**; sporangia in, *see* sporangia; sporophytes of, *see* sporophytes; stem of, *see* stem; storage of materials in, 311, 315–16; time scale for, in geologic periods, **246**; vascular, *see* vascular plants

Grew, Nehemiah, 192; drawings from *Anatomy of Plants* by, **54**

Griffith, F., 548

growth, 4, 118, 482; and development, in animals, *see* development; of flowering plants, **325**, 325–26, **326**, 327, **327**, 328, **328**, 329, 330–31, **331**, **332**, 332–33, 334; food for, 118, 119

growth substances, for flowering plants, 331–34, **331**, **332**, **333**

guanine, **552**, 554, **554**, 555, 557, 565, 568, 569; molecular structure of, **552**

guard cells, **288**, 292, 293, 294, **294**, **295**, 299, 302, 334, 335

guinea pig, domestication of, **681**

gymnosperms, 697; classification of, **283**; flowering plants compared to, 652–53

habitats, 349; major types of, **692–93**, 695; *see also* desert; environment; forest; grassland; ocean

hair color, inheritance of, 519, 522

half-life of radioactive substance, 244

Hardy, G. H., 577

Hardy-Weinberg Principle, 577, 578, 585, 615, 622, 623

Harvey, William, and theory of blood circulation, 408, 409, **409**, 410

hay infusion: observation of life in, 34, **35**, 35–36, **36**, 37, 38, 41, 42; survival time of organisms boiled in, 42 (table)

heart: of frog, **442**, 442–43; of grasshopper, **401**, 402; of man, 402, **403**, **404**, 405, **405**, 406; pacemaker of, 443

heart attack, mechanism of, **405**

heartwood, **306**

heath hen, **715,** 716
helium, 97; atomic structure of, 98, **98**
hematoxylin, 58
heme group, 418
hemoglobin, 105, 406, 414, 418, 426; formula for, 106, 419; molecule of, 418, 563; and oxygen, 105, 109, 340, 406, 414, 418, 419; sickle-cell, 563, 600
hemophilia, 539, **540,** 540–41, 585
hepatic portal vein, **403**
hepatitis, infectious, 186
herbaceous stem, **302,** 302–04, **303**
heredity: and blood types, 521, 573; chromosome theory of, 532–33, 535, 542, 544, 546; code of, 567–69; defined, 507; and environment, 508–10; evidences from, for evolution, 601–02; human, 584–87; *see also* breeding; chromosomes; DNA; genes; genetics; sex determination; traits
hermaphrodites, 368, 371, 462, 465–66
heron, night, **377**
Hershey, Alfred, 550
heterogamous sexual reproduction, 250, 251, **251,** 263
heterogamy, defined, 250
heterosporous plants, 274, 279
"heterotroph hypothesis," 637, 653–54, 721–23
heterotrophs, 199, 243, 248, 343, 637; evolution of, 242, 245; *see also* animals
heterozygote, defined, 515, 516
high-energy phosphate bonds, 130, 135, **556,** 557
Hill, A. V., 458
Historia Animalium, quoted, 27
Holtfreter, J., 500
homeostasis, 406, 428, 448; defined, 6, 351
Hominidae, 660, 661; defined, 360; evolution of, **666**
Homo sapiens, 358, 376, 669, 671; *see also* man
homology: in chromosomes, *see* chromosomes, homologous; in classification, 361, 362, **363,** 364, 607; evidences from, for evolution, 605–07
homozygote, defined, 515
Hooke, Robert, 192, 305; first to describe cells, 52, 53, 61, 63; *Micrographia* by, 49–52, 53, 54, 55
Hooker, Joseph, 592, 594
hookworm, 209, 369

hormones, 396, 443, 444, 445, 447, 470; defined, 390; female reproductive cycle controlled by, 475–77, 479–80; ovarian, 475–77, 478–79; pituitary, 479–80, 586; placental, 480; *see also* endocrine system
horse: domestication of, 680, **681;** evolution of, 605, **606,** 624, 626, **653**
horsetails, **271,** 273, **274;** Devonian, 646, **647**
host: entered by pathogens, 183, 187, **188,** 189, 210–11, 212; pathogens resisted by, 213–16
housefly: and insecticides, 719; under microscope, **47,** 48
hummingbird, pollination by, 322, 615, **616**
Hürzeler, Johannes, 661
Huxley, Thomas Henry, 594
hybrid corn, 524–25, **525,** 581
hybrids: and genetic isolation, 628–29; polyploid, 629–30; *see also* heterozygote
Hydra, 366, 367, **367, 368;** digestion in, **383,** 383–85; excretion in, 421–22, 423; nervous system of, **437,** 437–38; number of chromosomes in, 528; reproduction in, **463,** 464; respiration in, 413; transportation in, 398–99, **399**
hydrogen, 80, 81, 83, 94, 97, 101 (table), 114, 635, 637; abundance of, 95 (table); atomic structure of, 96, **96,** 97, 98, **98,** 101 (table); in carbon-hydrogen-oxygen cycle, 164, **165,** 166; as constituent of water, 99, 100; as element in organisms, 101 (table); ions, 101, 104, 133, 419; molecule of, 98, **99,** 100; and oxidation of glucose, 132, 133; symbol for, 101 (table)
hydrogen acceptor, 122, 164, 228, 297
hydrogen donor, 122
hydrogen peroxide, 80, 81, 82, 219
hydrolysis, 108, 111, 112, 114, 120, **121,** 345
hydrosphere, defined, 166
hydroxide ions, 101, 104
hydroxyl group, 113, 120
hyphae, 242; of mushroom, 235; of *Rhizopus,* 232, 233, **234**
hypocotyl, **320,** 321, **322**
hypothesis: deductions from, 14, 15, 16, 34, 63, 69, 150; distinguished from theory, 56; suggested by observation, 13,

15, 28–29; testing, 14–15, 16–17, 21, 29, 34, 56, 150
Hyracotherium, **653**

IAA, 332, 333, 334
Ice Ages, 661
identical twins, **463,** 464, 509–10, **510,** 584
igneous rocks, 244, 245
immunity: active, 214–16; passive, 216
independent assortment, in genetics, 524, 529–30, **524,** 541
indole acetic acid, 332, 333, 334
inferior vena cava, 402, **403, 404**
Ingenhousz, Jan, 286
Ingram, Vernon, 563
inorganic compounds, 83, 93
insecticides, 20, 719
insects: as arthropods, **373,** 374–75; fossil record of, 653; gall, 30, 31, **32;** pollination by, 276, 277, 322, 324, 335; resistant to chemical agents, 719; respiration in, 414; *see also* grasshopper
insulin, 106, 107, 108, 396, 447, 586; secreted by islets of Langerhans, 444; molecular structure of, **106,** 107, 108
integument, around sporangium, 275
intelligence, in man, 586, 672
interdependence, of plants and animals, 335
internode, of stem, 302, **302, 303**
intestinal juice, 391, 392, 396
intestine: large, *see* large intestine; small, *see* small intestine
intracellular digestion, **344,** 345, 347, **383**
invertebrates, 364–76, **365, 368, 369, 372, 373,** 376; Cambrian, 641; Carboniferous, 647; *see also Hydra;* planarians; earthworm; grasshopper
in vitro and *in vivo,* defined, 119
iodine, 95, 197, 219, 258
ionic bonds, 100
ionic compounds, 101
ionization, 101, 103, 104, 133
ions, 100, 101, 103, 104
iron, 418, 635; abundance of, 95 (table); and chlorophyll, 310; dietary requirement of, 710
islets of Langerhans, 444, **445,** 446, 447
isogamous sexual reproduction, 250, **251,** 263
isogamy, defined, 250
isolation, 580, 581, 602, 610, 624; genetic, 581, 628–29;

petiole, 287, **287**
Petrified Forest, 157, 603
pH scale, 104, **105**
pH values: in canning process, 222; for enzyme activity, 121–22, 122 (table), 389
phagocytes (white blood cells), 211, 212, 213, **214**, 406, 407, **407**, 503
pharynx: of chordates, 376, 605; of earthworm, 385, **386**; of man, **415**, 416
phenotype, defined, 516
phenylalanine, 568, 569; converted into tyrosine, 562; and pepsin, **394**
phenylpyruvic idiocy, 586
phenylthiocarbimide, 575, 576, 578, 580
Philosophical Transactions, 53, 75
phloem, 261, 268, **268**, **273**, 295, **303**, 304, **305**, **306**, 307, 309, **309**, 316, 328, **328**; movement of materials in, 313; primary and secondary, 328, **328**
Phlogiston Theory, 72, 73, 77, 80
phosphate ions, 101
phosphoric acid, 550, 551, 552, **554**
phosphorus, 73, 74, 76, 77, 79, 101 (table), 114, 310, 550; abundance of, 95 (table); cycle, **162**, **163**; as element in organism, 101 (table); symbol for, 101 (table)
phosphorus-32, 96
phosphorus cycle, **162**, **163**
photosynthesis, 103, 104, 136, 160–61, 162–63, 164, 166, 170, 260, 286–300, 314, 316, 691; in algae, 254, 255, 263, 297, 638, 691; amount of, worldwide, 297; in bacteria, 200; biochemistry of, 295–300, **298**; carbon dioxide absorbed in, 136, 162–63, 164, 260, 263, 286, 291–93, 300; and chlorophyll, **289**, 290–91; dark reactions in, 297, **298**; equations for, 164, 295, 296; and evolution, 243, 245, **246**, 249, 260, 722, 723; in herbaceous stem, 303; leaf as organ of, **287**, 287–95, **288**, **294**, 299, 300; light reactions in, 136, 286, 287, 288–90, 297, **298**; and oxygen, 136, 161, 296, 635; summary of reactions in, diagrammatic, **298**; water as factor in, 286, 293–95
phototropism, 329, **330**
phylloquinone, 709

phylum (phyla): animal, survey of, 364–78, **375**, **378**; defined, 360; plant, **282–83**
Physarum, 232
physiology: in classification, 362, 363, 364; defined, 4; *see also individual processes of plant and animal functioning*
Phytophthora infestans, 238
pig: domestication of, 679; embryonic development of, **609**
pigeon, passenger, **715**
pineal body, 67, **445**
pineapple: flowering controlled by NAA, 333; asexual reproduction in, 317
pink bread mold, 241, **241**; *see also Neurospora*
pinocytosis, 126, **126**, 383
pistil, **276**, 319, **320**, **323**
pith, of stem, **273**, 302, **303**, **328**
pithecanthropines, 665
Pithecanthropus erectus, see Java man
Pithecanthropus pekinensis, see Peking man
pits, in tracheids, 303, **305**
pituitary gland, 444, **445**, 447, 479, 480, 502
placenta, 470, 473, 474, 475; hormonal control by, 480
planarians, 367–68, **369**, **370**; digestion in, 385, **385**; excretion in, 422, **422**; locomotion of, 452, 453; nervous system in, 438, **438**; regeneration in, 501, **503**; respiration in, 413; transportation in, 399, 411
planation, 271
plankton, 259, 691
plants: alternation of generations in, 251–53, **254**, 265–66, **267**, 278–80, 281; and animals, similarities to and differences from, **341**, 342, 343; classification of, **282–83**; cultivated, origins of, 676, 678, 679, 680, **680**; evolutionary levels of, **282–83**; flowering, *see* flowering plants; green land, *see* green land plants; heredity in, *see* genetics; regeneration in, 501; responses to environment, 329–33, **330**, **331**; time scale for, in geologic periods, **246**, 640 (table); vascular, *see* vascular plants; *see also* algae; bacteria; fungi; liverworts; mosses
plasma, 406, 410, 430
plasmodium, of slime mold, 231, 232, **232**, 234
Plasmodium: asexual reproduction in, 464; discovery of, 13–

14, 19; malaria caused by, 14–15, 16, 17, 18, 209, 364; under microscope, **14**; mosquitoes as carriers of, 16, 17, 21; and temperature cycle of malaria, **19**
platelets, 406, 407, **407**
Platyhelminthes, 366–68, **369**, **370**; *see also* flatworms; planarians
platypus, duckbill, 470, **471**, 652
Pleistocene epoch, 640 (table), 660, 661, 665, **666**, 667
Pliny, 46
Pliocene epoch, 640 (table), 652, 661, **666**
pneumococcus, 548; transformation in, 548, 549
pneumonia, bacterial, 197, 209, 211, 217, 407, 548
polar nuclei, **320**, 321
poliomyelitis, 215; vaccine for, 215, 216; virus as cause of, 185, **185**, 186, 215
pollen grains, 275, 276, 279, 320, 321, 512
pollen tubes, 275–76, **320**, 321, 512, **512**; evolution of, 275–76
pollination, 276–77, **320**, 321, 322, 324, 335, 512, **512**, 615, 629, 653
pollution of water supply, 714
polymyxin, 218
polypeptide chain, 567, **567**, 569
polyploid species, 629–30, **631**, 682
Polytrichum, 261
Pongidae, 660
population genetics, 537–87
populations: emigration of, 580, 623; in equilibrium, 577, 578, **579**, 580; genes in, 573–87; immigration of, 580; and gene pool, 575–78, 581; genetics of, 573–87; isolation of, *see* isolation; model of, 574; sampling of, 574–75, **575**, 576; size of, as factor in evolution, 624; in transition, 580–81
Porifera, 364, **365**, 366
positive charge, of protons, 96, 97
potassium, 95, 101 (table), 310; as element in organisms, 101 (table); ions of, 101; kelp as source of, 261; symbol for, 101 (table)
potassium-argon dating, 660, 661
potato: asexual reproduction of, 317, **318**; fungus disease of, 238; number of chromosomes in, 528; sprouting prevented by NAA, 333

potential energy, 89

Pouchet, F. A., 37–38, 41, 42

Pre-Cambrian period, 245, **246**, 247, 639, 640 (table), 641, **642**

preformation, 494, 496, **496, 497**, 498; evidence for, 494–95

pregnancy, 479, 480; human, 474, 475; length of, for various species, 474

preservatives for food, 224

preventive medicine, 43

Priestley, Joseph, 84, 88, 93, 166; and discovery of oxygen, 76–79, **77, 78**, 286; quoted, 74, 75

primary consumers, 161, 170, **171**, 172, **176**, 691, **696**, 699

primary sex characteristics, 466

primates: brachiation by, 460; defined, 360; evolution of, **662**, 662–65, **663, 664, 665, 666**; first, 662, 663, **663**

probability, in genetics, 516

Proconsul, 660–61, 664

producers, as green plants, 160, 164, **171, 176**, 691, **696**, 699

progesterone, 476, 477, 478, 479, 480

prolactin, 479, 480

Pronuba, 277

prosimians, evolution of, **662**, 662–63, **663, 666**

protease, 225

protective coloration, **598**, 598–99, **599**

protein molecules, 102, 106, 107, 108, 109, 120, 129, 390; Fox's suggestion as to origin of, 636–37

proteins, 114, 167, 168, 345, 568, 710; built with amino acids, 106, 107, 114, 129, 130, 168, **566**, 566–67, **567**, 709; in cells, 104–09, 129; dietary requirement of, 709, 710; digestion of, 389, 390, 392, **394**, 396, 397; energy from, 135; as enzymes, 119, 121; nitrogen in, 114, 310, 345, 420; and RNA, in synthesis of, 565–67, **566, 567**; stored in plants, 315; sulfur in, 114, 310

Protista, 194, 360

protons, 96, **97**, 98

protozoans, 346, 357, 360, 364, **365**, 691; algae as food for, 256; asexual reproduction in, 462, **463**; destroyed by boiling, 42; disease caused by, 209, 364; fossil, 641; fungi evolved from, 233, 234, 242; in hay infusion, 34; locomotion in, 451, **451, 452**; *Paramecium*

and its way of life, as example of, 343–57, **347, 348, 351, 353, 354, 355**; slime molds evolved from, 234

pseudopodia, 248, 451, **452**, 455

Psilotum, 269, 273

psyche, Aristotle's ideas of, 66, **67**

ptarmigan, 599, **599**

PTC, 575, 576, 578, 580

Pteranodon, 648, **650**

pulmonary artery, 402, **403**, 404, **404**, 405

pulmonary veins, 402, **403, 404**

pump, vacuum, 312

pupae, 28

purines, 551, **551**, 552; molecular structure of, **552**, 554, **554**, 555, 556, 558, 565, 567, 568, 569, 637

pyramid of numbers, 172, **173**

pyrimidines, 551; molecular structure of, **551**, 552, 554, **554**, 555, 556, 558, 565, 567, 568, 569, 637

pyruvic acid, 133, 134, 135, 424, 457, 458; and fermentation, **227**, 228; molecular structure of, 132, **425**

python, 607; vestigial hip bones of, **608**

Quaternary period, **246**, 640 (table), **642**

quina-quina, 11, 12

quinine: discovery of, 11–12; malaria treated with, 12, 15, 18; source of, lost to Allies in World War II, 19; substitutes for, 20

rabbit: appendix in, 607; genes of, influenced by food and temperature, **596**, 597, **597**, 598; locomotion of, 453, **454**

races, ring of, 627, **628**

radial symmetry, 366, 376, **449**, 451

radiation, high-energy, gene mutations caused by, 546

radioactive isotopes, 96, 243–44, 296, 604–05; and time measured by, 157, 243–44, 604–05

radish, crossed with cabbage, 629, **631**

radium, 296

rain forest, **5**; as habitat, 700, 701; monthly rainfall variation in, **701**; monthly temperature variation in, **700**

random genetic drift, 622, 624

rat: estrus in, 477; experiments on reproductive cycle of, 476, **478**, 479; specialized teeth of, **654**

Ray, John, 358

Recent epoch, 640 (table), **666**

receptors, **435**; defined, 434; in man, 439; *see also* animals, coordination in; neurons

recombination, genetic, *see* genetic recombination

rectum, **388**

red blood cells, 195, 406, 407, **407**; and malaria, *see* malaria

Redi, Francesco, experiments of, 28–32, **30, 31**, 36

reduction, chemical, 90, 133, **134**

redwood trees, giant, 273, 311, **311**, 324, 716, **718**

reflex arc, **436**; defined, 436

refrigeration, of food, 223–24

regeneration, 501–02, **502, 503**

renal artery, **427**

renal vein, **427**

reproduction: asexual, *see* asexual reproduction; sexual, *see* sexual reproduction

reptiles: early, 646–48, **649**, 655; eggs of, 468; evolution of backbone of, 459, 460, **460, 461**; Mesozoic, 460, 648–49, **650, 651**, 656

resources, living, 714–19

respiration, 166, 342; aerobic, 226, 227, 228; anaerobic, 226, 228; and carbon dioxide, 412, 414, 419; and combustion, 76, 82, **85**, 166; in earthworm, **413**, 413–14; electron transport in, 228, 297; equation for, 164, 412; in frog, 412; in grasshopper, **401**, 414; in *Hydra*, 413; in man, 414–20, **415, 416, 417, 429**; oxygen in, 412, 414, 418–19; in *Paramecium*, 412; in planarian, 413

retina, 154

Rh blood type, 573, 584, 585

rhinoceros, woolly, **655**

rhizoids, 263

Rhizopus nigricans, 232, 233, **234**, 242

Rhynia, **268**

riboflavin, 228, 709, 710

riboflavin coenzyme, 133, **134**

ribonucleic acid, *see* RNA

ribose, 551, 565; molecular structure of, **551**

ribosomes, 59–60, 61, **124**, 128–29, **129**, 130, 136, **137**, 195, 565, 566, **566**, 567, 568

rice civilizations, 315

synapse, 434, **435**, 443
synapsis, of chromosomes, 529, 530, 542
synthesis, chemical, 83; (synthesize), defined, 83; of fat, 113–14, **114–15**; of maltose, 111, **112–13**; of polypeptide, **566–67**, 567; RNA and protein, 565–567, **566–67**; of urea, 83, 424–26, **425**
syphilis, 222
Systema Naturae, Linnaeus', 359

tadpole, and Spemann's experiments, 499, **500**
tagged molecules, 296
tapeworm, 209, 366, **463**, 466
taproot, 308, **308**
tarsier, 663, **663**, **666**
Tatum, Edward L, 201, 202, 204, 561, 562
technology, defined, 46
teeth, specialized, of mammals, 651, **654**
tentacle, defined, 449
Terblanche, Gert, 659
Tertiary period, **246**, 640 (table), **642**
terramycin, 218
test cross, in genetic analysis, 519
testes, 465, 466, 470, 479; in man, 444, **445**, 470, **473**
testosterone, 444
tetanus, 212, 213, 215, 216
tetrapod, defined, 459
Thallophyta, evolutionary level of, **282**, **283**
thallus, 262, **262**, 263
theory: defined, 56–57, 535; establishment of, 535; prediction as test of, 535
thiamine, 709, 711
thorax, movements of, during breathing, **417**
thymine, molecular structure of, **551**; 554, **554**, 555, 557, 565, 568, 569
thymus gland, 444, **445**
thyroid gland, 444, **445**
thyroxin, 444
tiger, specialized teeth of, **654**
tincture of iodine, 219
tissue, defined, 154
TMV (tobacco mosaic virus), 183, 184, **184**, 185, **187**, 211
toadstool, 235, 236, **236**
tobacco mosaic disease, 181, 183, 184, **184**
tomato, 322, 583, **680**
tongue, **388**, **416**
tools, and culture, 669, **671**
toxins, 181, 211, 212, 213

toxoids, 215, 216
TPN, 296
trachea, **388**, 415, **415**, 416, **416**, 417
tracheal tubes, of grasshopper, 401, **401**, 414
tracheids, 303, 304, **305**, **306**, 313, 316
traits: continuously varying, 524–25; cultural, 683, 684; dominant, 513, 514; improvement of, in domestic plants and animals, 581–82; recessive, 513, 514; sex-linked, 536, 538–39, **539**, **540**, 540–41, 542, 544, **544**; inheritance of, 514–16, 517, 519, **520**, 522–24; *see also* genes; genetics; heredity
transportation: of carbon dioxide, 419; within earthworm, 399–401, **400**, 413; within grasshopper, **401**, 401–02, 411; within *Hydra,* 398–99, **399**; within man, 402–11, **403**, **404**, **405**, **407**, **408**, **410**, 418–19, **429**, 430; of oxygen, 418–19; within planarian, 399, 411; in plant roots, 310–11; in plant stems, 303–04, **305**, 307, 311–15, **314**; problems of, for multicellular animals, 398; *see also* circulatory system
tree trunk: cross section through, **306**; petrified, **156**; *see also* woody stem
trees, *see* forest community
Triassic period, **246**, 640 (table), **642**
Triceratops, **650**
Trichinella, 369, 370
trichinosis, 369
trilobites, 641, **643**
triphosphopyridine nucleotide, 297
triple nutritional mutant, 202, 205
tropism, defined, 329
trypsin: pH value for, 122 (table); in protein digestion, **394**
Tschermak, E., 527
tuberculosis, 208, 209, 213, 217, 711; bovine, 223; genes for resistance to, 586
tundra, Arctic, 174, 699, **699**; monthly rainfall variation in, **701**; monthly temperature variation in, **700**
tunicates, **377**
turkey, domestication of, 680
twins, identical, **463**, 464, 509–10, **510**, 584
Tyler, S. A., 245
typhoid fever, 210, 213, 223

tyrosine, 568; and pepsin, **394**; phenylalanine converted to, 562
tyrothricin, 218

Uintatherium, **653**
ulcer, 389
ultraviolet radiations, mutations induced by, 201
Ulva, 250, 252, 253, **254**, **255**, 263, 265, 266, 281
umbilical cord, 474, 475
unconscious activity, 440–41
undulant fever, 223
unicellular organisms, 57, 194, **248**, **249**, 380, **381**; as ancestors of multicellular organisms, 247–50; *see also* microorganisms
uninucleate cell, 231
United Nations, 710, 711, 712
United States, vital statistics for, 708 (table), 709 (table)
unsaturated fatty acid, molecular structure of, **113**
uracil, 565, 569
uranium: isotopes of, 296; structure of, 97
uranium-lead dating, 243–44, 605, 661
urea, molecular structure of, 102, **102**; 125, 345, 406, 421, 423, 424, 426, 427, 428; first synthesized by Wöhler, 83, 102; formula for, 102, 424; process of formation of, 424, **425**, 426
ureter, 426, **426**, **427**
urethra, 426, **426**, **473**, **474**
Urey, Harold, 635, **635**
uric acid, 421, 423, 424, 428
urine, 428
uterus, 472, 474, **474**, 475, 476, 478, 479, 480

vaccination, 214, **215**
vacuoles, 61, 125, 126, **126**, **137**, 195, 197; of *Paramecium,* 347, **347**, 348, **348**, 349, 351, **351**, 352
vagina, 474, **474**
vagus nerve, 442, **442**, 443
valine, 563, 568
valves: of heart, 402, 404, **404**; of veins, 406, 410
Van Helmont, Jean-Baptiste, 28, 71, 73, 79; experiment with willow tree, 69–70, **71**, 82
variation: defined, 507; hereditary, as factor in evolution, 596, 601, 608, 610, 611; in species, 625, **625**